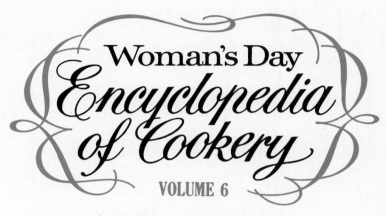

Woman's Day
Encyclopedia of Cookery
VOLUME 6

in 12 volumes—over 2,000 pages—
with more than 1,500 illustrations in color,
1,000 entries and 8,500 recipes
1,200 menus, 50 specialty cook books
and a host of delightful features by distinguished food writers.

Prepared and edited by the Editors of Woman's Day
Editor: EILEEN TIGHE
Managing Editor: EVELYN GRANT   *Food Editor:* GLENNA MCGINNIS
Art Consultant: HAROLD SITTERLE   *Photographic Editor:* BEN CALVO
Associates: OLIVIA RISBERG, CHARLOTTE SCRIPTURE,
CAROLYN STORM, JOHANNA BAFARO

SPECIAL PROJECT STAFF
Editor: NIKA STANDEN HAZELTON   *Art Director:* LEONARD A. ROMAGNA
Associates: L. GERALDINE MARSTELLER, HELEN FEINGOLD,
SUSAN J. KNOX, INEZ M. KRECH

FAWCETT PUBLICATIONS, INC.   NEW YORK

PRINTED AND BOUND BY
FAWCETT-HAYNES PRINTING CORPORATION
ROCKVILLE, MARYLAND

Table of Contents

VOLUME 6

HADDOCK TO KID

Definitions and 740 Recipes
How to buy, store, prepare, cook, and serve •
Nutritive Food Values • Caloric Values

To help you plan more varied meals
with the recipes in this volume.

Foreword

To the best of our knowledge, no work of this magnitude ever has been undertaken by any author, editor, or publisher in America. The editors of Woman's Day, with a special staff of experts, present to you this Encyclopedia of Cookery, a comprehensive and colorful library on all culinary matters. The twelve-volume encyclopedia contains in its 2,000 pages over 8,500 recipes from all over the world, 1,500 food illustrations in color, 1,200 menus, 50 special cook books and over 1,000 food definitions. In addition, there are full details about all foods, their nutritive and caloric values, how to buy, serve, prepare, and cook them. There is a history of food and cooking, articles on nutrition, diet, entertaining, menu planning, herbs and spices. Every topic of culinary interest is covered. Five years of intensive work have gone into its preparation, backed by twenty-five years of food and cookery experience in the publication of Woman's Day.

We think you will find this Encyclopedia of Cookery the most complete and authoritative work ever published on the subject. It is a library for everyone who cares about good food and the fine art of preparing it.

The Editors

HADDOCK—This salt-water fish is one of the most important food fish of the North Atlantic, from Nova Scotia to Cape Hatteras. It is closely related to the cod, but the two fish can easily be told apart; the haddock has a black lateral line and a patch below it and above the pectoral fin. The haddock is much smaller than the cod. In New England waters, haddocks on the average weigh between two and six pounds. Haddock is an all-season fish, and is as popular in northern Europe as it is in the United States.

The flesh is firm and white, with a pleasant flavor which is on the bland side. Smoked haddock is called finnan haddie.

Haddock can be successfully cooked in any desired way. Fillets are a favorite.

Availability and Purchasing Guide—Fresh haddock is available all year round, whole and in fillets. Frozen haddock is available in fillets.

Fresh haddock should be firm-fleshed and have a fresh odor.

Storage—Wrap haddock in moisture-proof covering or place in a tightly covered container. Keep fish in the coldest part of the refrigerator. Plan to use within 2 days.

Frozen haddock should be kept solidly frozen until ready to use. Once thawed, use immediately.

- [ ] Refrigerator shelf, raw: 1 to 2 days
- [ ] Refrigerator shelf, cooked: 3 to 4 days
- [ ] Refrigerator frozen-food compartment, prepared for freezing: 2 to 3 weeks
- [ ] Freezer, prepared for freezing: 1 year

Nutritive Food Values—Haddock is a very good source of protein and contains phosphorus, potassium, niacin, and thiamine.

- [ ] 3½ ounces, raw = 79 calories
- [ ] 3½ ounces, fried = 165 calories
- [ ] 3½ ounces, smoked = 103 calories

Basic Preparation—Wash fish quickly in cold, salted water. Frozen fish should be thawed in the refrigerator; allow about 8 hours for 1 pound of fish. Haddock may be cooked by dry or moist heat.

- [ ] **To Freeze**—Haddock can be frozen in steaks, chunks, or fillets. Dip fish into salted water, ¼ cup salt to 4 cups cold water, for 30 seconds. Drain. Wrap in moisture- vapor-proof material, excluding as much air as possible. Seal.

BROILED HADDOCK FILLETS

1½ pounds haddock fillets
1 teaspoon salt
⅛ teaspoon pepper
¾ cup small soft bread cubes
3 tablespoons butter or margarine, melted
¼ teaspoon crumbled dried thyme
12 fresh grapefruit sections

Wipe fillets with a damp cloth. Sprinkle both sides of fish with salt and pepper. Place in a shallow buttered baking pan or on buttered broiler rack. Mix bread cubes with 2 tablespoons of the butter and the thyme. Sprinkle over fish. Top with grapefruit sections. Brush with remaining butter. Place under broiler with oven control set to hot (400°F.) and broil for 25 minutes, or until fish is flaky and crumbs are brown. Makes 5 or 6 servings.

Haddock Plaki

FLAKED HADDOCK, NEWBURG

- 3 tablespoons butter or margarine
- 1½ tablespoons flour
- 1 teaspoon salt
- ½ teaspoon paprika
- ¼ teaspoon ground nutmeg
  Dash of cayenne
- ¾ cup light cream
- ⅓ cup milk
- 1½ pounds haddock fillets, cooked and flaked
- 3 tablespoons sherry
- 2 egg yolks
- 4 slices of toast

Melt butter and blend in the flour and seasonings. Add cream and milk slowly; cook until thickened, stirring constantly. Add fish and heat. Add sherry mixed with egg yolks and cook for 2 or 3 minutes longer. Serve at once on hot toast. Makes 4 servings.

HADDOCK-POTATO PATTIES

- 4 medium potatoes
- 1 pound haddock fillets, cooked and flaked
- 1 egg, beaten
- 2 tablespoons minced onion
- 1 teaspoon poultry seasoning
  Salt and pepper
  All-purpose flour
  Fat for frying

Cook potatoes and mash. Add fish, egg, onion, poultry seasoning, and salt and pepper to taste. Shape into 8 flat patties. Roll in flour and panfry in hot fat until brown. Makes 4 servings.

HADDOCK PLAKI

- 3 tomatoes or about 1 cup canned tomatoes
- 2 large onions, sliced
- 1 garlic clove, chopped
- 1 parsley sprig, finely chopped
- ¼ cup olive oil or butter
- 1 haddock large enough for 2 persons
- 1 lemon, sliced
  Ground sage, salt, and pepper to taste
  Bread crumbs

Lemon juice, if desired

Peel and mash tomatoes; add onion, garlic, and parsley. Add olive oil. Place mixture in shallow pan and let simmer over low heat until onion is tender. Place fish in pan and cover with lemon slices. Add sage, salt, and pepper and sprinkle with bread crumbs. Cook in oven until fish is browned. Let the *Plaki* cool and serve cold. Squeeze a little lemon juice on it, and you'll find it is an appetizing hot-weather dish. Makes 2 servings.

HAKE—The hake is a salt-water food fish which lives in the Atlantic and northern Pacific. It is a relative of the cod. Hakes are slender, dark-gray fish with fins on their backs; the first small and triangular, the second long and narrow. Their aver-

Poached Halibut Steaks with Curry Sauce

age market weight is between one and four pounds. The meat is soft and white with a delicate flavor.

Hake is marketed whole or filleted, and also fresh, frozen, salted, and smoked. A great deal of it is sold, along with cod, haddock, and other white fish, under the label of "deep-sea fillets." It can be prepared and frozen in any manner suited to cod and haddock.

Caloric Value
☐ 3½ ounces, raw = 74 calories

HAKE CASSEROLE
2 pounds hake fillets
4 potatoes, sliced
3 onions, sliced
  Few celery tops
1 bay leaf
4 whole cloves
1 garlic clove
¼ teaspoon dillseed
¼ teaspoon white pepper
2½ teaspoons salt
½ cup butter or margarine
½ cup dry white wine
2 cups boiling water
2 cups light cream
  Chopped parsley

Put all ingredients except last 2 in 3-quart casserole. Cover; bake in preheated moderate oven (375°F.) for 1 hour. Add scalded cream. Garnish with parsley. Makes 6 servings.

SESAME BAKED HAKE
2 pounds hake fillets
  Salt to taste
  Melted butter (about ⅔ cup)
3 cups soft bread crumbs
¼ teaspoon pepper
¼ cup sesame seeds, toasted in moderate oven (350°F.)
½ teaspoon dried thyme

Put fish in a shallow baking dish. Sprinkle with salt and pour on ¼ cup melted butter. Mix 1 teaspoon salt, ⅓ cup melted butter, and remaining ingredients. Spread on fish. Bake in preheated moderate oven (375°F.) for about 30 minutes. Makes 6 servings.

CURRIED HAKE
3 onions, chopped
1 garlic clove, minced
1 small green pepper, chopped
1 tablespoon curry powder
¼ cup butter or margarine
4 whole cloves
1 cinnamon stick
½ cup undiluted evaporated milk
1 pound hake fillets, cubed
  Salt
  Hot cooked rice

Cook first 4 ingredients in the butter for 5 minutes. Add next 5 ingredients, cover, and simmer for 10 minutes. Season to taste. Serve with rice. Makes 4 servings.

HALF AND HALF—A dairy product consisting of a mixture of milk and cream. The mixture is usually homogenized, and used for coffee or table cream. Half and half, on the average, contains between ten and twelve per cent butterfat. Whole sweet milk contains three and nine-tenths per cent butterfat, light cream twenty per cent, medium cream between thirty-six to forty per cent.

In the British Isles, half and half is the term used for a mixture of mild and bitter draught beer. It is one of the most popular drinks in the pubs which are known as the "workingman's clubs." Playing darts in an English pub, and gossiping with the locals over a glass of half and half, or " 'alf and 'alf" as the London Cockney would say, is a pleasing and soothing experience for Englishman and foreigner alike.

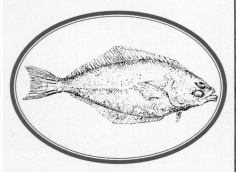

HALIBUT—A cold-water fish which lives in all the seas of the world and is one of the finest and most important of salt-water food fish; there are several varieties. The fish is flat and resembles a gigantic flounder. Female halibuts have been known to weigh as much as 600 pounds; males seldom exceed 100 pounds and more usually weigh around fifty.

The flesh is white and excellent in flavor and texture, but the large female halibuts do not make for the best eating since their flesh is coarse. Chicken halibuts, weighing up to ten pounds, are considered the finest.

Availability—Fresh halibut is available all year round; it is most abundant from March to September. Halibut is also available frozen in steaks and fillets.

Purchasing Guide—Fresh halibut is sold as steak or fillets. It should be firm-fleshed and have a fresh odor.

Storage—Fresh fish should be wrapped in a moisture-proof covering and kept in the coldest part of the refrigerator. Plan to use within 2 days. Frozen fish should be kept solidly frozen until ready to use. Once thawed, use immediately.
☐ Refrigerator shelf, raw: 1 to 2 days
☐ Refrigerator shelf, cooked and covered: 3 to 4 days
☐ Refrigerator frozen-food compart-ment, prepared for freezing: 2 to 3 weeks
☐ Freezer, prepared for freezing: 1 year

Nutritive Food Values—A very good source of protein, low in fat. Halibut liver oil is a rich source of vitamin A.
☐ 3½ ounces, raw = 100 calories
☐ 3½ ounces, broiled = 171 calories

Basic Preparation—Wash halibut in cold, salted water. Do not allow fish to remain in water as it may lose flavor and nutrients. Frozen halibut should be thawed in the refrigerator; allow about 8 hours for 1 pound of fish. Halibut may be cooked by dry or moist heat; poached, broiled, baked, fried, or used for soufflé or steamed pudding. To freeze at home see Haddock, page 845.

BAKED WHOLE HALIBUT
Stuff whole halibut lightly with well-seasoned bread stuffing. Cut 3 or 4 gashes in skin and insert thin slices of salt pork or bacon. Put a pinch of dried thyme or marjoram, 1 minced onion, 3 tablespoons minced parsley, and 2 tablespoons fat in baking pan. Put fish in pan; bake in pre-heated moderate oven (350°F.) until fish flakes easily with a fork.

POACHED HALIBUT STEAKS WITH CURRY SAUCE
Cut 1½ to 2 pounds halibut steaks into individual pieces. Cover with boiling water; season with a slice of onion, a parsley sprig or a few celery tops, salt, and a few peppercorns. Simmer gently for 10 to 15 minutes, or until fish is tender. Reserve stock and remove fish to hot platter. Serve with Curry Sauce. Makes 3 to 4 servings.

Curry Sauce
3 tablespoons butter or margarine
½ onion, grated
1½ tablespoons flour
2 to 4 teaspoons curry powder
½ teaspoon salt
1¼ cups fish stock (add water if necessary)
¼ cup cream or undiluted evaporated milk

Cook onion in butter for a minute or two. Blend in flour and seasonings. Add fish stock gradually; cook until thickened, stirring constantly. Add cream before serving. Makes about 1½ cups.

DEVILED HALIBUT STEAKS
Mix 2 tablespoons prepared mustard, 1 tablespoon salad oil, 2 tablespoons chili sauce, 2 tablespoons prepared horse-radish, and 1 teaspoon salt. Spread half of mixture on 4 halibut steaks (about 2 pounds). Put on greased broiler rack and broil for about 6 minutes under medium heat. Turn fish, spread with remaining sauce, and broil for 5 or 6 minutes longer. Makes 4 servings.

PLANKED HALIBUT STEAKS
8 small white onions
4 to 6 carrots, cut into strips
1 package (10 ounces) frozen broccoli
2 pounds halibut steaks (about 1 inch thick)
Salt and pepper to taste
Melted butter or margarine
Juice of 1 lemon
Paprika and parsley

Cook vegetables separately until almost tender. Meanwhile, if plank is used, oil well and heat in hot oven (400°F.). Sprinkle fish with salt and pepper. Brush with melted butter. Put on heated plank or on greased ovenproof baking dish. Bake in hot oven (400°F.) for 30 to 40 minutes, or until fish flakes easily when tested with a fork. If fish is not browned enough, put under broiler for a few minutes. Brown vegetables lightly in small amount of butter. Arrange around fish. Top fish with butter mixed with lemon juice; sprinkle with paprika and garnish with parsley. Serve on plank. Makes 4 servings.

BARBECUED HALIBUT STEAKS
1 small onion, minced
½ green pepper, chopped
3 tablespoons butter or margarine
½ cup chili sauce
½ cup ketchup
Juice of 2 lemons
2 tablespoons brown sugar
½ cup water
1 teaspoon powdered mustard
1 tablespoon Worcestershire
½ teaspoon each of salt and pepper
4 halibut steaks (2 pounds)

Cook onion and green pepper in butter for 5 minutes. Add remaining ingredients except fish and simmer for 10 minutes. Broil halibut until done, brushing from time to time with the sauce. Makes 4 servings.

HALIBUT WITH CREAMY MUSTARD SAUCE
1½ pounds halibut steaks
¼ cup butter or margarine
¼ cup all-purpose flour
½ teaspoon powdered mustard
½ teaspoon steak sauce
¾ teaspoon salt
Dash of pepper
2 cups milk
1 tablespoon minced chives
Paprika

Poach fish in seasoned simmering water to cover until fish flakes. Drain and leave fish in covered pan. Melt butter and blend in flour and seasonings. Add milk and cook until thickened, stirring. Put fish on hot platter and pour sauce over fish. Sprinkle with chives and paprika. Makes 4 servings.

HAM—The rear leg of a hog, from the aitchbone (hipbone) through the meaty part of the shank bone, is called a ham.

The hog has been a domestic animal since prehistoric times and although no one knows for sure just when salt was first used to cure ham, this was one of the earliest methods of food preservation, and cured ham was traditional at the pagan spring festivals which predated the Christian Easter.

Tradition says that Columbus brought eight pigs with him on his second trip to the Americas, and Cortés brought swine to Honduras in 1524. When de Soto landed at Charlotte Harbor, Florida, in 1539, he brought with him 600 soldiers, 350 horses, and thirteen hogs. It did not take the Indians long to find out how good roast pork could be, and records show the whole Spanish encampment was burned twice by the Indians in their efforts to get it. In 1542, the survivors of the expedition killed 700 pigs to provide meat for the return voyage down the Mississippi. Fifty years later, when the French explored the river, the Indians fed the explorers pork raised from the descendants of the original de Soto herd. These, as well as others brought west from the English colonies, especially Virginia, sired the "razorbacks" and "stump rooters" from which the famed country-style hams of Virginia, Georgia, Kentucky, and Tennessee are made today.

The differences in the taste of ham lie in the breed of the hog and the food it is fed. In the case of cured hams, taste is also affected by the flavors of the brines used in curing, and the fuel, such as hickory logs, over which the meat is smoked. Razorbacks forced to forage for their own food produce a different flavor from the corn-fed breeds developed on America's pig farms and agricultural experiment stations. The final effect on taste is, of course, provided by the liquids, spices, and sauces used in cooking, roasting, and basting the ham in the home.

FRESH HAM
(UNCURED LEG OF PORK)

Availability—All year round, with the supply most plentiful at the New Year and Easter. The most common range of weight for a whole fresh ham is 10 to 14 pounds.

Purchasing Guide—The inspection stamp, federal, state, or city, guarantees the wholesomeness of the meat. At the present time U. S. grade identification does not appear on retail cuts of pork, but in high-quality ham the layer of external fat is firm and white; the color of the lean is grayish-pink in young pork, and turns a delicate rose color in older animals; the lean is well marbled with fat; the texture of the lean is firm and fine-grained; bones are porous and pinkish in color.

The cuts of fresh ham most commonly sold, bone-in or boneless, are: whole ham; half ham, shank or butt; ham end, shank or butt; center slice, from ½ to 3 inches thick.

The following rule of thumb may be used for determining the amount to buy:
- ☐ ¾ to 1 pound per serving for ham with bone
- ☐ ¼ to ⅓ pound per serving for boneless ham

Storage—Loosen or remove market paper; store unwrapped or loosely wrapped in coldest part of refrigerator. If fresh ham cannot be used within time suggested, wrap closely and seal tightly in moisture-vapor-proof material and freeze quickly.

To store cooked ham and gravy, cool quickly, cover tightly, and place in coldest part of refrigerator. Or freeze quickly. Do not refreeze.
- ☐ Refrigerator shelf, uncooked: 5 to 6 days
- ☐ Refrigerator frozen-food compartment, prepared for freezing, uncooked: 2 to 3 weeks
- ☐ Freezer, prepared for freezing, uncooked: 3 to 4 months
- ☐ Refrigerator shelf, cooked, with gravy: 4 to 5 days
- ☐ Refrigerator frozen-food compartment, cooked, with gravy, prepared for freezing: 2 to 3 weeks
- ☐ Freezer, cooked, with gravy, prepared for freezing: 2 to 3 months

Nutritive Food Values—Fresh ham is a very good to excellent source of high-quality protein and thiamine, fair to good source of iron and niacin, and fair source of riboflavin.
- ☐ 3½ ounces, fat, roasted = 394 calories
- ☐ 3½ ounces, medium-fat, roasted = 374 calories
- ☐ 3½ ounces, lean, roasted = 346 calories

Basic Preparation—Fresh ham should be thoroughly cooked to bring out its full flavor, as well as to kill any trichinae organisms present. The cooked lean of fresh ham should be grayish-white without any tinge of pink. This does not mean overcooking, which reduces juiciness, flavor, tenderness, and food value. Low cooking temperatures are recommended.

☐ **To Roast (Bake)**—Place the ham, fat side up, in a shallow open pan, on a rack to keep the meat out of the drippings. Insert a meat thermometer into the center of the meat, making sure the point does not rest on fat or bone. Roast at an oven temperature between 325°F. and 350°F. until the meat reaches an internal temperature of 185°F. A 10- to 14-pound whole ham, bone-in, needs approximately 25 to 30 minutes per pound; a boneless whole ham weighing 7 to 10 pounds needs 35 to 40 minutes per pound; a half ham, bone-in, weighing 5 to 7 pounds needs 40 to 45 minutes per pound.

Boneless half hams, and shank and butt ends which weigh less than 7 pounds vary so in shape that it is impossible to give approximate cooking times per pound for them. Use a meat thermometer, and cook until the meat reaches an internal temperature of 185°F. If you don't have a meat thermometer, check on doneness by cutting into the meat. Roast slices more than 2 inches thick in the same way.

For center slices, bone-in or boneless, calculate cooking time by the thickness of the piece. A 2-inch slice should roast for about 60 minutes. A 1-inch slice takes about 40 minutes.

☐ **To Panbroil Slices**—Only slices 1 inch or less thick should be panbroiled. Trim fat from edge of slices, and rub over heated skillet. Snip fat edges of slices in several places to keep edge from curling. Put in skillet, and panbroil until browned on both sides, about 5 to 10 minutes on each side.

☐ **To Panfry Slices**—Follow directions given for panbroiling, but cook ham in a small amount of fat.

☐ **To Cook in Liquid**—Cover ham with cold water. Season to taste with herbs, onions, etc. Cover. Simmer slowly, that is, cook just *below* or *at* the boiling point. This is important. Allow 25 minutes for each pound of ham. A 10- to 12-pound fresh ham will take approximately 4 to 6 hours.

CURED AND SMOKED HAM

Availability—All year round, cured or cured and smoked, whole and in a variety of cuts, uncooked (cook-before-eating) or fully cooked (ready-to-eat), and as standard or specialty hams.

Cured ham and cured and smoked ham are also available canned. Other canned ham products available include deviled ham and spiced ham.

Purchasing Guide—Standard ham is available in the following cuts: Whole hams, bone-in, semiboneless (the aitchbone and shank bone are removed, leaving only the leg bone to hold the shape), and boneless; half hams, bone-in, shank or butt; ham ends, bone-in, shank or butt; center slices, bone-in, from about ½ inch to 3 inches thick (the thinner slices are also known as ham steaks); ham boned and rolled, from slices of any weight requested to a whole ham, which may weigh as much as 14 pounds; thinly sliced ham, boneless, fully cooked (often called boiled ham).

A wide variety of specialty hams are produced in this country, and Italian, Danish, Polish, German, Czechoslovakian, Hungarian, French Bayonne, and English York hams are imported. Among the best-known of these specialty hams are:

American Country-Style Hams (Georgia, Kentucky, Smithfield, Tennessee, and Virginia)—Heavily cured and smoked, but uncooked, they are generally available as whole hams in the localities in which they are cured, and by mail or in specialty food stores nationally. Some cooked Smithfield hams are found in specialty food stores, too.

Italian Prosciutto and German Westphalian Hams—Cured, pressed, smoked, aged in spices, and ready-to-eat. They are usually sold sliced paper-thin.

Note: Picnic shoulders and shoulder butts are not hams, although often called hams, especially when cured.

Storage—Refrigerate in original wrapper or container. Do not freeze. Country-style hams, uncooked, can be stored in a cool place for several months. Canned hams should generally be refrigerated. Be sure to check label for special instructions.

☐ Whole ham, refrigerator shelf, uncooked: 2 weeks
☐ Half ham or ham end, refrigerator shelf, uncooked: 1 week
☐ Center slices and thinly sliced ham, refrigerator shelf, uncooked or cooked: 3 days
☐ Whole ham, half, or end, refrigerator shelf, cooked and covered: 1 week
☐ Canned ham, refrigerator shelf, unopened: 1 year, unless label directs otherwise
☐ Canned deviled or spiced ham, kitchen shelf, unopened: 1 year
☐ Canned ham, deviled, or spiced ham, refrigerator shelf, opened and covered: 1 week

Nutritive Food Values—Cured ham has approximately the same food values as fresh ham. The caloric values of 3½ ounces of various hams are as follows:
☐ Standard, fat, baked = 394 calories
☐ Standard, medium-fat, baked = 374 calories

☐ Standard, lean, baked = 346 calories
☐ Boiled = 234 calories
☐ Specialty, fat = 460 calories
☐ Specialty, medium-fat = 389 calories
☐ Specialty, lean = 310 calories
☐ Canned = 193 calories
☐ Canned deviled = 351 calories
☐ Canned spiced = 294 calories

Basic Preparation—Remove rind of uncooked standard whole ham, half ham, or ham end. If necessary, rinse and pat dry before cooking.

Soak, parboil, and remove rind of specialty hams before baking.

Fully cooked hams may be served without heating, or they may be heated to an internal temperature of about 130°F.

☐ **To Prepare Specialty Ham for Baking**—Unwrap ham and soak 24 to 30 hours in cold water to cover; drain. Put ham in large kettle, cutting off tip of ham, if necessary. Cover with water; bring to boil and simmer, covered, until tender (allow about 25 to 30 minutes per pound), or until large bone in heavy end of ham becomes loose and protrudes. Remove ham from water, and cut off rind. The ham is now ready to be sliced and eaten, or to be glazed.

☐ **To Bake**—For uncooked or fully cooked ham, put ham, fat side up, on rack in open roasting pan. Insert meat thermometer so the bulb is in the center of thickest part and does not touch bone. (Do not add water.) Put in preheated oven and bake as directed in Timetable for Baking, below.

To glaze a ham, remove it from the oven 45 minutes before it is done, score, stud with cloves, and spread with glaze. Return to oven and finish baking.

Specialty hams which have been parboiled are simply scored, spread with a glaze, and baked, glazed-side up, in a preheated slow oven (300°F.) for about 1 hour.

To bake slices, put a 2-inch-thick fully cooked ham slice on a rack in a shallow plan, and bake in a preheated slow oven (325°F.) for 40 minutes. An uncooked ham slice requires 60 minutes. The slice can be studded with whole cloves, and topped with a glaze before baking, if desired.

HAM GLAZES

■ Applesauce—Mix ½ cup corn syrup, 1 cup strained applesauce, and 2 tablespoons prepared mustard.
■ Butterscotch—Mix ¾ cup brown sugar, 2 teaspoons powdered mustard, and small amount of ham fat.
■ Honey—Use ¾ cup strained honey.
■ Jelly—Mash 1 cup cranberry, currant, or other tart jelly.
■ Marmalade—Use ½ cup orange, peach, or apricot marmalade.
■ Molasses—Mix ½ cup each of vinegar and molasses.
■ Mustard—Mix ¼ cup prepared mustard, ½ cup brown sugar, and 2 tablespoons honey.
■ Pineapple—Mix ½ cup crushed pineapple and ¾ cup brown sugar.
■ Sweet Pickle—Use liquid drained from gherkins or other sweet pickles.

☐ **To Broil Slices**—Slash the fat edges in several places to prevent curling. Broil 3 inches from unit. A 1-inch-thick slice of fully cooked ham requires 5 minutes per side. Allow 10 minutes per side for uncooked ham slices.

☐ **To Panbroil Slices**—Ham slices ¼ to ½ inch thick should be panbroiled. Trim fat from edge of slices, and rub over heated skillet. Snip fat edges of slices in several places to keep edge from curling. Put in skillet, and panbroil until browned on both sides, 2 to 5 minutes on each side for uncooked slices and 1½ to 2 minutes for fully cooked slices.

☐ **To Panfry Slices**—Follow directions given for panbroiling but cook ham in a small amount of fat.

TIMETABLE FOR BAKING
UNCOOKED AND FULLY COOKED STANDARD CURED HAM

CUT	APPROXIMATE WEIGHT (POUNDS)	OVEN TEMPERATURE	INTERNAL TEMPERATURE	APPROXIMATE COOKING TIME (MINUTES PER POUND)
Uncooked Ham				
Whole	10 to 14	300°F. to 325°F.	160°F.	18 to 20
Half	5 to 7	300°F. to 325°F.	160°F.	22 to 25
End	3 to 4	325°F.	160°F.	35 to 40
Fully Cooked Ham				
Whole	12 to 16	325°F.	125°F. to 130°F.	10 to 15
Half	6 to 8	325°F.	125°F. to 130°F.	18 to 24

HAM COOK BOOK

The Perennial Pleasure of Ham: A meat for all seasons ■ A meat for all meals ■ A meat for young and old ■

FRESH HAM

ROAST FRESH HAM
1 fresh ham
1 garlic clove, cut
　Salt and pepper to taste
1 tablespoon caraway seed
4 onions, sliced
2 carrots, sliced
2 celery stalks, sliced
1 bay leaf
3 whole cloves
1 cup water
1 cup dry white wine

Allow ½ pound uncooked meat for each serving. Score skin of ham in 2 directions, making a diamond pattern. Rub meat on all sides with garlic, salt, pepper, and caraway seed. Put onions, carrots, celery, bay leaf, and cloves on bottom of large baking pan. Add water. Lay ham,

fat side down, on vegetables. Roast, uncovered, in preheated slow oven (325° F.) for 1 hour. Baste frequently with pan juices and wine. Turn meat fat side up and roast until done. Roasting time is about 4½ hours for a 5-pound ham from the time the meat is put in the oven. Or roast to 185°F. on a meat thermometer.

COLD FRESH HAM
　Fresh ham, 6 to 7 pounds, boned
　　and rolled
　Salt and pepper to taste
　Rosemary
2 garlic cloves

Season meat with salt, pepper, and just a little rosemary. Cut each garlic clove in several pieces. Bury each garlic piece just under the surface of the meat by making tiny gashes and inserting pieces. (Remove garlic before serving.) Put on

rack in roasting pan, and roast in preheated slow oven (325°F.) for 30 to 35 minutes per pound (185°F. internal temperature on a meat thermometer). Cool, but do not refrigerate. Serve with one of the ham sauces on page 859 and spiced fruit. Makes 6 to 8 servings.

PORK FRICASSEE FILIPINO
1 fresh ham (about 8 pounds)
½ cup soy sauce
　Juice of 1 lemon
2 teaspoons poultry seasoning
1½ teaspoons salt
½ teaspoon pepper
1 teaspoon ground ginger
2 medium onions, chopped
2 cups water
6 tablespoons cornstarch

Have meat sliced into 1-inch slices. Remove bones, trim off fat, and cut slices into pieces about 1 x 1½ inches. Combine remaining ingredients except water and cornstarch. Pour over meat. Let stand for at least 30 minutes. Put in large kettle, add water, and bring to boil. Cover and simmer for 1½ hours, or until tender. Skim fat from broth. Thicken with cornstarch mixed with a little cold water. Simmer for about 5 minutes. Makes 12 servings.

CURED HAM

Note: In the recipes that follow, the ingredients specify fully cooked (ready-to-eat), uncooked (cook-be-fore-eating), or cooked ham. As an ingredient "cooked ham" refers to either fully cooked or uncooked ham which has been baked, broiled, etc., at home. It may also be fully cooked ham, as bought.

APPETIZERS

HAM-STUFFED CHICKEN LEGS
8 chicken legs
8 cooked ham pieces, about 2 x 1 x 1 inches
2 eggs, slightly beaten
Fine dry bread crumbs
Melted butter or margarine

Remove bone from chicken pieces, keeping skin intact. With skin side down, pound chicken to flatten slightly. In center of each put a piece of cooked ham. Fold chicken over, pull skin to cover, and fasten with skewer or strong wooden toothpicks. Dip into eggs and roll in crumbs. Put in shallow baking dish and pour over each a little melted butter. Cover; bake in preheated slow oven (325°F.) for about 1¼ hours. Remove skewers. Serve plain or with gravy made from drippings in baking dish. Makes 8 servings.

HAM DIP
1 cup ground cooked ham
3 tablespoons mayonnaise
2 tablespoons chili sauce
1 tablespoon prepared mustard
½ teaspoon each of chili powder and brown sugar

Mix all ingredients well and chill in refrigerator. Serve with hot potato chips. Makes about 1¼ cups.
Note: This keeps well in refrigerator.

HAM AND CHEESE BITES
Remove crusts from 6 slices of white bread. Slice thin 1 package (8 ounces) Mozzarella cheese. On each of 3 bread slices place cheese, a slice of boiled ham, and another layer of cheese. Cover with other 3 slices of bread. Fry gently

in butter until golden on both sides. With a sharp knife, cut each sandwich into quarters. Serve hot. Makes 12.

SMITHFIELD HAM CANAPÉS
Make 24 small baking powder biscuits, or heat beaten biscuits from a package. Split biscuits and place bits of cooked Smithfield ham (about ¼ pound altogether), sliced paper-thin, between halves. Serve with a little bowl of Dijon mustard, so the guests may season the canapé if they like. Makes 24.

HAM TURNOVERS
1¼ cups ground cooked ham
1 teaspoon curry powder
1 teaspoon Worcestershire
Dash of cayenne
Mayonnaise (2 to 3 tablespoons)
1 box pastry mix
1 egg yolk
1 teaspoon cold water

Mix first 4 ingredients. Add enough mayonnaise to moisten. Roll prepared pastry mix to ⅛-inch thickness. Cut in 3-inch squares. Put about 1 tablespoon of the mixture in one corner of each square. Moisten edges with water and fold over to form a triangle. Crimp edges with fork, and cut 1 or 2 gashes in top to allow steam to escape. Put on baking sheet and brush with egg yolk beaten with 1 teaspoon water. Bake in preheated very hot oven (450°F.) for 15 minutes, or until golden brown. Serve hot. Makes 12 to 14.

HAM-AND-CHEESE APPETIZERS
1½ cups grated process American cheese
¼ cup evaporated milk
1 cup ground cooked ham
¼ cup ketchup
1 teaspoon powdered mustard
6 slices toast

Melt cheese in milk in top part of double boiler over boiling water. Add remaining ingredients, except toast; mix well. Trim crusts from toast; spread one side of slices with mixture. Cut into fingers and reheat in preheated moderate oven (350°F.). Makes 1½ dozen.

SOUP

HAM AND CORN POTATO SOUP
Baked-ham bone
Water
4 cups diced potatoes
1 onion, chopped
About 2 cups (one 1-pound can) cream-style corn
2 cups milk
¼ cup minced parsley
Salt and pepper to taste
4 slices of rye bread, cubed
¼ cup ham-fat drippings

Break bone at joints; cover and simmer in 6 cups water for 1½ hours. Remove bone and take off meat. Add meat, pota-

toes, and onion to broth. Cook until potatoes are tender. Add corn, milk, and parsley. Season. Heat. Serve with the bread cubes already browned in drippings. Make 4 large servings.

HAM-LIMA BEAN SOUP
1 box (1 pound) dried Lima beans
10 cups cold water
1 ham bone with scraps
1 onion, peeled and sliced
2 celery stalks, sliced
8 whole black peppercorns
2 carrots, peeled and cut in chunks
¼ teaspoon powdered mustard
1 bay leaf
1 leek, sliced (optional)
3 tablespoons butter or margarine
2 tablespoons all-purpose flour
1½ cups milk

Pick over and wash beans. Put in large kettle and add the water. Bring to boil and boil for 2 minutes. Cover and let stand for 1 hour. Add next 8 ingredients. Bring again to boil, cover and simmer for about 1½ hours. Remove bone and force mixture through sieve or food mill. Or whirl in blender until smooth. Melt butter and blend in flour. Add milk and cook, stirring, until thickened. Add to bean mixture with any ham scraps removed from bone. Heat. Makes 2½ quarts, or 6 to 8 servings.

HAM DUMPLINGS
1 cup ground lean cooked ham
¾ cup all-purpose flour
¼ teaspoon salt
1 teaspoon baking powder
¼ teaspoon each thyme and sage
Dash of mace
⅓ cup milk
Chicken broth or other stock or soup

Mix lightly all ingredients, except broth. Drop by teaspoonfuls into boiling broth. Cover and simmer for 10 minutes, or until dumplings are cooked. Makes about 16, or 4 servings.
Note: Try them in split pea soup if you have hearty eaters.

MAIN DISHES

BAKED HAM WITH SPICY SAUCE
1 cup orange or pineapple juice
¾ cup light brown sugar, packed
2 teaspoons powdered mustard
¼ teaspoon ground cloves
⅛ teaspoon nutmeg
½ teaspoon ginger
3 teaspoons rum extract
6–pound rolled, boneless fully cooked ham (or 5-pound canned ham)
Whole cloves
½ cup raisins, plumped in boiling water
1 tablespoon fresh lemon juice
1 tablespoon arrowroot or cornstarch
1 tablespoon water

Mix first 6 ingredients and bring to boil. Simmer, stirring, until sugar is dissolved. Add 2 teaspoons rum extract. Pierce ham several times with fork and cover with marinade. Let stand for 4 hours, basting occasionally with marinade. Remove ham, put on rack in roasting pan and bake in preheated slow oven (325°F.) for 1 hour. Remove from oven and score with knife. Stud with cloves. Increase heat to 425°F. and bake for 30 minutes longer, basting frequently with marinade. Remove ham. Add drained raisins and lemon juice to pan drippings. Blend arrowroot and 1 tablespoon water and stir into mixture. Cook, stirring, until thickened. Add remaining 1 teaspoon rum extract. Serve sauce with ham. Makes 8 to 10 servings.

HAM IN CIDER

- ½ bone-in uncooked ham (about 6 pounds)
- 2 large carrots, scraped and sliced
- 3 medium onions, peeled and sliced
- 3 stalks celery, diced
- Few parsley sprigs
- 12 whole cloves
- 6 whole black peppercorns
- 1 bay leaf
- Cider (about 2 to 3 quarts)

Put ham in kettle and add remaining ingredients, except cider. Add enough cider to cover ham. Bring to boil, cover and simmer for 2 hours, or until tender. Serve hot, or let cool in the broth, remove and chill. Makes 8 servings.

GLAZED COLD HAM

Put ⅔ cup cold water in small bowl; sprinkle with 4 envelopes unflavored gelatin. Put 1 cup sugar in heavy skillet and cook, stirring constantly, until golden brown and syrupy. Remove from heat and very gradually stir in ¼ cup hot water. Then add 1 cup sugar mixed with ⅛ teaspoon ground cloves and 1 teaspoon powdered mustard. Stir and cook for 2 or 3 minutes longer, or until mixture is of the consistency of whipped cream. Remove from heat and add gelatin; stir until dissolved. Add ½ cup cold water; cool. Put scored ham on rack on a tray. Pour glaze over top and sides of ham, spreading evenly with spoon. Add remaining glaze for a second coat. Let ham stand until glaze is firm, about 15 minutes. Canned hams are especially attractive when glazed this way. Makes enough glaze for one 5-pound canned ham or an 8- to 10-pound cooked ham.

HAM-AND-BEAN BAKE

- ⅔ cup chopped baked-ham fat
- 1 onion, chopped
- 2 tablespoons ketchup
- 1 tablespoon molasses
- 1 teaspoon powdered mustard
- ½ teaspoon salt
- ⅛ teaspoon pepper
- 1 teaspoon Worcestershire
- ¾ cup ground baked ham
- About 2¼ cups (one 1-pound, 4-ounce can) dried Lima beans
- About 2¼ cups (one 1-pound, 4-ounce can) red kidney beans

Fry ham fat until crisp. Pour off drippings. Add onion and cook slowly for 5 minutes. Add remaining ingredients. Pour into shallow baking dish. Bake in preheated moderate oven (350°F.) for 25 minutes, or until thoroughly heated. Makes 4 servings.

HAM BAKED IN CLARET

- 1 center-cut fully cooked ham slice, 1 inch thick (about 2 pounds)
- 1 teaspoon powdered mustard
- 2 cups chopped peeled tart apples
- ½ cup firmly packed brown sugar
- 1 cup claret

Put ham in large shallow baking dish. Sprinkle with mustard. Top with apples and sprinkle with brown sugar. Pour claret over ham. Cover; bake in preheated moderate oven (350°F.) for 1 hour. Uncover; bake for 30 minutes longer. Makes 4 servings.

SPICED HAM AND BANANAS

- Few whole cloves
- 1 center-cut fully cooked ham slice (about 2 pounds)
- Prepared mustard
- Brown sugar
- ½ cup water
- Juice of 1 lemon
- 2 or 3 firm ripe bananas

Insert cloves into fat of ham. Put ham in shallow baking dish and spread with mustard. Sprinkle with brown sugar. Add water and half of lemon juice. Bake in preheated slow oven (300°F.) for about 50 minutes. Peel bananas, cut into halves lengthwise, and arrange on ham. Sprinkle with brown sugar and remaining lemon juice. Bake for 10 to 15 minutes longer, basting bananas several times with the drippings in pan. Makes 4 servings.

STUFFED HAM SLICES

- 2 center-cut fully cooked ham slices, 1 inch thick (about 3 pounds)
- 24 whole cloves
- ½ pound fresh spinach
- Chopped tops from 1 bunch of green onions
- 1 cup chopped celery leaves
- 6 parsley sprigs, chopped
- 1 teaspoon salt
- ¼ teaspoon pepper
- Dash of cayenne
- Dash of ground mace or nutmeg

Score edges of ham slices and insert 12 cloves into the fat of each. Mix remaining ingredients and use to stuff ham slices, sandwich fashion. Insert several skewers to hold slices together. Put on rack in shallow baking pan and bake in preheated slow oven (325°F.) for about 1½ hours. Makes 6 servings.

HAM AND BROCCOLI CASSEROLE

- 1 box (11 ounces) frozen cut-up broccoli
- 1 cup diced cooked ham
- 1 cup (one 8-ounce can) midget potatoes, drained
- ¼ cup butter
- 1¼ cups all-purpose flour
- 2⅓ cups milk
- ¼ teaspoon seasoned pepper
- ½ teaspoon steak sauce
- 2 teaspoons prepared mustard
- ¼ cup grated Cheddar cheese
- Seasoned salt
- 1½ teaspoons baking powder
- ½ teaspoon salt
- 2 tablespoons chopped parsley
- 2½ tablespoons cooking oil

Cook broccoli until just tender; drain. Combine with ham and potatoes in shallow 1½-quart baking dish. Melt butter and blend in ¼ cup flour. Gradually add 2 cups milk and cook, stirring, until thickened. Add next 4 ingredients and seasoned salt to taste. Mix next 3 ingredients with remaining flour. Mix oil and remaining milk and stir into flour mixture with fork. Drop from tablespoon onto mixture in baking dish. Bake in preheated hot oven (425°F.) for 25 to 30 minutes. Makes 6 servings.

HAM AND GREEN-NOODLE CASSEROLE

- 2 cups green noodles, cooked and drained
- 1 cup dairy sour cream
- 1 cup diced cooked ham
- ½ cup sliced ripe olives
- ½ cup chopped dry-toasted or dry-roasted peanuts
- 1 can (3 ounces) chopped mushrooms, drained
- 1 teaspoon prepared mustard
- ¼ teaspoon pepper
- 1 can Cheddar cheese soup
- 1 cup grated sharp Cheddar cheese

Mix well all ingredients, except cheese. Put in shallow 1½-quart baking dish. Sprinkle with cheese. Bake in preheated moderate oven (350°F.) for 25 minutes. Makes 6 servings.

HAM AND POTATOES AU GRATIN

- 1½ cups diced cooked ham
- 3 cups diced cooked potato
- 4 tablespoons margarine
- 1 small onion, minced
- 3 tablespoons all-purpose flour
- 2 cups milk
- Seasoned salt and pepper to taste
- ½ cup grated sharp Cheddar cheese
- 2 tablespoons fine, dry bread crumbs

Put ham and potato into shallow 1½-quart baking dish. Melt 3 tablespoons margarine, add onion and cook until golden. Blend in flour. Gradually add milk and cook, stirring until thickened. Season with salt and pepper; pour over ham and potato. Sprinkle with cheese and crumbs. Dot with remaining margarine. Bake in preheated hot oven (400°F.) for about 20 minutes. Makes 4 servings.

BAKED CRANBERRY HAM CUBES

- 4 cups diced cooked ham
- 3 tablespoons butter or margarine
- ½ cup water
- ½ cup sugar
- 1½ cups cranberries
- 2 tablespoons grated orange rind
- Salt and pepper

Lightly brown ham in the butter. Bring water and sugar to boil, stirring until sugar is dissolved. Add ¾ cup of the cranberries and simmer, covered, for 15

Baked Ham with Pineapple Glaze

minutes. Add orange rind and salt and pepper to taste. Mix ham and sauce in shallow 1½-quart baking dish. Bake, uncovered, in preheated moderate oven (350°F.) for 20 minutes. Add remaining cranberries and bake for 10 to 15 minutes longer. Makes 6 servings.

HAM AND SWEETS
2 cups small slices of cooked ham
About 2 cups (one 1-pound, 2-ounce can) sweet potatoes
4 slices of canned pineapple
8 whole cloves
½ cup pineapple juice
2 tablespoons brown sugar
¼ teaspoon ground cinnamon
Dash of ground nutmeg

Arrange ham slices and halved potatoes alternately in shallow casserole or large pie pan, standing ham upright when possible. Cut pineapple slices into halves and arrange on top of ham and potatoes. Insert cloves in ham; pour juice over top. Sprinkle with sugar and spices. Bake in preheated moderate oven (350°F.) for about 25 minutes. Makes 4 servings.

BAKED HAM-AND-PORK BALLS
¾ pound ground fully cooked ham
½ pound lean pork, ground
½ cup milk
½ cup cracker crumbs
¾ cup brown sugar, packed
½ cup vinegar
½ cup water
6 whole cloves
1 tablespoon powdered mustard

Mix first 4 ingredients and shape in 12 balls about 2 inches in diameter. Put in shallow baking dish. Bring remaining ingredients to boil and pour over ham balls. Bake, uncovered, in preheated slow oven (325°F.) for about 2 hours. Makes 4 servings.

HAM AND CABBAGE WITH TOMATOES
½ medium cabbage, shredded
1 center-cut, uncooked ham slice, 1 inch thick, cut in 4 serving pieces
1 can (1 pound) tomatoes
½ teaspoon pepper
½ teaspoon monosodium glutamate
1 teaspoon steak sauce
1 teaspoon sugar

Put cabbage in shallow 1½-quart baking dish. Arrange ham pieces on top. Mix remaining ingredients and spread on ham. Bake uncovered, in preheated moderate oven (350°F.) for about 1 hour. Makes 4 servings.
Note: A fully cooked ham slice can be used in the recipe above. Reduce cooking time to 45 minutes.

CHICKEN IN HAM BLANKETS
3 cups diced cooked potatoes
3 tablespoons butter or margarine
3 tablespoons all-purpose flour
2 cups milk
1 cup diced sharp Cheddar cheese
Salt and pepper
8 small slices of cooked chicken
8 slices of boiled or baked ham
Paprika

Put ¾ cup potato in each of 4 individual baking dishes. Melt butter in saucepan; blend in flour. Gradually add milk and cook, stirring, until thickened. Add cheese and stir until cheese is melted. Season to taste with salt and pepper. Reserve about ½ cup sauce and pour remainder over potato. Put a slice of chicken at one side of each ham slice and fold ham over to form a triangle. Arrange two on each dish of potato. Top with remaining ½ cup sauce and sprinkle with paprika. Put in preheated hot oven (400°F.) for 10 minutes, or until thoroughly heated. Or broil under medium heat until lightly browned. Makes 4 servings.

HAM AND VEAL LOAF
1½ pounds ground uncooked ham
½ pound ground raw veal
2 eggs
 Dried bread rolled to make 1½ cups fine crumbs
1 teaspoon celery salt
⅛ teaspoon pepper
¾ cup milk
 Creamy Horseradish Sauce (see page 859)

Mix all ingredients except Sauce. Shape into two rolls to fit into two greased No. 2½ cans (3½ cups each). Shake mixture; then press down lightly. Cover each can with foil or several layers of wax paper and tie securely. Put on rack in large kettle; surround with water half the depth of cans. Cover kettle and bring water to boil. Reduce heat and simmer for 3 hours. Turn hot or cooled loaves onto board and slice; cut slices into halves if preferred. Serve hot or cold with Creamy Horseradish Sauce. Makes 8 servings.

HAM CORN-BREAD RING WITH CREAMED PEAS
¾ cup yellow cornmeal
1 cup all-purpose flour
¼ cup sugar
2 teaspoons baking powder
½ teaspoon baking soda
¾ teaspoon salt
1 cup dairy sour cream
¼ cup milk
1 egg, beaten
2 tablespoons margarine, melted
1 cup ground cooked ham
 Creamed cooked peas

Mix all ingredients, except peas, just to blend. Pour into well-greased 6-cup ring mold, patting mixture down and leveling off top. Bake in preheated hot oven (425°F.) for about 20 minutes. Let stand for 2 or 3 minutes. Then turn out on hot serving plate. Fill center with hot peas. Makes 6 servings.

Note: Other creamed vegetables such as onions, asparagus, broccoli, or mixed vegetables can be substituted for the peas.

HAM BISCUIT ROLL WITH CHEESE SAUCE
¼ cup butter or margarine
¼ cup all-purpose flour
2 cups milk
1½ to 2 cups ground cooked ham
1 tablespoon instant minced onion
 Salt, pepper, and powdered mustard
 Biscuit dough (recipe using 2 cups flour)
¾ cup grated Cheddar cheese

Melt butter and blend in flour. Gradually add milk and cook, stirring, until thickened. Mix ham, onion, ¼ teaspoon each salt and pepper, and ¼ teaspoon powdered mustard. Stir in enough of the first mixture to hold ingredients together. Roll out biscuit dough to form a rectangle about 12 x 10 inches. Spread with ham mixture. Roll up from 10-inch end as for jelly roll. Cut in 1-inch slices and put, cut side down, on greased cookie sheet. Bake in preheated very hot oven (450°F.) for 15 to 20 minutes. Add cheese to first mixture and heat, stirring, until cheese is melted. Season to taste with salt, pepper, and powdered mustard. Serve on ham biscuits. Makes 6 servings.

CURRIED HAM AND FRESH-PORK LOAF
1 pound boiled ham ends
1 pound fresh lean pork
1 garlic clove, minced
1 small onion, chopped
3 teaspoons salt
1 teaspoon pepper
2 teaspoons curry powder
1 to 2 teaspoons crumbled dried sage
1 egg white
½ cup evaporated milk
4 slices of bacon
2 quarts boiling water
¼ cup vinegar

Force meats through food chopper twice, using medium blade. Add garlic, onion, 2 teaspoons salt, the pepper, curry powder, sage, egg white, and evaporated milk. Mix lightly but thoroughly, and shape into a rounded loaf about 9 inches long. Lay bacon out on a square of cheesecloth. Put meat loaf on bacon and roll up in cloth. Tie ends with cord. Put on trivet in large kettle. Add boiling water, vinegar, and remaining salt. Cover and simmer for 2½ hours. Remove from liquid and let stand until cold. Chill, unwrap, and cut in thin slices. Makes 6 to 8 servings.

ORANGE-GLAZED HAM LOAF
1 pound uncooked ham
1 pound ground veal
2 eggs, beaten
1 cup fresh orange juice
½ teaspoon salt
¼ teaspoon pepper
1 cup fine, dry bread crumbs
 Orange Juice Glaze
 Orange slices

Mix lightly ham, veal, eggs, orange juice, salt, pepper, and bread crumbs. Shape in loaf and put in shallow baking pan. Bake in preheated moderate oven (350°F.) for 1½ hours, basting frequently with half the Orange Juice Glaze. Ten minutes before ham loaf is done, top with orange slices. Serve with remaining Glaze. Makes 6 servings.

Orange Juice Glaze
Combine 3 tablespoons sugar and 1 tablespoon cornstarch in saucepan. Add 1½ cups fresh orange juice and cook, stirring, until slightly thickened.

GLAZED BANANA-HAM ROLLS
Cut 4 firm ripe bananas in half crosswise, then cut each half in 2 lengthwise pieces. Spread one cut side with peanut butter and cover with matching piece, sandwich fashion. Wrap each of the 8 pieces in a long, thin slice of cooked ham. Sauté rolls lightly in hot margarine until browned on both sides. Cover with a glaze of ¼ cup honey and ½ cup fresh orange juice, mixed together. Cook for a few minutes longer, basting with the glaze in the pan. Makes 4 servings.

HAM AND CORN FRITTERS
 About 1 cup (one 8½-ounce can) cream-style corn
2 eggs
¾ cup diluted evaporated milk
2 teaspoons baking powder
2 cups all-purpose flour
1 teaspoon salt
¼ pound boiled ham, diced
 Fat for deep frying

Mix all ingredients except fat. Drop by heaping tablespoonfuls into hot deep fat (365°F. on a frying thermometer) and fry until golden brown and done. Serve hot, with applesauce if desired. Makes 4 servings.

HAM CROQUETTES
¼ cup butter or margarine
¼ cup all-purpose flour
1 small onion, minced
1 cup milk
2 eggs
1 tablespoon fresh lemon juice
1½ cups ground cooked ham
 Salt and pepper
 Fine dry bread crumbs
 Fat for deep frying

Melt butter; blend in flour and onion. Add milk and cook, stirring constantly, until very thick. Stir into 1 egg beaten with lemon juice. Add ham and salt and pepper to taste. Pour into a shallow dish; cool. Shape into 4 croquettes. Chill. Dip into crumbs, then into 1 egg beaten with 2 tablespoons water. Dip again into crumbs and let stand for 30 minutes. Fry in hot deep fat (390°F. on a frying thermometer) for 2 minutes, or until done. Serve with a Creamy Horseradish Sauce or Hot Mustard Sauce (page 859). Makes 4 servings.

HAM HAWAIIAN
¼ cup butter or margarine
½ medium green pepper, chopped
2 cups slivered cooked ham

**Mustard-Glazed
Ham Slices**

Glazed Cold Ham

About 4 slices (one 9-ounce can)
of pineapple
2 tablespoons brown sugar
1½ tablespoons cornstarch
1½ tablespoons vinegar
1½ teaspoons prepared mustard
⅛ teaspoon pepper
¾ cup cold water
1⅓ cups packaged precooked rice
⅛ teaspoon ground cloves

Melt half of butter in skillet. Add green pepper and ham; cook for 5 minutes. Drain pineapple, reserving liquid. Cut slices into bite-size pieces. Mix liquid and next 6 ingredients. Stir into ham mixture; cook, stirring, until thickened. Add pineapple; heat. Prepare rice as directed on the package; then add remaining butter and the cloves. Serve with the ham mixture. Makes 4 servings.

HAM À LA CRÈME
6 green onions, chopped fine
¼ cup butter or margarine
¼ cup all-purpose flour
¾ cup each of milk and light cream
2 tablespoons tomato purée
¼ cup white wine
Salt and pepper
8 thin slices of baked or boiled ham

In top part of double boiler over direct heat, cook onions in butter for 5 minutes. Blend in flour. Add milk and cream; cook, stirring, until thickened. Put over boiling water and stir in purée and wine. Add salt and pepper to taste. Cut ham into strips and put in shallow broiler-proof dish. Pour sauce over ham and put under broiler until lightly browned and bubbly. Makes 4 servings.

HAM-ASPARAGUS ROLLS WITH MACARONI AND CHEESE
8 slices boiled ham
16 to 24 spears cooked asparagus
2 tablespoons butter or margarine
1 quart milk
1 tablespoon instant minced onion
2 teaspoons seasoned salt
1 teaspoon powdered mustard
¼ teaspoon pepper
2 cups broken macaroni
2 cups grated Cheddar cheese

Roll each slice of ham around 2 or 3 spears of asparagus. Heat lightly in butter in skillet. Remove and keep warm. Pour milk into skillet, add onion, salt, mustard, and pepper. Bring to boil. Gradually add macaroni, keeping mixture boiling. Cook, uncovered, stirring often, for 20 minutes. Stir in cheese and top with ham rolls. Heat for a few minutes if necessary. Makes 4 servings.

HAM FRIED RICE
1 cup uncooked rice
2 eggs, slightly beaten
¼ cup cooking oil
¼ cup sliced green onions with tops
2 tablespoons soy sauce
½ teaspoon sugar
¼ teaspoon monosodium glutamate
1 cup diced cooked ham

Cook rice without salt until tender. Drain

and cool. Scramble eggs slightly in 1 tablespoon oil; set aside. Heat remaining 3 tablespoons oil in skillet. Add green onion and heat for 1 minute, stirring. Add rice and stir quickly to coat with oil. When heated, stir in remaining ingredients, including eggs. Serve with additional soy sauce, if desired. Makes 4 servings.

HAM KEDGEREE
⅔ cup uncooked rice
1 cup diced cooked ham
2 hard-cooked eggs, chopped
1 teaspoon curry powder
2 tablespoons minced parsley
¼ cup heavy cream (or enough to moisten)
Salt and pepper to taste

Cook and drain rice. Add remaining ingredients and heat, stirring gently. Makes 4 servings.

HAM HASH
4 medium potatoes, peeled and cooked
1 small onion
½ green pepper
1 cup diced cooked ham
¼ teaspoon salt
⅛ teaspoon pepper
Dash of dried thyme
3 tablespoons butter or margarine

Force first 4 ingredients through food chopper, using coarse blade. Stir in seasonings. Heat butter in skillet, add the hash and cook until well browned, stirring frequently. Makes 6 servings.

FRIZZLED HAM WITH PIQUANT SAUCE
In a little margarine in skillet, frizzle enough thinly sliced cooked ham for 4 servings. Put on hot platter. Take skillet off heat and add 3 tablespoons vinegar; 1½ teaspoons prepared mustard; ½ teaspoon sugar; ⅛ teaspoon paprika; and 1 tablespoon guava, currant, grape, or apple jelly. Heat, stirring, until blended. Pour over ham. Makes 4 servings.

BAKED HAM WITH CUMBERLAND SAUCE
Cut cold baked ham into thin slices, arrange on platter, and serve with Cumberland Sauce. To make sauce, mix in saucepan 1 teaspoon powdered mustard, 1 teaspoon paprika, ½ teaspoon ground ginger, a dash of salt, 1 tablespoon water, grated rind of 2 oranges, 2 tablespoons fresh orange juice, and 1 tablespoon fresh lemon juice. Let stand for 30 minutes. Add ¼ cup currant or apple jelly and heat, stirring, until jelly is dissolved. Cool and strain. Add 2 tablespoons port wine and quartered slices of ½ orange. Makes 4 servings.

● SALADS AND SANDWICHES ●

HAM SALAD
2 cups diced cooked ham
½ cup chopped salted peanuts
1 cup diced celery
Mayonnaise
Salad greens

Mix first 3 ingredients. Moisten with mayonnaise. Serve on greens. Makes 4 servings.

BROILED HAM SALAD
2 cups finely diced cooked ham
1½ cups finely diced celery
¼ cup lightly seasoned French dressing
½ cup salad dressing or mayonnaise
⅓ cup dairy sour cream
¼ cup toasted slivered almonds
2 cups finely crushed potato chips
1 cup grated Cheddar cheese
Salad greens

Marinate ham and celery in French dressing in refrigerator for 1 hour. Add salad dressing and sour cream and mix lightly. Put in 9-inch metal pie pan or 4 individual broiler-proof ramekins. Chill until almost ready to serve. Sprinkle with almonds. Mix potato chips and cheese and press on top of mixture. Put under broiler for 2 or 3 minutes, or until cheese is melted. Tuck greens around edge and serve. Makes 4 servings.

MOLDED HAM SALAD
2 envelopes unflavored gelatin
½ cup water
1 cup pineapple juice
1 tablespoon fresh lemon juice
½ teaspoon salt
1 tablespoon prepared mustard
1 teaspoon sugar
½ teaspoon paprika
1½ cups mayonnaise
1 cup finely diced celery
1 cup finely diced cooked ham
Salad greens
Broiled Ham Salad or fruit salad, optional

Soften gelatin in water. Dissolve over hot water. Add fruit juices and seasonings. Beat in mayonnaise. Chill until slightly thickened. (If mayonnaise is cold, it will not be necessary to chill mixture.) Fold in celery and ham. Pour into 6-cup mold and chill until firm. Unmold on salad greens. If desired, fill center with ham salad, using recipe for Broiled Ham Salad and omitting potato chips and cheese, or fill with fruit salad. Makes 6 servings.

HAM FRUIT SALAD
1 cup diced cooked ham
½ cup diced peeled orange
½ cup diced unpeeled apple
¾ cup diced pineapple or tidbits
½ cup diced banana
Salad greens
Fruit Dressing

Mix lightly all ingredients, except last 2.

Serve on greens with the Fruit Dressing. Makes 4 to 6 servings.

Fruit Dressing

In heavy saucepan mix 2 teaspoons grated orange rind, 1 teaspoon grated lemon rind, juice of 1 orange and 1 lemon (there should be ½ cup; if not enough, add a little water), 1 beaten egg, dash of salt, and ½ cup sugar. Bring to boil, stirring. Cool; then chill. When ready to serve, fold in ¼ cup dairy sour cream.

HOT HAM-CHEESE ROLLS

    8 sandwich rolls
1½ cups ground cooked ham
    1 cup shredded process American
       cheese
 ¼ cup chopped olives
 ½ cup minced celery
    1 tablespoon prepared mustard
    1 small onion, grated
 ⅛ teaspoon pepper
 ½ cup salad dressing
    1 teaspoon Worcestershire
       Melted butter or margarine

Cut a 1½-inch circle out of each roll so that the part beneath the crust is cone-shape; cut each top into halves. Scoop out some crumbs from each roll. Mix crumbs with remaining ingredients except butter. Fill rolls; replace tops. Brush with butter. Bake on ungreased cookie sheet in preheated slow oven (325°F.) for about 20 minutes. Makes 4 servings.

HAM SALAD BOATS

    2 cups chopped cooked ham
    1 cup diced celery
 ½ cup chopped green pepper
    1 onion slice, minced
    2 hard-cooked eggs, chopped
 ¼ cup chopped sweet pickle
    2 tablespoons prepared mustard
    8 frankfurter rolls
 ¾ cup mayonnaise

Mix all ingredients except last 2. Cut tops from rolls; remove centers. Crumble tops and centers coarsely and add to mixture. Add mayonnaise and mix well. Heap in rolls. Makes 4 servings.

WESTERN LONG BOYS

       French bread
       Butter or margarine
    1 small onion, chopped
 ⅓ cup chopped green pepper
    1 cup chopped cooked ham
    6 eggs, slightly beaten
 ½ cup milk
 ½ teaspoon salt
 ¼ teaspoon pepper
       Ketchup or chili sauce

Cut bread into four 6-inch lengths. Split, butter, and toast. Sauté onion, green pepper, and ham in 3 tablespoons butter in large skillet. Mix eggs, milk, salt, and pepper and pour into skillet. Scramble gently for 2 or 3 minutes, or until set. Top half of each Long Boy with egg mixture. Add top halves. Serve with ketchup. Makes 4.

HAM AND POTATO-SALAD SANDWICHES

Put a slice of baked or boiled ham and a layer of potato salad between slices of bread. Spread both sides of sandwiches with softened butter or margarine. Grill slowly until browned on both sides.

SAUCES FOR HAM
Spicy Cranberry Sauce

Crush 1¾ cups (one 1-pound can) cranberry jelly with fork and beat until smooth. Add ⅛ teaspoon each of ground cloves and cinnamon and 2 tablespoons port or Madeira.

Hot Mustard Sauce

Mix ¼ cup English-type or Dijon prepared mustard, 1 teaspoon powdered mustard, ¼ cup salad dressing or mayonnaise, and 2 tablespoons dairy sour cream.

Creamy Horseradish Sauce

 ½ cup heavy cream
 ½ teaspoon salt
       Dash of cayenne
 ½ teaspoon prepared mustard
    3 tablespoons mayonnaise
    2 to 4 tablespoons prepared
       horseradish

Whip cream until stiff. Stir in remaining ingredients. Serve on ham. Makes about 1 cup.

50 WAYS TO USE LEFTOVER HAM

HAM STRIPS

1. Creamed Potatoes—Combine in skillet 1 quart diced raw potatoes, 2 cups light cream, slivered ham (about 1½ cups), salt and pepper to taste, and dash of ground nutmeg. Simmer, covered, until potatoes are tender. Makes 4 generous servings.

2. Ham-Banana Salad—Combine ham with slivers of celery, bananas, and mustard-mayonnaise dressing for a delicious salad.

3. Ham-Bean Salad—Combine drained canned kidney beans with ham, chopped celery, chopped green pepper, pimiento, capers, salad dressing, and salt and pepper to taste.

4. Ham-Cheese Salad—Mix ham with strips of Swiss cheese and celery. Add wedges of tomatoes and toss with French dressing.

5. Rice—Combine ham with cooked rice, pineapple tidbits, and mayonnaise to taste.

6. Salads—Add ham strips to mixed-vegetable salad, potato salad, chicken salad, or macaroni salad.

7. Sauerkraut—Cook sauerkraut with 1

chopped onion and 1 chopped apple for about 30 minutes. Add ham and cook for 15 minutes longer.

8. Slaw—Mix ham with shredded raw carrots and cabbage; add mayonnaise, salt, pepper, and vinegar to taste.

9. Tomatoes—Combine ham strips with canned tomatoes and hominy. Simmer for about 30 minutes. Season to taste.

10. Tossed Salad—Combine ham with strips of cheese, canned peas, chopped celery, sliced cucumber, head lettuce broken into chunks, wedges of tomato, and French dressing.

HAM CHUNKS OR CUBES

11. Baked Beans—Add ham chunks to baked beans with a little sweet-pickle relish. Sprinkle with brown sugar and heat or bake.

12. Creamed Ham, Eggs, and Mushrooms—For 6 servings, combine 2 cans cream-of-mushroom soup and ¾ cup milk. Add about 1½ cups cubed ham, and heat. Add ½ pound lightly browned mushrooms and 6 quartered hard-cooked eggs; stir lightly. Heat gently. Serve on toast or in patty shells.

13. Curried Ham and Rice—Combine 1 can cream-of-chicken soup with 2 cups cooked rice and 1 cup cubed ham. Season with curry powder. Garnish with chunks and cubes. Makes 3 or 4 servings.

14. Ham-and-Egg Shortcake—Heat cream-of-mushroom soup with a little milk. Add ham and diced hard-cooked eggs; heat. Serve on shortcake made with prepared biscuit mix. Sprinkle with chopped parsley.

15. Ham Creole—Cook 1 chopped onion and 1 chopped green pepper in 2 tablespoons fat for a few minutes. Add 2 cups (one 1-pound can) tomatoes. Simmer for 10 minutes. Add 2 cups ham and cook for 5 minutes longer. Makes 4 servings.

16. Ham Macédoine—Mix 2 cups cooked mixed vegetables with 1 can condensed cream-of-chicken soup, undiluted, and 1½ cups ham chunks. Sprinkle with buttered bread crumbs; bake, uncovered, in preheated moderate oven (350°F.) for about 30 minutes. Makes 4 servings.

17. Ham Pie—Heat canned cream-of-mushroom soup with a little milk. Add ham and cooked peas. Top with mashed potatoes and sprinkle with grated Parmesan cheese. Bake in preheated hot oven (425°F.) until potatoes are brown. Sprinkle with chopped parsley.

18. Ham Succotash—Heat ham with cooked Lima beans and whole-kernel corn. Season with onion and salt and pepper.

19. Kabobs—Alternate chunks of ham with pineapple and green pepper. Sprinkle with brown sugar and broil until lightly browned and hot.

20. Luncheon Salad—Combine ham with chunks of hard-cooked eggs, celery, green pepper, mayonnaise, and salt and pepper. Serve on salad greens.

21. Paprika Ham—Mix 1 cup tomato sauce with 1 tablespoon prepared mustard, 1 teaspoon paprika, and 1 teaspoon instant minced onion. Add 1½ cups ham; simmer for 10 minutes. Stir in 1 cup dairy sour cream and heat slightly. Serve on noodles. Makes 4 servings.

22. Rice Casserole—Add 1 to 1½ cups ham to packaged Spanish rice with canned or cooked shrimps before cooking.

23. Veal and Ham Stew—Brown 1 pound stewing veal in 2 tablespoons butter or margarine. Add 1 can cream-of-mushroom soup and 1 cup water. Cover and simmer until tender. Add 1 cup ham, 2 sliced pimientos, and 8 chopped ripe olives. Simmer for about 10 minutes. Serve on noodles or rice. Makes 4 servings.

GROUND OR MINCED HAM

24. Baked or Stuffed Potatoes—Cut potatoes into halves; scoop from shell, mash, add ham, and season with salt and pepper. Pile in shell and brown in preheated hot oven (400°F.).

25. Cabbage Rolls—Cut core from medium head of cabbage. Cover with boiling water, removing leaves as they become tender. Stuff with 2 cups ham mixed with 2 cups cooked rice, salt, pepper, and onion salt. Add one 1-pound can of sauerkraut, 1 teaspoon caraway seeds, and 1 cup water. Cover and simmer for 1 hour. Makes 4 servings.

26. Deviled Eggs—Add ham to filling for deviled eggs; serve on toast with a hot cheese sauce.

27. Egg-Salad Sandwich Filling—Combine ham with chopped hard-cooked eggs, chopped olives, prepared mustard, and salad dressing to make a tempting sandwich filling.

28. Ham and Pickle Sandwich Filling—Combine ham with chopped sweet pickle, mayonnaise to moisten, and prepared mustard and pepper to taste.

29. Ham-Broccoli-Noodle Casserole—Combine 2 cups ham with 1 cup cooked chopped broccoli, 3 cups cooked noodles, and 1 can cream-of-mushroom soup, thinned with ½ cup milk. Sprinkle with shredded cheese and bake in preheated moderate oven (350°F.) for about 15 minutes.

30. Ham Shirred Eggs—Put 2 tablespoons ham in bottom of a custard cup and add 2 tablespoons heavy cream and 1 raw egg. Put on rack in skillet with 1 cup water. Cover and cook to desired doneness. Makes 1 serving.

31. Ham-Stuffed Buns—Combine minced ham with an equal amount of shredded cheese; moisten with mayonnaise; season with mustard and horseradish. Fill buns, wrap, and heat.

32. Hash—Combine ham with chopped cooked potatoes; season with onions and pepper. Fry in small amount of fat until lightly browned.

33. Hot Ham and Cheese Sandwich—Mix ham with shredded cheese, chopped olives, minced celery, and mayonnaise to moisten. Season with prepared mustard, pepper, Worcestershire, and onion to taste. Scoop out center from sandwich rolls. Fill with mixture. Bake in preheated slow oven (325°F.) for about 15 minutes.

34. Pancakes—Fill pancakes with ham and pour over them hot cream-of-mushroom soup, thinned with a little milk.

35. Scrambled Eggs—Mix 1 cup diced process cheese with ½ cup water and 1 cup ham. Bring to boil, stirring. Add 6 slightly beaten eggs and scramble. Add ham to scrambled eggs. Makes 3 or 4 servings.

36. Sour-Cream Casserole—Mix 1½ cups ham with 1 cup dairy sour cream, 2 cups cooked noodles, 2 beaten eggs, and chopped parsley. Bake in shallow dish in preheated moderate oven (350°F.) for about 20 minutes. Makes 4 servings.

37. Stuffed Eggplant—Parboil eggplant in boiling water for about 10 minutes. Split into halves lengthwise and scoop out pulp. Combine with cooked rice, ham, onion, and salt and pepper to taste. Line a casserole with eggplant shells. Add mixture. Sprinkle with grated Parmesan cheese and bread crumbs; dot with butter. Bake in preheated hot oven (400°F.) for about 30 minutes.

38. Stuffed Mushrooms—Chop and cook mushroom stems and a little chopped onion in fat for a few minutes. Combine with ham, bread crumbs, and salt and pepper to taste. Fill mushroom caps. Put in pan with a little water. Bake in preheated moderate oven (375°F.) for about 15 minutes, or until tender.

39. Stuffed Onions—Parboil large onions. Remove centers, chop, and mix with ham. Season with salt and pepper. Stuff onions and bake for about 15 minutes. Sprinkle with chopped parsley.

40. Stuffed Peaches—Fill canned peach halves with ham; sprinkle with bread crumbs. Bake in preheated moderate oven (375°F.) for about 20 minutes.

41. Stuffed Peppers—Combine ham with cooked rice to stuff peppers.

42. Stuffing—Add ham to stuffing for breast of veal.

43. Sweet-Potato Bake—Add ham to mashed sweet potatoes, sprinkle with brown sugar, and bake in preheated moderate oven (350°F.) until lightly browned.

44. Waffles—Add ham to waffle batter before baking.

HAM BONES, SCRAPS, AND FAT

45. Black Beans and Rice—Cover ham bones with 2 quarts water. Add 1 pound dried black beans; bring to boil and boil for 2 minutes. Cover and let stand for 1 hour. Cook 1 cup chopped onions, 1 chopped green pepper, and 1 minced garlic clove in ½ cup olive oil for about 5 minutes. Add to beans with 2 bay leaves. Bring to boil and simmer, covered, for 2 hours, or until beans are tender, adding more water if necessary. Add ¼ cup wine vinegar. Serve with rice, chopped hard-cooked eggs, sliced red onions, and chopped parsley. Makes 6 to 8 servings.

46. Cracklings—Use cracklings (see Ham Fat, below) in biscuits, corn bread, or muffins.

47. Ham Fat—Save scraps of fat from ham. Cut into small pieces and render until pieces of fat are brown and crisp (cracklings). Pour off fat. Use liquid fat for frying eggs or potatoes and for making pastry.

48. Lentil Soup—Use directions for Pea Soup (below) adding 2 cups canned tomatoes.

49. Pea Soup—Cover ham bones with 2 quarts water. Add 1 onion, 1 celery stalk, and 1 pound split green peas. Simmer, covered, for 2 hours, or until thick. Remove bone and cut off any bits of ham. Add to soup. Season with salt, add more water if necessary, and heat.

50. Vegetable Dinner—Cover ham bone with 2 quarts water. Simmer for about 1 hour. Add potatoes, carrots, onions; cook until almost tender. Add wedges of cabbage and cook until all is tender. Remove bone, cut off any bits of ham, and add.

By Helen Evans Brown

Ham and eggs," says the American as he slides onto a stool at a quick lunch counter. "A grunt and two cackles," echoes the cook in the kitchen behind, and soon two amber-tinged slices of juicy pink ham and two perfectly fried eggs are set before the eager customer. Not far away, at a more exalted restaurant, a waiter discusses the *spécialités de maison:* "Quiche Bourbonnaise," perhaps, or *Wiener Eierkuchen*? Eggs Benedict? Very good, sir." And another dish of ham and eggs is polished off with relish.

In France, *soufflé de jambon* and *croque monsieur* are favorites. In China it's eggs fu yung, in Italy *spaghetti alla carbonara;* and so it is the whole world over. Ham weds happily with eggs, in dishes lowly or elegant, but nourishing and delicious every one.

Rule number one in any successful ham and egg dish is that the eggs must be so fresh that when they are broken the white clings closely to the yolk and doesn't run all over the pan. (True, very fresh eggs are hard to peel when cooked, but I have found that the electric egg cookers eliminate that difficulty. If that device is not included among your cooking equipment, make a tiny hole in the pointed end of the egg with a needle before putting it in the simmering water, and plunge the cooked eggs immediately into cold water. Crack the shells gently; peel from the large end.)

Rule number two pertains to the ham. Get a good one, an "old-fashioned" or "country-cured" one, if possible, or a good reliable brand. Or use Virginia-type ham (they're wonderful in North Carolina, too, and Arkansas, and probably many other southern states). Or use a Danish or Polish canned ham, or one of the famous hams of Europe such as Bayonne, Parma, Westphalia, prosciutto, York, or Alsace.

PHILLIP'S HAM AND EGGS
I was once advised by a gastronome, whose business took him around the countryside, that almost any American lunchroom could turn out a good dish of fried ham and eggs; therefore it was always the safest choice. The dish can be truly called gourmet fare if it is prepared with loving care. My husband does ham and eggs this way, and they never fail to make a hit. Allow 2 slices of ham about ¼ inch thick for each serving. Fry them gently in a little butter until they show a touch of golden color, but not until they are tough and dry. Remove them to a warm platter and keep hot. Allow 2 eggs to a serving, and for each egg add another teaspoon of butter to the fat in the pan. Break in the eggs; add 1 tablespoon of water, cover, and cook over very low heat until the eggs are done to your liking. Toward the end baste eggs with the pan juices, or turn if "over easy" is desired. Sprinkle the whites with salt and put on the platter with the ham. Add a little garnish of parsley and some nicely buttered toast.

FRIED EGGS À L'AMÉRICAINE
According to French chefs, this is the way we serve our fried eggs! Well, it's good. Fry eggs as above, place them on pieces of fried ham, sprinkle with French-fried parsley, and serve with tomato sauce.

HUEVOS CON TORTILLAS Y JAMON
(Ham and Eggs with Tortillas)
The Mexicans do ham and eggs this way for a goodly snack, with a glass of their excellent beer. Fry 6 tortillas in a little lard or shortening until crisp. Top each with a slice of ham. Mash 6 hard-boiled eggs with 2 canned peeled green chilies (or 2 teaspoons chili powder), a little salt, and enough tomato juice (or Mexican chili sauce) to moisten. Spread on the ham, put it in the oven for 1 to 2 minutes to heat, pour on a little more Mexican chili sauce, and serve with green olives.

■ **Another Version**—Scramble 6 eggs in 2 tablespoons butter with ¼ cup chopped ham and 2 chopped green chili peppers. Stir in 3 tablespoons heavy cream just as the eggs set. Divide the mixture among 6 fried tortillas. Makes 6 servings.

OEUFS COCOTTES AU JAMBON
(Eggs in Ramekins with Ham)
A favorite dish in France, not only at home but at the more elegant restaurants, are these little egg cocottes with ham. If you have no cocottes, small custard cups or ramekins do beautifully. Butter the cups well (allow 1 cocotte per serving); in the bottom of each put 1 tablespoon minced ham mixed with 1 teaspoon minced fresh parsley. Break 1 egg into each; sprinkle with salt and pepper and 1 tablespoon heavy cream. Put the cups in a pan of water, cover with a sheet of aluminum foil, and bake in preheated moderate oven (350°F.) for 10 minutes, or until the whites are set. This makes a nice dish for a ladies' luncheon. With it serve croissants; follow with a fresh strawberry salad.

EGGS PARMESAN
Butter a shallow baking dish well (a glass pie pan will do nicely) and break into it the required number of eggs. For each egg allow ½ ounce (2 tablespoons) slivered prosciutto or domestic ham, 2 teaspoons grated Parmesan cheese, and 2 teaspoons butter. Top eggs with ham, sprinkle with grated cheese, drizzle on the butter, and bake in preheated moderate oven (350°F.) until the whites are set.

■ **Another Version**—Put 2 cups cream sauce in the dish, sprinkle with ½ cup diced prosciutto, break 6 eggs onto this, sprinkle with 3 tablespoons grated Parmesan and 3 tablespoons melted butter, and bake as above. Either of these dishes, served with a simple green salad, makes an excellent lunch.

Note: This recipe uses prosciutto, but any other ham may be substituted.

TORTILLA CON JAMON
(Spanish Omelette with Ham)
Cook a small chopped onion in 3 tablespoons olive oil or butter until golden. Add ½ cup minced ham and ½ cup cooked peas and heat, mixing well. Beat 6 eggs slightly, season with pepper, pour over the hot vegetable mixture, and allow to set, shaking the pan so that it will not stick. When just set, but still moist on top, roll and slide onto a hot platter. Makes 4 servings.

■ **Another Version**—Fry small slices of ham and sliced potatoes until crisp, pouring the beaten eggs over them, and, when set on the bottom, turning by using a buttered plate. When both sides are cooked, slide onto a plate and cut into wedges.

HAM AND EGGS IN ASPIC
Here is another distinctive dish that is nice for lunch or to begin a summer dinner. There are two ways of preparing it, using poached eggs or eggs mollet (eggs cooked for 6 minutes in water just under the boil, then plunged into cold water and peeled).

For the first: Poach 6 very fresh eggs in water to which 1 tablespoon vinegar has been added. When set, lift with a slotted spatula and slide into cold water. In the meantime, cut fairly thin slices of ham into rounds and arrange on a flat pan. Trim eggs and place one carefully on each slice. Cool aspic until it is of the consistency of unbeaten egg white. Drizzle a little on each egg, and decorate with leaves of fresh tarragon, if available, or with tiny slivers of green pepper or pimiento. Chill for a few minutes, then pour the remaining aspic carefully around the eggs so that they are covered. Allow to set; then, using a round cutter (½ inch larger than the one used for the ham), cut each ham and egg from the aspic, lift with a spatula, and slide onto plates. Garnish with watercress.

For the second, with the eggs mollet: Pour ¼ inch of cooled aspic into cups, allow to set, decorate as above, top with the cooled egg, then with a slice of ham cut to fit the cup. Fill with aspic and allow to set before unmolding. To make the aspic, soften 1 envelope unflavored gelatin in ¼ cup water; dissolve in 1¼ cups (one 10½-ounce can) consommé that has been brought to the boil. Add 1 tablespoon Madeira or dry sherry, and use as above. Makes 6 servings.

HAM AND EGG SMØRREBRØD

Smørrebrød, those delectable open-faced sandwiches of the Danes, are never better than when made with ham and eggs. Here are two versions.

For the first *smørrebrød,* butter a whole slice of rye bread generously with sweet butter and cover with a good slice of Danish ham. Hard-scramble an egg, spread on a plate to cool, and cut into strips. Arrange 2 strips of egg on the sandwich, making three sections. Fill the middle one with chopped aspic and the two outer ones with sliced sautéed mushrooms. Garnish with a pickle slice. For the aspic, soften 1 teaspoon unflavored gelatin in 1 tablespoon cold water, and dissolve in 1¼ cups (one 10½-ounce can) consommé; add 1 teaspoon each of sherry and fresh lemon juice. Allow to set, then turn out and chop with a French knife.

For the second *smørrebrød,* cover half of a buttered slice of dark bread with chopped ham, the other half with chopped cooked chicken liver (or one half with sliced ham, the other with sliced liver pâté). Top with a medium-fried egg and garnish with a little fried onion. Serve while the egg is still hot.

QUICHE DE BOURBONNAISE
(Ham and Swiss-Cheese Pie)

Line a 9-inch pie pan with rich pastry, flute the edges prettily, and brush with slightly beaten egg white. Bake in preheated hot oven (450°F.) until the crust is set, but do not brown. Dice 6 ounces of cooked ham (1½ cups) and distribute on the bottom of the pastry shell. Sprinkle evenly with 1 cup grated Swiss cheese; then pour over a mixture of 1 cup scalded heavy cream, 2 beaten eggs, and 1 egg yolk; add grinding or two

of black pepper, a little freshly grated nutmeg, and ¼ teaspoon salt. Bake in moderate oven (350°F.) until the mixture has set like a custard. Serve warm or cold, for lunch or supper, or for a wonderful picnic dish. This, baked in a square pan and cut into squares, makes a delectable hors-d'oeuvre. Makes 6 servings.

HAM AND EGG PIE

Here's a simple dish that never fails to delight. Line a pie pan with pastry, sprinkle with slivers of cooked ham, break eggs on top, season with pepper and a very little salt (depending on the saltiness of your ham), and sprinkle with more ham slivers. Top with pastry and flute the edges; if you feel ambitious, decorate with pastry cutouts and glaze with slightly beaten egg. Bake in preheated hot oven (400°F.) until the crust is brown. Serve hot or cold. Makes about 4 servings.

HAM AND EGG TART

Here again we have a luncheon dish, or one that can begin a party dinner or make a family one. Line 12 small or 6 larger tart shells with pastry. Combine 1 cup minced cooked ham, 3 chopped hard-boiled eggs, 3 raw egg yolks, 1 cup heavy cream, and salt, pepper, and nutmeg to taste. Brush tart shells with egg white, allow to dry, and fill with the mixture. Bake in preheated moderate oven (375°F.) until nicely browned. Serve as is, or with a tomato or mushroom sauce.

ENGLISH HAM AND EGG CAKES

Chop 4 hard-cooked eggs, combine them with 1 cup chopped ham (¼ pound), ½ cup bread crumbs, 1 egg, 1 tablespoon minced parsley, and a little pepper. Taste; add salt if necessary. Form into flat cakes, dust lightly with flour, and sauté in butter or shortening until brown on both sides. Try these for breakfast with a broiled canned peach. Makes 4 servings.

CUSCINETTI FILANTI AL PROSCIUTTO
(Pillows with Italian Ham)

This is made in various ways, the one following being the simplest. Make sandwiches with sliced Mozzarella cheese and sliced prosciutto. For each 2 sandwiches allow ¼ cup milk, ¼ cup all-purpose flour, and 1 egg. Dip the sandwiches into the milk, then into the flour, and finally into the egg. Fry on both sides in olive oil; cut each sandwich into four triangles. Serve at once.

CROQUE MONSIEUR
(Fried Sandwich, French Style)

This glorified sandwich, well liked in France, is becoming popular in our own country. For each sandwich allow 2 slices

of white bread, 1 slice of ham, and 1 of Swiss cheese, a little butter, 1 egg, and 1 tablespoon milk. Make a sandwich with the buttered bread, ham, and cheese. Beat the egg slightly with the milk; dip the sandwich into the mixture; turn so that all the egg is absorbed. Fry in butter or shortening until brown on both sides.

SPAGHETTI ALLA CARBONARA
(Spaghetti and Eggs on Ham)

A peasant recipe, this is made with the available foods in the more inaccessible parts of Italy. It is a delicious change from better known ways of preparing pasta.

- 1 pound spaghetti
- 1 garlic clove, crushed
- 2 tablespoons olive oil
- 2 cups diced ham (with some fat)
- 4 eggs
- ¼ cup minced parsley (preferably Italian)
- ¾ cup grated Pecorino cheese

Cook spaghetti in salted water until just tender, not mushy. In the meantime, cook the garlic in the olive oil for 2 minutes; discard garlic. Add the ham to pan and cook until slightly crisp. Beat the eggs slightly, add the parsley and cheese, and mix with the well-drained spaghetti. Then pour over the very hot ham and the fat in the pan and mix well. If the mixture seems raw, cook over the burner for a minute or two, stirring well. Serve with more grated Pecorino cheese, if desired. Makes 6 servings.

HUEVOS ESCALFADOS FRITOS
(Poached Eggs and Ham, Fried)

Tricky to prepare, but worthwhile for anyone who likes to cook and eat. Poach 4 very fresh eggs in acidulated water, drain, and trim. (Don't let the eggs get too hard!) Make a thick white sauce with 3 tablespoons butter, ¼ cup all-purpose flour, and 1 cup milk. Add 1 tablespoon minced parsley and 1 cup ground ham. Add pepper and salt if needed and allow to cool. Dust each egg lightly with flour, then coat thickly with the ham mixture, using your hands. Dust again with flour; dip into egg that has been slightly beaten, then into crumbs. Allow to dry, then fry in deep fat (380°F. on a frying thermometer) until nicely browned. If these are properly done, they will be crisp outside, and the inside yolk still soft. One egg is sufficient for each serving, as it expands considerably. Makes 4 servings.

OEUFS SUR LE PLAT
À L'ANDALOUSE
(Andalusian Egg Platter)

For an individual serving, cook ½ cup shredded ham in 3 tablespoons butter, add ½ cup cooked peas, 2 diced pimientos, ½ cup diced fried potatoes (such as

Home-Fried Ham and Eggs

— *Spaghetti alla Carbonara* — — *Eggs Carmen* —

cut-up leftover French-fries), and a diced artichoke bottom. Heat all together; add ¼ cup tomato purée. Spread in a shallow ovenproof pan (a glass pie pan will do), make depressions in the mixture, and break egg into each. Pour ½ teaspoon butter over each; bake in preheated moderate oven (350°F.) until set.

HAM AND EGG PIROSHKI
(Little Russian Pies)
These little Russian pastries were originally served with soup, but they make delightful appetizers. Cook ½ cup chopped onions in 2 tablespoons butter until wilted. Add ½ cup chopped ham, 2 chopped hard-cooked eggs, 1 tablespoon chopped parsley, 1 teaspoon chopped dill or dillweed, and sour cream or stock to moisten. Roll pastry thin; cut into 2½- or 3-inch rounds. Put a spoonful of the

mixture in the middle of each, moisten edges, and pinch together firmly along the top, making little pointed canoe-shape pastries. Brush with beaten egg and bake in preheated hot oven (400°F.) until brown. Makes 24 piroshki.

PIZZA CON UOVA E PROSCIUTTO
(Ham and Egg Pizza)
Make hot-roll mix according to directions on the box. Divide dough into halves and roll each into a 10- to 12-inch circle. Put one on a cookie sheet generously brushed with garlic olive oil. Arrange halves of hard-boiled eggs on the dough, having rounded sides up. Sprinkle chopped prosciutto between the eggs, drizzle on a little more garlic-flavored olive oil, top with the other dough circle, and press edges together. Again paint with olive oil; bake in preheated hot oven (400°F.)

until brown. Makes 4 servings.

HAM AND EGG SALAD
For each head of romaine lettuce, heat ½ cup ham fat and in it cook ½ cup diced ham. Chop 3 hard-boiled eggs. Break lettuce into a bowl. Add eggs and 3 chopped green onions. To the ham and fat in the pan add 2 tablespoons wine vinegar and some pepper. When hot, pour over lettuce, mix thoroughly, and serve at once. Makes about 4 servings.

EGGS CARMEN
For each serving, put a slice of cooked ham on a lettuce leaf and spread with a mixture of 1 tablespoon each of shredded cooked carrots, shredded cooked beets, and shredded raw green pepper. Top with a cold poached egg; cover with a

dressing of half ketchup and half mayonnaise.

SWEDISH HAM CUSTARD

This is a favorite *smörgåsbord* dish. Mix 1½ cups diced cooked ham with 2 tablespoons all-purpose flour. Scald 3 cups milk, beat it gradually into 4 slightly beaten eggs, and add ¼ cup tomato ketchup and the ham. Pour into a greased 2-quart casserole and set in a pan of hot water. Bake in preheated moderate oven (350°F.) for 35 minutes, or until an inserted knife comes out clean. Makes 6 servings.

HAM TIMBALES

An old favorite with a new sauce. Cook ¾ cup milk and 1 cup bread crumbs together until they form a smooth paste. Add 1 cup chopped cooked ham, 2 egg yolks, and salt and pepper to taste. Beat 2 egg whites stiff and fold into the mixture. Fill custard cups two thirds full, put in a pan of hot water, cover with foil, and bake in preheated moderate oven (350°F.) until firm. Let rest for a moment before unmolding. Serve with a thin cream sauce (2 tablespoons each of flour and butter, 2 cups thin cream or rich milk) to which ¼ cup chopped ripe olives and 2 teaspoons chopped dill or dillweed have been added, along with salt and pepper. Makes 6 servings.

EGGS ZURLO

This classic dish may be made with leftover ham and leftover mashed potatoes. Chop the ham and add ½ cup of it (for each serving) along with 1 tablespoon chopped parsley and, if desired, 1 tablespoon chopped truffles, to 1 cup thin cream sauce. Make flat oval potato cakes with the mashed potato, dip into egg and crumbs, and fry brown on both sides. Top each cake with an egg mollet (eggs cooked for 6 minutes in water just under the boil, then plunged into cold water and peeled); pour sauce around them.

MOUSSE DE JAMBON
(Ham Mousse)

There are three kinds of mousses: the frozen, the hot, and the cold kind. This one is cold and mighty good eating. Soak 1 envelope unflavored gelatin in ¼ cup water. Heat ¾ cup milk. Beat milk into 3 egg yolks and cook over hot water until custardy. Add gelatin and stir until dissolved, then stir in 1 cup very finely ground ham. Cool. When almost set, fold in 3 egg whites, beaten stiff, ½ cup heavy cream, whipped, and ¼ cup mayonnaise. Taste; add salt if necessary. Pour into a mold and allow to set before unmolding. Makes about 6 servings.

HAM SOUFFLÉ

Cook together ¼ cup butter and ¼ cup all-purpose flour for 2 minutes. Add 1 cup milk and cook until thick; then stir in ¼ cup grated Cheddar cheese and 1 cup finely chopped ham. Beat 4 egg yolks until thick and combine with hot mixture. Taste for salt. Allow to cool; then beat 5 egg whites stiff and mix half of them thoroughly into the mixture. Fold in the remaining whites lightly, pour into a buttered soufflé dish, and bake in preheated moderate oven (350°F.) for 45 to 50 minutes. Serve with sautéed mushrooms or with parsley sauce. This is a white sauce made with part cream, a little prepared mustard, and a generous amount of freshly chopped parsley. Makes 4 to 6 servings.

HUEVOS EN TOLEDO
(Eggs in Toledo)

For each serving cook 1 cup minced ham and ¼ cup chopped mushrooms in 2 tablespoons olive oil. Add 1 cup hot cooked peas and spread on a platter. Top with fried eggs and garnish with stuffed green olives.

WIENER EIERKUCHEN
(Viennese Egg Cake)

Viennese, this, but more a casserole than a cake. Mix 2½ cups soft bread crumbs (about a fourth of 1-pound loaf) with 1½ cups milk, 6 well-beaten eggs, ½ cup chopped cooked ham, 1 tablespoon finely chopped onion, a little pepper, and salt to taste. Beat well together, pour into a greased casserole, and bake in preheated moderate oven (350°F.) for 45 minutes, or until set and nicely browned. Makes about 6 servings.

FRIED RICE WITH HAM

The Chinese add many different things to their fried rice, but none is better than when it's ham. Cook 1½ cups slivered ham in 2 tablespoons cooking oil for 3 minutes, along with 2 tablespoons chopped water chestnuts or mushrooms and 2 tablespoons chopped green onion. Stir in 3 cups cooked rice, brown lightly, then add 2 beaten eggs and 1 tablespoon soy sauce. Cook, stirring, until the eggs are cooked. Serve with more chopped green onion sprinkled on top. Makes about 4 servings.

EGGS FU YUNG

Combine ½ cup chopped water chestnuts, ¼ cup each of chopped green onions and chopped bamboo shoots (or celery), ½ cup bean sprouts, and ½ cup slivered cooked ham. Cook these for 2 minutes in 2 tablespoons cooking oil. Then combine with 6 slightly beaten eggs and salt or soy sauce to taste. Drop by the half-cupful onto a well-greased griddle, using a spatula to fold up the thin

part of the egg over the vegetables as soon as egg sets. When lightly brown on one side, turn and brown on the other. (Or make in one large cake, in a greased skillet, if preferred.) Serve with a sauce: Heat 1 cup chicken bouillon with 1 tablespoon soy sauce; cook until clear with 1½ tablespoons cornstarch dissolved in 2 tablespoons cold water. Makes about 6 servings.

VIENNESE HAM FLECKERL
(Ham and Noodle Casserole)

This recipe is a little complicated, but it's lots of fun to make and to eat. Make a noodle dough with 1 whole egg, 1 egg yolk, and ½ teaspoon salt, adding as much all-purpose flour as needed to make a stiff dough (about 1 cup). Knead until very smooth, then roll, but not too thin. Let dry slightly; then roll like a jelly roll and cut into ½-inch slices. Cut ribbons into ½-inch pieces, making squares. Allow to dry, then cook in boiling salted water for 5 minutes, or until tender. Drain thoroughly, then turn out on a clean cloth to drain some more. Sauté in ⅓ cup butter until lightly colored. Beat ¾ cup sour cream with 4 eggs; add 1 cup chopped ham and the noodles. Add salt if necessary, put in a buttered casserole, sprinkle with crumbs, and bake in preheated moderate oven (350°F.) for about 40 minutes, or until nicely browned. Makes 4 to 6 servings.

DEVONSHIRE FRIED EGGS

A strange combination, you may say, but try it for supper and change your mind. Fry slices of ham in butter, and in the same fat sauté fillets of sole, lightly dusted with flour. Then fry the eggs and serve all together on a sizzling hot platter.

QUICK HAM AND EGG DISHES

■ **Eggs Celestine**—Broiled ham on a toasted English muffin, with a poached egg on top. Cover with cheese sauce and brown under the broiler.

■ **Eggs à la Bayonne**—Fried eggs on a slice of fried ham, with a sauce made by combining equal parts of Béarnaise and tomato sauce.

■ **Eggs Italienne**—Broiled ham on a mound of rice or risotto, topped with an egg mollet, and covered with tomato sauce.

■ **Eggs Beauvilliers**—Put a fried egg on a slice of fried ham and cover with *sauce Madère* (Madeira sauce). To make the sauce, add 1 tablespoon butter, 1 teaspoon finely minced green onion, and a pinch of dried tarragon to the fat and juices in the skillet in which the ham was cooked. Stir in 1 tablespoon all-purpose flour. Gradually add ½ cup condensed consommé and ¼ cup dry Madeira wine and stir until sauce thickens.

POTTED HAM AND EGGS

You'll find this English dish is handy to spread on biscuits for tea or a snack. For each cup of finely ground leftover ham, chop 2 hard-cooked eggs equally fine and mix with 3 tablespoons soft butter and a dash of pepper or powdered mustard. Put in little pots or jars, cover tops with melted butter, and refrigerate until hungry time. Makes about 1⅓ cups.

HAM AND EGG BUTTER

This and the recipe above are kissin' kin. Mix 1 cup finely ground cooked ham with 3 sieved hard-cooked egg yolks, ½ cup butter, and 1 teaspoon paprika. Pound well together and serve on hot toasted crackers. Makes about 1½ cups.

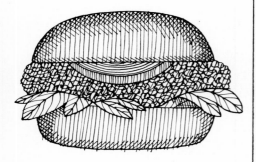

HAMBURGER—This term stands for ground beef prepared from the less tender cuts. After steak, hamburger is America's favorite meat, either in patties, or in meat loaves and countless other dishes.

The origin of the name hamburger for ground beef is open to speculation, although it was probably named for the German seaport of Hamburg. As one of the greatest ports in Europe, Hamburg had long engaged in trade with the Baltic provinces of Russia. The Balts of Estonia, Latvia, and Finland were fond of red meat, shredded with a dull knife and eaten raw. This dish, today a gourmet affair when made with fine steak, and called Beefsteak Tartare, may have pleased the Balts because of their origin, which connects them with the tribes of Tartary, or Mongolia, great riders, hunters, and meat-eaters all. After the people of Hamburg were introduced to this delightful novelty, their liking for it was great enough to immortalize the dish with their name. Or so the legend goes.

The reason for using ground meat, on the other hand, is not obscure at all: grinding tough cuts (and the meat of the past was infinitely tougher than ours) is a good way of tenderizing them. The ancient Egyptians ate ground meat, and through the ages ground meat has been shaped into patties and eaten in all of Europe under different names; in France, it is called *bifteck*. Hamburger in a bun is a great American institution. It is said to have originated at the great St. Louis Exposition of 1904.

Hamburger, aside from being so popular a dish that the aroma of the meat sizzling on a grill should be captured like a perfume from home for American exiles abroad, has also become a symbol of modern, Americanized living. It is good; it is fast; it is inexpensive; it is easy to serve alone or in countless ways as a patty or in a ground-beef dish. Small wonder that hamburger stands have traveled from the United States to all parts of the globe.

Availability—Available in all stores selling meat, sold ready-ground by the pound or ground to order. It comes in various grades and prices determined by the cut of meat from which it is ground, and the amount of fat ground in with the meat. Also sold preshaped and frozen into hamburger patties. May be sold as a part of a ready-ground meat-loaf mixture which includes ground veal and pork.

Purchasing Guide—Price is determined by the amount of fat in the meat, which affects the degree to which the meat will shrink during cooking. The best all-round hamburger buy is ground chuck which has enough fat to make it juicy, but not enough to make it shrink excessively. Lean ground meat may be desirable when meat needs to be shaped and must be more compact; also good for low-calorie diets.

Meat should be a deep-red color with small flecks of white fat. Meat should be packaged in flat packages because a large round chunk of ground meat may spoil in the center since cold cannot penetrate the meat too quickly.

Have meat ground once for hamburgers and ground twice for meat loaf.

Storage—Wrap meat lightly and store in the coldest part of the refrigerator. When freezing meat, shape into patties or make into a large flat patty so that cold will penetrate meat quickly. Wrap well to keep air out and prevent meat from becoming gray and developing off-flavors. Place a double thickness of freezer paper or foil between each patty for easy separation.

☐ Refrigerator shelf, raw: 1 to 2 days
☐ Refrigerator shelf, cooked and covered: 3 to 4 days
☐ Refrigerator frozen-food compart-
ment, raw, prepared for freezing: 2 to 3 weeks
☐ Freezer, raw, prepared for freezing: 6 months to 1 year

Nutritive Food Values—Good source of protein and a variable source of fat, depending on the type of meat ground.
☐ Market ground, 3½ ounces, raw = 268 calories
☐ Ground lean, 3½ ounces, raw = 179 calories

Basic Preparation—Ground meat is generally shaped into a flat round patty and served in a round hamburger bun with relishes, ketchup, onion slices, etc. The patties may be broiled, panfried, or panbroiled. During cooking, they may be coated with slices of American cheese and broiled until cheese is melted. However, hamburger is very versatile and can be mixed and shaped to suit the need and occasion, and cooked with countless other ingredients to make a little meat go a long way.

☐ **To Broil**—Place meat on rack of broiler pan. Adjust rack and pan so that top of meat is approximately 2 inches below heat for a ¾-inch-thick patty. Broil about half of time indicated below. Season. Turn. Complete broiling; season and serve. For ground-beef patties, the time for total cooking is: rare 8 minutes, medium 12, and well done 14 minutes.

☐ **To Panfry**—Shape hamburgers, and cook in frying pan in a small amount of fat.

☐ **To Panbroil**—Preheat skillet. Do not add fat. When pan is very hot, put in meat; brown quickly on both sides. Do not cover pan. Reduce heat and cook slowly until done. If fat collects in pan, pour it off. Season meat before serving.

HAMBURGER COOK BOOK

A mealtime favorite of all families.
From appetizers and soups to stews and
casseroles, meat loaves and pizzas,
the versatile hamburger
is delicious, nutritious,
and economical.

HAMBURGER PRINCESS

½ cup all-purpose flour
1 teaspoon sugar
  Salt
1 egg
¾ cup tomato juice
1 pound beef chuck, ground
  Butter or margarine (about 2 tablespoons)
6 slices of process American cheese

Mix flour, sugar, and ½ teaspoon salt. Beat egg with tomato juice and add to first mixture; beat until smooth. Mix meat and 1 teaspoon salt; shape into six 4-inch patties. Melt 1 teaspoon butter in 6-inch skillet. Pour in enough of tomato-juice mixture to cover pan thinly (one sixth of mixture). When done on bottom, turn and place a meat patty on cooked side. When underside is done, turn again. Sauté for about 4 minutes for medium to well done. Lift onto cookie sheet and roll up with meat on inside and edges underneath. Repeat until 6 rolls are made. Top each with a slice of cheese and put under broiler until cheese is just melted. (Loose beef can be browned, then rolled up in cooked pancakes.) Makes 6 servings.

HAMBURGER GUACAMOLE

1 pound beef chuck, ground
1 avocado
1 tomato, chopped
1 medium onion, chopped
¼ teaspoon hot pepper sauce
1 tablespoon fresh lemon juice
4 slices of toast

Shape meat into 4 good-size patties. Cook to desired doneness. Mash avocado and add next four ingredients. Put meat on toasted rounds of bread. Spoon some of mixture over each. Put under broiler or heat in oven for a few minutes. Serve with remaining sauce. Makes 4 servings.

HAMBURGER STEW

1 pound ground beef
1 tablespoon butter
1 onion, sliced
1½ teaspoons salt
¼ teaspoon pepper
1 tablespoon steak sauce
2⅓ cups (one 1-pound, 3-ounce can) tomatoes
3 medium potatoes, peeled and sliced
3 medium carrots, sliced
2 celery stalks, diced
  Split hot biscuits (optional)

Brown beef lightly in the butter, stirring with fork to break up meat. Add onion and cook for a few minutes longer. Add remaining ingredients except biscuits. Bring to boil and simmer, covered, for 30 minutes, or until vegetables are tender. Serve on biscuits if desired. Makes 4 to 6 servings.

LEMON PIE-PAN STEAK

1½ pounds beef chuck, ground
1 onion, sliced
6 lemon slices
1 cup ketchup
1 tablespoon Worcestershire
¼ cup water

Pat beef into deep 9- or 10-inch pie pan. Top with onion and lemon slices. Mix ketchup with remaining ingredients and pour over top of meat. Bake in preheated hot oven (400°F.) for about 30 minutes. Pour off some of the fat. Cut pie into wedges. Makes 4 to 6 servings.

SALISBURY STEAK WITH MUSHROOM SAUCE

1 pound beef chuck, ground
1 teaspoon salt
¼ teaspoon pepper
1 can (4 ounces) chopped mushrooms, drained
2 tablespoons butter or margarine
2 tablespoons flour
1 teaspoon curry powder
1 cup water
1 beef bouillon cube

Mix meat, salt, and pepper and shape into 4 patties. Panfry in lightly greased skillet until of desired doneness. Remove from skillet and keep hot. Cook mushrooms in butter for 2 or 3 minutes. Blend in flour and curry powder. Add water and bouillon cube; cook until smooth and thickened. Pour over meat patties and serve. Makes 4 servings.

SMOTHERED HAMBURGER STEAKS AND ONIONS

1 pound beef round or chuck, ground
½ cup water
1 teaspoon salt
¼ teaspoon pepper
¼ cup fine dry bread crumbs
4 medium onions, sliced
1 can (10¾ ounces) beef gravy

Mix first 5 ingredients. Shape into 4 large patties. Brown on one side, turn, add onion, and brown lightly. Add gravy, cover, and simmer for about 35 minutes. Makes 4 servings.

SWEET-AND-SOUR HAMBURGERS

1 pound ground beef
½ pound pork-sausage meat
1 teaspoon salt
⅛ teaspoon pepper
1 large onion, sliced
2 tablespoons soy sauce
½ cup water
¼ cup vinegar
⅓ cup firmly packed brown sugar

Mix first 4 ingredients and shape into 6 large patties. Brown on both sides in skillet. Add onion. Mix remaining ingredients and pour over patties. Cover, bring to boil, and simmer for 15 minutes. Makes 6 servings.

HAWAIIAN HAMBURGERS

1 pound beef round or chuck, ground
1 medium onion, minced
1 garlic clove, minced
½ cup soy sauce
¼ teaspoon ground ginger
  Sliced pineapple

Mix beef and onion and shape into 8 patties. Put in shallow dish. Mix next 4 ingredients and pour over patties. Let stand for 30 minutes, turning once. Drain; broil or panfry. Serve with sliced pineapple. Makes 4 servings.

PIZZA-BURGERS

1½ pounds chuck, ground
  Canned pizza sauce
  Sliced Muenster cheese
  Oregano
  Onion salt
  Anchovy fillets
  Grated Parmesan

Shape meat into 8 patties. Handle lightly; do not season. Panbroil slightly less done than desired and put on ovenproof platter. Pour a little pizza sauce over each, top with Muenster cheese, and sprinkle lightly with oregano and onion salt. Crisscross with anchovy fillets and sprinkle with grated Parmesan. Put in preheated moderate oven (375°F.) for 10 minutes. Or put under broiler until thoroughly heated. Makes 4 servings.

PEPPER-RING BURGERS

1 pound beef chuck, ground
¾ cup soft bread crumbs
1 teaspoon salt
⅛ teaspoon pepper
¼ cup milk
6 green-pepper rings, 2½ inches across, ½ inch thick
1 tablespoon fat
  Bottled barbecue sauce
6 split sandwich rolls, heated

Mix first 5 ingredients and shape into 6 patties. Press mixture into pepper rings, having meat cover cut edge of pepper on both sides. Brown patties on both sides in hot fat in skillet. Baste with sauce so both sides are covered. Cook to desired doneness and serve in rolls. Makes 6 servings.

HAMBURGERS, POLISH STYLE

1 onion, peeled
1 carrot, peeled
1 celery stalk
1 medium potato, peeled
  Few parsley sprigs
¾ pound beef chuck, ground
2 slices of bread, crumbled
1 egg
1½ teaspoons seasoned salt
¼ teaspoon seasoned pepper
2 tablespoons butter or margarine
1 cup dairy sour cream
⅔ cup canned French-fried onion rings

Force first 5 ingredients through medium blade of food chopper. Add to next 5 ingredients and mix lightly but thoroughly. Shape into 8 patties and brown on both sides in butter. Remove from skillet and blend sour cream into drippings. Put patties back in skillet. Cover and simmer for about 20 minutes. Top with onion rings. Makes 4 servings.

SAUERBRATEN HAMBURGERS
1½ pounds beef chuck, ground
1 tablespoon instant minced onion
1 egg
1½ teaspoons salt
¼ cup fine dry bread crumbs
⅓ cup milk
½ teaspoon grated lemon rind
1 tablespoon butter or margarine
1 can (10¾ ounces) beef gravy
2 tablespoons wine vinegar
½ teaspoon ground ginger
¼ cup firmly packed brown sugar
Dash of ground cloves
1 bay leaf

Mix first 7 ingredients lightly and shape in 6 large patties. Brown on both sides in butter in skillet. Remove patties and pour off fat. Mix remaining ingredients in skillet and bring to boil. Add patties, cover, and simmer for 30 minutes, turning once or twice and basting with the sauce. Makes 6 servings.

STUFFED HAMBURGER PATTIES
1 pound beef chuck, ground
1 medium onion, minced
1 teaspoon salt
¼ teaspoon pepper
1⅓ cups soft bread crumbs
¼ teaspoon poultry seasoning
¼ teaspoon seasoned salt
¼ cup margarine, melted
2 tablespoons fresh lemon juice

Mix beef, onion, salt, and ⅛ teaspoon pepper. Divide into 8 equal parts. With rolling pin flatten each between pieces of wax paper until about 5 inches in diameter. Leave on paper. Mix ⅛ teaspoon pepper and remaining ingredients. Spread on 4 patties and top with remaining 4 patties. Crimp edges with a fork. Remove from paper; broil until of desired doneness, turning once. Makes 4 servings.

PAPRIKA HAMBURGERS
1½ pounds beef chuck, ground
1 egg
1½ teaspoons salt
¼ teaspoon pepper
¼ cup fine dry bread crumbs
⅓ cup milk
¼ cup minced onion
1 tablespoon butter or margarine
1 teaspoon flour
½ cup vegetable-juice cocktail
1 tablespoon paprika
½ teaspoon steak sauce

1 can (10½ ounces) cream-of-vegetable soup
½ cup dairy sour cream
Hot cooked noodles (optional)

Mix lightly first 6 ingredients and 2 tablespoons onion. Shape into 8 patties. Brown on both sides in butter in skillet. Remove patties and pour off all but 1 teaspoon fat. Blend flour into fat in skillet. Add remaining onion, vegetable-juice cocktail, paprika, and steak sauce. Bring to boil and put patties back in skillet. Cover; simmer for 15 to 20 minutes. Remove patties and keep warm. Blend soup and sour cream into mixture in skillet and heat, stirring. Add patties and serve in skillet with noodles. (If preferred, put patties on a hot platter and pour sauce over the top.) Makes 4 servings.

BACON NUTBURGERS
6 slices of bacon
1½ pounds beef chuck, ground
1½ teaspoons salt
⅛ teaspoon pepper
6 tablespoons chopped nuts
3 tablespoons chopped parsley
2 tablespoons grated onion

Cook bacon until crisp; drain. Mix beef, salt, and pepper; divide into 12 equal portions and roll with rolling pin between 2 sheets of wax paper to form thin patties about 5 inches in diameter. Mix last 3 ingredients and spread on 6 patties. Top each with a bacon slice. Cover with remaining 6 patties and pinch edges together. Broil to desired doneness, turning once. Makes 6 servings.

BEEF CHEESEBURGERS DE LUXE
1½ pounds beef chuck, ground
2 cups shredded sharp Cheddar cheese
3 tablespoons grated onion
1½ tablespoons steak sauce
Pepper to taste
8 slices of bacon, partially cooked
Hot buttered French-bread slices
¼ cup soft butter or margarine
2 tablespoons minced stuffed olives

Mix first 5 ingredients and shape into 8 patties. Wrap a slice of bacon around each and secure with a wooden pick. Sauté for about 5 minutes on each side; serve on French bread. Mix butter and olives and top each patty with a dab of the mixture. Makes 8 servings.

HAMBURGERS WITH SHERRY-CHEESE SAUCE
½ pound process cheese, shredded
¼ cup milk
¼ cup sherry
1 pound beef round or chuck, ground
1 teaspoon salt
¼ teaspoon pepper
¼ cup sweet-pickle relish
4 slices of toast

Melt cheese in top part of double boiler over boiling water. Stir in milk and sherry; keep hot. Mix meat, salt, pepper, and relish; shape into 4 patties. Broil or panfry to desired doneness. Put on toast; top with cheese sauce. Makes 4 servings.

CHEESE-NUT BURGERS
Mix lightly 1 pound ground beef chuck, ¼ cup wheat germ, ¾ cup finely diced sharp Cheddar cheese, ½ teaspoon instant meat tenderizer, ½ cup chopped cashews or other nuts, and ¼ cup water. Shape into 4 to 6 thick patties and broil until of desired doneness. Makes 4 to 6 servings.

TENNESSEE HAMBURGER
1 pound beef round or chuck, ground
1 teaspoon salt
⅛ teaspoon pepper
1 garlic clove, minced
¼ cup prepared mustard
2 cups thinly sliced onions

Mix beef, salt, pepper, and garlic; shape into 2 large thin patties. Put one in a metal pie pan or layer-cake pan. Spread with mustard and cover with onions. Put second patty on top. Put under broiler until top browns lightly; turn and brown the other side of the double patty. Cover pan; bake in preheated moderate oven (350°F.) for about 50 minutes. Makes 4 servings.

BURGUNDY MEATBALLS WITH RAISIN SAUCE
1½ pounds beef chuck, ground
1 egg
1½ teaspoons salt
Dash of pepper
¼ cup fine dry bread crumbs
⅓ cup milk
2 tablespoons instant minced onion
1 tablespoon butter
1½ tablespoons flour
¼ teaspoon garlic powder
1 cup condensed beef bouillon or consommé
2 tablespoons tomato paste
½ cup seedless raisins
¼ cup dry red wine
Salt and pepper

Mix lightly first 6 ingredients and 1 tablespoon onion. Shape into 18 balls and brown on all sides in butter in skillet. Remove meatballs. Blend flour and garlic powder into drippings in skillet. Add remaining onion, next 3 ingredients, and meatballs. Cover and simmer for 10 minutes. Remove meatballs to a hot serving dish. Stir wine into sauce in skillet and season to taste. Pour over meatballs. Makes 4 to 6 servings.

MEATBALLS IN CURRIED TOMATO SAUCE

About 3½ cups (one 1-pound, 12-ounce can) tomatoes
¾ cup soft bread crumbs
1½ pounds ground beef
1 small onion, minced
1½ teaspoons seasoned salt
½ teaspoon salt
   Pepper
3 tablespoons all-purpose flour
2 tablespoons margarine or other fat
½ teaspoon sugar
1 teaspoon curry powder
½ teaspoon monosodium glutamate
   Hot cooked rice

Drain ½ cup juice from tomatoes and mix with bread. Add meat, onion, 1 teaspoon seasoned salt, the salt, and ⅛ teaspoon pepper. Mix lightly and shape into 24 balls. Dredge with the flour and brown on all sides in hot margarine. Remove meatballs and pour off fat. To skillet add remaining tomatoes and seasoned salt, ⅛ teaspoon pepper, the sugar, curry powder, monosodium glutamate, and meatballs. Bring to boil, cover, and simmer for 15 to 20 minutes, stirring occasionally. Serve hot with rice. Makes 6 servings.

CHILI MEATBALLS

1 pound ground beef
½ cup uncooked rice
1 small onion, chopped
1 teaspoon salt
¼ teaspoon pepper
2 tablespoons butter or margarine
2 cans (8 ounces each) tomato sauce
   or 1 can (15 ounces)
1 cup water
1 teaspoon chili powder
½ teaspoon ground cuminseed

Mix first 5 ingredients. Shape into 16 to 20 balls. Brown lightly on all sides in hot butter. Add remaining ingredients, bring to boil, cover, and simmer for about 45 minutes. Makes 4 servings.

KÖNIGSBERGER MEATBALLS

1 roll or 1 slice of firm bread
¾ pound beef chuck, ground
¼ pound ground pork
2 medium potatoes, cooked and mashed
2 anchovies, chopped
1 egg
   About ½ cup all-purpose flour
   Salt and pepper
   Water
3 tablespoons butter
1 beef bouillon cube
1 tablespoon capers
   Juice of ½ lemon

Moisten roll or bread with water and squeeze dry. Mix very thoroughly with meats, potatoes, anchovies, egg, 3 tablespoons flour, 1 teaspoon salt, and ⅛ teaspoon pepper. Shape into 16 balls, dredge with flour, and drop into simmering salted water. Cover and simmer for about 15 minutes. Melt butter and blend in 2 tablespoons flour. Add 1 cup water and bouillon cube; cook, stirring, until thickened. Add capers, lemon juice, and pepper to taste. Add cooked meatballs and simmer for a few minutes. Makes 4 servings.

MEATBALLS WITH ALMOND-MUSHROOM NOODLES

1 can (10½ ounces) condensed tomato soup
1 cup dairy sour cream
1 pound beef chuck, ground
2 parsley sprigs, chopped
1 teaspoon salt
⅛ teaspoon pepper
⅓ cup fine dry bread crumbs
1 egg
3 tablespoons butter or margarine
1 medium onion, minced
1 garlic clove, minced
1 bay leaf
1 teaspoon fresh lemon juice
1 teaspoon paprika
2 cups wide noodles
¼ cup almonds, slivered
1 can (4 ounces) sliced mushrooms, drained

Mix soup and sour cream. Add ¼ cup of this mixture to beef, parsley, salt, pepper, crumbs, and egg; mix well. Shape into 16 small balls. Cook in 1 tablespoon butter until well browned. Remove meatballs. Cook onion and garlic in fat remaining in skillet until lightly browned. Drain off any remaining fat. Add meatballs, remaining soup mixture, bay leaf, lemon juice, and paprika. Bring to boil, cover, and simmer for 20 minutes. Uncover and cook for 10 minutes longer. Cook and drain noodles. Sauté almonds and mushrooms slowly in 2 tablespoons butter until almonds are golden brown, stirring frequently. Mix with noodles and arrange in a border on hot platter. Put meatballs and sauce in center. Makes 4 servings.

PEANUT HAMBURGER BALLS

¾ pound beef chuck, ground
¾ cup crunchy peanut butter
1 onion, minced
3 tablespoons chili sauce
1¼ teaspoons salt
⅛ teaspoon pepper
1 egg, beaten
2 tablespoons fat
2 cans (8 ounces each) tomato sauce

Mix first 7 ingredients and shape into 12 balls. Brown on all sides in hot fat. Remove meat and pour off fat. Put meat back in skillet with tomato sauce. Cover and simmer for about 30 minutes. Makes 4 servings.

BEEF, CARROT, AND OLIVE LOAF

2 pounds beef chuck, ground
1½ cups corn flakes
½ cup chopped parsley
½ cup shredded raw carrot
1 can (4½ ounces) chopped ripe olives
1 medium onion, chopped
2 garlic cloves, minced
2 tablespoons butter or margarine
2 teaspoons salt
½ teaspoon pepper
½ teaspoon each of ground sage and oregano
1½ cups milk
1 egg

Mix first 5 ingredients. Cook onion and garlic in the butter and add to first mixture with remaining ingredients. Mix well. Shape into a loaf in a baking pan. Bake in preheated moderate oven (350°F.) for about 1 hour. Makes 8 servings.

BEEF LOAF, FARMER STYLE

2 medium potatoes, peeled
1 large onion, peeled
1 small apple, peeled
2 canned pimientos
1¼ pounds beef chuck, ground
½ pound sausage meat
1¼ teaspoons salt
⅛ teaspoon pepper
⅔ cup undiluted evaporated milk

Force first 4 ingredients through medium blade of food chopper. Do not drain. Add remaining ingredients and mix thoroughly. Pack in loaf pan (9 x 5 x 3 inches) and cover top with a buttered piece of foil. Bake in preheated moderate oven (350°F.) for about 1¾ hours. Remove foil 15 minutes before loaf is done. Makes 6 servings.

BEEF-AND-TOMATO LOAF

2 pounds ground beef
⅓ cup milk
1¼ cups soft bread crumbs
1 medium onion, chopped
¼ cup chopped green pepper
2 teaspoons salt
¼ teaspoon pepper
1 teaspoon monosodium glutamate
1 tablespoon each of prepared horseradish and Worcestershire
2 eggs, beaten
3 firm tomatoes, peeled and cut into 1-inch pieces

Mix all ingredients except tomatoes lightly but thoroughly. Gently stir in tomatoes. Pack in loaf pan (9 x 5 x 3 inches). Bake in slow oven (300°F.) for about 1½ hours. Let stand for 10 minutes. Drain off liquid and turn loaf out on a hot platter. Makes 8 servings.

ORANGE-GLAZED MEAT LOAVES

6 tablespoons brown sugar
½ teaspoon powdered mustard
6 slices of small orange, unpeeled
1½ pounds beef, round or chuck, ground
2 cups soft bread crumbs
1 egg
1 medium onion, minced
1 medium green pepper, minced
¼ teaspoon pepper

Paprika Hamburgers

1 teaspoon salt
½ cup fresh orange juice
Juice of 1 lemon

Put 1 tablespoon brown sugar in each of 6 greased small baking dishes. Sprinkle with mustard; put an orange slice in each dish. Mix remaining ingredients well. Press into baking dishes. Bake in preheated moderate oven (350°F.) for about 1 hour. Let stand for a few minutes before turning upside down on heated platter. Makes 4 to 6 servings.

CANADIAN HAMBURGER PIE
1 package (10 ounces) pastry mix
½ cup grated sharp Cheddar cheese
½ teaspoon paprika
Dash of cayenne
1½ pounds beef chuck, ground
1 small onion, minced
1½ cups dry bread cubes
1 can (10½ ounces) beef bouillon or consommé
½ teaspoon salt
½ teaspoon pepper
¼ teaspoon each of ground thyme and marjoram
2 teaspoons Worcestershire

Prepare pastry mix as directed on the label, adding cheese, paprika, and cayenne before adding the liquid. Roll half of pastry on lightly floured board; fit into 9-inch pie pan. Cook beef and onion in skillet until meat loses its red color, breaking up meat with fork. Mix bread cubes and bouillon and let stand for a few minutes. Add beef mixture and remaining ingredients. Mix well and pour into pastry-lined pan. Roll remaining pastry and put over top, crimping edges. Bake in preheated moderate oven (375°F.) for about 45 minutes. Serve warm or cold. Makes 6 servings.

MEATBALL SHEPHERD'S PIE
1 pound ground beef
1 egg
2 cups soft bread crumbs
Salt and pepper
3 tablespoons butter or margarine
1 large onion, minced
1 tablespoon flour
1 can (3 ounces) mushrooms, undrained
2 cups (one 1-pound can) tomatoes
1 package (10 ounces) frozen peas and carrots, thawed
⅛ teaspoon ground oregano
1 package (14 ounces) frozen whipped potatoes, thawed

Mix beef, egg, crumbs, 1 teaspoon salt, and ⅛ teaspoon pepper. Shape into 12 large balls. Brown on all sides in 2 tablespoons butter in Dutch oven or large skillet. Remove meatballs and brown onion in drippings remaining in pan. Blend in flour; add mushrooms and to-

matoes. Add meatballs and bring to boil. Cover and simmer for 30 minutes. Add peas and carrots and bring to boil. Add oregano, and season to taste. Pour into shallow 2-quart baking dish. Melt remaining butter in small saucepan, add potatoes, and heat. Spread on top of meat mixture. Put under broiler until lightly browned. Makes 4 to 6 servings.

HAMBURGER AND KIDNEY PIE
1 beef kidney
1 tablespoon fat
2 cups boiling water
1 pound beef chuck, ground
1 medium onion, chopped
2 tablespoons flour
¼ cup cold water
1½ teaspoons salt
¼ teaspoon pepper
1 teaspoon steak sauce
Rich pastry (made with 1½ cups flour)

Cut kidney into crosswise slices; remove fat and gristle; then cut kidney into small pieces. Rinse in cold water and wipe dry. Brown on all sides in the fat. Add boiling water, cover, and simmer for 1 hour, or until tender. Meanwhile cook beef and onion, stirring with fork, until meat loses its red color. Add cooked kidney and liquid. Blend flour with cold water and stir into mixture. Cook until slightly thickened, stirring. Add seasonings and pour into 1-quart casserole. Roll pastry to ⅛-inch thickness and cut into strips. Arrange on mixture, lattice fashion. Brush with undiluted evaporated milk, top milk, or slightly beaten egg white, if desired. Bake in preheated hot oven (400°F.) for 20 minutes, or until pastry is brown. Makes 4 servings.

TEXAS SOMBREROS
1 pound beef chuck, ground
1 teaspoon monosodium glutamate
1 teaspoon salt
⅛ teaspoon pepper
½ teaspoon steak sauce
1 to 2 teaspoons chili powder
2 tablespoons butter
½ cup finely chopped celery
¼ cup finely chopped onion
¼ cup finely chopped green pepper
2 cups (one 1-pound can) tomatoes
1 can (8 ounces) tomato sauce
Large corn chips
Shredded lettuce

Sprinkle meat with monosodium glutamate, salt, pepper, steak sauce, and chili powder. Melt butter in skillet and add celery, onion, and green pepper; cook until almost tender. Add meat and cook, stirring with fork, until meat loses its red color. Add tomatoes and tomato sauce. Simmer, uncovered, for 30 minutes, or

until quite thick. Serve on corn chips and top with lettuce. Makes 4 servings.

BEEF AND NOODLE PLATTER
1 pound ground beef
1 tablespoon butter
Salt and pepper to taste
1 can (10½ ounces) tomato soup
½ soup-can water
1 can (3 ounces) mushrooms, drained
6 ounces wide noodles
1 can (3 ounces) chow-mein noodles, heated in oven
Green-pepper and pimiento strips

Brown meat lightly in butter, stirring with fork to break up meat. Season. Add soup, water, and mushrooms. Bring to boil and simmer, uncovered, for about 15 minutes. Cook and drain wide noodles. Put in center of hot platter. Pour meat mixture over noodles. Arrange chow-mein noodles around edge and garnish with strips of pepper and pimiento. Makes 4 servings.

CREAMED HAMBURGER AND CABBAGE
¾ pound beef chuck, ground
1 medium onion, minced
3 tablespoons butter or margarine
4 cups coarsely chopped cabbage
3 tablespoons all-purpose flour
2 teaspoons salt
¼ teaspoon pepper
¾ teaspoon paprika
½ teaspoon celery seeds
1½ cups milk

Brown meat and onion lightly in butter, breaking up meat with fork. Add cabbage and sauté lightly. Blend in flour and seasonings. Add milk, cover, and simmer for 15 to 20 minutes. Makes 4 to 6 servings.

BEEF AND RICE CASSEROLE
1 pound ground beef
1 cup uncooked rice
1 small onion, chopped
2 tablespoons butter or margarine
1 teaspoon seasoned salt
½ teaspoon pepper
½ teaspoon monosodium glutamate
1 teaspoon paprika
1 bottle (2 ounces) stuffed olives (⅓ cup), sliced
2½ cups (one 1-pound, 4-ounce can) tomato juice
1½ cups boiling water
½ cup grated sharp Cheddar or process American cheese

Cook first 3 ingredients in butter until lightly browned, breaking up meat with fork. Add remaining ingredients except cheese and bring to boil. Put in 2-quart casserole. Cover; bake in slow oven (300°F.) for 1 hour. Sprinkle with cheese and put back in oven, uncovered, for 5 minutes, or until cheese is melted. Makes 6 servings.

HAMBURGER-MACARONI CASSEROLE
4 ounces elbow macaroni
1 garlic clove, minced

1 pound beef chuck, ground
1 can (10½ ounces) condensed onion soup
¾ teaspoon salt
Dash of pepper
½ cup shredded sharp Cheddar cheese
3 slices of bread, crumbled
3 tablespoons butter or margarine, melted

Cook macaroni until tender; drain. Brown garlic and beef lightly in skillet, stirring with fork to break up meat. Add soup, salt, and pepper; mix well. Add macaroni and pour into 1-quart casserole or shallow baking dish. Sprinkle with cheese. Mix crumbs and butter and sprinkle on top. Bake in preheated moderate oven (350°F.) for 15 minutes. Makes 4 servings.

BEEF CASSEROLE WITH ALMONDS
1 pound ground beef
1 cup uncooked rice
2 small cans (10½ ounces each) or 2 envelopes chicken-noodle or beef-noodle soup mix
1 small onion, chopped
1 cup sliced celery
3 cups water
1 tablespoon soy sauce
½ cup slivered almonds

Cook beef until lightly browned, stirring with fork to break up meat. Put in 3-quart casserole. Mix remaining ingredients and pour over meat. Cover; bake in preheated moderate oven (350°F.) for 1 hour, or until rice is done, adding a little more water if necessary. Makes 6 servings.

BEEF, POTATO, AND BEAN CASSEROLE
1 pound ground beef
1 teaspoon monosodium glutamate
1 teaspoon salt
¼ teaspoon pepper
⅛ teaspoon ground oregano or thyme
2 cups thinly sliced peeled potatoes (2 large)
About 2 cups (one 1-pound can) red kidney beans, drained
2 medium onions, sliced
½ cup chili sauce

Mix first 5 ingredients lightly. Put in skillet and cook, stirring with fork to break up meat, until lightly browned. Put meat and remaining ingredients in layers in 2-quart casserole, beginning and ending with meat. Cover; bake in preheated moderate oven (375°F.) for 40 minutes. Uncover; bake for about 20 minutes longer. Makes 6 servings.

BEEF-STUFFED CABBAGE ROLLS
1 pound ground beef
½ cup uncooked rice
1 onion, minced
2 garlic cloves, minced
1 egg

Salt and pepper
1 white cabbage with tight leaves (about 4 pounds)
1 pound sauerkraut
3¼ cups (one 1-pound, 12-ounce can) tomatoes
¼ cup butter or margarine
1½ cups boiling water

Mix first 5 ingredients, 2 teaspoons salt, and dash of pepper. Cut core out of cabbage to depth of 3 inches. Put cabbage in a large kettle of boiling water over high heat. With tongs remove about 20 leaves as they wilt. Let leaves stand until cool enough to handle. Carefully cut out coarsest part of ribs. Cool remaining cabbage and cut coarsely or chop. Put half of chopped cabbage in a large kettle. Put a spoonful of meat mixture in center of each leaf; roll up, tucking ends under. Put on top of cabbage in kettle. Top with remaining cabbage, sauerkraut, tomatoes, and butter. Season with salt and pepper to taste. Add the boiling water. Bring to boil, cover, and simmer for 45 minutes. Makes 5 servings.

HAMBURGER-CORN SKILLET DINNER
1 pound beef chuck, ground
1 cup soft bread crumbs
1¾ teaspoons salt
⅛ teaspoon pepper
2 tablespoons margarine
About 1½ cups (one 12-ounce can) whole-kernel corn, drained
1 medium onion, sliced
2⅓ cups (one 1-pound, 3-ounce can) tomatoes, drained

Mix meat, crumbs, 1 teaspoon salt, and pepper. Melt margarine in covered skillet and cook meat mixture, stirring frequently, until well browned. Add corn and onion; sprinkle with ¾ teaspoon salt. Add tomatoes, cover, and simmer for about 25 minutes. Serve in skillet. Makes 4 to 6 servings.

HAMBURGER-ZUCCHINI SKILLET DINNER
1 pound ground beef
1 can (3 ounces) mushrooms, drained
2 tablespoons flour
1 teaspoon salt
¼ teaspoon pepper
1 teaspoon onion salt
¼ teaspoon garlic salt
½ teaspoon hot pepper sauce
½ teaspoon monosodium glutamate
2 medium zucchini, sliced thin
About 1¼ cups (one 10-ounce can) tomatoes
1 tablespoon vinegar
½ teaspoon seasoned salt

In skillet cook beef and mushrooms until meat loses its red color, breaking up meat with fork. Drain off most of fat.

Blend in flour and next 6 ingredients. Arrange zucchini on meat mixture and pour tomatoes over top. Add vinegar and sprinkle with seasoned salt. Cover and simmer for 30 minutes. Makes 4 servings.

FRENCH-FRIED HAMBURGER SANDWICHES
8 slices of very fresh bread
¾ pound beef round or chuck, ground
Salt and pepper to taste
2 eggs, beaten
¾ cup milk
Fat for deep frying

Remove crusts from bread. Shape meat into 4 patties and put one in center of each of 4 slices of bread, and season; top with remaining slices. Press the two together with hands. Seal edges with tines of fork dipped into hot water. Dip each sandwich into batter made by mixing eggs and milk. Put in wire basket and fry in hot deep fat (375°F. on a frying thermometer) until golden brown. The meat will be rare. (If you prefer the meat less rare, cook it first.) Makes 4 servings.

LASAGNE AL FORNO
2 tablespoons olive oil
1 medium onion, minced
1 garlic clove, minced
1 pound beef chuck, ground
1 teaspoon salt
½ teaspoon pepper
2 teaspoons grated lemon rind
¼ cup chopped parsley
2 cans (10¼ ounces each) meat sauce (about 2½ cups)
8 ounces lasagna, cooked and drained
1 pound Mozzarella cheese
1 pound ricotta (or creamed cottage cheese)
½ cup grated Parmesan cheese

Heat oil and cook onion and garlic in it until soft and transparent. Add beef, stirring with fork. Cook until lightly browned, stirring. Stir in salt, pepper, lemon rind, parsley, and meat sauce. Simmer over low heat for 15 minutes, stirring frequently. Spread about ¼ of sauce mixture on bottom and sides of a very large shallow baking dish. Top with a layer of lasagna placed lengthwise. Cover with a layer of half of Mozzarella and top this with half of ricotta. Sprinkle with ⅓ of grated Parmesan. Repeat procedure. Top with a third (and last) layer of lasagna, the remaining sauce, and Parmesan. Bake in preheated moderate oven (350°F.) for 30 minutes. To serve, cut into squares. Makes 6 servings.

Wild West Hamburger gains flavor from herbs and wine

Hail to the Hamburger

by Mary Hemingway

Whoever it was who first hit upon the idea of slicing meat thinly lengthwise and then chopping crosswise (a Chinese probably, and many years B.C.), deserves a curtsy, a salaam, and a salute. Not all together, please. To the doctors of Padua, Italy, who, in the eighth century, began prescribing chopped beef and onions fried together to cure their patients' colds, we owe at least a bow on a short winter afternoon.

At Aiguesmortes, the lovely golden-walled ancient town in the south of France from which King Louis IX, later Saint Louis, launched the Sixth and Seventh Crusades in 1248 and 1270, they say that it was the king's chef who invented the food grinder. A man in leather pedal pushers and a chef's apron, he is supposed to have been devoted both to his king and his vocation. He also knew the problems of cuisine aboard the ships which took the Christians through the Mediterranean to recover the Holy Land for Christendom. Each crusader had to bring his own fresh water for drinking. Even the king's chef had minimum space for preparing food and, come bad weather, minimum time over his fire to prepare something succulent and flavorsome for lunch. It was with these restrictions in mind, so they say, that the chef to King Louis IX invented the little wheel with its cutting edges and the small tunnel through which you push the food, and had the king's armorer make him the first meat grinder. (Fresh meat couldn't have lasted more than a day or two, but that was his problem.) My profound respects, herewith, to that cook and his invention, or to the legend.

Hoity-toity cooks may sneer, but approval and praise naturally follow to the public-service-minded man who decided, "Let us butchers do this job." And to all the other butchers who caught on, from Denmark to Costa Rica to Tasmania, saving housewives time and energy cutting away the muscle and the hard edges, pro-

viding the base for who knows how many hundreds of main-dish recipes. Here are some of Ernest's and my favorite ways of dealing with ground beef and some hamburger ideas, including the Wild West hamburger, which I invented to fortify us for tramping through sagebrush after pheasant, partridge, or ducks, or, after such hikes, to console us for not having shot our limits.

WILD-WEST HAMBURGER
(Papa's Favorite)

- 1 pound lean beef, ground
- 1 heaping teaspoon dried sage
- ½ teaspoon mixed-herb seasoning
- ½ teaspoon monosodium glutamate
- ½ teaspoon sugar
  Salt and pepper
- 2 spring onions, or shallots, finely chopped
- 2 garlic cloves, minced
- 1 heaping teaspoon India relish
- 2 tablespoons capers
- 1 tablespoon minced parsley, or 1 tablespoon dried parsley
- 1 egg, whipped in a cup
- ⅓ cup dry white wine
- 2 tablespoons oil for frying

What to do: Break up the meat with a fork and thoroughly mix into it first all of the dry ingredients (and afterwards all of the wet ingredients, including the wine), and let the bowl sit at room temperature for an hour, or at least for ½ hour. Make 4 fat, juicy patties which are soft but not runny.

There is only one correct way to fry a hamburger, I think, just as there is only one correct way to fry an egg. Have the oil in your skillet hot but not smoking when you drop in the patties, then turn the heat down, or take the pan off the stove for a minute. Fry the burgers for 4 minutes. Take the pan off the burner and turn the heat high again. Flip the burgers over, put the pan back on the high heat, and let them sizzle 1 minute. Lower the heat again and cook another 3 minutes. Both sides of the burgers should be crispy brown and the middle pink and juicy, and GOOD. Makes 2 servings.

COTTAGE PIE

The classic British treatment of ground beef, which you find properly done only in their homes. (The customary restaurant version is apt to taste like warm, wet blotting paper.) My jazzed-up variation:

- 2 tablespoons cooking oil
- 1 large garlic clove, chopped fine
- 1 large Spanish onion, chopped coarsely
  Salt and pepper to taste
- ¼ teaspoon sugar
- ½ teaspoon mixed-herb seasoning
- ½ teaspoon monosodium glutamate
- 1 pound lean beef, ground
- 2 large celery stalks, chopped horizontally

- 1 large carrot, coarsely grated
- ⅓ cup dry red wine
  Mashed potatoes

What to do: 1. Fry in the oil, the garlic, onion, salt, pepper, and other dry seasonings; stir until they are half-cooked, about 5 minutes. Add meat; stir until it is crumbled and mixed with the other things. Remove pan from the heat and add everything else, except potatoes, and let it sit, keeping warm, to blend the flavors.

2. Make a batch of smooth, creamy mashed potatoes with plenty of white pepper in them, using at least 4 fair-size potatoes.

3. Put the meat-and-vegetable mixture in a warmed casserole, spread the mashed potatoes on top (the potatoes should be 2 inches thick) and put the dish under the broiler to "tan" the potatoes. Enough for 3 to 5 people depending on appetites and the rest of the menu.

P.S. For a richer dish, mix ⅓ cup of grated Cheddar cheese with ⅓ cup of grated Parmesan cheese and spread it on top of the potatoes before putting the casserole under the broiler.

STIR-FRY GROUND BEEF
(As taught to me by the Chinese in Havana)

No self-respecting Chinese cook would use ground beef in a stir-fry dish, of which there are infinite varieties. They would buy their beef in a solid piece and thinly slice it. But the Chinese cooks have more time, or more patience, or they wield their knives more skillfully than I do, or they have all these sterling attributes together. Their end result is better food, but my cut-corner dish is good, too. You can order the fresh gingerroot from any Chinatown grocery. (No garlic, for once.)

- 1 large onion, coarsely chopped
- 3 tablespoons cooking oil
- 1½ cups Special Vegetable (see below)
- 1 pound lean beef, ground
- 1 heaping tablespoon fresh gingerroot, finely sliced
- 1 small can of water chestnuts, each chestnut sliced twice
- 2 tablespoons soy sauce
- 3 tablespoons dry white wine
  Pinch of pepper
- ½ teaspoon monosodium glutamate
- ¼ teaspoon sugar
  Rice or noodles

Special Vegetable: Now comes your freedom of selection. You need about 1½ cups of almost any fresh or frozen juicy vegetable, *finely sliced*. Pick out whatever you happen to have available that you fancy. It can be green pepper, green beans, wax beans, beets (good), cabbage, celery, broccoli, asparagus, fresh mushrooms (very good), green peas, or whatever.

What to do: You need three frying pans, one for the onions, one for the beef, one for your Special Vegetable.

1. Fry the onion slowly in a covered pan, to hold in its vapor and keep it warm. Use as little oil as possible.

2. Fry your Special Vegetable in as little oil as possible (this depends on the moisture in the vegetable) and add a little water, if necessary. Two minutes should do it, since you want your vegetable still fresh and in good form.

3. Fry the ground beef in a little oil, breaking it up and stirring it, three to four minutes. Then add to it the gingerroot, water chestnuts, soy sauce, wine, and seasonings (no salt), and cook two minutes more, until the new things are heated.

4. Into the meat pan, dump the onions, the Special Vegetable and its native juices. Stir a couple of times and serve with either white rice, wild rice, Chinese noodles, tagliatelli (big flat Italian noodles), macaroni, or spaghetti. Enough for 3 to 5 people, depending on appetites and what else you serve.

PICADILLO (pronounced "pee-kah-dee-yo")

This is what the Cubans do with ground beef instead of making hamburgers. There are many different versions of it but this one is the most authentic. (I leave out the tomatoes.)

    2 tablespoons cooking oil
    2 large garlic cloves, minced
    1 large onion, chopped coarsely
      Salt and pepper to taste
    ½ teaspoon monosodium glutamate
    1 pound lean beef, ground
    ⅓ cup dry white wine
    2 large ripe tomatoes, peeled and
      chopped
    ½ cup dark or light raisins, plumped
      up in hot water
    ⅓ cup pimiento-stuffed olives, sliced
      in thirds
    1 seeded green pepper, chopped in
      half-inch squares

What to do: In the oil, fry the garlic and onion for five minutes, stirring frequently. Add the seasonings, the meat, the wine, and stir again. Add the tomatoes, raisins, and olives, and stir. Add the green pepper and cook only long enough for it to get thoroughly hot; it should retain crispness and color.

One of *Picadillo's* charms is that all the chopping and slicing can be done in advance, the cooking requiring only a few (10) minutes' time. The Cubans serve this dish with plain white rice, either in a separate dish or with the *Picadillo* on top of the rice and its juices trickling down. (Enough for 3 to 5 people.)

HAMBURGER

A year ago and a month ago and a week ago, I saw served to helpless customers in various restaurants, rounds of gray, greasy, paper-thin agglomerations of meat and seasonings being presented as hamburger. A national disgrace! A hamburger worthy of the name should be at least 1 inch thick and 3 inches across; 4 inches is nobler. It can (why not?) contain all sorts of surprises besides salt, pepper, and ketchup. Here are some additions I have tried with success. Use ¼ pound of ground lean beef per hamburger. Never any bread or bread crumbs. Bind it with an egg, beaten up in a cup. For juiciness, in a pound of meat use a ¼, even ⅓ cup dry wine, red or white, depending on the other ingredients and seasonings. Take the ground beef out of the refrigerator an hour before you plan to cook it, mix in the extras, and let it rest comfortably at room temperature, the wine soaking into the meat. You'll see.

SURPRISE HAMBURGERS

With your 1 pound of lean ground beef, try mixing in one of the following:

1. A cup of grated Cheddar cheese, 1 clove of minced garlic, white wine, salt and pepper to taste.

2. A 5-ounce can of chopped water chestnuts, 2 chopped spring onions or shallots, 2 pinches of oregano, 2 tablespoons of soy sauce (no salt).

3. Three-quarters cup of finely chopped mushrooms, 3 pinches of marjoram, a big dollop of piccalilli, white wine, salt and pepper to taste.

4. Three-quarters cup of grated carrot, 1 minced garlic clove, 1 chopped onion, 3 pinches of thyme, red wine, salt and pepper to taste.

5. One-half of a 6-ounce can of tomato paste, diluted with ½ cup of tomato juice, ¼ teaspoon of sugar, 1 tablespoon of chopped dill pickle, salt and pepper to taste. (No wine.)

6. Three-quarters cup of finely chopped walnuts, 1 scant teaspoon of fresh, or a heaping teaspoon of dried dill seed, red wine, salt to taste.

7. One-half cup of grated tart apple, one chopped shallot, ⅓ cup of toasted, chopped almonds, red wine.

HARD COOKED—A term used to describe a method of cooking eggs in the shell to the stage where the egg white is firm yet tender and the egg yolk is firm but not rubbery. Eggs so cooked are often called "hard boiled." To achieve this result, it is necessary to cook eggs at a simmering, not hard-boiling, temperature during the entire cooking time. There are two ways to do this:

Cold-Water Method—Add cold water to eggs until 1 inch above eggs. Bring to a boil and simmer for 15 minutes. Place eggs in cold water to cool thoroughly. Roll egg to crack shell on its entire surface. Peel.

Boiling-Water Method—Carefully, with a spoon, lower room-temperature eggs into boiling water. Simmer for 12 minutes. Cool, and shell as above.

HARD SAUCE—This sauce is made by creaming butter with sugar, and flavoring it with brandy, rum, whisky, wine, or with extracts or spices. The sugar can be granulated, confectioners' sugar, or brown sugar. Cream is sometimes added to make the creaming easier. The sauce is chilled before use to stiffen it. It is served with a hot dessert such as a steamed pudding. It can also be served as an icing with fruit- or spicecakes.

Hard sauce is the traditional sauce for plum pudding. The combination of the brown, crumbly, hot pudding and the smooth, white, cold sauce is delicious. The sauce is of English origin, and in Great Britain it is called Brandy Butter, since it is flavored with brandy.

It takes time to make a good hard sauce. The sugar must be creamed into the softened, but not melted, butter slowly, and in small amounts. The sauce should be so thoroughly blended that no sugar crystals remain. The brandy or other flavoring should be added by pouring it over the last few tablespoons of sugar, thus blending it well into the mixture.

BASIC HARD SAUCE

Cream ⅓ cup butter, softened but not melted. To it add, a little at a time, 1 cup confectioners' sugar, beating after each addition. Beat in ½ teaspoon vanilla, a few drops at a time. Shape in balls or individual servings and chill, or put in serving dish to be spooned onto pudding. Makes 6 to 8 servings.

Sherry Hard Sauce

Make Basic Hard Sauce and beat in 1 to 3 tablespoons sherry.

Brandy Hard Sauce

Make Basic Hard Sauce and beat in 1 tablespoon brandy.

Creamy Hard Sauce

Make Basic Hard Sauce and beat in ¼ cup heavy cream.

Mocha Hard Sauce

Make Basic Hard Sauce and beat in 2 tablespoons strong coffee, 2 teaspoons cocoa, and ¼ cup heavy cream.

Lemon Hard Sauce

Make Basic Hard Sauce and beat in 1 teaspoon fresh lemon juice and 1 tablespoon lemon rind.

Orange Hard Sauce

Make Basic Hard Sauce and beat in 2 tablespoons fresh orange juice and 2 tablespoons orange rind.

Spicy Hard Sauce

Make Basic Hard Sauce and beat in ½ teaspoon ground cinnamon and ¼ teaspoon ground cloves.

Cherry-Nut Patties

Chop candied cherries and nuts. Make Basic Hard Sauce recipe, shape into a roll, and roll in cherries and nuts. Chill. At serving time, cut into serving-size slices.

FLUFFY HARD SAUCE

1 cup sugar
1 tablespoon soft butter
3 tablespoons heavy cream
3 egg whites, beaten until stiff
1 teaspoon vanilla extract

Mix sugar with butter and cream. Blend well. Gradually fold in egg whites and vanilla. Makes about 1½ cups.

BROWN-SUGAR HARD SAUCE

1½ cups firmly packed dark brown sugar
½ cup butter
⅓ cup light cream
1 teaspoon vanilla extract or 2 tablespoons rum

Mash brown sugar to remove all lumps. Cream butter until soft and gradually beat in brown sugar. Gradually beat in cream and vanilla. Blend well. Chill. Makes about 1⅔ cups.

HARDTACK—A large, hard biscuit made of unsalted dough and dried after baking to make it easy to store and preserve. Hardtack is also called "ship biscuit" or "pilot bread" because of the custom of serving it on shipboard during the prolonged sea voyages of the past when it was impossible to store fresh bread.

Hardtack is used in army and navy commissaries and is also available in food stores. It is often served with chowders, soups, and stews, sometimes broken into pieces and added to the dish.

Hardtack is an excellent biscuit for those who like dry, light biscuits.

HARE—Hare is a cousin of the rabbit and belongs to the *Leporidae* family of rodents. Generally speaking, hares are European and rabbits are American. There are many varieties of each.

Although the names are often used interchangeably, genuine hares are not found in the United States and the two animals are quite different. Rabbits are born naked and blind; hares are born furred with eyes opened. After a month's suckling, hares are able to look after themselves. They are generally bigger than rabbits and have longer ears and feet. Their coats are beautiful, often silky. There are blue-gray hares in the far north of Europe, with black-tipped ears which turn white in the winter. In Ireland, russet-colored hares never show a trace of white in their furs. Some French hares have coats the color of ripe corn. Some hares grow huge, like Belgian hares, reaching thirteen pounds.

The meat of a hare differs greatly in taste depending on its age. A tender leveret, as young hares are called, has white meat that tastes like chicken. It can be cooked as chicken is cooked. Older hares have strong-flavored, tougher meat. They are treated like game and cooked slowly, often after being marinated to make the meat more tender. Hare is seldom available in the United States.

HARICOT—A French word meaning "bean." *Haricots blancs* are "white beans," *haricots verts* are "green beans."

In French culinary language, a *haricot* can also be a mutton or lamb stew made with potatoes and onions. A *"haricot"* does not contain beans; the name is a corruption of the French *halicot,* meaning "chopped very fine."

HASENPFEFFER—The literal translation of this German word is "hare pepper." In practice it stands for a highly seasoned stew of rabbit or hare, which has been marinated to make the meat more tender. The marinade can be wine, or equal parts of vinegar and water, seasoned with onion slices, bay leaf, salt and pepper, juniper berries, or any other marinade seasonings. The meat rests in the marinade for one or several days (depending on its age). It is then browned in fat and braised in the marinade. Sweet or sour cream is added to the final gravy.

Hasenpfeffer is a hunter's dish that has been adopted for family use. It is an excellent way of serving rabbit or hare. Any venison or game can be cooked in the same manner.

HASENPFEFFER

1 cup each of water and vinegar
1 clove
1 bay leaf
1 teaspoon salt
6 peppercorns
1 onion, sliced
1 rabbit or hare, cut into serving pieces
¼ cup butter or margarine
¼ cup all-purpose flour

Cook water, vinegar, spices, and onion together for 5 minutes. Pour over rabbit pieces and let stand in refrigerator for 2 days. Remove rabbit from marinade, and pat dry. Fry in the butter until brown. Reserve marinade. Add flour and let it brown lightly. Add 1 cup strained marinade and simmer gently for 1½ hours, until rabbit is tender. Add more marinade if necessary. If desired, add ½ cup dairy sour cream to sauce when meat is cooked and removed from heat. Makes 4 servings.

HASH—A mixture of foods chopped into small pieces and mixed. The word is most commonly applied to a mixture of meat or poultry, potatoes, and seasonings. Other vegetables may be added. For that matter, hash may be made of almost any other ingredients: there is even a marshmallow dessert which bears the name "Heavenly Hash."

Corned-beef hash and roast-beef hash are available canned and frozen.

HASH COOK BOOK

HASH PREPARED WITH FRESH INGREDIENTS

HASH WITH MUSHROOMS
¼ cup butter or margarine
½ pound sliced fresh mushrooms
2 cups diced cooked beef, lamb, chicken, or turkey
1½ cups brown gravy
Salt and pepper
Crumbled dried thyme, basil, or rosemary
Hot toast
1 tablespoon chopped parsley

Heat butter and sauté mushrooms until tender. Add meat and gravy, and heat until piping hot. Season to taste with salt and pepper and crumbled dried thyme. Serve on hot toast garnished with chopped parsley. Makes 4 servings.

VEAL HASH
3 cups diced cooked veal
1 onion, minced
3 tablespoons butter or margarine
1 cup diced cooked potatoes
1 cup veal broth
1 pimiento, diced
1 cup heavy cream or undiluted evaporated milk, scalded
2 egg yolks, slightly beaten
Salt and pepper

Use leftover meat or simmer a knuckle of veal in well-seasoned water until tender. Cut meat into very small even cubes. Cook onion in butter for 2 or 3 minutes. Add potatoes and broth; heat to boiling. Add meat and pimiento; simmer for 2 or 3 minutes. Pour hot cream slowly over egg yolks. Add to meat mixture. Heat gently until thickened, stirring carefully. Add more salt and pepper if necessary. Serve at once. Makes 4 servings.

FRANKFURTER HASH
4 cups finely diced cold boiled potatoes
1 medium onion, chopped
3 tablespoons all-purpose flour
Salt and pepper
¼ cup milk
½ pound frankfurters, thinly sliced
3 tablespoons butter or margarine
½ cup shredded sharp Cheddar cheese

Combine potatoes and onion. Sprinkle with flour and season to taste. Add milk and frankfurters. Put in shallow baking dish or pie pan. Dot with butter. Bake in preheated hot oven (425°F.) for 30 minutes. Top with cheese. Bake for 5 minutes longer, or until cheese is melted. Makes 4 servings.

MAINE CORNED-BEEF HASH
4 cups cold cubed cooked corned beef
3 cups cubed boiled potatoes
¼ cup butter or margarine
¾ cup boiling water
Salt and pepper

Trim meat free from gristle and fat. Place with potatoes in chopping bowl. Chop until meat and potatoes are in shreds. Melt butter in heavy skillet. Add boiling water and meat and potato mixture. Season with salt and pepper to taste. Cook over lowest possible heat for about 15 minutes, or until a thin brown crust has been formed on the bottom of the hash. Fold over as for an omelet. Slide onto heated serving dish. Makes 4 to 6 servings.

CHICKEN HASH À LA RITZ
4 large chicken breasts or 3 to 4 cups cooked chicken, white meat only
Chicken bouillon
2 tablespoons butter
1 cup mushrooms, sliced
½ cup minced green pepper
¼ cup minced pimiento
⅔ cup light dry sherry
1 cup heavy cream
1½ cups medium white sauce made with light cream instead of milk
1 teaspoon salt
White pepper

Simmer chicken breasts in chicken bouillon to cover for 30 to 45 minutes, or until tender. Remove skin, bones, and tendons. Cut chicken into ¼-inch or smaller dices. In heavy skillet heat butter until golden, but do not let brown. Cook mushrooms, pepper, and pimiento in butter for 5 minutes. Add chicken, ⅓ cup of the sherry, and the heavy cream. Simmer over low heat, stirring frequently, for 10 minutes, or until sauce has cooked down to about half the initial quantity. Add white sauce and blend thoroughly. Season with salt, and pepper to taste. Just before serving, stir in remaining sherry and a little more heavy cream if sauce looks too thick. Serve on buttered toast, or with asparagus and wild rice. Makes 2 or 3 servings.

TURKEY HASH
¼ cup butter
2 tablespoons flour
½ cup heavy cream
¾ cup chicken bouillon
Grated rind of 1 lemon
¼ teaspoon white pepper
⅛ teaspoon ground mace
½ pound mushrooms, sliced, or 3- to 4-ounce can sliced mushrooms
3 cups diced turkey
1 cup oysters (optional)

Melt 2 tablespoons butter and stir in flour. Cook, stirring constantly, until smooth and golden. Combine cream and bouillon. Stir gradually into flour mixture. Cook, stirring constantly, until thickened and smooth. Stir in lemon rind, pepper, and mace. Cook mushrooms in remaining butter for 3 minutes. Add mushrooms and turkey to sauce. Cook over lowest possible heat, stirring frequently, until thoroughly heated through. Just before serving, add oysters. Serve with plain or wild rice, or with corn pudding. Makes 3 servings.

POTATOES HASHED IN CREAM
1 medium onion, minced
2 tablespoons butter or margarine
About 2 cups (1-pound can) potatoes, drained and chopped
½ cup light cream
Salt and pepper
Chopped parsley
Paprika

Cook onion in butter in skillet until lightly browned. Add potatoes and cream; simmer for 5 minutes. Season with salt and pepper to taste. Put in serving dish and sprinkle with parsley and paprika. Makes 4 servings.

PEPPER HASH
12 sweet red peppers
12 sweet green peppers
12 medium onions
6 cups white or cider vinegar
2 cups sugar
¼ cup salt

Remove stems and seeds from peppers and peel onions. Put vegetables through food grinder, using medium blade. Cover with boiling water and let stand for 15 minutes. Drain and repeat. Drain again. Add vinegar, sugar, and salt. Cook gently for 30 minutes. Pour into hot sterilized jars, and seal. Makes about 4 pints.

HEAVENLY HASH
25 marshmallows
25 candied cherries
2 cups heavy cream
1 cup blanched almonds, chopped
½ teaspoon each of vanilla and almond extracts

Cut marshmallows into 4 pieces each; use scissors for easier working. Slice all but 6 cherries. Combine marshmallows and heavy cream. Refrigerate for 1 hour. With rotary beater, whip mixture until stiff. Fold in other ingredients. Chill for 2 to 4 hours; dessert must be very cold. Cut remaining cherries into halves. At serving time, decorate hash with halved cherries. Makes 6 servings.

CANNED HASH

BAKED CORNED-BEEF HASH AND TOMATOES
1- pound can corned-beef hash
2 tomatoes, halved

Heavenly Hash

Chicken Hash à La Ritz

Prepared mustard
Salt and pepper
Onion salt
Worcestershire
Sugar
Butter
Fine dry bread crumbs

Put hash in small shallow baking dish or pie pan. Press tomato halves into hash and spread with mustard. Sprinkle with salt, pepper, onion salt, Worcestershire, and sugar to taste. Dot with butter and sprinkle with crumbs. Bake in preheated hot oven (400°F.) for 25 minutes. Makes 2 servings.

BROILED CORNED-BEEF-HASH MOUNDS

4 thin slices of bread
1- pound can corned-beef hash
¼ cup chili sauce
⅓ cup shredded sharp Cheddar cheese
1 medium onion, cut into rings
1 tablespoon melted butter

Toast bread in broiler on one side. Mix hash and chili sauce and heap on un-toasted sides of bread, taking care to cover edges. Broil under medium heat for 15 minutes, or until slightly browned. Sprinkle with cheese and top with onion rings. Brush rings with butter; broil only until cheese is melted. Makes 2 servings.

CORNED-BEEF HASH WITH CREAMED EGGS

1- pound can corned-beef hash
1 tablespoon margarine
½ can cream-of-mushroom soup
¼ teaspoon Worcestershire
¼ cup heavy cream
2 hard-cooked eggs, quartered
1 pimiento, cut into strips

Open both ends of can and push out hash. Cut across into 4 slices. Brown slowly in margarine in skillet, turning to brown both sides. Meanwhile, combine soup, Worcestershire, and cream in top part of double boiler; heat over boiling water. Add eggs and pimiento; heat. Serve as sauce on hash. Makes 2 servings.

CORNED-BEEF HASH WITH MUSTARD SAUCE

1- pound can corned-beef hash
1 tablespoon bacon fat
Hot Mustard Sauce

Heat hash thoroughly in fat in skillet. Serve in mounds with hot Mustard Sauce. Makes 2 servings.

Mustard Sauce

1 medium onion, minced
2 tablespoons margarine
1 tablespoon all-purpose flour
½ teaspoon salt
Dash of pepper
¾ cup milk
1 tablespoon prepared mustard

Cook onion in margarine in heavy sauce-pan until yellow. Stir in flour, salt, pepper, and milk. Cook slowly until slightly thickened. Add mustard. Makes 1 cup.

CORNED-BEEF HASH LYONNAISE

1 tablespoon margarine
2 medium onions, sliced
2 cans (1 pound each) corned-beef hash

Melt margarine in skillet; add onions and cook for a few minutes. Add hash, mix well, and cook until brown. Makes 4 servings.

CORNED-BEEF HASH O'BRIEN

1 small onion, minced
½ medium green pepper, chopped
1 tablespoon margarine
1 pimiento, chopped
1- pound can corned-beef hash

Cook onion and green pepper in margarine until onion is lightly browned. Add pimiento and hash; cook, stirring occasionally, until hash is browned. Makes 2 servings.

HASH-STUFFED CABBAGE ROLLS

6 large cabbage leaves
1 small onion, minced
1 tablespoon margarine
1- pound can corned-beef hash
2⅓ cups (one 1-pound, 3-ounce can) tomatoes, drained
1 garlic clove, minced
¼ teaspoon ground oregano
½ teaspoon salt
⅛ teaspoon pepper
½ cup grated Parmesan cheese

Cook cabbage leaves in boiling water for 3 minutes. Drain and dry on absorbent paper. Cook onion in margarine until lightly browned. Add to hash. Divide mixture among cabbage leaves. Roll leaves; tuck ends under and arrange in shallow baking dish. Mix tomato pulp and remaining ingredients except cheese. Pour over cabbage rolls. Bake in preheated hot oven (400°F.) for 35 minutes. Sprinkle with cheese; bake for 10 minutes longer. Makes 2 servings.

ROAST-BEEF HASH CASSEROLE

1 can (12 ounces) roast-beef hash
¼ cup butter or margarine
1 cup sharp Cheddar cheese
Dash of Worcestershire
1 egg white, stiffly beaten

Spread roast-beef hash in shallow casserole. Cream butter; mix in cheese and Worcestershire, and then the egg white. Spoon over hash in casserole. Bake in preheated hot oven (425°F.) for 15 minutes, or until puffy. Makes 4 servings.

BARBECUED BEEF HASH

1½ tablespoons onion, chopped
1 teaspoon butter
1 can (12 ounces) roast-beef hash
⅓ cup ketchup
1½ tablespoons vinegar
1 tablespoon Worcestershire
⅓ teaspoon salt
Pepper to taste
4 hamburger rolls, toasted

Brown onion in butter. Add next 6 ingredients and mix well. Heat slowly and serve on toasted rolls. Makes 4 servings.

HAZELNUT—This grape-size, smooth-shelled nut grows on shrubs and trees belonging to the genus *Corylus*. The nuts grow in clusters and each is wrapped in a fuzzy outer husk that opens as the nut ripens. The hazelnut is also known as a cobnut or filbert.

Hazelnuts are an essential nut in European dessert cookery and baking. The nuts are often toasted for a browner color and a better flavor; they are never blanched.

Whole hazelnuts can be salted, or sugared, or eaten as is. Chopped hazelnuts can be used in candies, baked goods, and desserts. Sliced hazelnuts can be added to salads and to main dishes for texture.

Availability and Purchasing Guide—Hazelnuts are sold in the shell, in bulk or by the pound. Look for nuts with clean shells that are free from scars, cracks, or holes. The shells should be well filled so that the kernel does not rattle.

Shelled salted hazelnuts are sold in bulk and packaged in film bags. Fresh-shelled kernels should be plump, meaty, crisp, and brittle.
□ 2¼ pounds in-shell = 1 pound shelled = 3½ cups

Storage—Keep tightly covered and away from light.
□ Kitchen shelf: 1 month
□ Refrigerator shelf: 3 to 4 months
□ Refrigerator frozen-food compartment, prepared for freezing: 6 months
□ Freezer, prepared for freezing: 1 year

Nutritive Food Values—Hazelnuts provide protein, fat, iron, and thiamine.
□ 3½ ounces = 634 calories

Basic Preparation—To shell hazelnuts, use

a nutcracker as the shell is brittle. Remove the kernel intact. To slice or chop nuts, use a long sharp knife and a cutting board.

□ **To Toast**—Place nuts on a cookie sheet in preheated moderate oven (350° F.) for 5 to 6 minutes, stirring once. Turn them out on a rough cloth and rub them briskly in the cloth. This will remove fine skin fibers. The nuts must then be picked over. They can be ground in a blender or a nut mill, and used like other nuts.

□ **To Roast in Oven**—Spread nutmeats in a shallow pan and place in preheated hot oven (400°F.) for about 7 minutes, or in preheated slow oven (275°F.) for 20 minutes. Stir nuts frequently to prevent scorching. For salted nuts, add 1 teaspoon salt per cup of nutmeats. If desired, while nutmeats are warm, rub off skins with cloth or between fingers.

□ **To Skillet-Roast**—Heat 2 teaspoons cooking oil in a skillet over low heat. Add nutmeats and 1 teaspoon salt per cup of nuts. Stir constantly until thoroughly heated. Drain well on paper towels.

□ **To Grind**—Use a special nut grinder or an electric blender; when butter or paste is desired, use a meat grinder. Hazelnuts are excellent when ground, with a dry grain that is not oily.

HAZELNUT AND MUSHROOM SAUCE
½ cup sliced hazelnuts
½ onion, minced
¼ cup sliced mushrooms
¼ cup butter or margarine
2 tablespoons all-purpose flour
1 teaspoon salt
¼ teaspoon pepper
2 chicken bouillon cubes
2 cups hot water

Brown hazelnuts, onion, and mushrooms in butter; remove from skillet. To fat, add flour and seasonings, mixing well. Add bouillon cubes which have been dissolved in the hot water; cook until thickened. Return hazelnuts, onion, and mushrooms to sauce; serve hot over rice. Makes about 2½ cups.

HAZELNUT CREAM
½ cup shelled hazelnuts
1 cup milk or light cream
2 egg yolks
¼ cup sugar
1 teaspoon vanilla extract
1½ teaspoons unflavored gelatin
1 tablespoon water
½ cup heavy cream, whipped

Spread hazelnuts in pie pan and toast in moderate oven (350°F,) until skins are coming loose. Place in towel and rub to remove skins. Grind in nut grinder or blender. Combine with milk, egg yolks, and sugar. Cook over lowest possible heat, stirring constantly, until *almost* boiling. Remove from heat. Add vanilla.

Soften gelatin in water. Stir into hot custard until completely dissolved. Cool; fold in whipped cream. Pour into glass serving dish and chill until set. Makes 3 large servings.

CHOCOLATE DIAMONDS WITH HAZELNUTS
2 ounces (2 squares) unsweetened chocolate
½ cup butter
1 cup sugar
2 eggs
½ cup sifted all-purpose flour
¼ teaspoon salt
½ teaspoon vanilla extract
⅔ cup chopped hazelnuts

Melt chocolate and butter over hot water. Add remaining ingredients except nuts and mix well. Spread in greased pan (1 x 10 x 15 inches). Sprinkle with nuts. Bake in preheated hot oven (400° F.) for about 12 minutes. Cool slightly and cut into 1½-inch diamonds in pans. Makes about 4 dozen.

HAZELNUT TARTS
Pastry (2-cups flour recipe)
½ cup firmly packed brown sugar
1 tablespoon all-purpose flour
⅛ teaspoon salt
1 cup dark corn syrup
2 eggs, well beaten
2 tablespoons melted butter or margarine
1 teaspoon vanilla extract
1 cup chopped hazelnuts
Evaporated milk

Line tart shells with pastry. Mix sugar, flour, and salt; add syrup, eggs, butter, and vanilla; pour into pastry. Sprinkle nuts over top and brush edges of tarts with evaporated milk. Bake in preheated moderate oven (350°F.) for 10 minutes; reduce heat to slow (325°F.) and bake for 25 minutes longer. Makes 8 tarts.

HAZELNUT CINNAMON BUNS
2 cups sifted all-purpose flour
2 teaspoons baking powder
½ teaspoon salt
5 tablespoons shortening
⅔ cup milk
¼ cup butter or margarine
¼ cup firmly packed brown sugar
1 teaspoon ground cinnamon
½ cup sliced hazelnuts
¾ cup light corn syrup

Sift dry ingredients together; cut in shortening. Add milk and knead for 1 minute. Roll out on floured board into a sheet 12 x 6 inches. Spread with butter, brown sugar, cinnamon, and nuts. Roll as for jelly roll. Cut into 1-inch slices. Pour 1 tablespoon syrup into each greased muffin pan; put slice of dough in each. Bake in preheated very hot oven (450° F.) for 12 minutes. Makes 1 dozen.

HEAD CHEESE—Head cheese is a well-seasoned cold cut made of the edible parts of a calf's or a pig's head such as the cheeks, snouts, and underlips, to which sometimes brains, hearts, tongues, and feet are added. The meat is boiled, stripped from the bones, skinned, cut into pieces, and seasoned with onions, herbs, and spices. Then it is put into a mold and pressed into a firm, jellied mass.

Head cheese is named so misleadingly because, at one time, cheese was added to the meat. It is available in food stores, as are other cold cuts, but it can also be made at home.

Head cheese is used in Scandinavian *smörgåsbord*, in French hors-d'oeuvre, and in German, Swiss, and Austrian sandwiches. Every country where farm people butcher meat has its own version of head cheese.

HEAD CHEESE
1 calf's or pig's head
Water
White wine
1 onion, studded with 4 cloves
6 celery stalks with leaves
4 parsley sprigs
1 carrot, sliced
1 bay leaf
12 peppercorns
2 teaspoons salt
Cayenne, ground nutmeg, and ground sage

Have butcher clean the head and remove the snout. Reserve tongue and brains. Wash head well and place in a kettle large enough to cover the head with equal parts of water and wine. Add tongue and onion studded with cloves. Tie celery, parsley, carrot, bay leaf, and peppercorns in a cheesecloth bag. Add. Bring water to a boil and simmer for about 4 hours, skimming the surface as it cooks. Remove tongue from water after 1½ hours. Skin tongue and cut into 1-inch cubes. Remove head from water and reserve cooking liquid. Remove meat from head and cut into 1-inch cubes. Drop brains into cooking liquid and simmer for 15 minutes. Cut brains, after removing the membrane, into 1-inch cubes. Toss with tongue and meat from head, and season to taste with salt, cayenne, nutmeg, and sage. Spoon mixture into a loaf pan or mold, pressing firmly. Pour ½ cup of the cooking liquid into the pan. Cover pan and weight to keep meats under the liquid. Cool, and then chill for 48 hours. Serve chilled and cut into slices. Makes 8 servings.

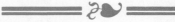

HEART—The hearts of beef, veal, lamb, and pork are used in cookery, especially in Scandinavia and in central Europe. Poultry hearts are usually used as giblets.

Hearts are tasty meat when properly cooked. Since they are one of the less tender cuts, they must be cooked slowly in moist heat, by braising and stewing. Stuffing adds to the interest of the dish.

Hearts are nutritious and inexpensive; and when seasoned with thyme, marjoram, or other herbs, and cooked in a good sauce, make a good family dish.

Hearts can be used in any recipe calling for sliced, diced, or ground meat.

Availability and Purchasing Guide—Beef heart is the largest and averages 3 to 3½ pounds; it may weigh as much as 5 pounds. One heart makes about 8 servings. Veal (calf's heart) is smaller and more tender. It weighs ¾ to 1 pound and makes 2 or 3 servings. Pork heart averages ½ pound and makes 1 or 2 servings. Lamb heart is the smallest and weighs ¼ to ½ pound. Usually one heart is allowed per serving. Occasionally two very small lamb hearts are served as a single portion.

Storage—Keep in refrigerator loosely wrapped. Maximum storage time is 3 to 4 days as heart spoils rapidly. Quality is best when used within 24 hours.

☐ Refrigerator shelf, raw: 3 to 4 days
☐ Refrigerator shelf, cooked: 5 to 6 days
☐ Refrigerator frozen-food compartment, prepared for freezing: 2 to 3 weeks
☐ Freezer, prepared for freezing: 6 months to 1 year

Nutritive Food Values—Heart is high in protein, iron, riboflavin, and niacin, and has fair amounts of thiamine.

☐ Beef, 3½ ounces, raw = 108 calories
☐ Veal, 3½ ounces, raw = 124 calories
☐ Pork, 3½ ounces, raw = 113 calories
☐ Lamb, 3½ ounces, raw = 162 calories

Basic Preparation—Wash heart. Cut out fat, veins, and arteries. Use whole, sliced, or ground. Braise or cook in liquid.

☐ **To Braise**—If desired, stuff heart before braising. Brown the heart on all sides in a small amount of shortening. Add about ½ cup of liquid. Season with salt and pepper. Simmer, covered, over low heat on top of the range or in preheated slow oven (300° to 325°F.). Check occasionally for moisture; if necessary, add a little more hot liquid to prevent scorching.

☐ **To Cook in Liquid**—Add 1 teaspoon

●● TIMETABLE FOR COOKING HEARTS ●●

	BRAISED (After Browning) (Hours)	COOKED IN LIQUID (Hours)
Beef		
Whole	3 to 4	3 to 4
Sliced	1½ to 2	
Veal (calf)		
Whole	2½ to 3	2½ to 3
Pork	2½ to 3	2½ to 3
Lamb	2½ to 3	2½ to 3

Cooking times are based on top of the range or cooking in a slow oven (300°F. to 325°F.). A pressure cooker shortens the cooking time to about 1 hour. Follow manufacturer's directions for accurate cooking times.

salt for each quart of water to be used. Place heart in deep heavy saucepan. Add water to cover and any desired seasonings. Simmer, covered, until tender.

SAVORY STUFFED HEART
1¼ cups rice, cooked
    Few celery leaves, chopped
  3 onions, chopped
  1 teaspoon poultry seasoning or
    ½ teaspoon each of ground thyme and sage
    Salt and pepper
  1 beef heart
  2 tablespoons fat
  2 cups beef bouillon or water

Mix rice and next 3 ingredients; season to taste with salt and pepper. Trim heart and remove large tubes, excess fat, and blood vessels. Season well inside and out with salt and pepper. Fill with some of rice mixture and sew edges together. Brown well in hot fat in heavy kettle. Cover; cook slowly without added water for 2 hours. Remove meat and pour off all fat. Put remaining rice mixture in kettle; add bouillon and season to taste. Put heart on top, cover, and simmer for 1 hour longer, or until meat is tender. Makes 8 servings.

BEEF HEART WITH VEGETABLES
  1 beef heart
  2 teaspoons salt
  ¼ teaspoon pepper
  1 teaspoon mixed pickling spice
  1 celery stalk
  4 carrots, sliced
  4 onions, sliced
  4 potatoes, sliced
    Bottled gravy sauce

Trim heart; remove large tubes, excess fat, and blood vessels. Cover with water. Add salt, pepper, pickling spice, and celery. Cover and simmer for 2 hours, or until tender. Remove heart, reserving stock, and slice. Put vegetables in bottom of casserole and cover with sliced heart. Add strained stock and a little gravy sauce. Cover, bake in preheated moderate oven (375°F.) for 1 hour. Makes 4 servings.

SCOTCH HEART PATTIES
1¼ pounds beef heart
  1 medium onion
  ½ cup quick-cooking rolled oats
1½ teaspoons salt
  ⅛ teaspoon pepper
    All-purpose flour
  2 tablespoons fat
1½ cups water

Wash and trim heart and remove large tubes, excess fat, and blood vessels. Force heart and onion through food grinder, using fine blade. Add oats, salt, and pepper. Let stand for at least 30 minutes. Then, with well-floured hands, shape mixture into 8 thin patties, coating each patty with flour. Brown slowly on both sides in hot fat. Remove patties and keep hot. Blend 1½ tablespoons flour into drippings remaining in skillet. Add

water and cook until thickened. Season with additional salt and pepper if necessary. Serve as a sauce with the patties. Makes 4 servings.

HEART STEW
1½ pounds beef or veal heart
  2 tablespoons all-purpose flour
  1 teaspoon salt
    Dash of pepper
  2 tablespoons cooking oil
  2 onions, sliced
1½ cups water
    Hot mashed potatoes

Trim heart; remove large tubes, excess fat, and blood vessels. Cut meat into thin slices. Dredge with flour, salt, and pepper. Brown lightly in hot oil. Add onion and water. Cover and simmer for 45 minutes. Serve with potatoes. Makes 4 servings.

DANISH VEAL HEARTS
  2 veal hearts (about 1½ pounds)
  6 parsley sprigs, chopped
  2 onions, sliced thin
  1 tablespoon fat
  ½ bay leaf
  4 peppercorns
  1 teaspoon salt
    Dash of pepper
  2 small carrots, diced
  1 celery stalk, diced
  1 cup water
  ¼ cup heavy cream

Trim hearts and split lengthwise. Remove large tubes, excess fat, and blood vessels. Stuff hearts with parsley and half of onion; close with skewers or sew with string. Brown on all sides in fat in heavy kettle. Add remaining onion, the seasonings, carrots, celery, and water. Cover; simmer for 2 hours, or until hearts are very tender. Remove to hot serving platter. Strain broth, add cream, and pour over hearts. Makes 4 servings.
Note: Pork or lamb hearts may be substituted for the veal.

FRIED HEART SLICES
  2 veal hearts (about 1½ pounds)
  3 tablespoons cooking oil
  1 garlic clove, halved
    Salt and pepper
    Fresh lemon juice
  1 tablespoon chopped scallion tops or parsley

Trim hearts; remove large tubes, excess fat, and blood vessels. Slice very thin. Heat oil and garlic slowly for 3 minutes; remove garlic. Add heart slices; brown quickly on both sides. Remove to platter; sprinkle with salt and pepper to taste. Squeeze a little lemon juice over all. Sprinkle scallions on top. Makes 4 servings.
Note: Pork, beef, or lamb hearts may be substituted for the veal.

VEAL HEARTS WITH FRUIT STUFFING
  2 veal hearts (about 1½ pounds)
    Salt and pepper to taste
  8 pitted dried prunes
  2 tart apples, peeled and sliced

3 tablespoons butter or margarine
1 cup water
¾ cup light cream

Trim hearts and split lengthwise. Remove large tubes, excess fat, and blood vessels. Sprinkle hearts inside and out with salt and pepper. Stuff hearts with prunes and apple slices. Skewer or sew opening together. Brown hearts on all sides in butter. Gradually add water and 1 teaspoon salt. Bring to a boil, cover, and simmer for 1½ hours, or until hearts are tender. Remove hearts and slice. Stir cream into pan juices. Reheat but do not boil. Serve over heart slices. Makes 6 servings.

HERB—An aromatic plant used to add flavor to food. These plants usually owe their flavoring qualities to essential oils which are readily soluble or easily volatized by heat and quickly permeate the foods with which they are mixed. For culinary use the seeds of some of these plants are the seasoning agent, in others it is the foliage. The herbs most used in American kitchens are parsley, sage, thyme, marjoram, dill, fennel, tarragon, basil, chives, oregano, and savory.

Strictly speaking, only seed plants which do not develop woody persistent tissue can be considered herbs, but certain plants which do not qualify botanically have long histories of use in cooking as flavoring agents. These include such flowers as the rose, marigold, violet, and scented geranium.

From the earliest times herbs have been used in cooking and medicine and for their sweet scent. They have played a large part in folklore and all sorts of magical properties have been accredited to them. The Assyrians, shapers of one of the earliest of recorded civilizations, who settled along the Tigris in what now is Iraq about 3000 B.C., used herbs. Among the 200 plants they were familiar with were dill, fennel, origanum, and thyme. The Egyptians sprinkled parsley on the graves of their dead, and both Greeks and Romans put sweet marjoram in funeral wreaths.

The Greeks and Romans also believed in love potions made from various herbs, including anise, basil, fennel, and garlic. It was thought that anise made one's face young, that basil attracted scorpions (especially if pounded together with crabs), and that thyme could not grow unless it was blown upon by sea winds. Herbs were also used for all sorts of medical cures, and of course, in cookery.

The Middle Ages continued the use of culinary herbs and the herb gardens of monasteries and castles were lovely to behold. Anise, mint, and parsley were favorites for gravies, sauces, and relishes. Dill added flavor to vegetables. Puddings, tarts, pastries, cakes, and conserves were made with the addition of sweet marjoram, thyme, savory, and anise. Some more unusual culinary preparations included marigolds for soup and drinks (as well as for "angry words"), and cumin for roasted peacock. Borage flowers were used as a garnish, and rue was much more popular than it is now. Basil was "for potage," and also to "make a woman shall not eat of anything that is set on the table." This feat was accomplished by serving the food on a hidden bed of basil, because "men say that she will eat none of that which is on the dish whereunder the basil lieth."

Herbs have always been used for beverages, both alcoholic and nonalcoholic. Today, country people and herbalists are still fervent supporters of herb teas and wines. Woodruff is a traditional and continuing ingredient in the *Maibowle* of the Germans, while wormwood is used for absinthe.

Many herbs, including geranium leaves and mint, were said to have healing powers for wounds, and various common and unpleasant ailments have been thought to be curable by herbs. Present-day herbalists continue the tradition, and modern pharmacists use herbs in preparation of some medicines. The type of herb for the type of ailment has differed in different times and different countries. Baldness, a problem throughout the ages, has been thought to be stopped by onions, parsley, and southernwood.

Queen Victoria's mother, a demanding woman, recommended a violet drink to "soothe the system" in case of bronchitis, fevers, and catarrhs.

Herbs have long been used for a cosmetic effect. Sir Hugh Platt, an Englishman writing in 1609, claims they "relieue," or relieve, for ladies, "The wrongs that Nature on their person wrought/Or parching sun with his hot firie rayes." Sir Hugh recommends sorrel "to take staines out of ones hands presently." "To take away the freckles in the face," according to Sir Hugh, you must "wash your face in the wane of the moone with a spunge, morninge and euening with the distilled water of Elder Leaues, letting the same drie into the skinne. Your water must be distilled in Maie."

The careful instructions as to the time of day and year which are necessary for this herbal remedy to be efficient are not uncommon in herb lore. Herbs have always been connected with magic and superstition, and have sometimes been explained in terms of astrology. From earliest times the influence of the moon upon plants has been considered important. The 17th-century astrologers had complicated charts where they reckoned that each disease was caused by a planet. The illness could be cured either by use of herbs belonging to an opposite sign, or by sympathy, with the herb of the same sign.

Garlic has been worn in an amulet or carried in the pocket or eaten, to ward off all sorts of evil, including vampires, the evil eye, and witches. The plant is used in many spells and charms, and was thought, because of its humanlike form, to screech when it was uprooted. There was also a belief that whoever pulled up the root would himself die. Its juice acted as an anesthetic, as a love potion, to help abscesses, and to soften ivory, as well as "for devil sickness or insanity," "sterility," or "heavy mischief in the home." In fact, it was claimed that it "cures every infirmity except only death where there is no help."

The smell of the aromatic leaves of the herbs, as well as the flowers of some of them, contributes to their flavor and probably accounts for some of the magical properties given to them. But they have long been used for their smell alone. Today the essential oils from roses and sweet calamus are used commercially in perfume, scented soaps, and other sweet-smelling preparations. The early burning of aromatics for the gods was to unleash their smell. In medieval days lavender and sweet flag were often strewn on the floor. Sweet woodruff, which smells like new-mown hay, lent its fragrance to floors and was put among clothes in chests. Costmary and bay scented the medieval version of finger bowls at tables. Potpurris, a mixture of dried flower leaves, are improved with the addition of herbs now, as they have been for years.

Considering the wide uses of herbs, it is not surprising that rulers throughout the ages have been interested in information about them. The Roman Emperors had botanists all over the empire sending back herbs to the capital. Physicians in the later Middle Ages and Renaissance constantly checked herbal experiments in an attempt to keep them up-to-date and free from error. Partly because of the great financial value of herbs and spices in the Middle Ages, when they were used extensively by the rich to flavor and preserve food in those days of nonrefrigeration, Columbus was allowed to set forth on his famous voyage to the New World by Ferdinand and Isabella, who hoped he would discover the spice islands of the East.

Our colonial ancestors set great store

by herbs and used them much as they had in the old country. All gardens had their corner where herbs were grown, if not an herb garden proper. Many of these herb gardens of the old colonial mansions were ravishingly planted in formal designs in the English fashion. We can still see them in colonial Williamsburg, for instance, filling the air with their sweet scent. The Indians of America used many of the weeds growing in the fields and forests for herb teas and medicines. The colonial housewife often had to consult her Indian squaw neighbor to find out if an interesting-looking and smelling plant was poisonous.

Today, herbs have become once more part of daily living. They are easy to cultivate, in a backyard garden or in pots or a box on a kitchen window sill. They prefer light, moderately rich, well drained soil, and a sunny exposure. The great majority of culinary herb plants are annuals which are replaced each spring with new fresh plants. The perennials such as sage and tarragon are propagated by stem cuttings. Few gardening efforts are less troublesome or more rewarding than growing herbs of one's own, for nothing adds such zest and flavor to one's cooking as a pinch of a favorite herb.

When cooking with herbs, here is a word of caution: Be selective about the kinds of herbs used and conservative about the amounts. Use preferably only one herb to flavor a dish if the herb has a pronounced flavor, and don't use too many different herbs in the course of a meal, or the palate will be confused. How little or how much of an herb to use is essentially a question of personal taste, arrived at by experimentation. But remember that a little goes a long way when it comes to herbs, and that not everybody likes the same herbs.

Use ⅓ to ½ teaspoon dried herbs for every tablespoon fresh herbs. This proportion depends on the age of the dried herbs as the flavor of dried herbs deteriorates on standing. Crumble herbs before using to release flavor.

The leaves and/or roots of some herbs, called "potherbs," are themselves cooked and served as vegetables. These include the leaves of borage, chervil, chicory, Good-King-Henry, lovage, orach, rampion, and sorrel; the leaves and roots of sweet cicely and rampion; the roots of skirret. When cooking potherbs, boil leaves as you would spinach, roots as you would turnips.

A CHART OF THE BEST-KNOWN HERBS AND THEIR CULINARY USES

NAME	ORIGIN AND DESCRIPTION	PART USED—FORM AND FLAVOR	CULINARY USES	
			Appetizers & Soups	Meat & Poultry
ANGELICA (Angelica archangelica)	Grows in northern Europe, western Asia, but is not grown in this country now except in a few private gardens. Usually biennial, with care is a weak perennial. It grows about 7 ft. high on hollow stems. The leaves are large, yellow-green, and serrated; roots are long and fleshy; small flowers are greenish-white.	Leaves, leafstalks, and stems, dried or fresh roots, and dried seeds are used. The stems are imported from France. The leaves are not available here. The flavor is bitter and aromatic, resembling juniper berries.	Use chopped fresh leaves as garnish for fish canapés. Flavor vegetable or bean soup with cut-up root and seeds.	Use whole leaves as garnish for meat dishes, stews.
ANISE (Pimpinella Anisum)	Grows in Europe, Asia Minor, India, Mexico, South America, and other temperate and hot countries. An annual, it reaches up to 2 ft. high with light-green leaves, notched 3 times, and yellowish-white flowers. The seeds are downy and ridged, brown with tan stripes when dried.	Fresh and dried leaves, and powdered flowers are used. All have sweetish licorice flavor.	Refreshing flavor for lobster or shrimp cocktail, for cream-of-cabbage or cauliflower soup.	Add to beef or veal stew for a subtly sweet taste and aroma.
BASIL, SWEET (Ocimum Basilicum) **BASIL, DWARF** (O. minimum) **BASIL, ITALIAN** (O. crispum) Also called Curly Basil **BASIL, LEMON** (O. citriodora)	Native to Near East; grown throughout the world. Sweet basil is an annual plant growing 1 to 2 ft. tall. The leaves are large (up to 2 in.), glossy, dark green. Dwarf basil comes with purple or green leaves and is smaller and more bushy than sweet basil. The bush grows up to 10 in. with leaves a maximum of ½ in., or in truly dwarf size with leaves ¼ in. or less. Italian basil has large wrinkled, light-green leaves. Lemon basil grows about 18 in. tall. Its leaves are not so shiny as those of sweet basil.	Leaves with leaf stems, fresh, dried, or ground, are used. The flavor of the standard sweet basil is like spicy cloves. The smaller varieties have much the same taste, while the lemon basil has a more fruity flavor. Italian basil has a stronger odor and taste and must be used with care.	A pinch gives variety to seafood cocktails and dips; or to bean, pea, beef, tomato, or turtle soups.	Sweetly fragrant with hamburger, sausage, veal, beef, pork, duck, and lamb or beef stews. Rub hare or venison lightly with basil before roasting.
BAY LEAF (Laurus nobilis) Also called Laurel Leaf	Mediterranean, Asia Minor, Portugal, Central America, southern United States. Leaf of a small evergreen tree with spreading branches. The leaves are smooth, waxy, and from 1 to 3 in. long and 1 in. or more wide. When fresh, only the underside is pale yellowish-green but the brittle dried leaf is yellowish-green all over, shiny on top and dull underneath.	The dried leaf, whole or ground, is used in cooking. Its bitter pungent flavor is even stronger when the leaf is crushed.	A tempting seasoning in tomato juice, chowders, and beef, lamb, mutton, or game soups, either alone or in an herb bouquet.	Add it to game, pot roasts, stews, tripe, or shish kabobs. Try with chicken or duck, roasted or in pies.
BORAGE (Borago officinalis)	Grows widely throughout the world, including Europe, Asia, and eastern United States. An annual, it is over 2 ft. tall, and is covered with grayish hairs which make it look grayish-green and fuzzy. Some of the oval leaves are as long as 6 in. The bright blue flowers are star-shape.	Leaves and flowers, dried or fresh, can be used. The foliage has the flavor and aroma of cucumber.	Dried or fresh leaves add a pleasant flavor to soups. May take the place of parsley.	
BURNET (Sanguisorba minor)	Asia, North America. Leaflets are very long and deeply toothed. This gives them a fernlike effect. There are 10 varieties of this herb, but this is the one used in cooking.	Fresh or dried leaves have delicate odor and flavor like cucumber. Seeds, dried and pounded, have limited use for vinegar.	Place fresh or dried leaves in soups at beginning of cooking. Goes well in asparagus, celery, Lima-bean, or mushroom soups.	Use in stews.

CULINARY USES

Fish & Seafood	Cheese & Eggs	Breads & Stuffings	Sauces & Gravies	Vegetables & Salads	Desserts & Beverages
Add fresh or dried leaves to water in which fish is poached. Use fresh whole leaves as garnish for baked and broiled fish.		Use chopped dried leaves sparingly in poultry stuffing.		The blanched stalk may be eaten like celery, cooked as a vegetable, or prepared with sugar and eaten like rhubarb. The stems may be cooked with sugar, rhubarb, and a little lemon. Add leaves, whole or chopped, to green salads. Cook fresh leaf shoots like spinach, although they have a somewhat bitter flavor. Roast or boil roots.	Leaflets and stems are good candied in sugar syrup with lemon or lime added, and, if desired, green food coloring. Use as decoration for cakes, confections. Sprinkle chopped fresh leaves on fruit salad; add whole leaves as garnish to cold drinks. Dried roots and fruits flavor cakes and candy; cooked stems flavor rhubarb jam.
A sprinkling in fish stuffings gives subtle flavor.	Add a little to cottage cheese as a lunch salad.	Gives an unusual taste to rolls, scones, or to stuffing for fish.	Use a little to give an elusive, licoricelike flavor to pudding sauce.	Add to beets, carrots, pickles, sauerkraut; to apple, beet, cucumber salad.	Sprinkle seeds over a coffeecake; mix into cookies, fruit compote, preserved fruit.
Try it with crab, lobster, mackerel, shrimps, swordfish, eel, or in fish dressings and butters.	A pungent addition to rarebits, omelets, scrambled eggs, soufflés.	Its clovelike flavor is delectable stirred into corn bread or muffins. Try adding to other herbs or alone in stuffing for duck.	Add to herb butters, in stuffings, marinades, tomato sauce.	Use it with eggplant, onions, rutabaga, squash, tomatoes, for sure, and in green, or seafood, carrot, cauliflower, cucumber, or tomato salads. Sprinkle over boiled potatoes or peas.	Its sweet, warm quality adds to the deliciousness of fruit compotes.
Gives fine flavor to fish stews, pickled fish, or to steamed lobster, shrimps.		Tasty in poultry stuffings.	Pleasant bitter taste to spark meat or tomato sauce, marinades, or gravies.	Cook with artichokes, beets, carrots, tomatoes, or crumble into fish or potato salad. Delicious in salad dressing for tomato salad or in jellied seafood.	Consider using a bit when making custards.
				The young leaves are similar to spinach and may be cooked with other greens or used alone as a vegetable. Add a few fresh leaves to water in which green peas, beans, or salsify (oyster plant) are cooked. In salads, leaves may be combined with cabbage, cucumber, lettuce, or mixed greens.	The beautiful star-shape borage flowers may be candied and used to decorate cakes and cookies. Sprigs of flowers and leafy tips give fragrance and elegance to iced tea, fruit and wine drinks, and to lemonades.
		Use chopped leaves like parsley in stuffings.	Leaves or dried and pounded seeds used as flavoring for salad dressings and vinegar.	Toss fresh young leaves in beet, cabbage, carrot, celery, lettuce, mixed-green, or tomato salad; or mix dry herb with dressing. Fresh or dried leaves may be added to mayonnaise dressing before serving. Boil fresh young leaves like spinach, or place leaves in water in which vegetables are cooking.	Use leaves for tea, and fresh sprigs to garnish iced drinks.

A CHART OF THE BEST-KNOWN HERBS AND THEIR CULINARY USES

NAME	ORIGIN AND DESCRIPTION	PART USED— FORM AND FLAVOR	CULINARY USES Appetizers & Soups	Meat & Poultry
CAPER (Capparis spinosa)	A native of the Mediterranean, now cultivated in southern Europe and North Africa as well as in southern United States. The caper plant is a low (about 3 ft.) trailing bush, with pinkish flowers and oval green leaves.	Capers are small unopened flower buds, gathered in the early morning before they have opened. They are usually pickled in brine, but are also available dried in bulk.	Add capers to canapés in place of olives.	Use as a garnish for leftovers, especially cold roasts.
CARAWAY (Carum Carvi)	Grows in Europe, temperate Asia, Japan, and parts of United States and Canada. Usually a biennial, it grows over 2 ft., with feathery bright-green leaves like a carrot and with small flowers, usually white, growing like Queen Anne's Lace in umbrellalike clusters.	The dried fruit, caraway seed, is often used whole or ground, as are the fresh young leaves, leaf stems, and roots. Seeds have a sharp flavor like a mixture of anise and dill; leaves are milder in taste. The sweet root has a much more delicate flavor than parsnips.	Chopped leaves and young shoots, as well as seeds, give a distinctive flavor to bean or cabbage soups or to clam chowder.	Adds subtly pungent quality to beef à la mode, goulash, or sauerbraten. Place sprigs in bottom of pan for roast goose or pork. Use leaves as garnish for meat.
CELERY, CULTIVATED (Apium graveolens, var. dulce) **CELERY, WILD** (A. graveolens) Sometimes called Smallage	Celery grows in temperate zones throughout the world. Usually biennial, although sometimes annual, it has wrinkled pale-green leaves and tiny white flowers which grow in large umbrella-shape clusters. Golden Heart celery has bleached white stalk; Pascal, a green stalk. The seeds which form on the flower stalks are less than 1/16 in. long. Wild celery is a lower plant that resembles lovage, with which it has sometimes been confused.	All parts: root, stalk, leaves (fresh and dried), and seeds (dried, whole, or ground) can be used in cooking. All parts have a somewhat sweet flavor. The root is considerably sweeter than the stalk, which has a mildly sweet aromatic flavor. The leaves are more sharp and pungent. The seeds have the flavor of the fresh celery, but the seed covering provides a somewhat bitter taste.	Canapés, cheese, fish, shellfish may be sprinkled lightly with seed just before serving. Or add chopped celery to ingredients and garnish with stalk and leaves. Fresh leaves especially good in soups.	Add to meat loaves, stews, and pot roasts.
CHERVIL (Anthriscus Cerefolium)	Native of Europe; naturalized in northeast United States. An annual growing up to 2 ft., it has delicate, fernlike bright-green leaves, much like parsley. The flowers are small and white and grow in clusters.	Leaves, fresh or dried, as well as whole sprigs, are used in cooking and as a garnish. The root of the tuberous variety may be cooked and eaten like a carrot. The leaves and stalk have a mild parsley flavor, sometimes with a whiff of licorice or tarragon. A curly-leafed variety has a definite anise-like flavor and smell.	The tender leaves garnish a dish, or season asparagus, chicken, spinach, or sorrel soups.	Is friendly with beef, game, lamb, pork, veal, poultry. Good in meat loaf.
CHIVES (Allium Schoenoprasum)	Grows in Europe and temperate Asia, as well as extensively in United States. A relative of the onion, chives grow in clumps, with a tiny bulb under the ground and tubular green leaves rising above to a height of 10 in. The thin flowers are lavender.	The tiny bulb and the freshly picked flowers can be used as well as the fresh, frozen, freeze-dried, or dried leaves. The green leaves and the bulb have a mild onion flavor.	Garnish for dips, soups, or appetizers; happy addition to seafood cocktails or to Vichyssoise.	Chop the slender leaves over beef, game, lamb, pork, veal, or poultry dishes. The bulbs are used in sausage.
CLARY SAGE (Salvia Sclarea)	Native to southern Europe and Mediterranean countries. This 3- to 4-ft. biennial has unusually large leaves (about 9 in.) at its base. They are gray-green and quite broad. The leaves at the top are smaller. Although a member of the sage family, it is commonly referred to as Clary.	Leaves, fresh or dried, ground or whole, have a lavenderlike odor, and taste, naturally enough, like sage.	Try a teaspoon of chopped dried leaves in meat soups.	A fresh or dried leaf in the roasting pan; use dried powdered leaf in sausage.
COSTMARY (Chrysanthemum Balsamita) Also called Bible Leaf or Alecost	A native of western Asia, it grows wild in some parts of North America. A perennial, it grows over 3 ft., with shrubby stems, and light-green, slightly downy leaves. The flowers are like small daisies, although sometimes there are no white petals.	Leaves, fresh and dried, are used and have a lemony mint odor.		Crushed fresh leaves or dried leaves flavor beef and hamburgers. Place a costmary leaf in the bottom of the roasting pan for chicken, wild duck, or venison.

CULINARY USES

Fish & Seafood	Cheese & Eggs	Breads & Stuffings	Sauces & Gravies	Vegetables & Salads	Desserts & Beverages
			Most fish and meat sauces are enhanced by the addition of capers. Use with oily sauces or dressings.	Always use in antipasto. Use as a garnish for other green and vegetable salads.	
	A pleasant smooth taste in cheese spreads, cream or cottage cheese, creamed eggs.	Seeds, of course, in rye bread. Also widely used in muffins, rolls, and scones.	Add a little to give zest to sour-cream dressing for salads.	Add sprigs of leaves to water in which cabbage, cauliflower, potatoes, or turnips are boiled. Combine seeds with beets, sauerkraut, potatoes, noodles, creamed onions, turnips, or cabbage. Use fresh herb in cabbage, cucumber, lettuce, potato, and tomato salads. Cook leaves like spinach or use as salad green; boil roots as vegetable and eat plain or with cream sauce.	Use seeds in baked pears, baked apples, applesauce, spice cake, poundcake, sugar cookies, and pumpkin pie, or sugar-coated as candy.
Shredded codfish and salmon croquettes are good flavored with seed. Use in chowders and stews. Add a stalk to water in which fish is poached.	Scrambled eggs, cream and cottage cheese pep up with seed. Add chopped celery to creamed or deviled eggs or omelets.	Biscuits and salty bread are enhanced by celery seed.		Put seed in cauliflower, cabbage, and stewed tomatoes. Mix chopped celery with carrots, onions, peas, tomatoes, green peppers. Use with fish, potato, and vegetable salads; seeds especially good with cabbage salad. For fruit salads add seed to your favorite dressing and serve; or mix chopped celery in with ingredients. Serve cooked celery plain or with sauce.	
Goes well with all kinds of fish.	Stir some into cream or cottage cheese, omelets, or scrambled eggs.		Mild parsleylike flavor for Béarnaise and butter sauces and French dressing.	Try a little chopped leaf with asparagus, beets, carrots, eggplant, or spinach. Green or potato salads are sparked by this parsleylike herb. Cook the herbage as a potherb, or use as salad green.	
Less pungent than the onion, this is a happy seasoning for any fish.	Chop the leaves fine and mix with cottage or cream cheese or into omelets. Use dried leaves in fondues.		Chop them into sour-cream dressing or try some in vinaigrette sauce.	Chopped leaves are good in creamed vegetables, with potatoes, green salads. For an exotic touch, add some of the flowers to a green or cucumber salad. Try pickling the tiny bulbs like onions.	
	Chopped fresh leaves are good in omelets and for flavoring bland cheeses.	May be used like sage in stuffings.	Use leaves in salad dressing and in spice-hot sauce for barbecue.	Add a touch to the water in which yellow vegetables are cooking.	
					Place a leaf in the bottom of the baking pan when baking poundcake. The flavor is very dominant, so take care to use only 1 leaf. It is an ingredient in herb teas. Use in eggnog, or to garnish strawberry shrub.

A CHART OF THE BEST-KNOWN HERBS AND THEIR CULINARY USES

NAME	ORIGIN AND DESCRIPTION	PART USED— FORM AND FLAVOR	CULINARY USES Appetizers & Soups	Meat & Poultry
DILL (Anethum graveolens)	Native to Europe; naturalized in North America. This 2- or 3-ft. high plant, grown as an annual, has fine wispy bluish-green leaves and a hollow gummy stem. The yellow flowers are in large umbrella-shape clusters. The seeds are very tiny.	The leaves and stems, fresh and dried (the fresh are better), as well as the seed of this herb are used. Leaves are quite pungent and stems are bitter; both should be finely chopped for use. The aromatic seeds are available whole or ground; have a sharp taste.	Sprinkle in avocado or fish cocktails, or into bean, borscht, split-pea or tomato soup.	Fresh pungent flavor for lamb chops, stew, or a bowl of rich creamed chicken. Sprinkle over broiled steak or cook with corned beef.
FENNEL, WILD (Foeniculum vulgare) **FENNEL, SWEET** (F. vulgare, var. dulce) Also called Finocchio or Florence Fennel **CAROSELLA** (F. vulgare, var. piperitum)	Wild fennel and the form cultivated in gardens (sweet) are known primarily for their wispy bright-green leaves. Both are erect perennials, the wild variety growing over 4 ft. high. The stems are smooth and glossy and thin in comparison to those of the Carosella, a variety of the garden-grown fennel. It has thickened stalks like celery and grows to the height of about 2 ft. Finocchio is considerably shorter than the wild, and the base of the stems is very thick, overlapping like celery.	Seeds, fresh, as well as dried whole or ground; leaves; stems; bulbous bases and roots of finocchio and carosella are all edible and used in cooking. Flavor is sweet, like anise. Finocchio is especially sweet.	Try this to give a faint sweet quality to fish or seafood cocktails; or try in cabbage or fish soup.	Liver, pork, lamb stew, duck, or goose gain new flavor from this herb.
FENUGREEK (Trigonella Foenum-Graecum)	Grows in Europe and the Orient as well as in United States. An annual, it grows, usually not branching, to about 2 ft. The leaves are as long as 1 in. and the plant has white flowers, growing alone or in pairs.	Dried seeds, available whole, suggest a burnt-sugar or maple taste. The fresh leaves and stems are also used.	Use in meat and vegetable soups.	Good in moderation with beef, lamb, pork, and veal dishes.
HORSERADISH (Armoracial apathifolia or Radicula armoracia)	Although there is no agreement on the botanical name for this perennial, native to southeastern Europe, it is widely known for its long thick branching wrinkled white root, which grows deep into the ground. The flowering stem above the ground is as high as 3 ft.; the leaves are of 2 kinds: the first look like combs, about 9 ft. long and 4 in. across; the next are long (14 in.) oblong leaves, shiny and green, with scalloped edges.	Root and leaves are used. Whole fresh root has no odor; the sharp familiar horseradish aroma is only unloosed when it is grated or ground. It is available fresh or preserved in vinegar. The early leaves taste of bitter herbs, with a biting after-taste.	Use ground root with cream cheese and sour cream for a pleasing dip for fresh vegetables.	Good to accompany roast or boiled beef, lamb, or mutton.
HYSSOP (Hyssopus officinalis)	This perennial, 1 to 2 ft. tall, has long stems with narrow pointed stalkless dark-green leaves, 1 to 2 in. long. Variations of hyssops have different leaf formations, and other than the blue flowers of this type.	Leaves, flowers, stems, and young shoots, fresh or dried, have a bitter aromatic flavor.	Crush 1 or 2 tender young leaves in bottom of bowl for fruit cocktail; particularly good with cranberries. Add a little freshly minced or dried leaves to sweet vegetable soups while cooking.	Minced herb cuts grease on all fatty meats. Sprinkle duck or pheasant lightly with minced herb before roasting. Fresh or dried leaves give additional flavor to game, kidney, or lamb stews.
LEMON BALM (Melissa officinalis)	Native to southern Europe; now in all temperate climates, including eastern United States. It is a very leafy perennial which grows higher than 2 ft. tall. The leaves, which are up to 3 in. long, are almost round, dark green, and slightly hairy. The flowers are pale yellow and grow in clusters.	Leaves, fresh or dried, are used for their lemon-minty smell and flavor.	Cream soups may be sprinkled lightly with minced leaves just before serving.	Rub roast lamb lightly with crushed fresh or dried leaves before you place it in the oven.

Fish & Seafood	Cheese & Eggs	Breads & Stuffings	Sauces & Gravies	Vegetables & Salads	Desserts & Beverages
An unusual flavoring for your favorite fish dish; or add a few seeds to water in which fish is boiled.	Both leaves and seeds excellent for cheese spreads, cottage or cream cheese.	Sprinkle a few seeds in rye or other dark-bread dough to give carawaylike flavor.	Warm, sharp taste to liven drawn butter or sour-cream dressings; good in vinegars. Beef gravy peps up with addition of a few chopped leaves of dill.	A few seeds improve beets, cabbage, carrots, cauliflower, peas, snap beans, potato salad. Leaves flavor cabbage, cauliflower, or turnips. Seeds, with some stems and leaves, used, of course, to pickle cucumbers.	Slightly sharp flavor of seeds adds savor to apple dumplings or stewed pears, and is tasty in cake.
A delicious sweet flavor to add to fish puddings.	It adds importance to omelets or to scrambled eggs.	Italian bakers stud bread and rolls with it. It is good in muffins, too.	Try it in egg or fish sauces.	Delightful seasoning for beets, celery, lentils; mixed in rice or squash; added to sweet pickles. Use leaves in salad, or boil them as potherb. Eat raw stems like celery. Try seeds to spice beets, or put them in sauerkraut.	Adds unusually good flavor to apple dishes, to coffeecakes, and to sugar cookies. Flavor wine with base of finocchio.
				Try with blackeye peas.	Cookies, gingerbread, and rice puddings are flavored with this herb.
Freshly ground root good with most seafoods, a classic with oysters.			Cream sauces for beef, fish, ham, and other meats are livened with ground root. Gives dash to cocktail sauces for fish and shellfish. Good in salad dressings and flavored mayonnaise.	Fresh young leaves, finely chopped, may be added to green salads.	
Garnish any fatty fish sparingly with minced fresh leaves.				Toss freshly minced herb in vegetable salads.	Use with sweet fruit in pies such as apricot or peach.
		Crushed dried leaves may be added to traditional stuffings; especially good for pork or turkey.	Delicious in cream sauces and those served with fish. Add chopped fresh leaves just before serving.	Chopped fresh leaves may be added to fruit, mixed, or tossed green salad. Or try cooking leaves with chard.	This herb is a welcome addition to tea, fruit drinks, lemonades, or wine cups. If the drink is cold, garnish with a sprig of balm; if the drink is hot, crush 1 or 2 leaves in the bottom of the cup.

A CHART OF THE BEST-KNOWN HERBS AND THEIR CULINARY USES

NAME	ORIGIN AND DESCRIPTION	PART USED— FORM AND FLAVOR	CULINARY USES	
			Appetizers & Soups	Meat & Poultry
LEMON VERBENA (Lippia citriodora)	Originally from Argentina and Chile; now is found in many mild climates. A perennial shrub which grows from 10 ft. in warm climates and to 10 in. in pots. The yellow-green leaves are long, narrow, and pointed at the end and grow in whorls of 3 or 4 woody branches.	Dried or fresh leaves of this plant are used; they have a delicate lemony flavor and smell.	Garnish fruit cups with a tiny leaf.	
LOVAGE (Levisticum officinale)	Native of southern Europe; United States' North Atlantic seaboard also grows wild Scotch Lovage, used for medicinal purposes. True lovage is a tall (5 to 7 ft.) plant, with large heavy light-green leaves like celery, and with clusters of yellowish flowers.	Fresh and dried leaves, stem bases, leafstalks, root, and seeds are used. Greens have celerylike flavor; root tastes and smells strong.	Add a few leaves to tomato-juice cocktail. Leaves give celery flavor to soups.	Cook beef, lamb, mutton, veal, rabbit, or venison stews with seeds in cheesecloth bag. Leaves give celery flavor to stews.
MARIGOLD (Calendula officinalis) Also called Pot Marigold	Native to southern Europe and eastern Asia. A hardy annual, growing from 1 to 2 ft. tall, it has curling green pinnate leaves and bright golden flowers. Flowers, which can be as large as small sunflowers, have oval golden-yellow and orange petals around circular heads.	Dried heads and petals pulverized into powder are used as well as fresh ones. They have a somewhat bitter taste, but lend a subtle flavor and golden color to foods if they are added in moderation. A very little goes a long way.	Try adding 2 or 3 petals to your favorite fish-chowder recipe. A very little powder may be added in cooking chicken broth. Flowers added to vegetable soup is a good idea, too.	Add ½ teaspoon powder to venison stew. Try flavoring braised beef or pot roast with ½ teaspoon powder.
MARJORAM (Majorana hortensis) More exactly, Sweet or Knotted Marjoram	Native to Mediterranean area as a perennial, but usually grown as an annual in cooler regions such as northern United States. It grows over 1 ft. tall and the leaves are downy light-green ovals of up to 1 in. The minute flowers sometimes are pinkish or lilac. The herb has a fragrant odor and a spicy taste. It resembles sage in flavor although it is considerably less strong. A smaller variety, M. onites, resembles M. hortensis, except it has milder flavor. Pot marjoram is usually only sweet marjoram under another name.	Although flowering tips are used in medicine and industry, the leaves are the only part employed in cooking. They have a fragrant aroma and a spicy taste, somewhat resembling sage although considerably less strong.	Add a pinch to avocados, mushrooms, pâtés, to clam chowder or onion soup.	Delightful seasoning for beef, pork, veal, pot roasts, and savory stews.
MINT (Mentha)	There are over 30 varieties of mint, and about a dozen cultivated in the United States. The varieties listed below, the most useful for culinary purposes, are found in temperate zones throughout the world. Other mints, not listed here because their use is limited, include Corn Mint and Water Mint. The mints differ somewhat in appearance, but all have square red-tinged stems and purple flowers, in whorls or spikes.	The fresh leaves of all the mints listed can be used for flavoring. Tastes vary slightly, but all mints have aromatic refreshing aroma. The oil from leaves is used commercially. Spearmint is widely available dried and powdered as "mint." Uses for "mint," fresh or dried, follow. Some experimentation with substitution of different types is possible, for most members of the mint family mix well.	Aromatic addition to cranberry juice, fruit cup, or to soups such as pea.	Delicate flavoring for lamb, ham, veal, ragouts.
MINT, AMERICAN APPLE (M. gentilis)	The only one of 2 varieties of apple mint used for cooking (the other has woolly leaves). A hardy perennial with smooth grayish-green leaves with yellow streaks. Shorter than some mints, as it is low growing with a tendency to spread. Its purple flowers blossom in whorls and there are almost square stems.	Leaves have a delicate fruit aroma and taste, refreshing and with a trace of apple.		
MINT, BERGAMOT (M. citrata) Also called Orange and Lemon Mint	Smooth oval leaves, edged with purple, up to 2 in. long. The leaves are broader than those of the more familiar peppermint.	The leaves have a fragrance mixed with lavender, although orange predominates after they have been smelled for a while.		

Fish & Seafood	Cheese & Eggs	Breads & Stuffings	Sauces & Gravies	Vegetables & Salads	Desserts & Beverages
				Fresh or canned fruit salads may be garnished with a small leaf.	A crushed leaf may be placed at the bottom of the cup or glass before pouring drink. Delicious for making jellies. Lemon Verbena tea is one of the most popular of the herb teas.
				Blanched root can be served like celery. Boil leaves as a potherb. Add a few seeds to salad dressing and serve over mixed fruit. To give a celery flavor to salads rub inside of bowl with a few leaves.	Candy the root, or, for an even more adventurous sweet, candy the leaf stalks and stem bases. Use lovage seeds as a garnish or ingredient as you would caraway seeds.
Add a few petals to other vegetables in a seafood stew.	A little powder will give color to butter and cheese.	Color buns with a dash of powder.		Cook rice with ¼ teaspoon marigold powder instead of saffron.	Add a few crushed petals to baked or boiled custard or to custard sauce. Color cakes with a dash of powder. Try making marigold cordial.
Sprinkle it over fish before baking or into a cream sauce for fish.	Gives subtle variety of flavor to omelets, scrambled eggs, soufflés.	Delicious in poultry stuffing, or added to biscuit dough or herb breads.	Delicate flavoring for spaghetti sauce or your favorite gravy.	Adds interest to corn, beans, carrots, eggplant, Lima beans, peas, spinach, beans, or to a crisp green salad.	
Refreshing change when cooked with any fish.	Tantalizing flavor for cream or cottage cheese.		Make it into mint sauce to serve with roast lamb. Add to French dressing for green salads. Make flavored vinegar.	Add to cabbage, carrots, celery, potatoes, snap beans, or to jellied salads.	Sweet and tangy in custards, fruit compotes, ice cream, in fruit punch, juleps, mint tea. Make a sugar syrup to add flavor to beverages. Make your own mint jelly or add to currant jelly.
				Preferred with cabbage to spearmint because it is more delicate.	Especially recommended in applesauce and pie.
				Used with chopped cabbage instead of spearmint, as Bergamot is more delicate.	Especially recommended for jelly.

A CHART OF THE BEST-KNOWN HERBS AND THEIR CULINARY USES

NAME	ORIGIN AND DESCRIPTION	PART USED— FORM AND FLAVOR	CULINARY USES	
			Appetizers & Soups	Meat & Poultry
CURLEY MINT (M. spicata, var. crispa)	The mint has dull-green crinkly wide leaves and grows 2 ft. at its tallest. As it has long weak stems and many slender branches, it has tendency to sprawl during summer. The spikes are tipped with violet flowers.	Leaves have piny-resinous odor.		
PEPPERMINT (M. piperita)	There are 2 varieties: Black (var. vulgaris) and White (var. officinalis). Both have pointed leaves 1 to 2 in. long and ½ in. wide, with toothed edges. The flower spikes are thick and blunt. Black has dark-green leaves tinged with purple, and purple flowers tinged with red. It is taller than white variety. The white has light-green leaves.	One of the most popular mints. The oil from white mint is considered of best quality, as the black's is stronger. Largely used commercially, but fresh leaves can be employed by the home cook for an aromatic pungent flavor.		
SPEARMINT (M. spicata, var. viridis)	The most popular of the culinary mints, it resembles peppermint, but the lance-shape leaves are stemless and longer. The flower spikes are long and narrow and pointed. Pale-purple flowers.	Fresh leaves, as well as dried and powdered ones, are used. Recommended for all uses of mint. Very sweet aromatic, one of best mints for flavorings.	See Mint.	See Mint.
MUSTARD, BLACK (Brassica nigra) **MUSTARD, WHITE** (B. alba or B. hirta)	Native to Europe and western Asia and cultivated in western United States, this mustard grows wild throughout country. Black mustard is a hardy annual, growing up to 4 ft., with yellowish-green smooth leaves and the bright yellow flowers characteristic of mustard. The white mustard is a small 18-in. plant, with tender green leaves that spread very quickly.	Both mustards are grown for their seed, which is commercially prepared as mustard flour, the basis of prepared mustard; available also as powdered mustard. Whole seeds of both varieties can be used, but only the leaves of the white are eaten. The black seeds are smaller and considerably more pungent than those of the white.	Tender young white-mustard leaves may be used sparingly in sorrel or lettuce soup.	Season roasts lightly with powdered mustard. Use a bit to flavor creamed chicken or turkey.
NASTURTIUM (Tropaeolum majus or minus)	These annuals, one tall and climbing (T. majus) and one low and bushy (T. minus), have flowers and leaves used in cooking. The small plant, native to Peru, has more flowers and in brighter hues. The leaves are almost circular; the flowers all shades of yellow, orange, and dark red. The light-green seeds turn light brown, and are ridged and wrinkled.	Young stems, leaves, and flowers have peppery taste. Pickled seeds and pods used in place of capers.		
OREGANO (Origanum vulgare) Often called Wild Marjoram	Native to Eurasia, also grows widely in northeast United States and Canada. There are many varieties of this plant, differing in appearance. In general, an erect perennial, growing up to 3 ft., with branching hairy stems (sometimes purplish) and dark-green leaves shaped like a roundish egg.	Fresh or dried leaves and tops are used, and have sweet aromatic flavor like sweet marjoram or thyme. Oregano is stronger than these two and should be used with care.	Try a pinch in vegetable-juice cocktails, in bean, beef, game, or tomato soup.	It's pungent, so use with care to season beef, lamb, pork, veal, sausages, Swiss steak, or any poultry.
PARSLEY (Petroselinum crispum)	there are more than 30 forms of this carrot-type plant. The main varieties include double-curled, moss-leaved, fern-leaved, and turnip-rooted, whose names describe their leaves or roots. A small green plant, its leaves and flowers vary according to kind.	Leaves have familiar refreshing taste and aroma.	Use it as a garnish, as an ingredient in soup bouquets.	A nutritious flavorful addition to beef, lamb, pork, veal, poultry.

Fish & Seafood	Cheese & Eggs	Breads & Stuffings	CULINARY USES Sauces & Gravies	Vegetables & Salads	Desserts & Beverages
					Especially recommended in juleps and punches.
					Try making your own peppermint wafers instead of buying them. Or boil leaves and add marmalade for an unusual dessert sauce.
See Mint.	See Mint.	See Mint.	Best kind for traditional mint sauce, chopped leaves in sweetened vinegar.	Adds strong sweet flavor to cabbage, carrots, potatoes, snap beans, or to jellied salads.	Add to sugar syrup to flavor iced beverages.
Add powdered mustard to other ingredients in making deviled crab.	Use powdered mustard in deviled eggs. Flavor cottage cheese and cream cheese with a pinch of powdered mustard.			Cook greens as potherb. Use 1 teaspoon chopped fresh leaves in salad or add ½ to 1 teaspoon seed with mixed green-vegetable salad. A bit of seeds peps up coleslaw. Sprinkle a few seeds onto hot boiled beets, or boil cabbage with a few seeds. White seeds are used in preparing pickles.	
	Chopped fresh leaves and stems are good, like watercress, with cream- or cottage-cheese spreads.		Use pickled seeds in sauces in place of capers. Especially good with brown sauce for mutton.	Toss chopped young stems and leaves or whole leaves into mixed-green or vegetable salads. Use flowers as edible garnish.	For an exotic and pretty touch, float flowers in tea.
Adds intriguing taste to any fish, but it's pungent, so take care.	Aromatic flavor to give distinction to cheese spreads or omelets.	A favorite with Mexican and Italian cooks. Good in pizzas, rolls, stuffings.	Sprinkle it in fish butter sauce; in cream, meat, spaghetti, or tomato sauces. Add to marinades for game.	Use a little with broccoli, beans, carrots, Lima beans, mushrooms, onions, peas, potatoes, tomatoes. Add to aspics or potato salad. On its own can be boiled as potherb.	
Exciting flavor for fish stuffings, creamed seafood, or for salmon.	Add a pinch to cheese sauces, deviled or scrambled eggs, or to omelets.	Mild and good in biscuits, herb breads, muffins, stuffings, or added to butter for toast.	Seasoning for butters, marinades.	Seasoning and garnish for most vegetables and salads.	

A CHART OF THE BEST-KNOWN HERBS AND THEIR CULINARY USES

NAME	ORIGIN AND DESCRIPTION	PART USED— FORM AND FLAVOR	CULINARY USES	
			Appetizers & Soups	Meat & Poultry
ROSE (Rosa, various species)	There are countless varieties of the rose. Some of the most well known include the Damask rose, the Cabbage rose, and the China rose. The beautiful petaled flowers growing from thorny stems are known to gardeners throughout the world.	Petals, preferably fresh with the base cut off, and hips, fresh or dried, are used. (Hips are the small berries left after the flowers dry, and are the rosebush's fruit.) Rosewater is available commercially, although it may be made at home. The heavily perfumed rose varieties used in cooking have a honeyed scent.	Crush a rose petal into fruit cups. Try making rose-hip soup.	For an exotic delight, glaze baked chicken with rosewater and honey. Rub deer and venison with dried hips, mashed and blended with seasonings and marjoram, before baking. Add hips to rabbit stews.
ROSEMARY (Rosmarinus officinalis)	Grows wild in southern Europe, cultivated in Europe and United States. It grows slowly, but reaches height of 4 or 5 ft. Not hardy in the north. An evergreen shrub, has branching stems which bear long (up to 1½ in.) thin dark-green leaves, curving a bit like pine needles. The undersides are grayish and slightly hairy. The flowers are bluish.	Leaves, fresh and dried, and the fresh tops are used in cooking and garnishing. They have a pungent spicy flavor.	Fresh or dried, it gives exciting flavor to fruit cups, chicken, pea, spinach, and turtle soups.	Its affinity for hearty foods fits it well to blend with beef, game, lamb, pork, veal, poultry.
RUE (Ruta graveolens)	Southern Europe was its home. The little perennial, growing up to 2 ft., has evergreen deeply cut grayish-green leaves, which are thick and covered with a nonhairy bloom which rubs off when touched. The pretty four-petaled flowers are yellow.	Leaves, fresh and dried, are used but are very bitter and should be used sparingly.	Blend into chicken broth. Gives a delightfully different flavor to minced chicken or mushroom canapés. Try a few minced (or if you're feeling adventurous, whole) leaves between buttered brown bread for different sandwiches.	Add a few leaves to beef, lamb, chicken, or kidney stews, during or before cooking.
SAGE (Salvia officinalis)	Native to northern Mediterranean countries, but grows now in all temperate zones. Yugoslavia raises one of the best varieties of sage, Dalmatian sage, which is imported by United States. There are over 500 varieties of this popular herb. Besides the imported Dalmatian sage and the Garden sage (Salvia officinalis), there are White sage, Cyprus sage, a garden variety known as S. horminum, Meadow sage, Pineapple sage (with pineapple fragrance), and Clary sage (see Clary). Most are perennial shrubs with grayish leaves. Garden sage grows 1 to 2 ft. high and has bluish or purplish flowers.	Leaves, fresh and dried, chopped or powdered, are used. The flavor is aromatically bitter; the Pineapple and Dalmatian sages are milder.	A pinch adds extra flavor to cheese dips, pâté, chowders, consommé, and bland cream soups.	It's vital for sausage, and a happy thought in stews, with poultry, or to season rabbit. Rub on a little ground sage before roasting beef, lamb, pork, mutton, or veal.
SAVORY, SUMMER (Satureia hortensis) **SAVORY, WINTER** (S. montana)	Summer savory is native to Mediterranean; now cultivated throughout Europe and United States. Bushy, with many branches, this annual grows up to 18 in. on its weak stems, but falls down easily. The leaves are dark green, and the bush has a great mass of pinkish, bluish, or purplish flowers. Winter savory is similar, but is an annual, somewhat shorter and woodier and falling down and spreading. Its leaves are stiffer than those of summer savory.	Leaves, fresh and dried, are used and have a somewhat resinous aroma. Winter savory has a stronger flavor, but can be used with discretion where summer savory is used.	A piquant touch for pâté, vegetable juices, consommés, chowders, bean or lentil soups.	Adds a deliciousness to a chicken loaf, hamburger, lamb, veal, to stews and poultry stuffing.

Fish & Seafood	Cheese & Eggs	Breads & Stuffings	Sauces & Gravies	Vegetables & Salads	Desserts & Beverages
Try poaching fish in milk with a little rosewater sprinkled over fish.	Add a few chopped fresh petals to scrambled eggs.	Coffeecakes flavored with rosewater or syrup are good.	Rose petals in sauces and gravies for game help remove "gamy" taste.	Fresh or canned fruit salads may be spiced with 1 or 2 fresh petals.	Rose-petal syrup, made with petals and sugar, or rosewater, deliciously flavors custards, puddings, cookies, cakes, chiffon pies, fruit jello, dessert pancakes, and ice creams. Blend crushed rose leaves with orange-blossom honey, or add to fruit and mint jellies and jams.
Exciting flavor for fish stuffings, creamed seafood, or for salmon.	Add a pinch to cheese sauces, deviled or scrambled eggs, or to omelets.	Sweet fresh-tasting herb to crumble into herb breads, stuffings.	Sweet fresh-tasting herb to add to cheese, cream, jelly, or game sauces, or to use in marinades.	Tonic addition to lentils, mushrooms, peas, potatoes, spinach, squash, fruit salads.	
	Mix finely minced leaf with cottage or cream cheese for a delicious spread.			Sprinkle a little minced rue over boiled potatoes. Or add to dressing for chicken, veal, tuna-fish, or vegetable salad.	
Belongs in fish stuffings, where it adds appetizing flavor, a faint fragrance. Put a sage leaf inside mild-flavored fish when baking or add to the water in which you boil fish.	Warm astringent taste to give variety to Cheddar cheese, or to your cheese spreads.	Especially good in cheese bread, and, of course, in stuffings.	Appetizing seasoning for brown sauce, French dressing, or for meat gravies.	Try with Brussels sprouts, carrots, eggplant, Lima beans, onions, peas, or tomatoes.	
Happy with baked or broiled fish.	Its aromatic flavor will improve cream cheese. Try it with scrambled eggs.	Fragrant flavorful addition to herb bread and to meat or poultry stuffings.	Aromatic flavoring for barbecue, fish, seafood, or poultry sauces and gravies.	Add a bit when cooking artichokes, beets, cabbage, peas, rice, sauerkraut. Classic with green beans. Fresh leaves are good tossed into salad.	Tastes good in stewed pears, or used with quinces.

NAME	ORIGIN AND DESCRIPTION	PART USED— FORM AND FLAVOR	CULINARY USES	
			Appetizers & Soups	Meat & Poultry
SWEET CICELY (Myrrhis odorata) Also called Sweet Chervil and Myrrh	Native to Europe, this perennial's hairy stems grow 2 to 3 ft. high. The leaves are fernlike, the flowers small and whitish. The long seed (up to 1 in.) is narrow and ribbed.	Fresh leaves and seeds are used. Seeds should be sliced and eaten with other herbs. All have an aniselike flavor, although the leaves are weak in taste.	Chopped leaves flavor cream soups with faint anise flavor.	Good in stews.
SWEET FLAG (Acorus Calamus) Often called Calamus	Grows in North Temperate Zone throughout world. The plant has yellow-green sword-shape leaves rising from base up to 3 ft. The flower is a dry spike. It grows from a large underground rhizome into a smaller underground stem. Not to be confused with the poisonous blue flag, which has dark-green leaves with no smell.	Leaves, stem, roots, and rhizome, fresh and dried, have strong spicy ginger-like aroma. Rhizome is apt to be tough and requires long boiling.	Young leaves are good addition to chicken soup. Or for winter, use dried and ground leaves or root.	Add to chicken stew young leaves dried and ground or fresh.
TARRAGON (Artemisia dracunculus) Often called French Tarragon	Native to western and southern Asia, now grows in temperate and cold United States and southern Europe. A perennial, it grows somewhat like a shrub to a height of above 18 in. The dark-green leaves are long, narrow, and pointed, and occur along the woody stems at intervals.	Leaves, fresh and dried, are used in cooking. Their flavor is somewhat like anise.	Piquant addition to chicken livers, vegetable juices, chowders, consommés.	Highly valued for use with pheasant, sweetbreads, tongue, veal, chicken, or turkey dishes.
THYME, GARDEN (Thymus vulgaris) Also called English Thyme **THYME, WILD** (T. Serpyllum) Also called Creeping Thyme	Garden thyme grows widely in Europe, United States, and Canada; wild thyme, a native to Europe, temperate Asia, and North Africa, grows in North America from southeastern Canada to North Carolina. Garden thyme is a bushy little perennial, about 1 ft. tall, with gray-green leaves, ½ to 1 in. long. English thyme is a variety with broad leaves. There are many varieties of the wild thyme, which, as its name implies, creeps along the ground, rising to varying heights. It becomes firmly matted and its leaves are of many colors as well as green, according to the variety. Some are striped white, some greenish-yellow; flowers may be bluish, purplish, white, or red.	Leaves and the leafy and flowering tops, fresh or dried, of both thymes are used. Both wild and garden thyme have pungent flavor and a sweet fragrance. Leaves and flowers of certain varieties of thyme have particular aromas which are distinctive. Of the creeping thymes, Lemon thyme (T. citriodorus) has lemony scent; Caraway thyme (T. Herbabarona) smells and tastes as name implies; Thymus azoricus has fruity citrus aroma. The chart indicates where a certain variety is especially recommended for use.	Sprinkle a little in seafood or vegetable-juice cocktails; in a gumbo or fish chowder.	Use with restraint with beef, game, lamb, pork, veal, or in meat loaf. Rub caraway thyme over meat to preserve it and flavor it.
WATERCRESS (Nasturtium officinale)	Native to temperate Europe. Naturalized in North America in brooks and ponds. A short perennial, it has very small round shiny dark-green leaves, paler green stems, and small white flowers.	The fresh leaves and stems have a slightly peppery flavor and are crisp.	Garnish canapés and seafood appetizers with chopped leaves. Or mix into fruit and vegetable-juice cocktails. Try minced watercress in cheese, fish, and meat sandwich fillings. Add a half bunch of minced sprigs to fish chowders, and creamed potato or vegetable soups. Or use as sorrel.	A pretty garnish for broiled, boiled, or roasted meats and poultry.

CULINARY USES

Fish & Seafood	Cheese & Eggs	Breads & Stuffings	Sauces & Gravies	Vegetables & Salads	Desserts & Beverages
				Root, raw or boiled, can be eaten with oil and vinegar alone or in salads. Fresh leaves add to salads.	Use seeds like cloves or caraway in dessert flavoring.
Use dried root as substitute for ginger in a fish dish.			Young leaves flavor fish sauce.	Slice tiny unborn leaves in center of the young stalk into green salads.	Candied root makes a delicious confection alone or to flavor cream, custard, or rice pudding.
Delicious seasoning for baked or broiled fish, especially for lobster.	Sprinkle it over scrambled eggs or omelets.		Best known in tarragon vinegar; good, too, in butters, marinades, and added to mustards and flavored mayonnaise. A must for Sauce Béarnaise.	Has an almost spicy taste which adds to asparagus, beans, beets, broccoli, cabbage; tossed green, tomato, fish, or jellied salads.	
Pungent warm addition to any type of fish.	Mix it with cream or cottage cheeses, sprinkle on shirred or creamed eggs.	Important in poultry and vegetable stuffings; adds taste to biscuits, herb breads, or waffles.	Delightful addition to an herb bouquet or to seafood sauce.	Try with beans, beets, carrots, onions, potatoes, or in aspics.	Use T. azoricus in creams and custards. Lemon thyme especially good in jellies.
Minced or whole, garnishes whole fish.	Blend into cottage or cream-cheese spread or into omelets and scrambled eggs.	Minced cress added to biscuit dough or piecrust is delicious and nutritious.		Use as sorrel in your favorite recipe. Sprinkle minced leaves over carrots, cauliflower, potatoes, green beans, and sweet vegetables. Or boil as potherb and serve with your favorite sauce.	

HOW TO BUILD AND PLANT THIS HERB GARDEN IN YOUR OWN BACKYARD

When you discover how easy herbs are to grow, you will collect them avidly and tuck them into odd places about your yard. To start you on your way with herbs, here is a collection of 18 different culinary kinds growing in clay-colored flue tiles and arranged in a group to be viewed from all four sides; a perfect feature for a sunny terrace or patio. And you may adapt the idea to your site by regrouping the tiles any way you wish; they might even be set into a slope. Flue tiles are obtained in various shapes and heights from building supply dealers. Tiles may be cut into halves; let a mason show you how. When you decide on an arrangement that pleases you, sink the tiles two inches or more into the ground and fill them with good garden soil after first loosening the earth beneath the tiles with a spade to insure drainage. You may grow your herbs from seed sown in the soil-filled tiles when the weather warms in spring. But with the exception of the parsley and sweet woodruff you need only two or three plants of a kind so it may be more practical to buy them from a garden center or an herb specialist.

1 Sweet woodruff
2 Chives
3 Mint
4 Sweet Marjoram
5 Dill
6 Thyme
7 Winter savory
8 Summer savory
9 Basil

10 Rue
11 Lemon Balm
12 Burnet
13 Oregano
14 Catnip
15 Sage
16 Fennel
17 Parsley
18 Nasturtium

HERMIT—A dark, spicy cookie filled with fruits and nuts. The dark color comes from molasses or brown sugar and ground spices. Hermits may be served plain or with a glaze.

Hermits are early American cookies that originated in New England. They are also found in the South and other parts of the country. Their origin is as obscure as their name. They belong to the group of spicy cookies of the clipper-ship and the spice-trade days. They bear enchanting names like Snickerdoodles, Kinkawoodles, Brambles, Tangled Britches and they all resemble each other; the difference is that one may contain cinnamon, but not other spices, the other raisins and no citron, etc.

BROWN-SUGAR HERMITS
½ cup soft butter
1 cup firmly packed brown sugar
2 eggs
2 cups sifted cake flour
1 teaspoon baking powder
½ teaspoon salt
1 teaspoon ground cinnamon
¼ teaspoon each of ground cloves and nutmeg
2 cups seeded raisins, chopped
½ cup chopped nuts

Cream butter and sugar. Add eggs, one at a time, beating until light after each addition. Add sifted dry ingredients, raisins, and nuts; mix well. Drop by tea-spoonfuls onto greased cookie sheets. Bake in preheated moderate oven (350° F.) for about 10 minutes. Makes about 4 dozen.

MOLASSES HERMITS
¾ cup soft butter or margarine
1½ cups light brown sugar, packed
½ cup molasses
3 eggs
4 cups sifted cake flour
1 teaspoon each of salt, cinnamon, and ground nutmeg
½ teaspoon each of cloves, allspice, and mace
¼ cup strong coffee
1 cup chopped nuts
1 cup each of raisins and currants
Confectioners' sugar

Cream butter and sugar until light. Beat in molasses. Add eggs, one at a time, beating thoroughly after each addition. Sift flour, salt, and spices and add to first mixture alternately with coffee, beating until smooth. Fold in nuts and fruit. Pour into pan (15 x 10 x 1 inches) lined with wax paper. Bake in preheated moderate oven (350°F.) for about 20 minutes. Turn out on rack and peel off paper. Slip onto cutting board and cut in 35 bars about 3 inches x 1½ inches. Sprinkle with confectioners' sugar.
Note: These will stay moist a long time.

MINCEMEAT HERMITS
1 cup sifted all-purpose flour
¼ teaspoon each of salt, baking soda, and ground nutmeg
½ teaspoon ground cinnamon
⅓ cup butter
⅓ cup firmly packed light brown sugar
1 egg
½ cup mincemeat
1 tablespoon dairy sour cream
Vanilla Glaze

Sift first 5 ingredients and set aside. Cream butter and sugar. Add egg, and combine mixtures. Then add mincemeat and cream, mixing by hand. Drop by heaping teaspoonfuls in mounds onto ungreased cookie sheet, leaving 2 inches between mounds. Bake in preheated hot oven (400°F.) for 10 to 12 minutes. Remove from oven and frost with Vanilla Glaze while hot. Makes 20.

Vanilla Glaze
Mix 1½ cups sifted confectioners' sugar, dash of salt, 1 teaspoon vanilla extract, 2 tablespoons melted butter, and about 2 tablespoons heavy cream.

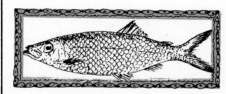

HERRING—These small, salt-water fish belong to the family *Clupeidae,* and the shad, alewife, and sardine are related to them. Also related to this family is a fresh-water variety, lake herring, some-times called "cisco." Herring is an impor-tant food fish, both for human consump-tion and as the basic diet of other food fishes.

Herring have small heads; they are streamlined and covered with silvery, iridescent scales. Mature herrings meas-ure around ten inches, but they can be larger. They are migratory fish, and appear to spend most of their lives in the deep waters offshore. In the spring they come to the beaches in enormous numbers in order to spawn. The sight of schools of herring, several miles wide, shimmering in the moonlight like an iridescent tapestry as they progress to the shore, is an unforgettable one. Their migrations are uncertain, and no one knows why sometimes they stay away from some shores for years.

Herring females lay an average of 10,000 to 60,000 eggs at each spawning. At spawning time, the female rubs her-self against rocks, sand, or seaweed, on which she drops her eggs. These can be seen floating on top of the sea, re-sembling sawdust. Both eggs and herring are preyed upon by other fish and gulls, porpoises, and sharks.

The economics of many nations were based upon herring. The spawning ground influenced the location of cities, and the capricious habits of the herring often brought disaster, for when the fish did not come, there was no food. Herring have always been fished commercially on a vast scale. Holland's great foreign trade was built upon her successful her-ring fisheries. One of the reasons why Charles I of England (1600-1649) was overthrown by his subjects (and eventu-ally lost his head) was because he inter-fered with their free fishing rights. He wanted to tax the fishing rights to get money to fight the Dutch herring trade of the time.

In Europe, especially in Great Britain and in the countries that border on the North Sea, fresh herring is greatly appreciated.

Preserved herring in many varieties is a staple food of Holland and the Scan-dinavian countries. The herring is salted, pickled, or smoked and dressed with sauces. Many of these herring delicacies are imported into the United States and, along with our own preserved herring, can add considerable variety to a budget diet.

Kippers and bloaters are two herring specialties of England. The fish are cured by salting and smoking. They are baked or broiled just long enough to heat them through. Kippers (a contraction of "kip-pered herring" referring to the method and ingredients used in the process of curing them) and bloaters (the latter are larger herring) are tasty English break-fast food and are served also at high teas and suppers.

Rollmops, the favorite German herring dish, is a rolled-up pickled herring. Like other pickled herring, it can be bought in food stores.

Availability and Purchasing Guide — All year round, although the supply fluctu-ates depending upon the catch.

Herring is sold fresh, salted in brine, mild-smoked, hard-smoked, pickled in wine sauce or other seasoned sauces or with sour cream, and kippered.

Canned herring is available pickled in tomato or wine sauce, as grilled fillets, and rolled with anchovies. Pickled her-ring in wine sauce or with sour cream is available in jars.

Storage
- ☐ Fresh and mild-smoked, refrigerator shelf: 1 to 2 days
- ☐ Fresh and mild-smoked, refrigerator frozen-food compartment, prepared for freezing: 2 to 3 weeks
- ☐ Fresh and mild-smoked, freezer, pre-pared for freezing: 1 year
- ☐ Salted in brine, refrigerator shelf: 1 week
- ☐ Hard-smoked, pickled, and kippered,

Rollmops

refrigerator shelf: 2 to 3 months
☐ Canned, kitchen shelf, unopened: 6 months to 1 year
☐ Canned, kitchen shelf, opened and covered: 3 to 4 days

Nutritive Food Values—Good source of protein and fat. Fresh herring is high in phosphorus. The caloric value of 3½ ounces of fresh salt-water herring can vary from 98 to 176 calories depending on the variety. The value of 3½ ounces of smoked herring varies from 196 to 300 calories depending on variety and method of smoking.
☐ Fresh-water herring (cisco), 3½ ounces, raw = 96 calories
☐ Salad in brine, 3½ ounces = 218 calories
☐ Kippered, 3½ ounces = 211 calories

Basic Preparation—*Fresh herring* is prepared as is any other fresh fish.

Herring in brine should be soaked in fresh water for 24 hours. Water should be changed several times. After soaking, remove head, split, fillet, and skin fish. Prepare as desired.

Smoked herring should be soaked in water or in half milk and half water for several hours. The longer it is soaked the less smoky it will taste.

Kippers and bloaters, if heavily salted, may have to be soaked as other smoked herring is. They should be just heated through or they will be dry. Serve as a breakfast dish with eggs and toast.

Pickled herring is eaten as is and can be chopped and mixed with other foods, with salads, sandwich spreads, etc.

GRILLED ENGLISH HERRING

Cut heads, tails, and fins off washed and gutted herrings. Split open along the backbone; draw out the backbone with as many fine bones as possible. Wipe fish and sprinkle with pepper and salt. Dip fish into fine oatmeal, coating it both inside and out. Place fish on broiler rack. Dot each with 1 teaspoon bacon fat. Broil for 10 minutes on each side, or until crisp and golden brown. Serve immediately with mustard sauce or with lemon.

PICKLED HERRING

    6 herring in brine
    1 onion, sliced
    ½ lemon, sliced
    1½ cups cider vinegar
    3 bay leaves
    ⅛ teaspoon crushed red pepper
    1½ teaspoons mustard seeds
    ½ teaspoon sugar

Clean herring and soak in cold water for 24 hours, changing water several times. Remove head and bones; rinse and drain. Arrange in covered refrigerator dish in layers with onion and lemon. Combine vinegar with remaining ingredients. Bring to boil; cool; pour over her-ring. Store, covered, in refrigerator for 3 to 4 days before serving. Makes 6 servings.

ROLLMOPS

    6 herring in brine
      Prepared mustard
    2 small sour pickles, sliced
    2 onions, thinly sliced
    1 tablespoon capers
    1 red pepper, cut up
    6 peppercorns
    2 bay leaves
    1½ cups cider vinegar
    1 cup water

Clean herring and soak in cold water for 24 hours, changing water several times. Remove head and bones. Rinse and drain. Spread herring with prepared mustard, pickle slices, onion slices, and capers. Roll up each herring and secure with toothpicks. Place in small container with red pepper, peppercorns, and bay leaves. Do not use a metal container. Boil together vinegar and water. Cool; pour over herring. Cover and let stand for 3 to 6 days. Drain before serving. Serve with sour cream, if desired. Makes 6 servings.

HERRING IN SOUR CREAM

    5 herring in brine
    1 cup dairy sour cream
    2 tablespoons cider vinegar
    1 teaspoon Worcestershire
    ½ teaspoon powdered mustard
    2 onions, sliced
      Dash of cayenne
      Chopped parsley

Clean herring and soak in cold water for 24 hours, changing water several times. Remove head, skin, and bones. Rinse and drain. Cut into 1-inch pieces. Combine remaining ingredients; add herring and mix lightly. Place in glass jar; cover. Let stand in refrigerator for about 12 hours before serving. Makes 6 servings.

BROILED CISCO

Preheat broiler. Wash fish and dry quickly with damp cloth. Lightly dust with flour. Put fish on broiler pan, brush with butter, margarine, or oil. Broil fillets, 2 inches from heat, for 5 to 7 minutes; do not turn, but baste once during broiling. Broil whole fish 6 inches from heat; broil for 4 minutes, then turn and broil for 5 minutes on second side.

BROILED KIPPERED HERRING

    8 mild kippers
    ¼ cup melted butter
      Juice of 1 lemon
      Paprika
    3 teaspoons chopped scallions

Without breaking the skin along the back, split kippers and spread butterfly-style, skin-side down in shallow baking dish. Brush with butter and lemon juice, sprinkle with paprika, and bake in preheated moderate oven (350°F.) for 10 minutes. Garnish with scallions. Makes 4 servings.

FRIED SMOKED HERRING

    8 smoked herring
      Pepper
    1 cup cornmeal
      Fat for cooking

Wash herring and soak in cold water for 24 hours, changing water twice. Rinse and dry. Sprinkle with pepper and roll in cornmeal. Fry in shallow fat (⅛ to ¼ inch) in skillet for about 12 to 15 minutes or until brown and crisp, turning once. Makes 4 servings.

HERRING BUTTER

Mix ¼ cup creamed butter, 2 teaspoons ground smoked herring or herring paste, and a few drops of fresh lemon juice. May be spread on bread for canapés, alone, or as a base for another food.

HICKORY—A large family of American trees of the genus *Carya*, all of which have hard wood suitable for timber. Many have rich green leaves in summer which turn a brilliant yellow in fall. Some hickory varieties are raised commercially.

The extremely hard wood of the tree has made hickory a synonym for firmness. Andrew Jackson, who was elected president of the United States in 1828, was known as Old Hickory to point up his toughness in war or peace.

Pecan and pignut trees are both members of the hickory family. The thin-shelled nuts of these trees are known as pecans and pignuts. The "hickory" nuts available commercially come from the shagbark or shellbark hickories and have a hard shell.

The hickory nut was eaten by the Indians before the first American colonists arrived in the new country. The name pohickery, mentioned as early as 1653, is a shortened form of the word used by the Virginians to describe an Indian food of water and pounded nuts.

The Indians in Florida used hickory nuts to make a milky liquor which they called "milk of nuts." A contemporary observer, writing in 1775, reported that "this milk they are fond of and eat it with sweet potatoes in it."

Modern cooks find hickory nuts more useful in cakes, cookies, sweet breads, and candies. They can also be used in any recipe calling for pecans.

The shells of hickory nuts are so hard that it is usually necessary to use a hammer to crack them in order to remove the nutmeats.

Availability and Purchasing Guide—Hickory nuts are available only in certain localities. They are sold by the pound in bulk, unshelled; they are rarely available shelled.

☐ 3 pounds hickory nuts = 1 pound shelled meats

Storage—Store, in a covered container, in a cool dry place, refrigerate or freeze.

☐ In shell, kitchen shelf, covered: 1 year
☐ Shelled, kitchen shelf, covered: 2 to 3 months.
☐ Shelled, refrigerator shelf: 4 months
☐ Shelled, refrigerator frozen-food compartment: 6 months
☐ Shelled, freezer: 6 months to 1 year

Nutritive Food Values—Hickory nuts are high in fat.

☐ 3½ ounces = 673 calories

HICKORY NUT CAKE
1 cup butter or margarine
2 cups sugar
3 cups sifted all-purpose flour
1 tablespoon baking powder
1 cup milk
½ teaspoon each of vanilla and orange extracts
1 tablespoon grated lemon rind
7 egg whites, beaten until very stiff
1 cup hickory nuts, chopped

Cream butter until soft. Gradually beat in sugar, a little at a time. Beat until fluffy. Sift together flour and baking powder. Add flour and milk alternately with butter mixture, beginning and ending with flour. Stir in vanilla and orange extracts and grated lemon rind. Fold in beaten egg whites. Pour into greased 9-inch angel-food pan. Scatter hickory nuts on top of batter. Bake in preheated moderate oven (350°F.) for about 1 hour. Cool in pan. Makes one 9-inch cake.

HICKORY NUT CREAMS
3 cups firmly packed light brown sugar or maple sugar
1 cup light cream or evaporated milk
½ teaspoon vanilla extract
1 tablespoon butter
2 cups hickory nuts

Mix sugar with cream until sugar is dissolved. Bring to a boil and boil to 234° F. on a candy thermometer, or until a small amount dropped into cold water forms a soft ball. Cool mixture to 110° F., or lukewarm. Add vanilla, butter, and nuts. Beat with a spoon until creamy. Drop by teaspoons onto wax paper. Makes about 36 creams.

NUT BREAD
3 cups sifted all-purpose flour
1 cup sugar
1½ teaspoons salt
4 teaspoons baking powder
¼ cup shortening
1 egg, well beaten
1¼ cups milk
1 cup coarsely chopped hickory nuts

Sift flour with sugar, salt, and baking powder. Cut in shortening until mixture resembles coarse cornmeal. Beat egg with milk and add liquid all at once to dry ingredients. Stir until just blended. Stir in nuts. Pour mixture into a well-greased pan (9 x 5 x 3 inches). After baking, cool on a rack and slice while warm.

HICKORY CRESCENTS
1 cup ground hickory nuts
1 cup butter
¾ cup sugar
2½ cups sifted all-purpose flour
1½ teaspoons vanilla extract
Vanilla Sugar

Combine nuts, butter, sugar, flour, and vanilla. Knead to a smooth dough and shape about 1 teaspoon of dough at a time into a small crescent about 1½ inches long. Bake on ungreased cookie sheets in preheated moderate oven (350° F.) until slightly browned, about 15 to 17 minutes. Cool for 1 minute. While still warm, roll cookies in Vanilla Sugar. Cool completely, and roll again in Vanilla Sugar. Makes about 6 dozen.

Vanilla Sugar
Cut 2 or 3 vanilla beans into 1-inch pieces. Put in jar with 1 pound sifted confectioners' sugar. Let stand for 3 days. The longer the sugar stands, the more fragrant it becomes.

HIGHBALL—An American drink made from whisky or other hard liquor, mixed with water, soda water, or ginger ale and served with ice in a tall glass.

HOECAKE—This is the cornmeal cake of the early American settlers, which often served as bread. The cooking facilities of colonial households were generally primitive, and ovens, even when existing, could not be heated easily. The inventive settlers baked a cornmeal and water mix-

ture on the blades of their hoes on hot coals in front of a wood fire and called them "hoecakes."

Today's hoecakes are baked in a frying pan or on a griddle like any other hot cake.

OLD-FASHIONED HOECAKE
1 cup white cornmeal
½ teaspoon salt
Boiling water

Mix the meal and salt and add enough boiling water to make a dough that is soft, but not thin enough to be a batter. Heat a well-greased 6- or 8-inch frying pan, and spread the dough on it in one cake, flattening with a spoon or spatula. Cook until very brown on one side, then turn with a pancake turner and let brown as long as can be done without burning.

HOLLANDAISE—A rich sauce of French origin made with egg yolks and butter. It is served with eggs, fish, vegetables, and, occasionally, meat. The origin of the name is obscure; there is no historical evidence that it originated in Holland. There may be a slight clue in the old French culinary language where we find that fish served with melted butter was called *à la hollandaise,* since the sauce we know today as hollandaise is so rich in butter.

How to Cook Superbly: Hollandaise

by Helen Evans Brown

Hollandaise sauce is not only a classic accompaniment for asparagus, broccoli, and other vegetables, it is the base of other famous sauces: Béarnaise, mousseline, maltaise, and choron. It is also a chef's way of obtaining a beautiful brown glaze on many entrées and a necessary ingredient for many famous dishes including eggs Benedict. It is really no great feat to make hollandaise perfectly for, unlike an omelet, it requires no practice. There is just one simple thing to remember, and that is not to let it cook over too high heat. If you do, it will break or separate. But even that catastrophe can usually be remedied.

There are three ways to make hollandaise. The one usually found in most cook books I will skip, because I consider the other two better, each for a different reason. The first of these, the method used by most European-trained chefs, has the advantage of perfect flavor and consistency and is easy to make. The second, or blender method, is even easier, although the resulting sauce has two small faults, probably recognized only by experts: the egg yolks have a slightly raw taste and the consistency is a bit too fluffy.

FIRST METHOD

EQUIPMENT

You will need a kitchen bowl, preferably a heavy crockery one (not metal) that will heat slowly and hold the heat. Select a size that will fit over a saucepan or the bottom part of a double boiler without touching the hot water beneath. A 3-cup bowl is usually right as it allows room for beating. You will also need a wire whisk. The French type (called a *fouet* in France) is perfect but there are American whips that do very well. One is a spoon-shape device edged with a coil of

wire; the other is also spoon-shape, but crisscrossed with wire. A split or slotted spoon, or a bundle of twigs such as those used in Sweden, can also be used, as can a spoon or plastic scraper if you work fast. A fork doesn't reach the curves of the bowl; therefore some of the mixture may overcook. You will also need a knife for cutting the butter or a small pan for melting it, if you prefer that method.

INGREDIENTS

3   egg yolks
¼   cup hot water
1   tablespoon fresh lemon juice (or to taste)
    White pepper or cayenne to taste
    Ground nutmeg to taste (optional)
½   cup (¼ pound) soft butter, cut into slices, or melted butter

HERE'S HOW

1. Put the bowl over the pan of warm water, making sure that the bottom is at least ½ inch from the top of the water. Place over low heat.
2. Put the egg yolks in the bowl and, while whisking or stirring vigorously, drizzle in the hot water. Add lemon juice and pepper or cayenne, continuing to beat. Add nutmeg if you wish (early French recipes called for it, but it is rarely used today). Don't let the water boil or you'll have scrambled eggs. If it approaches that point, remove from heat. If it does boil, put bowl in cold water for a minute to cool it slightly. The egg-and-water mixture will become fluffy and thickened, the whisk coated, and the yolks will lose their raw taste.
3. When the egg mixture reaches that point, add a slice of the butter and stir until it melts. The sauce should begin thickening. Add more butter, whisking the while, until all is added and the sauce is so thick that the bottom of the bowl will show for a split second when you stir. If it doesn't thicken properly, give it more heat but not too much. A quicker method is to melt the butter and drizzle it in with one hand while beating with the other. This works very well if you are careful to pour very slowly, at least at first until the mixture starts to thicken. It has an added advantage in that you can leave the milky residue in the melting pan, thus improving the flavor of the sauce.
4. Your sauce is now done and can be held over warm (never hot) water until you're ready to serve (up to 1 hour or more). Remember that hollandaise is a warm, not hot, sauce. Makes about 1½ cups.

SECOND METHOD

EQUIPMENT

All you need is an electric blender.

INGREDIENTS

Cut egg yolks to 2 and hot water to 1 tablespoon. All of the other ingredients remain the same. Melt butter until it is very hot, almost boiling.

HERE'S HOW

1. Rinse container of blender with hot water; put in place, add egg yolks, hot water, lemon juice, and seasonings, and whirl at high speed for 3 seconds.
2. Remove top (just the small opening if your blender is so provided, otherwise just lift lid enough to add butter). Pour the foaming butter in very slowly, keeping the blender turned on. (You may get splattered if you stand too close, so watch it!) As soon as all the butter (but not the milky residue) is added, your hollandaise is ready to serve. Makes about ⅔ cup.

HINTS

■ **Separation**—If your hollandaise should separate from overheating, try adding a few drops of boiling water or thick cream while beating vigorously.

■ **Thinness**—If it is too thin, it means you haven't cooked it enough or have added the butter too fast. If you suspect the first, just return the bowl to water that is under the boil and beat until thickened. If you think you may have added the butter too quickly, warm a bowl in hot water, then put about 1 teaspoon of heavy cream and 1 tablespoon of the sauce in it and whisk vigorously. Gradually add the remaining sauce, 1 spoonful at a time, until all is added and the sauce is thick.

■ **Reheating**—Hollandaise can be kept in the refrigerator for 2 or 3 days or frozen for weeks. (Remember that egg yolk is a perfect culture for bacteria, so don't let it stand around in a warm place.) When reheating, put a bowl over warm water, as above, and add 1 spoonful of the sauce at a time, beating after each addition. If it should separate, treat as above. Or put it over warm water all at once and beat hard until smooth and warm.

VARIATIONS

■ **Béarnaise Sauce**—Follow Hollandaise recipe but omit lemon juice. Instead soak 1 teaspoon dried tarragon in 2 tablespoons tarragon vinegar and cook with 2 teaspoons chopped shallots or green onions until the vinegar is absorbed. Add to the hot water and continue as above. Omit nutmeg but add a pinch of powdered mustard, if desired. Strain if you wish. Serve with steaks, lamb, meat loaf, fish, and vegetables.

■ **Choron Sauce**—Add 2 tablespoons tomato paste to 1 recipe of Béarnaise Sauce. Serve with fish, eggs, steaks, meat-

Frankfurter, Hominy, and Green-Pea Casserole

balls, or meat loaf.

■ **Mousseline Sauce**—Combine 1 recipe of Hollandaise Sauce with ½ cup heavy cream, whipped. Serve with soufflés, vegetables.

■ **Maltaise Sauce**—Follow Hollandaise recipe but substitute ¼ cup fresh orange juice for the hot water, in either method; in the blender method use 3 egg yolks. Also add 1 teaspoon grated orange peel. Serve with boiled vegetables or fish.

SPECIAL USES

■ Add 2 or 3 tablespoons hollandaise to 1 cup Béchamel or cream sauce.

■ Or add ¼ cup hollandaise to 1 cup whipped cream (or ½ cup each of whipped cream and cream sauce) and use for masking foods that are to be glazed or browned under the broiler.

HOMESTYLE—The word describes a home-kitchen way of cooking food or a home-cooked meal. When food is cooked for hotels, restaurants, institutions, and factories, the dishes taste differently from those prepared at home. The difference in flavor and texture is due to the fact that the food is cooked in large amounts at one time, that many of the ingredients are prepared in advance rather than just at cooking time, and that the food is kept hot on steam tables and other equipment instead of being cooked just before serving.

To cook homestyle is to try to approximate the methods used in home cooking: small quantities, good seasonings, and cooked to order, which means cooked fresh for the meal.

HOMINY—Kernels of hulled dried corn from which the germ has been removed. It is also known as "samp." Ground hominy is called grits. Hominy is apparently a word of Algonquian Indian origin, implying small particles. It is a truly American food, unknown anywhere else.

Hominy is cooked in water or milk, and may then be fried, baked, or served with a sauce. It is a popular staple in the South and Southwest.

Availability and Purchasing Guide—Sold by the pound as pearl, hominy (hull removed mechanically), and lye hominy (hull removed chemically). Hominy grits are available in three grinds: fine, medium, and coarse.

Canned hominy is also available.

Storage

- ☐ Kitchen shelf: stores indefinitely
- ☐ Refrigerator shelf, cooked and covered: 4 to 5 days

Nutritive Food Values—Good source of carbohydrate.

- ☐ Hominy and hominy grits, 3½ ounces, cooked = 51 calories

Basic Preparation

☐ **To Cook Hominy**—Soak overnight in water to cover. Pour hominy into salted boiling water (1 part hominy to 4 parts water). Cook over low heat. Cover and simmer for 4 to 5 hours, or until hominy is tender. Stir often during cooking. Use as is or beat butter into the hominy before serving. Beating whitens hominy. Milk or cream (½ cup for each 1 cup raw hominy) may be beaten into the hominy before serving.

☐ **To Cook Hominy Grits**—Soak 1 cup grits in water to cover for 1 hour. Drain. Add 3 cups boiling water and 1 teaspoon salt, and cook in double boiler up to 1 hour, or until tender. Length of cooking time will depend on whether grits are fine, medium, or coarse.

SALT PORK, BEANS, AND HOMINY

½ pound navy beans
½ pound hominy
½ pound salt pork
Salt and pepper
Crumbled dried marjoram

Soak beans and hominy overnight. Drain and cover with fresh water. Cut salt pork into strips and mix with beans and hominy. Season to taste with salt, pepper, and marjoram. Simmer, covered, for at least 5 hours, or until beans and hominy are tender. Makes 6 to 8 servings.

FRANKFURTER, HOMINY, AND GREEN-PEA CASSEROLE

In a greased 2-quart casserole, arrange in 3 pie-shape portions the following: 1 pound frankfurters, brushed with melted margarine and scored with sharp knife; 3½ cups cooked hominy (one 1-pound, 13-ounce can), drained; 2 cups (one 1-pound can) peas, drained. Pour ¼ cup margarine over hominy and peas. Sprinkle with 4 slices of cooked bacon, chopped. Bake for 25 minutes in preheated moderate oven (350°F.). Makes 4 servings.

HOMINY AU GRATIN

3½ cups (one 1-pound, 13-ounce can) hominy
1 cup water
1 teaspoon salt
½ cup grated sharp cheese
¼ cup butter or margarine
1 cup warm milk

In a skillet combine all ingredients except milk. Simmer over low heat for 10 minutes, or until butter and cheese are melted. Stir occasionally. Gradually stir in milk and cook, stirring occasionally, over low heat until thick and bubbly. Put under broiler and cook until top is golden-brown. Makes 8 servings.

MEXICAN HOMINY

1 medium onion, minced
1 medium green pepper, chopped
¼ cup butter or bacon fat
3½ cups (one 1-pound, 13-ounce can) cooled hominy, drained
1 teaspoon chili powder
½ teaspoon salt
⅛ teaspoon pepper

Cook onion and green pepper in the butter in top pan of chafing dish over direct heat for about 10 minutes. Add remaining ingredients, and heat. Makes 4 servings.

HOMINY AND CHEESE

3½ cups (one 1-pound, 13-ounce can) cooked hominy, drained
¾ pound sharp Cheddar cheese, cut into pieces
¾ cup milk
½ teaspoon salt
2 eggs, beaten
⅛ teaspoon pepper
⅛ teaspoon celery seed

Put all ingredients in skillet. Cook over low heat, stirring frequently, until cheese is melted. Makes 4 servings.

BUTTERY GARLIC GRITS

1 cup fine hominy grits
4 cups boiling water
Salt
½ cup butter
¼ pound garlic-smoked cheese, shredded
2 eggs, beaten, and water to make 1 cup
½ cup crumbled corn flakes

Cook grits in boiling salted water for 7 to 10 minutes. Remove from heat. Stir in butter, shredded cheese, eggs and water. Pour into ungreased 1½-quart baking dish. Sprinkle corn flakes on top and cook in preheated moderate oven (350°F.) for about 45 minutes. Serve in casserole hot from the oven. Makes 4 servings.

FRIED SALT PORK AND MILK GRAVY ON HOMINY GRITS

Boil ⅓ cup fine hominy grits with 1¾ cups water and ¼ teaspoon salt for 10 minutes. Cut rind from 3 ounces of salt pork and slice pork thin. Cover with boiling water and let stand for 5 minutes, then drain and dip into flour. Fry slowly until brown and crisp. Remove salt pork and pour off all but 1 tablespoon fat drippings. Stir in 1 tablespoon flour and 1 cup skim milk. Bring to boil; cook until slightly thickened, stirring constantly. Season to taste with salt and pepper. Serve pork and gravy on grits. Makes 2 servings.

BAKED HOMINY GRITS

2 cups cooked hominy grits
⅔ cup milk
3 tablespoons melted butter or margarine
2 eggs, beaten

Combine all ingredients and pour mixture into a buttered shallow 1-quart baking dish. Place pan in a pan of hot water. Bake in preheated moderate oven (375° F.) for 1 hour. Makes 6 servings.

GRITS BATTER BREAD

1 egg, beaten
½ cup cooked hominy grits
1 cup white or yellow cornmeal
1 teaspoon salt
Boiling water
1 tablespoon shortening

Combine egg, grits, cornmeal, and salt. Pour enough boiling water over mixture to make a batter of the consistency of light cream, about 1½ cups. Melt shortening in 8-inch square pan. Pour batter into pan. Bake in preheated moderate oven (350°F.) for 40 minutes. Bread will not brown. Makes 4 servings.

FRIED HOMINY GRITS

2 cups cooked hominy grits
2 eggs, beaten
2 tablespoons milk
¼ cup fine cracker crumbs
½ cup shortening
Bacon

Press hominy into a small loaf pan (7⅜ x 5⅜ x 2¼ inches). Chill for several hours. Unmold. Cut into ½-inch slices. Beat eggs with milk and dip slices into mixture. Roll slices in cracker crumbs and coat well. Heat shortening; fry slices to a golden brown on both sides. Serve with slices of crisp bacon. Makes 4 to 6 servings.

HOMINY PUFFS

2 cups cooked hominy grits
2 eggs, separated
¼ cup all-purpose flour
1½ teaspoons baking powder
½ teaspoon salt
Fat or lard for deep frying

Mix hominy with egg yolks. Stir in flour sifted with baking powder and salt. Beat egg whites until stiff but not dry, and fold them into the hominy mixture. Drop by tablespoonfuls into hot deep fat (360° F. on a frying thermometer). Fry until deep brown. Makes about 18 puffs.

HOMOGENIZE—This is a word of Greek origin, composed of *homos,* meaning "the same," and *"genos,"* kin or kind. In culinary language, "to homogenize" is to reduce an emulsion to particles of the same size and to distribute them evenly. The word is most frequently used for milk, but also for salad dressings and mayonnaise.

The homogenized milk we drink is pasteurized milk that has been processed mechanically to break up the fat globules into a tiny size so that they will stay in the liquid part of the milk rather than rise to the top. In other words, the cream is incorporated into the milk so that the milk is uniform rather than consisting of thin milk topped by cream.

The origin of homogenized milk lies in patents granted to two Frenchmen in 1892. They wanted to make margarine and invented machines that were the first homogenizing machines. These machines blended fats and water into a smooth whole. Their use for milk came later, in 1899, when another French inventor, Auguste Gaulin, noticed the fat globules in milk and decided to make a smooth, homogenous milk emulsion, which he did, adapting the principles of the homogenizing machines and taking out his own patents. This new milk appeared for the first time at the World's Fair in Paris in 1900, where it stirred up great curiosity. The milk was called Gaulin's Milk or *lait homogénéisé*, and from this developed our name.

The first time American readers heard about homogenized milk was in April 1904, when it was described to them in *The Scientific American*. The first introduction, in Quebec, Canada, in 1904, was not successful. The new milk was reintroduced in Ottawa in 1927, and by 1932 it could be found in many large Canadian cities.

In the United States, the first homogenized milk was introduced experimentally at the University of Illinois in 1921, but it did not become popular until the early thirties. Studies made at the Children's Hospital in Philadelphia, which proved that homogenized milk was more digestible for babies than ordinary milk, led to its acceptance in American homes. Today, over two thirds of all American milk is homogenized.

HONEY—A sweet sticky liquid made by honeybees from the nectar of plants. The bees suck the nectar from the flowers and store it in their honey sacs where it undergoes certain changes. Later the bees deposit the liquid in honeycombs where, with other changes, it becomes honey.

Honey is the oldest sweetener known to man, and was just about the only one until sugar cane was discovered in the New World and cultivated on a large scale to produce sugar.

All ancient literature mentions honey and honeybees with much feeling and gratitude for their bounty. The Bible perhaps expressed this best, speaking of a land "flowing with milk and honey."

In the early days, honey was gathered from the hives of wild bees in rocks,

crevices, and trees. Later on, tame bees and their hives were part of every monastery, castle, or farm garden. As honey was the principal sweetener until the 18th century, almost every small rural household kept its bees. We read in old English manor account books how the tenants often paid their rent in honey, and in old cook books how hams were originally cured in honey, and fruits preserved in honey solutions. The rinsings of the combs were used to make mead, the ancient honey drink that was known to all the people of antiquity, from the Druids in Britain to the Persians.

Throughout the world honey was used not only in cooking, but also for medicinal purposes, in ceremonials, and in worship. The wax from the combs was equally part and parcel of daily life. Strips of clean linen dipped into melted wax were used to bind up wounds. The wax was used to waterproof leather, smooth sewing yarn, and even to make a kind of primitive chewing gum.

Reading the literature of the past, we may marvel at the enormous amounts of honey consumed. But we must remember that in those days there were many more flowered meadows and wild lands, and that beekeeping was not a hobby as it is now, nor was honey a special food product, but part of the household's economy.

Honey is served plain on bread, muffins, biscuits, waffles, or pancakes. It blends well with butter or peanut butter for sandwiches. Honey is used in cooking in cakes, cookies, breads, and sauces. It may be used as a sweetener for milk, fruit drinks, or hot beverages and is popular on hot or cold cereal, ice cream, and fruits. Honey is also used as a glaze for baked ham. It can be used to glaze carrots and sausage links, to drizzle warm over ice cream or on broiled grapefruit, to sweeten lemonade or iced tea, to mix with cream cheese for salad, to sweeten baked apples, and to sweeten raw cranberry relish.

Availability and Purchasing Guide—Honey is available year round in jars, cans, pails, and cardboard containers. The flowers from which bees gather nectar largely determine the color, flavor, and aroma of honey. When there is no designation of the flower source on the container, the honey is a blend of different floral types. Sweet clover, clover, and alfalfa honey constitute well over half of the honey produced in this country.

Color—The color varies from the water-white of sage honey through the golden color of clover honey to the reddish brown of buckwheat honey. Usually the lighter the color of honey, the milder the flavor.

Style—Honey is available in three styles: extracted, comb, and chunk. About three fourths of the yearly crop is sold as extracted honey.

☐ Extracted honey—This is the liquid honey separated from the comb. Some processors filter it to make it clear. It is the type most used in honey cookery.

The crystallized or granulated form of extracted honey with its fine creamy texture makes a smooth spread for breads. This is labeled granulated, creamed, fondant, spread, or spun. Whipped honey is crystallized honey which has been whipped to make it light and fluffy. Also available is honey butter, a blend of honey and butter.

☐ Comb honey—Sections of the waxen comb, filled with honey just as the bees stored it. Section-comb is sold from the hive in wooden frames usually weighing about 1 pound. Cut-comb honey has been taken from the frames and cut into small squares. Both of these are fragile and hard to handle so few stores stock them but they are available at farm markets and roadside stands.

☐ Chunk honey—Consists of parts of the comb in a container with extracted honey filled in around the chunks.

Storage—Honey should be stored in a tightly covered container at room temperature in a dry place. If container is left open, the honey will absorb moisture and may ferment. If tightly covered, honey may be kept for several months at room temperature (about 70°F.) at a low relative humidity. Do not store in refrigerator for the cold temperature hastens crystallization of the sugar. Crystallization will occur if kept too long but this does not harm the honey. To reliquefy, place the container in a pan of warm water until the crystals disappear. The water should not be hotter than the hand can stand.

Nutritive Food Values—Honey is almost pure carbohydrate. It is a predigested sweetener, and as such is valuable in certain special diets.

☐ 3½ ounces, extracted = 304 calories

Basic Preparation—Use low to moderate oven temperatures for baking, for honey caramelizes at a low temperature and will brown quickly. Honey cakes and cookies will remain moist longer than those made with sugar and are generally leavened with baking soda.

Honey should be measured accurately. Thick honey rounds up over the top of a measuring spoon or cup, so cut off with a spatula. Be sure to scrape all the honey from the measuring container; heated honey will pour more easily than cold honey and heating makes it easier to measure. Honey becomes darker and thicker with age and is not desirable for baking. It can be used as a spread or syrup.

When honey is substituted for sugar it is necessary to adjust the amount of liquid in the recipe. To substitute honey for sugar: 1 cup honey contains about ¼ cup water, therefore deduct ¼ cup liquid from the amount in the recipe for each cup of honey used. One cup honey is as sweet as 1 cup sugar so no adjustment is necessary for taste. Honey's tendency to absorb moisture presents problems when it is substituted for sugar in frostings, confections, and crisp cookies. Since the amount of moisture absorbed tends to make baked products temperamental, the amount of flour used in any recipe in which honey is substituted for sugar may have to be changed from what the recipe specifies. This has to be done by experimentation, adding flour a little at a time until the desired consistency of dough is achieved.

HONEY BUTTER

Blend ½ cup each of soft butter and honey. Store in refrigerator. If a thinner butter is desired, use ¾ to 1 cup honey to ½ cup butter. Serve with hot biscuits or on hot waffles or pancakes. Good, too, in making cinnamon toast.

Honey-Fruit Butter

To recipe for Honey Butter, add a little grated orange or lemon rind; chopped nuts, dates, or dried apricots. Serve on raisin bread.

HONEY GLAZES

■ For Baked Ham—Mix 1 cup honey with ½ cup orange juice, cranberry sauce, or cider. About 45 minutes before ham is baked, remove rind. Score fat and insert whole cloves in center of squares. Cover with glaze and finish baking, basting frequently.

■ For Carrots or Onions—In saucepan melt ¼ cup butter or margarine. Add ¼ cup honey, and blend. Add hot cooked whole carrots or white onions and cook until glazed, turning frequently.

HONEYED BEETS

3 cups cooked beets, diced
2 tablespoons butter
1 tablespoon grated orange rind
¼ cup fresh orange juice
½ cup honey
½ teaspoon salt
½ teaspoon pepper

Place beets in heavy saucepan. Add all other ingredients. Cook over low heat, stirring constantly, until liquid has evaporated and honey forms a glaze over beets. Do not brown. Makes 4 servings.

STRAWBERRY-HONEY BAVARIAN

1 package strawberry-flavored gelatin
1 cup undiluted evaporated milk
  Juice and grated rind of 1 lemon
¼ cup honey

Honey: Extracted, Chunk, and Comb

18 ladyfingers, split
1 package (12 ounces) frozen strawberries

Dissolve gelatin in 1 cup hot water. Chill until partially set. Pour milk into refrigerator tray and freeze until mushy. Turn into chilled bowl and whip until stiff. Add lemon juice and rind and honey. Beat until well blended. Fold in gelatin; chill until set. Just before serving, arrange 6 ladyfinger halves around edge of each sherbet glass. Spoon Bavarian into glasses; top with partially thawed strawberries. Makes 6 servings.

HONEY MOUSSE

3 egg yolks
¾ cup strained honey
1 cup heavy cream, whipped
2 egg whites, stiffly beaten

Beat together egg yolks and honey until light. Fold in whipped cream first, then beaten egg whites. Pack into 1½-quart mold, and freeze. Makes 6 to 8 servings. **Note:** A fragrant flower honey, such as orange or rose honey, would be excellent for this French recipe.

PENNIES FROM HEAVEN

½ cup water
1 cup honey

Combine water and honey and bring to a boil. Cook until it reaches the soft-ball stage, or 240°F. on candy thermometer. Drop hot mixture, 1 teaspoon at a time, into a dish filled with firmly packed crushed ice. The ice must be as firm as the ice in snow cones.

HONEY-GLAZED APPLES

Peel and core 4 cooking apples. Bring 1 cup each of water and honey to boil in deep saucepan. Slowly cook 2 apples at a time in syrup until tender, turning apples occasionally. Remove to serving dishes. Boil syrup until thick. Cool slightly and pour on apples. Serve warm or cold, topped with dairy sour cream and a grating of nutmeg. Makes 4 servings.

HONEYED PEARS

7 pounds ripe but firm pears
1 cinnamon stick
1 teaspoon ground ginger
   Grated rind of 1 lemon
2 cups cider vinegar
3 pounds honey

Peel and core pears, but leave whole. Combine all other ingredients and bring to a boil. Cook pears in syrup over medium heat until tender; test with cake tester. Cook only a few pears at one time. Remove pears with slotted spoon and place in sterilized jars. Remove cinnamon stick from syrup. Cook syrup until reduced by half. Pour over pears. Seal jars. Makes about 3 quarts.
Note: Use firm pears, such as Seckel pears, and serve as a relish with roast meats and poultry.

HONEY-NUT-APPLE PIE

3 tablespoons all-purpose flour
¼ teaspoon salt
1 teaspoon ground cinnamon
½ teaspoon ground nutmeg
½ cup dairy sour cream
¾ cup honey
½ cup chopped pecans
6 medium tart apples
   Pastry for 2-crust 9-inch pie, unbaked

Mix first 4 ingredients; then add sour cream, honey, and pecans. Peel and slice apples and stir into first mixture. Line pie pan with half of pastry, add filling, and adjust top crust. Bake in preheated hot oven (425°F.) for 30 minutes. Reduce heat to moderate (350°F.) and bake for about 15 minutes longer. Makes 6 to 8 servings.

HONEY-ORANGE-ALMOND CAKE

½ cup shortening
½ cup sugar
½ cup honey
   Grated rind of 1 orange
5 egg yolks
2 cups sifted cake flour
2 teaspoons baking powder
½ teaspoon salt
½ cup milk

Honey-Orange-Almond Cake   Strawberry-Honey Bavarian

¼ cup ground blanched almonds
Confectioners' sugar
Slivered almonds

Cream shortening; add sugar gradually, beating until light and fluffy. Add honey and orange rind and mix well. Then add egg yolks, one at a time, beating thoroughly after each addition. Add sifted dry ingredients alternately with milk, beating until smooth. Add nuts. Line greased pan (9 x 9 x 2 inches) with unglazed brown paper, then grease again. Pour mixture into pan. Bake in preheated moderate oven (350°F.) for 50 minutes, or until done. Sprinkle with confectioners' sugar and garnish with slivered almonds.

DUTCH HONEY CAKE

½ cup firmly packed dark brown sugar
1 egg
½ cup honey
3 tablespoons dark molasses
1 teaspoon baking soda
½ teaspoon baking powder
¼ teaspoon pepper
¼ teaspoon each of ground allspice, cinnamon, nutmeg, and mace
3 tablespoons butter, melted
1½ cups sifted all-purpose flour

Beat together sugar and egg. Beat in honey and molasses. Soften baking soda in 2 teaspoons water and stir into mixture. Combine baking powder, spices, and melted butter. Beat into mixture. Gradually beat in flour, a little at a time. Thoroughly grease and flour a loaf pan (9¼ x 5¼ x 2¾ inches). Pour mixture into it. Bake in preheated moderate oven (350° F.) for 30 to 45 minutes, or until knife blade inserted in center comes out clean. Cool in pan for 5 minutes. Remove, and cool on wire rack.

HONEY-DATE BARS

1 cup honey
3 eggs, well beaten
1 teaspoon vanilla extract
1⅓ cups sifted all-purpose flour
1 teaspoon baking powder
¼ teaspoon salt
2 packages (6½ ounces each) pitted dates, cut up
1 cup chopped nuts
Fine granulated sugar

Mix honey, eggs, and vanilla; beat well. Add sifted dry ingredients, dates, and nuts. Spread in greased pan (13 x 9 x 2 inches). Bake in preheated moderate oven (350°F.) for about 45 minutes. Cool in pan. Cut into bars 1 x 3 inches; roll in sugar. Makes 39.

BUTTERED HONEY NUTS

6 ounces shelled unsalted nuts
1 tablespoon melted butter
1 tablespoon honey

Spread nuts on a cookie sheet. Bake in preheated slow oven (300°F.) for 15 minutes. Mix butter and honey and pour over nuts. Stir until nuts are completely coated with the honey mixture. Store in airtight container until ready to serve. Makes 1⅓ cups.

HONEY-CREAM SAUCE

Mix ½ cup honey, ½ cup light cream, and 2 tablespoons butter; cook over low heat for 10 minutes. Add a little rum flavoring if desired. Makes about 1 cup.

LEMON-HONEY SPREAD

2½ cups honey
Grated rind of 1 lemon
¾ cup strained fresh lemon juice
⅓ cup liquid pectin or ½ bottle

Combine honey, lemon rind, and lemon juice in saucepan. Bring to a rolling boil, stirring constantly. Stir in pectin. Bring again to a full boil. Boil for exactly 1 minute. Remove from heat when jelly sheets from spoon. Skim; pour into hot sterilized jelly glasses. Seal with paraffin. Makes 1 quart.

Note: This is delicious on hot toast, pancakes, waffles, or with cold meats.

HONEY TOPPING

½ cup sweet butter
¼ cup honey
¼ teaspoon ground cinnamon, nutmeg, mace, ginger, or any combination of these spices to taste
½ cup heavy cream, whipped

Cream butter until soft and fluffy. Beat in honey and spices. Gradually beat in whipped cream, beating until mixture is smooth and fluffy. Chill until serving time. Use as a quick topping for cakes, pancakes, waffles, or French toast. Makes about 1 cup.

═══════ ✑ ═══════

HONEYDEW MELON—These melons belong to the muskmelon family, whose varieties include cantaloupes, honeydews, casaba, and Persian melons. Honeydews have a smooth yellowish-white rind, and their flesh is sweet and green.

Honeydews were enjoyed by the Egyptians as early as 2400 B.C. The Persians knew them before that, since muskmelons had been grown in Persia since antiquity. So fragrant were the melons that they reminded the Persians of a favorite perfume, musk. There is a tale of a jeweled Persian prince who had himself wakened at night to eat a melon that had reached the peak of perfection at that particular moment.

Honeydews were brought to the United States about sixty years ago. At first, they were grown under climatic and soil conditions similar to those of their Asiatic ancestors, in low hot river valleys and deltas, but now they flourish in all the irrigated parts of the Southwest, and in California.

Honeydew, cut into wedges, is served with lemon or lime slices. It is a fine accompaniment for meat, seafood, sliced cheese, and, served as melon balls, combines well with other fruits in salads and desserts. Wedges of honeydew are good garnished with other fruits, especially berries.

Availability—Honeydews are available from May to October, with August and September the most plentiful months. A combination of honeydew and cantaloupe balls is available frozen, in sugar pack.

Purchasing Guide—These oblong melons average 4 to 6 pounds and are 7 to 10 inches long. Select melons with creamy yellow rinds that feel velvety. Ripeness is also indicated by a softening at the blossom end.

Storage—Allow underripe melons to ripen at room temperature. Rinse ripe melons, dry well, and wrap in wax paper, foil, or plastic bag. Chill in refrigerator. The tissues of melons held too long at low temperatures break down rapidly at room temperature. Cut melon should be wrapped well and kept in the refrigerator.

Nutritive Food Values—Honeydew contains vitamin C.

☐ Fresh, 3½ ounces = 33 calories
☐ Frozen melon balls, syrup pack, 3½ ounces = 62 calories

HONEYDEW RINGS WITH SHRIMP SALAD

1 medium-size ripe honeydew melon
Head lettuce
Shrimp Salad
Fresh parsley
Mayonnaise

Wash honeydew and cut into 6 rings. Save end pieces to add to fruit cup or fruit salad. Remove seeds from rings, peel, and cut into 1-inch wedges. Shred lettuce and place in each of 6 individual salad plates, over which arrange honeydew wedges in circles. Fill center of each with Shrimp Salad. Garnish with fresh parsley and serve with mayonnaise as a main-dish salad. Makes 6 servings.

Shrimp Salad

3 cups diced cold cooked shrimps
1½ cups diced celery
½ teaspoon finely chopped onion
½ teaspoon salt, or to taste
⅛ teaspoon pepper
2 tablespoons fresh lemon juice
⅓ cup mayonnaise

Combine all ingredients. Toss lightly, and chill. Makes 4½ cups.

AVOCADO-MELON SALAD

Halve avocados and remove seeds. Scoop out pulp carefully. Reserve shells. Cube avocado pulp. Lightly toss avocado cubes with watermelon and honeydew balls. Pile in scooped-out avocado shells. Sprinkle with lemon juice.

HONEYDEW AND ORANGE DESSERT

Place 3 cups fresh honeydew melon balls and 2 cups fresh orange sections in a bowl. Combine 6 tablespoons fresh lemon juice, 2 tablespoons fresh lime juice, and ¼ cup sugar and pour over fruit. Chill, and serve in sherbet glasses. Makes 6 servings.

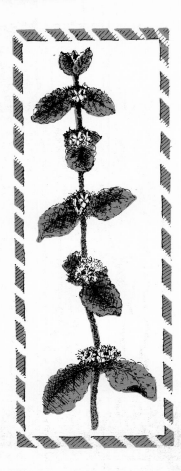

HOREHOUND (Marrubium vulgare)—

Horehound is a member of the mint family, a large family of plants including herbs such as thyme, marjoram, and basil. It shares an aromatic odor with its better-known relatives, but is very bitter in taste. Horehound also refers to the extract or candy made from the plant and used for coughs and colds.

Horehound is native to the Old World countries of southern Europe, northern Asia, and the Orient, but it is now found in most parts of the world except the tropics. Although it is used mainly for horehound candy, it was known to the ancient Egyptians, whose priests referred dramatically to it as "Seed of Horus," "Bull's Blood," and "The Eye of the Star." As early as the 1st century Pliny the Elder, the famous Roman scholar and historian, recommended it as a medicinal plant of great value. His contemporary, Columella, added that it had great use in killing flies. A dish of milk with horehound should be put in the place bothered by the pests. The 13th-century German philosopher and theologian, Albertus Magnus, mentions it as a cough medicine and Michael Drayton, the English poet (1563-1631) gives other explicit uses: "For comforting the spleen and liver—get for juice, Pale Horehound."

Now, after a long history as a popular medicine and cough remedy, horehound is most often used to make horehound candy, a brittle sugar candy made with brown sugar and leaves or stems of horehound. But the adventurous cook can also use a leaf to flavor braised beef or beef stew and cakes and cookies.

HORS-D'OEUVRE—

The literal translation of these French words is "outside of the main work." Hors-d'oeuvre are small appetizers that are not part of the menu, but serve as an introduction to a meal.

In American culinary language the terms hors-d'oeuvre, appetizer, and canapé are often used interchangeably for foods served with drinks or as a first course. To be literal about the matter: while it is true that both hors-d'oeuvre and canapés are appetizers, canapés are morsels of food with a base of bread or crackers and are eaten with the fingers; hors-d'oeuvre, which can be hot or cold, are eaten at the table with a knife and fork.

An endless variety of foods lend themselves to hors-d'oeuvre: oysters, shrimps, canned fish, meat, crisp vegetables, cold cuts, and cheeses. All the foods served on a Scandinavian smörgåsbord or an Italian antipasto table are perfect hors-d'oeuvre foods. Many hors-d'oeuvre can be prepared beforehand, frozen, and reheated at serving time.

MUSHROOM PASTRIES

1 can (3 ounces) chopped mushrooms
2 tablespoons butter or margarine
2 tablespoons all-purpose flour
2/3 cup heavy cream and mushroom liquid
1/2 teaspoon instant bouillon
1/2 teaspoon paprika
1/4 teaspoon pepper
Dash of garlic salt
1 teaspoon instant minced onion
1/2 teaspoon bottled thick meat sauce
1 egg yolk, slightly beaten
Potato Pastry Shells

Cook mushrooms lightly in butter; blend in flour. Stir in cream and liquid, bouillon, and seasonings. Cook until thickened, stirring. Stir small amount of mixture into egg yolk. Add to remainder of filling and cook for a few minutes longer. Fill Potato Pastry Shells. Bake in preheated very hot oven (450°F.) for 10 to 15 minutes. Serve warm or cool. Makes 30 tiny pastries.

Note: Make these shortly before serving.

Potato Pastry Shells

1/2 cup shortening
1 cup sifted all-purpose flour
1/2 teaspoon salt
1/2 cup cold riced potato

Cut shortening into flour and salt. With fork, stir in potato. Put a rounded meas-

uring teaspoon of the mixture into each of 30 tiny tart pans. Press with finger firmly on bottom and sides of pans, leaving center hollow.

DEVILED EGGS

3 hard-cooked eggs
1 1/2 teaspoons mayonnaise
1/2 teaspoon prepared mustard
1/2 teaspoon pickled-onion juice
1/4 teaspoon celery salt
Salt, pepper, and paprika
Pickled onions, halved

Cut eggs into halves lengthwise. Remove yolks and mash with mayonnaise, mustard, onion juice, and celery salt. Add salt and pepper to taste. Fill whites with seasoned yolks. Sprinkle with paprika and top each egg half with half a pickled onion. Makes 3 servings.

ANCHOVY EGGS

Shell hard-cooked eggs and cut into halves lengthwise. Spread each half with mayonnaise and top with a drained rolled anchovy fillet.

WILTED CUCUMBERS AND ONIONS

2 large cucumbers
1 large onion, sliced thin
1 cup cider vinegar
1 teaspoon celery seed
1 teaspoon sugar
1/2 teaspoon salt
1/4 teaspoon pepper

Peel cucumbers; slice thin. Add remaining ingredients. Let stand in refrigerator for at least 2 hours before serving. Makes about 2 pints.

CURRY PUFFS

2 garlic cloves, mashed
1 slice of green gingerroot, mashed
1 1/2 tablespoons minced onion
1 tablespoon curry powder (or more to taste)
2 tablespoons butter
1/2 pound ground beef
1 tablespoon fresh lime juice
1/2 teaspoon salt
1 recipe plain pastry (2 1/2 cups flour recipe) made with half butter, half lard

Sauté garlic, gingerroot, onion, and curry powder together in butter for 5 minutes. Add meat and stir constantly until meat loses red color. Add lime juice and salt, and mix well. Cool. Roll pastry and cut into 2-inch rounds. Place a bit of meat mixture on one round. Moisten edges of round with water and cover with another pastry round, pinching edges well to hold them together. Bake on ungreased cookie sheet in preheated very hot oven (450° F.) for 15 minutes, or until nicely browned. Makes about 2 dozen.

CLAM PASTRIES

Potato Pastry Shells (at left)
1 can (10 1/2 ounces) minced clams, drained
1 tablespoon instant minced onion
1/4 cup minced green pepper
1 egg
1/2 cup heavy cream
2 tablespoons minced celery and leaves

½ cup fine dry bread crumbs
1 tablespoon melted margarine
Dash of cayenne
¾ teaspoon salt
¼ teaspoon pepper

Prepare Potato Pastry. Put 1 rounded teaspoon of pastry into each of 2 dozen 1¾-inch muffin-pan sections, pressing firmly with finger onto bottom and sides of pans; leave centers hollow. Bake in preheated very hot oven (450°F.) for about 12 minutes. Mix remaining ingredients and fill baked shells. Put under broiler until golden-brown. Serve hot. Makes 2 dozen.

FRENCHED HAM AND SWISS

Cut the crusts off thin-sliced bread and spread each slice with a mixture of grated Swiss cheese and cream, mixed well to make a paste. Place a thin slice of ham between each two slices of bread. Dip into beaten egg; then fry in butter. Cut into bite-size pieces. Serve hot.

CHEESE OLIVE PUFFS

2 cups grated sharp Cheddar cheese
1 cup all-purpose flour
½ teaspoon paprika
¼ pound (½ cup) butter or margarine
3 to 4 dozen small stuffed olives

Combine all ingredients except olives; mix very well; chill. For each puff, use a generous teaspoonful and shape into a ball. Push finger into center to make a deep depression, put olive in and shape dough around to fully cover olive. Bake in preheated hot oven (400°F.) for about 15 minutes, or until baked but not browned. Serve hot. Makes 3 to 4 dozen.

CRABMEAT STUFFED MUSHROOMS

¼ teaspoon powdered mustard
Salt and cayenne
1 teaspoon Worcestershire
½ cup hot water
½ cup soft bread crumbs
1 tablespoon cream
1 tablespoon butter
1 cup crabmeat
15 to 20 medium-large mushroom caps
Melted butter
Buttered crumbs

Combine all ingredients except last 4 in saucepan and simmer for about 5 minutes. Add crabmeat. Meanwhile sauté mushroom caps in melted butter. Fill with crab mixture, top with buttered crumbs, and broil just enough to brown crumbs.

CUCUMBER CUPS

1 medium cucumber, diced
¼ cup ketchup
¼ cup chili sauce
2 tablespoons fresh lemon juice
1 teaspoon Worcestershire
1 teaspoon prepared horseradish
Dash of hot pepper sauce
1 head bibb lettuce

Combine all ingredients except lettuce and toss to mix. Serve on lettuce leaves. Makes 8 to 10 servings.

SAVORY APPLE SLICES

Apples
Fresh lemon juice
Shredded sharp Cheddar cheese
Deviled ham or chicken

Slice apples in rings ¼ inch thick. Remove core and dip in lemon juice. Spread some with cheese, and the rest with ham. Broil just enough to heat.

HERRING SALAD

2 herring in brine
2 cups diced cooked potato
1½ cups diced pickled beets
¼ cup diced sweet pickles
1 large apple, diced
1 small onion, minced
1 cup diced cooked veal
¼ cup vinegar
2 tablespoons water
2 tablespoons sugar
¼ teaspoon pepper
2 hard-cooked eggs, quartered

Clean and soak herring in cold water for 24 hours, changing water several times. Remove head, skin, and bones. Rinse, and drain; cut in cubes. Mix with potato, beets, pickles, apple, onion, and veal. Toss lightly. Combine vinegar, water, sugar, and pepper; pour over salad ingredients; toss lightly until all is well seasoned. Chill. Garnish with eggs. Makes 6 to 7 cups.

TOMATO-AVOCADO HORS-D'OEUVRE

1 avocado
1 teaspoon grated onion
½ teaspoon Worcestershire
Dash of cayenne
½ teaspoon salt
2 tablespoons salad oil
1 tablespoon vinegar or fresh lemon juice
½ pound tomatoes
Watercress

Peel and mash avocado with fork; add seasonings, oil, and vinegar, and chill. Peel and cut tomatoes into 6 thick slices; chill. Top each tomato slice with a spoonful of avocado, and garnish with watercress. Makes 6 servings.

AVOCADO HORS-D'OEUVRE

Peel avocado, cut in two, and remove seed. Slice and marinate in highly seasoned French dressing for 30 minutes. Sprinkle with chopped stuffed olives.

INDIAN BROILED SHRIMPS

1 pound raw shrimps, shelled and deveined
1 cup boiling water
1 teaspoon salt
1 teaspoon ground coriander
½ small onion, minced
8 peppercorns
¼ cup cooking oil
1 teaspoon salt
½ teaspoon ground cuminseed
1 teaspoon ground turmeric
1 tablespoon fresh lemon juice or lime juice
1 large lemon or lime, cut into wedges

Combine shrimps, boiling water, salt, coriander, onion, and peppercorns in saucepan. Bring to a boil; cook for 2 to 3 minutes, or until shrimps just begin to turn pink. Remove from water; reserve. Heat oil in skillet; remove from heat. Stir in salt, cuminseed, turmeric, and lemon juice. Add shrimps and toss to coat shrimps with mixture. Place shrimps in shallow baking pan. Broil under medium heat for about 5 minutes, or until shrimps are pink and slightly browned on the edges. Serve with lemon or lime wedges. Makes 4 to 6 servings.

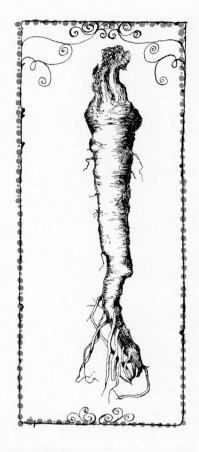

HORSERADISH (Armoracia lapathifolia)—This tall, hardy plant with glossy green, toothed leaves and large amounts of small white flowers is grown for its pungent roots. These are large, fleshy, white, and cylindrical. When grated they have a sharp flavor and a pungent odor. The roots are usually dug in the fall. Peeled and grated, served as is or in vinegar, they are used as a condiment for fish, seafood, meats, game, and in sauces.

Horseradish is a native of southeastern Europe. It has been used since antiquity, long before Christian times. It is one of the five bitter herbs of the Jewish Passover festival, when it is served symbolically during the Seder services.

Horseradish is sold fresh as a root or commercially prepared as preserved white or red horseradish, which is the grated root mixed with vinegar or beet juice and bottled.

Fresh horseradish should be grated as soon as possible after purchase.

Dried horseradish root is also available. To reconstitute, add 2 tablespoons water to each tablespoon dried horseradish. Do this 30 minutes before serving to develop full flavor. Add ½ cup heavy cream for additional flavor. The flavor of dried horseradish is not as strong as that of fresh-grated horseradish.

Horseradish is also sold blended into various seafood sauces.

HORSERADISH SAUCE

1 small onion, minced
2 tablespoons butter or margarine
1 cup light cream
2 egg yolks
¼ cup freshly grated or prepared horseradish, well drained
Salt and cayenne

Brown onion lightly in butter. Add cream and bring to boil. Pour over slightly beaten egg yolks. Add horseradish and return to heat. Cook gently until slightly thickened, stirring. Season with salt and cayenne to taste, and serve hot on boiled beef, fish, or tongue. Makes about 1 cup.

HORSERADISH WHIPPED-CREAM SAUCE

½ cup heavy cream
¼ cup prepared horseradish, well drained
¼ teaspoon salt
1 teaspoon sugar
Paprika

Whip cream until thick. Fold in horseradish, salt, and sugar. Pile lightly in serving dish, and sprinkle with paprika. Serve on cold roast beef, fish, or vegetables. Makes about 1 cup.

TUNA SALAD WITH SOUR-CREAM HORSERADISH SAUCE

Shredded lettuce or other greens
2 cans (7 ounces each) tuna, flaked
1 cup dairy sour cream
1 teaspoon fresh lemon juice
2 teaspoons sugar
½ teaspoon salt
½ teaspoon powdered mustard
2 teaspoons prepared horseradish
2 eggs, hard-cooked
Paprika
Dill pickles
Cherry tomatoes

Arrange lettuce on serving dish. Arrange tuna in center. Mix sour cream, lemon juice, sugar, salt, mustard, horseradish, and finely chopped egg whites. Pour over fish. Sprinkle top with finely chopped egg yolks, and paprika. Garnish with dill pickle wedges and tomatoes. Makes 6 servings.

GREEN BEANS WITH HORSERADISH SAUCE

1 tablespoon butter
2 tablespoons all-purpose flour
Salt and pepper to taste
1 cup milk
3 tablespoons prepared horseradish
2½ cups (one 1-pound, 4-ounce can) cut green beans, drained

Melt butter in a saucepan. Stir in flour, salt, and pepper; blend. Gradually stir in milk; cook over low heat, stirring constantly, until thickened. Add horseradish and drained beans. Heat quickly. Serve with beef, lamb, or veal. Makes 4 servings.

HOT CAKE—This is another term for a griddle cake, pancake, flannel cake, or flapjack. It is a thin, golden-brown cake, always served hot and with butter, syrup, corn syrup, jelly, jam, or honey.

HUBBARD SQUASH—A large winter squash, with a thick, hard, and warty skin. The plant is a long running vine with compound tendrils and large round leaves. There are several varieties, such as the Green, Blue, or Golden Hubbard. Some of them, like the Blue Hubbard, grow so large that they are sold in pieces or sections.

Squash, and its first cousin the pumpkin, are vegetables of American origin.

Availability and Purchasing Guide—Fresh squash is available from late August to March. It is also available canned and frozen.

Look for fresh squash with hard warted rind free from blemishes. Avoid squash with watery spots.

Storage—Will keep well for months in a dry cool place at temperature of about 50°F. For long storage, select squash which are unbruised and have stem attached.

☐ Refrigerator shelf, uncut: 4 to 6 months

☐ Refrigerator shelf, cooked: 4 to 5 days

☐ Refrigerator frozen-food compartment, cooked and prepared for freezing: 2 to 3 months

☐ Freezer, cooked and prepared for freezing: 1 year

Nutritive Food Values—Excellent source of vitamin A, ½ cup providing more than a day's quota. Contains a fair amount of iron and riboflavin.

☐ 3½ ounces, raw = 39 calories

Basic Preparation—Wash thoroughly. Cut into serving pieces or pieces small enough to handle. A large knife and a mallet are useful. Remove seeds and stringy portion. Peel if desired.

☐ **To Cook**—Use 1 inch of boiling salted water and cook, covered, for 25 to 30 minutes. Remove from rind with a spoon and mash, adding seasonings and butter, or serve in individual pieces with rind.

☐ **To Bake**—Season with salt and pepper. Put a small piece of butter in each piece of squash; add a little honey, if desired. Bake, covered, in preheated moderate oven (375°F.) for 45 to 60 minutes.

☐ **To Freeze**—Use firm squash. Wash, cut into pieces, and remove seeds. Cover with water and cook until tender. Remove rind and press pulp through a sieve. Cool. Pack in containers, leaving ½-inch headspace. Seal.

SQUASH CASSEROLE

2 cups mashed cooked Hubbard squash
4 tablespoons butter or margarine
3 tablespoons brown sugar
1 tablespoon prepared mustard
1 egg, slightly beaten
Salt and pepper to taste
½ cup crushed corn flakes or corn-flake crumbs

Mix squash with 2 tablespoons each butter and brown sugar, the mustard, egg, and salt and pepper. Put in shallow 1-quart baking dish or 9-inch pie pan. Mix corn flakes with remaining butter and brown sugar and sprinkle on top. Bake in preheated moderate oven (350°F.) for 20 minutes, or until thoroughly heated. Makes 4 to 6 servings.

SQUASH BAKED IN SHELLS

3 pounds Hubbard squash
Butter or margarine
2 tablespoons minced onion
2 slices of bread
1 egg
1 teaspoon salt
⅛ teaspoon pepper
Fine cracker crumbs

Remove seeds and stringy portion, and cut squash in 2- to 3-inch pieces. Put in baking pan, and top each piece with a little butter. Bake in preheated moderate oven (350°F.) for 1 hour, or until tender. Scoop out squash, keeping shells intact. Mash squash. Cook onion lightly in 2 tablespoons butter. Add squash. Dip bread in water, squeeze dry, and add to squash. Cook over low heat, stirring frequently, for 15 minutes. Stir in egg and seasonings. Pile lightly in reserved shells and sprinkle with crumbs. Dot with butter and bake in preheated moderate oven (350°F.) for 15 minutes, or until golden-brown. Makes 6 servings.

SQUASH PATTIES

Use cold leftover mashed Hubbard squash. Shape in flat cakes, dip in slightly beaten egg, and roll in fine dry bread crumbs. Sauté in hot margarine until browned on both sides.

SQUASH MUFFINS

2 cups sifted all-purpose flour
2 teaspoons baking powder
2 tablespoons sugar
¾ teaspoon salt
1 egg, beaten
⅔ cup milk
1 tablespoon cooking oil
1 cup strained cooked Hubbard squash

Sift dry ingredients into bowl. Mix egg and remaining ingredients, and add all at once to first mixture. Stir only enough to dampen dry ingredients. Fill greased muffin cups half full with the mixture, and bake in preheated very hot oven (450°F.) for 15 to 20 minutes. Makes 16 medium-size muffins.

COMPANY SQUASH PIE

1 cup strained cooked Hubbard squash
1 cup heavy cream
1 cup sugar
3 eggs, slightly beaten
2 tablespoons brandy
1 teaspoon each cinnamon and nutmeg
½ teaspoon ginger
½ teaspoon salt
Unbaked 9-inch pie shell

Mix all ingredients, except pie shell. Pour into shell and bake in preheated moderate oven (375°F.) for about 45 minutes, or until firm. Cool before serving.

HUCKLEBERRY

HUCKLEBERRY—An edible berry of the species *Gaylussacia,* and the shrub of the same name. The huckleberry is dark blue to black in color and is found growing from the tropics to the arctic. There are a number of varieties, growing on low or high bushes and in an acid soil. The bushes are very prolific, and they can take over a neglected field.

In many parts of the United States the term huckleberry is also applied indiscriminately to blueberries, which belong to the genus Vaccinium, but a huckleberry is more acid than a blueberry, and each huckleberry contains ten hard little seeds, whereas a blueberry has a larger number of seeds so minute they are hardly noticeable.

Availability—June, July, and August, usually sold locally since they do not ship well.

Purchasing Guide—Select clean, plump, and dry berries with a deep-black or dark-blue color. Berries may have a light bloom; this varies with the species.
□ 1 pint = about 2 cups berries

Storage—Sort first if necessary, but do not wash until ready to use.
□ Kitchen shelf: 1 to 2 days
□ Refrigerator shelf: 1 to 2 weeks
□ Refrigerator frozen-food compartment, prepared for freezing: 2 to 3 months
□ Freezer, prepared for freezing: 1 year

Caloric Value

□ 3½ ounces = 62 calories

Basic Preparation—Wash berries gently just before using. Do not allow berries to soak in water. Remove any stems. Serve huckleberries with cream or milk. Use to make jam, in tarts, puddings, and pies, and in any recipe calling for blueberries.

□ **To Freeze**—Wash berries in cold water. Drain. Dip berries into boiling water for 20 to 30 seconds. Chill quickly in cold water.

□ **To Freeze, Loose Pack**—Spread berries in a single layer on a shallow pan with sides or tray. Freeze until firm. Pour into freezer container, leaving no headspace.

□ **To Freeze, Sugar Pack**—Mix 4 cups berries with ½ cup sugar. Stir gently until sugar dissolves. Pack in containers, leaving ½-inch headspace. Seal.

HUCKLEBERRY GRIDDLE CAKES

2 cups unsifted all-purpose flour
2 teaspoons baking powder
½ teaspoon salt
3 tablespoons sugar
1 egg, well beaten
2 cups milk
2 cups washed and well-drained huckleberries, coated lightly with flour

Sift flour with baking powder, salt, and sugar. Beat egg with milk and add all at once to the flour. Beat until smooth. Fold in huckleberries. Bake pancakes on a lightly greased hot griddle. Serve with whipped butter and honey, if desired. Makes 4 to 6 servings.

HUCKLEBERRY SHORTCAKE

4 cups sifted all-purpose flour
4 teaspoons baking powder
1 teaspoon salt
½ cup butter or margarine
2 eggs
1¼ cups milk
4 cups washed and well-drained huckleberries
Sugar
Grated orange rind

Sift flour with baking powder and salt. Cut in butter until mixture resembles coarse cornmeal. Beat egg with milk and add all at once to the flour mixture. Stir only until just blended. Place dough on a lightly floured board and knead a few times to form dough into a smooth ball. Cut dough into halves and roll each half into a rectangle 12 x 8 inches. Place one oblong on a well-greased cookie sheet.

Mix huckleberries with sugar and orange rind and spread on dough, making a layer of berries about ¾ inch thick. Moisten outside edges of rectangle with water. Top with second rectangle and pinch edges to seal. Bake in preheated moderate oven (350°F.) for 30 to 40 minutes, or until top is deeply browned. Cut into squares and serve with thick cream. Makes 10 to 12 servings.

HUCKLEBERRY COTTAGE PUDDING

¼ cup butter or margarine
⅔ cup sugar
1 egg, slightly beaten
2 cups all-purpose flour
3 teaspoons baking powder
¼ teaspoon salt
1 cup huckleberries, washed
1 cup milk
Lemon Hard Sauce, see page 878

Cream butter until light and fluffy. Add sugar and beat until light. Add egg and beat well. Sift dry ingredients; sprinkle ¼ cup of mixture on berries. Add remainder alternately with milk to first mixture, beating until smooth. Fold in berries. Bake in greased pan (8 x 8 x 2 inches) in preheated moderate oven (350° F.) for about 35 minutes. Serve hot with Lemon Hard Sauce. Makes 6 large or 9 small servings.

HUCKLEBERRY CREAM-CHEESE PIE

1½ cups fresh huckleberries
12 ounces cream cheese
1 tablespoon all-purpose flour
3 egg yolks
2 egg whites
3 tablespoons sugar
½ teaspoon salt
¾ cup dairy sour cream
Pastry for 1-crust 8-inch pie, unbaked

Rinse huckleberries in colander and let drain thoroughly, or dry on paper towels. With fork stir softened cream cheese until smooth. Add flour and mix thoroughly. Lightly beat egg yolks with 1 egg white; add sugar, salt, and sour cream. Combine egg mixture with cream-cheese mixture, stirring well. Line 8-inch pie pan with pastry and brush lightly with remaining egg white. Dust huckleberries lightly with flour and place in thick layer in pastry-lined pan. Smooth cream-cheese mixture evenly over huckleberries and bake in preheated moderate oven (350°F.) for 30 minutes, or until set. Makes 6 servings.

HUNGARIAN COOKERY

The incomparable cuisine
of Hungary,
from goulash to apple strudel,
is an expression of
people who care greatly
for excellent food.

by Nika Hazelton

Hungary is a country blessed with an original and delicious cookery of her own, developed and refined by a people who care greatly for excellent food.

Hungary lies at the crossroads of West and East. Through the centuries, many people crossed, fought, and settled in the lands of the Magyars, which is the name the Hungarians use for themselves. The Magyars came from the distant slopes of the eastern part of the Ural Mountains, in what is now Russia, as long ago as 896 A.D., and founded their state on the banks of the Danube. Turks, Slovaks, Serbs, Croats, Poles, Slovenes, Russians, Germans, and Austrians mingled in Hungary in the centuries that followed and contributed to the Hungarian kitchen and to the country's food habits and traditions.

The Turkish conquest of Hungary in the 16th and 17th centuries left a lasting influence, for the Turks introduced coffee, melons, spices, nuts, and, above all, the use of paprika.

But strains from even farther away can be found in Hungarian cooking. Through the centuries, the cooks brought by the princes and princesses who married Hungary's royalty introduced new ways of cooking and seasoning. The influence of the courts of France and Austria was especially marked since the Hungarians adopted their ways with enthusiasm, as we see in the old Hungarian cook books which are full of French cooking terms. In their turn, these foreign recipes were translated into dishes that are still part and parcel of present-day Hungarian cooking, such as the meats and fish dishes cooked with wine, the use of fruit, etc. To Austrian influences goes some of the credit for Hungary's excellent dumplings and superlative cakes, to which the Hungarians added their own twist, such as filling strudel dough with ground poppy seed.

Another factor that contributed to the excellence of Hungarian food was the resources of the country. In the warm yet temperate climate, fruits and vegetables grow to rare lusciousness. The plains yielded tender beef and lamb, the farmyards fattened pigs into famous hams and pork products, and fattened geese and ducks as well. Hungarian goose liver is comparable to the renowned goose liver of Alsace. The deep forests abounded in game, including wild boar, and hunting was a favorite sport. Hungary has no access to the sea, but the trout of her mountain streams and, above all, the unrivaled *fogas,* a very white and extremely delicate kind of perch-pike found in beautiful Lake Balaton, is famous throughout Europe. And finally, the wheat of the great Hungarian plains was considered the finest for baking. In the old days, European cook books specified that fine baking required Hungarian flour.

The most typical ingredients of Hungarian cooking are paprika powder, onions, green peppers, tomatoes, sour cream, lard or goose fat, instead of other shortenings, noodles and other pastas.

The Hungarian housewife does not use paprika as a garnish the way we do, but by the tea- or tablespoonfuls as an integral part of a meat, soup, or vegetable dish, to give it flavor and a rosy color.

The color of paprika is a fiery-red, but the spice itself need not be any hotter than pepper, if as hot. This spice with the exquisite aroma and mildly pungent taste is made from the capsicum pepper, which grows especially well on Hungarian soil. The ground spice is produced from special pepper varieties which are grown for the purpose and widely exported. There are many degrees of pungency in the spice, ranging from the hottest to the mildest, and they are graded according to government specifications. It is important that paprika, whatever its degree of pungency, be used as freshly ground as possible, when fragrance is most enticing. In fact, Hungarian paprika, called "noble and sweet" by the people, has a fragrance unmatched by the paprika of any other country. In cooking, it should not be added to the sizzling fat, but rather to the dish, one school of cooks says. And of course, hot or mild paprika, and the grades in between, are a matter of individual preference, in Hungary as well as anywhere else.

Other Hungarian food specialties whose fame has spread are the sausages, Herz salami, quite possibly the best dry salami ever made, and *tarhonya,* a kneaded dough of flour and eggs which is broken into pieces the size of small peas. The paste is then dried quite hard, so that it will keep for a long time. *Tarhonya* can be cooked in water or broth like noodles and served like them as an accompaniment with gravy dishes, or browned first in lard with minced onions and paprika and then simmered in as much liquid as it will absorb.

When it comes to noodles, the Hungarians use them often in an original manner combined with cottage cheese, nuts, or poppy seeds. Some noodle dishes are sugared and used as desserts.

The most famous Hungarian desserts are dumplings filled with fresh fruit, pancakes, and strudels. Every kind of fruit and nuts is used for strudel fillings, and there are also nonsweet ones, such as cabbage and cheese.

Among the many delicious fruits grown in Hungary which are liberally used by all of the population fresh, as compotes, or in jams, special mention must be made of the apricots. They are exquisite in flavor and either as fruit or distilled into brandy, they are delicious.

SOUPS

GULYÁSLEVES
(Goulash Soup)
    3 medium onions, chopped
    2 tablespoons butter or margarine
1½ pounds beef chuck, cut into ½-inch
      cubes
    2 tablespoons paprika
  ½ teaspoon caraway seeds
    1 garlic clove, crushed
  ½ teaspoon grated lemon rind
    4 cups beef bouillon
      Salt to taste
    2 medium potatoes, peeled and cut
      into ½-inch cubes

Cook onions in butter until golden. Add beef and paprika and cook, stirring constantly, until slightly browned. Add caraway, garlic, lemon rind, and bouillon. Season to taste. Simmer, covered, for 1½ hours. Add potato and cook for 30 minutes longer. Makes 4 to 6 servings.

SÓSKA LEVES
(Sorrel Soup)
  ½ pound sorrel
    4 cups chicken consommé
    2 egg yolks
    2 tablespoons heavy cream
      Salt and white pepper
    1 cup dairy sour cream

Clean sorrel and chop into fine pieces. Cook for 10 minutes in consommé. Mix egg yolks and cream and add slowly to soup, beating constantly with wire whisk. Season to taste. Cool, then chill in refrigerator. Just before serving, beat in sour cream, and top with a spoonful of the sour cream. Makes 4 servings.
Note: To serve hot, beat in sour cream and heat gently.

KÖMÉNY LEVES
(Caraway Soup)
    6 cups water
    1 teaspoon salt
    2 tablespoons caraway seeds
    3 tablespoons bacon fat or butter
  ¼ cup all-purpose flour
    1 egg yolk
  ½ cup dairy sour cream
    6 slices of roll, toasted

Bring water to boil. Add salt and caraway and simmer for 20 minutes. Strain soup through fine sieve. Blend fat or butter with flour. Blend with some of the soup, return to soup, and bring to boil. Beat egg yolk with sour cream;

add a little of the soup to it. Remove soup from heat and beat mixture into it. Serve with a slice of toasted roll in each soup plate. Makes 6 servings.

MEAT, FISH, AND POULTRY

MAGYAR GULYÁS
(Hungarian Goulash)

2 pounds lean beef chuck, cut into 1½-inch squares
Salt and pepper to taste
¼ pound lard or sweet butter
1 to 1½ pounds onions, sliced
2 tablespoons sweet paprika or
1 tablespoon hot paprika
1 tablespoon flour
Hot water or dry white wine
2 cups dairy sour cream

Season meat with salt and pepper. Heat lard almost to smoking point in heavy saucepan. Brown meat in it on all sides. Add onions. Stir in paprika; there should be enough paprika to color meat and onions a reddish brown. Over low heat cook, stirring, until all the pan juices have been absorbed. Sprinkle with flour and cook for 1 minute. Add hot water or wine to cover meat. Simmer, covered, over low heat for 1 to 1½ hours, until meat is tender and the onions have cooked down to a pulp. Check occasionally for liquid; if necessary, add a little more. Stir in sour cream and heat through but do not boil. Serve with buttered noodles sprinkled with caraway seeds. Makes 4 to 6 servings.

MAJORANNÁS TOKÁNY
(Beef Stew with Marjoram)

2 pounds beef chuck or round, in one piece
2 tablespoons lard
1 pound (3 medium) onions, coarsely chopped
2 teaspoons ground marjoram
Salt
Pepper (there should be quite a lot of pepper)
2 cups water
1½ cups dry white wine
½ pound lean bacon
1 cup dairy sour cream

Cut beef into strips 1 x 3 inches. Heat lard in Dutch oven to smoking point. Cook onion in hot lard until soft and golden. Add meat. Sprinkle with marjoram and season to taste with salt and pepper. Add water and wine. Simmer, covered, over lowest possible heat for 45 minutes, or until half done. While meat is cooking, cut bacon into strips the same size as the meat. Cook bacon partially until limp and until most of the grease has cooked out. Drain bacon and add to meat. Continue to simmer, covered, for 45 minutes longer, or until meat is tender. Remove from heat and stir in sour

cream. Return to heat; heat through but do not boil again. Serve with rice or noodles. Makes 4 to 6 servings.

SAVANYU ÖKÖRFAROK
(Sour Oxtail Ragout)

2 oxtails, disjointed
½ cup cider vinegar
1 onion
1 carrot
1 garlic clove
Grated rind of 1 lemon
2 bay leaves
2 whole cloves
6 peppercorns
½ teaspoon salt
Boiling water
2 tablespoons fat
2 tablespoons all-purpose flour
¼ cup dairy sour cream
Paprika

In a large saucepan combine oxtails with vinegar, onion, carrot, and seasonings. Cover with boiling water and cook, covered, over low heat until meat is tender. Drain, and reserve 1 cup liquid. Melt fat and stir in flour. Gradually stir in liquid from meat. Cook over low heat, stirring constantly, until smooth and thickened. Add oxtail pieces. Just before serving, stir in sour cream and sprinkle with paprika. Makes 6 servings.

BORJÚ PÖRKÖLT
(Veal Paprika)

2 pounds veal cutlet, sliced thin
2 tablespoons butter or margarine
1 garlic clove, minced
1 tablespoon sweet paprika
1 cup water
1 cup heavy cream
½ teaspoon salt

Pound veal well. Pat dry with absorbent paper. Melt butter. Brown veal quickly with garlic and paprika. Add water, cover, and simmer for 1 hour. Add cream and salt. Heat through, and serve. Makes 4 to 6 servings.

DISZNÓKARAJ MAGYAROSAN
(Hungarian Pork Chops)

6 pork chops, about ½ inch thick
Salt and pepper
1 medium onion, chopped
1 garlic clove, minced
3 tablespoons lard or butter
1 bay leaf
¾ cup chicken bouillon
1 cup dairy sour cream
2 teaspoons paprika

Trim excess fat from pork chops and sprinkle chops with salt and pepper. Sauté onion and garlic in lard until soft and golden. Push aside or remove from skillet. Add pork chops and brown on all sides. Pour off fat. Lower heat and add bay leaf and bouillon. Cook, covered, over low heat for about 1 hour. Transfer chops to hot serving plate and keep hot. Reduce pan juices to half by cooking over high heat. Add sour cream and paprika and blend thoroughly with pan juices. Heat through, but do not boil. Pour sauce over chops. Makes 4 to 6 servings.

BÁRÁNY PÖRKÖLT ÁRPAKÁSÁVAL
(Lamb and Barley Stew)

2 pounds lamb shoulder, cut up and trimmed of excess fat
Flour
Salt and pepper to taste
2 tablespoons cooking oil
1 cup chopped onions
4 medium tomatoes, quartered
2 bay leaves
2 tablespoons pearl barley
6 dried prunes, pitted
1 garlic clove, minced
1 teaspoon sweet paprika
1 cup water or bouillon
2 tablespoons sweet or dairy sour cream (optional)

Coat lamb pieces evenly with flour mixed with salt and pepper. Brown on all sides in oil in heavy skillet or Dutch oven. Add onions and cook until onions are soft but not brown. Add all other ingredients except cream. Cover and simmer over low heat for 1½ to 2 hours; or bake in very slow oven (250°F.) for 3 to 4 hours. (This stew should cook as slowly as possible.) Check for moisture; if too dry, add a little more water or bouillon, 1 tablespoon at a time. Remove from heat and stir in cream. Do not cook again. Makes 4 to 6 servings.

HÉT VEZÉR TOKÁNY
(Seven Chieftains' Tokany)

2 tablespoons lard
4 slices of bacon
½ pound onions, sliced
1 tablespoon paprika
1 pound lean boneless pork, cut into strips 3 x 1 inch
1 pound beef chuck or round cut into strips 3 x 1 inch
1 pound boneless veal cut into strips 3 x 1 inch
1 cup water
2 green peppers cut into strips
2 small tomatoes, peeled, seeded, and chopped
Salt and pepper
½ cup dairy sour cream
1 tablespoon flour

Heat lard in Dutch oven. Cook bacon until limp. Remove bacon and cut into strips; reserve. Cook onions in hot fat until soft and golden-brown. Stir in paprika. Cook for 2 minutes. Add pork. Simmer, covered, over low heat for 30 minutes. Add beef and veal and simmer for 45 minutes. Add a little hot water, about 1 cup, to prevent sticking. Add green peppers, tomatoes, salt and pepper to taste, and bacon. Simmer, covered, for 20 minutes, or until peppers are tender, stirring occasionally. Combine sour cream and flour to a smooth paste. Stir into stew. Simmer over low heat for 4 minutes, stirring constantly. Serve with steamed rice or noodles. Makes 6 to 8 servings.

Note: Hungarians often combine different meats in their stews for a tastier effect. The seven chieftains are national heroes who led the Magyars to the present country in the 9th century.

SZÉKELY GULYÁS
(Szekely Sauerkraut Goulash)
1 pound boneless beef chuck
1 pound boneless veal shoulder
½ pound lean pork
2 small onions, sliced
2 teaspoons butter
1 pound sauerkraut
  A few peppercorns
2 teaspoons paprika
1 teaspoon caraway seeds
1 cup bouillon
2 cups dairy sour cream

Cut the meat into cubes as you would for any stew. Cook the onions in butter to golden-yellow. Add meat, sauerkraut, peppercorns, paprika, caraway seeds, and bouillon. Cook, covered, for about 1 hour in an ordinary pan, or in a pressure cooker for about 15 minutes at 15-pound pressure. Very slowly pour the juice from the cooking pan into a dish with the sour cream, stirring all the while so it will not curdle. Thicken with a little flour, if necessary. Pour the mixture back into the pan and let it stand on an asbestos pad over low heat until used. It improves with waiting and can be reheated. The use of salt depends on taste and on the saltiness of the sauerkraut. If the kraut is too salty, wash it. Makes 5 or 6 servings.

SONKÁS PALACSINTA
(Pancakes Layered with Minced Ham)
1 cup cold milk
1 cup cold water
4 eggs
1 teaspoon salt
2 cups sifted all-purpose flour
¼ cup melted butter or margarine
  Ham Filling
¼ cup buttered bread crumbs

Beat together milk, water, eggs, and salt. Add flour gradually, beating constantly until smooth. Add melted butter. The consistency should be that of heavy cream. Refrigerate for at least 1 hour before baking pancakes. Lightly grease a 7-inch crêpe pan or skillet, heat to smoking, and pour in just enough of the batter to coat the bottom lightly. Tilt pan to be sure that all is covered. Brown lightly on one side. Turn and brown on the other. Put one pancake in a baking dish, spread some of the Ham Filling on it, then top with another pancake. Keep warm in slow oven (300°F.). Continue layering in this manner until all pancakes (about 12) and Ham Filling are used. Sprinkle top with buttered bread crumbs. Bake in preheated moderate oven (350° F.) for 20 minutes, until filling is set. Cut into wedges to serve. Makes 8 servings.

Ham Filling
1 pound cooked ham, minced
4 eggs, separated
1 cup dairy sour cream
  Salt

Mix ham, egg yolks, and sour cream.

Beat egg whites until stiff. Fold into mixture. Season to taste.

CSIRKE PAPRIKÁS
(Chicken Paprika with Sour Cream)
1 frying chicken (about 3 pounds), cut into pieces
2 medium onions, chopped fine
2 tablespoons sweet paprika
3 tablespoons butter or margarine
½ cup chicken bouillon
1 cup dairy sour cream
  Salt and pepper

Brown chicken, onions, and paprika in the butter. Add bouillon. Simmer, covered, over low heat for 30 minutes, or until tender. Stir in sour cream and heat through. Season to taste. Makes 4 servings.

SZEGEDI CSIRKE PAPRIKÁS
(Chicken Stew)
3 tablespoons lard
4 large onions, sliced
1 tablespoon sweet paprika
1 teaspoon caraway seeds, crushed
2 frying chickens (about 3 pounds each), cut into pieces
  Salt
3 cups water
1 pound potatoes, peeled and quartered
3 medium carrots, thickly sliced
3 cups canned tomatoes
  Pepper

Heat lard in Dutch oven. When smoking hot, add onions. Cook until soft and golden-brown. Add paprika, caraway seeds, and chicken pieces. Toss and cook over medium heat for 5 to 10 minutes, or until chickens are golden-brown. Sprinkle with salt. Add water. Simmer, covered, over lowest possible heat for 30 minutes, or until chicken is half done. Add potatoes, carrots, and canned tomatoes. Season to taste with salt and pepper. Continue to simmer, covered, for 30 minutes longer, or until chicken and vegetables are tender. Serve with buttered *tarhonya* or buttered noodles and a green salad. Makes 6 servings.

TEJFELES SÜLT PONTY
(Pike Baked in Cream)
2 pounds pike fillets
1 teaspoon caraway seeds
½ teaspoon salt
½ cup fine dried bread crumbs
1 cup dairy sour cream

Place ⅓ of fish in greased baking dish. Sprinkle with ⅓ of caraway seeds, salt, bread crumbs, and sour cream. Repeat until all ingredients are used. Bake in preheated slow oven (325°F.) for 20 to 30 minutes, or until fish is flaky. Makes 4 servings.

VEGETABLES, PASTAS, AND SALADS

RAKOTT KRUMPLI
(Potato and Egg Casserole)
6 slices of bacon, chopped

1 tablespoon butter
6 medium potatoes, boiled and sliced
6 hard-cooked eggs, sliced
  Salt and pepper
2 tablespoons chopped parsley
½ to ⅔ cup dairy sour cream

Cook bacon in hot butter until crisp. Drain; reserve fat. Place alternate layers of potatoes, hard-cooked eggs, and bacon in greased 2-quart baking dish. Season each layer with salt and pepper to taste, but remember that bacon may be very salty. Sprinkle with parsley. Stir reserved bacon fat into sour cream. Pour over potato mixture. Bake, covered, in preheated moderate oven (350°F.) for 15 to 20 minutes, or until golden. Makes 4 servings.

TEJFELES BAFFŐZELÉK
(Dried Beans in Sour Cream)
½ pound dried white beans, washed
  Salt
1 medium onion, chopped fine
2 tablespoons butter or margarine
2 tablespoons flour
1 tablespoon vinegar
1 cup water
½ cup dairy sour cream

Soak beans in water overnight. Drain. Cover with fresh water, add 1 teaspoon salt, and simmer for 2 to 3 hours, or until tender. Brown onion in butter; blend in flour. Add vinegar and water, and stir until thickened. Drain beans when done and mix into sauce. Stir in sour cream and allow to heat through but do not boil. Season to taste. Makes 4 to 6 servings.

ZELLER SALÁTA
(Celery-Root Salad)
3 celery roots
  Boiling salted water
  Salt, pepper, and mayonnaise

Peel celery root and cut into julienne strips. Drop into boiling salted water and cook for 15 to 20 minutes, until tender. Cool. Season with salt, pepper, and mayonnaise to taste. Chill for 2 hours. Makes 6 servings.

ZÖLD PAPRIKA SALÁTA
(Green-Pepper Salad)
4 large green peppers
½ cup olive oil
2 to 4 tablespoons vinegar, depending on strength (dressing should be mild)
  Salt and pepper to taste
½ teaspoon sugar

Remove seeds and inside ribs of peppers. Cut into ½-inch slices. Drop for 1 minute into boiling water. Drain. Place in glass serving dish. Make a French dressing with remaining ingredients. Pour over peppers. Marinate at room temperature for 1 hour. Serve as is or chilled. Makes 4 servings.

TARHONYA
(Egg Barley)
4 cups all-purpose flour
5 eggs
1 teaspoon salt

Sift flour. Make a well in the center. Break eggs into well and mix together with the flour. Add salt. Knead dough until it is perfectly smooth. Allow to dry a little. Chop with a knife until pieces resemble barley in size. Or press through a special sieve which will make pieces of the same size. Spread pieces out and allow to dry for 24 hours. Store in jars with tight lids. To cook, brown *tarhonya* lightly in butter; then add water to cover and simmer for 15 minutes. Or, if it is to be served in a soup, it can be cooked in that without browning.

DIÓS TÉSZTA
(Boiled Noodles with Walnuts)

- 8 ounces fine noodles
- ½ cup chopped walnuts
- 2 tablespoons butter or margarine

Cook noodles in salted water according to package directions. Drain. Meantime, sauté walnuts in butter until lightly browned. Add to drained noodles. Place in top part of double boiler over hot water for 30 minutes before serving to meld the flavors. Makes 4 servings.

Makos Tészta
(Boiled Noodles with Poppy Seeds)

Cook noodles as above. Drain. Toss with ¼ cup butter and 2 tablespoons ground poppy seeds. Omit nuts. Or, substitute 1 tablespoon caraway seeds for the poppy seeds. Omit nuts.

DESSERTS

SZILVÁS GOMBÓC
(Plum Dumplings)

- 12 plums
  Almond extract
- 12 small lumps of sugar
- ⅓ cup butter
- 2 cups sifted all-purpose flour
- 2 cups cooked potatoes, riced and chilled
- 1 teaspoon salt
- 2 eggs
- 2 tablespoons butter
- ¾ cup fine dry bread crumbs

Cut plums just enough to remove pits. Keep fruit as intact as possible. Sprinkle a drop of almond extract on each lump of sugar. Push 1 sugar lump into cavity of each fruit. With pastry cutter or two knives, cut butter into flour until it resembles coarse meal. Stir in potatoes and salt. Add eggs and mix thoroughly. With hands work dough until smooth. On slightly floured board roll out dough to ¼-inch thickness. Cut into 3- or 4-inch squares, depending on size of fruit. Place a plum on each square. Moisten edges of dough and fold dough over fruit. Pinch edges together. With floured hands roll dumplings into round balls. Cook a few at a time in kettle of gently boiling water. The water must continue to boil. Cook for 10 to 15 minutes, depending on size. Carefully lift out with slotted spoon and keep warm. Heat butter and brown crumbs in it. Roll dumplings in buttered crumbs. Serve hot. Makes 6 servings.

Savanyu Ökörfarok   *Diós Tészta*

■ **Variation** — Use apricots instead of plums.

CSERESZNYE KISÜTVE
(Deep-Fried Cherries)

    1 cup sifted all-purpose flour
    ¼ cup sugar
    ½ teaspoon ground cinnamon
    ⅓ cup milk
    ½ cup dry white wine
    3 eggs, lightly beaten
    1 pound ripe firm sweet cherries,
        with stems
        Shortening for deep frying
        Confectioners' sugar

Combine flour, sugar, and cinnamon. Stir in milk and wine to make a smooth paste. Beat in eggs. Let batter rest for 30 minutes. Tie 4 or 5 cherries into clusters with thread. Dip each cluster into batter, making sure cherries are well coated. Carefully lower clusters into hot deep fat (370°F. on frying thermometer). When browned, remove with slotted spoon. Cook only a few clusters at one time. Drain on absorbent paper and sprinkle with confectioners' sugar. Serve immediately. Serve 1 or 2 clusters for each individual helping.

ALMÁSRÉTES
(Apple Strudel)

Strudel Dough:

    1 egg, slightly beaten
    ½ teaspoon salt
        Cooking oil
    1 cup unsifted all-purpose flour
        Butter
        Sugar

Apple Filling:

    ¼ cup seedless raisins
        Water
    6 to 8 medium apples
        Sugar
    ¾ cup fine soft bread crumbs
    ⅓ cup butter
    ½ cup chopped blanched almonds
    1 tablespoon ground cinnamon

Mix egg, salt, 2 tablespoons oil, and the flour. Add 1 tablespoon warm water and mix to form soft dough. On lightly floured board knead for 10 to 15 minutes, or until dough is very smooth and very elastic. Brush top with oil and cover with a warm bowl. Let stand for 30 minutes. Soak raisins in 2 tablespoons water. Peel apples, slice thin, and sprinkle with ½ cup sugar. Brown crumbs in ⅓ cup butter. Roll strudel dough as thin as possible on a large lightly floured cloth, (about 36 inches square). Melt ½ cup butter and brush some on top of dough. With palms up, slip hands underneath dough and stretch dough carefully to paper thinness, working from the center out. If edges remain thick, cut them off. Dough should almost cover the cloth. Brush with more melted butter to keep pliable. Pile apples in a row about 2 inches from one end of dough. Combine undrained raisins, bread crumbs, almonds, cinnamon, and ½ cup sugar; spread over remaining dough. Fold over the dough about 1 inch along the edges of dough at the top and bottom of the row of apples. Lift edges of cloth nearest the apples so that the dough falls

Sóska Leves   *Sonkás Palacsinta*   *Cseresznye Kisütve*

over apples; continue to roll dough over and over with the help of cloth. Put roll on cookie sheet in a U shape. Bake in preheated hot oven (400°F.) for 30 minutes. Brush 2 or 3 times with melted butter. Five minutes before strudel is done, sprinkle thickly with more sugar. Makes 12 3-inch pieces.

Cheese Strudel
Strudel Dough (see recipe page 921)
1 tablespoon butter
¼ cup sugar
4 eggs
1 pound cottage cheese, sieved
3 tablespoons dairy sour cream
⅓ cup seedless raisins
2 tablespoons melted butter

Prepare dough as for Apple Strudel. Cream butter with sugar. Beat in eggs. Mix in cottage cheese, sour cream, and raisins. Spread mixture evenly over the dough which has been brushed with melted butter. Bake as for Apple Strudel.

Nut Strudel
Strudel Dough (see recipe page 921)
1 cup ground nuts
1 cup sugar
½ cup milk
Grated rind of 1 lemon
½ cup yellow raisins
2 tablespoons melted butter

Prepare dough as for Apple Strudel. Mix nuts with sugar and milk. Cook over low heat until mixture is slightly thickened. Add lemon rind and raisins. Spread filling on strudel dough which has been brushed with melted butter. Bake as for Apple Strudel.

Cherry Strudel
Strudel Dough (see recipe page 921)
2 tablespoons melted butter
½ cup dry bread crumbs
½ cup ground blanched almonds
1½ cups dark sweet cherries, pitted
1 cup sugar
¼ cup dairy sour cream

Prepare dough as for Apple Strudel. Brush with melted butter and sprinkle with bread crumbs and almonds. Scatter cherries over the dough and sprinkle with sugar. Roll up and brush with sour cream. Bake as for Apple Strudel.

Cabbage Strudel
3½ cups grated cabbage
1 tablespoon salt
1½ tablespoons sugar
2 tablespoons fat
½ teaspoon white pepper
Strudel Dough (see page 921)
2 tablespoons melted butter

Mix cabbage with salt. Let stand for 30 minutes. Squeeze out liquid. Add sugar and cabbage to hot fat and cook until lightly browned and tender. Stir in pepper. Prepare dough as for Apple Strudel. Spread cooled cabbage mixture over the dough which has been brushed with melted butter. Bake as for Apple Strudel.

Poppy-Seed Strudel
Strudel Dough (see page 921)
1 pound freshly ground poppy seeds
½ cup sugar
Grated rind of 1 lemon
½ cup milk
⅓ cup raisins
2 tablespoons melted butter

Prepare dough as for Apple Strudel. Mix poppy seeds with sugar, lemon rind, and milk. Cook over low heat until thickened. Add raisins and blend well. Cool, and then spread on strudel dough which has been brushed with melted butter. Bake as for Apple Strudel.

DIÓS TEKERCS
(Hungarian Walnut Roll)
1 package active dry yeast or 1 cake compressed
½ cup lukewarm water*
4 cups sifted all-purpose flour
½ teaspoon salt
6 egg yolks
¾ cup warm milk
Filling
1 cup chopped walnuts
⅓ cup milk, scalded
2 tablespoons sugar
1 small vanilla bean, grated

Sprinkle dry yeast or crumble cake yeast into warm water. *Use very warm water (105°F. to 115°F.) for dry yeast; use lukewarm water (80°F. to 90°F.) for compressed. Let stand for a few minutes, then stir until dissolved. Place sifted flour and salt in a large mixing bowl; form a well in the center and place in it the yeast, egg yolks, and milk. Gradually incorporate the flour into the other ingredients; knead in bowl until mixture is smooth. Cover and let rest while preparing the Filling. Roll out dough to a rectangle ½ inch thick; spread with Filling and sprinkle with 1 cup chopped walnuts. Roll as for jelly roll. Cut into 1½-inch pieces and place, cut side up, in a buttered ring mold or tube pan. It may be necessary to make 2 layers. Let rise in a warm place until doubled in bulk. Bake in preheated moderate oven (350°F.) for 25 minutes. Remove from oven and pour over ⅓ cup scalded milk mixed with 2 tablespoons sugar and 1 small vanilla bean, grated. Return to oven for 15 minutes longer. Remove from oven and cool on a rack.

Filling
Cream together ¾ cup sugar and ¾ cup sweet butter; add a 1½-inch piece of vanilla bean, grated.

HUSZÁRCSÓK
(Hussar's Kisses)
⅔ cup sweet butter (must be butter and sweet is the best)
⅓ cup sugar
1 egg yolk
2 eggs
1⅓ cups sifted all-purpose flour
⅓ cup finely chopped nuts
⅓ cup raspberry jam

Cream butter with sugar. Add egg yolk

and 1 egg. Blend in flour. Chill. Pinch off walnut-size pieces of dough and shape into balls with floured hands. Put on ungreased cookie sheet. With pencil or finger make a deep depression in center of each ball. Beat remaining egg and brush cookies with it. Sprinkle with nuts. Bake in preheated moderate oven (350°F.) for 15 minutes, or until golden. Cool. Fill depressions with jam. Makes about 32.

HYDROGENATE—Hydrogenation is a process which converts liquid oils into semisolid, malleable fats. Further processing incorporates air or an inert gas, resulting in a solid bland fat (hydrogenated fat) which is soft and creamy in consistency and creamy-white in color. When melted, it has the same keeping quality for successive fryings and the same high smoking point as the original oil. It will not acquire food flavors if foods are properly cooked in it. This hydrogenated fat is sold under many trade names and is excellent both for frying and baking. Corn, cottonseed, and soybean are the oils most frequently used to make hydrogenated vegetable fats. The process of hydrogenation is also employed to better the consistency of animal fats such as lard, in the manufacture of some margarine, and for industrial purposes such as soapmaking.

The importance of the hydrogenation of fats cannot be overemphasized. It is done on an enormous scale, and has made possible the use of vegetable-seed oils as substitutes for the more expensive animal (hog and beef) fats and for butter in cooking and baking.

The first research in hydrogenation was done by French chemists between 1897 and 1905. It was carried on in England, where a process was patented by W. Norman in 1903. An English firm is said to have hydrogenated whale oil in 1906 or earlier.

Today, practically every American producer of shortening oils and margarine uses the hydrogenation process and so do comparable manufacturers throughout the world. Processors of nonedible oils and fats use it, too.

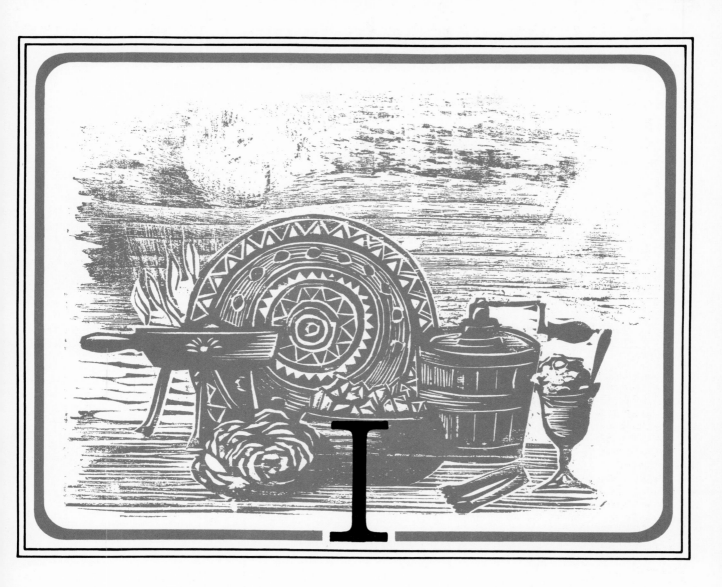

ICE—When water solidifies, it is called ice. Water, like all liquids, when sufficiently cooled becomes solid. The freezing point of water is 32°F. or 0°C. Ice is transparent in color; it is also lighter than water, which accounts for the familiar sight of ice floating on water. Ice is greater in bulk than the corresponding amount of water. It expands almost ten per cent in mass upon freezing.

The verb "to ice" means to cover or to chill or cool with ice. It is also applied to coating, as, a cake, with an icing, although the more common term for this is frosting.

For most household purposes, ice is frozen in the refrigerator frozen-food compartment or freezer in a variety of shapes, generally as ice cubes. Ice for household purposes can also be bought commercially in blocks varying from twelve and a half to 300 pounds, as snow, marbles, cubes, etc.

Today, anyone with a refrigerator can cool drinks with ice. This was not always so; ice has a history as a luxury product. Cooled wines, drunk by Solomon, are mentioned in the Bible. Hippocrates, the early Greek physician, thought cold drinks to be unhealthy. He wrote that "it is dangerous to heat, cool, or make a commotion all of a sudden in the body—let it be done which way it may—because anything that is excessive is an enemy to nature. But for all this, people will not take warning, and most men would rather run the hazard of their lives or health than be deprived the pleasure of drinking out of ice."

In the 1st century A.D., the Roman Emperor Nero sent slaves to the nearby mountains to gather ice for chilling. Pliny the Elder, the famous Roman naturalist, shared Hippocrates' distrust of iced drinks, but for sanitary reasons. He put his drinks in jars in the ice and snow, to prevent contamination.

Another disapproving statement on the practice of chilling by ice was made by Seneca, a Roman philosopher of the same time. His objection was not only on sanitary grounds, but also because of the great trouble and expense. He tells how the snow carried from the mountains was used to pack perishable foods. Snow, packed in chaff or straw pits, solidified into ice and was used to ice drinks. So many slaves had to be sent out to the mountains to gather snow, that it was an expensive practice that only the rich could afford.

A refinement on the packing of snow into pits to turn it to ice was the discovery that boiled water in a container packed in the middle of the snow would turn to ice. In mid-16th century, the Italians, who were the primary drinkers of iced drinks, discovered that saltpeter added to the packing around the container hastened the cooling process.

Experiments in ice-making were common during the 17th century. Francis Bacon, one of the first great English experimental scientists, died in 1626 as a direct result of a cold caught while stuffing a fowl with snow to try to preserve it.

Ice was used and stored in America from early colonial days in the North, where it could be gathered from frozen ponds and streams. The ice business in America started in 1799 when a shipload was sent from New York to South Carolina. Five years later a Boston entrepreneur shipped ice to the West Indies, and shortly afterward another Boston firm introduced ice to the English.

In the 19th century every southern plantation had its own icehouse, and all industrial centers built ice storage houses. The supply of natural ice was limited, however, and it seemed as if ice would end its history as it had begun it, by being a luxury item.

But, from 1755 when Dr. William Cullen of Scotland had attempted to make ice by mechanical means, experimenters had been working on the problem. The 19th-century experimenters who worked on means of mechanical freezing were justifiably proud of their work. One inventor, the Englishman Thomas Masters, wrote in 1844 about the age as an "age of invention." He continued: "Art has, however, not rested content with providing the luxuries and preparing the necessaries of humanity; it has dared to imitate nature in the production of its most wonderful phenomena, and *ice,* once the sole produce of her mighty laboratory, has been made by the skill and enterprise of her subject; man."

By 1870 there were four commercial ice-making plants in the United States. At the end of the century, pressed by the need for ice, the industry expanded rapidly. In 1944, 6,800 plants were producing almost fifty million tons. Today the great growth in mechanical refrigerators and freezers, electric or gas, has turned almost every American home into its own ice-making plant, and coin-operated ice-cube dispensers are found in convenient public locations.

The Uses of Ice in Cookery

■ Ice Cubes—The most popular ice form used is the ice cube which can be frozen in special ice-cube trays at home. Ice cubes may be plain water, water mixed with fruit juices or punches, and double-strength coffee or tea. They can be frozen plain or for decorative use by placing cherries, mint leaves, gumdrops, small pieces of lemon and lime, strawberries and pineapple into the water before freezing.

■ Ice Rings and Blocks—Water, plain or colored with vegetable coloring, may be frozen in ring molds or pans and used to chill large bowls of punch. Flowers, leaves, fruits may be placed on top of the ice or may be frozen into the ice.

To keep ice clear, use boiled cooled water or distilled water for freezing. Freeze ice quickly; when ready to unmold, keep ice mold in the refrigerator for thirty minutes and then remove to room temperature until ice melts slightly. Unmold and place into chilled punch. If ice is subjected to too rapid temperature changes, it will crack.

■ Ice Bowls—An ice bowl may be made by filling a large bowl with water and pressing a smaller bowl into the water. Hold in place with a weight. Tape the bowls together so they will not move during freezing. Freeze until firm. Dip bowls into lukewarm water for a few seconds to loosen ice bowl. Leave the ice bowl in the freezer until ready to fill. Fill with ice cream or chilled fruits or chilled seafood or sherbet. Be sure to use a serving dish under it which can accommodate a certain amount of melting.

■ Shaved Ice—The ice is shaved or crushed finely and used in preparing mint juleps and daiquiris; to chill melon, grapefruit, relishes, shrimp cocktail, vichyssoise, jellied consommé, oysters, clams on the half shell, and other dishes which must be served and eaten icy cold.

Shaved ice is also shaped into cones. Sweet flavored syrup is spooned over it and it is eaten much as one would eat ices.

■ Ice Sculpture—Many restaurants and hotel chefs specialize in ice sculpture of great beauty. However, this is an art in itself which requires years of skill and a cold room in which to work. Simple ice molds can be made using the various metal molds usually used for molding gelatin desserts. Handle and unmold as directed in Ice Rings and Blocks above. Dry ice underneath the mold can prevent its melting during the meal.

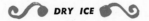

DRY ICE

Dry Ice is the trademarked name of a product made of solidified carbon dioxide. It can burn if touched, and dissipates when it melts. Any room in which Dry Ice is being used should be ventilated. It serves as a refrigerant and is usually available at ice supply houses or from distributors who supply it to manufacturers. Any home owner who stores an appreciable amount of food in a freezer should know who the local suppliers are since, in the event of a power shutdown lasting more than a day or two, dry ice

obtained quickly can be used to prevent the deterioration or spoilage of frozen food.

ICE—The word ice is used to describe a frozen mixture of a fruit juice or purée, a sweetener, and water. Occasionally ices are made with coffee or wine instead of fruit juice. Such mixtures are often called "water ices" to distinguish them from the sherbets, ice creams, and other frozen desserts to which eggs, milk, cream, etc., are added.

Most ices are stirred often during the freezing process so that the finished product has a smooth texture, and they are frozen firm. Frappés are ices frozen only to a mushy consistency and granités are ices which, although frozen firm, are stirred very little so that their texture is rough and icy.

Ices are usually one part sugar to four parts liquid. Ices may be frozen in a refrigerator or freezer, or, for best results, churned in a crank freezer. When ices are not frozen in a crank freezer, they must be stirred every thirty minutes to break up ice crystals and make them smaller. They may also be frozen halfway, then whipped with a beater, and frozen until firm. Ices can be frozen in any kind of container or mold or even in individual molds.

Ices are sold commercially in a variety of flavors, both in bulk and prepackaged containers.

The bright fresh flavor of ices allows them to be served very simply or in elegant style. Place scoops into fruit juices or punches, in fruit cups, on melon wedges, any fresh or canned fruit; ices can be used to fill hollowed-out apples, oranges, grapefruit, drizzled with liqueurs, or topped with candied fruits and nuts.

Flavored ices have been a delicacy from the earliest days. It is thought that the Chinese were the first to perfect this art and that they taught it to the Indians, Persians, and Arabs. It might also be a development of the early Greek and Roman practice of putting ice and snow in their beverages.

Marco Polo, the famous 13th-century Italian voyager to China, brought back reports, if not recipes, of the oriental custom of eating water ices. They became popular, first in Venice and then throughout Italy, from the 14th century on. It is said that Bernard Buontalenti, a 16th-century Italian architect, was the first to manufacture frozen drinks and desserts.

Catherine de Medici helped spread the custom of eating ices. When she came to France in 1533 as a fourteen-year-old bride to marry the future Henry II, she brought with her Italian cooks who knew the secret of ices. The frozen desserts became so popular that Catherine's son, Henry III, is said to have eaten ices every day.

Until 1660, when an Italian cook who was to Gallicize his name into Procope arrived in Paris from Italy, ices were the province solely of the court. When the Café Procope was founded as a place serving ices, the eager Parisians ate the ices to such an extent that soon other restaurateurs were following the lead of the clever Italian. By 1676 there were so many shops that they had to incorporate and the members of the corporation had to be officially authorized to sell their popular products.

In the 18th century the development of ices was rapid. Ices, frozen into fantastic shapes and equally fabulously decorated, were popular desserts at elegant banquets. The late 18th century and the first French Empire set up ices as the height of fashionable elegance.

Some modern versions of ices provide a striking contrast to their royal history. It was in America in 1926 that a California fair concessionaire named Epperson came to New Jersey to visit friends. He left his glass of lemonade, with a spoon in it, on his windowsill one cold day. When he returned he found the lemonade frozen, with the spoon rigid in the middle. Carrying the glass to the bathroom he ran water on it, and the ice came out in a single piece with the spoon frozen in, acting as a handle. He was quick to see the possibilities of his discovery and christened it the "epsicle." Later this was changed to the now famous "popsicle."

APPLE AND GRAPE-JUICE ICE
2 cups apple juice
1 cup grape juice
½ cup light corn syrup
Few grains of salt

Combine ingredients and pour into chilled freezing can of ice-cream freezer; cover. Surround with mixture of 4 parts crushed ice and 1 part rock salt. Turn crank slowly and steadily until turning becomes difficult. Remove dasher; repack in ice and salt. Let stand for at least 1 hour. Makes 1½ quarts.

APRICOT ICE
1 cup sugar
2 cups water
2 cups apricot nectar
¼ cup fresh lemon juice

Combine sugar and water, and cook for 5 minutes. Cool. Stir in apricot nectar and lemon juice. Pour into freezer trays and freeze until almost firm. Remove to bowl, and beat until smooth. Return to

trays and freeze until firm. Makes 4 to 6 servings.

Note: Any nectar can be substituted for the apricot.

CANTALOUPE ICE
4 cups peeled, seeded, ripe cantaloupe, cut into pieces
Juice of 2 lemons
½ cup sugar

Strain cantaloupe through a sieve or whirl in blender. Add lemon juice and sugar. Place in freezing trays and freeze until almost firm. Place in bowl and beat until smooth. Return to trays and freeze until firm. Makes 4 to 6 servings.

FRESH COCONUT ICE
2 large coconuts to yield 6 cups grated coconut and 4¼ cups extracted coconut milk
3½ cups boiling water
½ teaspoon vanilla extract
1 cup coconut water
1 cup sugar
Grated coconut

Crack coconuts and reserve coconut water. Grate; there should be 6 cups grated coconut meat. Pour boiling water over grated coconut. Let stand for 15 minutes. Strain through a triple layer of cheesecloth, squeezing out as much of the milk as possible. Add vanilla, coconut water, and sugar, and stir until sugar is dissolved. Freeze in refrigerator trays or in ice-cream freezer as usual. Serve with additional grated coconut sprinkled on top. Makes 6 to 8 servings.

COFFEE ICE WITH WHIPPED CREAM
1½ cups ground Italian-style coffee
⅓ cup sugar
5 cups boiling water
Whipped cream, sweetened to taste

Combine coffee, sugar, and water in top part of double boiler. Steep over simmering water for 30 minutes. Cool. Strain through a strainer lined with a triple thickness of cheesecloth. Freeze in ice-cube tray until almost firm. Remove to bowl and beat until smooth. Return to trays and freeze until almost firm; the ice should be a little on the mushy side. Spoon into glasses and top with whipped cream. Makes 6 servings.

CURRANT-JELLY AND RASPBERRY ICE
12 sprigs of fresh mint
1 cup currant jelly
1¼ cups boiling water
1 cup fresh raspberries

Cut mint fine, using scissors. Combine with jelly and boiling water; simmer for 5 minutes. Cover and let stand until cold. Strain. Add raspberries. Pour into chilled freezing can of ice-cream freezer. Cover; surround with mixture of 4 parts crushed ice and 1 part rock salt. Turn crank slowly and steadily until turning becomes difficult. Remove dasher; repack in ice and salt. Let stand for at least 1 hour before serving. Makes 5 to 6 servings.

FRUIT-JUICE ICE
4 cups water
1½ cups sugar
2 cups orange, pineapple, apple, cranberry, etc., juice, or ¾ cup fresh lemon juice

Cook water with sugar until it boils, and boil for 5 minutes. Cool, and add fruit juice. (Use one fruit juice or a blending of many fruit juices.) Pour mixture into freezer container and freeze until very firm, stirring mixture every 30 minutes if frozen in a freezer tray. Makes 8 to 10 servings.

INSTANT BLENDER LEMON ICE
6 or 8 ice cubes
⅓ to ½ cup sugar
1 lemon, cut into small pieces, peel and pulp

Put all ingredients into a blender. Whirl until well combined. Serve at once. Makes about 4 servings.

LEMON FRAPPÉ
1 cup fresh lemon juice, or more, depending on tartness desired
Grated rind of 1 large lemon
3 cups water
1 cup sugar

Combine lemon juice and lemon rind. Boil water and sugar together for 5 minutes. Cool; stir in juice and rind. Freeze in refrigerator trays at coldest temperature. Stir twice during freezing, the second time stirring to a firm mush just before serving. Makes 4 servings.

MUSCATEL ICE
1 can (29 ounces) canned apricot halves
1½ cups sugar
2 cups boiling water
1 cup cold water
Juice of 2 lemons
1 cup Muscatel wine (or Tokay or Malaga)
¼ teaspoon salt

Drain apricots and reserve juice. Purée in a blender or food mill. Return fruit to fruit juice. Dissolve sugar in the boiling water; cool. Add apricots with juice and remaining ingredients. Pour into container of ice-cream freezer. Pack ice around with rock salt, and churn. Makes about 2 quarts.

ORANGE ICE
4 cups freshly squeezed orange juice
1 can (6 ounces) frozen orange-juice concentrate, undiluted
1 tablespoon grated lemon rind
Juice of 1 lemon
¼ cup light corn syrup or honey

Combine all ingredients. Freeze in refrigerator trays until mushy. Beat and freeze again. Serve with a dash of orange liqueur or on fruit salad, if desired. Makes 6 to 8 servings.

Note: This may be frozen in cubes to flavor drinks.

PEACH ICE

1 package (12 ounces) sweetened
  frozen peaches
⅛ teaspoon almond extract
1 egg white
  Few grains of salt

Thaw peaches and put through ricer or coarse sieve. Add almond extract. Pour into freezing tray and freeze until thick and mushy. Remove to well-chilled bowl; beat with rotary beater until mixture is fluffy. Fold in stiffly beaten egg white and salt. Beat again with rotary beater; return to freezing tray until ready to serve. Makes 4 to 6 servings.

FRESH PINEAPPLE ICE

1 large ripe fresh pineapple
½ cup honey
4 cups water
  Grated rind of 1 lemon
  Juice of 1 lemon

Pare pineapple, removing all dark eyes. Grate on cheese grater or force through food chopper. Combine with honey, water, and lemon rind. Simmer, covered, for 10 minutes. Strain and cool. Stir in lemon juice. Freeze in freezer trays until mushy. Beat until smooth and freeze again. Serve frozen mushy with additional fresh pineapple. Makes 4 to 6 servings.

PLUM ICE

12 to 20 (one 1-pound, 14-ounce can)
  plums or prunes
½ cup fresh orange juice
  Juice of 2 lemons
⅓ cup honey

Pit fruit, and force pulp with juice through ricer or sieve. Add remaining ingredients; mix thoroughly. Pour into refrigerator tray. Put tray in lowest compartment of freezing unit. With temperature control at coldest point, freeze until partly frozen. Remove to ice-cold bowl; beat with chilled rotary beater or electric mixer until light. Return to tray and freeze until firm. Makes 6 servings.

RHUBARB ICE

1½ teaspoons unflavored gelatin
¼ cup cold water
4 cups diced pink rhubarb
  Grated rind of 1 orange
1⅓ cups light corn syrup
  Few grains of salt

Soften gelatin in cold water. Cook rhubarb, orange rind, and corn syrup for about 20 minutes. Add softened gelatin and salt, stirring until gelatin dissolves. Pour into freezing tray; freeze until thick and mushy. Remove to well-chilled bowl and beat with rotary beater until the mixture is fluffy. Return to tray and freeze until firm. Makes 6 servings.

STRAWBERRY ICE

2 quarts fresh strawberries
1½ cups sugar
1 cup water

  Juice of 1 lemon

Wash and hull strawberries. Combine with all other ingredients. Rub through a fine sieve or whirl in blender. Pour into freezing trays. Freeze until almost firm. Place in bowl and beat until smooth. Return to trays and freeze until firm. Makes 6 servings.

STRAWBERRY, APRICOT, RASPBERRY, OR PEACH FRAPPÉ

2 cups fruit purée made from fresh or
  canned fruit
  Fresh lemon juice
4 cups water
1½ cups sugar

Purée fruit, which has been cooked if fresh and firm. If fruits are soft, purée them as they are and do not cook. Add lemon juice to taste. Cook water with sugar and let boil for 5 minutes. Cool, and add to puréed fruit. Pour mixture into freezer tray or into an ice-cream freezer. If using a freezer tray, stir ice every 30 minutes to keep ice crystals small, or freeze until half frozen and beat with a rotary beater until smooth. Freeze again to a thick mush just before serving. Makes 8 to 10 servings.

TANGERINE ICE IN ORANGE SHELLS

2 cans (6 ounces each) frozen
  tangerine juice
1 envelope unflavored gelatin
½ cup sugar
6 large thick-skinned oranges

Set refrigerator control for fast freezing. Blend tangerine juice with 3 juice-cans water. Soften gelatin in ½ cup juice. Put over low heat and stir until dissolved. Add gelatin and sugar to remaining juice. Pour into refrigerator trays and freeze until firm, stirring occasionally. Remove to cold bowl and beat until fluffy. Return to trays and freeze until firm. Cut tops from oranges about one third of way down. Scoop out pulp; reserve for later use. Cut edges of shells sawtooth fashion. Fill with ice and put in freezing section until ready to serve. Makes 6 servings.

THREE-FRUIT ICE

½ cup sugar
1 cup water
2 bananas
  Juice of 2 lemons
1 cup bottled grape juice

Cook sugar and water together for 5 minutes. Add mashed bananas, lemon juice, and grape juice. Cool; pour into refrigerator tray. Put tray in lowest compartment of freezing unit. With temperature control at coldest point, freeze until partly frozen. Remove to ice-cold bowl; beat with chilled rotary beater or electric mixer until light. Return to refrigerator tray and freeze until firm. Makes 5 to 6 servings.

WATERMELON GRANITÉ

4 cups ripe watermelon meat, seeds
  removed
2 tablespoons fresh lemon juice
½ cup sugar

Purée watermelon in blender or food mill; add lemon juice and sugar and stir until dissolved. Pour into refrigerator tray and freeze for 30 minutes to 1 hour. It is better not to let it get too solid. Makes 4 to 6 servings.

ICE CREAM—America's favorite dessert is a frozen food made from milk products, sweetening, flavoring, and other ingredients, depending on whether it is homemade or made commercially. By far the largest amount of ice cream consumed in the United States is commercial ice cream. Homemade ice cream has become a delicacy, made only for special occasions.

Ice cream may contain cream, fresh or evaporated milk, a sweetener such as sugar or honey or an artificial sweetener. Fruits, nuts, and flavorings are added to suit the fancy. The choice of flavorings is varied: from vanilla to liqueurs.

Commercially made ice cream also contains milk fat (also called butterfat), stabilizers added to improve the body of the ice cream, to make the ice cream smooth by keeping the ice crystals small, and to give it more resistance to melting. It may contain some nonfat milk solids.

It is impossible to say who invented ice cream. Marco Polo, who traveled extensively through China in the late 13th century, reported the oriental practice of making water and milk ices. Water ices were popular in Venice and Italy from the 14th century on. In 1660 an Italian confectioner set up in Paris a café serving ices, which was soon copied throughout Paris. It is possible that some of these early water ices may have contained milk and cream.

The first recorded occasion of the appearance of ice cream was at an elaborate banquet given by the English king, Charles I, around 1640. The frozen "cream ice" was such a surprise and such a success that Charles called in the cook and ordered him to keep the recipe a secret forever. To prove that he was serious, the king pensioned off this cook for a generous sum. But the cook did not keep his word and ice cream became a popular, if at first strictly luxurious, specialty.

Later in the century, across the channel in France, Louis XIV's guests at a state dinner were surprised to see, as one of them has reported, "in silver gilt cups, what apparently was a freshly laid egg colored like those of Easter, but before the company had time to recover from their surprise at such a novelty for dessert, they discovered that the supposed eggs were delicious sweet-meats, cold and compact as marble."

The American colonists were not far behind their European neighbors. A guest of Governor Bladen of Maryland describes a dinner of 1744: "We had a dessert no less curious; among the rarities of which it was compos'd was some fine Ice Cream which, with the Strawberries and Milk, eat Most Deliciously."

In 1774 there was a public announcement of the delicacy. Philip Lenzi of London would prepare special orders of ice cream, declared an advertisement in a New York paper. Three years later an ice-cream advertisement read: "Ice cream of what sort they will please to order."

Many leaders in American government were connected with the rise in popularity of ice cream in this country. The first President, George Washington, had two "pewter ice cream pots," presumably for making ice cream at Mount Vernon. He was introduced to ice cream by Mrs. Alexander Hamilton, the wife of the Secretary of the Treasury, in 1789. Thomas Jefferson, the third president, was an enthusiastic gastronome and had learned recipes for ice-cream dishes while in France. Guests at his state dinners were sometimes served such luxuries as meringue glacée and baked Alaska.

Perhaps the most famous American patroness of ice cream was Dolly Madison, who served as hostess for the wifeless Jefferson as well as for her own husband, James Madison, the fourth president. A contemporary speaks of the great moment of one of Dolly's parties: "Mrs. Madison always entertains with grace and charm, but last night there was a sparkle in her eye that set astir an air of expectancy among her guests. When finally the brilliant assemblage—America's best—entered the dining room, they beheld a table set with French china and English silver, laden with good things to eat, and in the center, high on a silver platter, a large shining dome of pink ice cream." She served strawberry ice cream at the second Inaugural Ball of 1812.

Ice cream's rich flavor and taste was so soothing and popular that Emerson, the famous Concord writer, complained about the lack of conversation in homes in 1841: "We dare not trust our wit for making our house pleasant to our friends and so we buy ice cream."

As early as 1893, only forty-two years after the making of the first American commercial ice cream in 1851 by Jacob Fussel, an American magazine called ice-cream sodas "the national beverage." Ice-cream cones first appeared at the St. Louis Fair in 1904. Credit for their dis-

covery goes to Mr. E. Hamwi, a Syrian waffle vendor. Ice cream was sold in little dishes at the Fair. One day, an ice cream vendor located next to Mr. Hamwi's stand ran out of dishes. Mr. Hamwi, observing the predicament, helped out by rolling one of his thin, wafer-like waffles into the shape of a cone. This hardened as it cooled. The ice cream was put into it to the customer's delight, and a great new American institution was born.

Ice cream is, without doubt, along with pie, America's most beloved dessert. The consumption of it has risen greatly during the last thirty years; between 1935 and 1939 Americans consumed an average of 8.4 quarts a year. In 1963 they ate 15.4 quarts each. In fact, it often appears that ice cream has transcended its role as dessert and become a staple food, eaten at all times. Vanilla ice cream outsells all other flavors, with chocolate second and strawberry third in popularity.

Making Ice Cream at Home

Homemade ice cream is made by either the stirred or the still-frozen method. The *stirred method* uses a crank freezer surrounded by ice and salt and turned by hand or by an electric motor. It is important to be sure that the lid, can, and dasher (scraper) are sterilized in boiling water, that the lid fits properly, and that melted ice does not seep into the can. For freezing ice cream, a mixture of one part salt to six parts ice by weight, or one part salt to twelve parts ice by measure, is frequently used. Coarse ice-cream salt must be used, as table salt dissolves too rapidly. The dasher is turned slowly until it begins to be difficult to turn so that the warm mixture will not be churned, then the dasher is turned more quickly to whip air into the ice cream. A hardening period of about 1 hour is necessary to complete freezing.

The *still-frozen method* (refrigerator ice cream) requires some means other than continuous stirring to keep the ice crystals small and to incorporate air. Rapid freezing and the use of a variety of materials that interfere with crystal formation are relied on to keep the crystals small. Rapid freezing is aided by setting the controls of the refrigerator at the lowest setting. The mixture can also be removed from the refrigerator occasionally and stirred to remove it from the sides of the container. Air can be incorporated by folding in a fluffy beaten product such as whipped cream, or by taking the ice cream from the refrigerator and beating before freezing is completed.

Even when a good recipe is skillfully used, the texture of refrigerator ice cream is usually less smooth than that of ice cream made in a crank freezer and

becomes coarser on storage because the ice crystals grow. Refrigerator ice cream is best eaten soon after freezing.

Commercial Ice Cream

Commercial ice-cream mixtures are pasteurized, homogenized, aged, frozen, and hardened. By federal or state standards ice cream must contain per gallon a minimum of 10 per cent milk fat, minimum 20 per cent total milk solids, stabilizer maximum .5 per cent (not more than .2 per cent emulsifier permitted), as well as a weight of minimum 4.5 pounds per gallon and minimum 1.6 pounds food solids per gallon.

There are some diet ice creams available in which noncaloric sweeteners are used.

Milk sherbet or fruit sherbet is a frozen dessert made of a milk product such as milk, or milk and cream, fruit or fruit juice, and sweetening. Water, flavorings, and stabilizers may be added. The number of calories supplied are slightly less than those from plain ice cream.

Frozen custard, French ice cream, or *French custard ice cream* are all frozen products in which eggs or egg yolks are added to the usual ice cream ingredients.

Ice milk is a frozen dessert similar to ice cream but contains less milk fat and total milk solids. Ice milk is often served from the freezer in the soft state at refreshment stands, under various trade names.

Imitation ice cream or *mellorine* is a frozen dessert in which fats other than butterfat are used. It may resemble ice cream or ice milk depending on its fat content, as the other ingredients are similar. The fat most commonly used is a blend of hydrogenated vegetable oils. Its sale is regulated by state laws and is permitted in fourteen states.

Storage—Refrigerate in refrigerator frozen-food compartment with temperature control at coldest setting.
☐ Refrigerator frozen-food compartment, in ice-cream carton: 2 to 3 days
☐ Freezer, in ice-cream carton: 8 months

Nutritive Food Values—Small amounts of protein and calcium, depending on the amount of milk solids used in making the ice cream. High in fat content, especially when made with cream.

The caloric value of 3½ ounces of ice cream product varies with the ingredients used and the amount of fat content, from about 193 to 222 calories. The diet ice creams contain about 150 calories in 3½ ounces. For 3½ ounces of ice milk the caloric value is 152.

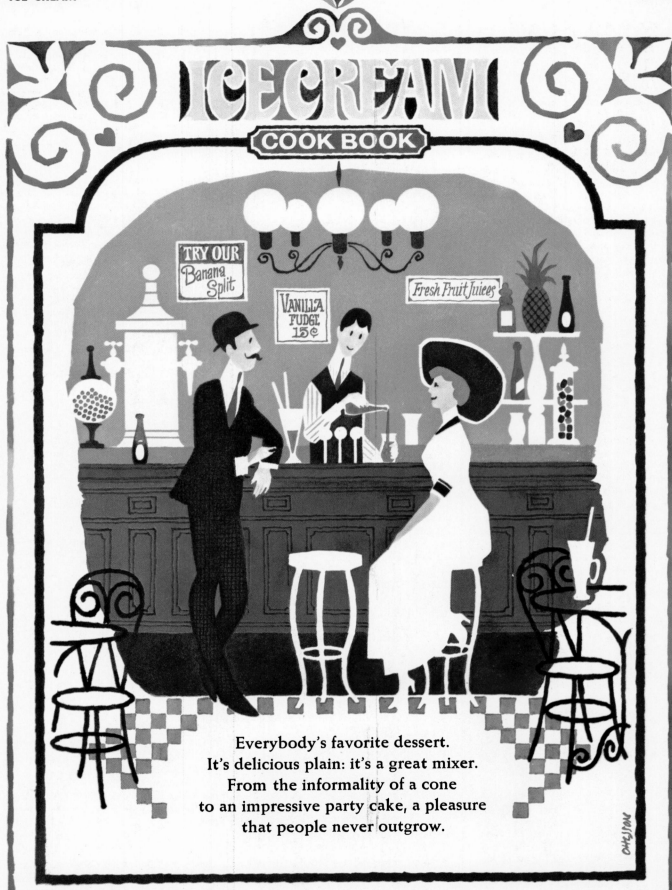

Everybody's favorite dessert.
It's delicious plain: it's a great mixer.
From the informality of a cone
to an impressive party cake, a pleasure
that people never outgrow.

STILL-FROZEN ICE CREAMS

VANILLA ICE CREAM

4 cups milk
1 box (3 ounces) vanilla pudding mix
1 cup light corn syrup
1 teaspoon vanilla extract
1 teaspoon almond extract
1 cup heavy cream or chilled evaporated milk

Add milk gradually to pudding powder; add corn syrup; mix until smooth. Cook over low heat until thickened, stirring constantly. When cool, freeze in refrigerator trays. When frozen around the edges, remove to chilled bowl and beat well with rotary beater. Add vanilla and almond extracts. Whip cream; fold into partially frozen pudding mixture. Freeze until firm. If desired, serve with fruit sweetened with honey. Makes about 1½ quarts.

CHOCOLATE ICE CREAM

4 cups milk
3 ounces (3 squares) unsweetened chocolate
1 cup sugar
1 tablespoon flour
¼ teaspoon salt
2 eggs
1 envelope unflavored gelatin
¼ cup cold water
2 teaspoons vanilla extract
1 cup heavy cream

Pour half of milk into top part of a double boiler; add chocolate; heat until melted. Combine half of sugar with flour and salt; add hot milk slowly, stirring well. Return to double boiler; cook for 10 minutes, stirring frequently. Combine remaining ½ cup sugar and 2 cups milk with beaten eggs; add to hot mixture; add gelatin soaked in water. Cook until custard coats a silver spoon. When cool, freeze in refrigerator trays. When partially frozen, beat well; add vanilla. Whip cream or chilled evaporated milk until stiff; fold into mixture; freeze. Makes about 1½ quarts.

PINEAPPLE ICE CREAM

½ cup sugar
1 cup water
Dash of salt
About 1 to 1¼ cups (one 9-ounce can) crushed pineapple
1 cup heavy cream, whipped

Bring first 3 ingredients to boil and boil for 5 minutes. Cool. Add pineapple; pour into tray. Freeze in freezing compartment of refrigerator or in freezer until mushy. Fold in cream; freeze until firm. Makes 1 quart.

RUM-RAISIN ICE CREAM

2 egg yolks
½ cup sugar
Few grains of salt
1 cup light cream
1 cup heavy cream
1½ teaspoons vanilla extract
½ cup seeded raisins, slivered or ground, soaked for several hours in 2 to 3 tablespoons Jamaica rum

Beat yolks until light, add sugar, then salt and light cream; blend well. Fold in whipped heavy cream and vanilla. Partially freeze. Stir once, and when it is of frappé consistency add the raisins. Continue freezing. Makes 6 servings.

ALMOND ICE CREAM

3 eggs
¾ cup sugar
¼ cup water
¼ cup fresh milk
1¾ cups heavy cream or 1 can (14½ ounces) undiluted evaporated milk, partially frozen
¾ teaspoon almond extract

Beat eggs and sugar until light in top part of double boiler; stir in water and fresh milk. Cook, stirring constantly, over hot, not boiling, water until thick enough to coat a metal spoon. Chill. Whip partially frozen cream until stiff. Fold in egg mixture and almond extract. Freeze in refrigerator tray at coldest temperature until frozen 1 inch in from edge of tray. Turn into chilled bowl and beat with a rotary beater until creamy. Return to tray and chill until firm. Makes 6 servings.

ICE 'N CREAM

1 cup grape juice
1 cup apple juice
¼ cup lime juice
¾ cup superfine sugar
1½ cups heavy cream
1 teaspoon vanilla extract
⅔ cup chopped nuts

Combine fruit juices and ½ cup sugar. Pour into refrigerator tray, and freeze. Whip cream with remaining ¼ cup sugar; add vanilla and half of nuts. Pour over frozen fruit juices, and freeze. Serve garnished with remaining nuts. Makes 8 servings.

STIRRED ICE CREAMS

FRENCH VANILLA ICE CREAM

6 egg yolks
2 cups milk
1 cup sugar
¼ teaspoon salt
2 cups heavy cream
1 tablespoon vanilla extract

In top part of double boiler beat egg yolks and milk with rotary beater. Add sugar and salt; cook, stirring constantly, over hot, not boiling, water until thick enough to coat a metal spoon. Let cool, then add cream and vanilla. Freeze in a crank-type freezer, using 8 parts cracked ice to 1 part rock salt. Makes about 1½ quarts.

Banana Ice Cream

Use recipe above, omitting all but 1 tea-spoon vanilla. Force 3 large ripe bananas through sieve and add pulp to ice-cream mixture. Freeze.

Peach Ice Cream

Use recipe for French Vanilla Ice Cream, substituting 1 teaspoon almond extract for vanilla. Partially freeze. Add 2 cups sweetened crushed fresh peaches, or use thawed frozen peaches. Finish freezing. Makes 8 to 10 servings.

Strawberry Ice Cream

Use recipe for French Vanilla Ice Cream, omitting vanilla. Partially freeze. Add 2 cups sweetened crushed fresh strawberries, or use thawed frozen strawberries. Finish freezing. Makes 8 to 10 servings.

Raspberry Ice Cream

Use recipe for French Vanilla Ice Cream, omitting vanilla. Partially freeze. Add 2 cups sweetened strained fresh raspberries, or use thawed frozen raspberries. Finish freezing. Makes 8 to 10 servings.

CHOCOLATE FREEZER ICE CREAM

4 cups milk
2 ounces (2 squares) unsweetened chocolate
1 cup sugar
1 tablespoon flour
¼ teaspoon salt
2 eggs
2 cups light cream
1 tablespoon vanilla extract

Pour half of milk into top part of a double boiler; add chocolate; heat until chocolate melts. Combine half of sugar with flour and salt, add hot milk slowly and stir until well mixed. Return to double boiler; cook for 10 minutes, stirring frequently. Combine remaining sugar with eggs; add to hot-milk mixture; cook until custard coats a silver spoon. Add remaining milk, cool, and strain into freezer can of ice-cream freezer. Add unbeaten cream and vanilla. Pack in ice and salt, using 8 parts chopped ice to 1 part rock salt. Freeze as usual. Makes about 1½ quarts.

BLUEBERRY ICE CREAM

4 cups fresh blueberries
¼ cup water
1 cup sugar
¼ teaspoon salt
Juice of 1 lemon
2 cups light cream

Put berries in saucepan with water. Cover and simmer for 10 minutes, or until berries are soft. Mash; put through a sieve. Add sugar, salt, and lemon juice; cool. Mix with cream and freeze in a crank freezer. Makes 1½ quarts.

FRESH STRAWBERRY ICE CREAM

2 quarts strawberries
2 cups sugar
3 quarts heavy cream
Pinch of salt

Clean and hull berries and sprinkle them

with sugar. Cover and let stand for 1½ to 2 hours. Mash them lightly. Mix cream with salt and pour into freezer; freeze until mushy. Remove cover of freezer and stir in strawberries. Re-cover and continue freezing until solid. Makes about 1½ gallons.

ICE CREAM PARFAITS

CINNAMON CHOCOLATE PARFAIT

To softened chocolate ice cream add ground cinnamon to taste. Pour some Chocolate Fudge Sauce (page 931) into parfait or other tall glass (fruit-juice glass can be used). Fill with alternating layers of cinnamon-chocolate ice cream and Chocolate Fudge Sauce. Top with whipped topping. Sprinkle with ground cinnamon.

TWO-TONE CHERRY PARFAIT

Flavor softened vanilla ice cream with a little maraschino-cherry juice and some chopped cherries. Fill parfait or other tall glass (fruit-juice glass can be used) alternately with the cherry-ice cream mix-

ture and pistachio ice cream. Top with whipped cream and a whole maraschino cherry or chopped pistachio nuts. Put in freezer for a short time before serving.

MOCHA PARFAIT

Fill parfait or other tall glass (fruit-juice glass can be used) with alternate layers of Chocolate Fudge Sauce (pg. 931) and coffee ice cream. Top with whipped cream or other whipped topping. Decorate with Chocolate-Covered Coffee Beans (right). Serve at once or store in freezer.

STRAWBERRY PARFAIT

Alternate layers of thawed frozen strawberries and vanilla ice cream in a parfait glass. Top with whipped ice cream and a maraschino cherry.

BLUEBERRY PARFAIT

Spoon a little Blueberry Sauce (right) into bottom of a parfait or other tall glass (fruit-juice glass can be used). Alternate layers of vanilla ice cream and Blueberry Sauce. Top with whipped cream or whipped topping and whole blueberries.

SAUCES FOR ICE CREAM

■ **Apricot Cherry Sauce**—Combine 2 cups (one 1-pound jar) apricot jam and ½ cup coarsely chopped red maraschino cherries. Makes about 2 cups.

■ **Blueberry Sauce**—In saucepan blend 2 teaspoons cornstarch and 1 tablespoon water. Add ¼ cup sugar, ⅓ cup water (or syrup from canned blueberries), and ⅛ teaspoon salt. Cook until clear and slightly thickened, stirring. Add 2 cups washed fresh blueberries, or drained canned or frozen. Boil for 2 or 3 minutes. Makes 2 cups.

■ **Butterscotch Sauce**—Combine in saucepan 2 cups firmly packed brown sugar, ½ cup undiluted evaporated milk, ¼ teaspoon salt, ⅓ cup light corn syrup, and ⅓ cup butter. Bring to boil and cook rapidly for 3 minutes (to 220°F. on a candy thermometer). Makes 2 cups.

■ **Chocolate-Covered Coffee Beans**—Melt semisweet chocolate over hot water. Put each bean on tip of teaspoon and dip into chocolate until coated. Place on wax

paper. Allow to harden in refrigerator.

■ **Chocolate Fudge Sauce**—Melt 3 ounces (3 squares) unsweetened chocolate in ¾ cup milk over low heat, stirring constantly. Beat until smooth. Add ¼ teaspoon salt, 1½ cups sugar, and 3 tablespoons light corn syrup; cook, stirring, for 5 minutes. Add 1 tablespoon butter or margarine and ¾ teaspoon vanilla extract. Serve warm or cold. Makes about 2 cups.

■ **Pineapple Mint Topping**—Drain well 1 to 1¼ cups (one 9-ounce can) crushed pineapple. Combine pineapple with 2 tablespoons crème de menthe or melted mint jelly. Makes 1 cup.

■ **Raspberry Sauce**—Thaw 1 package (12 ounces) frozen raspberries. Press through fine sieve or whirl in blender; strain. Add 3 tablespoons sugar; dissolve in saucepan over medium heat. Cook rapidly for 3 minutes. Cool. Makes about 1 cup.

■ **Flavored Whipped Cream**—Before whipping, try adding one of the following to flavor heavy cream:
1. Instant coffee powder
2. Instant cocoa mix
3. Quick strawberry-flavored beverage mix
4. Brown sugar instead of granulated sugar
5. Your favorite flavoring extract

Or, fold one of these into the whipped cream:
1. Chopped nuts
2. Macaroon crumbs
3. Chocolate sprinkles
4. Chopped raisins
5. Grenadine instead of sugar

TOPPINGS FOR ICE CREAM SUNDAES

ORANGE AND BLUE SUNDAE
Top peach ice cream with equal parts of orange segments, sliced bananas, blueberries.

STOP-AND-GO SUNDAE
Mix chopped green and red maraschino cherries; add a little light corn syrup.

HOT CARAMEL SUNDAE
Melt ½ pound caramels with 2 tablespoons water over hot water.

ORIENTAL SUNDAE
Cut up undrained preserved kumquats. Good on chocolate ice cream.

MARSHMALLOW SUNDAE
Top ice cream with bought marshmallow cream. Best on peach, pineapple, chocolate.

NUTMEG SUNDAE
Grate fresh nutmeg generously over vanilla or peach ice cream.

GINGER SUNDAE
Top ice cream with ginger marmalade or chopped preserved gingerroot in syrup.

PEACH SUNDAE
Top vanilla ice cream with frozen or sweetened sliced fresh peaches.

MAPLE-RUM SUNDAE
Top coffee ice cream with hot maple syrup flavored with rum or rum extract.

BRITTLE SUNDAE
Sprinkle crushed nut brittle over coffee, vanilla, chocolate, or caramel ice cream.

CHOCOLATE-MINT SUNDAE
Melt thin chocolate mints over hot water; serve on vanilla, chocolate, pistachio.

Two-Tone Cherry Parfait
Orange and Blue Sundae
Cherry Ice Cream Soda
Ice 'n Cream
Harlequin Crinkle Cups

BRANDIED FRUIT SUNDAE

Serve cut-up brandied fruit on coffee, pineapple, coconut, banana, or vanilla.

MOLASSES CHIP SUNDAE

Top vanilla, banana, or chocolate ice cream with crushed molasses chips.

PINEAPPLE SUNDAE

Serve canned pineapple pie filling on vanilla or banana ice cream.

CRANBERRY-ORANGE SUNDAE

Add orange segments to cranberry sauce. Or use raw-cranberry relish to top vanilla.

ARABIAN SUNDAE

Moisten chopped dates with honey. Serve on butter-pecan or burnt-almond ice cream.

CANDIED FRUIT SUNDAE

Serve moist mixed candied fruits on vanilla or pistachio ice cream.

TROPICAL SUNDAE

Add chopped coconut, white raisins, and nuts to Butterscotch Sauce.

JUNIOR SUNDAE

Pour junior apricot-and-applesauce over vanilla ice cream. Top with raisins.

CEREAL SUNDAE

Top vanilla, coffee, chocolate, or banana ice cream with sugar-coated cereal.

CHOCOLATE-RUM SUNDAE

Melt chocolate rum wafers over hot water; serve on vanilla or chocolate ice cream.

JAM OR PRESERVES SUNDAE

Serve cherry, plum, apricot, or berry jam or preserves on choice of ice cream.

COOKIE SUNDAE

Top choice of ice cream with crushed fig cookies, coconut bars, or macaroons.

ZIPPY SUNDAE

Top choice of ice cream with Cointreau, crème de menthe, or any cordial.

MOCHA SUNDAE

Flavor bought chocolate syrup with powdered coffee for chocolate ice cream.

MINCEMEAT SUNDAE

Spike warm mincemeat with rum or brandy—best on vanilla ice cream.

COCONUT SUNDAE

Roll balls of strawberry or other ice cream in coconut. Serve with any sauce.

ORANGE SUNDAE

Top chocolate or vanilla ice cream with frozen orange juice concentrate.

PINEAPPLE-GINGER SUNDAE

Add a small amount chopped candied gingerroot to pineapple jam; serve on vanilla.

PARTY PINK SUNDAE

Top vanilla ice cream with 1 or 2 tablespoons grenadine.

ICE-CREAM SODAS

Each recipe makes one serving.

- *Black-and-White*—Follow the directions for Chocolate Soda (below), substituting vanilla for chocolate ice cream.
- *Chocolate*—Put 2 to 3 tablespoons chocolate syrup in a large glass. Add ¼ cup milk and a large scoop of chocolate ice cream. Almost fill with chilled soda water. Stir.
- *Cherry*—Put 2 tablespoons bought cherry-sundae topping in tall glass. Add ¼ cup milk and vanilla ice cream. Fill with chilled soda water; stir; top with cherries.
- *Coffee*—Several hours before making sodas, mix in a saucepan ½ cup sugar, ½ cup light corn syrup, ¾ cup water, and a dash of salt. Bring to boil, stirring constantly. Remove from heat and stir in 2 tablespoons instant coffee. Cool. Add ½ teaspoon vanilla extract. Refrigerate. For each soda, put 2 to 3 tablespoons syrup in large glass; add ¼ cup milk and large scoop of vanilla or coffee ice cream; almost fill with chilled soda water; stir.
- *Cola, Root-Beer, Sarsaparilla, or Ginger-Ale*—Put a scoop of vanilla ice cream in a large glass. Almost fill with chilled beverage desired. Stir.
- *Lemon*—Put 2 tablespoons frozen, concentrated lemonade in tall glass. Add a scoop of vanilla ice cream. Almost fill with chilled soda water. Stir.
- *Peach or Apricot*—Put ⅓ cup mashed frozen, canned, or sweetened ripe fresh peaches or apricots in a large glass. Add ¼ cup milk, a large scoop of peach or vanilla ice cream, and almost fill with chilled soda water. Stir.
- *Pineapple*—Put ⅓ cup sweetened, drained, canned crushed, or fresh shredded pineapple in large glass. Add ¼ cup milk and a large scoop of vanilla or pineapple ice cream. Almost fill with chilled soda water. Stir.
- *Strawberry or Raspberry*—Put ⅓ cup frozen or crushed, sweetened, fresh berries in a large glass. Add 3 tablespoons milk and a large scoop of vanilla ice cream. Almost fill with chilled soda water. Stir.

ICE-CREAM CAKES AND DESSERTS

ICE-CREAM SHADOW CAKE

    1 large angel-food cake ring
    2 pints chocolate ice cream
    2 cups heavy cream, whipped and
      sweetened
      Chocolate sauce

Cut angel cake into three layers. Spread 1 pint ice cream (softened) between each two layers. Spread whipped cream on top and sides of cake; freeze. When ready to serve, remove from freezer and dribble chocolate sauce over top and sides of cake. Cut into wedges to serve. Makes 12 servings.

Note: If freezer isn't available, chill cake and have cream whipped before filling cake. Fill with ice cream; spread with cream. Dribble sauce over top and sides and serve at once.

LADYFINGER ICE-CREAM CAKE

Line a 2-quart mold or mixing bowl with about 2 dozen ladyfingers, split. Pack with 3 pints peppermint-stick ice cream. Cover with foil; freeze for several hours or overnight. Unmold and garnish with a wreath of whipped cream; sprinkle with "shot" candies; arrange candy fruit slices around the cake base. Makes about 8 to 10 servings.

ICE-CREAM CAKE

Cover bottom and sides of three 8-inch layer-cake pans with one piece of wax paper or foil; spread 1 pint softened ice cream in each. Strawberry, coffee, or any desired flavor or combination of flavors may be used. Put in freezer until firm. Split two 8-inch sponge layers into halves, making 4 layers. Cover with foil a circle of cardboard cut to fit the cake. On it assemble cake by placing ice-cream layers between sponge layers; remove wax paper or foil from ice cream. Press slightly so layers will stay together. Put in freezer until ice cream is hard. Whip 1½ cups heavy cream, ¼ cup confectioners' sugar, and 1 teaspoon vanilla extract until stiff; spread on top and sides of cake. Reserve some of cream and use in pastry tube to decorate cake. Return cake to freezer; let stand until cream is frozen. Package, and keep in freezer until ready to serve. Cut and serve while it is frozen. Makes 12 to 16 slices.

CHOCOLATE ICE-CREAM ROLL

    4 eggs
      Sugar (about ¾ cup)
    ½ cup sifted cake flour
    ½ teaspoon baking powder
    ¼ teaspoon salt
    1 teaspoon ground cinnamon
    ¼ teaspoon baking soda
    3 tablespoons cold water
    2½ ounces (2½ squares) unsweetened
      chocolate, melted
      Ice cream (French Vanilla or
      Banana, page **929**)

Beat eggs slightly. Gradually add ⅔ cup sugar and beat until thick and lemon-colored. Sift flour, baking powder, salt, and cinnamon. Add to egg mixture and

Strawberry Parfait   Blueberry Parfait   Ladyfinger Ice-Cream Cake   Melon à la Mode

blend well. Add 3 tablespoons sugar, the soda, and water to chocolate; mix. Fold into batter. Grease a jelly-roll pan (15½ x 10½ x 1 inch), line with wax paper, and grease again. Pour in batter. Bake in preheated moderate oven (375°F.) for about 15 minutes. Turn out on damp towel; remove paper carefully. Roll lengthwise with towel; cool. Unroll, and spread with softened ice cream; re-roll. Freeze until firm. Cut into slices to serve. Makes 8 servings.

HARLEQUIN CRINKLE CUPS
Melt separately 6 ounces each of semi-sweet chocolate and butterscotch pieces in top part of double boiler over hot water. Place 10 to 12 paper baking cups (3 to 4 inches in diameter) in muffin-pan sections. With spatula, line half the inside and bottom with melted chocolate and the other half with melted butterscotch. Put muffin pan in refrigerator until ready to use. Then quickly peel off paper cups. Fill crinkle cups with butter-pecan ice cream. Decorate with pecan half.

JELLY-ROLL SANDWICHES
For each serving use two ½-inch slices of jelly roll or poundcake; put together with a slice of ice cream. Serve at once, or package airtight in foil and freeze. Top with sundae topping or strawberry jam, if desired.

COFFEE-CHOCOLATE PIE
½ cup fine chocolate-cookie crumbs
1 quart coffee ice cream
¼ cup chocolate syrup

Butter a 9-inch pie pan and sprinkle with cookie crumbs, reserving 2 tablespoons for top of pie. Carefully spread softened ice cream over crumbs. Sprinkle remaining crumbs on top around edge of pie. Place in freezer until hard. Run tines of fork deeply over pie; pour chocolate syrup into hollows thus formed. Freeze uncovered; then cover with foil; keep in freezer until ready to serve. Cut into 6 or 8 pieces.

APRICOT ICE-CREAM PIE
9- inch pastry shell, baked
¼ pound marshmallows
  Apricot preserves
2 egg whites
⅛ teaspoon salt
¼ cup sugar
2 pints vanilla ice cream

Chill pastry shell. Heat marshmallows and 2 tablespoons preserves in top part of double boiler over boiling water until marshmallows are half melted. Remove from heat and beat until smooth. Beat egg whites with salt until foamy; gradually add sugar and beat until stiff. Fold in marshmallow mixture. Press ice cream quickly into chilled shell. Spread with ½ cup preserves. Cover with marshmallow meringue, spreading to cover ice cream

completely. Put under preheated broiler for 1 or 2 minutes, or until lightly browned. (This meringue browns very quickly.) Cut into wedges and garnish each with spoonful of preserves. Makes 6 to 8 servings.

SUMMER SNOWBALLS
Scoop vanilla ice cream onto cookie sheets; cover with transparent plastic wrap; freeze firm, package in plastic bags, and store in freezer until ready to use.

If preferred, cut bulk ice cream into cubes. Roll in one of the following coatings and serve with sauce:

● Plain or toasted coconut coating with butterscotch or chocolate sauce
● Chocolate "shot" candy or chopped candied-fruit coating with soft custard or nesselrode sauce
● Crushed peppermint candy or chopped nut coating with chocolate or marshmallow sauce
● Crushed peanut-brittle coating with chopped peaches or soft custard sauce

STRAWBERRIES À LA MODE
Stud a large bowl of vanilla ice cream with whole fresh strawberries dipped into sugar. When ice cream has softened slightly, spoon into individual dishes. Also good with fresh raspberries or sliced peaches.

MERINGUES GLACÉES
⅛ teaspoon salt
½ teaspoon cream of tartar
2 egg whites
½ cup sugar
½ teaspoon vanilla extract
1 pint strawberry ice cream
1 package (10 ounces) frozen strawberries, thawed

Add salt and cream of tartar to egg whites and beat with rotary beater until foamy; gradually add sugar and continue beating until very stiff. Add vanilla. Spoon some onto lightly buttered brown paper on cookie sheet and flatten to make 4 thin bases about 1½ inches in diameter. With a pastry tube or spoon, surround bases with remaining meringue to height of 2 inches, leaving center unfilled. Bake in preheated very slow oven (250°F.) for 1¼ hours. Transfer paper to a damp board and remove meringues with a spatula. When cold, fill with ice cream and top with strawberries. Makes 4 servings.

FROZEN CRÊPES
■ **To make crêpes:** Beat until smooth 2 egg yolks, ¾ teaspoon salt, 2 teaspoons each of melted butter and sugar, ½ cup all-purpose flour, and 1 cup milk. Beat 2 egg whites until they form soft peaks. Fold into batter and let mixture stand for about 1 hour. Brush a 5- or 6-inch skillet with oil. Heat until very hot. Pour on batter by scant ¼ cupfuls. Tilt until

pan is completely covered. Turn crêpe after about 15 seconds. Makes 16.
■ **To fill:** Place narrow roll of ice cream in center of each crêpe. Bring edges to center. Store in freezer as each is made. Serve with hot Chocolate Fudge Sauce (page 942). Top with chopped nuts.

MELON À LA MODE
For each serving, fill a chilled cantaloupe or honeydew half with two or more contrasting flavors of ice cream, or ice cream and sherbet or berries.

ICE-CREAM BONBONS
1 quart ice cream
2 cups chopped pecans or other nuts
12 ounces (1 large package) semisweet chocolate pieces
½ cup margarine
1 tablespoon instant coffee powder

Make ice-cream balls with large melon-ball scoop. Immediately roll each ball in nuts. Put in freezer until thoroughly frozen, at least 1 hour. Melt chocolate and margarine in top part of double boiler. Add coffee, and mix. Remove from heat, but keep warm over hot water. Use a fork to dip ice-cream balls into chocolate, working as quickly as possible. When you've dipped 10 or 12, place them in freezer and continue. When chocolate is thoroughly firm, set bonbons in paper cups, 3 or 4 to each individual serving. Cover or wrap with foil or plastic wrap; store in freezer. Makes 30 to 36.

BANANA SPLIT
1 ripe banana
1 scoop each of vanilla, chocolate, and strawberry ice cream
2 tablespoons strawberry preserves
2 tablespoons pineapple preserves
2 tablespoons chocolate sauce
  Whipped cream
2 tablespoons chopped nuts
1 maraschino cherry

Cut banana into halves lengthwise. Put on plate, cut side up. Arrange ice cream scoops in row between banana halves. Spoon strawberry preserves over one scoop, pineapple over another, and chocolate sauce over the last. Top with cream and garnish with nuts and cherry. Makes 1 serving.

ICE CREAM AS A DESSERT SAUCE

Serve softened vanilla ice cream over:
● Fresh strawberries with Cointreau
● Toasted angel-food cake wedges
● Chocolate cake or gingerbread
● Brownies with chocolate sauce
● Sliced bananas and oranges
● Peach or apple crisp, oven-warm
● Strawberry or peach shortcake
● Fruited or plain gelatin dessert
● Waffles with fruit or berry sauce

INDIA'S COOKERY

By William Clifford

*The subtle cuisine of the vast land of India is a culinary tour
of a fascinating country whose civilization, including the art of
good eating, began thousands of years before our own.*

India is a world apart, a land unto itself. From the Vale of Kashmir to Cape Comorin, from Gujarat to Assam, it spans nearly as much of the globe as all of western Europe from Scandinavia to Greece. The sacred earth of Mother India nurtures even more human beings (not to mention cows, buffaloes, monkeys, insects, and cobras) than there are Europeans. So many people, living in such a vast expanse of land, tropical and temperate, lush and arid, mountainous and flat, naturally enough, enjoy all sorts of food.

The foods of India and the Indian ways of serving them have evolved over thousands of years. By contrast, classical French cooking dates only from the 18th century. Age alone is no proof of greatness, but anything that survives so long a test of time is certainly worth close scrutiny. What one finds, on looking closely at India, is a national cuisine of such variety and subtlety that it is rivaled only by the Chinese and the French. This will come as a great surprise to most westerners, who tend to think of Indian cooking as beginning and ending with curry. While it is true that a simple curry does not exemplify all the treasures stored away in the many chambers of the house of Indian cuisine, it is also true that an understanding of curry opens the door to that house.

One sometimes hears that curry is not really Indian or that Indians do not use ready-mixed curry powders. The first claim is not true. The word curry appears in languages of both north and south India, and to Indians it means a dish of vegetables or meat with a spicy sauce, not a dry dish. The claim that Indians never use prepared curry powder has more truth, but an Indian wife who grinds and mixes fresh spices every day ends up with powders and pastes much like the ones you can buy prepackaged. She changes the quantities and combinations according to the food she is cooking, family preferences and traditions, or her mood. You can do the same by adding individual spices to commercial curry powders.

Curry powders vary greatly in strength and taste, and you might like to make a taste test of several of them. Include both American and Indian-made ones, together with curry pastes, which are made of the same spices as the powders, mixed with oil and vinegar. Generally the Indian powders and pastes are hotter. All of them, domestic and foreign, contain the same basic six ingredients: coriander, turmeric, cuminseed, fenugreek, black pepper, and cayenne or chili pepper. The proportions vary from brand to brand, or from home to home in India. Although more coriander than anything else is generally used, I have seen formulas where it was used in equal measure with turmeric or with both turmeric and cuminseed.

After these basic six there are at least twenty other ingredients that turn up in curry powders in smaller amounts. These include mustard, anise, poppy, celery, and caraway seeds; various dried green leaves including bay; dried peas, onion, and garlic; ginger, dill, nutmeg, mace, cardamom, cloves, cinnamon, orange peel, sugar, and salt. The sweeter spices such as cardamom, cloves, and cinnamon are less often found in Indian curry mixtures than in American ones. Indians tend to reserve them for puddings and other sweets, elaborate rice dishes, and other special preparations.

The reason Indians began to prepare food with all these spices and seasonings is not positively known. One theory holds that curry was invented to cover up the taste of food that was of inferior quality or that had gone bad in the tropical climate. The trouble with this idea is that a good blend of curry brings out the fundamental flavor rather than kills it. Spices will help to preserve good food, but they do not make bad food palatable.

Another possibility is that the eating of highly spiced, hot foods is done instinctively in tropical lands because this causes perspiration, opening the pores and offering relief from the heat. A third and most reasonable explanation holds that the spices came to be used because they were there. If you live in a land where cloves stud the trees and tempt you with their aroma as you walk by, you are likely to use more of them than if they must be shipped thousands of miles and sold by the ounce in a store.

To taste and compare curry powders, I recommend first frying the powder in a couple of tablespoons of oil or butter, then adding chopped onions and more butter, and finally whatever principal ingredient you want to flavor with the sauce. This can be meat or chicken, or for a shorter cooking time something precooked like hard-cooked eggs or fish balls. Add water if necessary, simmer for a few minutes to blend flavors, add salt, and taste. This gives you a much more authentically Indian sauce than the cream sauce into which curry powder is so often blended in western cooking.

While properly blended spices enhance the flavor of the food you put them with, too much hot pepper can scorch your tongue and kill your taste temporarily. If you get accidentally burned in your curry experiments, be reassured that the fire will die away in half an hour or less and leave no scars, and the knowledge you gain is worth the risk. Until you taste eggplant in curry, you do not know the full taste of eggplant. A delicate fish that gives up the ghost when deep fried and served with tartare sauce will reveal hidden depths of taste in the right spices.

After tasting your curry powders, try out the basic six ingredients individually in the same way. Black and cayenne peppers you already know. Coriander, the plant that dominates curry powder, is a member of the parsley family. It grows in every Indian garden, and its fresh green leaves look something like our big-leaved Italian parsley, which is another carrot cousin. It has a strong pungent flavor, one you may have encountered in both Mexican and Chinese cooking, where fresh coriander leaves are used extensively. The ground seeds of the coriander that go into curry powder are much milder than the leaf, and a dish seasoned with ground coriander alone may remind you faintly of a mild chile con carne or a curry. It has no hot peppery quality.

Cuminseed used alone has a pleasant taste, one that might again call to mind a mild chile con carne. Turmeric has a bright yellow color; a pinch of it will color a whole dish, like saffron. Indians use saffron too, but it is very expensive and its assertive flavor is considered most suitable for sweets and fancy rice dishes. The yellow color in most meat and vegetable dishes comes from turmeric. Turmeric alone has a somewhat bitter taste, but it can be combined very effectively with mustard seed and hot pepper in seasoning a fish. Fenugreek alone is generally too rank, although it serves brilliantly to season a dish of creamed spinach, the way the French do it with mace. This illustrates the exciting principle of combining spices, that an ingredient which fails to please on its own may make an invaluable contribution in a mixture.

My own introduction to food in India, twenty years ago, was not so scientific as this.

Ashore in Bombay after a three-week voyage from Liverpool in 1945, I tasted my first food on Indian soil at the venerable Taj Mahal Hotel. A table-d'hôte lunch at the Taj in those days began with an hors-d'oeuvre that was basically European but included an Indian taste or two. It is instinctive with an Indian cook to put a bit of coriander leaf into the ravigote, minced hot green chili to pep up anything calling for chopped onion, and a pinch of curry powder in the mayonnaise. Then followed an important main dish, a choice of something European or a curry. And finally a macédoine of tropical fruits or ice cream of an indigenous flavor such as mango, coconut, pomegranate, or pistachio.

By a stroke of luck my first curry at the Taj was the most unusual: a curry of quail. I have since been told that in the refined Moghul cooking of Lucknow chicken is served only in the winter and quail only in the summer. It was August, the monsoon season in Bombay, and the tiny birds had been brought in from the nearby marshes. The quail curry of the Taj was rich with butter, coconut, and poppy seeds, included tomatoes and yogurt, and was finished in the Moghul style, with cream, saffron, lime juice, and cashew nuts. Cashews are the chief nuts of southern India. Almonds and pistachios predominate in the North, and peanuts are found everywhere. Any nuts, ground, help to enrich and thicken a curry, as do yogurt and cream, and such minced vegetables as onions, tomatoes, squashes, and cucumbers. Indians do not thicken sauces with flour or cornstarch or meat gelatin.

The Taj curry was positively paraded to the table by a trio of bearers. Number One filled oversize dinner plates with mountains of rice, not ordinary boiled rice, but extra-quality (India is said to have 200 varieties) rice pilaf, rich with onions and spices, butter and stock, saffron and edible silver leaf. Number Two heaped on the curry. Number Three offered an enormous silver tray of condiments. These included thin crisp wafers made of split-pea flour, usually seasoned with crushed black pepper and cumin-seeds in north India but plain in the South, called *popadam* or *papar;* deep-fried bits of dried fish with the saltiness of bacon, called Bombay duck; a mango chutney (sweet) and a mango pickle (sour); coconut scrapings with minced hot chilies and coriander leaves; and a mixture of sliced onions, tomatoes, and fresh lime with minced chilies and coriander. There were no raisins or sieved hard-cooked eggs.

This service was what certain colonials would have called a three-boy curry. A six-boy or ten-boy curry meant that many bearers and more dishes to sample and combine. Actually even the third bearer, the one with the condiments, was superfluous with two such nobly seasoned dishes as a Moghul curry and rich pilaf.

When I had gone through the Taj repertory of curries I began to look around Bombay for other types of food. There were several places popular with the British army, but they seemed to serve everything fried: fried mutton or fish cutlets with Indian seasonings, fried steak with fried eggs, fried tomatoes and onions, fried chips, even fried bread. About the only thing not fried was the Sergeant Major's tea, made with condensed milk, strong and sweet. Then I found the India Coffee House, where snacks were available, including small meat or vegetable fritters, together with fine strong south India coffee.

South India grows some of the world's choice coffee, but there isn't enough for export. You can't even get a good cup of it in north India, except at the India Coffee Houses in the few big cities. Young intellectuals use these coffeehouses as people do everywhere in the world, for meeting friends and seeing a bit of life and having long hours of conversation. They and the coffee-loving populace of southern India mostly drink their coffee mixed with hot milk and sugar, and aerated—poured back and forth from metal tumbler to bowl in flashing streams that contribute to the scene at coffee stalls and on railway platforms in the south. The aeration introduces oxygen, which improves the coffee's flavor. Cashew nuts, either salted or spiced, go well with an after-dinner coffee enriched with cream.

What coffee is to the south, tea is to northern India. It grows in excellent quality on the slopes around Darjeeling and extensively in Assam. It is drunk in the morning, often twice, and in the afternoon at teatime. Some people enjoy it throughout the day. All Indian tea is black, that is to say fermented, and virtually everyone takes it with milk and sugar. It should be brewed in a clean pot, for at least six minutes to get full flavor, and any that is left in the pot should be thrown away after fifteen minutes, when the undesirable tannin starts to come out. The thing that affects the flavor of tea most, after the quality of the leaf itself, is the quality of the water. If you don't get good tea with your city water supply, you can try bottled or well water.

One day while searching for new eating places in Bombay I came upon Joshi's Bangle Shop. "Genuine Bombay Bangles," the sign said, "S. Joshi, Prop." The walls of the small open-front shop were solidly lined with racks of bangles—glass bracelets, mostly, encrusted with tiny mirrors, gilt wires, beads, imitation pearls and stones. They were dazzling, full of life, as colorful as the tropical birds of India. S. Joshi was hopping about in the shop like a bird, chattering to himself the glib phrases of the pitch-man, like a pianist practicing scales. We became friends, and I went back many times.

When one of Joshi's important customers arrived in her curtained automobile or carriage, he would pull a large flowered curtain across the whole front of his shop. If I came to call during one of these visits (the curtain gave me the feeling that a seance must be going on inside), I waited for Joshi at the India Coffee House or at a small vegetarian restaurant that sold a safe glass of ice water for a penny. This restaurant also made good ice cream and sold dishes of spicy vegetables for about ten cents each.

Most people of India are vegetarians, most of all in the West and the South. This may be largely on account of poverty or tradition, but in Joshi's case it was conviction. He pointed out to me that man is the only animal that appears to eat both meat and vegetables by nature, and that can make a choice. He was throwing in his lot with the peaceful vegetarian cow rather than the destructive carnivorous tiger. He and other Indian vegetarians get their protein mainly from dried peas and beans and from milk products. Here, in fact, are two of the basic four or five items in the diet of the ordinary Indian villager, who is nearly always a vegetarian out of poverty. Dried peas and beans are cooked with a little salt and hot pepper or spice into a soup, which may be thick or thin, called *dal*. Milk is drunk mainly with tea or coffee, or is turned into curds or yogurt or buttermilk.

Then every Indian eats grain, mainly rice in the East and South, wheat in the North and West. Whole wheat is ground and made into thin rounds of unleavened bread called *chapati*. Variations include mixing whole wheat and white flours or wheat and rice, rolling and folding the bread into many thin layers with butter in between, and deep-frying rather than frying on a dry griddle, then on the coals, as *chapati* are cooked. In northwest India a popular bread called *nan* is made of white flour, lightly leavened, and baked in a clay oven. There are other breads thin as paper, some baked in ovens, some made of fermented dough, some made with milk. But the poor man's bread is the *chapati* of whole-wheat flour and plain water, cooked without fat.

In the South rice is ground to a paste with lentils and water, fermented, and made into a light steamed cake called *idli,* or into a thin pancake called *dosa. Masala dosas* are these pancakes stuffed with a spiced vegetable such as potatoes.

The only remaining item in the ordinary villager's diet is tea or coffee, drunk with milk and sugar. As he moves up the economic ladder he is likely to add more milk and sugar for making sweets, and more fat for cooking or dribbling on cooked food. Except in certain richly endowed regions he isn't likely to take to high-quality animal protein or fruits or even a wide range of vegetables.

One of the exceptional regions is the Punjab, in northwest India, where the climate permits the richest farms and best diet of the whole land. Here live the tall bearded Sikhs, who love to eat. Another exception to the ordinary village diet is found along the seacoast and in riverine areas such as Bengal. There fish are eaten by a good part of the people. Lobsters are transported a thousand miles from Bombay and Calcutta to Delhi, largely for the delectation of the Bengali community in the capital.

I was very pleased when Joshi felt that he could invite me to his home for lunch. We had been talking about the curries served at the Taj and other European-style eating places in Bombay. None of them, he said, represented the way people ate at home in Bombay or anywhere in India. They were adaptations of north Indian dishes, made for the British taste. Why wasn't more authentic Indian food available to visitors, in public hotels and restaurants, I wanted to know. Because the British didn't care, Joshi explained, and neither did the Indians.

The important day came, and Joshi took me to his house in the Bombay suburbs. We sat on the veranda, and when lunch was ready we washed our hands there, pouring the water from a brass pot and letting it fall on the flowerbeds. At the dining table our metal trays had been filled with *chapati*. We each received a small metal cup of thin *dal* with tomatoes, hot pickles, and a couple of milk sweets. It is a regional peculiarity of Gujarat to eat both wheat and rice at the same meal, and to have sweets at the beginning, with the bread. When our *chapati* were gone, we got a mound of plain rice, together with more *dal* and curds. Several dishes of spiced vegetables were passed, including a delicious okra with buttermilk. There was one dish of curried minced lamb, called *keema,* that had been made because the family feared I couldn't be satisfied unless I had some meat. Feeling rather like a tiger, I ate it, but tried to explain that with so many other wonderful dishes it wasn't necessary.

Joshi's luncheon party was a success, and his brother's children entertained their schoolmates for days afterward with accounts of the American sahib who ate with his fingers. Joshi and I met many more times and made several excursions into the neighboring countryside, where we took along picnic lunches. On a trip to the Elephanta Caves in Bombay Harbor there was cold rice with buttermilk, hot chilies, and coriander leaves for my vegetarian friend, and for the carnivorous American delicious little chicken sandwiches with Indian seasonings, wrapped in fresh cool green leaves to keep them moist.

One had to travel only a few miles outside Bombay to see villages with the primitive qualities of Biblical times, and to realize that India is living in many different centuries, in many stages of development, simultaneously. One thing that ties the modern cities and the primitive villages together is the common celebration of festivals. Religious festivals, harvest festivals, fertility festivals, patriotic festivals—India celebrates some thirty of them as national holidays, more than one every two weeks. Maharajas and schoolchildren, shopkeepers and housewives, officials and laborers, all of them love holidays.

No month of the year is without its celebrations, beginning in January with the rice-harvest festival of the South, Pongal. The newly gathered grain is ceremoniously cooked and shared by the whole family, including the beloved cows and bullocks, whose horns are painted bright orange and blue and festooned with tinsel for the occasion. The liveliest and most colorful festival, Holi, is enjoyed all over north India in March. Grateful for the warming sunshine and riotously colored flowers of spring, people throw colored powders or colored water on their friends and even on strangers in the street. If you have old clothes, that's the day to remember to wear them. Indians who have nothing but old clothes, and no change of them, may go around for weeks afterward looking like harlequins. Formal greetings and sweetmeats are given at Holi.

In September comes Ram Lila in the North (called Durga Puja in Bengal) and the great spectacle of Dasara in the South. In Mysore the former Maharaja parades his palace elephants, which have charming flower designs painted around their ears and down their trunks. Their toenails are also decorated. Here are shown the royal howdahs and ceremonial mahouts, leftovers of colonial and princely India. October brings Diwali, the night when the whole country becomes a fairyland of flickering oil lamps. Diwali honors the goddess Lakshmi, or Kali in Bengal. This holiday has recently become the chief annual occasion for exchange of gifts, and stores in all the big cities advise you to "Do Your Diwali Shopping Early."

Nationally or locally India honors the holidays of every major religion. In December, Christmas is celebrated by Christians, in Kerala and scattered throughout the land. Hindus and Moslems in big cities may also mark December 25, especially if their children go to English schools and if they have foreign friends.

Soon after independence in 1947, India was divided into a series of large states, some old, some new, some familiar names with reduced territory, some familiar territory with altered names. Bengal in the East and the Punjab in the West—each lost a large part of its land to Pakistan. The United Provinces in north-central India kept the same initials while changing the name to Uttar Pradesh. Travancore and Cochin on the southwest coast became Kerala. Madras remained Madras but lost its northern part to Andhra, which took in most of Hyderabad. The division was made along linguistic lines. Except for Hindi, a different major language is spoken by almost all the people in each state. While the boundaries between cooking styles are not so sharp or easy to define as between the languages, I think it is clear that there are major regional differences.

Just as France can be divided into areas where food is cooked principally in butter, olive oil, or lard, India has cooking fats that predominate in certain areas sufficiently so that at least one authority has said the country could be divided up according to oils rather than languages. In Madras the common oils are sesame and peanut; in Kerala, coconut; in Bombay, sesame; in Bengal, mustard; in the Punjab, butter oil or ghee. Ghee is clarified butter, with the solids and water removed. Clarified butter, unlike butter with impurities, apparently keeps forever. Some of it was found in the ruins of Mohenjo-Daro, more than 3,000 years old, and it hadn't turned rancid yet.

In the last analysis, just about every food known to man is eaten by at least a few of the diverse people in some corner of India's climatic and geographic spectrum. The variety of fruits is staggering: a dozen kinds of bananas in one city market at one season, many different mangoes, papayas, sweet limes, pineapples, custard apples, sour limes or lemons, pomegranates, guavas, tangerines, apples, pears, grapes. I have eaten large yellow raspberries in Kashmir, where all the familiar temperate-climate fruits and vegetables are grown. The Indian Ocean and certain rivers teem with fish. Nonvegetarian Hindus normally eat only chicken, mutton, and goat, but Moslems eat beef as well, when they can get it. Only Christians and aborigines eat pork, and a scattering of hunters eat game birds and animals.

Despite her great variety, India's countryside is still impoverished, communications are poor, and a traveler stopping at a rural *dak* bungalow may be offered nothing better than brown soup and mutton cutlets or Country Captain, a dish named for colonial officers who dropped in unannounced and were given hash. And just as fine cooking has largely been home cooking in India, the influence of Indian food in the West has been so slight that it almost escapes detection. A pinch of curry powder in soup or mayonnaise; a curry-flavored white sauce with shrimps, chicken, or lamb; Major Grey's chutney; Indian tonic or quinine water—these are about all most of us have ever been offered from the cuisine of this vast and varied subcontinent. For us the best of Indian cooking is still a world apart, a land unto itself, waiting to be discovered.

NOTE

Estimated servings are based on using a single meat or fish dish as a main course. If many dishes are offered on a buffet table, more servings are possible from each dish.

PACHADI
(Yogurt Salad)

Here is a thin soupy salad in the style of Madras, cool and nourishing, delicious on a hot day. You can drink it or eat it with a spoon, have it as a first course, or serve it with a hot curry.

    1 pint plain yogurt
    1 medium tomato, peeled and diced
    1 teaspoon minced hot green chili
        pepper
    1 small onion, minced
    ¼ cup chopped fresh coriander leaves
        or parsley
    1 teaspoon mustard seed
    ½ teaspoon cuminseed
        Salt to taste

Stir all ingredients together until well mixed. (Juice from the tomato will thin out the yogurt.) If fresh hot green peppers are unavailable, use canned Mexican or Italian ones, adjusting quantity to taste. Makes 4 servings.

MURGHA KARI
(Chicken Curry with Tomatoes)

This dish from the Punjab takes only 30 minutes to prepare. In India, fresh

tomatoes would be simmered, seasoned, skinned, and strained, but for us all this work is done by the makers of canned tomato sauce.

    4 medium onions, chopped
    2 tablespoons curry powder
    ½ cup butter or cooking oil
    1 cup or 1 can (8 ounces) tomato
        sauce
    2 teaspoons salt
    1 frying chicken (2 to 3 pounds)
    ¾ cup hot water

Use a casserole or large skillet with lid. Cook onions and curry powder in butter for 10 to 15 minutes. Add tomato sauce and salt. Disjoint and skin chicken, and place in sauce. Cook, uncovered, over medium heat, turning frequently until sauce becomes quite dry and chicken tests done with fork, about 15 minutes. Add hot water, cover pot, and cook over low heat for 5 minutes. Makes 4 servings.

Note: When making the dish again, increase or decrease curry powder according to its strength and your taste. Or add an additional flavor such as ½ teaspoon ground cloves or ginger, or chopped fresh tarragon or mint.

KEEMA MATAR
(Chopped Meat with Peas)

A simple north Indian dish (the one prepared especially for me at Joshi's lunch), this is one of the best ways to dress up chopped meat. Indian spices take especially well to lamb, but ground beef can be used if you prefer.

    1½ pounds lamb or beef, ground
    1 tablespoon minced garlic
    2 tablespoons curry powder
    1 cinnamon stick
    1 teaspoon minced fresh gingerroot
        or ½ teaspoon ground ginger
    1 teaspoon salt
    1 package (10 ounces) frozen peas

Sauté meat in skillet, chopping and turning to break it up. As soon as pan becomes moist, add all other ingredients except peas. Stir and cook until meat is done, keeping it crumbly, not caked. Add peas and cook and stir until just thawed and heated through. Makes 4 servings.

■ **Variation**—Substitute for green peas ½ cup split peas soaked in 1 cup water. Add peas and water to meat at beginning of cooking, cover, and cook until peas are tender.

PALAK GOSHT
(Lamb with Spinach)

This Punjab dish is relatively dry.

    1½ pounds lamb cut into 1-inch cubes
    1 cup plain yogurt
    1 medium onion, chopped
    1 tablespoon ground coriander
    1 teaspoon each of ground turmeric
        and cuminseed
    ⅛ teaspoon cayenne
    2 teaspoons salt

    ¼ cup butter or margarine
    1 pound spinach, washed and chopped

Place lamb in yogurt to marinate for at least 2 hours, preferably overnight. Sauté onions and all spices in butter. Add lamb with yogurt, and mix together. Sauté for another 5 minutes. Place spinach on top of meat, cover, and cook over low heat for 40 minutes, or until meat is done. Stir as necessary to prevent sticking; in the end, meat and spinach will be mixed together. Makes 6 servings.

SOOWAR KA GOSHT VINDALOO
(Sour Pork Curry)

This is the sour curry popular in Bombay. In this recipe it is made with pork, but it can be made with any meat, with poultry, or even with shrimps.

    2 pounds lean pork, cut into ¾-inch
        cubes
    ½ cup vinegar
    4 medium onions, chopped
    1 teaspoon minced garlic
    1 tablespoon minced gingerroot or
        1½ teaspoons powdered ginger
    1 tablespoon mustard seed
    1 teaspoon ground turmeric
    ½ teaspoon cayenne
    ¼ cup cooking oil
    1 cup chicken bouillon
    6 medium potatoes, peeled and
        quartered

Marinate meat in vinegar, onions, garlic, and seasonings for 2 hours or more. Place in top-stove casserole with oil and bouillon. (Sesame oil is used in western India, but any cooking oil will do.) Cook over medium heat for 20 minutes. Add potatoes and cook slowly, covered, for about 40 minutes, or until they are tender. Add more bouillon if necessary. Makes 6 servings.

ROGAN GOSHT
(Lamb Curry)

An exceptionally rich dish of the Punjab, this type of lamb curry needs plain rice or *chapati* to go with it. It may also be made with beef.

    2 medium onions, chopped
    1 cup butter or margarine
    1 pound small white turnips, peeled
        and halved
    2 pounds lamb in large cubes
    1 tablespoon sugar
    1 cup plain yogurt
    1 tablespoon ground coriander
    ¼ to ½ teaspoon cayenne
    2 teaspoons salt
        Hot water
    ½ teaspoon each of ground cardamom,
        cloves, and saffron

Brown onions in the butter. Add all other ingredients except saffron, and cook for 25 minutes, or until meat is browned. Add 1 cup hot water. Reduce heat and simmer, covered, for 45 minutes, or until meat is tender. Dissolve saffron in 1 tablespoon hot water and add just before serving. Makes 6 servings.

Chapati

Rogan Gosht

Pachadi

Gajar Halwa

Bhaji Malida Machli

SARSON BHARA KEKDA
(Shrimps with Mustard)

Here is the Bengali specialty that features the taste of turmeric, without the other curry-powder spices.

    2 tablespoons mustard seed, ground
    1 teaspoon ground turmeric
    ¼ cup mustard oil or any cooking oil
    1 large onion, ground
    1½ pounds shrimps, peeled and deveined
    1 tablespoon minced hot green chili peppers
    1 teaspoon salt

Make a paste of the mustard seed and turmeric with a little water. Add all other ingredients, cover, and cook at the gentlest simmer until shrimps are fully pink, 5 to 10 minutes, depending on size of shrimps. Makes 4 servings.

KEKDA BENGALI
(Bengali Crab)

This recipe may also be made with fresh lobster meat, scallops, or shrimps. As a matter of fact, the word *kekda* means either crab or shrimp.

    2 packages (6 ounces each) frozen King crabmeat
    2 medium onions, chopped
    6 tablespoons mustard oil or cooking oil
    1 tablespoon minced gingerroot or 1 teaspoon powdered ginger
    1 cup plain yogurt
    1 teaspoon each of ground coriander, turmeric, cuminseed, and salt
    1 teaspoon minced hot green chili pepper

Allow crabmeat to thaw partially. Cook onions in the oil until brown, add all other ingredients except crabmeat, and simmer for 5 minutes. Add crabmeat and simmer until thoroughly thawed, then simmer for another 5 minutes. Makes 4 servings.

BHAJI MALIDA MACHLI
(Stuffed Fish with Greens)

    1 whole striped bass or haddock (3 to 4 pounds)
    ½ cup chopped fresh coriander or parsley
    ½ cup chopped green onions, including tops
    2 tablespoons hot green chili pepper
    2 tablespoons minced gingerroot or 1 teaspoon powdered ginger
    2 teaspoons salt
    ¼ cup cooking oil
    2 tablespoons fresh lime juice

Wash fish and wipe dry. Combine all other ingredients and place as much in cavity of fish as it will hold. Brush remainder over outside of fish and place on rack in fish steamer or boiler. Steam with small amount of water until flesh tests done with fork. If no steamer is available, fish may be wrapped in foil and baked in preheated moderate oven (350°F.) for 45 to 50 minutes. Makes 4 servings.

CHANNA KARI
(Chick-Pea Curry)

This provides the vegetable protein required by the many Indians who eat no meat. If you use canned rather than dried chick-peas, it is quick to prepare.

    1 tablespoon curry powder
    1 tablespoon minced garlic
    ½ cup chopped sweet green pepper
    ¼ cup cooking oil
    2 cans (each 1-pound, 4 ounces) chick-peas
    1 teaspoon salt
    ¼ cup chopped fresh coriander or parsley

Sauté curry powder, garlic, and green pepper in oil. Add chick-peas and salt, stir, and heat through. Simmer for 5 minutes and serve sprinkled with coriander. Makes 6 servings.

MOONG KI DAL
(Mung Beans)

Another of India's best-known foods, rich in protein, this *dal* is made with either mung beans, the dark-green beans used for bean sprouts, or green split peas.

    1 cup mung beans or split peas
    2 tablespoons curry powder
    1 teaspoon salt
    2 whole hot green chili peppers
    2 medium onions, sliced
    ¼ cup cooking oil

Soak beans in water to cover for several hours. Bring to boil, add curry powder, salt, and peppers, and cook for 1 to 2 hours, depending on desired texture of finished dish. Peppers will have lost most of their heat and may be given to anybody who wants them. Amount of water used will determine whether the result is a thick soup or a mush. Fry onions in the oil until very brown and place on top of *dal* with any unabsorbed oil when serving. Makes 6 servings. ings.

DAHI BHATH
(Rice with Buttermilk)

This is Joshi's cold rice, as it was made for our picnics. Carry it in foil or eat it at home in hot weather.

    1½ cups cold cooked rice
    1 cup buttermilk
    1 teaspoon each of minced garlic and hot green chili pepper
    ¼ cup chopped fresh coriander
       Salt to taste

Combine all ingredients. If rice does not hold together, add more buttermilk until desired stickiness is reached. Makes 4 servings.

PONGAL

This rice dish has the same name as the January harvest festival in South India. It can be made either hot or (as follows) sweet.

    ½ cup mung beans or green split peas
    ½ cup butter or margarine
       Water

    ¾ cup uncooked rice
    ⅔ cup sugar
    ½ cup cashew nuts
    ¼ cup raisins
       Pinch each of ground cloves and cardamom

Fry beans in 1 tablespoon of the butter until lightly browned. Bring to boil 3½ cups water, add beans and rice, and cook until very soft. Add 2 tablespoons water to sugar and boil to a syrup, about 10 minutes. Add cooked rice and beans to syrup and stir, adding remaining butter, nuts, and raisins. Serve hot, sprinkled with cloves and cardamom. Makes 6 servings.

GAJAR HALWA
(Carrot Dessert)

One of India's most delicious and nutritious desserts.

       Water
    1 can (14 ounces) sweetened condensed milk
    2 cups grated carrot
    1 cup cooking oil, butter, or margarine
    2 tablespoons each of chopped blanched almonds and raisins
    ¼ teaspoon ground saffron
    1 tablespoon fresh lime juice, heated

Add 1 can of water to condensed milk and bring to boil. Add carrot and cook over low heat for about 45 minutes, stirring occasionally. Add oil gradually. Cook until fat begins to separate. Then add almonds and raisins, and the saffron dissolved in lime juice. May be eaten hot or cold. Makes 6 servings.

INVERT SUGAR—A mixture that results from the process used in making jelly, jam, candy, and frosting. With the use of heat and an acid, sugar is changed from sucrose to a mixture of glucose and fructose. Invert sugar keeps the sugar crystals small; therefore, the resulting product is creamier and smoother. The acid used may be vinegar, lemon juice, or cream of tartar. Heat alone can cause inversion of sugar but it occurs more quickly when an acid is added.

Acid in fruit juice also stops jellies and jams from recrystallizing; therefore, it keeps them clear and smooth.

IRISh cookeRY

BY MAURA LAVERTY □ <u>Cead mile failte,</u> *a hundred thousand welcomes,*
this is the flavoring we offer with every dish in Ireland.
Not, indeed, that Irish food needs sauce or embellishment.
Thanks to our soft, mild climate, the lush grazing of our pasturelands
gives us prime meat and dairy products, and the richness of
our soil gives us the best of vegetables and fruits.
To serve a plump Irish chicken other than plain boiled or roast
would be a sin against its tender goodness
and an insult to the skilled woman who reared it.

Plain boiled in its jacket is how we prefer our potato, the vegetable which is a "must" at least once a day in every home. It may be that there are four hundred ways of preparing potatoes, but I have yet to sample one which equals the flavor of the boiled Irish potato. Of course, we serve our potatoes in many other ways. Potato cakes dripping with butter may not be a weight reducer, but they are certainly a delight to the eye and to the palate. Boxty, the traditional dish eaten on Shrove Tuesday, is composed of grated raw potatoes and mashed cooked potatoes with a binding of flour. You may have your boxty baked on the griddle or fried in the pan, but whichever method you choose, you must never forget to stir into the mixture that all-important ring wrapped in paper which foretells an early marriage for the lucky finder.

Although the potato blight of Black '47 which decimated our population taught us not to place too much reliance on the "spud," we in Ireland still believe that a day without potatoes is a day without nourishment. In the West, no one uses the cold term "potato field"; with affection they speak of "the potato garden." The very names of Irish potatoes are gastronomic poetry: Ulster Chieftain, Golden Wonder, Aran Banner, May Queen, Skerry Champion, etc.

According to the World Health Organization, we Irish rank high on the list of well-fed peoples. I have often wondered if this is not due mainly to the fact that forty-nine per cent of our population is agricultural, and that most of our farms are small holdings of from thirty to forty acres. Because of this, our farmers produce enough food for themselves and for town dwellers. And the short distances between towns and farms make us independent of processed and frozen food. "Plastic food," as we call it, and no one will ever convince us that it can be as flavorsome and nutritious as the food which comes straight from the good earth.

Long, long ago a poet sang, "A plenteous place is Ireland of hospitable cheer." Part of that cheer is the bread made in our own kitchens with our own grain and buttermilk. White bread, griddle bread, brown bread, potato bread, buns, scones, and potato cakes—the making of these is a daily ritual in most Irish homes. The eating of them is a thrice-daily delight whether served plain with golden butter or with our heather-scented honey or with the homemade jams of which we are proud. Sometimes, but not often enough, our bread is accompanied by cheese, for cheese making

on an industrial scale is comparatively new in this pastoral land of ours.

Being gemmed with lakes and rivers, it is natural that Ireland should abound in fish. The lazy Suir, the tree-fringed Blackwater, the broad Boyne, and the lovely lakes of the Shannon—these are the principal sources of that noblest of fish, the gleaming salmon. I have stood on Galway Bridge and watched those arcs of silver take the leap with an indolence which bespoke their fatness.

Every lake and river in Ireland offers a wealth of trout, both brown and speckled. From the Liffey to the smallest lake in Connemara, you will find trout galore. So well stocked are our rivers and lakes with salmon and trout that these are among our chief exports to France and Britain where, no doubt, cooks have their own ways of preparing them. Here, at home, we like our salmon poached and served whole with melted butter and lemon; or cut into thick slices and simmered golden in butter. And I know of no better way with a good-size trout than to split it, remove the backbone, dip it into seasoned rolled oats, and fry it in butter. Some people like to add a little vinegar and mustard to the butter in which the trout has been fried.

As in so many other countries, Christmas is the great Irish feast. It commences on Christmas Eve with the lighting of the Christmas candle which is placed in the window of every house in the country as a sign to any homeless strangers who may be abroad that we are eager and willing to try to compensate for the cold welcome offered to Mary and Joseph on the first Christmas Eve. When midnight ends the Christmas Eve fast, there is a meal of spiced beef, corned brisket rich in spices, simmered to tenderness and served cold. For dinner on Christmas Day there is the special fattened fowl, a goose stuffed with sage-and-onion dressing, or a roast turkey ringed with golden sausages and bursting with parsley-and-thyme dressing. In either case, a boiled ham accompanies the fowl. The time-honored pudding on Christmas Day is, of course, a flaming plum pudding which may have been made for as long as six months in advance, since its brandied, fruity spiciness improves with keeping. The same is true of the cake of the year: every cook worth her salt makes a rich fruitcake well in advance. Layered with marzipan and coated with snowy icing, it is decorated to taste. In our house, for many years the choice has been a miniature crib.

● ● ●

BREADS

BASIC RECIPE FOR SODA BREAD
2 cups unsifted all-purpose flour
1½ teaspoons baking powder
¾ teaspoon salt
¼ teaspoon baking soda
1 cup buttermilk

Mix dry ingredients. Add buttermilk and stir to make a soft dough. Turn out on lightly floured board and knead for about 1 minute. Shape the dough into a round loaf about 8 inches in diameter. Put in a greased round pan or on a greased cookie sheet. With a sharp knife, cut a cross on the top. Bake in preheated moderate oven (350°F.) for 40 minutes, or until done. Bread is done if it sounds hollow when tapped with the knuckles. Cool on its side before cutting. For a soft crust, wrap loaf in a tea towel and stand on its side to cool.

BOXTY-ON-THE-GRIDDLE
For this recipe I am indebted to Grannie Doyle of Lennox Street, Dublin, who told me, "Now I'll tell you how our boxty bread was baked. My mother took a couple of grated raw potatoes and a skillet of hot mashed potatoes, 3 or 4 handfuls of flour with a bit of butter rubbed in and a generous grain of salt— all mixed well and rolled out on the board, cut into squares, and baked on a well-greased griddle to the tune of the children singing:

Three pans of boxty, baking all the day, What use is boxty without a cup of tay?

The children in those days got very little 'tay.' Each one got a nice tin porringer of m'lk and sat up to the table and ate hot buttered boxty to the fill—and we lived."

BOXTY-ON-THE-PAN
1 cup each of grated raw potatoes, all-purpose flour, and mashed potatoes
2 teaspoons each of baking powder and salt
2 eggs
Milk to mix (about ¼ cup)

Squeeze the grated raw potatoes in a cloth to remove as much moisture as possible. Sift the flour with baking powder and salt. Mix all potatoes and dry ingredients well together with beaten eggs; add sufficient milk to make a dropping batter. Drop by tablespoonfuls onto a hot buttered frying pan and cook over moderate heat, allowing about 4 minutes on each side. Serve hot and well buttered, with or without sugar. Makes 4 to 6 servings.

SOUPS

COCK-A-LEEKIE SOUP

When the Scottish planters came over the border and took over the rich Ulster farms, ordering their rightful owners "to Hell or to Connaught," they brought with them just one good thing: their cock-a-leekie soup.

- 1 elderly fowl (stewing chicken, about 4 pounds)
- 4 pounds boneless shin of beef
- 3 dozen leeks
- 3 quarts cold water
- 1 tablespoon salt
- 1 teaspoon pepper
- 1 cup pitted dried prunes

Truss the fowl as for boiling. Cut up the beef into small pieces. Wash the leeks, cut into thin slices, using as much as possible of the green part. Put all ingredients except prunes in a large pot. Simmer for 3 hours, then add pitted prunes and simmer for 1 hour longer. Take up the fowl, remove skin, gristle, and bones; chop the meat small and return to the pot. Correct seasoning. The prunes should be left in the soup. Makes 5 quarts.

PRIDE OF ERIN SOUP

- 1 green cabbage (about 1 pound)
- 2 tablespoons butter
- 3 tablespoons chopped onion
- ¼ cup chopped raw potato
- ½ teaspoon ground mace
- 2 tablespoons all-purpose flour
- 2½ cups milk
- 2½ cups water or chicken bouillon
    Salt and pepper
- ¼ cup heavy cream, whipped
- 2 tablespoons chopped parsley
- 2 tablespoons grated cheese (Parmesan preferably)

Quarter the cabbage; cut away the hard stalk. Cover with boiling water and leave for 5 minutes. Drain, pat dry, and shred. Melt the butter in a heavy pan over low heat and simmer the chopped onion until tender, but without browning. Add cabbage and potato and stir over low heat. Add mace. Stir in the flour to coat all ingredients, but do not brown. Add the liquids, bring to a boil, and simmer for 20 minutes, or until vegetables are tender. Rub through a sieve. Reheat and add salt and pepper to taste. If soup is too thick, add a little boiling milk. Serve with a spoonful of whipped cream on each serving. Sprinkle parsley and grated cheese on the cream. Makes about 7 cups.

WATERCRESS SOUP

- 3 cups milk
- 3 cups mashed potatoes
- 2 teaspoons salt
- 2 cups chopped watercress leaves
- 2 tablespoons butter

Combine boiling milk, mashed potatoes, and salt. Stir until smooth and boiling. Add watercress and cook for 5 minutes. Remove from heat and stir in butter. Makes about 7 cups.

FISH

DINGLE MACKEREL

- 6 small mackerel
- ¼ cup white vinegar
- ¾ cup water
    Few grains of cayenne
- 6 peppercorns
- 1-inch piece of cinnamon stick
- 1 bay leaf
- 3 parsley sprigs
- 2 teaspoons salt

Cut off head and fins. Wash and clean mackerel, split, and remove backbones and tails. Roll up and place in a 1½-quart casserole. Bring vinegar, water, spices, bay leaf, parsley, and seasoning to boil and pour over fish. Cover and bake in preheated moderate oven (375° F.) for 45 minutes. Makes 6 servings.

LIFFEY TROUT WITH MUSHROOM SAUCE

I have known the delight of preparing and eating this dish after catching the trout myself in a leaf-dappled stretch of the Liffey. And, on the way home, I stopped at a field where *cuppeens* (little button mushrooms) nestled like fallen stars among the tufts of grass. There are few joys on earth to compare with gathering mushrooms in the early morning. Next best is to buy your trout and your mushrooms and to prepare the fish in this way:

- 4 small trout
- 6 tablespoons all-purpose flour
    Pepper and salt
- 6 tablespoons butter
    About 12 button mushrooms
- 1 cup half cream and half milk
- 1 tablespoon chopped parsley

Clean, wash, and dry the trout. Roll in ¼ cup of the flour seasoned with pepper and salt. Fry in ¼ cup of the butter. Drain, and keep hot. Wipe and slice the mushrooms and sauté in the same pan in which the trout were fried. Melt remaining butter in a small saucepan; stir in remaining flour. Add cream and milk and season to taste. Add mushrooms and reheat to serving point. Garnish the trout with parsley and serve sauce separately. Makes 4 servings.

MEAT AND POULTRY

STUFFED PORK FILLETS

- 2 fresh pork fillets or tenderloin
- 1 cup fine dry bread crumbs
- 1 parboiled onion, chopped
- ¼ teaspoon ground sage
    Butter
    Milk or chicken bouillon
    Salt and pepper
    Thick brown gravy
    Apple sauce

Split fillets lengthwise and flatten them well. On half of each fillet place stuffing made as follows: Combine bread crumbs with onion, sage, 1 tablespoon melted butter, sufficient milk to bind, and salt and pepper to taste. Fold over each fillet and secure in place by sewing or skewering. Weigh. Place in baking pan, dot with butter, and roast in preheated moderate oven (350°F.) allowing 40 minutes to the pound. Serve with brown gravy and apple sauce. Makes 4 servings.

BEEF-AND-KIDNEY PUDDING

    All-purpose flour
- 1 teaspoon baking powder
    Salt
- 1 cup finely chopped beef suet
- 1 cup fine stale-bread crumbs
    Water to mix
- ¾ pound round steak, cut into small pieces
- ¼ pound beef kidney, cut into small pieces
- ¼ pound mushrooms, sliced
- 2 tablespoons chopped onion
- 1 tablespoon chopped parsley
- ¼ teaspoon pepper
- ⅔ cup beef bouillon or water

Sift 1 cup flour with the baking powder and ½ teaspoon salt. Add suet and crumbs and mix well. Add enough water to make a stiff dough. Line a 1-quart casserole with half the dough. Put meats, mushrooms, onion, and parsley in layers in lined casserole, sprinkling each layer with 3 tablespoons flour, seasoned with 1 teaspoon salt and the pepper. Add the bouillon. Cover with remaining dough, moisten edges, and press together well. Cover with greased foil and steam for 3 hours. Makes 4 servings.

VEAL HOT POT

- 2 pounds lean veal
- 2 large onions
- 8 young carrots
- ¼ pound sliced bacon
- ¼ cup all-purpose flour
    Salt and pepper to taste
- 2 tablespoons dry sherry
- 1 cup chicken bouillon or water

Dice veal, peel and slice onions, wash and slice carrots, dice bacon. Mix flour with salt and pepper; combine sherry with

*Irish Stew, Colcannon, Barmbrack,
and Irish Coffee*

bouillon. Put layer of onion and carrot in a greased 2-quart casserole; add a layer of bacon and veal. Repeat until all are used, sprinkling each layer with some seasoned flour. Add combined sherry and bouillon. Cover closely and cook in preheated very slow oven (275°F.) for about 2½ hours. Makes 4 to 6 servings.

BAKED LIMERICK HAM

Long ago a whole pig would have been baked in a pit lined with stones previously heated in the fire. Or it might have been cooked in one of the great bronze caldrons which were the most treasured possessions of well-to-do households. Pork was always the favorite meat of the Irish. Wasn't it as a swineherd that St. Patrick first came to us? When the meat was cooked the various cuts were served according to the social importance of the guests:

A thigh for a king and a poet;
A chine for a literary sage;
A leg for a young lord;
Heads for charioteers;
A haunch for a queen.

"The hero's morsel" was the choice tidbit reserved for the man who had performed the greatest or bravest exploit . . . and woe betide anyone who helped himself to it if he was not entitled to the honor. One of the biggest battles in Irish history occurred because a chieftain wrongfully appropriated "the hero's morsel."

1 Limerick ham (10 pounds)
1 tablespoon whole cloves
¾ cup honey
1 cup Madeira wine

Soak the ham in cold water for 12 hours. Place in a pot, cover well with fresh water, and bring slowly to a boil. Allow to simmer for 2 hours. Place the ham in a baking pan, remove the skin, and stick cloves over the entire surface. Pour the honey mixed with Madeira wine over the ham and bake in preheated moderate oven (350°F.) for 2½ hours, or until the knuckle bone can be removed. Makes about 20 servings.

SEVENTEENTH-CENTURY BEEF POT ROAST

1 cup very finely ground veal
1 egg white
3 pounds beef (select a thick solid piece)
4 slices of bacon
Pepper and salt
6 tablespoons all-purpose flour
3 tablespoons beef drippings
1½ cups water or beef bouillon
1 cup red wine
4 medium mushrooms, sliced

Mix veal and egg white. Make holes here

and there in the beef and fill with veal mixture. Lay the strips of bacon on top and tie in place. Mix pepper and salt with 2 tablespoons of the flour; rub into the meat. In heavy pan sear meat quickly on all sides in smoking hot drippings. Add water, wine, and a sprinkling of salt and pepper. Cover and simmer until tender, about 3½ hours. When done, place meat on a platter, remove bacon and string, and keep the meat hot. Skim fat from the liquor and cook down until liquor measures about 2 cups. Add the sliced mushrooms, and thicken with remaining flour blended to a paste with a little cold water. Correct seasoning; serve the gravy separately. This beef is excellent cold. Makes 8 servings.

COCK OF THE NORTH

1 capon, about 6 pounds
Juice of 2 lemons
¼ cup all-purpose flour
Salt and pepper
1 cup butter
½ pound bacon, diced
5 small yellow onions
¾ cup Irish whisky
1 garlic clove
½ teaspoon ground allspice
1 cup dry red wine
1 cup water
2 egg yolks
2 tablespoons light cream
1 pound pearl onions
1 pound mushrooms

Cut up capon as for fricassee. Dip the pieces into lemon juice and then into 3 tablespoons of the flour, seasoned with salt and pepper. Brown in butter. Add bacon and small yellow onions; sprinkle with 1 tablespoon flour, and brown again. Flame the capon with Irish whisky. Add salt, pepper, garlic, and allspice. Cover with wine and water, and simmer gently for 45 to 60 minutes.

For the sauce make a broth with the neck, feet, and giblets. Strain off the liquor from the bird and add to the broth. Reduce to half by rapid boiling. Thicken with the raw egg yolks and cream.

Serve the capon in a dish garnished with the pearl onions and mushrooms, each cooked separately in water and lemon juice. Pour part of the sauce over the capon and serve the remainder separately. Makes 8 to 10 servings.

IRISH STEW

The original Irish stew was made with spareribs. Today we make it with mutton.

2 pounds neck of mutton or lamb
½ pound streaky bacon
3 pounds (9 medium) potatoes
10 to 12 small onions
Salt and pepper
2 cups cold water

Cut the meat into neat pieces and trim away as much fat as possible. Remove rind from bacon and cut into 1-inch pieces. Pare the potatoes and slice the onions. Place a layer of meat in a heavy stewpan, add a layer of bacon, onions, and potatoes, and sprinkle with seasoning. Repeat layers, finishing with potatoes. Add the water, let it come slowly to a boil, remove any scum, cover, and simmer gently for 2½ hours. The potatoes should be cooked to a pulp. Makes 4 servings.

VEGETABLES

BRAISED CABBAGE

1 medium Savoy cabbage
2 tablespoons butter
¼ cup chopped onion
2 large tomatoes, skinned, seeded, and chopped
1 tablespoon all-purpose flour
1 cup chicken bouillon
Salt and pepper to taste
2 teaspoons finely chopped parsley
¼ cup dairy sour cream

Quarter cabbage, remove most of stalk, cover with boiling water, and leave to blanch for 10 minutes. Drain and pat dry in a towel. Place in a glass baking dish. Melt butter over moderate heat and sauté onion until tender but not brown; add chopped tomatoes, stir in flour, add bouillon, and bring to a boil, stirring constantly. Add seasoning and parsley, mix well, and spoon the mixture over the quartered cabbage. Cook, covered, in preheated moderate oven (375°F.) for 30 minutes, basting occasionally. Stir several tablespoons of liquid from cabbage into sour cream. Pour over cabbage, and bake for 15 minutes longer. Makes 4 to 6 servings.

SLIEVE na mBAN CARROTS

The ruddy crest of *Slieve na mBan* (The Mountain of the Women) rising above its stole of milk-white mist gives its name to this dish of cream-wreathed carrots.

12 young carrots
3 tablespoons butter
½ cup milk
Salt and pepper to taste
½ cup heavy cream
2 egg yolks
1 teaspoon finely chopped parsley

Trim and wash carrots and halve lengthwise. Melt butter over moderate heat, add milk, season with salt and pepper, add carrots, and cook gently until tender. Remove from heat, stir in cream and beaten egg yolks, and reheat but do not boil, stirring until eggs thicken. Correct sea-

soning and add parsley. Makes 4 servings.

COLCANNON

This delectable mixture of buttered greens and potatoes is yet another way of foretelling the future at Halloween. A heaped portion is served on each plate. A well is made in the center of the heap to hold a generous amount of butter. The colcannon is eaten from around the outside of the heap, each person dipping his fork first into the colcannon and then into the melted butter. The perfect accompaniment is a glass of fresh buttermilk.

In the Midlands colcannon is called "Thump." In the North and West it is called "Champ." Here is a recipe for colcannon. Put the cooked potatoes through a sieve or ricer. Beat in a good lump of butter and enough hot cream or milk to make the mixture light and fluffy. Add to the potato mixture half its bulk of finely chopped cooked kale and 1 tablespoon minced onion. Add salt and pepper to taste, beat well, and reheat thoroughly. And don't forget the ring and that all-important silver coin.

HAGGERTY

3 medium potatoes
1 large onion
2 tablespoons bacon fat
¾ cup grated Cheddar cheese
Salt and pepper to taste

Wash and pare potatoes, cut into paper-thin slices, and pat dry in a towel. Slice onion very thin. Heat half of bacon fat in a heavy frying pan and fill pan with alternate layers of potatoes and onion and cheese, finishing with potatoes. Sprinkle each layer with salt and pepper. Dot the top layer of potatoes with remainder of bacon fat. Cook over moderate heat until potatoes are almost tender. Turn the Haggerty carefully onto a platter, slip it, top side down, back into the pan, and continue cooking until done. To serve, cut into wedges. Makes 4 servings.

POTATO COLLOPS

There is no denying that the best way of all to cook potatoes is to boil or bake them in their jackets. And, notwithstanding the advice of foreign cooks, the skins of potatoes should not be gashed when being put to cook. If the skins should burst slightly in the boiling and subsequent drying (boiled potatoes should always be shaken for a minute or two over low heat after being drained) it is all to the good: there is no more appetizing sight than the floury "grin" of a burst boiled potato.

Admittedly, during the weeks before the new potatoes are ready for digging, last season's potatoes begin to show their age and sometimes need dressing up. And I know of few better potato dishes than Collops ("collop," by the way, means a small portion of any foodstuff). Originally "collope," the 16th century Irish referred to our famous rashers and eggs as "collopes and eggs."

3 medium potatoes
1 large onion
Salt and pepper to taste
2 teaspoons chopped parsley
¼ pound raw bacon, diced (to be omitted on fast days)
2 tablespoons butter
1 cup milk, boiled
3 tablespoons grated cheese

Pare potatoes and cut into very thin slices. Chop onion. Place a layer of vegetables in a greased baking dish. Sprinkle with seasonings, parsley, and diced bacon (rind removed), and dot with butter. Repeat layers until all ingredients are used, finishing with potatoes. Pour in milk and sprinkle top with grated cheese. Cover and bake in preheated moderate oven (350°F.) for 45 minutes. Uncover and continue cooking until potatoes are done and top layer is brown. Makes 4 servings.

DESSERTS

APPLE PUDDENY-PIE

4 medium cooking apples
1 teaspoon ground cinnamon
½ teaspoon grated nutmeg
½ cup sugar
½ teaspoon salt
⅓ cup water
2 teaspoons fresh lemon juice
1 teaspoon grated lemon rind
½ teaspoon baking soda
1 cup quick-cooking oats
⅓ cup butter

Pare and core apples. Cut into eighths and place in greased baking dish about 10 x 6 inches. Sprinkle with combined spices, sugar, and a little of the salt. Mix water, lemon juice, and grated rind and pour over apples. Add baking soda and remaining salt to oats; work butter into this mixture until crumbly. Spread oatmeal mixture over apples and bake in preheated moderate oven (375°F.) for 40 minutes. Makes 4 to 6 servings.

LENTEN CAKE (EGGLESS)

½ cup butter
3 tablespoons molasses
1 cup milk
4 cups sifted all-purpose flour
¾ cup sugar
3 teaspoons ground allspice
2 teaspoons baking powder

1 teaspoon baking soda
½ teaspoon salt
½ cup raisins

Melt butter, add molasses and milk, and cool. Sift together flour, sugar, allspice, baking powder, baking soda, and salt. Stir butter mixture into dry ingredients. Add raisins and mix well. Pour into buttered pan (13 x 9 x 2 inches) and bake in preheated moderate oven (350°F.) for 30 minutes.

BARMBRACK

The term *barmbrack* for an Irish fruit loaf or cake does not derive from barm or leaven. It is a corruption of the Irish word *arán breac*, "speckled bread."

Halloween in Ireland would be unthinkable without barmbrack, the sweet and sticky-crusted loaf which foretells one's fortune for the coming year. Into the dough we knead (paper-wrapped to guard against choking or appendicitis) a ring for marriage, a silver coin for wealth, and a button for single blessedness.

7 cups sifted all-purpose flour
2 teaspoons ground allspice
1½ teaspoons salt
1 cup sugar
2 packages active dry yeast
3 cups warm milk and water (half and half)
6 tablespoons butter
2½ cup raisins
¾ cup dried currants
¾ cup chopped citrus peel

Sift flour, allspice, salt, and sugar into a large bowl. Dissolve yeast in half the warm milk and water. Add yeast and remaining liquid to dry ingredients, and mix thoroughly. Knead into a ball and turn out on a floured board. Knead until the dough no longer feels sticky and comes away clean from the board. Wash and grease the bowl, return the dough to it, cover, and let stand in a warm place until dough is double in bulk, about 1½ hours.

Turn the dough onto a floured board and flatten to a large round. Place butter, fruits, and peel in the middle, and work in these ingredients by squeezing and kneading until they are evenly incorporated in the dough. At this point, work in the paper-wrapped charms. Return the dough again to the greased bowl, cover, and leave to rise for about 45 minutes. Divide the dough into two parts and shape to fit 2 loaf pans (each 9 x 5 x 3 inches). Half fill the pans, cover, and leave in a warm place to rise to the top of pans. Bake in preheated hot oven (450°F.) for about 50 minutes, reducing the heat to 425°F. for the last 15 minutes

of baking. Five minutes before the barmbracks are done, brush with sugar and water in equal quantities. Makes 2 large barmbracks.

POTATO SEEDY CAKE

1½ cups sifted all-purpose flour
½ cup sugar
2 teaspoons baking powder
1 teaspoon salt
½ teaspoon ground allspice
¼ cup butter
1 teaspoon caraway seeds
½ cup dried currants
1 cup mashed potatoes
2 large eggs, well beaten

Sift together flour, sugar, baking powder, salt, and allspice; rub in the butter. Add caraway seeds. Add currants and mashed potatoes, mixing well. Add eggs. Place in a well-greased flat pan (8 x 8 inches), and bake in preheated hot oven (425°F.) for 30 minutes. Cut into squares and serve hot. Makes 9 squares.

PETTICOAT TAILS

This rather peculiar name is probably a corruption of *petite galette* (little cake).

1¼ cups butter
4 cups sifted all-purpose flour
¾ cup sugar
1 egg, beaten

Work butter into flour and mix in sugar. Add beaten egg and mix well. Although the mixture will be dry and crumbly, no other liquid should be added. The paste should be worked well with the hands to make it a cohesive mass. Cut it into 4 parts and roll each into a 9-inch round about ⅛ inch thick. In the center of each round stamp a circle with a 2½-inch pastry cutter. Cut the outside part into 8 equal segments. Lift carefully with a spatula onto a well-greased cookie sheet and bake in preheated moderate oven (350°F.) for 12 to 15 minutes. They should be very pale brown in color. Makes 36 pieces.

Note: If desired, brush cookies before baking with a little beaten egg white and sprinkle with a cinnamon-sugar mixture.

IRISH COFFEE

Pour 1 jigger Irish whiskey into a warmed goblet or coffee cup. Add 1 to 2 teaspoons sugar. Add hot strong coffee to within ½ inch of the top. Top with chilled sweetened whipped cream. Makes 1 serving.

IRISH MOSS or CARRAGEEN—

A species of small edible seaweed, varying in color from greenish yellow to purplish brown, named after Carragheen, Waterford County, Ireland. This seaweed is found along the coast of the British Islands, the rocky shores of continental Europe, and the eastern shores of the northern United States and Canada. The moss used domestically is obtained principally from New Hampshire and Massachusetts. The plants are washed in salt water and spread on the beach to dry and bleach, the process being repeated several times. The greater part of the supply is used for clarifying malt beverages. The remainder is retailed through druggists and health-food stores. It was formerly used in New England and still is, occasionally, to make a blancmange-type dessert.

IRISH MOSS BLANCMANGE

¾ cup Irish moss
Cold water
4 cups milk
Dash of salt
½ teaspoon lemon or vanilla extract
Sugar and cream

Soak moss in cold water for 5 minutes. Then tie moss in cheesecloth and put in top part of double boiler with milk and salt. Put over boiling water and cook, covered, for 30 minutes. Remove cheesecloth bag and add flavoring to milk mixture. Pour into bowl and chill until firm. Serve with sugar and cream, or with fruit. Makes 4 servings.

Italian Cookery

Italian cuisine is divided into butter and oil cooking. Northern Italy, cooler and pastoral, produces and uses excellent butter. Central and Southern Italy produce and use oil and cured pork fats, which do not suffer from the heat. Within these two basic divisions, the variety in foods is also very great, for historical, geographical, and economic reasons.

Italy's history has been one of independent tribes, cities, duchies, and kingdoms until the country was united, in 1870, into one nation. After the Second World War, the kingdom became a republic. In spite of the unification, an intensive local patriotism is part of the Italian character. Villages, towns, and regions look askance at each other, as exemplified in the Italian proverb of *moglie e buoi dei paesi tuoi*, "wives and cattle from your own locality."

This regional feeling has produced an independent, nonstandardized people and an infinite variety of architecture, customs, products, and cooking. Verona and Venice, for instance, are only a few hours' train journey apart, but their food is quite different.

Economically, the Italians have been until recently a very poor but imaginative people. In what other country have two simple ingredients, such as flour and water, resulted in so many pastas, food that is deliciously filling and an ideal stretcher of such expensive foods as meats and fats.

Throughout Italy the cooking is careful, with an instinctive feeling for flavor and texture combination. The laborer who eats his bread sprinkled with oil and chopped herbed tomatoes, the cook who can take a piece of cheese, put it between two slices of bread, fry it, and serve it with anchovy sauce, or transform a few little pieces of veal into dozens of delightful dishes are people who enjoy good food and are discriminating about it.

In Italy, it is always worthwhile to find out what foods and wines can be had locally, because many of them are not transported away from home, and many of them are strictly seasonal. Quite a number of dishes are made only in certain seasons or for certain holidays. Similar dishes turn up in many regions, but under various names and with their own special character. *Ravioli*, for instance, is called *ravioli* only in Piedmont and Genoa, and *tortellini*, *tortelli*, *agnolotti*, *anolini*, *cappelletti*, and *melfatti* in other places, and is everywhere filled with different stuffings.

No writing about Italian cookery would be complete without mention of Italian wines. All of Italy is a vineyard, and wine is part of the daily food, drunk at meals. The best-known Italian wine is red Chianti. But any Italian region, town, or village produces its own excellent wines, which should be savored by travelers in Italy.

A superb collection of exceptional Italian recipes for appetizers, soups, salads, main dishes, and desserts illustrates the wide and wonderful range of Italian cuisine.

 **APPETIZERS**

ANTIPASTO MISTO
(Antipasto Plates)

The *antipasto* (meaning "before the meal") platters and plates can be a little salad or a meal in itself. The idea is to combine vegetables, meats, fish, and eggs in as colorful an assortment as possible. Great care is taken in arranging the foods in an attractive and orderly way.

Antipasto Combinations

■ Arrange the following on a platter or plate: slices of Italian salami; rolled-up prosciutto or other ham; tuna in olive oil; black and green olives; eggs sliced or stuffed and topped, in both cases, with a parsley sprig or 3 capers; pickled mushrooms; radish roses; tomato slices, strips of red pimientos, and green peppers marinated in olive oil; celery stuffed with mashed Gorgonzola or other blue-veined cheese; eggplant salad; artichoke hearts marinated in a mixture of olive oil, white wine, basil or other herb, and salt and pepper; rolled anchovies, sardines, and any relishes such as pickled peppers, cauliflower, artichokes, labeled Italian style in food stores.

■ Cantaloupe or honeydew melon wedges wrapped in slices of prosciutto; pare chilled melon and cut into wedges; wrap with wafer-thin slices of prosciutto (allow 2 melon wedges for each person to be served); mushroom salad; anchovy-stuffed eggs; tomatoes; sliced fennel; slices of Italian salami; potato salad; pimiento marinated in olive oil; green olives; anchovies; sardines.

■ Meatless antipasto: overlapping slices of tomatoes and hard-cooked eggs, surrounded by chunks of tuna in olive oil and rolled anchovies, garnished with mayonnaise and decorated with parsley sprigs.

MEDAGLIONI DI MOZZARELLA
(Medallions of Mozzarella Cheese)

Cut medallions (diameter of fifty-cent piece and ½ inch thick) of Mozzarella or other cheese. Roll each piece of cheese in flour, well-beaten egg, and fine bread crumbs. Deep fry in ¼ inch of olive oil in skillet until golden-brown.

MELANZANE ALLA MARINARA
(Marinated Eggplant Appetizer)

1 large unpeeled eggplant, cut into 1-inch cubes
½ cup white vinegar (preferably wine vinegar)

1 teaspoon salt
½ teaspoon white pepper
1 garlic clove, minced
1 teaspoon dried oregano
½ teaspoon dried basil
¾ cup olive oil

Boil eggplant in boiling water to cover for 8 to 10 minutes. Drain. Cubes should be soft but retain their shape. Mix other ingredients except oil. Place drained eggplant in large bowl and pour marinade over. Toss thoroughly. Marinate overnight, or for at least 8 hours. Before serving, toss with oil. Makes 6 to 8 servings.
Note: This will keep for about 1 week in the refrigerator.

PROSCIUTTO WITH FRUITS

One of the most typical of Italian first courses for luncheon is the ham of Parma called prosciutto. This specially cured ham is eaten in thin slices. It is combined with various fruits and eaten with a little freshly ground black pepper and in some cases with a squeeze of lemon. These paper-thin slices of ham are always laid over the fruits they are to complement. Try them with:
■ Luscious ripe melon wedges
■ Quarters of peeled ripe pears
■ Wedges of ripe pineapple
■ Whole ripe figs with ham slices wrapped around them cornucopia fashion
Crisp bread and fresh butter go with this exciting appetizer.

 SOUPS

MINESTRONE MILANESE

¼ cup olive oil
1 garlic clove, minced
1 onion, minced
1 leek, washed and diced (when in season)
1 tablespoon chopped parsley
1 teaspoon dried thyme
1 tablespoon tomato paste
¼ cup water
3 canned or fresh tomatoes, peeled, seeded, and chopped
3 celery stalks, chopped
2 carrots, diced
2 potatoes, diced
¼ small cabbage, shredded
2 zucchinis, diced
6 cups hot water or bouillon
Salt to taste
½ teaspoon pepper
⅓ cup uncooked rice
1 to 1½ cups cooked and drained

dried beans
Grated Parmesan cheese

Put olive oil in large kettle. Add garlic, onion, leek, parsley, and thyme and cook until soft. Add tomato paste thinned with ¼ cup water and cook for 5 minutes. Add all remaining ingredients except rice, beans, and cheese. Simmer, covered, for 1 hour. Bring to boil, add rice, and cook until soft. Add beans; heat. Serve with cheese. Makes 3 quarts, or 6 servings.
Note: In this northern version of Italy's national soup, rice replaces pasta.

PAVESE
(Egg Consommé)

6 cups beef or chicken consommé
1 tablespoon minced parsley
3 eggs
3 tablespoons grated Parmesan cheese

Bring consommé to a boil. Beat parsley, eggs, and cheese together. Stir into consommé and cook, stirring, for a few seconds, or until eggs are set. Makes 1½ quarts, or 4 to 6 servings.

ZUPPA VENEZIANA DI PESCE
(Venetian Fish Soup)

3 pounds white-fleshed fish, including heads
3 cups water
1 onion, studded with 2 cloves
2 bay leaves
3 parsley sprigs
1 teaspoon salt
¼ teaspoon pepper
½ teaspoon crumbled dried marjoram
½ cup olive oil
1 garlic clove
½ cup dry white wine
1 cup stewed tomatoes

Trim fish and cut flesh into bite-size pieces. Reserve. Combine trimmings, including heads, water, onion, 1 bay leaf, parsley, salt, pepper, and ¼ teaspoon marjoram. Simmer, covered, for 30 to 40 minutes, stirring occasionally. Drain and reserve fish stock; there should be about 2 cups. Discard everything else. Fry fish pieces in the hot olive oil with remaining marjoram and bay leaf and the garlic. Add stock, wine, and tomatoes. Simmer, covered, for 15 minutes. Remove garlic. Makes 1½ quarts, or 4 to 6 servings.
Note: This fish soup is almost a stew.

MINESTRONE DI PASTA E FAGIUOLI
or PASTA FAZULA
(Thick Soup of Macaroni and Beans)

Wash 1 pound dried pinto or navy beans and soak overnight in 2 quarts water. Cook beans in the same water. Prepare sauce. Sauté ½ cup chopped salt pork, bacon, or ham with 1 minced garlic clove

Antipasto Misto

Minestrone Milanese

Prosciutto with Honeydew

or 2 tablespoons minced onion and a dash of chili pepper. Add to the beans and let cook until tender. Just before serving, add 1 pound cooked and drained *ditalini* (macaroni) and let simmer for 5 minutes. Stir well, and serve topped with grated Romano cheese. Makes 8 to 10 servings.

 ## FISH AND SEAFOOD

PESCE LESSO
(Poached Fish, Italian Style)
- 2 tablespoons minced parsley
- 1 garlic clove, minced
- 3 tablespoons olive oil
- 1 cup hot water
- 1½ pounds flounder fillets
- 1 teaspoon salt
- ⅛ teaspoon pepper
- Pinch of dried oregano

Cook parsley and garlic in olive oil in skillet for 3 minutes. Add hot water and bring to boil. Add fish and seasonings. Cover, bring again to boil, and cook for 5 to 10 minutes. Serve with the liquid. Makes 4 servings.

PESCE ALLA SICILIANA
(Sicilian Fish)
- 4 slices of halibut or swordfish (or other thick fish), 1¾ to 2 pounds
- ¼ cup olive oil
- 1 tablespoon chopped parsley
- 1 garlic clove, minced
- ½ cup white vinegar
- 2 pounds tomatoes, peeled, seeded, and chopped
- Salt and pepper to taste
- 1 package (10 ounces) frozen peas, thawed

In skillet brown fish in hot oil. Add parsley, garlic, and vinegar. Cook until liquid has almost evaporated. Add tomatoes, salt, and pepper. Simmer, covered, for 5 minutes. Add peas. Simmer, covered, for about 30 minutes. Put fish on hot platter and pour sauce over it. Makes 4 to 6 servings.

PESCE FRITTO
(Fried Fish Fillets, Italian Style)
- 4 medium fish fillets
- ½ cup all-purpose flour
- ½ cup olive oil
- Salt to taste
- Lemon wedges

Coat fillets with flour and fry in hot oil for about 8 minutes on each side. Drain on absorbent paper. Sprinkle with salt and serve with lemon wedges. Makes 4 servings.

Note: The olive oil gives fried fish a different flavor.

SCAMPI AI FERRI
(Garlic Broiled Shrimps)
- 2 pounds raw shrimps
- ½ cup olive oil
- 2 garlic cloves, minced
- 2 teaspoons salt
- ⅓ cup chopped parsley
- Lemon wedges

Split shrimp shells with scissors. Remove shells and devein shrimps. Arrange shrimps in shallow baking pan. Sprinkle with olive oil, garlic, salt, and half of parsley. Broil about 4 inches from source of heat for 5 to 7 minutes on each side, depending on size of shrimps. Sprinkle with remaining parsley and serve with lemon wedges. Makes 4 servings.

 ## MEAT AND POULTRY

SCALOPPINE DI VITELLO
(Veal Scaloppine)
- 1 pound veal scaloppine, cut very thin
- ⅓ cup all-purpose flour, seasoned with salt and pepper
- 6 tablespoons butter
- ¼ cup dry white wine

Coat scaloppine with flour. Sauté in hot butter for about 3 minutes on each side. Add white wine. Simmer for 2 minutes longer. Serve at once. Makes 3 or 4 servings.

COSTOLETTE ALLA PARMIGIANA
(Veal Chops Parmigiana)
- ½ cup fine dry bread crumbs
- ½ cup grated Parmesan cheese
- ¾ teaspoon salt
- ¾ teaspoon paprika
- 4 large loin veal chops (2 to 2½ pounds)
- 1 egg, beaten
- 3 tablespoons butter
- 4 thin slices of Mozzarella cheese
- 2 cups well-seasoned tomato sauce

Mix crumbs, Parmesan, salt, and paprika. Dip chops into egg and roll in crumb mixture. Heat butter and brown chops on both sides. Cover each with a slice of Mozzarella. Pour tomato sauce over chops. Cover and simmer for about 45 minutes. If sauce is too thick, add a little hot water. Makes 4 servings.

PETTO DI VITELLO
(Veal Breast)
- 3 pounds breast of veal
- Boiling water
- 2 teaspoons salt
- 1 celery stalk
- 1 carrot
- 1 onion
- ¼ teaspoon pepper
- ⅛ teaspoon ground nutmeg
- 1 tablespoon chopped parsley

- 3 tablespoons olive oil
- 3 tablespoons fresh lemon juice
- 2 eggs, beaten
- 1 tablespoon melted butter
- Fine dry bread crumbs

Simmer veal in boiling water to cover with salt, celery, carrot, and onion for 1 hour, or until tender. Remove meat and reserve broth for soup and other uses. Cool meat and cut into 1- or 2-inch strips. Combine pepper, nutmeg, parsley, oil, and lemon juice. Add meat and marinate for at least 2 hours, turning occasionally. Remove meat from marinade and dry with paper towels. Mix eggs and melted butter. Dip meat into mixture, roll in crumbs, and put in one layer in greased shallow baking dish. Bake in preheated moderate oven (375°F.) for 30 minutes, turning once after 15 minutes. Makes 4 servings.

ARROSTO DI AGNELLO
(Roast Lamb)
Taking a leg of lamb or an entire baby lamb, rub it well with garlic, rosemary leaves, and salt and pepper. Pour ½ cup olive oil into the roaster. Set lamb in it and roast, uncovered, in preheated moderate oven (350°F.), turning occasionally until practically done, allowing 30 minutes to the pound. Place peeled tiny new spring potatoes around meat and continue roasting until they are tender.

Note: Lamb prepared with a blend of herbs is an Easter delicacy throughout Italy, as is turkey on Thanksgiving in America.

AGNELLO ALLA CACCIATORA
(Lamb Cacciatora)
- 4 pounds shoulder or leg of lamb, trimmed of all fat and cut into 1½-inch cubes
- ⅓ cup olive oil
- 1 small garlic clove, minced
- 1 teaspoon crumbled dried rosemary
- ½ teaspoon crumbled dried sage
- 2 teaspoons all-purpose flour
- ½ cup white or wine vinegar
- ½ cup water
- Salt and pepper to taste

Brown meat in hot oil. Add garlic, rosemary, and sage. Sprinkle flour on meat. Add vinegar and water, stirring thoroughly. Cover and simmer for 1 hour, or until meat is tender. Season with salt and pepper. Stir frequently during cooking, and add a little hot water if necessary. Makes 6 servings.

MAIALE AFFOGATO
(Stewed Pork with Celery)
- 1 garlic clove
- 2 tablespoons olive or cooking oil

1 carrot, minced
2 pounds lean boneless pork, cut into bite-size pieces
1 cup dry red or white wine
1½ teaspoons salt
½ teaspoon pepper
2½ cups sliced celery
  Bouillon or water
1 cup chopped fresh or canned tomatoes

Brown garlic in oil and discard garlic. Add carrot, pork, wine, and salt and pepper. Cook, covered, over low heat for 1½ hours. Cook celery in bouillon until almost tender. Drain. Add cooked celery and tomatoes to pork mixture for the last 15 minutes of cooking time. Makes 4 to 6 servings.

SALSICCIE E FAGIOLI
(Italian Sausages with Beans)

1 pound sweet or hot Italian sausages
2 tablespoons olive oil
2 tablespoons tomato paste
¼ teaspoon salt
⅛ teaspoon pepper (omit if hot sausage is used)
4 cups drained cooked kidney beans
¼ cup bean liquid or water

Prick sausages and put in skillet with cold water to cover. Cook over moderate heat until water evaporates. Then cook for 20 minutes, allowing sausages to brown on all sides. Remove from pan and keep hot. Add oil to fat in pan. Stir in tomato paste, salt, and pepper. Cook for 5 minutes. Add kidney beans, liquid, and sausages to pan. Simmer for 15 minutes, stirring occasionally. Garnish with parsley, if desired. Makes 4 servings.

Note: Use the sweet or hot variety of sausage, according to taste.

POLLO ALLA CACCIATORA
(Chicken Cacciatora)

¼ cup olive oil
1 chicken (2½ to 3 pounds), cut up
2 onions, sliced
2 garlic cloves, minced
2 cups (one 1-pound can) Italian tomatoes
1 can (8 ounces) tomato sauce
1 teaspoon salt
¼ teaspoon pepper
½ teaspoon celery seed
1 teaspoon crushed dried oregano
2 bay leaves
½ cup dry white wine

Heat oil in large deep skillet. Brown chicken in it. Remove chicken and keep hot. Cook onions and garlic in oil in skillet until tender. Add other ingredients except wine, and blend. Cook for 5 minutes. Return chicken to skillet. Cover and simmer for 45 minutes. Add wine and cook, uncovered, for about 15 min-

utes. Arrange on hot platter. Skim excess fat from sauce and remove bay leaves. Pour sauce over chicken. Makes 4 to 6 servings.

Note: Serve on spaghetti or noodles with a sprinkling of cheese.

PETTI DI POLLO ALLA PIEMONTESE
(Chicken Breast, Piedmont Style)

2 whole chicken breasts, boned and halved
2 tablespoons all-purpose flour
1 teaspoon salt
½ teaspoon white pepper
2 tablespoons butter
  Slices of truffles or 4 large mushrooms, sliced and sautéed in butter
4 very thin slices of Swiss cheese

Trim chicken of skin, fat, and gristle. Put between sheets of wax paper and roll thin with a rolling pin. Coat with flour seasoned with salt and pepper. Heat butter and cook chicken until tender, about 5 or 6 minutes on each side. Remove to shallow baking pan. Arrange truffle slices on each breast and cover each with cheese. Put under broiler just long enough to melt cheese. Makes 4 servings.

FEGATINI DI POLLO ALLA SALVIA
(Chicken Livers with Sage)

Season chicken livers with salt and pepper and coat with chopped fresh or dried sage (about 1 tablespoon fresh sage or ½ teaspoon crumbled dried sage leaves per liver, depending on taste). Wrap chicken livers in strips of prosciutto or partly cooked lean bacon. Thread on small skewers. Broil over a campfire or an outdoor grill or a rotisserie or under the range broiler, turning occasionally. Allow about 8 to 10 minutes of broiling time. If livers are wrapped in prosciutto, baste with melted butter.

EGGS AND CHEESE

UOVA IN PURGATORIO
(Eggs in Purgatory)

¼ cup chopped onion
¼ cup minced parsley
  Salt and pepper to taste
1 tablespoon olive oil
2 cups chopped, peeled tomatoes (or canned)
8 eggs
4 slices of buttered toast

Sauté onion and parsley with salt and pepper in oil for 10 minutes. Add tomatoes and simmer for 30 minutes, stirring often. Bring to a boil, then care-

fully drop in the eggs, one at a time, to poach. Serve on buttered toast with the sauce. Makes 4 servings, allowing 2 eggs for each portion.

CROSTINI ALLA MOZZARELLA
(Italian Mozzarella Skewers)

Mozzarella originally came from the marshy farming districts around Naples, where buffaloes from India are used as beasts of burden. Their milk goes into cheese making. Our Mozzarella is more bland than the Italian and it is therefore a good idea to serve the *crostini* with anchovy butter.

Remove the crust from a loaf of French bread. Cut loaf into slices about ⅓ inch thick. Cut Mozzarella into slices the same size and thickness as bread. Place alternate slices of bread and cheese on a skewer until there are 3 of cheese and 4 of bread, beginning and ending with bread. Preheat baking dish and place skewers on it. Bake in a very hot oven (450°F. to 475°F.) just long enough for the cheese to melt and the bread to brown. Serve very hot with Anchovy Butter.

Anchovy Butter

Melt 1 cup butter. Chop 8 anchovy fillets and simmer in butter for 5 minutes. Pour sauce over each skewer serving.

PASTA, PANCAKES, AND RICE

SPAGHETTI CON LE POLPETTINE
(Spaghetti with Meatballs)

Tomato Sauce:

3½ cups (one 1-pound, 12-ounce can) tomatoes
3 cans (6 ounces each) tomato paste
4 cups water
1 onion, minced
1 garlic clove, minced
¼ pound salt pork, minced
2 tablespoons olive oil
2 tablespoons chopped parsley
2 teaspoons salt
½ teaspoon pepper
1 teaspoon sugar
½ teaspoon dried oregano
1 bay leaf, crushed
¼ cup grated Parmesan or Romano cheese

Meatballs:

½ pound each of ground beef, veal, and pork
2 eggs, beaten
1 teaspoon salt
¼ teaspoon pepper
¼ teaspoon dried oregano
½ cup grated Parmesan cheese

Salsiccie e Fagioli

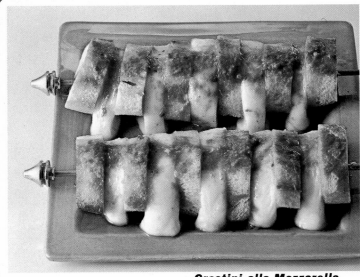

Crostini alla Mozzarella

Spaghetti con le Polpettine

Insalata Bandiera

Cassata Napolitana

2 tablespoons chopped parsley
2 teaspoons grated lemon rind
¼ cup fine dry bread crumbs
Cooked spaghetti

Combine tomatoes, tomato paste, and water; bring to boil. Sauté onion, garlic, and salt pork in hot olive oil. Add to tomato mixture. Add remaining ingredients except cheese and simmer, covered, for about 1 hour, stirring frequently. Combine all meatball ingredients and mix thoroughly with hands. Shape into balls. Add to tomato sauce and simmer, covered, for about 40 minutes, stirring occasionally. Before serving, stir in the ¼ cup grated cheese listed in sauce. Pour over hot cooked spaghetti. Makes 6 servings.

SPAGHETTI AL QUATTRO FORMAGGI
(Spaghetti with Four Cheeses)
½ cup butter
⅔ cup shredded Mozzarella cheese
⅔ cup grated Gouda or Edam cheese
⅔ cup grated imported Swiss cheese
⅔ cup grated Parmesan cheese
1 pound spaghetti
Salt and pepper

Melt butter in top part of a double boiler; have cheeses ready. Cook spaghetti to your taste in boiling salted water. Drain well and turn into a chafing dish or electric skillet turned to low. Add Mozzarella and Gouda and toss well. Then add half of butter and the Swiss cheese. Give it a thorough mixing and add freshly ground pepper. Finally add remaining butter and the Parmesan cheese. Toss again and serve very hot. Makes 4 servings.

LASAGNE CON LE POLPETTINE
(Lasagna with Meatballs)
¾ pound lean beef, ground
½ teaspoon salt
¼ teaspoon pepper
1 teaspoon grated lemon rind
2 tablespoons olive oil
3 cups favorite tomato sauce
1 pound lasagna, cooked and drained
1 pound ricotta or cottage cheese
1 pound Mozzarella cheese, cubed
1½ cups grated Parmesan cheese

Season beef with salt and pepper, add lemon rind, and shape into balls the size of a large marble. Brown in hot oil. Cover bottom of a large 2- to 3-inch-deep baking dish sparingly with tomato sauce. Line with lasagna. Dot with half of cheeses. Spread with half of remaining sauce; top with meat. Cover with remaining lasagna, sauce, and cheeses. Bake in preheated slow oven (325°F.) for about 45 minutes. Cool slightly. Makes 10 to 12 servings.

VERMICELLI ALLA PASTORA
(Fine Noodles for the Shepherdess)
1 pound vermicelli
1 pound ricotta, well creamed
1 cup hot water
3 tablespoons olive oil
Salt and pepper to taste

While noodles cook in rapidly boiling water, dilute cheese with hot water and olive oil, stirring constantly. Strain noodles and mix them thoroughly with the cheese sauce. Season. Makes 6 servings.

CANNELLONI ALLA PARMIGIANA
(Stuffed Pancakes, I)
½ pound sausage meat, cooked and drained
1 package (10 ounces) frozen spinach, cooked and chopped fine
1 cup finely chopped cooked chicken
¼ cup grated Romano cheese
⅛ teaspoon ground thyme
⅛ teaspoon pepper
Butter
1 cup milk
2 eggs, beaten
½ cup sifted all-purpose flour
1 teaspoon baking powder
½ teaspoon salt
Parmesan Sauce

To make stuffing mix first 6 ingredients.
To make Cannelloni heat 2 tablespoons butter and the milk until butter is melted. Cool slightly. Add next 4 ingredients and mix until smooth. Drop by spoonfuls onto hot buttered skillet to form eighteen 3-inch pancakes. Fry until browned on both sides. Cool, and spread each with stuffing. Roll up and put in broilerproof shallow baking dish. Cover with Parmesan Sauce. Broil for 5 minutes. Makes 6 servings.

Parmesan Sauce
Melt 3 tablespoons butter; blend in 3 tablespoons flour. Add 1½ cups light cream; cook, stirring, until thickened. Stir in ½ cup grated Parmesan cheese. Season.

MANICOTTI
(Stuffed Pancakes, II)
1 cup sifted all-purpose flour
1 cup water
Salt
7 eggs
2 pounds ricotta cheese
Grated Parmesan or Romano cheese
¼ teaspoon pepper
½ pound Mozzarella, cut into 12 strips
3 cans (8 ounces each) tomato sauce

To make pancakes combine flour, water, and ¼ teaspoon salt; beat until smooth. Beat in 4 eggs, one at a time. Heat a 5- to 6-inch skillet and grease with a few drops of oil. Put about 3 tablespoons

batter in hot skillet and roll around pan to distribute evenly. Cook over low heat until firm; do not brown. Turn, and cook lightly on other side. Continue making pancakes until all batter is used. This amount will make 12 to 14 pancakes. Do not grease skillet a second time.
To make filling mix ½ teaspoon salt, 3 eggs, ricotta, ¼ cup Parmesan, and the pepper. Put about 2 tablespoons filling and a strip of Mozzarella on each pancake and roll up. Pour 1 can tomato sauce into large shallow baking dish. Put pancakes, seam side down, in sauce. Cover with remaining 2 cans sauce and sprinkle with ½ cup Parmesan. Bake in preheated moderate oven (350°F.) for 45 minutes. Makes 6 generous servings.

RISOTTO ALLA MILANESE
(Rice, Milan Style)
¼ cup butter
¼ cup chopped beef marrow or 2 tablespoons butter
1 onion, minced
2 cups uncooked rice
½ cup dry white wine
About 5 cups boiling chicken bouillon
½ teaspoon ground saffron, steeped in a little chicken bouillon
Salt to taste
½ teaspoon white pepper
⅔ cup grated Parmesan cheese

In heavy saucepan melt butter and beef marrow. Cook onion in it until soft but not brown. Add rice and cook for 3 or 4 minutes, stirring. The rice must be transparent but not brown. Stir in wine and cook for 3 minutes. Add ½ cup boiling bouillon. Cook until bouillon is absorbed, stirring. Add remaining bouillon by half cups, allowing it to become absorbed after each addition, and stirring constantly. The cooking time should be 20 to 25 minutes after the bouillon has been first added, depending on the kind of rice used and the degree of doneness desired. (Italians eat it *al dente.*) After about 15 minutes of cooking time, add saffron, salt, and pepper. When done, stir in cheese. Serve with more cheese. Rice can be served plain or with chicken livers or mushrooms. Makes 4 to 6 servings.
Note: The finished product should be moist and creamy, not dry.

VEGETABLES

MELANZANE ALLA PARMIGIANA
(Eggplant Parmigiana)
2 cups olive oil, about

1 garlic clove, minced
1 large onion, chopped
5 cups canned Italian-style tomatoes
½ teaspoon dried basil
Salt and pepper to taste
1 cup all-purpose flour
2 eggs, beaten
1 cup milk
2 medium eggplants, cut into ½-inch slices
1 cup grated Parmesan cheese
8 ounces Mozzarella cheese, diced
¼ cup butter

Heat ¼ cup of oil in skillet. Sauté garlic and onion in it until soft. Add tomatoes, basil, salt, and pepper. Cook, covered, stirring occasionally, for 30 minutes. Make batter with flour, eggs, and milk. Dip eggplant slices into batter and fry slices in remaining shallow hot oil until just browned on both sides. Add more oil after each frying. Arrange alternate layers of eggplant, sauce, and cheeses in casserole, sprinkling each layer with salt and pepper; dot with butter. Bake in preheated moderate oven (350°F.) for 30 minutes. Makes 6 to 8 servings.

PISELLI E PASTA
(Peas and Shell Macaroni)

¼ cup butter
¼ cup olive oil
1 onion, minced
1 garlic clove, minced (optional)
½ pound shell macaroni, cooked and drained
3 cups cooked peas
1 cup chopped parsley
½ cup finely cooked ham (optional)
Grated Parmesan cheese
Salt and pepper

Heat butter and oil. Sauté onion and garlic in it until onion is soft. Add other ingredients except cheese and season to taste with salt and pepper. Simmer, covered, for 10 minutes. Serve with cheese. Makes 4 to 6 servings.

Note: This dish is also served without the cheese in Italy.

PEPERONI CON PATATE
(Peppers and Potatoes)

1 pound sweet peppers
¼ cup olive oil
1 garlic clove, minced
1 onion, minced
5 potatoes, peeled and sliced or cubed
1 cup tomato juice
Salt and pepper to taste

Trim peppers and cut into strips lengthwise. Heat olive oil and sauté garlic and onion in it. Add peppers and all other ingredients. Cook, covered, over low heat, for 30 minutes, or until potatoes are tender. Stir occasionally and add a little more tomato juice if necessary. Makes 4 servings.

Note: Served with eggs, this makes a good luncheon dish.

SPINACI STUFATI
(Steamed Spinach)

¼ cup olive oil
1 garlic clove, peeled
2 pounds fresh spinach or 2 packages (10 ounces each) frozen spinach
Salt and pepper to taste

Heat oil and garlic; add spinach. Cook for 7 minutes, or until spinach is just tender. If too dry add ¼ cup water, although usually the water that clings to the spinach is enough to cook it. Season with salt and pepper; remove garlic clove before serving. Makes 4 servings.

ZUCCHINI AL BURRO
(Squash with Butter)

If squash is young, slice it without peeling. If skin is tough, peel it first. Cut into ½-inch slices. When all slices are in the skillet, add a large piece of butter, salt and pepper to taste, and a dash of ground cinnamon. Cover and simmer until done, stirring when necessary.

ZUCCHINI FRITTE
(Fried Squash)

8 small zucchinis, unpeeled
½ cup seasoned all-purpose flour
½ cup olive oil

Wash zucchinis, dry, and cut into ¼-inch rounds. Coat with flour. Fry in hot oil until crisp and golden. Drain on absorbent paper. Makes 4 to 6 servings.
Note: Wonderful with veal.

 SAUCES

SALSA PARMIGIANA
(Basic Tomato Sauce)

¼ cup minced onion
1 garlic clove, minced (optional)
¼ cup olive oil
¼ cup minced raw carrot
1 cup minced celery
¼ cup minced sweet basil
Salt and pepper to taste
3 cups canned tomato sauce or two 6-ounce cans tomato paste diluted with 3 cans water

Sauté onion and garlic (if used) in oil until golden-brown. Add carrot, celery, sweet basil, and salt and pepper and continue cooking until vegetables are wilted. Add tomato sauce and simmer for 45 minutes, until tasty and thick. Serve this sauce over your favorite cooked pasta. Makes about 2¾ cups.

SALSA ALLA MARINARA
(Mariner's Sauce)

3 garlic cloves, minced
¼ cup minced parsley
½ cup olive oil
2 cups chopped, peeled tomatoes
1 teaspoon crumbled dried oregano
Salt and pepper to taste

Sauté garlic and parsley in oil. When garlic is delicately brown, add tomatoes, oregano, and salt and pepper, and simmer for 30 minutes, or until well blended and thick. Makes about 1½ cups.
Note: For noodle-dough preparations.

SALSA DI VONGOLE
(White Clam Sauce)

3 tablespoons butter
1 garlic clove, minced
1 tablespoon all-purpose flour
2 cans (10½ ounces each) minced clams
¼ cup chopped parsley
Salt and pepper to taste
¾ teaspoon dried thyme or basil

Heat butter and cook garlic in it for 1 minute. Blend in flour. Add other ingredients and simmer, covered, for about 10 minutes, stirring frequently. Makes 3 cups sauce.
Note: Serve over hot cooked spaghetti or linguine.

SALSA VERDE PICCANTE
(Piquant Green Sauce)

½ cup minced parsley
¼ cup chopped pignon nuts
2 tablespoons drained capers, chopped
½ cup fine dry bread crumbs
6 pitted black olives, minced
3 tablespoons olive oil
1 tablespoon wine vinegar
Salt and pepper
1 teaspoon crushed chili pepper
1 teaspoon minced chives, onion, or garlic

Mix all ingredients thoroughly. Makes about 1 cup.
Note: Serve with fish.

SALSA DI ALICI
(Anchovy Sauce)

¼ cup olive oil
¼ cup butter
4 garlic cloves, minced
2 cans (2 ounces each) flat anchovy fillets, drained
¼ cup chopped parsley

Heat oil and butter and add garlic. Cook until garlic is soft, stirring. Add anchovies and cook, stirring, until anchovies have disintegrated. Stir in parsley. Makes about ¾ cup sauce.
Note: For fried Mozzarella, pasta, and boiled-fish dishes.

 SALADS

INSALATA DI FAGIOLINI E PATATE
(Green-Bean and Potato Salad)

4 large potatoes
1 pound fresh green beans (Italian preferred)
2 medium-size onions, chopped
Salt and pepper
Olive oil and wine vinegar

Wash potatoes and boil until tender; drain, peel, and cool. Boil beans in salted water until tender but firm; drain and cool. Slice or dice potatoes into a large bowl. Add beans, onions, and salt and pepper to taste and mix all carefully. Pour in about 3 tablespoons olive oil and 1 tablespoon wine vinegar, according to taste. Stir salad carefully; marinate in refrigerator for at least 2 hours. Stir again just before serving. Makes 6 to 8 servings.

INSALATA BANDIERA
(Flag Salad)

Fresh tomatoes, sliced or diced
Green beans, cooked, drained, cooled
Chopped carrots, raw or cooked and cooled
Florets of cauliflower, cooked, drained, cooled
Potatoes, cooked, peeled, and diced with a bit of chopped green onion
Red beets, cooked, peeled, and sliced or diced
Finely cut endive or other greens

In preparing Flag Salad, make your own choice among the vegetables, parboiling, straining, and cooling each vegetable separately. (Drop it into rapidly boiling salted water and leave it for just a few minutes, until cooked but firm.) Do not cook the tomatoes or members of the lettuce family (romaine, endive, chicory, escarole, dandelion). When each vegetable is cooled, sprinkle it with salt and pepper and salad dressing to taste. Toss well, and place in individual dishes of a Lazy Susan so that each dish is different from the others.

CANNELINI AL TONNO
(White-Bean and Tuna Salad)

5 cups (two 1-pound, 4-ounce cans) cannelini or 1 pound dried white beans
1 onion stuck with 2 cloves and 1 bay leaf (if using dried beans)
2 cans (7 ounces each) white-meat tuna fish
2/3 cup finely chopped scallions
1/2 cup finely chopped parsley
1 garlic clove, finely minced
About 1/2 cup olive oil
Vinegar or fresh lemon juice
Salt and pepper

Open and drain the canned beans, or soak and prepare the packaged beans with onion and bay leaf and cook until tender. Cool. Combine with coarsely shredded tuna fish and other seasonings and dress to suit your taste with olive oil, vinegar, and salt and pepper. Chill before serving. This may be prepared while the beans are hot and eaten hot, although it is best when served cold for an appetizer or a luncheon salad. Makes 6 salad servings.
Note: Cannelini are long white beans which may be found canned or dried. If you do not find them in your locality, substitute white pea beans or small dried Limas.

 SWEETS AND DESSERTS

CASSATA NAPOLITANA
(Rich Dessert Cake)

One 9- or 10-inch spongecake or 2 sponge layers
1 1/2 pounds ricotta cheese
1/3 cup sugar
1/2 cup light cream
1 teaspoon vanilla extract
1/4 teaspoon almond extract
1 ounce (1 square) semisweet chocolate or 1/4 cup semisweet chocolate pieces, chopped
1/4 cup chopped toasted almonds
2/3 cup finely diced mixed candied fruit
1/4 cup rum
Frosting
Candied cherries

If a whole cake is used, cut into 2 layers. Chill. Combine ricotta, sugar, light cream, and flavorings and mix well. Rub through a sieve or whip until smooth. Add chocolate, almonds, and fruit. Chill. Place 1 cake layer on serving plate and spread with filling. Top with remaining layer. Sprinkle with rum. Chill until shortly before serving time; then frost top. Reserve some of the Frosting to tint pink and use it for decorative swirls on cake. Decorate with cherries.

Frosting

1 egg white
2 cups confectioners' sugar
1 teaspoon almond extract
1 tablespoon fresh lemon juice

Mix all ingredients until smooth. If necessary, add a little water, 1/2 teaspoon at a time, to achieve right spreading consistency.

BUDINO DI RICOTTA
(Cream-Cheese Custard)

1/2 pound ricotta cheese
1/4 cup grated milk chocolate
1/4 cup finely chopped walnuts
2 tablespoons heavy cream (more if needed)

Cream the ricotta. Add chocolate and nuts and blend thoroughly. Add cream as needed for desired consistency. Serve in sherbet glasses. Makes 4 servings.
Note: This "custard" can also be used as a filling for many cakes and cookies.

FRAGOLE ALL' ITALIANA
(Italian Strawberries)

2 tablespoons sugar, or more, depending on berries
4 cups washed and hulled strawberries
2/3 cup dry white wine or fresh orange juice

Sprinkle sugar over strawberries and cover with wine. Chill before serving. Makes 4 to 6 servings.

GROSTOLI
(Crisp Cookies)

3 eggs, lightly beaten
5 cups sifted all-purpose flour
1/2 cup granulated sugar
1 teaspoon baking powder
1 cup milk
1 teaspoon salt
1 grated lemon rind (optional)
1 ounce of brandy (2 tablespoons)
Lard
Confectioners' sugar

Mix first 8 ingredients into smooth noodle dough and roll thin as a dime. With pastry cutter, form rectangles 2 by 3 inches. Deep fry in pure lard. Drain, and dust with confectioners' sugar. Makes about 8 dozen.

JAM—A preserve of fruit which is usually crushed, or may even be ground, cooked with sugar until thick, and stored in sterilized jars. The crushed particles of fruit remain in the finished product. The fruit used can be fresh, canned, frozen, or dried. Jam is sometimes made of fruits mixed with vegetables.

Making jam is one of the most satisfying branches of the ancient art of preserving foods. Before the general availability of canned and frozen foods and commercially made jams, homemade jams were the homemaker's pride and the joy of her family during many a long winter, when the jam's fragrance and sparkle brought summer sunshine to the cold dark season. Housewives slaved over hot stoves on many a summer day when the fruit was perfect for the purpose.

Success in jam making depends on the kind of fruit used, the cooking, handling, and storing. Because of the products available today, the homemaker has a choice of several methods for making jam:

☐ Jam Made without Added Pectin— (Pectin is a water-soluble substance present in plant tissue. It yields a jelly when it is properly combined with acid and sugar.) Some fruits contain enough natural pectin to eliminate the necessity for adding commercial fruit pectin. These fruits include tart apples, blackberries, cranberries, currants, gooseberries, Concord grapes, quinces, and raspberries.

Even when using them, however, some underripe fruits (they contain more pectin than ripe ones) should be included with the ripe fruits to insure the presence of enough pectin for gelling.

☐ Jams Made with Commercial Fruit Pectin—Liquid pectin is added to the cooked fruit and sugar after it is removed from the heat. Or powdered pectin is added to the unheated crushed fruit.

☐ Jams Made without Cooking—Some fresh, canned, or frozen fruits can be used without cooking if liquid or powdered fruit pectin is added and a long storage life is not desired. These fruits include blackberries, raspberries, strawberries, cherries, and peaches. No-cook jams cannot be stored at room temperature. If kept in the freezer, they will last up to one year; in the refrigerator their storage life is three to four months.

TO MAKE JAM

☐ Follow recipe directions for preparing and cooking fruit and for handling it after cooking.

☐ Stir well during cooking to prevent sticking and scorching.

☐ Remember that the mixture will thicken more as it cools. Jams made without added pectin take longer to cook than jams made with pectin, and it is more difficult to tell when the jam is finished. To determine this, use a candy and jelly thermometer, and cook mixture to 220°F. If you do not have a ther-

mometer, you can use the spoon, or sheet, test (the old "jelly test") although it is not absolutely dependable: Dip a cool metal spoon into the boiling mixture. Then raise it at least 1 foot above the kettle, out of the steam, and turn the spoon so that the syrup runs off the side. If the syrup forms drops that flow together and fall off the spoon as one sheet, the jam should be done.

☐ Prepare jars or glasses properly. Have them ready for use when jam is finished cooking. Jars and lids should be covered with hot, not boiling, water and brought to a boil. No further boiling is necessary. Keep hot in water or in a very slow oven until they are needed.

☐ To Seal Jam—Jam which will not be kept more than two months does not need any special sealing. Jam which will be kept longer should be kept in canning jars or sealed with paraffin.

Canning jars, such as the new all-purpose jars with two-piece metal screw-top lids, should be filled to the top, the rim wiped, and the clean hot metal lids placed on the jar with sealing compound next to the glass. The metal band is screwed on firmly, the jar cooled on a metal rack or folded cloth; then labeled, and stored in a cool, dry place.

If using paraffin to seal glasses, the paraffin should be kept hot without overheating. A double boiler is good for this. As soon as jam is in the glasses, filled to within ½ inch of top, cover immediately

with a ⅛-inch layer of paraffin. Be sure jam is completely covered by paraffin, and prick any air bubbles that may appear in the jam. A thin single layer of paraffin is preferable to either a thick or two thin layers as this gives a tighter seal with no chance for air bubbles.

JAMS MADE WITHOUT PECTIN

APRICOT-PINEAPPLE JAM
- 1 package (11 or 12 ounces) dried apricots
- 3½ cups (one pound, 14-ounce can) chunk-style pineapple
- 3½ cups water
- 1 jar (8 ounces) maraschino cherries
- 6 cups sugar

In large saucepan combine apricots, pineapple and syrup, water, and cherry syrup; let stand for 1 hour. Cook slowly until apricots are tender. Add sugar and cook slowly, stirring often, until thick and clear (216°F. on candy thermometer). Add cherries, cut into quarters; cook for a few minutes longer (220°F.). Pour into hot sterilized jars and seal. Makes six ½-pint jars.

SPICED BLACKBERRY JAM
- 4 cups canned blackberry pulp
- 1 teaspoon ground allspice or combination of ground spices
- 1¼ cups sugar*
- 2½ cups corn syrup
- 1 tablespoon fresh lemon juice

Bring pulp to boil in heavy 6-quart kettle. Boil hard for 15 minutes. Add spice, sugar, and syrup. Boil rapidly until jam forms thick jellied drops that adhere to edge of spoon, about 45 minutes. Add lemon juice. Cool slightly; stir; pour into sterilized glasses and seal. Makes four or five ½-pint jars.
*Or use 3 cups sugar, omitting syrup.

CRANBERRY AND FIG JAM
- 3 cups dried figs
- 3 cups water
- Grated rind of 1 orange
- 4 cups cranberries
- 3 cups sugar
- ¼ teaspoon salt

Wash figs and remove the hard stem ends. Put through food chopper, using medium blade. Add water and boil for 30 minutes, stirring frequently. Add rinds, cranberries, sugar, and salt and boil for another 30 minutes. Stir often to prevent burning. Pour into hot sterilized glasses and seal. Makes six ½-pint jars.

CRANBERRY, ORANGE, AND HONEY JAM
- 4 cups cranberries
- 2 cups boiling water
- Grated rind of 1 orange
- 1 cup sugar
- ¾ cup strained honey

Pick over, wash, and drain cranberries. Add water and orange rind; boil for 20 minutes. Force cranberries through a fine sieve. Bring to rapid boil and add sugar and honey, stirring until thoroughly mixed. Boil for 3 minutes longer. Pour into hot sterilized glasses or small molds and seal. Makes about four ½-pint jars.

SPICED GRAPE JAM

1½ pounds stemmed Concord grapes (2½ cups pulp and skins)
Grated rind of 1 orange
½ cup water
2¼ cups sugar
½ teaspoon each of ground cloves and cinnamon

Wash grapes and slip skins from pulp. Heat pulp to boiling and rub through a coarse sieve to remove seeds. Add orange rind and water and cook for 10 minutes. Add grape skins, bring to boil, and add sugar and spices. Cook until thickened. Pour into hot sterilized jars and seal. Makes four or five ½-pint jars.

GRAPE AND PINEAPPLE JAM

2 pounds Concord grapes
1 lemon
Dash of salt
1½ cups sugar
1 cup canned crushed pineapple

Wash grapes, drain, and stem. Slip skins from pulp and reserve. Heat pulp to boiling and rub through coarse sieve to remove seeds. Slice lemon thin and remove seeds. Add to grape pulp and skins; add salt, and cook over moderate heat for 15 minutes, stirring constantly. Add sugar and pineapple; cook to consistency of marmalade, about 20 minutes. Pour into hot sterilized jars and seal. Makes four or five ½-pint jars.

SPICED PEACH JAM

4 cups peach pulp
4 cups sugar
3 or 4 peach pits
1 tablespoon whole gingerroot
¾ teaspoon whole allspice
½ tablespoon whole cloves
1 cinnamon stick
Juice of ½ lemon

Chop peach pulp; mix with sugar in preserving kettle. Crack peach pits; remove kernels and add to peach pulp. Add spices tied in a bag. Simmer until clear and thick, stirring occasionally to prevent sticking. Remove spice bag and add lemon juice. Fill hot sterilized jars; seal. Makes about four ½-pint glasses.

PINEAPPLE-STRAWBERRY JAM

8 cups hulled strawberries, quartered
4 cups chopped pineapple
4 cups sugar

Combine ingredients in large preserving kettle; let stand for 1 hour. Heat slowly until sugar is dissolved, stirring occasionally. Cook rapidly for 30 to 40 minutes, or until thick, stirring frequently to prevent sticking. Pour into hot sterilized

jars and seal. Cover and store. Makes five ½-pint jars.

PLUM-ORANGE JAM

1 large orange
½ pound seedless raisins
½ cup cold water
½ cup honey
24 large plums

Remove rind from orange in sections and discard all white membrane. Cut yellow rind into very small pieces or force through food chopper; dice pulp. Combine rind and pulp with raisins, water, and honey. Add plums which have been pitted and cut into eighths. (1 cup seedless grapes may be added if desired.) Cook over medium heat, stirring frequently, until thick, about 1 hour. Skim and pour into hot sterilized jars. Let cool slightly, and seal. If desired, ¼ cup chopped nuts may be added to the preserve just before jars are filled. Makes eight ½-pint jars.

RED-PEPPER JAM

Wash and seed 1 dozen large sweet red peppers. Force through medium blade of food chopper. Add 1 tablespoon salt and let stand overnight. Drain well, pressing out all liquid. Put in kettle with 2 cups white vinegar and 3 cups sugar. Cook, uncovered, for 45 minutes, or until of marmalade consistency, stirring frequently. Pour into hot sterilized jars and seal. Makes four or five ½-pint jars.

GOLDEN JAM

2 large oranges
6 cups diced rhubarb
3 cups ground raw carrots
3 cups light corn syrup
2 cups sugar*

Remove seeds and grind oranges. Combine with remaining ingredients and let stand overnight. Bring to a boil and cook slowly until rhubarb is transparent and mixture is thickened. Pour into hot sterilized jars and seal. Makes ten ½-pint jars.
*Or use 4 cups sugar, omitting corn syrup.

OLD-COUNTRY STRAWBERRY JAM

6 cups hulled strawberries
3 cups sugar

Put strawberries in a large heavy saucepan and mash. Cook over moderate heat until fairly thick, stirring frequently. Gradually add sugar; stir constantly over low heat until sugar is dissolved. Bring to boil and boil rapidly for 15 to 20 minutes, or until juice sheets from spoon, stirring occasionally to prevent sticking. Skim, and pour into hot sterilized jars. Seal. Makes four ½-pint jars.

TOMATO-APRICOT JAM

1 package (12 ounces) dried apricots
7 cups (two 1-pound, 12-ounce cans) tomatoes

1 teaspoon whole cloves
3 cinnamon sticks
1 teaspoon salt
7 cups sugar
Juice of ½ lemon

Soak apricots overnight in tomatoes. Add spices, tied in a bag, and salt. Bring to boil and cook for 15 minutes. Add sugar and cook until clear and of consistency of marmalade. Remove spice bag; add lemon juice. Pour into hot sterilized jars and seal. Makes about five ½-pint jars.

QUINCE AND PEAR JAM

3 cups quince pulp
2 cups pear pulp
3½ cups sugar
Salt
1 cup water

Wash and cut quinces; cover with water and cook until tender and mushy. Drain and use liquid for making Quince Jelly (page 984). Meanwhile wash and cut up pears and cook, covered with water, until tender. Put through food mill, and measure. Put quinces through food mill to remove seeds and cores, and measure. Put measured pulp purée into kettle with sugar, salt, and water, and cook, stirring to prevent scorching, until thick. Pour into hot sterilized jars and seal. Makes four ½-pint jars.

Note: This is sometimes called Quince and Pear Honey.

RASPBERRY CURRANT JAM

2 cups currant pulp
2 cups crushed raspberries
3 cups sugar

To prepare currant pulp, cook currants (about 3 cups) until soft, press through a sieve or food mill. Measure pulp. Combine currant pulp, raspberries, and sugar. Bring slowly to boil, stirring occasionally until sugar dissolves. Cook rapidly to jellying point, about 30 minutes. As mixture thickens, stir frequently to prevent sticking. Pour, boiling hot, into sterilized jars and seal. Makes four ½-pint jars.

JAMS MADE WITH PECTIN

PINEAPPLE-MINT JAM

3½ cups (one 1-pound, 13-ounce can) crushed pineapple
¾ cup water
Juice of 2 lemons
7½ cups sugar
1 bottle (6 ounces) liquid pectin
1 teaspoon peppermint extract
Green food coloring

Mix first 4 ingredients. Bring to a boil, stirring. Boil for 2 minutes. Add pectin, peppermint, and coloring. Stir and skim for 5 minutes. Pour into hot sterilized jars and seal. Makes five ½-pint jars.

THREE-MINUTE STRAWBERRY JAM

2 cups mashed or sieved strawberries
4 cups sugar

1 box (1¾ ounces) powdered fruit
   pectin
1 cup water

Combine berries and sugar. Let stand for about 20 minutes, stirring occasionally. Stir pectin into water; bring to boil and boil rapidly for 1 minute, stirring constantly. Remove from heat, add berries, and stir constantly for about 2 minutes. Pour into sterilized jars; cover and let stand at room temperature for 48 hours, or until gelled. Seal and store in freezer, where jam will keep well for several months. Or it will keep for 6 to 8 weeks stored in refrigerator. Makes five ½-pint jars.

Note: To use liquid fruit pectin for this jam, omit powdered pectin and water and use ½ bottle liquid pectin (½ cup). It is not necessary to heat liquid pectin; just stir strawberry-sugar mixture into it and proceed as directed above.

TOMATO JAM

Scald, peel, and chop about 2¼ pounds ripe tomatoes. Bring to boil and simmer for 10 minutes. Measure 3 cups into large saucepan. Add 1½ teaspoons grated lemon rind, ¼ cup fresh lemon juice, and 6 cups sugar. Mix well and bring to a full rolling boil. Boil hard for 1 minute, stirring. Remove from heat and at once stir in 1 bottle (6 ounces) liquid pectin. Skim, then stir and skim by turns for 5 minutes. Ladle into hot sterilized jars and seal. Makes about seven ½-pint jars.

Note: Serve with any cold meat.

BERRY JAM

2 quarts blackberries, boysenberries, dewberries, strawberries, or youngberries or any mixture of these
7 cups sugar
½ bottle (6 ounces) liquid pectin or
1 box (1¾ ounces) powdered pectin

Wash berries and crush. If berries are very seedy, sieve half of berries to remove part of seeds. Combine 4 cups crushed berries and the sugar in saucepan. Mix well and bring to a full rolling boil. Boil for 1 minute, stirring constantly. Remove from heat and stir in pectin. Skim off foam and stir and skim alternately for 5 minutes. Fill hot sterilized jars and seal. Makes seven or eight ½-pint jars.

Note: If berries are lacking in tartness, substitute ¼ cup fresh lemon juice for ¼ cup of the fruit.

Loganberry or Red Raspberry Jam
Follow Berry Jam recipe, but use only 6½ cups sugar.

Gooseberry Jam
Follow Berry Jam recipe, but use only 6 cups sugar and grind berries instead of crushing.

BLUEBERRY JAM

Wash and pick over 1½ quarts ripe berries and crush; there should be 4½ cups. Combine in kettle with 2 tablespoons fresh lemon juice and 7 cups sugar; mix well. Bring to full rolling boil over high heat; boil hard for 1 minute, stirring. Remove from heat and stir in 1 bottle (6 ounces) liquid pectin. Skim off foam. Continue stirring and skimming for 5 minutes to prevent floating fruit. Ladle into hot sterilized jars and seal. Makes nine ½-pint jars.

RED-CHERRY JAM
2½ cups (one 1-pound, 3-ounce can) pitted red sour cherries
3½ cups sugar
½ bottle (6-ounce size) liquid pectin

Drain juice from cherries. Crush cherries thoroughly; add sugar, and mix in large preserving kettle. Bring quickly to a full rolling boil and boil rapidly for 1 minute, stirring constantly. Remove from heat, add pectin, and mix well. Skim, and pour into hot sterilized jars. Seal. Makes four ½-pint jars.

SOUR CHERRY JAM
1 quart ripe sour cherries, about
4 cups sugar
¾ cup water
1 box (1¾ ounces) powdered fruit pectin

Pit and grind the cherries and measure 2 cups into large bowl or pan. Add sugar to fruit, mix well, and let stand. Mix water and pectin in small saucepan. Bring to a boil and boil for 1 minute, stirring constantly. Stir into fruit mixture. Continue stirring for about 3 minutes. There will be a few remaining sugar crystals. Ladle quickly into glasses. Cover at once with tight lids. When jam is set, store in freezer. If jam will be used within 2 or 3 weeks, it may be stored in refrigerator. Makes about seven ½-pint jars.

PEACH JAM
3 cups canned sliced peaches
1 jar (8 ounces) maraschino cherries
1 large lemon
7½ cups sugar
1 cup liquid pectin

Drain peaches before measuring, then chop them. Add cherries, cut into quarters, juice from cherries, and juice of the lemon. Add peach syrup if necessary to make 4 cups of fruit mixture. Combine with sugar, bring to boiling point, and boil hard for 2 minutes. Stir almost constantly during the cooking. Remove from heat, stir in pectin, and let stand for 5 minutes, stirring frequently. Turn into hot sterilized jars and seal. Makes about six ½-pint jars.

PEAR-RASPBERRY JAM
Thaw 1 package (10 ounces) frozen raspberries. Peel and core about 2 pounds

fully ripe pears and force them through medium blade of food chopper. Measure raspberries and enough ground pears to make 4 cups fruit. Put in kettle with ¼ cup fresh lemon juice, 1 tablespoon grated orange rind, and 6 cups sugar. Bring to full rolling boil over high heat; boil hard for 1 minute, stirring. Remove from heat and stir in half of 6-ounce bottle of liquid pectin. Skim off foam. Continue stirring and skimming for 5 minutes to prevent floating fruit. Ladle into hot sterilized jars and seal. Makes seven or eight ½-pint jars.

JAMS MADE WITHOUT COOKING

NO-COOK BLACKBERRY JAM
2 cups fully ripe blackberries (about 1 quart)
4 cups sugar
2 tablespoons fresh lemon juice
½ bottle liquid pectin

Crush berries. (*For a less seedy jam, allow 1 more cup berries; strain half the berries and discard this half of the pulp.) Put fruit in large bowl and add sugar. Mix well. Combine lemon juice and pectin, and add to fruit. Continue stirring for 3 minutes. If a few sugar crystals remain they will do no harm. Pour into glasses or freezer jars. Cover with tight lids and let stand 24 hours to set. Store in freezer or for up to 3 weeks in refrigerator. Makes six ½-pint jars.

No-Cook Red-Raspberry Jam
Substitute red raspberries for blackberries in recipe above. Makes about six ½-pint jars.

No-Cook Strawberry Jam
Substitute 1¾ cups crushed strawberries for 2 cups berries in No-Cook Blackberry Jam recipe. Makes about five ½-pint jars.

No-Cook Peach Jam
2¾ cups peeled, pitted, and ground peaches (about 2¼ pounds, whole)
6½ cups sugar
⅓ cup fresh lemon juice
1 bottle liquid pectin

Proceed as in No-Cook Blackberry Jam recipe. Makes about nine ½-pint jars.

No-Cook Sour Cherry Jam
1¾ cups pitted and ground sour cherries (about 1 quart)
4 cups sugar
¼ cup fresh lemon juice
½ bottle liquid pectin

Proceed as in No-Cook Blackberry Jam recipe. Makes about five ½-pint jars.

JAMAICAN SOUPS

by Leila Hadley

Hearty and deliciously different, these soups capture the flavor of one of the loveliest islands in the Caribbean. Admittedly, there is something in my nature that finds much of the Caribbean cuisine unappealing. Roasted breadfruit sings no siren song for me. I have no truck with peanut stew, and I turn a rich shade of antique green when confronted with curried goat. Sweet-potato pone makes my teeth scream with anguish. To my notion, the best cooking is simply the best there is, but not necessarily the strangest or the most complicated or the most original.

And so, on coming to live in Jamaica, it was a matter of pure joy to find that no matter how disturbingly sweet and glutinous their pudding desserts, nor how scaringly seasoned their meat curries, the Jamaicans are masters at the preparation of fish and soup.

When fish and soup come together in a chowder, the combination is delectable and soul-warming. If you don't want to cope with anything more than a one-dish meal, yet feel like something more inventive than chicken, more delicate than steak, a fish chowder such as the one I'm about to describe is the perfect solution. At lunch or supper, accompanied by a green salad, hot buttered popovers, some fruit, or perhaps lemon sherbet with an extra tang of grated lemon, it makes a thoroughly delicious and satisfying meal. Jamaicans are connoisseurs of fish, and savor their fish bright-eyed and firm-fleshed, fresh from the sea. So in the morning, when the fishermen return in their dugout canoes, we go down to the beach to do our marketing. No matter how early we go, the higglers are there before us. The higglers (a polite corruption of the word hagglers) are the local peddlers. Traditionally, the fish higglers are women whose speech, colorful as their bright-printed cotton skirts, is shot through with startling endearments. "My darlin'," one of the women says, bargaining with a fisherman straight from his boat with a basket of fish, "you greedy as a old hog for make me pay such a price. Man, you two-face like a star-apple leaf. You is a real terrible t'ief for true."

She walks away, her hips penduluming with indignation, but the round wicker basket she balances on her head is nevertheless filled with fish. Purple doctorfish with curious smiling mouths, groupers, parrot fish—turquoise and shining—and red-spotted butterfish. After doing a little higgling myself, I buy shrimps, a lively lobster, a mirror-smooth kingfish, and a snapper the color of a pink sunset, all carefully weighed on a battered brass-pan scale.

Back home again in the kitchen, Miss Gladys, our cook, sets the final seal on my shopping pleasure by saying, "Them didn't rob you. Everything them lovely for true, Mistress." So now we are ready to make the chowder. By the way, if you live inland where fresh lobster and shrimps aren't available, there's no reason why you shouldn't use frozen seafood. Don't let the long list of ingredients put you off. The recipe, which appears on page 967, is actually simpler than it looks.

Another house specialty of ours is a Jamaican Pepperpot, and I'm sure that somewhere in the pot is a touch of white magic. For after that first spoonful has spread its influence on tongue and palate, strong taciturn men, previously all too plainly impervious to my charms as a temptress, have indicated in giddy phrases that I am the moon of all delight. Women, who would just as soon shred me into pieces and clap me into a Saratoga trunk, dimple at me sweetly, kowtow with fitting humility, and beg me to give them the recipe.

This Jamaican soup is an island specialty, and although there are innumerable ways of making it, this is the way it is prepared at the Myrtle Bank, the oldest hotel in Kingston, justly famed for its charm and comfort. In the evening, the tourists, unburdened of their complex of cameras, raffia-embroidered straw hats and baskets, souvenir shells and bundles of duty-free merchandise, sit out in the cool of the broad hotel veranda, listening to the palm trees clacking in the wind. Down by the bar, the band strikes up a Jamaican *mento,* or work song, soft and pleasing, and then sends out an animated Trinidadian calypso. A departing liner gives a resonant farewell hoot. The fireflies in the moonlit garden flash mating signals to each other. In a pleasantly lazy, calypso-collapse mood, you go in to dinner and, with a certain well-bred greediness, you wait for the pepperpot soup to appear.

MYRTLE BANK JAMAICAN PEPPERPOT SOUP

- 2 pounds spinach (locally known by the fetching name of Callaloo!) or 2 packages (10 ounces each) frozen spinach, thawed
- 2 pounds beef, cut into 1-inch cubes
- ½ pound diced salt pork
- 3 onions, coarsely chopped
- 4 cups water
- ½ teaspoon dried thyme
- 3 scallions or chives, minced
- 1 seeded green pepper, minced
- 1 bay leaf
- 2 tomatoes, sliced
- 2 teaspoons salt
- ⅛ teaspoon cayenne or ½ teaspoon freshly ground black pepper
- 12 okras, stemmed
  Butter
- ½ cup heavy cream
  Paprika

Wash spinach, drain thoroughly, then chop coarsely. Put in large soup pot and add beef, salt pork, onions, and water. Bring these ingredients to the boiling point and then let simmer gently for 1 hour. Add thyme, scallions, green pepper, bay leaf, tomatoes, salt, and cayenne; allow to simmer for about 30 minutes. Slice okras into rings and sauté gently in butter. They musn't brown but must absorb the butter as flowers absorb the sun. Add them to the soup for last 10 minutes of cooking time. Just before serving, add cream. Sprinkle each serving with a wisp of paprika. Makes about 6 servings.

JAMAICAN SPLIT-PEA SOUP

- 2 cups split peas
- 2 onions, coarsely chopped
- 6 cups water
- 3 cups chicken or beef bouillon or consommé
  Salt and pepper
- 4 strips of bacon, cooked and crumbled
  Croutons

Boil split peas and onions in water for 30 minutes. Then simmer for 1½ hours. Whirl this purée in a blender for a few seconds. Return to pot and add bouillon. Season to taste. Garnish with crumbled bacon and croutons. Makes about 6 servings.

JAMAICAN CONGO-PEA OR KIDNEY-BEAN SOUP

- 4 cups water
- ½ cup Congo peas (pigeon peas) or kidney beans
- ¼ pound salt pork or a ham bone with meat

1 bay leaf
4 peppercorns
Milk or light cream
Croutons
Chopped parsley

Bring water to a rapid boil. Drop peas in slowly so as not to lower boiling point. When last pea has been added, add meat, bay leaf, and peppercorns; simmer for about 2½ hours, or until peas are soft. Remove meat and mince finely. Whirl soup in a blender and return to the pot. Return meat. Thin soup as desired with milk. Garnish with croutons and parsley. Makes about 6 servings.

CHICKEN SOUP WITH SHERRY

Bones and scraps of 1 chicken
2 onions, chopped
2 teaspoons salt
½ teaspoon ground ginger
8 cups water
3 tablespoons sherry

Put chicken bones and scraps, onions, salt, and ginger in the pot with cold water and quickly bring to a boil. Reduce heat and simmer for 1½ hours. Add sherry and simmer for another 30 minutes. Strain, and serve. Very easy and very good. Makes about 6 servings.

JAMAICAN ONION SOUP WITH CHEESE

2 tablespoons soft butter
2 egg yolks
2 cups milk
1 can (10½ ounces) condensed consommé with enough water added to make 2 cups
1 cup sautéed, coarsely chopped onions
½ cup grated Gruyère cheese
Salt and pepper

Beat butter together with egg yolks. When thoroughly mixed, add milk and consommé. Bring to boiling point, stirring as you go. Reduce heat. Add onions, cheese, and salt and pepper to taste. Serve piping hot. Makes about 6 servings.

KINGSTON POTATO SOUP

6 tablespoons butter
6 leeks, sliced
2 onions, sliced
6 large potatoes, sliced
6 cups chicken bouillon
½ cup cooked green peas
Dash of cayenne
1½ teaspoons salt
1 cup milk
1 avocado, peeled and sliced

Melt butter in a saucepan. Add leeks and onions and sauté until golden-brown. Add potatoes and bouillon and let simmer for 30 to 40 minutes. When potatoes are well done, put soup through a sieve or whirl in a blender. Return to saucepan, add peas, cayenne, and salt, and

cook for 5 minutes longer. Thin with heated milk. Place a slice or two of avocado in each soup plate and pour the soup over the avocado. Serve very hot. Makes about 6 servings.

JAMAICAN FISH CHOWDER
Fish

1 large or 2 small lobsters
1 pound shrimps
2 pounds fish fillets (cod or haddock)

Fish Stock

8 cups water
1 carrot, coarsely chopped
1 onion, coarsely chopped
1 celery stalk, coarsely chopped
1 garlic clove
1 bay leaf
1½ tablespoons salt
6 peppercorns
2 whole cloves
½ lemon

Chowder

½ cup olive oil
¾ cup sliced onions
1 tablespoon minced garlic
¼ cup parsley leaves
½ teaspoon dried basil
1 bay leaf
3 peppercorns
2 cups (one 1-pound can) solid-pack tomatoes
½ teaspoon salt
Pinch of ground saffron
¼ teaspoon grated lemon rind
1 cup dry white wine, or more

Garnish

3 tablespoons minced parsley

If you have brought home a live lobster, start by plunging it into enough boiling water to cover it generously. Add 2 tablespoons salt for each quart of water. When the water has returned to a rollicking boil, count the cooking time from this minute and allow 5 minutes for each pound of lobster. Remove the lobster from the water with kitchen tongs. When it is cool enough to handle, clip out the hard sac near the head, remove the dark intestinal vein, and draw out the meat from the shell. Cut the meat into serving pieces. If you've brought home a cooked lobster, all you have to do is remove the meat from the shell, discard the intestinal vein and the hard sac near the head, and cut the meat into serving pieces. Cover the chunks and put them in the refrigerator. Don't save the water in which the lobster was boiled in the hope you can use it for the stock. Take my word for it, you can't.

Now on to the shrimps, the fish, and the fish stock. Wash, shell, and devein the raw shrimps. Set aside. Cut the filleted fish into 2-inch cubes, wrap cubes in wax paper, and refrigerate until needed. Next

step is to simmer for 10 to 15 minutes all the ingredients listed under Fish Stock. Then add the fish scraps, if you had a whole fish, and the shrimps. Let these simmer for 10 minutes. Let the shrimps cool in the stock. Remove shrimps and store them, covered, in the refrigerator until needed. Strain the stock and set aside.

Now then, get out a large soup pot. Pour in olive oil and place the pot over medium heat. Add sliced onions, minced garlic, and parsley leaves. Cook and stir until these are lightly browned. Then add basil, bay leaf, peppercorns, tomatoes, salt, and saffron. Simmer these ingredients, covered, for 30 minutes. You may want to place a slice of toast in each soup plate, and, if so, now is a good time to make the toast. Some people prefer plain crackers with the chowder, but others prefer the chowder ladled over a slice of toast plus a liberal offering of popovers. After the soup has simmered for 30 minutes, add stock. Stir. Then add fish cubes, and do give these a last-minute pinch to find any bones that might have remained. Let fish simmer for 10 minutes. Then add lobster, shrimps, and lemon rind, and let this supreme concoction simmer for 5 more minutes. Add white wine, ladle the chowder into soup plates, garnish with minced parsley, and bring to the table at once! Makes about 6 servings.

PUMPKIN SOUP

Scooped-out chunks and pulp of a large pumpkin
2 onions, coarsely chopped
2 teaspoons salt
⅛ teaspoon cayenne
4 cups chicken bouillon
1 teaspoon grated onion
½ cup heavy cream, whipped
Pepper

Remove the seeds and strings from pumpkin. Add pumpkin, coarsely chopped onions, and salt and cayenne to bouillon and simmer until pumpkin is tender. Put soup through a sieve or whirl in a blender. Reheat to boiling point, but do not allow to boil. Just before serving, add grated onion. Top each serving with whipped cream and a grating of freshly ground black pepper. Makes 6 servings.

JAMBALAYA—A New Orleans Creole dish, made with combinations of ham, sausage, fowl, shrimps, oysters, tomatoes, onions, garlic, and other seasonings.

The origin of the dish is obscure, although it is evidently based upon elements of French and Spanish cooking. The Spanish *paella,* a mixture of rice, meat, and seafood, is a close relative. The origin of the name is obscure, too. It may derive from the French word for "ham," *jambon,* or it may come more directly from a Provençal word, *jambalaia* meaning "a dish of rice and fowl."

Jambalayas make excellent party dishes since they can be prepared beforehand. For a party, cook the jambalaya until it is almost done, refrigerate, and finish cooking just before serving. A green salad is a good accompaniment, and a creamy bland dessert provides a pleasant flavor contrast to the well-seasoned jambalaya.

CREOLE JAMBALAYA
- 2 tablespoons butter
- 1 pound raw smoked ham, coarsely diced
- 2 large onions, chopped
- 2 garlic cloves, minced
- 1 medium green pepper, cut up
- 4⅔ cups (two 1-pound, 3-ounce cans) tomatoes
- 3 cups meat broth or 2 chicken cubes and 3 cups water
- 1 bay leaf, crushed
- ½ teaspoon dried thyme
- ½ teaspoon chili powder
- ¼ teaspoon pepper
- 2 cups long-grain rice
- 1 pound fresh shrimps, cooked, shelled, and cleaned or 1 package (12 ounces) frozen shelled cleaned shrimps, cooked

Melt butter in top-of-stove casserole or Dutch oven. Add ham, onion, and garlic; cook until lightly browned. Add remaining ingredients except rice and shrimps and bring to boil. Gradually stir in rice. Cover and simmer for 30 minutes, or until rice is tender and liquid is absorbed. Add shrimps, and more seasoning if desired. Makes 6 servings.

JAPANESE COOKERY

a gourmet's
tour of
the exotic
and economical,
nutritious
and delicious
cookery of Japan.

Although some Japanese dishes seem very foreign to Americans, there are many of them that are ideally suited to our everyday life. They have many advantages, chief of which is their economy and healthfulness. Because meat is expensive in Japan, it is stretched with vegetables, and fish, which is plentiful, is used in many fascinating ways. Raw fish is eaten in the form of *sushi* and *sashimi* but it is more often served cooked. Few Japanese kitchens have ranges, as we have, so much of the food is cooked on a *hibachi* (a small grill) by broiling, steaming, boiling, and frying. Baked or roasted dishes are practically unknown.

One of the most entrancing things about Japanese food is its beauty. As much care is taken with the arrangement of the food, its color contrast, and even shape, as with the cooking and seasoning. This makes it especially appropriate for party food, when one wants the meal to look as attractive as possible. Also *nabe* cookery (cooking at the table) is wonderful for the busy hostess with no help. The guests do their own cooking and love it.

Japanese meals are served very differently from American ones. Not only because the guests sit on the floor, eat from low, usually individual, tables, and use chopsticks, but because the order in which the courses are served is very different from ours. For instance, although they have delicious soups, they do not necessarily come at the beginning of the meal. They don't have salads as we know them, and rice or noodles take the place of bread. Green tea is the national beverage, but beer is popular and sake, heated and served in tiny cups, is often served throughout the meal. Fruit is served as dessert, especially melons, berries, and tangerines, but the Japanese have sweets, usually made of bean paste, that are more appealing to Americans' eyes than to their palates. Pickles are very popular, as are salted plums (a breakfast treat), and vegetables. These and the other ingredients used in these recipes can be found in Japanese markets in large American cities. Recipes, unless otherwise noted, serve 6, and there is no reason in the world why they can't be incorporated into a meal that is otherwise typical of the United States.

GLOSSARY

JAPANESE INGREDIENT	TRANSLATION	SUBSTITUTE
Aburage	Fried soybean curd*	None
Ajinomoto	Monosodium glutamate	
Azuki	Japanese red beans	Red kidney beans
Beni-shoga	Pickled gingerroot*	Soak crystallized gingerroot in vinegar
Daikon	Japanese radish	Radish, perfectly white
Dashi	Japanese soup stock	Fish, chicken stock, consommé, or recipe at right
Ginko	Ginkgo nuts*	None
Kamaboko	Fish cakes *	Recipe, page 972
Katsuobushi	Dried bonito*	Dried shrimps
Konbu	Seaweed*	None
Matsutake	Wild mushrooms*	Regular mushrooms may be substituted, but the taste is not comparable
Mirin	Japanese wine	Sherry or whisky
Miso	Fermented bean paste*	Recipe at right
Nori	Seaweed in sheets*	None
Nou	Variety of seaweed*	None
Sake	Rice wine	Dry beer or dry white wine
Sashimi	Sliced raw fish	
Sembei	Soy-coated rice cracker*	None
Shichimi togarashi	Seven spices: mixture of pepper, poppy seed, cayenne, sesame, orange peel, hemp seed, and seaweed*	None
Shiitake	Mushrooms (a variety cultivated on trees)*	Regular mushrooms may be substituted, but the taste is not comparable
Shinsen-shoga	Fresh gingerroot*	Crystallized gingerroot, rinsed of sugar
Shirataki	Cellophane, transparent, or yam noodles*	Fine noodles or vermicelli
Shoyu	Japanese soy sauce	Soy sauce
Shungiku	Edible chrysanthemum*	None
Soba	Buckwheat noodles*	Fine noodles
Somen	Fine noodles	
Tofu	Soybean curd*	Tiny dumplings
Udon	Broad noodles	
Wasabi	Horseradish	
Yakidofu	Broiled bean curd*	None

* Available in Japanese food stores

EXAMPLES OF JAPANESE MEALS

BREAKFAST

Rice; *miso shiru* (bean paste soup); egg; *tsukudami* (fish cooked in *shoyu*); *konomono* (pickles); *umeboski* (salted plum); tea. The egg is usually raw, beaten with *shoyu* and poured over the hot rice.

NOON MEAL

Rice or any noodles (soba, udon, or somen); boiled vegetables; broiled fish; tea.

DINNER

Rice; *suimono* (clear soup); *sashimi* (raw fish); broiled or fried fish; *chawan mushi* (steamed custard); *tsukemono* (pickles); *tempura*; tea.

HOT TOWELS

This is a lovely Japanese custom, passed after any food is served. The towels (our fingertip terry towels are ideal) are wrung out in very hot water, rolled up tight, and passed to each guest while still steaming hot. A good way to do this is to wet the towels in hot water, twist each one into a figure eight, and keep on a hot tray, covered with foil, until time to serve.

DASHI
(Soup Stock)

This is the Japanese national soup stock, used in many recipes. It can be bought in little envelopes, like large tea bags, and made by boiling in water according to directions on the package.

4 cups water
Konbu
Shaved katsuobushi
½ teaspoon ajinomoto

Use a piece of *konbu* about 4 inches square. Put in the water and bring to a boil. Remove *konbu* and add shaved *katsuobushi*, available already shaved or in a rocklike piece; dried shrimps may be used instead. Add the amount specified on the package. Bring again to a boil and remove from heat. Add *ajinomoto*. When *katsuobushi* sinks to bottom of pot, pour off the clear liquid. This is *dashi*, and many of these recipes call for it. Makes about 4 cups.

MISO
(Fermented Bean Paste)
Miso is available in Japanese markets. If not available, this is a fairly reasonable facsimile

1 cup dried beans, white or pinto
2 tablespoons Japanese rice vinegar
2 tablespoons mirin
1 teaspoon salt

Cook beans in water to cover until they are very soft, adding more water to keep from sticking. Drain; mash smooth or whirl in a blender. Add remaining ingredients. Makes about 3 cups.

 SOUPS

SUIMONO
(Clear Soup)

This clear soup is simply *dashi*, sometimes with a few drops of *shoyu* added, with some beautiful garnish. The garnish may be almost anything: a few green peas, a thinly sliced mushroom, a chicken gizzard cut like a chrysanthemum (cut a half gizzard into squares, almost to the bottom; when cooked it will open up like a flower), a few slices of carrot cut with a tiny scalloped cutter, a lemon slice, a split shrimp or two, a triangle egg (drop a raw egg into the corner of a piece of greased foil folded into quarters, stand foil on point, and cook in boiling water), a few matchlike pieces of turnip, carrot, or onion, watercress leaves, shreds of chicken. Often two or three things are used. For instance, half a split shrimp, 2 slices of mushroom, 5 green peas. Whatever it is, it must look pretty!

TAMAGO SUIMONO
(Egg Soup)
    6 cups dashi (page 970)
    1 tablespoon shoyu
    4 eggs
    4 green onions, minced

Heat *dashi,* add *shoyu,* and bring to a boil. Beat eggs well, turn off heat under soup, and stir in eggs gradually, beating constantly. The eggs will set. Divide among 6 bowls and garnish each portion with a little of the minced onion. Makes 6 servings.

MISO SHIRU
(Bean Paste Soup)
    4 cups dashi (page 970)
    ½ pound (¾ cup) miso (page 970)

Heat *dashi* to a boil. Add *miso* and cook until *miso* is melted. Add almost any-thing—shredded *daikon* or sliced green onions, for instance. *Aburage* is often cut into squares and added. Makes 4 servings.

CHAWAN-MUSHI
(Steamed Custard)
This delicious dish may be served as a soup or a first course. In Japan, it's served warm, but when cold it is a de-lightful beginning for a summer meal. It is usually made with chicken or shrimps, often with both.

    1 chicken breast, boned (about 10 ounces)
    6 medium shrimps (optional)
    6 eggs
    3 cups dashi (page 970)
    2 tablespoons sake
    ⅓ cup shoyu
    3 medium-large mushroom caps
    ¼ cup cooked peas or 18 canned ginkgo nuts
    3 green onions, sliced thin
    3 water chestnuts, sliced thin or 6 thin slices of bamboo shoot
    6 spinach leaves or 6 small watercress springs

Use cooked chicken breast and shrimps or—and this is preferable—steam raw

shelled and cleaned shrimps and skinned and boned chicken breast over boiling water or *dashi* for 5 minutes. They will be firm enough to slice, but still juicy.

Beat eggs slightly and add cooled *dashi,* sake, and *shoyu;* mix well. Slice chicken and/or shrimps as thin as pos-sible (or dice, if you prefer); slice mush-rooms (if raw ones are used, they must be paper-thin); divide these ingredients evenly among six 1-cup bowls or custard cups. Add the other ingredients (any or all), cutting the greens into shreds and dividing everything as evenly as possible. Strain the egg mixture over all and steam over simmering water for 10 to 15 min-utes, or until the custard is set. Over-cooking will ruin the dish. Serve each bowl with a thin slice of lemon, if desired. Makes 6 servings.

FISH AND SEAFOOD

CHIRINABE
(Fish Sukiyaki)
    6 cups dashi (page 970)
    ¼ cup sake
    2 pounds fish
    8 green onions, sliced
    3 squares tofu
    1 pound spinach or edible chrysanthemum
      Juice of 3 lemons
    1 ounce grated fresh gingerroot
    1 lemon, sliced

Heat *dashi* and sake in a chafing dish, electric skillet, or *sukiyaki cooker.* Cut fish into pieces, bones and all (the Japanese include head and tail). Add about one-fourth of it to stock. Add 1 of the onions, about one-fourth of *tofu* (each piece cut into 4 or 6 squares), and one-third of spinach leaves. Bring to a boil and add ingredients again, a few at a time. Each guest helps himself to a ladleful of the soup and uses his chop-sticks to eat the solids directly from the common pot. They are dipped into the lemon juice and grated gingerroot, which are divided among the guests. The sliced lemon is a garnish. Makes 6 servings.

SASHIMI
(Sliced Raw Fish)
This is just raw fish without benefit of *sushi* rice. The fish, which must be very very fresh, is boned and sliced ¼ inch thin or thinner, then cut into pieces about 1 by 2 inches. Serve with grated horse-radish, *daikon,* and gingerroot, *shoyu* and

mustard. Each guest mixes his own sauce and dips fish into it with chopsticks. Bonito, albacore, shrimps, and scallops are popular for *sashimi,* although other fish are also used.

NIGIRI SUSHI
(Raw Fish Rice Ball)
    Raw tuna fish
    Grated fresh horseradish
    Cooked Sushi Rice
    Shoyu

Slice the tuna ¼ inch thick and cut into pieces 2 inches long and 1 inch wide. Sprinkle a little grated horseradish (or grated gingerroot) on it. Then pick up some of the rather gooey rice (about 2 tablespoons) and form it into an oval. Put a slice of fish on top and mold as symmetrically as possible. Serve with *shoyu.* Mackerel, clams, whitefish, prawns, and other fish can be used the same way. If you can't bear the idea of raw fish, use smoked salmon.

Sushi Rice
    1 pound polished rice
    2½ cups water
    1¼ cups white vinegar
    3 tablespoons salt

Wash rice 3 hours before cooking. Boil water, add rice, and bring to a rolling boil. Then lower heat and cook until rice is tender and water absorbed. Spread out in a shallow bowl. Cool quickly by fan-ning. (If you have an electric fan, fine!) Mix in 1¼ cups white vinegar (prefer-ably Japanese) and 3 tablespoons salt. You now have *sushi* rice.

TEMPURA
(Tempura)
Many Americans think of *tempura* as shrimps dipped into batter and fried in deep fat. That is one form, and a very good one, but in Japan all kinds of sea-food and vegetables are also used. Some, such as ginkgo nuts in little edible sea-weed baskets and shoots of young ginger, are impossible for us to find. The food should be fried at the table and served immediately. An electric skillet or deep fryer is fine, or a *tempura nabe* (cooker), which must be used over an electric plate.

Ingredients (use any or all):
    Shrimps, shelled and cleaned
    Small fish, cleaned but whole
    Clams, scallops, mussels, or oysters, shelled but whole
    Lobster, cut into slices across the grain
    Fillet of fish, cut into strips with the

grain
Mushrooms, sliced if large, whole if
 small
Spinach, whole perfect leaves
Carrots, cut into thin diagonal slices
Green onions, cut into thin diagonal
 slices or whole if small
Celery, cut into thin diagonal slices
Chinese or snow peas, whole, strings
 removed
Eggplant, cut like French-fried
 potatoes
Sweet potatoes, cut into thin slices
Watercress, whole sprigs
String beans, whole, cooked for 5
 minutes

Batter:

2 eggs
¾ cup all-purpose flour
1 cup water
1 tablespoon cornstarch
½ teaspoon salt
½ teaspoon baking powder
 Peanut or other cooking oil

Beat eggs until fluffy, add remaining ingredients, and mix—a few lumps are of
no concern to the Japanese. Have plenty
of oil heated to 350°F. on a frying thermometer and have all ingredients dry.
Dip into batter; shrimps may be held by
their tails; spinach, watercress, and small
green onions by the stems; other ingredients may be dropped into the batter,
then lifted out with a slotted spoon or
tongs and allowed to drain for a second
before putting into the fat. The batter
coating should be very thin. The Japanese sometimes shake a few extra drops
of the batter onto the food in the fat,
using their chopsticks. This makes little
beads of crispness on the food. Small
pieces of food, such as string beans or
snow peas, are usually dipped and fried
2 or 3 at a time. The food is turned so
that it will brown evenly, then drained;
the tempura cooker has a perforated shelf
for this purpose; a cake rack on a plate
does nicely. The food should be served on
a paper napkin, to absorb extra fat, as
soon as it is done. Each guest should dip
his portion into the Sauce (below) and
eat at once. (If preferred, *shoyu* alone
may be used for sauce.) The hostess
may officiate at the cooking, or guests
may take turns cooking while the others
eat. Usually one variety of food is cooked
and served at a time, as shrimps, fish,
mushrooms, beans, etc. Makes enough
batter for 6 servings.

Sauce

1 cup dashi (page 970)
⅓ cup shoyu
⅓ cup sake
 Sugar to taste (optional)

Combine all ingredients and mix well.
Each guest should be given a small dish
of sauce, and grated radish and grated
fresh gingerroot should be on hand to
add to it.

Note: In Japan, small amounts of anything left—not enough to go around—are
chopped, stirred into the remaining batter, then dropped by spoonfuls into the
fat—a mixed fritter!

TENDON, short for TEMPURA DOMBURI
(Tempura over rice served
in a covered casserole)

Tendon, in its simplest form, is shrimps
or lobster fried like *tempura,* but served
on a bed of rice. Sometimes watercress
or other vegetables are cooked like *tempura* and added to the shrimps and the
sauce is poured over all. Instead of rice,
the Japanese noodles *(udon)* or buckwheat noodles *(soba)* may be used.

TEMPURA SEMBEI
(Cracker-Fried Shrimps)

This is very appealing to the occidental
palate. It can be made with any fish or
shellfish, but is perhaps best made with
jumbo shrimps.

2 pounds jumbo shrimps or prawns
2 eggs
1 teaspoon shoyu
1 cup sembei crumbs (see note)
 Fat for deep frying

Shell shrimps, split down the back, remove veins, and open. Beat eggs slightly;
add *shoyu*. Roll *sembei* or whirl in the
blender to make crumbs. Dip shrimps
into egg mixture, then into crumbs, and
allow to dry for 30 minutes. Fry in deep
fat (360°F. on frying thermometer) until
nicely browned, 2 to 3 minutes. Serve
with *tempura* sauce. Makes 4 servings.
Note: *Sembei* are Japanese crackers.
There are many varieties, but the one to
use here is the small salty one with a
shiny varnished look.

TEMPURA SOBA
(Fried Foods with Noodles)

This is very good. Cook a bundle (10 to
12 ounces) of *soba* until tender. Put in
a *domburi* (casserole) and top with small
strips of lemon peel and with *tempura*
of small shrimps, *Kamaboko* (see recipe
below), shellfish such as clams, and assorted vegetables. Serve with *Kakejiru*
(see recipe at right above)

Kamaboko
(Fish Cakes)

Kamaboko are available in Japanese
markets. If you can't get them, here is a
recipe.

1 pound fillet of any white fish
2 tablespoons cornstarch
1 teaspoon sugar
½ teaspoon ajinomoto
 Water

Grind fish, add cornstarch, sugar, *ajinomoto,* and just enough water to make a
thick paste. Knead well, form into a
sausage-shape, or mound on a narrow
clean board so that you have a half-
cylinder, and steam for 15 minutes. Slice
before dipping into batter for *tempura*.
Makes 6 to 8 servings.

Kakejiru
(Sauce)

3 cups dashi (page 970)
3 tablespoons shoyu
½ teaspoon sugar
½ teaspoon ajinomoto

Heat *dashi,* add other ingredients, and
serve.

ONIGARI YAKI
(Broiled Shrimps)

These are delicious and make a delicious
appetizer served before an occidental
meal. Allow 6 medium-size shrimps for
each person. Leave them whole, with the
shells on, and thread 3 on each bamboo
skewer, putting the skewer first just below
the head (or where the head would have
been), then near the tail, so that each
shrimp is U-shape. Cook together ¾
cup shoyu, ½ cup *mirin,* and 2 teaspoons
sugar (the sugar can be omitted to ap-
peal more to American palates) for 4
or 5 minutes. Soak shrimps in this mixture, then broil over charcoal or in the
oven, basting with the marinade. Don't
overcook—5 or 6 minutes should suffice.
Note: You and your guests may be hap-
pier if the shrimps are shelled before
cooking, but if they're not, be sure to
serve hot towels after this dish has been
eaten.

NUTA
(Seafood Salad)

1 pound raw scallops
3 bunches green onions, sliced
1 teaspoon salt
¼ cup miso
1 tablespoon sugar
2 tablespoons vinegar
2 tablespoons ajinomoto
1 large head celery
2 cups shredded daikon or sliced radish
 Lettuce

Cut scallops into thin slices; use raw, or
cook for 2 minutes. Blanch green onions.
Mix salt, *miso,* sugar, vinegar, and *ajinomoto*. Combine with vegetables and scallops. Serve cold on shredded lettuce.
Makes 4 to 6 servings.

Sashimi   Onigari Yaki
Butaniku-Teriyaki

Nuta
Tempura Sembei

MEAT

JYUNIKU-TERIYAKI
(Broiled Beef)
2 pounds beef tenderloin
1 tablespoon grated fresh gingerroot
¼ cup shoyu
1 garlic clove, mashed
¼ cup mirin
2 tablespoons peanut oil

The meat may be cut into individual steaks; or cut into ⅛-inch slices and then into strips, then woven on bamboo skewers; or it may be cut into ¾-inch cubes and strung on skewers. Mix gingerroot, *shoyu*, garlic, and *mirin* and marinate skewered meat for 1 hour. Brush with oil and broil or sauté, basting with the marinade. The meat should be shiny when done, but not dried out. Time of cooking varies with the thickness of the meat. This may be used as an appetizer or an entrée. Makes 6 to 8 servings.

Note: Although *teriyaki* may be made with fish or chicken, beef is the most popular.

BUTANIKU-TERIYAKI
(Broiled Pork)
2 pounds lean pork, cut into ¾-inch cubes
½ cup shoyu
¼ cup sake
2 tablespoons sugar
1 garlic clove, crushed (optional)
½ ounce fresh gingerroot, sliced

Marinate meat in other ingredients for 1 hour, turning once. Broil over charcoal or in a broiler, basting with the marinade and turning so that all sides become brown and shiny. Cook until pork is thoroughly done, but not dry, for 20 to 25 minutes. Makes 6 to 8 servings.

UMANI
(Meatballs)
½ pound ground beef or pork
1 tablespoon water
  Cornstarch
1½ cups water
3 tablespoons shoyu
½ teaspoon sugar
½ teaspoon ajinomoto
1 cup sliced carrots
1 cup cooked string beans

Mix meat with water and 1 tablespoon cornstarch and form into small balls. Combine water, *shoyu*, sugar, and *ajinomoto* and cook meatballs in it for 10 minutes. Remove meatballs and cook carrots in same sauce. Return meatballs to mixture and add beans. Heat, and serve. Makes 4 servings.

NABE RYORI
Nabe ryori means "cooking at the table," and is an ancient form of Japanese cookery, which is growing in popularity in this country. Called "friendship dishes," the best known is *sukiyaki,* but there are many others, some included here. *Mizutaki,* originally just chicken, precooked in the kitchen and finished at the table, is now made with other meats and can include vegetables. A *hokotsu,* or copper cooker with a chimney for charcoal, surrounded by a moat for the cooking food, is used in Japan, but a Japanese casserole or *domburi,* placed on a charcoal burner or electric plate, is also used. An electric skillet makes a fine table cooker.

SUKIYAKI
(Plough-Roasted)
This is the Japanese dish best known to Americans. It can be made in many different ways, and is. It is inexpensive, low in calories, and good eating. This basic recipe may be varied to suit, and American vegetables can take the place of Japanese ones.

1 cup mirin
1 cup shoyu
1 teaspoon ajinomoto
2 pounds beef tenderloin or sirloin
1 cup beef suet
2 large onions
6 green onions
1 or 2 bamboo shoots
1 can tofu
1 small can shirataki
  Optional: Spinach, mushrooms, carrots, Chinese cabbage, celery, eggplant, bean sprouts, watercress, snow peas
  Sugar
6 raw eggs

First make the *warishita,* which is the cooking mixture, by combining *mirin, shoyu,* and *ajinomoto.* Some people use *shoyu* and sugar, thinned with *dashi.* Have mixture in a pitcher at the table. The beef is preferably tenderloin or sirloin, but as it is sliced paper-thin, it does not have to be top grade. It is easier to slice if it is partially frozen, but Japanese markets sell it sliced. Arrange it tastefully. Cut suet into 3 or 4 pieces. Cut onions into halves from top to bottom, then slice ⅜ inch thick. Cut green onions into 2-inch pieces. Slice bamboo shoot. Cut *tofu* into 1-inch cubes. Drain *shirataki* (if dried *shirataki* is used, soak in cold water for 2 hours and cut into 4-inch lengths). The optional vegetables are sliced thin, except spinach leaves and watercress which are stemmed, and snow

peas, which are trimmed of tips and strings. Arrange all these attractively as possible on bamboo trays or dishes. Use electric skillet or put *sukiyaki* pan on the table over heat. Using chopsticks, put the suet in the pan and rub around so that it melts. Add about ¼ of ingredients at a time, keeping them in separate little heaps and turning with chopsticks as they cook. Sprinkle 2 teaspoons sugar over the mixture. Stir lightly. Add about ½ cup of the *warishita* and when everything is almost done, add the beef. As soon as it loses color, serve the guests with some of each ingredient and repeat the procedure. Each guest breaks his own egg into a small bowl, beats it with his chopsticks, and dips his food into it before eating, to cool food and coat it with a bland sauce. Makes 6 servings.

Note: Many Japanese start with beef, then add the *warishita* and other ingredients, but this way there is no danger of overcooking the beef.

BATAYAKI
(Butter-Cooked Meat)
1 pound beef tenderloin, sliced thin
2 onions, cut into ¼-inch slices
1 daikon, sliced
1 cucumber, sliced
4 green onions, cut into 2-inch lengths
1 bamboo shoot, sliced thin
  Sliced tofu (optional)
  Sliced mushrooms, spinach, or cooked shirataki (optional)
  Butter or beef suet
1 cup sake
½ cup shoyu
  Sugar (optional)

Batayaki is like *sukiyaki* except that it is marinated in sauce, then cooked in butter or suet. Many Americans prefer it to *sukiyaki.* Arrange beef and next 7 ingredients attractively and symmetrically on trays or plates. Heat butter in *sukiyaki* pan or electric skillet and add a few of the ingredients at a time, cooking until done to your liking. If the beef is added last, it can be cooked rare. Add more butter as needed. As soon as one batch is cooked, serve it, and add more ingredients to the pan to cook while guests are eating. For sauce to serve with *batayaki,* in small cups, combine sake, *shoyu,* and sugar to taste. Grated *daikon, shoyu,* mustard, and "7 spices," available at Japanese markets, are also put on the table for seasoning the sauce. Makes 4 servings.

JYUNIKU NO MIZUTAKI
(Table-Boiled Beef)
2 pounds beef, tenderloin or sirloin,

sliced paper-thin
1 Chinese cabbage
1 pound spinach
1 bamboo shoot, sliced, or one 5-ounce
   can, drained
1 tofu, cut into cubes
6 green onions, sliced diagonally
3 carrots, sliced diagonally
3 celery stalks, sliced diagonally
6 large mushrooms, sliced thin
8 cups dashi (page 970) or water
   Junidanya Sauce

Have beef sliced as for *sukiyaki* and arrange on a plate. (To make meat easier to handle, freeze until hard and then slice.) Steam Chinese cabbage and spinach until just wilted. Cool, and put a layer of the cabbage leaves on a cloth (the Japanese use a bamboo mat); on top of this put a layer of spinach leaves. With the help of the cloth, roll the long way, so that the cabbage will roll around the spinach. Press out all the moisture, then slice the roll into ½-inch slices and arrange on a plate. Also arrange, as attractively as possible, next 6 ingredients and put on the table, surrounding the cooker. Heat *dashi* in the kitchen and start charcoal outside. When ready to eat, bring hot *dashi* and glowing charcoal (in bucket with long-handled tongs) to the table. Pour about two thirds of *dashi* into cooker and immediately fill chimney with charcoal. (If you put charcoal in ahead of liquid, the solder may melt.) Now add (or have the guests add) about one third of ingredients. As the ingredients cook, the guests help themselves. The second batch is started while the guests are dipping their food into the sauce and eating it, and when that's done, the broth, now enriched, is served in cups. After the rest of the *dashi* and the ingredients are cooked, each guest mixes the remaining broth with what's left of his sauce. This is highly relished. This sounds complicated, but the ritual is the part that is most delightful, although the dish is delicious. Makes 6 servings.

Junidanya Sauce
½ cup sesame seeds
1 cup dashi (page 970)
½ cup shoyu
1 tablespoon vinegar
   Cayenne
1 tablespoon peanut oil
   Garlic (optional)

Toast the sesame seeds in a heavy dry pan, shaking until lightly browned. Grind to a paste in a mortar, or whirl in a blender. Add *dashi, shoyu,* and vinegar, stirring well. Add cayenne in judicious

amounts to the oil (Mr. Nishigaki, the originator, uses dry red peppers). If garlic is used, crush or purée it and add to taste. Each guest is given a small cup of this sauce. Also have finely minced green onions, grated gingerroot, and, if you wish, Japanese chili powder on hand for those who want to add them to the sauce. Makes about 1¼ cups.

 POULTRY

KUSHI-KATSU
(Fried Chicken on Skewers)
2 broiler-fryers (2½ to 3 pounds each)
1 cup sake
3 tablespoons shoyu
6 small onions
½ teaspoon salt
¼ cup all-purpose flour
2 eggs
1 cup sembei crumbs
   Deep fat
   Shoyu

Skin and bone chicken and cut meat into pieces. Marinate in sake and *shoyu* for 30 minutes. Cut onions into sixths from top to bottom. String chicken on bamboo skewers, alternating pieces with onion. Mix salt and flour and beat eggs slightly. Dip skewers into flour, then into egg, then roll in crumbs. Let stand for 30 minutes, then fry in deep fat (350°F. on a frying thermometer) until crisp and tender. Serve with *shoyu* and, if you wish, grated gingerroot and minced green onion. Makes 8 servings.

TORI NO MIZUTAKI
(Boiled Chicken)
2 broiler-fryers (2½ to 3 pounds each)
10 cups water
½ teaspoon ajinomoto
2 teaspoons salt

Sauce:
2 cups dashi (page 970)
2 tablespoons mirin
⅔ cup shoyu

Condiments:
   Minced green onions
   Grated gingerroot
   Lemon juice

Have chicken chopped into 2-inch pieces, bones, skin, and all. Cover with water in a large pot, add *ajinomoto* and salt, and simmer, covered, until tender. Bring to the table and transfer to the cooker. You may have to do this a little at a time. Each guest helps himself to chicken with his chopsticks, dips chicken into the

sauce, and adds such condiments as desired. The sauce is made by mixing the *dashi, mirin,* and *shoyu;* each guest is given a small cupful. At the end of the meal, the delicious broth from the chicken is served to the guests in cups. Makes 6 servings.

Note: This is *mizutaki* at its simplest. In recent years many vegetables are added: sliced mushrooms, sliced onions or leek, Chinese cabbage, spinach, sliced carrots, etc.

YOSE-NABE
(Mixed Cooked Foods)
This is cooked in a *hoko-nabe,* or Japanese cooker with a chimney for hot charcoal surrounded by a "moat" in which the food is cooked. It can be a mixture of almost anything, but the following is typical.

½ pound raw shrimps
½ pound skinned and boned raw
   chicken (about 1 pound before
   skinning and boning)
2 bamboo shoots
6 green onions
½ pound fresh mushrooms or three
   4-ounce cans sliced mushrooms
1 pound spinach
2 cups dashi (page 970)
   Ponzu

Shell and clean shrimps and split. Slice chicken as thin as possible (if you steam it for a few minutes, it's easier). Slice bamboo shoots, green onions, and mushrooms. Steam spinach until limp, stack in a neat pile, and cut into ½-inch slices. Arrange ingredients attractively on a platter. Heat *dashi* and put in cooker; add hot charcoal to chimney with tongs (lacking the cooker, an electric skillet can be used). The hostess or guests add the ingredients to the hot *dashi* with chopsticks and remove them as soon as they're done. The food is dipped into *Ponzu* and eaten at once. When all the food is eaten, the by now rich soup is ladled into bowls and drunk. This amount makes 4 servings—enough for *nabe* cooking.

Ponzu
(Dipping Sauce)
½ cup shoyu
½ cup fresh lime juice
2 tablespoons grated fresh gingerroot
2 tablespoons minced green onion
2 tablespoons grated daikon

Combine *shoyu* and lime juice. Divide among 4 bowls and pass other ingredients in tiny dishes, for guests to add at will.

RICE, NOODLES,
AND VEGETABLES

GOHAN
(Rice)
Wash rice very well under running water. Put in a heavy kettle with a tight-fitting lid. Add 1¼ cups cold water for each cup of rice. Cover and bring rapidly to a hard boil. Turn heat to medium-low and cook for about 12 minutes, then turn heat as low as possible for another 15 minutes. Turn off heat and let stand, still covered, for another 10 minutes before serving. If you wish, you may add ½ teaspoon salt for each cup rice at beginning of cooking.
Note: In Japan the water content of rice varies during the year and allowance for that is made in the amount of cooking water. Japanese rice is sticky, not in separate grains, to make it easier to pick up with chopsticks. The bland flavor of rice is used to offset the spicy flavor of other foods.

CHAZUKE
This is the lowliest of dishes, made with leftover rice with very hot tea poured over it—the Japanese version of milk toast. Here is a more elaborate version.

NORI-CHAZUKE
(Rice with Seaweed)
8 cups hot cooked rice
5 cups hot dashi (page 970) or tea
1 tablespoon wasabi, or to taste
  Shoyu to taste
5 sheets toasted nori
2 tablespoons toasted sesame seed

Put rice in a 1½-quart domburi. Season dashi with wasabi and shoyu. Sprinkle with nori and sesame. Pour liquid over all and serve at once. Makes 6 to 8 servings.
Note: To toast sesame seed, cook in a heavy deep skillet, stirring, until it begins to color. Toast nori under the broiler until crisp. If using dried wasabi, moisten it in a little water first.

ODAMAKI-MUSHI
(Egg Custard Noodles)
1 pound udon
1 chicken breast, steamed
2 tablespoons shoyu
  About 1 bamboo shoot, sliced (½ of 5-ounce can, or as much as needed for design)
2 green onions, sliced diagonally
3 cups dashi (page 970)
2 eggs, beaten

Cook udon in salted water until just tender, drain, and rinse. Divide among 6 soup bowls. Slice chicken breast thin and marinate in shoyu for 10 minutes. Arrange on top of udon along with bamboo and onions, making a design. Mix dashi with eggs, and divide among the bowls. Set bowls on a rack over simmering water, cover, and steam for 10 minutes. Serve at once. Makes 6 servings.

SOBA
(Buckwheat Noodles)
The Japanese are very fond of these noodles, which are delicious. They are available in Japanese markets in 14- and 16-ounce packages. Drop noodles into boiling water. When it again comes to a boil, stir, and add ½ cup cold water to stop boiling. Bring again to a boil and again add cold water. Do this 4 times altogether. Cover, turn off heat, and let stand for 15 minutes; then rinse well with cold water. Serve cold with shoyu. These noodles are also delicious served hot with butter.

HITASHIMONO
(Boiled Greens)
Any tender young greens such as spinach or lettuce or young turnip greens may be used. Cook them without salt in a minimum of water until tender but still green. Serve in small bowls with a mixture of 1 cup dashi (page 970) and ¼ cup shoyu.

MATSUTAKI DOBIN
(Steamed Mushrooms)
6 large mushrooms
1 teaspoon salt
2 tablespoons sake
1 chicken breast
½ pound fillet of sole or other white fish
1 bunch of watercress
¼ cup canned ginkgo nuts
1½ cups dashi (page 970)
1 tablespoon shoyu
1 tablespoon fresh lemon juice

Slice mushrooms thin and soak in salt and sake for 10 minutes. Steam chicken and fish for 8 minutes. Remove skin and bones from chicken and then slice chicken and fish. Remove stems from watercress and chop leaves. Divide mushrooms, chicken, fish, watercress, and ginkgo nuts among 6 bowls with covers. Mix dashi, remains of sake, shoyu, and lemon juice and divide among the cups. Cover and steam for 20 minutes. Makes 6 servings.
Note: Matsutaki, Japanese mushrooms, look like corks from opened champagne bottles. They are available dried in some Japanese stores and may be used in this recipe. They must be soaked before using.

Canned ones are also to be found; they need no soaking. In Japan this dish is steamed in individual dobin, or teapots, hence the name. The juice is poured from the spout into little cups and drunk. Makes 6 servings.

OSHITASHI
(Spinach with Sesame)
1 pound spinach
¼ cup sesame seeds
¼ cup shoyu

Pile spinach evenly in stacks of 6 to 8 leaves. Lay in a skillet and pour boiling water over them. Cook for 2 minutes, or until wilted. Drain, rinse with cold water, and press all moisture from the leaves. Cut piles in 1-inch pieces. Toast sesame seeds in a dry pan until they begin to color, then crush in a mortar or whirl in a blender. Add shoyu and pour over spinach. Serve cold. Makes 4 servings.

NOPPE JIRU
(Vegetable Stew)
3 cups dashi (page 970) or consommé
½ cup diced daikon
¼ cup diced carrot
¼ cup diced turnip
½ cup peas
1 tablespoon shoyu
4 teaspoons cornstarch
¼ cup cold water
¼ teaspoon ajinomoto

Combine dashi with vegetables and cook until barely tender. Add shoyu and cornstarch, mixed with water and ajinomoto. Cook until thickened, and serve. Makes 4 servings.

GOMA-ZU
(Sauce for Vegetables)
This can be used on vegetables such as bean sprouts, spinach, cucumbers, or watercress. As the vegetables are usually served cold, the dish is comparable to a salad.

1 cup cider vinegar
1 tablespoon shoyu
1 teaspoon salt
2 tablespoons sugar, or to taste
¼ teaspoon ajinomoto
⅓ cup ground toasted sesame seeds
¼ cup mirin

Mix well before serving. Makes about 1⅔ cups.

 SALADS

JUJU GAKUAN
(Salad)
Chop 3 green onions and mix with 1 large peeled and chopped cucumber. Add

Sukiyaki

2 cups mashed bean curd (cottage cheese may be substituted) and season with salt and pepper. Mix with mayonnaise (widely used in Japan) or with oil and fresh lemon juice. Makes 4 to 6 servings.

KYURI-MOMI
(Vinegared Cucumber)
1 cucumber or daikon
2 tablespoons salt
2 tablespoons sugar
3 tablespoons vinegar

Peel cucumber and slice thin. Sprinkle with salt; let stand for 30 minutes. Drain and rinse. Add sugar and vinegar, and chill. Makes 2 servings.

 DESSERTS

AWAYUKI-KAN
(Snow Gelatin)
1 envelope unflavored gelatin
1 cup water
1 cup sugar
2 egg whites
2 tablespoons fresh lemon juice

Stir gelatin into water. Let stand for 5 minutes. Heat, stirring, until gelatin is dissolved. Add sugar and stir until dissolved. Chill until it begins to thicken. Beat egg whites until stiff. Fold egg whites and lemon juice into gelatin mixture. Pour into an 8-inch square pan and, when set, cut into 2-inch squares. Makes 16 squares.

Nishiki-Kan
(Two-Tone Jelly)
Follow recipe for *Awayuki-kan,* but divide gelatin-sugar mixture, after it has thickened slightly, into 2 parts. Mix one part with 2 beaten egg whites and pour into a moistened pan. Chill until firm. Mix the other part with 2 beaten egg yolks and pour on top of white mixture when it is firm. When set, cut into pieces.

CHAKIN SHIBORI
(Sweet-Potato Dessert)
1 cup well-drained canned fruit (pineapple, mandarin oranges, plums, etc.)
2 cups mashed cooked sweet potatoes
½ cup sugar
½ teaspoon salt

Cut fruit into cubes (mandarin sections may be left whole). Mix mashed potato with sugar and salt and cook over low heat, stirring, until moisture disappears and potato is very thick. Cool. Place about 3 tablespoons on a square of clean

cloth, put a piece of drained fruit on top, bring cloth up around, and twist into a ball. Remove cloth. You should have a round of potato paste stuffed with fruit. Serve at once. Makes about 10.

YOKAN
(Bean Cakes)
1 pound red Japanese beans
8 cups water
1½ cups sugar
2 envelopes unflavored gelatin
½ cup cold water

Buy Japanese red beans if possible, otherwise use kidney beans. Cook in water until very soft. Mash through a strainer or whirl in a blender. Add sugar, and gelatin dissolved in cold water (a little salt will make it more palatable to Americans). Cook until thick and pour into 8-inch square pan. When cold, cut into squares. Fancy-shape cookie cutters may be used. Sometimes these bean cakes are wrapped in cherry leaves before serving. Makes 3 dozen.

TSUJIURA
(Japanese Fortune Wafers)
⅓ cup butter
1¾ cups sugar
1 egg
¼ cup milk
2 cups all-purpose flour
1 teaspoon baking powder
¼ teaspoon salt
1 teaspoon almond extract or 2 teaspoons vanilla extract

Cream butter until light and fluffy. Beat in sugar. Add egg and mix well. Stir in milk. Sift flour with baking powder and salt. Add to batter and stir until smooth. Add flavoring. Spread as thinly as possible on the bottom of baking pans. Bake in preheated moderate oven (350°F.) for 8 to 10 minutes, or until very lightly browned. Working quickly, cut into 3½-inch squares, or cut into rounds with a 3-inch cutter, and while still warm put a "fortune" written on a piece of paper in the center. Fold and press edges together firmly. If the cakes cool, slip them back in the oven before attempting to roll. If rolled properly thin, this will make 6 dozen.

JELLIED—This adjective describes: 1) A semitransparent, semisolid, and somewhat elastic consistency of foods, due to the presence of such substances as agar, gelatin, Irish moss, isinglass, or pectin; 2) A completed dish containing, or covered with, gelatin such as jellied eggs, jellied salads, jellied meats, etc.

Jellied dishes include soups, aspics, molded salads, and desserts. They are extremely popular because they are colorful, attractive, and delicious to eat. Also, foods with a jellied coating do not dry out.

Jellied dishes should be stiff enough to hold their shape when unmolded, but they should be tender. Since they can be prepared in advance of serving, they are used a great deal for entertaining.

The gelling agents most often used in home cookery are gelatin and pectin. Gelatin is a protein substance made from animal tissues. It is available unflavored in granular form and in sheets, and fruit- and vegetable-flavored in granular form. It is combined with a liquid which can be fruit or vegetable juice, milk, or broth. The gelatin-liquid mixture can be used plain; it can have solids such as chopped meat, chicken, fish, vegetables, or fruit added; and it can be used to coat other foods. One of the characteristics of such jellied dishes is that the gelatin mixture retains its translucence.

When a richer mixture is desired, beaten egg whites and/or whipped cream are folded into the gelatin mixture and cloud it: Spanish cream, chiffon pies, charlottes, sherbets, and Bavarians are examples of this type of dish.

The second most widely used gelling agent is pectin, a water-soluble substance present in plant tissue which yields a jelly when properly combined with acid and sugar. Some fruits, such as tart apples, blackberries, cranberries, and quinces contain enough natural pectin, particularly when slightly unripe, to gel without the addition of any artificial gelling agent when they are properly cooked. Commercial liquid and dry pectins are available and are used in the making of jams, jellies, and preserves.

Agar, made from various kinds of algae or seaweed, bleached and dried; Irish moss, made from dried and bleached carrageen, a dark-purple seaweed; and isinglass, a semitransparent whitish gelatin prepared from the air bladders of certain fish, including carp, cod, and sturgeon, are other gelling agents. Their use in home cookery today is very limited and they are not widely available. Agar can be found in drugstores; Irish moss and isinglass in some health-food stores and perhaps in some country food stores.

A few jellied dishes gel because of the gelatin present in the original substance. Head cheese is an example of such a dish. Jellied soups and meats may be made by boiling meat and bones which are rich in gelatin. When the broth is strained and cooled, the mixture solidifies.

RUBY-GLAZED CHICKEN-LIVER PÂTÉ

½ pound chicken livers
2 tablespoons butter or margarine
2 hard-cooked eggs
2 packages (3 ounces each) cream cheese
2 tablespoons chopped parsley
¾ teaspoon salt
Dash of cayenne
1 tablespoon brandy
1 can (10½ ounces) consommé madrilene, undiluted

Sauté chicken livers in butter until lightly browned. Put chicken livers and eggs through fine blade of food chopper or blend in electric blender. Cream cheese with next 4 ingredients. Blend mixtures thoroughly. Pack into refrigerator dish. Pour consommé over pâté to cover. Refrigerate. Makes 1½ cups.

JELLIED CONSOMMÉ MADRILENE

3 envelopes unflavored gelatin
½ cup cold water
2 cups tomato juice
2 cups clear chicken bouillon
½ teaspoon grated onion
2 tablespoons dry sherry
Lemon wedges

Soften gelatin in cold water. Heat tomato juice, bouillon, and onion. Pour over gelatin, stirring until gelatin is dissolved. Add sherry, strain out onion, and chill consommé until firm. Beat slightly with a fork before serving. Garnish with lemon wedges. Makes 4 servings.

JELLIED FRUIT SOUP

½ cup each of dried prunes and apricots
½ cup seedless raisins
1 cinnamon stick
2 cooking apples, peeled
2 fresh pears, peeled
2 cups (one 1-pound can) unsweetened sour red cherries
1 box (3 ounces) cherry-flavored gelatin
1 cup boiling water
Lemon slices

In large kettle soak prunes, apricots, and raisins in 3 cups cold water for 1 hour. Add cinnamon stick, sliced apples and pears. Cover and simmer for 15 minutes, or until fruit is tender. Add undrained cherries and bring to boil. Dissolve gelatin in boiling water; stir gently into fruit. Chill overnight. Serve with lemon. Makes 8 servings.

MOLDED CRABMEAT SALAD

1 envelope unflavored gelatin
1 cup cold water
½ cup hot water
2 cans (6½ ounces each) crabmeat
½ cup mayonnaise or salad dressing
¼ cup ketchup
Juice of 1 lemon
½ cup diced celery
2 tablespoons each of chopped sweet pickle and stuffed olives
¼ teaspoon salt
Salad greens

Sprinkle gelatin on cold water and let stand for 5 minutes. Add hot water and stir until dissolved. Add remaining ingredients except salad greens. Chill until mixture begins to set. Stir well and pour into 1½-quart mold. Chill until firm. Unmold on greens. Makes 4 servings.

CLAM-ASPIC SALAD

1 envelope unflavored gelatin
1 tablespoon cold water
1 cup tomato juice
2 tablespoons fresh lemon juice
½ teaspoon salt
1 can (10½ ounces) minced clams, drained
2 hard-cooked eggs, chopped
2 tablespoons chopped sweet pickle
1 tablespoon grated peeled raw cucumber
½ cup diced celery
½ cup cubed avocado
Lettuce
Mayonnaise
6 stuffed olives, sliced

Soften gelatin in cold water for 5 minutes. Combine tomato juice, lemon juice, and salt in saucepan; bring to boil. Stir in softened gelatin; remove from stove and allow to cool. Chill until gelatin has the consistency of unbeaten egg white. Fold in clams, eggs, pickle, cucumber, celery, and avocado. Pour into a lightly oiled 1-quart loaf pan or ring mold. Chill until firm. Slice, and serve on lettuce; garnish with mayonnaise and olives. Makes 4 to 6 servings.

SAVORY SHRIMP MOLD

2 envelopes unflavored gelatin
½ cup cold water
1 cup boiling water
2 bouillon cubes
¼ cup mayonnaise
1 teaspoon horseradish
1 teaspoon instant minced onion
1 tablespoon minced parsley
2 tablespoons fresh lime or lemon juice
Dash each of Worcestershire and hot pepper sauce
1 pound shrimps, cooked, peeled, cleaned, and diced
½ cup heavy cream, whipped
Seasoned salt and pepper to taste
Salad greens

Soften gelatin in cold water; add boiling water and bouillon cubes; stir until gelatin and cubes are dissolved. Chill until slightly thickened. Fold in remaining ingredients except greens. Pour into 1-quart mold. Chill until firm. Unmold on greens. Makes 6 servings.

PORK AND VEAL HEAD CHEESE

1 pig's head, quartered
1 pound lean pork
1 pound veal
4 cups meat stock or bouillon
2 bay leaves
2 sprigs of fresh thyme
¼ teaspoon powdered cloves
2 teaspoons salt
8 peppercorns
1 teaspoon grated lemon rind
3 onions, peeled and sliced
1 carrot, peeled and sliced
1 celery stalk, sliced

Wash head thoroughly, remove ears, brains, eyes, tongue, and most of the fat. Soak in cold water for 12 hours, changing water several times. Combine head, ears, and tongue with remaining ingredients in large kettle; bring to a boil and simmer for about 4 hours or until the meat is falling from the bones. Cook brains for about 15 minutes in a little stock; cool, and dice. Separate the meat from the bones; discard bones. Dice ears. Slice pork, veal, tongue, and meat from head and alternate sliced and diced meats in a mold. Pour stock over meat. Cover with a cloth and put a weight on top. Chill. Serve cut into slices. Makes 10 to 12 servings.

JELLIED MEAT LOAF

1 envelope unflavored gelatin
1 cup chicken bouillon
½ medium green pepper, sliced
1 tablespoon diced onion
12-ounce can luncheon meat
½ cup undiluted evaporated milk
Dairy sour cream
Horseradish

Soften gelatin in ¼ cup of bouillon for 5 minutes. Put over low heat and stir until dissolved. Put gelatin mixture, remaining bouillon, pepper, and onion in container of electric blender; blend until smooth. Add luncheon meat and milk and blend well. Pour into lightly oiled loaf pan (9 x 5 x 3 inches). Chill until firm. Unmold; serve with sour cream seasoned with horseradish. Makes 6 servings.

JELLIED CHICKEN MOLD

5-pound fowl
4 cups boiling water
1 onion
2 celery stalks
1 bay leaf
Salt
Cooking oil
Pepper
Mayonnaise
Chopped fresh or crumbled dried herbs

Have fowl cut into pieces. Wash; put in kettle; add boiling water, onion, celery, bay leaf, and 1 teaspoon salt. Cover; bring to boil and simmer for 2½ hours, or until fowl is tender. Drain, reserving liquid. Cool fowl; remove meat from bones and cut into coarse pieces. Arrange in 6 oiled individual molds or 1½-quart mold. Skim fat from liquid; strain; reduce to 2 cups by boiling, uncovered. Season to taste with salt and pepper, and pour over chicken. Cool; then chill overnight, or until set. Unmold, and serve with mayonnaise seasoned with herbs. Makes 6 servings.

JELLIED COTTAGE-CHEESE AND TOMATO SALAD

1 envelope unflavored gelatin
¼ cup cold water
½ cup boiling water
½ teaspoon salt
1 onion, grated
2 tablespoons cider vinegar
½ pound cottage cheese
1 can (8 ounces) tomato sauce
Coleslaw
Green-pepper rings

Soak gelatin in cold water, add boiling water, and stir until dissolved. Add salt, onion, and vinegar. Add 3 tablespoons of this gelatin liquid to cottage cheese. To remaining gelatin liquid add tomato sauce. Pour half of tomato mixture into lightly oiled 1-quart mold; chill until set. Meanwhile keep cottage cheese and remaining tomato mixture at room temperature. Add cottage-cheese mixture to jellied tomato layer and chill until set. Then cover with remaining tomato mixture and chill once more. To serve, unmold on slaw; garnish with pepper rings. Makes 4 to 6 servings.

JELLIED VEGETABLE RING

1 envelope unflavored gelatin
¼ cup cold water
1½ cups boiling water
3 tablespoons sugar
¼ cup cider vinegar
1 teaspoon salt
½ teaspoon curry powder
Dash of pepper
1 tablespoon minced onion
1 cup celery strips
¾ cup finely shredded cabbage
¼ cup diced cooked beets
Salad greens
Mayonnaise or salad dressing

Soften gelatin in cold water for 5 minutes; then dissolve in boiling water. Add sugar, vinegar, seasonings, and onion. Chill until slightly thickened; stir and fold in vegetables. Pour into 1-quart ring mold. Chill until firm. Unmold on salad greens and serve with mayonnaise. Makes 4 to 6 servings.

JELLIED PEAR AND CREAM-CHEESE SALAD

1 box (3 ounces) lemon-flavored gelatin
Hot water
½ teaspoon salt
2 canned pear halves or 1 fresh pear, diced
1 banana, diced
4 maraschino cherries, cut up
1 package (3 ounces) cream cheese, softened
½ cup broken nut meats
Salad greens

Dissolve gelatin in 2 cups hot water. Add salt and chill until mixture begins to set. Divide gelatin. To one half add diced pear, banana, and cherries. Turn into 1-quart mold and chill until firm. Beat remaining gelatin until fluffy. Beat in cream cheese and fold in nut meats. Pour over first gelatin layer. Chill until firm. Unmold on salad greens. Makes 4 servings.

ASPIC GLAZE FOR SANDWICHES

1 envelope unflavored gelatin
½ cup cold water
1 cup boiling water
1 chicken bouillon cube

Soften gelatin in cold water for 5 minutes. Add boiling water and bouillon cube and stir until cube and gelatin are dissolved. Chill until thickened to the consistency of unbeaten egg white.

■ To Glaze Sandwiches—Place open-face sandwiches in refrigerator and chill for 30 minutes. Spoon gelatin mixture over sandwiches to completely cover. Chill for about 30 minutes. Makes enough glaze for 12 open-face sandwiches.

STRAWBERRY CHIFFON PIE

1 box (3 ounces) strawberry-flavored gelatin
⅔ cup boiling water
⅛ teaspoon salt
2 tablespoons fresh lemon juice
1 package (10 ounces) frozen sliced strawberries, thawed
3 egg whites
⅓ cup sugar
Ladyfinger Crust

Dissolve gelatin in boiling water. Add salt, lemon juice, and strawberries. Chill until thickened but not firm. Beat egg whites until foamy; gradually add sugar and beat until stiff but not dry. Fold into gelatin. Pile in Ladyfinger Crust and chill until firm. Makes 6 to 8 servings.

Ladyfinger Crust

Split 12 ladyfingers. Use some to line bottom of deep 9-inch pie pan. Cut some into halves crosswise and arrange around edge of pan. Break remainder into small pieces and fill in spaces in bottom of pan. Melt 2 tablespoons butter and pour over ladyfingers in bottom. Chill. Makes one 9-inch pie shell.

Raspberry Chiffon Pie

Use recipe for Strawberry Chiffon Pie, substituting raspberry gelatin for strawberry and 1 package raspberries for the strawberries.

VANILLA BAVARIAN CREAM

1 envelope unflavored gelatin
½ cup sugar
¼ teaspoon salt
4 eggs, separated
1 cup milk
1 teaspoon vanilla extract
1 cup heavy cream, whipped

Combine gelatin, ¼ cup sugar, and salt in saucepan. Beat egg yolks with milk; add to gelatin mixture. Cook over low heat, stirring constantly, until gelatin is dissolved. Remove from heat; add vanilla. Chill until mixture mounds slightly when dropped from spoon. Beat egg whites until foamy. Gradually beat in ¼ cup sugar, 1 tablespoon at a time, continuing to beat until stiff. Fold meringue and then whipped cream into

gelatin mixture. Pour into 2-quart mold. Chill for at least 4 hours, or until firm. Unmold. Serve plain or with fruit or crème de menthe, if desired. Makes 8 servings.

COFFEE-BANANA BAVARIAN

1 envelope unflavored gelatin
½ cup milk
1 cup strong hot coffee
⅓ cup sugar
⅛ teaspoon salt
1 teaspoon rum extract
1 cup heavy cream, whipped
1 ripe banana, diced
½ cup chopped nuts

Soften gelatin in milk for 5 minutes. Add coffee and stir until gelatin is dissolved. Add sugar, salt, and flavoring. Chill until slightly thickened. Fold in remaining ingredients. Chill until firm. Makes 6 servings.

SPANISH CREAM

4 eggs, separated
½ cup sugar
2 cups hot milk
1 envelope unflavored gelatin
¼ cup cold water
½ teaspoon vanilla extract

Beat yolks until thick and lemon-colored. Gradually beat in sugar. Gradually stir in hot milk. Cook over low heat, stirring constantly, until mixture coats a spoon. Soak gelatin in cold water. Let stand for 5 minutes. Add gelatin to hot custard mixture. Stir over ice until mixture is slightly thickened. Beat egg whites until stiff and fold into custard mixture. Add flavoring. Pour mixture into 1-quart mold. Chill until firm. Unmold by dipping mold into lukewarm water for a few seconds. Serve plain or with whipped cream, fresh or cooked fruit, or berries, if desired. Makes 6 servings.

ORANGE-HONEY SHERBET

1½ teaspoons unflavored gelatin
¾ cup cold water
½ cup honey
Grated rind of 2 oranges
1½ cups fresh orange juice
2 egg whites
Few grains of salt

Soften gelatin in ¼ cup cold water. Mix ½ cup water, the honey, and orange rind together; boil for 5 minutes. Add softened gelatin and stir until dissolved. Cool, add orange juice, and pour into freezing tray. Freeze until thick and mushy. Remove to well-chilled bowl and beat with rotary beater until mixture is smooth and fluffy. Fold in stiffly beaten egg whites and salt. Beat again with rotary beater, return to freezing tray, and freeze until firm, stirring occasionally. Makes 6 to 8 servings.

TROPICAL MARMALADE

1 orange
1 lemon

1 tangerine (or another kind of orange)
1 cup water
2½ cups, about (one 1-pound, 4-ounce can) crushed pineapple
1 package powdered pectin
5 cups sugar
½ teaspoon salt
½ teaspoon ground ginger

With 2-blade vegetable peeler, shave peel of fruits into strips. Then cut peel into thin slivers, ⅛ inch or less. Simmer for 20 minutes in water. Cut fruit into halves; with curved grapefruit knife scoop out pulp. Squeeze out juice; add with pulp to peel. Simmer for 10 minutes. Measure all fruit into saucepan, adding water to make 3½ cups. Add powdered pectin; bring to boil. Add remaining ingredients. Stir constantly. When mixture comes to rolling boil, remove from heat after 1 minute. Cool; ladle into hot sterilized jars; seal. Makes seven 8-ounce jars.

JELLY—A mixture of fruit juice, sugar, acid, and pectin, either natural or added, cooked to the stage at which gelation occurs. The resulting product is clear and bright-colored. It is firm enough to hold its shape when turned out of the container in which it was stored. Jelly has a quivering quality and is easily spooned; it should never be syrupy, sticky, gummy, or tough.

Unlike jams, which require only one cooking, jellies require two: one cooking prepares the fruit for juice extraction; in the second cooking the juice is mixed with sugar and cooked to the gelation stage. The first cooking can be eliminated, of course, by the use of frozen or canned juices.

Specific amounts of fruit juice, pectin, acid, and sugar are necessary to make a successful jelly.

The fruit gives the jelly its flavor and color, and supplies, at least in part, the pectin and acid needed. The fruit also has mineral salts which add to the flavor and aid gelation. Fruits with definite or distinctive flavors are best for jelly making because the flavor is diluted by the large proportion of sugar needed for proper consistency and good keeping quality.

Pectin, a water-soluble gelling agent, is found naturally in fruits; when accompanied by an acid and sugar in correct proportions, it makes the jelly gel. It also helps prevent recrystallization of the sugar. Some fruits have enough natural pectin, others do not; and all fruits have less pectin when they are fully ripe, hence fruit used for making jelly should be only ripe enough to be firm, or some underripe fruit should be included. Commercial fruit pectins are available in liquid or powdered form. These may be used with any fruit whether it is naturally high in pectin or not and the fruit may be fully ripe. The cooking time for these jellies is shorter, the formulas standardized, so there is no question about when the jelly has cooked enough. Also the amount of yield is greater.

Some acid is necessary for flavor in jelly making; also the acid aids the pectin to precipitate out, thus forming the jelly. There is a great variation in the amount of acid in various kinds of fruit, and in relation to acid, too, underripe fruit has more than ripe. If fruit is ripe, the acid in the recipe is increased by adding lemon juice or citric acid.

Sugar in the correct amounts is the last of the elements which together are responsible for the formation of the jelly. Sugar also serves as a preserving agent and contributes to the flavor.

Beet or cane sugar may be used in jelly making for they have the same composition. Sometimes corn syrup or honey may be used in place of part, but not all, of the sugar. Usually ¾ cup sugar to each 1 cup juice is the proportion; however, this may vary with the ripeness of the fruit and the amount of pectin present.

There are several ways to make jelly, and because of the products and facilities available today, jelly can be made successfully at any time of year.

□ Jellies Made without Added Pectin— The juice of fruits known to be high in natural pectin should be selected. Among such fruits are tart apples, blackberries, cranberries, currants, gooseberries, Concord grapes, quinces, and raspberries. It is usually best to have part of the fruit underripe. One fourth underripe to three fourths ripe is the ratio most commonly recommended to assure sufficient pectin. To find out whether or not fruit juice has enough natural pectin, add 4 to 5 tablespoons alcohol to 1 tablespoon fruit juice. If the pectin coagulates in a solid mass, the juice has enough.

□ Jellies Made with Commercial Fruit Pectin—In this method, liquid pectin is added to the boiling juice and sugar mixture. Use only recipes designed for this form. Fully ripe fruit may be used.

When powdered fruit pectin is used, it is mixed with the unheated fruit juice. Use only recipes designed for this form. Fully ripe fruit may be used.

□ Jellies Made without Cooking—These may be made with powdered or liquid fruit pectin if they can be stored in a freezer, or used within three to four months if kept in the refrigerator.

TO MAKE JELLY

□ In addition to the standard items found in most kitchens the following equipment is needed for making jelly: A large, broad-bottomed, wide-topped kettle, large enough so fruit juice will not boil over; a jelly bag or several thicknesses of cheesecloth, firm unbleached muslin, or Canton flannel (used with nap side in), to strain the juice; a stand for the jelly bag, or a colander; if making jelly without commercial pectin, a jelly and candy, or a deep-fat thermometer is helpful, as is a clock with a second hand, and household scales for weighing fruit.

□ Have glasses ready when they are needed. Glasses, or jars, and lids should be covered with hot, not boiling, water, and brought to a boil. No further boiling is necessary. Keep hot in water or in a very slow oven until they are needed.

□ To Prepare Juice—You can have the luxury of freshly made jelly in the winter by freezing or canning the juice when fruit is in season.

Select fruit of uniform ripeness; avoid either very green or overripe fruit, both of which may cause trouble. Use a 4- or 6-quart kettle with wide bottom. Sort, wash, and drain fruit; it is not necessary to remove stems, pits, or skins. Crush with potato masher. Add a small amount of water. Heat to simmering; if needed, simmer for 5 to 12 minutes to soften fruit; stir often. Pour fruit into dampened jelly bag or into two thicknesses of cheesecloth over bowl. Let drip for at least 1 hour. Bag may be pressed very lightly with back of spoon to extract juice.

To Freeze—Pour juice into liquid-tight containers, leaving 1-inch headspace for expansion. Freeze at 0°F.

To Can—Add sugar in the proportion of 1 cup sugar to 1 gallon juice. Reheat to simmering and pour into hot clean jars to within ½ inch of top. Seal according to manufacturer's instructions. Process in simmering water (180°F.) for 20 minutes. Label juice, giving kind, date canned, and the amount of sugar used in preparing. Store in cool, dry, dark place. If crystals form, strain before making jelly.

□ If making a jelly without added pectin, cook mixture at a rapid boil until it reaches 220°F. on a candy and jelly thermometer. If you do not have one you can use an old standby jelly test, the spoon, or sheet, test, although it is not as reliable as a thermometer: Dip a cool metal spoon into the boiling jelly mixture. Then raise it at least 1 foot above the kettle, out of the steam, and turn the spoon so that the syrup runs off the side. If the syrup forms drops that flow together and fall off the spoon as one sheet, the jelly should be done.

□ To Seal Jelly—See To Seal Jam, page 961.

JELLIES MADE WITHOUT PECTIN

APPLE JELLY

3 pounds tart red apples
4 cups water
3 cups sugar

Wash apples, cut out any blemishes and the stem and blossom ends, but do not peel or remove the core. Cut apples into eighths. Put fruit in a flat-bottomed saucepan and add water. Cover and simmer until the juice flows freely, about 15 minutes. Strain through a damp jelly bag or several layers of dampened cheesecloth. For crystal-clear jelly, do not squeeze or press the bag. Measure juice into a deep saucepan. (There should be 4 cups.) Boil for 5 minutes. Stir in the sugar and boil rapidly to the jelly stage, 220°F. on a candy and jelly thermometer. Skim any foam from mixture and pour into hot sterilized jars; seal. Makes four or five ½-pint jars.

SPICED APPLE AND BLUEBERRY JELLY

2½ quarts green apple parings or apples
1 cup blueberries
Rind of 1 orange
1 teaspoon ground mace
Few whole cloves
¼ cinnamon stick
2 cups sugar

Cook apple parings and cores, removing only blossom ends, with blueberries, orange rind, and spices in water barely to cover until juice is extracted. Strain through flannel cloth. There should be from 2½ to 3 cups juice. Add sugar and cook until juice sheets from spoon. Jelly should be skimmed several times during cooking. Pour into hot sterilized jars, and seal. Makes about four ½-pint jars.

CRANBERRY JELLY

2 cups cranberries
1 cup boiling water
1 cup sugar

Pick over and wash cranberries; drain. Add water and boil for 20 minutes; rub through sieve. Cook pulp for 3 minutes. Add sugar, mix well, and cook for 2 minutes longer. Pour into jelly glasses or small molds and chill for at least 24 hours. Makes 6 servings.

CONCORD LIME JELLY

4 pounds Concord grapes
Grated rind and juice of 5 small limes
Sugar

Wash grapes, drain, and stem. Put into large preserving kettle and crush slightly. Do not add water. Cook for about 30 minutes, stirring occasionally. Pour into flannel jelly bag and let drain for several hours; do not squeeze. Measure grape juice; bring to boil and boil rapidly for 5 minutes. Add lime rind, juice, and sugar, allowing ¾ cup sugar to each 1 cup juice. Cook until jelly sheets from spoon. Pour into hot sterilized jars, and seal. Makes four or five ½-pint jars.

GRAPE JELLY

3 pounds Concord grapes
About 2½ cups sugar

Crush grapes. Bring to boil and cook for 15 minutes. Strain juice through flannel jelly bag; chill. Dip out juice; do not use sediment at bottom as it may cause crystals to form. Add sugar, using 5 parts sugar to 4 parts juice by measure. Stir until sugar is completely dissolved; do not heat. Pour into hot sterilized jars, and seal. Makes about three ½-pint jars.

MINT JELLY

Use any apple jelly recipe, cooking 1 cup chopped mint leaves with each 1½ pounds apples when preparing juice for jelly. Color a delicate green with vegetable coloring.

QUINCE AND CRANBERRY JELLY

12 large quinces
2 pounds cranberries
Sugar

Wash fruit. Cut quinces into quarters, cover with water, and cook until tender. Add cranberries and cook until skins burst. Strain through jelly bag. Measure juice. For each 1 cup juice, measure ¾ cup sugar. Boil juice for 12 minutes; add sugar, stirring until well mixed. Boil until jelly sheets from spoon. Pour into hot sterilized jars, cool slightly, and seal. Makes about twelve ½-pint jars.
Note: Save this recipe until you find quinces and cranberries in the market in the fall.

JELLIES MADE WITH PECTIN

AROMATIC APPLE JELLY

2 cups apple juice
3½ cups sugar
1 tablespoon aromatic bitters
Juice of 1 lemon
Red food coloring
½ bottle (6-ounce size) liquid pectin

Put juice and sugar in large kettle and bring to boil. Add bitters, lemon juice, and few drops of coloring; bring to boil. Stir in pectin; when mixture boils, let boil for one minute, stirring. Skim, and pour into hot sterilized jars. Seal. Makes about four ½-pint jars.

BERRY JELLY

About 2½ quarts ripe blackberries, boysenberries, dewberries, loganberries, red raspberries, strawberries, or youngberries
7½ cups sugar
1 bottle (6 ounces) liquid pectin

Wash berries and crush thoroughly. Place in jelly cloth or bag, press out juice, and measure. Pour 4 cups juice into very large saucepan and add sugar. Mix well and bring to a full rolling boil, stirring constantly. Add liquid pectin and boil hard for 1 minute, stirring constantly. Remove from heat and skim off foam with a metal spoon. Pour quickly into hot sterilized jars, and seal. Makes about eight ½-pint jars.
Note: If berries are lacking in tartness substitute ¼ cup fresh lemon juice for ¼ cup fruit juice.

Black Raspberry Jelly

Use 3 cups juice, 5 cups sugar, and ½ bottle pectin. Heat crushed berries until the juice flows. Cover and simmer for 15 minutes. Place in jelly bag and press out juice. Combine 3 cups juice and ¼ cup fresh lemon juice in large saucepan. Proceed as with basic recipe above. Makes six ½-pint jars.
Note: This jelly may set slowly. Allow a week or longer.

BLACKBERRY-JUICE JELLY

2 cups canned unsweetened blackberry juice
1 tablespoon fresh lemon juice
½ package (1¾-ounce size) powdered fruit pectin
1¼ cups sugar*
¾ cup corn syrup

Strain juices through fine cloth into large kettle. Place over high heat; heat almost to boiling point; stir in dry pectin and let jelly come to a full boil. Add sugar and corn syrup; mix well and boil rapidly until jelly sheets from spoon. Remove from heat, skim, and pour at once into hot sterilized jars. Cool slightly; seal. Makes about three ½-pint jars.
* Or use 2 cups sugar and omit syrup.

CIDER-AND-SAGE JELLY

½ cup boiling water
3 tablespoons dried sage
1½ cups sweet cider
3¾ cups sugar
Yellow vegetable coloring
½ cup liquid fruit pectin

Pour boiling water over sage. Cover and let stand for 15 minutes. Strain through cheesecloth. Add more water, if needed, to make ½ cup. Add cider and sugar, and heat to boiling. Add enough coloring to tint mixture light yellow. Add pectin, stirring constantly. Boil rapidly for 1 minute. Skim, and pour into hot sterilized jars. Seal. Makes about four ½-pint jars.

GRAPE JELLY

3 pounds ripe Concord grapes
5¾ cups sugar
¾ cup water
1 box (1¾ ounces) powdered fruit pectin

Thoroughly crush the grapes, place in jelly cloth or bag, and squeeze out juice. Measure 3 cups into a large bowl or pan. Add sugar to juice and mix well. Mix water and pectin in small saucepan. Bring to a boil and boil for 1 minute, stirring constantly. Stir into fruit juice. Continue stirring for about 3 minutes. There will be a few remaining sugar crystals. Quickly pour into glasses. Cover at once with tight lid. When jelly is set, store in freezer. If jelly will be used within 2 or 3 weeks, it may be stored in the refrigerator. Makes about eight ½-pint jars.

Note: For best results in making grape jellies, squeeze crushed grapes through 4 thicknesses of dampened cheesecloth.

GRAPE-JUICE JELLY

6½ cups sugar
2½ cups water
  1 bottle (6 ounces) liquid pectin
  3 six-ounce cans (2¼ cups) frozen concentrated grape juice

Stir sugar into water. Place over high heat and, stirring constantly, bring quickly to a full rolling boil that cannot be stirred down. Boil hard for 1 minute. Remove from heat and stir in pectin. Add thawed concentrated grape juice and mix well. Pour immediately into hot sterilized jars, and seal. Makes about nine ½-pint jars.

GRAPE-AND-BASIL JELLY

½ cup boiling water
  1 tablespoon dried basil
1½ cups grape juice
  3 cups sugar
½ cup liquid pectin

Pour boiling water over basil. Cover and let stand for 5 to 10 minutes. Strain through cheesecloth. Add more water, if needed, to make ½ cup. Add grape juice and sugar and heat to boiling. Add pectin, stirring constantly. Boil for half minute. Skim, and pour into hot sterilized jars. Seal. Makes about four ½-pint jars.

Note: Dried thyme may be used in place of basil.

GRAPEFRUIT-AND-SAVORY JELLY

½ cup boiling water
  2 tablespoons dried summer savory
  1 cup grapefruit juice
3¼ cups sugar
  Green vegetable coloring
½ cup liquid pectin

Pour boiling water over savory. Cover and let stand for 15 minutes. Strain through cheesecloth. Add more water, if needed, to make ½ cup. Add grapefruit juice and sugar. Heat to boiling. Add enough coloring to tint mixture light green. Add pectin, stirring constantly. Boil rapidly for ½ minute. Skim, and pour into hot sterilized jars. Seal. Makes three ½-pint jars.

ORANGE JELLY

  6 medium oranges
  4 medium lemons
4½ cups sugar
½ bottle (6-ounce size) liquid pectin

Extract juice from oranges and lemons and strain. There should be 2½ cups juice. Put in large kettle, add sugar, and

mix well. Bring to a boil over high heat and add pectin, stirring constantly. Then bring to a full boil and boil for half minute. Skim, and pour into hot sterilized jars. Seal. Makes four or five ½-pint jars.

ORANGE-GRAPEFRUIT-JUICE JELLY

- 3¼ cups sugar
- 1 cup water
- 3 tablespoons fresh lemon juice
- ½ bottle (6-ounce size) liquid pectin
- 1 six-ounce can (¾ cup) frozen concentrated orange-and-grapefruit juice

Stir sugar into water. Place over high heat and, stirring constantly, bring quickly to a full rolling boil that cannot be stirred down. Add lemon juice and boil hard for 1 minute. Remove from heat and stir in pectin. Add thawed concentrated orange-and-grapefruit juice and mix well. Pour immediately into hot sterilized jars, and seal. Makes about four ½-pint jars.

PLUM JELLY

- 5 pounds ripe tart plums
- 1½ cups water
- 1 box (1¾ ounces) powdered fruit pectin
- 7½ cups sugar

Crush plums thoroughly. Do not peel or pit. Add water, bring to a boil, and simmer, covered, for 10 minutes. Put in jelly bag and press out juice to make 5½ cups. Combine with pectin in kettle and mix well. Bring to a hard boil over high heat, stirring. Add sugar and again bring to a full rolling boil. Boil hard for 1 minute, stirring. Remove from heat, skim off foam, and pour into hot sterilized jars. Seal at once. Makes nine ½-pint jars.

QUINCE JELLY

- 3 pounds ripe quinces
- ¼ cup strained fresh lemon juice
- 7½ cups sugar
- ½ bottle (6-ounce size) liquid pectin

Remove cores and blossom and stem ends from quinces, but do not peel. Put through food chopper. Add 4½ cups water, bring to boil, and simmer, covered, for 15 minutes. Put in jelly bag and press out juice to make 4 cups. Combine in kettle with lemon juice and sugar; mix well. Bring to boil over high heat, stirring. Add pectin, bring to a full rolling boil, and boil hard for 1 minute, stirring. Remove from heat, skim off foam, and pour into hot sterilized jars. Seal. Makes eight ½-pint jars.

RED RASPBERRY JELLY

- 2¼ quarts fully ripe red raspberries
- 6 cups sugar
- ¾ cup water
- 1 box (1¾ ounces) powdered fruit pectin

Thoroughly crush the raspberries, place in jelly cloth or bag, and squeeze out juice. Measure 3 cups into a large bowl

or pan. Add sugar to juice and mix well. Mix water and pectin in small saucepan. Bring to a boil and boil for 1 minute, stirring constantly. Stir into fruit juice. Continue stirring for about 3 minutes. There will be a few remaining sugar crystals. Quickly pour into jars. Cover at once with tight lids. When jelly is set, store in freezer. If jelly will be used within 2 or 3 weeks, it may be stored in the refrigerator. Makes about eight ½-pint jars.

JELLIES MADE WITHOUT COOKING

NO-COOK BLACKBERRY JELLY

- 1¾ quarts ripe blackberries
- 5 cups sugar
- 2 tablespoons fresh lemon juice
- ½ bottle liquid pectin

Crush blackberries and put in jelly cloth or bag. Squeeze out juice and measure 2½ cups into bowl. Add sugar and mix well. Mix lemon juice and liquid pectin; then stir into blackberry juice. Continue stirring for 3 minutes. If a few sugar crystals remain they will do no harm. Pour into glasses or freezer jars. Cover with tight lid. Let stand for 24 hours to set. Store in freezer or for up to 3 weeks in refrigerator. Makes about seven ½-pint jars.

NO-COOK GRAPE JELLY

- 2 pounds ripe Concord grapes
- 4 cups sugar
- 2 tablespoons water
- ½ bottle liquid pectin

Crush grapes and put in jelly cloth or bag. Squeeze out juice and measure into bowl. Add sugar and mix well. Mix water and liquid pectin; then stir into grape juice. Continue stirring for 3 minutes. If a few sugar crystals remain they will do no harm. Pour into glasses or freezer jars. Cover with tight lids. Let stand for 24 hours to set. Store in freezer or for up to 3 weeks in refrigerator. Makes about six ½-pint jars.

NO-COOK RED RASPBERRY JELLY

- 1½ quarts ripe red raspberries
- 5 cups sugar
- 2 tablespoons water
- ½ bottle liquid pectin

Crush raspberries and put in jelly cloth or bag. Squeeze out juice and measure 2½ cups into bowl. Add sugar and mix well. Mix water and liquid pectin; then stir into raspberry juice. Continue stirring for 3 minutes. If a few sugar crystals remain they will do no harm. Pour into glasses or freezer jars. Cover with tight lids. Let stand for 24 hours to set. Store in freezer or for up to 3 weeks in refrigerator. Makes about seven ½-pint jars.

NO-COOK STRAWBERRY JELLY

- 1½ quarts ripe strawberries
- 4 cups sugar
- 2 tablespoons fresh lemon juice
- ½ bottle liquid pectin

Crush strawberries and put in jelly cloth or bag. Squeeze out juice and measure 1¾ cups into bowl. Add sugar and mix well. Mix lemon juice and liquid pectin; then stir into strawberry juice. Continue stirring for 3 minutes. If a few sugar crystals remain they will do no harm. Pour into glasses or freezer jars. Cover with tight lids. Let stand for 24 hours to set. Store in freezer or for up to 3 weeks in refrigerator. Makes about six ½-pint jars.

JERUSALEM ARTICHOKE—This tuber, *Helianthus tuberosus*, is a native of North America and a hardy sunflower perennial which will grow from six to twelve feet in height. The tubers, which grow underground, vary in shape from oblong to elongated, in one piece or branched, and weigh three to four ounces. Their skin is very thin and the color ranges from light beige to a deep yellow, or to brown, reddish, or purplish tinges. The flesh of the Jerusalem artichoke is white and crisp, with a pronounced sweetish flavor of its own. The tubers shrivel quickly when exposed to air.

The Jerusalem artichoke is not even remotely related to the globe artichoke, nor does it resemble an artichoke in appearance. It was probably called an artichoke because its taste vaguely resembles that of the globe artichoke. What is more, it has nothing to do with the city of the Holy Land. The "Jerusalem" in its name is an adaptation of the Italian word for sunflower, *girasole*.

The American Indians cultivated it for centuries. Samuel de Champlain reported seeing the Jerusalem artichoke about 1605 in the gardens of Indians on Cape Cod, and it was introduced to Europe in 1616.

Availability—From October to March in specialty food stores.

Purchasing Guide—Select artichokes with a fresh appearance, free from blemishes.

Storage—Store in a cool dry place. When cooked, store in refrigerator.

☐ Refrigerator shelf: 4 to 5 days

Caloric Value

☐ 3½ ounces, raw = 70 calories

Basic Preparation—Wash and scrub well. Can be eaten raw: sliced and salted like radishes. Jerusalem artichokes are usually cooked with skins on since the skin is thin; however, they may be pared before cooking if preferred.

☐ **To Boil**—Wash and scrub well. Cook, covered, in boiling water to cover for 20 to 30 minutes, or until tender. Check artichokes during cooking period. Overcooking causes the tubers to become mushy. When tender, rub off skin. Season with salt and pepper and serve with melted butter.

Jerusalem artichokes can also be creamed after boiling, or prepared au gratin. They can be cooked, chilled, and cubed for a salad. Prepare as fritters by dipping cooked artichokes into batter, then frying. They can also be made into croquettes or French-fried.

☐ **To Mash**—Boil until tender. Rub off skin. Mash artichokes and season as desired.

☐ **To Fry**—Parboil artichokes and rub off skin. Cook thin slices in very hot deep fat until golden-brown. Drain. Season with salt and pepper. Serve immediately.

☐ **To Bake**—Wash and scrub well. Bake in preheated hot oven (400°F.) for 30 to 40 minutes, or in moderate oven (350° F.) for 40 to 60 minutes. Avoid overcooking.

JERUSALEM ARTICHOKES WITH TOMATOES

2 tablespoons butter
2 tablespoons olive oil
1 cup canned tomatoes
   Salt and pepper
½ teaspoon crumbled dried basil
2 cups sliced cooked Jerusalem artichokes

Heat butter and olive oil. Add tomatoes and salt and pepper to taste. Stir in basil. Cook over low heat, stirring constantly, until very hot. Add artichoke slices and reheat until hot. Serve immediately. Makes 4 servings.

JEWISH COOKERY

by Violet Leonard Kanfer

A varied and representative collection of favorite Jewish dishes, plus a special group of holiday recipes.

Many foods mentioned in the Bible are still used by Jewish people. This is especially true of dishes which are part of holiday tradition, for example the unleavened bread or matzo which is eaten during Passover. Honey, written of frequently in the Old Testament, is still served on the New Year table.

After the exodus from the Holy Land, Jews were scattered to communities throughout the world. In each country where they found themselves, the Jewish homemakers adapted the local produce and cuisine to the special requirements of their Dietary Laws (see below). Except for the foods proscribed by these laws, and the foods specifically associated with religious holidays, Jewish cookery is influenced by the country in which the Jews are or were living. For instance, French Jews ate food much influenced by French cookery, while the food of the German Jews was definitely German in character.

Dishes associated with Jews in the United States are mostly eastern European in origin since most of the American Jews came from eastern Europe. These foods were often modified by family taste and by local availability of ingredients. An illustration of the way in which a recipe traveled is cited by the 11th-century French-Jewish Biblical commentator and scholar, Solomon ben Isaac Rashi, who wrote that the Sabbath dish called *cholent* or *shalet* derived from the French word *chaud*. The dish, he speculates, came from Rome. From France this dish was carried to Germany, to Russia, and thence to Poland. It was brought to America by immigrants from these countries. This dish is served on the Sabbath, or Day of Rest. Since cooking is forbidden on this day, a blend of starches and meat is cooked slowly in the oven, and kept warm overnight. It is still served in homes and restaurants here.

WHAT IS KOSHER AND WHAT ARE THE DIETARY LAWS?

The act of eating is considered by Jews who observe their religious laws to be a religious experience. For this reason a prayer of thanksgiving is said over each meal, or between-meal snack. Blessings are invoked on bread, on wine, and on other foods, such as the first fruits of the season. This food is hallowed as a sacrament, and accepted as one of God's blessings.

The regulations as to the types of food which may or may not be eaten derive from Bible laws. Some theories have been set forth that the rules arose from early recognition of the importance of cleanliness and health and hygiene needs. However, these laws are also a rigid religious discipline which according to the philosopher Maimonides "train us to master our appetites, and accustom us not to consider eating and drinking as ends of man's existence."

Permitted foods are called "kosher" which means "fitting or proper." This includes ritually slaughtered herbiverous animals which "chew the cud and have cloven hooves," and specified birds. There are strict proscriptions against birds and animals of prey, scavengers, creeping insects, and reptiles, all seafood except those with scales and fins, and the blood of all animals (Leviticus 11:1-47). Blood is always extracted from meat and poultry. Even in the case of eggs, any with blood spots are unfit. In addition, meat from the hind quarters of all animals is prohibited. Kosher foods of all kinds are readily available in Jewish and many non-Jewish stores. They are often marked by a *U* in a circle, or by a *K* alone or in a circle. The first means that the foods are endorsed by the Union of Orthodox Jewish Congregations of America, the largest food-endorsing body in the country. The *K* means that other endorsing agencies guarantee that the food is kosher.

In addition, the mixing of meat and milk products is strictly forbidden. This stems from the Biblical injunction "thou shalt not seethe a kid in his mother's milk" (Deuteronomy 14:21). All dishes and utensils used in the preparation of meat and dairy dishes are kept separate.

However, there are foods that are *parve,* or neutral, which means they can be eaten with both meat or dairy dishes. Eggs, vegetables, and fish belong to this neutral group. In order to distinguish quickly such foods from others, their packages are often marked "parve."

The laws governing the slaughter of animals are based upon sparing the animals' suffering. The functionary is a respected person, especially trained, and uses a special knife.

JEWISH FOOD CUSTOMS

"There is no festive celebration without eating and drinking"—Talmud.

All Jewish holidays and holy days are associated with specific food traditions. The Sabbath, which starts at sundown Friday, is marked with an elaborate meal, the best of the week. Traditionally a fine loaf of unsliced twisted white bread called *challah* is blessed by the master of the house. It is then broken and passed to each person at the table, so that all are literally "breaking bread together." A blessing is pronounced over wine or grape juice. The menu is then at the homemaker's discretion, and depends on the locale and economic situation. It is always the finest that can be provided. Since cooking is forbidden until the following sundown, it is customary to serve dishes which can be kept warm in the oven.

All other holiday meals are based on the model of the Sabbath. The exception is the Passover, a spring festival which celebrates the exodus of the Israelites from bondage under the Pharoahs in Egypt. During the eight days of this holiday no bread or other leavened baked goods may be eaten. Nor may beans, peas, corn, rice, or other grains be used. This is a reminder of the haste with which these ancient people fled their homes, and of their privations during their sojourn in the wilderness. All leavening is removed from the house, and special utensils and dishes are used.

Passover—The week of Passover starts with a special ceremonial meal known as a *seder* or "order of service." The story of the Exodus is read and explained. Food symbols are tasted by everyone at table. These are:

1. Three matzos (unleavened bread) symbolizing the three groups into which each Jewish community was divided.

2. A roasted bone, usually lamb or chicken, which represents the sacrificial paschal lamb offered on the eve of the exodus.

3. Bitter herbs, usually horseradish root and watercress, as a reminder of the bitterness of slavery.

4. A roasted or hard-cooked egg, recalling the individual offering at the Temple; also a symbol of life.

5. A green vegetable, usually parsley

or celery tops, as a suggestion of spring's rebirth.

6. Salted water into which these greens are dipped as a token of the tears shed for suffering and persecution.

7. A blend of chopped apple, nuts, and wine called *charoses* which represents the bricks made without straw by the Israelites who were slaves in Egypt.

8. Wine, which is served in goblets four times during the ceremony, to symbolize the promise of redemption made four times in the Bible.

In addition, a large goblet of wine is placed on the table for the prophet Elijah, for whom a door is left ajar. Legend has it that this messenger of the Messiah may arrive at anyone's table during the Passover seder as a harbinger of peace and freedom throughout the world.

Special Passover dishes such as fried matzos and nut cakes are prepared throughout the week.

Other Holiday Food Traditions—Rosh Hashanah, New Year's Day, is in the autumn. Honey and apples are served as a wish for a sweet year to come. Other sweets are served.

Yom Kippur, Day of Atonement, is a day of strict fasting, and prayer. No food or drink is partaken of for twenty-four hours of penitence. Traditionally the fast is preceded by a festive meal, and the fast is broken with fish dishes to symbolize fruitfulness and plenty.

Sukkot, Harvest Festival, is celebrated by decoration with fruits and vegetables and by serving sweets. A citrus fruit and branches of myrtle, palm, and willow are part of the ceremony. In many countries a stuffed cabbage or vine leaves is traditional. Also, so is strudel.

Shevout, Giving of the Law, is celebrated by serving dishes prepared with milk and honey symbolizing the "sweetness of Torah (Ten Commandments and other laws) and the nutrition of learning." It is a time of confirmations and consecration of the children and many parties are given.

Hanukkah celebrates the heroism of Mattathias and his sons the Maccabees, who defied Antiochus in the 2nd century B.C. At this time a miracle occurred. It was thought that there was only sufficient oil for one night's illumination, but the oil was found to last for eight nights. Candles are kindled each night in cele-

bration, and games and gifts are usual. *Latkes,* potato pancakes, are traditional.

Purim, the Feast of Esther, commemorates the rescue of her people by Esther, the Jewish Queen, wife of Xerxes or Ahasuerus of Persia, whose evil Prime Minister Haman had plotted to kill all the Jews in the kingdom. This is a gay holiday celebrated with masquerades and fetes. Foods associated with the festival are triangular cakes filled with poppy seeds or fruits, often prunes and nuts. These are called *Hamantaschen* or Haman's pockets. Strudels and cookies are also served.

APPETIZERS AND SOUPS

CHOPPED CHICKEN LIVERS

½ pound chicken livers
Salt
1 medium onion
2 hard-cooked eggs
1 teaspoon salt
⅛ teaspoon pepper
Rendered chicken fat
Lettuce and tomato

Score chicken livers with a sharp knife. Wash, drain, and sprinkle with salt. Broil chicken livers for 3 to 5 minutes, or until cooked. Grind livers finely with onion and hard-cooked eggs. Add salt and pepper. Add enough chicken fat to make a mixture that is smooth and has the consistency of mashed potatoes. Serve on lettuce with a wedge of tomato. Makes 4 appetizer servings.

CHICKEN FAT AND GRIBENES
(Cracklings)

2 cups fat and skin of raw chicken, duck, or goose
1 onion, chopped

Cut fat and skin into small cubes. Fry slowly, stirring occasionally, in a skillet over medium heat. Drain fat as it fills pan. When fat is almost rendered, add onions and continue cooking until onions are golden-brown. Drain through a fine sieve. Store fat and use as rendered chicken fat. Reserve *gribenes* and use mixed into chopped chicken livers as a spread on bread to be served with soup, or as a snack tidbit. Makes 1 cup clear rendered chicken fat.

MUSHROOM BARLEY SOUP

6 dried mushrooms
¼ cup pearl barley
2 quarts water
2 teaspoons salt
¼ teaspoon pepper

2 onions, chopped
3 tablespoons butter
2 tablespoons flour
¾ cup milk

Soak mushrooms in cold water for 10 minutes. Slice. In a saucepan combine mushrooms with barley, water, salt, and pepper. Cover and simmer for 1 hour. Sauté onions in butter. Add to soup. Cook for an additional 30 minutes. Gradually, while stirring, mix flour with milk. Add mixture to soup. Cook, stirring, for 15 minutes. Makes 8 servings.

GOLDENE YOICH
(Golden Chicken Broth)

1 stewing chicken (4 to 5 pounds), and giblets
Boiling water
1 tablespoon salt
1½ cups diced carrots
¾ cup chopped celeriac or celery
½ cup diced parsnip

Use a fresh-killed fowl with a yellow skin with plenty of fat. Use gizzard, heart, and chicken feet if they are available. To clean chicken feet scald them in boiling water. Peel off membranes. Quarter chicken. Place chicken with gizzard, heart, and chicken feet in a large kettle. Cover with boiling water. Add salt and vegetables. Cover and simmer slowly. Do not remove scum. Simmer for 2 to 3 hours, or until fowl is tender. Remove chicken and serve separately; or place chicken pieces in a soup bowl and spoon soup over the top. Before serving soup, remove excess chicken fat and season to taste. Noodles may be added if desired. Makes 6 to 8 cups.

KNAIDLACH
(Matzo Balls)

2 eggs
¼ cup chicken or goose fat or shortening
1 scant cup matzo meal
¼ to ½ cup water (approximately)
1 teaspoon salt
Dash of ground ginger or cinnamon

Combine eggs, fat, and matzo meal and beat well. Add water and salt, stirring to make a stiff batter. Add seasoning, cover, and chill in refrigerator for at least 2 hours. About 30 minutes before serving, wet hands with cold water to prevent sticking and form balls of the batter. Drop the dumplings into boiling salted water, cover, and cook for 30 minutes. Drain, and serve with clear soup or as a substitute for potatoes.

■ **Variations**—Add 2 tablespoons chopped liver or 2 tablespoons finely chopped parsley to batter before chilling.

SCHAV
(Sorrel Soup)

1 pound schav (sorrel or sour grass)
2 onions, minced
8 cups water
2 teaspoons salt
1 tablespoon fresh lemon juice

Festive Tzimmes   **Gefilte Fish**

Passover Nut Cake   **Charoses**

¼ cup sugar (optional)
2 eggs
  Dairy sour cream

Wash sorrel, and shred. Place sorrel, onions, water, and salt in a large deep saucepan. Bring to a boil, lower heat, and simmer, covered, for 45 minutes. Add lemon juice and sugar, if desired. Beat eggs and gradually beat into soup. Chill; serve garnished with sour cream. Makes 1½ quarts.

   FISH

GEFILTE FISH
3 pounds fresh fish (1 pound each of whitefish, pike, and carp)
2 large onions, peeled and sliced
6 cups water
2 carrots, sliced
2 teaspoons salt
½ teaspoon white pepper
2 eggs
6 tablespoons ice water
1½ tablespoons matzo meal or cracker meal
  Horseradish

Have fish filleted but reserve head, skin, and bones. Place head, skin, and bones in a large saucepan. Add onions, water, carrots, salt, and pepper. Bring to a boil, lower heat, and simmer until fish is ready. Grind fish fillets finely. Put fish into a bowl; correct seasoning. Add eggs, ice water, and matzo meal. Chop until mixture is smooth and well blended. With wet hands, shape fish mixture into balls about the size of a small baking potato. Place balls into fish stock carefully, cover, and simmer slowly for 1½ hours. Remove cover during the last 30 minutes of cooking. Cool fish slightly and place on a platter or put in a bowl. Strain stock over fish. Place carrots around fish. Chill. Serve with horseradish, white or red. Makes 6 generous servings.

JELLIED FISH
1 whole fish, 4 to 5 pounds (haddock, carp, or other fish)
2 medium onions, sliced
1 bay leaf
1 carrot, sliced
½ lemon, sliced
1½ teaspoons salt
6 cups water

Clean fish; remove head and tail. Put head and tail in kettle with remaining ingredients. Cover and cook for 1½ hours. Strain broth and return to kettle. Add the fish, cut into 1-inch slices. Simmer for 15 minutes, or until fish is done. Remove pieces carefully and put in shallow serving dish. Continue boiling broth until liquid has reduced to about 1½ cups. Pour over fish. Chill until firm. As fish chills, spoon stock over fish so that fish is completely covered. Serve garnished with lemon, black olives, and mayonnaise. Makes 4 to 6 servings.

SWEET-AND-SOUR FISH

2 onions, thinly sliced
2 lemons, sliced
¼ cup firmly packed light brown sugar
¼ cup seedless raisins
1 bay leaf
6 slices of whitefish or pike
1½ teaspoons salt
2 cups water
1 cup gingersnaps, crushed
¼ cup cider vinegar
Slivered blanched almonds

Combine first 8 ingredients in a saucepan. Cover and simmer for 25 minutes. Remove fish with a spatula and place on a platter. Add gingersnaps and vinegar to pan juices. Cook over low heat, stirring constantly, until smooth and well blended. Pour sauce over fish, and sprinkle with nuts. Serve warm or cold. Makes 6 servings.

 **MEAT**

CHOLENT
(Jewish Sabbath Meal-in-One)

2 onions, diced
2 tablespoons vegetable shortening or chicken fat
½ pound dried Lima beans, soaked overnight in cold water
½ cup barley
6 to 8 potatoes, pared and quartered
2 pounds brisket of beef, in one piece
2 tablespoons flour
Salt, pepper, and paprika to taste
Boiling water

Brown onions in shortening in the bottom of a large Dutch oven or other heavy pan with a lid. Pour in presoaked beans, barley, and potatoes. Make a space in the center and sink the meat in this space. Mix flour and seasonings and sprinkle over other ingredients. Add enough boiling water to come almost to the top of pan. Cover tightly and simmer very slowly, using an asbestos pad over the heat. Cook for 5 hours or overnight. Do not stir, but shake the pot from time to time to prevent sticking. This dish may be cooked in the deep well of a stove or in an electric beanpot. In that case, set control to 150°F. and cook overnight. May also be cooked in an automatic oven at very slow (200°F.) overnight. Makes 6 servings.

POT ROAST

4 pounds beef chuck, boneless and in one piece
Salt and pepper

3 tablespoons rendered chicken fat
4 onions, peeled and sliced
2 cups canned tomatoes
8 medium potatoes, peeled and cut into halves
8 carrots, cut into 2-inch lengths
2 tablespoons flour, lightly browned

Sprinkle meat with salt and pepper. Melt fat in a Dutch oven and brown meat in it on all sides. Add onions and tomatoes. Cover and simmer for 3 hours, turning meat occasionally and adding more tomatoes to keep meat from sticking. About 30 minutes before meat is ready, add potatoes and carrots and cook until tender. Remove meat and vegetables. Slice meat and keep warm. Mix browned flour with a little water to make a smooth paste. Add to pan juices. Cook over low heat, stirring constantly, until sauce is smooth and thickened. Pour sauce over meat and vegetables. Serve with dumplings if desired. Makes 8 servings.

BRISKET OF BEEF

2- pound boneless fresh brisket of beef
Fat or shortening
2 cups dried beans, navy or Lima, soaked overnight
Salt and pepper
1 bay leaf
1 large onion, chopped

Brown meat in fat. Add drained beans. Add salt and pepper to taste, bay leaf, and onion. Add enough water just to cover the beans. Cover tightly and cook over low heat at a slow simmer, stirring occasionally, until meat and beans are tender, approximately 2 to 2½ hours. Can also be baked, tightly covered, in moderate oven (350°F.) for 2 to 3 hours. Makes 8 servings.

FESTIVE TZIMMES
(Main-Dish Meat and Vegetables)

5 large carrots, scraped
5 white potatoes, peeled
3 sweet potatoes, peeled
2½ pounds brisket or short ribs of beef
1 pound dried prunes, rinsed
1 teaspoon salt
½ cup honey or brown sugar
1 onion
Cold water to cover
2 tablespoons shortening or chicken fat
2 tablespoons flour

Slice vegetables 1 inch thick. Sear meat on all sides in a heavy Dutch oven or any other heavy saucepan. Add vegetables and prunes to meat. Add salt, honey, onion, and water to cover. Bring to the boiling point and skim. Reduce

heat to simmer. Cook, uncovered, for 2½ to 3 hours, or until the meat is very tender to the fork. Do not stir, but shake the pot to prevent sticking. More water may be added if required. Remove onion. Taste and correct seasoning. Make a *roux* of the fat and flour and add to the mixture. Turn into a casserole or baking dish and bake in preheated moderate oven (350°F.) for 30 minutes, or until brown on top. Makes 8 servings.

TONGUE WITH SWEET-AND-SOUR SAUCE

Pickled beef tongue (4 to 5 pounds)
Water
1 onion, sliced
1 garlic clove
1 bay leaf
3 tablespoons shortening
1 onion, chopped
2 tablespoons flour
⅓ cup cider vinegar
⅓ cup honey
½ teaspoon ground ginger
¼ cup seedless raisins
¼ cup slivered blanched almonds
1 lemon, thinly sliced

Wash pickled tongue. Cover with water; add sliced onion, garlic, and bay leaf. Cover and simmer for about 3 hours, or until tongue is tender. Drain, and reserve 2 cups broth. Skin tongue and discard root and other bones. Slice, and keep warm. Melt shortening and sauté chopped onion until golden. Stir in flour. Gradually stir in reserved broth. Add remaining ingredients and cook over low heat, stirring constantly, until smooth and thickened. Pour sauce over sliced tongue. Makes 6 servings.

STUFFED BREAST OF VEAL

6 pounds breast of veal
1 tablespoon salt
½ teaspoon pepper
1 teaspoon garlic powder
Bread Stuffing
¼ cup fat or shortening

Have butcher cut a pocket in the veal. Sprinkle meat inside and out with salt, pepper, and garlic powder. Lightly fill the pocket with Bread Stuffing. Fasten with skewers or sew opening. Melt fat in a roasting pan. Put veal in pan and roast in a slow oven (325°F.) for 3 hours, or until meat is tender. Baste every 30 minutes with the pan juices. Add water to the pan to keep meat from sticking, if necessary. Makes 8 servings.

Bread Stuffing

3 tablespoons fat
1 onion, minced

Challah   Holishkes   Cholent   Knaidlach in Goldene Yoich

1 green pepper, seeded and chopped
½ cup chopped celery
8 slices of white bread
 Salt, pepper, crumbled dried thyme
1 teaspoon paprika
1 egg, well beaten

Melt fat and sauté vegetables for 10 minutes, stirring constantly. Soak bread in cold water for 5 minutes. Squeeze out all excess moisture. Mix bread with vegetables and salt, pepper, and thyme to taste. Stir in paprika and egg. Mix well.

SALAMI AND EGGS
16 slices of salami (kosher salami)
 8 eggs
 Salt and pepper
¼ cup water

Cut salami into strips and place in a large skillet. Sauté over low heat until salami is well heated and bottom of pan is well greased with the fat from the salami. Beat eggs, add salt and pepper to taste, and beat in water. Pour mixture over salami and cook as you would an omelet. Makes 4 servings.

POTATOES, PASTA, AND PANCAKES

KARTOFFEL LATKES
(Potato Pancakes)
4 potatoes
1 tablespoon grated onion
1 large egg
⅓ cup all-purpose flour
¾ teaspoon salt
 Fat or oil

Peel potatoes and grate very finely; there should be about 3 cups grated. Squeeze out some of the moisture in the grated potatoes. Add onion, egg, flour, and salt. Beat until well blended. Put ½ inch of fat in the skillet. Drop batter by heaping tablespoonfuls into hot fat and fry until crisp and brown on both sides. Remove pancakes and drain on absorbent paper. Serve hot with sour cream, hot applesauce, cream cheese, or apricot or prune purée, if desired. Makes 4 servings.

POTATO KNISHES
2½ cups sifted all-purpose flour
 1 teaspoon baking powder
½ teaspoon salt
 2 eggs
½ cup cooking oil
 2 tablespoons water
 Potato Filling

Sift flour with baking powder and salt. Make a well in the center and add eggs, oil, and water. Mix with the hands and then knead on a lightly floured board until smooth. Roll out dough on a lightly floured board as thin as possible. Cut into 3-inch rounds. Place 1 tablespoon Potato Filling on each round. Moisten edges of dough and pull together to enclose filling completely and to form a ball. Place pinched side down on an oiled cookie sheet. Bake in preheated moderate oven (350°F.) for 35 minutes, or until brown. Makes about 2 dozen.

Note: Knishes can also be filled with pot cheese, ground meat or chicken, or with cooked and seasoned buckwheat groats.

Potato Filling

1 cup chopped onions
⅓ cup chicken fat
2 cups mashed potatoes
1 egg, well beaten
1 teaspoon salt
⅛ teaspoon white pepper

Sauté onions in fat until golden-brown. Beat in remaining ingredients.

KARTOFFEL CHREMSEL
(Potato Fritters)

4 potatoes, about 1½ pounds
2 egg yolks
1 teaspoon salt
⅛ teaspoon pepper
1 tablespoon potato starch
2 egg whites
Butter or fat

Cook potatoes and peel. Press potatoes through a ricer, or mash. Beat in egg yolks, salt, pepper, and potato starch. Beat egg whites until stiff but not dry. Fold egg whites into potato mixture. Heat butter in a skillet to depth of ½ inch. Drop mixture by tablespoonfuls into hot butter. Fry until crisp and golden-brown on both sides. Serve with sour cream or applesauce, if desired. Makes 6 servings.

FALAFEL (Chick-Pea Croquettes)

2 cups thick puréed cooked chick-peas
½ teaspoon salt
¼ teaspoon white pepper
¼ teaspoon mixed ground herbs— basil, marjoram, thyme
¼ teaspoon hot pepper sauce
Fine dry cracker or bread crumbs
2 eggs
2 tablespoons melted shortening or olive oil
Shortening for deep frying

Canned or cooked chick-peas should be drained and mashed. Grind chick-peas through the fine blade of a food chopper. Add salt, pepper, herbs, hot pepper sauce, and 2 tablespoons cracker or bread crumbs. Beat eggs and stir into mixture. Stir in 2 tablespoons melted shortening. Shape mixture into 2½- to 3-inch fingers about 1 inch in diameter. Roll each in dry cracker or bread crumbs. Fry a few at a time in deep hot shortening (360°F. on a frying thermometer) for 2 to 3 minutes, or until golden brown. Remove with a slotted spoon and drain on absorbent paper. Serve hot. Makes 18 to 20.

KASHA VARNISHKAS
(Buckwheat Groats with Noodles)

1 egg
1 cup buckwheat groats
½ teaspoon salt
2 tablespoons rendered chicken fat

2 cups boiling water
2 cups cooked bowknot noodles
Salt and pepper to taste

Combine unbeaten egg, groats, and salt. Place chicken fat in skillet and add groat mixture and boiling water. Cover tightly and cook over low heat, stirring occasionally, until kasha is tender, about 15 minutes. Add additional water or meat broth to keep mixture from sticking. Mix kasha with cooked noodles. Add salt and pepper to taste and reheat until piping hot. Serve with meat. Makes 6 servings.

KAESE BLINTZES
(Rolled Cheese Pancakes)

1 package (7 ounces) dry cottage cheese (farmer cheese)
1 carton (12 ounces) pot cheese
2 packages (3 ounces each) cream cheese
Sweet butter
8 eggs
1 tablespoon sugar
2 teaspoons salt
1½ cups sifted all-purpose flour
1½ cups milk
Parve margarine
Dairy sour cream

To make filling, beat cheeses, 1 tablespoon soft butter, 2 eggs, sugar, and ½ teaspoon salt together.

To make batter, beat 6 remaining eggs until frothy; add remaining 1½ teaspoons salt. Add flour, ½ cup at a time, stirring to make a smooth paste. Gradually add milk, stirring constantly. Heat a heavy 6½-inch skillet and grease well. Have a piece of brown paper and some *parve* margarine handy for greasing skillet when frying rest of pancakes. Into the hot skillet pour enough batter (2 to 3 tablespoons) to cover bottom when batter is quickly rolled around. Tilt pan to distribute batter. Cook until pancake is firm and browned on one side. Put on buttered plate, browned side up. Grease skillet if necessary and fry another pancake the same way. While second one is cooking, spoon about 1 tablespoon filling right on edge of first pancake. Fold up once, fold over two sides, and make one more turn. Put on buttered plate. Continue until batter and filling are used up. Should pancakes develop empty spaces during frying, fill spaces with a little batter.

When ready to serve, heat a small amount of butter in large skillet. Fry blintzes until golden-brown on all sides. Serve at once with sour cream. Fry only the number of filled blintzes desired for one meal. Unfried blintzes keep well for a day or two in the refrigerator. Or they can be wrapped in vapor-proof paper and frozen until ready to use. Makes about 2 dozen.

Cherry Blintzes

Mix 1½ cups drained canned pitted red sour cherries, 1½ tablespoons flour, ⅛

teaspoon ground cinnamon, and sugar to taste. Substitute for cheese filling in Blintzes recipe.

Blueberry Blintzes

Mix 1½ cups blueberries, 1½ tablespoons flour, ⅛ teaspoon ground cinnamon, and sugar to taste. Substitute for cheese filling in Blintzes recipe.

BREADS

CHALLAH
(Sabbath or Holiday Twist Bread)

1 package active dry yeast or 1 cake compressed yeast
2 tablespoons sugar
1½ cups lukewarm water*
About 5 cups sifted all-purpose flour
2 teaspoons salt
2 eggs
2 tablespoons oil
1 egg yolk
2 tablespoons poppy seeds

Combine yeast, sugar, and ¼ cup water. *Use very warm water (105°F. to 115°F.) for dry yeast; use lukewarm water (80°F. to 90°F.) for compressed yeast. Let stand for 5 minutes. Sift flour and salt into a large bowl. Make a well in the center and drop in eggs, oil, remaining warm water, and finally yeast mixture. Work liquids into the flour. Knead on a floured board until dough is smooth and elastic. Place in a bowl, brush top with oil, cover with a towel, and let stand in a warm place to rise for 1 hour. Punch down, cover, and let rise to double in bulk. Divide dough into 3 equal parts. Between lightly floured hands, roll dough into 3 strips of even length. Braid these and place on a greased cookie sheet. Cover and let rise to double in bulk. Brush with egg yolk and sprinkle with poppy seeds. Bake in preheated moderate oven (375°F.) for 45 to 50 minutes, or until golden-brown. This recipe makes 1 very large loaf or 2 smaller loaves. It may be used as a pan loaf or for rolls instead of for twisted bread.

MANDELBROT
(Almond Bread)

1½ cups sifted all-purpose flour
¼ teaspoon salt
1 teaspoon baking powder
4 eggs
1 cup sugar
3 tablespoons cooking oil
1 teaspoon vanilla extract
1 cup chopped blanched almonds
1 tablespoon ground cinnamon

Sift flour with salt and baking powder. Beat eggs until thick and lemon-colored. Gradually beat in sugar. Stir in oil and vanilla. Stir in flour and almonds. Grease and flour two loaf pans (9 x 5 x 3 inches). Cover the bottoms of the pans with batter. Sprinkle with cinnamon. Add another layer of batter and cinnamon and con-

tinue layering until all cinnamon and batter are used. Bake in preheated moderate oven (350°F.) for 25 minutes, or until cake is golden-brown. Breads will only be 2½ inches high. Remove from pans, and cool. With a sharp knife cut breads into ½-inch slices. Place slices on greased cookie sheet and brown in preheated hot oven (400°F.) for 5 to 6 minutes.

 PICKLES

PICKLED PUMPKIN

2 pounds pumpkin
1 cup firmly packed dark brown sugar
½ cup cider vinegar
¼ teaspoon ground allspice
½ teaspoon salt

Remove skin and cut pumpkin into small wedges. Combine brown sugar, vinegar, allspice, and salt. Cook until sugar is dissolved. Add pumpkin and continue simmering until pumpkin is tender. Spoon mixture into sterilized glass jars. Seal. Makes about 1½ pints.

GARLIC HALF-SOUR PICKLES

48 medium cucumbers about 4 inches long
  Coarse salt
  Garlic cloves
  Mixed pickling spices
  Dill sprigs

Wash cucumbers and place in an upright position in sterilized jars. To each quart of cucumbers add 1 teaspoon salt, 4 garlic cloves, and ¼ teaspoon pickling spices. Place 1 sprig of dill with seed heads on top of each jar. Fill with cold water and let stand for 5 minutes before sealing. Store in cool place for about 2 weeks. Makes 48.

PICKLED GREEN TOMATOES

48 small green tomatoes
  Salt
  Water
  Dill
  Garlic cloves
1 tablespoon pickling spices
1 cup cider vinegar

Wash tomatoes and use whole. Do not remove stem end. Put into a brine solution made by adding 1 cup salt to each 4 cups water. Let stand overnight. Drain. Arrange tomatoes in a large crock or earthenware bowl. Layer tomatoes with sprigs of fresh dill with seed heads. Place 1 garlic clove on each layer of tomatoes. Tie pickling spices in cheesecloth bag.

Add vinegar, spices, and 6 quarts water to the tomatoes. Make sure all tomatoes are covered by lacing a weighted cover on them to keep them under liquid. Cover loosely with cheesecloth. Let stand for 2 weeks. Then pack into sterilized jars with liquid covering them; store in cool place for later use. Makes 48.

 DESSERTS AND CAKES

FRUIT COMPOTE

¼ pound each of dried apricots, peaches, and pears
1 juice orange
  Pinch of ground allspice
2 tablespoons honey
2 tablespoons sugar
¼ cup walnuts or blanched almonds

Cover fruits with water and cook until tender. Drain juice from fruit and reserve it. Peel yellow rind from the orange and cut rind into slivers. Add rind to juice drained from fruit and cook over low heat until liquid simmers. Add spice, honey, and sugar. Continue to simmer until juice is slightly thickened. Pour syrup over fruit. Serve in compote dishes and sprinkle with nuts. Makes 4 servings.

LOKSHEN KUGEL
(Noodle Pudding)

3 tablespoons shortening or oil
½ pound broad noodles, boiled and drained
3 eggs, separated
1 teaspoon ground cinnamon
¼ teaspoon ground nutmeg
½ cup sugar
¼ teaspoon salt
¾ cup raisins (optional)
½ cup chopped nuts (optional)

Add fat to noodles. Beat egg yolks and add. Blend in spices, sugar, and salt. Beat egg whites until stiff but not dry and fold in. Pour into greased 1½-quart baking dish, adding one third of mixture at a time, alternating with raisins and nuts, if desired. Bake in preheated moderate oven (350°F.) for 45 minutes, or until set. Serve hot, with or without any desired pudding sauce, as a side dish with meats or as a dessert. Makes 6 servings.
Note: This is often varied with the addition of apples, chopped dried fruits, dates, etc.

LEKAH
(Honey Cake)

4 eggs
1 cup sugar

1 cup honey
½ cup strong black coffee
2 tablespoons oil
3½ cups sifted all-purpose flour
1½ teaspoons baking powder
1 teaspoon baking soda
½ teaspoon salt
1 teaspoon ground cinnamon
½ teaspoon ground ginger
¼ teaspoon ground nutmeg
  Dash of ground cloves (optional)
½ cup chopped nuts
½ cup raisins
¼ cup finely cut citron or other candied fruit
2 tablespoons brandy (optional)

Beat eggs until light. Gradually beat in sugar until mixture is fluffy. Dilute honey with hot coffee and cool to lukewarm. Add oil. Blend into eggs and sugar alternately with sifted dry ingredients. Add nuts and fruits. Blend well, but do not overbeat. Add brandy. Pour into a well-greased and paper-lined pan (9 x 13 x 2 inches). Bake in preheated slow oven (300°F.) for 1 hour, or until a tester inserted in the center comes out clean of crumbs. Invert on a rack to cool before cutting into squares of desired size.

PRUNE PIROSHKIS

2 cups sifted all-purpose flour
½ teaspoon salt
⅔ cup shortening
1 egg yolk
¼ cup ice water
  Prune Filling

Sift flour with salt. Cut in shortening until mixture resembles coarse cornmeal. Beat egg yolk with water and add to flour mixture. Stir until dough forms a ball. Roll out dough on a lightly floured board to ⅛-inch thickness. Cut into 3-inch rounds. Top each round with a spoon of Prune Filling. Moisten edges of dough and pull dough over the filling, forming a half-moon shape. Place on a greased cookie sheet. Bake in preheated hot oven (400°F.) for 15 minutes, or until brown. Makes about 2 dozen.
Note: Piroshkis can also be filled with chopped chicken livers, chopped fish, chopped mushrooms, or cheese.

Prune Filling

¼ cup honey
⅔ cup fresh orange juice
2 teaspoons fresh lemon juice
1 pound pitted prunes
2 teaspoons grated orange rind

Mix honey with orange and lemon juice and cook at a slow boil for 5 minutes. Add prunes, cover, and cook for 15 minutes. Drain and chop prunes. Stir in orange rind. Cool mixture before filling piroshki.

TAYGLACH MIT NESHOMAS
(Nut and Honey Sweetmeats)
3 cups sifted all-purpose flour
1 teaspoon baking powder
4 eggs
¼ teaspoon salt
   Filling
   Syrup

Sift flour with baking powder. Beat eggs with salt. Stir in flour. Knead lightly until smooth. Roll out on a lightly floured board to ⅛-inch thickness and cut into 1½-inch rounds. Place 1 teaspoon Filling on each round and fold dough around Filling to form a ball. Drop *tayglach* into hot Syrup and simmer for 15 minutes, or until Syrup has been absorbed. Shake pot occasionally to prevent dough from sticking. Place *tayglach* on a platter sprinkled with confectioners' sugar. Separate while still warm. Let cool and dry.

Filling
Mix 1 cup finely chopped or grated nuts and raisins with 1 teaspoon fresh lemon juice.

Syrup
Combine 1 cup honey with 1 cup sugar, ½ cup water, and ½ teaspoon ground ginger. Bring to a boil, lower heat, and drop in *tayglach*.

HOLIDAY SPECIALTIES

PASSOVER

PESACH RUSELL
(Passover Fermented Beet Juice)
10 to 12 pounds beets
   Water

Wash beets, peel, and cut into quarters. Place beets in a clean crock of stoneware or earthenware. Cover beets with water and cover crock with cheesecloth. Let stand at room temperature for 1 week. Uncover and remove all scum. Stir well and re-cover. Let stand for 2 to 3 weeks, or until liquid is scarlet and clear. Makes 2 to 3 quarts of *rusell*.

Note: The *rusell* liquid and beets are used in borscht, to cook pot roast, as a drink, and to make beet horseradish.

RUSELL CHRAIN
(Passover Horseradish with Fermented Beet Juice)
Peel horseradish root and grate very finely. Add just enough rusell liquid (above) to moisten and tint the desired color. Season with salt and sugar to taste.

CHAROSES
4 tart apples, cored and grated
1½ cups blanched shelled almonds, ground
¼ cup walnuts, ground
3 tablespoons sugar
½ teaspoon each of ground cinnamon and ginger
1½ teaspoons grated lemon rind
3 tablespoons fresh lemon juice
   Passover red wine

Combine all ingredients and blend with enough wine to give a spreading consistency. Makes 8 to 10 servings.

RUSELL BORSCHT
4 cups rusell liquid (at left)*
1 cup chopped rusell beets*
1 medium onion, chopped
   Salt, sugar, and fresh lemon juice

Heat *rusell* liquid with beets and onion. Cook over low heat until beets are tender. Add salt, sugar, and lemon juice to taste. Makes 4 servings.

■ **Variation**—Sliced hard-cooked egg may be added to borscht when served either hot or cold. Or, when borscht is hot and ready to be served, beat 2 eggs until well blended. Gradually beat borscht into the eggs. Reheat slightly but do not boil. *If *rusell* liquid and beets are not available, fresh cooked or canned beets may be used with their juice. Add extra lemon juice for the tartness required.

Note: When served hot, add hot boiled potato and sour cream to borscht. When served cold, add chopped cucumbers, scallions, and sour cream.

RUSELL FLEISCH IN BORSCHT
(Meat Cooked in Fermented Beet Juice)
4 cups rusell liquid (at left)
2 cups chopped rusell beets
3 cups water
⅔ cup chopped onions
3 pounds boneless brisket or chuck of beef
   Beef marrow bones
2 teaspoons salt
¼ teaspoon pepper
   Sugar and fresh lemon juice
1 egg
   Boiled potatoes

Place liquid and beets in a Dutch oven or deep kettle. Add water, onions, meat, bones, salt, and pepper. Cover and simmer for 2 to 3 hours, or until meat is tender. Remove meat, slice, and keep warm. Season broth to taste with sugar and lemon juice. Beat egg slightly and gradually beat broth from meat into egg. Spoon some of the sauce over the meat and serve the remainder in soup bowls. Serve boiled potatoes with the borscht in bowls. Makes 6 to 8 servings.

VEGETABLE CUTLETS
1¼ cups finely chopped cooked green pepper
1¼ cups tightly packed grated raw carrot
1¼ cups tightly packed chopped raw spinach
3 medium potatoes, boiled and mashed
1 tablespoon grated raw onion

1 tablespoon minced parsley
3 eggs
1½ teaspoons salt
1¼ cups matzo meal
   Melted fat or shortening

Mix vegetables and parsley. Beat eggs with salt and add to vegetables, beating until mixture is well blended and smooth. Stir in matzo meal and let stand for 30 minutes. Form into patties about 3 inches in diameter and fry in shallow fat until golden-brown on each side. Drain on absorbent towels. Makes 8 servings.

MATZO BRIE
(Fried Matzos)
4 eggs, well beaten
1 cup water
   Salt
4 matzos
   Shortening or fat

Beat eggs with water and a little salt. Break matzos into small bite-size pieces. Soak in water; drain. Stir matzos into eggs and let stand for 5 minutes. Pour mixture into a skillet with a thin layer of hot shortening. Fry over moderate heat until golden-brown on one side. Turn and brown the other side, stirring occasionally to break up the pieces. Can be served for breakfast or lunch. Makes 4 servings.

MATZO KUGEL
(Matzo-Meal Pudding)
3 matzos
   Water to cover
1 teaspoon salt
2 tablespoons melted chicken fat, shortening, or oil
3 eggs, separated
1 cup sugar
   Grated rind of 1 lemon
   Juice of 1 lemon
1 cup chopped apples
½ cup chopped nuts
   Matzo meal
¼ teaspoon ground cinnamon

Soak matzos in water to cover until they are soft. Squeeze out excess liquid. Stir until creamy. Add salt and melted fat. Beat egg yolks with sugar, rind, and juice. Blend into matzo mixture. Fold in stiffly beaten egg whites. Alternate the batter with apples and nuts in a greased 2-quart pudding dish, starting and ending with batter. Sprinkle with matzo meal and cinnamon. Bake in preheated moderate oven (350°F.) for 30 minutes, or until lightly browned and set. May be served with fruit or wine sauces, or garnished with berries. Serve warm. Makes 6 servings.

CHREMSLACH
(Matzo-Meal Fritters)
1 cup matzo meal
2 tablespoons chopped blanched almonds
2 teaspoons granulated sugar
¼ teaspoon salt
1 cup chicken bouillon, boiling
4 eggs, separated
   Fat or oil for deep frying

Confectioners' sugar
Honey

Mix matzo meal with almonds, sugar, and salt. Stir in boiling bouillon. Add mixture gradually to beaten egg yolks. Blend well. Beat egg whites until stiff but not dry. Use hands to fold egg whites into batter. Drop mixture by teaspoonfuls into deep hot fat (360°F. on a frying thermometer). Fry until golden-brown, 2 to 3 minutes. Drain on absorbent paper and sprinkle with confectioners' sugar. Serve with honey. Makes about 5 dozen.

PASSOVER NUT CAKE
- 6 eggs
- 6 tablespoons sugar
- 6 tablespoons matzo cake meal
- 1 tablespoon fresh lemon juice
- 2/3 cup finely chopped almonds or walnuts
- 1/8 teaspoon salt
- Confectioners' sugar

Separate eggs and beat egg yolks until thick and lemon-colored. Beat in sugar and continue beating until thick and creamy. Gradually stir in matzo cake meal. Stir in lemon juice and nuts. Beat egg whites with salt until stiff but not dry and fold them into cake batter. Pour mixture into an ungreased tube pan (9 x 3 inches). Bake in preheated slow oven (300°F.) for 45 minutes; increase heat to 325°F. for 15 minutes, or until top of cake springs back when lightly touched. Remove from oven and invert pan. Cool thoroughly, and then cut out of pan. Sprinkle with confectioners' sugar. Makes one 9-inch cake.

 SUKKOT

MEAT KREPLACH (Dumplings)
- 2 cups sifted all-purpose flour
- 1/2 teaspoon salt
- 2 eggs
- 2 to 3 tablespoons cold water
- Meat Filling

Sift flour with salt, and make a well in the center of the flour. Add eggs and water. Mix with the hands until dough becomes a compact ball. Knead on a lightly floured board until smooth and elastic. Let stand for 1 hour. Roll out on a lightly floured board as thin as pos-

sible. With a sharp knife cut dough into 2-inch squares. Top each square with a small ball of Meat Filling. Moisten edges of dough, bring opposite corners together, and press firmly to shape a triangle. Then bring the other two opposite corners together to form caplike *kreplach*. Drop *kreplach,* one at a time, into boiling salted water. Simmer slowly for 15 to 20 minutes. *Kreplach* will rise to the top when they are done. Serve with gravy or in chicken soup. Makes 2 to 3 dozen.

Meat Filling
Mix 1½ cups finely ground cooked meat or chicken with 1 well-beaten egg and 1 teaspoon grated onion. Shape mixture into small balls about the size of a small olive.

HOLISHKES (Meat-Stuffed Cabbage)
- 2 pounds beef chuck, ground
- 3/4 cup cooked rice or kasha
- 2 eggs
- 1/4 cup grated onion
- 1/3 cup grated carrot
- 1/2 teaspoon salt
- 20 to 24 large green cabbage leaves
- 1/2 cup cider vinegar or 1/4 teaspoon sour salt (citric acid crystals)
- 3/4 cup firmly packed dark brown sugar
- 1 can (8 ounces) tomato sauce

Mix meat with rice, eggs, onion, carrot, and salt. With a sharp knife carefully slice off the back of the tough rib of each cabbage leaf, keeping surface of leaf in one piece. Pour boiling water over cabbage leaves and let stand until wilted. Drain. Place a ball of meat about the size of a small plum at one side of the leaf. Roll the cabbage tightly around the meat to enclose the filling completely. Place filled rolls in a heavy Dutch oven or deep saucepan. Add remaining ingredients mixed together. Cover and simmer for 50 minutes to 1 hour. Add water if necessary to prevent sticking. Makes 8 to 10 servings.

 *SHEVUOT*

MAMALIGA (Cornmeal Mush)
- 2 cups yellow cornmeal
- 1 cup cold water

- 1 teaspoon salt
- 4 cups boiling water
- 1/2 cup butter or margarine
- 1 cup grated cheese or 2 cups pot cheese

Mix yellow cornmeal with the cold water. Add salt to boiling water. Stir in paste and cook over low heat, stirring constantly, for 30 minutes. Add butter and cheese and stir until butter is melted. Serve with additional butter, and jam, sugar, or preserves if desired. Makes 12 servings.

 *PURIM*

HAMANTASCHEN
- 2½ cups sifted all-purpose flour
- 1 tablespoon baking powder
- 1 teaspoon salt
- 1/4 cup sugar
- 1 egg, beaten
- 3/4 cup milk
- 1/3 cup melted butter or margarine
- Poppy-Seed Filling or lekvar (puréed prune butter in a jar)
- 1 egg yolk, beaten

Sift flour with baking powder, salt, and sugar. Beat egg with milk and mix with melted butter. Pour mixture into the center of the flour and stir until a soft dough is formed. Knead on a lightly floured board until smooth and not sticky. Roll to 1/4-inch thickness. Cut into 3-inch circles. Top each with a small spoon of Poppy-Seed Filling. Moisten edges of circle and fold the three sides over the filling, leaving the filling exposed in the center and shaping the pastry into a tricorn shape. Brush with egg yolk and place on a greased cookie sheet. Bake in preheated moderate oven (350°F.) for 20 to 25 minutes. Makes 15 to 18.

Poppy-Seed Filling
Mix 1 cup finely ground poppy seed with 1 egg yolk, 2 tablespoons honey or sugar, 1½ teaspoons fresh lemon juice, and 3 tablespoons finely chopped nuts. Blend well.

JULEP—An alcoholic drink made with spirits, most often bourbon, but sometimes rum or brandy; and sugar, crushed ice, and mint. The name is of Arabic origin but the drink is associated with the southern United States, especially Kentucky.

The proper construction of a mint julep has produced a great deal of controversy. It would, therefore, be imprudent and presumptuous to give a final formula for this exquisite, cooling, decorative, and consoling concoction. Suffice it to say that most people agree that the classic julep is one made with bourbon. As to whether the mint in a julep should be crushed or not, and the drink sipped from a straw or directly from the glass, each to his own choice. To quote the English writer Charles Dickens who traveled in the American southern states in 1842: "the mounds of ices, and the bowls of mint julep and sherry cobbler that they make in these latitudes, are refreshments never to be thought of afterwards, in summer, by those who would preserve contented minds."

KENTUCKY MINT JULEP
Chill silver julep mugs, goblets, or tumblers in frozen-food compartment of refrigerator. For each mug, dissolve 1 lump sugar or 1 teaspoon sugar in a little water. Reserve. Fill mug with finely crushed ice. Pour in 1½ ounces of bourbon. Stir in dissolved sugar. Stir until the mug is heavily frosted on the outside. Garnish with 6 sprigs of fresh mint, tucked into the ice so that they protrude. Serve with or without a straw.

GEORGIA MINT JULEP
Proceed as above, but substitute equal parts of brandy and peach brandy for the bourbon.

RUM MINT JULEP
Proceed as above, but substitute dark or light rum for the bourbon.

JULIENNE—The term, of French origin, refers first to food cut into thin matchlike strips. Vegetables, meats, poultry, and cheese can be cut in this manner. Julienne strips of food are used in soups, salads, and many other dishes. These strips of food should be cut with a sharp knife and handled carefully during preparation and cooking to prevent breaking.

The second meaning of the culinary term julienne is a clear consommé to which a mixture of finely shredded vegetables has been added. The vegetables are first cooked slowly in a little butter and then added to the hot consommé. Consommé Julienne is highly thought of in French cookery, since it makes an excellent light soup to precede a substantial dinner.

CONSOMMÉ JULIENNE
Mix 3 cans condensed consommé and 2 cans water; simmer for a few minutes. When ready to serve, pour consommé into bowls and garnish with some of each of the following cooked vegetables cut julienne style: carrot, white turnip, green pepper, leek, mushroom, celery, green cabbage, and lettuce. Sprinkle each serving with a little chopped parsley or chervil. Makes 6 servings.

JUNIPER BERRY—The fruit of the evergreen *Juniperus communis*, a small tree or shrub. The berries, which vary in size from one-fifth to one-half inch in diameter, are purple in color with a greenish bloom. The berries of the common juniper plant are too pungent to be eaten raw. They are dried for cooking, which makes them black, and used to flavor meats, game, stuffings, sauces, and marinades. They remove the strong flavor of game and give foods an interesting taste. They should be crushed before using, since this releases the flavor. The flavor of freshly dried juniper berries is intense but it dissipates fairly quickly so that dried juniper berries should not be kept too long. They are available in specialty food stores.

Juniper berries are an inseparable part of gin. They were first used, it is said, by the 17th-century nobleman, the Comte de Moret, son of the French king Henry IV. The very name "gin" comes indirectly from juniper berries, for the French name for gin was *genievre*, corrupted into "Geneva" in Holland. Gin is still called *genievre* in France.

The juniper tree and berry have traditionally been associated with the protection of people. It is said that when the Virgin Mary and Jesus were trying to escape from the punishment of King Herod by fleeing into Egypt, they hid behind the juniper bush's spreading branches and were saved. And Elijah, the prophet, while escaping from the wicked Queen Jezebel, wife of Ahab, was protected by an angel of God when he slept under a juniper tree in the wilderness.

The Romans burned juniper trees to protect themselves from harm. Virgil, the Latin poet of the 1st century A.D., instructs: "But learn to burn within your sheltering rooms/Sweet Juniper." In India, the juniper tree, there the drooping juniper, is a sacred shrub. The twigs are burnt as incense.

In America juniper berries were one of the foods of the Indians, used both as spices and dried and ground into meal.

JUNIPER POT ROAST IN BURGUNDY
1 pot roast, about 5 pounds (rump, chuck, bottom round, or brisket of beef)
  Salt
10 juniper berries, crushed, or more to taste
6 onions, peeled
6 parsnips, peeled
2 cups of 1½-inch pieces of celery
6 carrots, scraped
2 cups Burgundy or dry red wine
2 cups boiling water or beef bouillon

Rub pot roast with salt and juniper berries. Put roast in a Dutch oven and surround with vegetables. Pour wine and water over roast. Cover tightly and simmer over low heat, turning meat occasionally, for 3 to 4 hours. (Meat can also be roasted, covered, in slow oven, 325° F., for 3 to 4 hours.) Remove meat and keep warm on a platter. Strain sauce and vegetables through a sieve or whirl all in a blender. Slice meat and serve with the sauce and hot sauerkraut. Makes 6 to 8 servings.

JUNIPER-BERRY SAUCE
2 tablespoons butter
2½ tablespoons all-purpose flour
2 cups beef bouillon
1 bouillon cube
½ cup Madeira
  Salt and pepper to taste
2 teaspoons ground juniper berries

Melt butter and stir in flour. Gradually stir in bouillon. Add bouillon cube and Madeira. Add salt and pepper to taste if necessary. Stir in juniper berries. Cook over low heat, stirring constantly, until sauce is smooth and slightly thickened. Serve with roast meats, fowl, and game. Makes about 2½ cups.

KABOB—The word, also spelled "kebab" and "cabob," means a small piece of roasted meat. The addition of the word *shish,* or "skewer," means that the meat was threaded on a skewer and then roasted.

In American usage, kabobs are small pieces of meat, fish, or poultry, with or without cubes of vegetables or fruits, which are sometimes marinated in a spicy sauce before being threaded on skewers. The skewers may be bamboo, wood, or metal. The food is then broiled or roasted until golden-brown and brushed with the marinade, if any, during cooking.

Kabobs are of Near Eastern origin and are a feature of the cuisines of Turkey, Iran, Iraq, Lebanon, Syria, and India.

LAMB SHISH-KABOB
2 pounds shoulder lamb chops,
  1½ inches thick
8 small onions, peeled
2 medium green peppers, cut into
  eighths
4 tomatoes, quartered
½ cup cooking oil
1 teaspoon salt
¼ teaspoon pepper
1 teaspoon crumbled dried marjoram
2 teaspoons fresh lemon juice

Bone chops and cut meat into cubes. Put meat and vegetables in bowl. Mix remaining ingredients and pour over contents of bowl. Store in refrigerator for at least 1 hour before starting to cook. Have ready some long metal skewers or firm slender green sticks. Push pieces of lamb and vegetables onto skewers or sticks, alternating meat with vegetables. Hold skewers over hot coals, turning to brown all sides. Take care not to burn sticks. Shish-kabob should be done in 10 to 15 minutes. Makes 4 servings.

SKILLET KABOBS
1½ pounds sirloin steak
2 tomatoes, each cut into 8 wedges
2 green peppers, cut into 1-inch pieces
1 can (8 ounces) onions, drained
  Salt and pepper to taste
  Cooking oil

Cut steak into 1-inch pieces. Thread meat and vegetables alternately on 8 short or 4 long skewers and sprinkle with salt and pepper. Heat small amount of oil in large skillet and brown kabobs quickly on all sides. Reduce heat, cover, and cook for 5 to 10 minutes, or until foods are of desired doneness. Serve on or off skewers, or hold food between toasted frankfurter rolls and pull out skewers. Makes 4 servings.

SPICY PORK KABOBS
2 pounds lean boneless pork
¼ cup smooth peanut butter
1 teaspoon ground coriander
1½ teaspoons salt
½ teaspoon cayenne
1 teaspoon ground cuminseed
½ teaspoon pepper
4 onions, grated
1 garlic clove, minced
1½ tablespoons fresh lemon juice
1 tablespoon brown sugar
3 tablespoons soy sauce

Cut pork into 1½-inch cubes. Mix remaining ingredients and add pork; stir until well coated. Cover, and refrigerate for several hours. Thread on skewers and broil in broiler or over coals for 20 to 25 minutes. Makes 6 servings.

PINEAPPLE-FRANKFURTER KABOBS

Cut frankfurters into 1-inch lengths. String on skewers alternately with drained pineapple chunks. Mix equal parts of prepared mustard and pineapple syrup; brush on frankfurters and pineapple chunks. Broil until sizzling hot. Serve with toasted split rolls.

SHRIMP KABOBS

Peel jumbo shrimps and remove veins. String on skewers, alternating with squares of bacon and pitted large ripe olives or cubes of pineapple. Dip into melted butter or oil and broil for 4 minutes on each side.

KALE—This member of the *Brassica* genus or cabbage family is also called "borecole," "cole," or "colewort." There are a number of varieties of the vegetable, ranging from dwarf to tall sizes, with leaves that vary from green to reddish or purplish. Kale is grown for its large curled or smooth leaves. It has a very high vitamin content. Kale can be cooked in any of the ways spinach is cooked, but the leaves should be chopped.

Availability and Purchasing Guide—Kale is most plentiful and inexpensive during the winter months. Look for crisp, clean leaves of good color.

Kale is also available canned and frozen.

Storage—Keep in refrigerator in moisture-proof bag or covered container.
- Refrigerator shelf, raw: 3 to 8 days
- Refrigerator shelf, cooked and covered: 4 to 5 days
- Refrigerator frozen-food compartment, cooked, prepared for freezing: 2 to 3 months
- Freezer, cooked, prepared for freezing: 1 year
- Canned, kitchen shelf: 1 year

Nutritive Food Values—Kale is a good source of vitamins A and C, and contains calcium, some riboflavin, and iron.
- 3½ ounces, raw = 38 calories
- 3½ ounces, cooked = 28 calories

Basic Preparation—Remove the tough stems and midribs; cut large leaves into pieces.
- **To Cook**—Add kale to 1 inch of boiling salted water; simmer for 10 to 15 minutes, until just tender. Drain. Season with salt, pepper, and butter. May be sprinkled with diced salt pork or bacon which has been cooked until brown and crisp.
- **To Freeze**—Wash kale thoroughly and remove tough stems and wilted leaves. Chop. Blanch in boiling water for 2 minutes. Drain. Chill in cold water for 5 minutes. Drain. Pack into containers, leaving ½-inch headspace. Seal.

KALE, COUNTRY STYLE

Cook 2 pounds of kale in 2½ cups of boiling salted water for 15 minutes, or until tender. Drain, and chop; put back in saucepan and add 3 tablespoons bacon fat and 1 tablespoon pickle relish. Heat well; season. Makes 3 servings.

KALE, BACON, AND OATMEAL

¼ pound bacon, diced
2½ cups water
2 pounds kale, washed, stemmed, and chopped
1 cup cooked oatmeal

Cook bacon over low heat until crisp; add water and kale. Cook for about 15 minutes, or until tender. Add cooked oatmeal; mix well. Season to taste with salt and pepper. Makes 6 servings.

KETCHUP—This highly seasoned, thick condiment sauce is also called "catchup" or "catsup." These two words derive from colloquial pronunciations of the real name, which comes from a Malay word *kechap* for spiced fish sauce.

Ketchup is a smoothly textured and brightly colored sauce, usually made with red-tomato pulp. It can also be made from green tomatoes, fruits, berries, vegetables, and even seafood.

Originally, ketchup meant a sauce in which the important ingredient was salted spiced mushrooms. In Great Britain, mushroom ketchup has been known for centuries and it is still widely used.

When making ketchup, the ingredients can be cooked until tender and then puréed through a sieve or food mill. Or the ingredients can be whirled in a blender before cooking and then cooked to the proper thickness. The two most important points to remember are first, to use a deep kettle to allow the mixture to "plop" without splattering the kitchen and second, to stir constantly when the mixture has cooked to a thick purée, to prevent sticking and scorching. Pour mixture while hot into sterilized jars, seal, cool, and store.

Ketchup can also be "cooked" in the oven. This eliminates watching and stirring. Bake mixture, uncovered, in preheated slow oven (325°F.) until volume is reduced by half. The length of time varies with the amount of moisture in the original purée.

Commercially made tomato ketchups are available, some more highly seasoned than others.

TOMATO KETCHUP

1 cup white vinegar
1½ teaspoons whole cloves
1½ teaspoons coarsely broken cinnamon stick
1 teaspoon celery seed
8 pounds (about 24) fully ripe tomatoes
2 cups water
1 tablespoon instant minced onion
½ teaspoon cayenne
1 cup sugar
4 teaspoons salt

Bring first 4 ingredients to boil and remove from heat. Scald and crush tomatoes. Put tomatoes in kettle with water, onion, and cayenne. Bring to boil and cook for 15 minutes. Put through food mill. Combine purée and sugar in kettle; cook, stirring frequently, for 45 minutes, or until reduced by half. Strain vinegar, discarding spices, and add with salt to tomato mixture. Continue cooking, stirring almost constantly, for 30 minutes, or until thick. Ladle into 4 hot sterilized ½-pint jars, and seal.
Note: To help retain color, wrap individual jars in brown paper before storing.

TOMATO COCKTAIL AND TOMATO KETCHUP

8 quarts tomatoes
4 celery stalks, minced
1 green pepper, minced
7 teaspoons salt
2 onions
1¼ cups sugar
1½ cups cider vinegar
1 teaspoon each of ground cinnamon and allspice
½ teaspoon ground cloves
¼ teaspoon pepper
Dash of cayenne

Wash, scald, peel, and quarter tomatoes. Simmer until very juicy. Strain juice through wire strainer or cheesecloth without pressing through any of the pulp. Reserve pulp for ketchup. To the juice add celery, green pepper, 4 teaspoons salt, and 1 onion, minced. Heat to simmering and strain into hot clean jars. Seal, and process in hot-water bath for 10 minutes.

Put tomato pulp through a sieve. Add sugar, vinegar, and remaining 3 teaspoons salt. Put spices and remaining onion, sliced, in a small muslin bag; tie securely and cook with tomato mixture. Cook until thickened, stirring often. Discard spice bag and pour ketchup into sterilized jars; seal. Makes about 4 quarts tomato cocktail and 1½ pints ketchup.

MUSHROOM KETCHUP

4 pounds mushrooms
Coarse salt (1 to 2 tablespoons)
1 cup vinegar
1 medium onion
1 garlic clove
1 teaspoon mixed pickling spice
¼ teaspoon nutmeg

Remove stems and peel mushrooms. Sprinkle undersides with salt, and let stand for 1 hour. Wipe with a paper towel. Wash stems and put stems and mushrooms in bowl. Sprinkle with salt and let stand in cool place for 3 days, stirring frequently with a wooden spoon. Put in kettle and add remaining ingredients. Simmer, covered, for about 1 hour, adding a little water or vinegar, if necessary. Strain, and put in hot sterilized bottles with screw tops. Fasten corks loosely and stand bottles in pan of water reaching to tops of bottles. Bring slowly to boil and keep at this temperature for 20 minutes. Remove from water, insert corks, and screw on caps. Makes about 4 cups.

FRUIT KETCHUP

6 tart apples, cored and sliced
1 medium onion, chopped
½ cup sugar
½ teaspoon each of white pepper, salt, powdered mustard, and ground cloves and cinnamon
Pinch of allspice
¾ cup white vinegar
¼ cup water

Cook apples in enough water to cover until tender. Press apples through sieve and add remaining ingredients. Cook over low heat, stirring occasionally, until thick, about 2 hours. Pour into sterilized jars, seal, and cool. Makes about 1 pint.

GRAPE KETCHUP

5 pounds Concord grapes
½ cup water
5 cups sugar
2 cups cider vinegar
1 teaspoon salt
½ cup mixed pickling spices tied in a cheesecloth bag

Remove grapes from stems. Cook grapes with water at a boil until grapes are tender. Press grapes through a sieve or food mill. Add remaining ingredients and cook over low heat, stirring occasionally, until mixture is thick. Remove spice bag. Pour ketchup into sterilized jars, seal, cool, and store. Makes about 4 pints.

KID—This is the meat of a young goat slaughtered before being weaned. Kid is a surprisingly bland and delicate meat, which is prized in the cooking of Latin countries in Europe and South America. It is often served as an Easter dish as a substitute for the traditional Easter lamb. The reason for this is that lambs can grow into sheep and yield precious wool, while goats are less expensive and easier-to-raise animals. In any case, kid can be prepared like any young lamb.

ROAST KID

1 cup vinegar
2 medium onions, minced
1 teaspoon dried thyme
1 garlic clove, minced
1 bay leaf
1 teaspoon salt
4 pounds kid, cut into serving pieces
½ pound salt pork, sliced

Mix first 6 ingredients, and pour over kid meat in bowl. Let stand to marinate for 1 hour. Drain, and put meat in roasting pan. Cover with sliced pork. Roast in preheated moderate oven (350°F.) for about 2 hours, basting occasionally with drippings in pan, and adding a little water if necessary to prevent drying out. Makes 4 to 6 servings.

100 Menus
to help you plan
more varied meals
for your family with
the recipes in this volume

*Recipes for all starred dishes found in this volume.

BREAKFAST

Sliced Oranges
with Cranberry Sauce
Broiled Kippered Herring*
Mamaliga (Cornmeal Mush)*
Butter
─────
Sauerkraut Juice
Phillip's Ham and Eggs*
Buttered Thin Rye Toast
Blueberry Jam*

Grapefruit Sections
Crisp Sausage Links
Huckleberry Griddle Cakes*
Whipped Cream Cheese
Honey
─────
Applesauce
Sonkás Palacsinta
(Pancakes Layered
with Minced Ham)*
Fried Tomatoes

Pears Stewed in Grape Juice
Crisp Bacon
Pecan Waffles
Honey Topping*
─────
Pineapple Juice
Tortilla con Jamon
(Spanish Omelet with Ham)*
Hominy and Cheese*

Stewed Apricots
Fried Salt Pork
and Milk Gravy
on Hominy Grits*
Eggs Parmesan*
Hot Biscuits
─────
Tomato Cocktail*
Haddock-Potato Patties*
with Poached Eggs
Old-Fashioned Hoecake*
Red-Cherry Jam*

LUNCH OR SUPPER

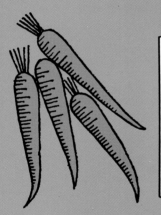

English Ham and Egg Cakes*
Broiled Peach Halves
Corn Bread Squares
Whipped Butter
─────
Sliced Bananas
in Cranberry Juice
Huevos Escalfados Fritos
(Poached Eggs and Ham, Fried)*
Toasted English Muffins

Apple and Apricot Juice
Corned-Beef Hash
with Creamed Eggs*
Broiled Tomato Slices
and Mushrooms
Hard Rolls
─────
Melon and Berries in Cream
Grilled English Herring*
Home-Fried Potatoes
Crumpets
Tomato Jam*

Jamaican Split-Pea Soup*
Cheese-Nut Burgers*
on Toasted Buns
Whole Apples or Pears
─────
Quiche de Bourbonnaise
(Ham and Swiss Cheese Pie)*
Insalata Bandiera
(Flag Salad)*
Chocolate Fudge
or Brownies

Savory Shrimp Mold*
Insalata di Fagiolini
e Patate (Green-Bean
and Potato Salad)*
Assorted Crisp Breads
Orange-Honey Sherbet*
─────
Jamaican Congo-Pea
or Kidney-Bean Soup*
Molded Crabmeat Salad*
Cracked Wheat Toast
Plum Jelly*

Baked Pea Beans
Boston Brown Bread
Pickled Green Tomatoes*
Jellied Pear and
Cream-Cheese Salad*
─────
Rollmops*
Jellied Vegetable Salad
Pumpernickel Bread
Sweet Butter
Honey-Date Bars*

Tuna Salad with Sour-Cream
Horseradish Sauce*
Dill Pickles   Cherry Tomatoes
Crackers
Honey-Orange-Almond Cake*
─────
Honeydew Rings
with Shrimp Salad*
Hominy Puffs*
Chocolate or Coffee
Ice Cream Sodas*

Kingston Potato Soup*
Pizza con Uova e Prosciutto
(Ham and Egg Pizza)*
Strawberries à la Mode*
─────
Grilled Frankfurters
or Hamburgers
Buttery Garlic Grits*
Tomato Lettuce Salad
Apple and Grape-Juice Ice*

Eggs Zurlo*
Pickled Beets on Greens
Ice-Cream-Sundae*

⬥

Minestrone Milanese*
Toasted Italian Bread
Banana Splits*

Goldene Yoich
(Golden Chicken Broth)*
Sour Rye Bread
Garlic Half-Sour Pickles*
Passover Nut Cake*

⬥

Crabmeat Stuffed Mushrooms*
Jellied Cottage-Cheese
and Tomato Salad*
Melba Toast
Cantaloupe Ice*

Ruby-Glazed
Chicken-Liver Pâté*
Crisp Rye Wafers
Cucumber Cups*
Huckleberry Cottage Pudding*
with Lemon Hard Sauce*

⬥

Jamaican Onion Soup
with Cheese*
Ham and Corn Fritters*
Waldorf Salad

Roast Fresh Ham*
Succotash
Baked Yams
Red Cabbage Slaw
Pocket Book Rolls
Strawberry Sundae

⬥

Mushroom Barley Soup*
Spiced Ham and Bananas*
Oshitashi
(Spinach with Sesame)*
Ice-Cream Shadow Cake*

Curried Ham
and Fresh-Pork Loaf*
Spicy Cranberry Sauce*
Braised Cabbage*
Green Beans and Celery Salad
Corn Sticks   Butter
Taylach mit Neshomas
(Nut and Honey Sweetmeats)*

⬥

Savory Stuffed Heart*
Broccoli Vinaigrette
Vienna Bread   Butter
Apricot Ice-Cream Pie*

Magyar Guylás
(Hungarian Goulash)*
Buttered Noodles
with Caraway Seeds
Honeyed Beets*
Celery Hearts
Rum-Raisin Ice Cream*
Petticoat Tails*

⬥

Pavese (Egg Consommé)*
Haddock Plaki*
Deviled Eggs* on Lettuce
Sliced Tomatoes
Challah*
Szilvás Gombóc
(Plum Dumplings)*

Veal Hearts
with Fruit Stuffing*
Risotto alla Milanese
(Rice, Milan Style)*
Green Beans
Sliced Cucumber Salad
Almond Ice Cream*

⬥

Pachadi (Yogurt Salad)*
Pickled Pumpkin*
Keema Matar
(Chopped Meat with Peas)*
Steamed Spinach
Sesame Crackers
Fresh Coconut Ice*

Consommé Julienne*
Stuffed Pork Fillets*
Squash Casserole*
Cabbage, Green and
Red-Pepper Salad
Rolls
Pineapple Ice Cream*

⬥

Tomato Juice
Flaked Haddock, Newburg*
on Squares of
Grits Batter Bread*
Green Bean, Onion, and
Cucumber Salad
Blueberry Parfait*

Veal Hot Pot*
Gohan (Rice)*
Green Pepper Salad
Squash Muffins*
Strawberry Chiffon Pie*

⬥

Gefilte Fish*
Red Horseradish
Festive Tzimmes
(Main Dish
Meat and Vegetables)*
Coleslaw
Dark Pumpernickel Bread
Watermelon Granité*
Lekah (Honey Cake)*

Pride of Erin Soup*
Seventeenth-Century
Beef Pot Roast*
Mashed Yellow Turnips
Pepper Hash*
Soda Bread*   Butter
Honeyed Pears*

⬥

Cock of the North
(Capon with Pearl Onions
and Mushrooms)*
Potato Collops*
Kale
Currant-Jelly and
Raspberry Ice*
Lenten Cake*

Beef-and-Kidney Pudding*
Green Beans
with Horseradish Sauce*
Sliced Tomatoes
Irish Moss Blancmange*
Grostoli (Crisp Cookies)*

⬥

Irish Stew*
(Mutton or Lamb)
Buttered Cabbage
Cucumber, Carrot and
Green Pepper Sticks
Crispy White Rolls
Apple Puddeny-Pie* Topped
with Vanilla Ice Cream*

Uova in Purgatorio
(Eggs in Purgatory)*
Crostini alla Mozzarella
(Italian Mozzarella Skewers)*
Mixed Green Salad
Ice 'n Cream* Cookies
Espresso

⬥

Anchovy Eggs* on Chicory
Scaloppine di Vitello
(Veal Scaloppine)*
Potato Pastry Shells*
Filled with Cream
Green Peas
Finocchio and Plum Tomatoes
Cassata Napolitana (Cake)*

Fegatini di Pollo alla
Salvia (Chicken Livers
with Sage)*
Spaghetti al Quattro
Formaggi (Spaghetti with
Four Cheeses)*
Escarole and Green Pepper
Salad with Italian Dressing
Honeydew and Orange Dessert*
Cookies

⬥

Smoked Salmon with Capers
Myrtle Bank Jamaican
Pepperpot Soup*
Hot Cornbread Squares
Coffee-Chocolate Pie*

Indian Broiled Shrimps*
Moong Ki Dal (Mung Beans)*
Dahi Bhath
(Rice with Buttermilk)*
Mango Chutney
Tangerine Ice
in Orange Shells*

⬥

Soowar Ka Gosht Vindaloo
(Sour Pork Curry)*
Rice   Spiced Peach Jam*
Crisp Rolls
Honey Mousse*
Sliced Mangoes
Darjeeling Tea

Pickled Herring*
Csirke Paprikás
(Chicken Paprika
with Sour Cream)*
Makos Tészta
(Noodles with Poppy Seed)*
Cseresznye Kisütve
(Deep-Fried Cherries)*

———◆———

Jellied Fruit Soup*
Holishkes
(Meat-Stuffed Cabbage)*
Wilted Cucumbers with Dill
Pumpernickel   Sweet Butter
Diós Tekercs (Hungarian
Walnut Roll)*

Grapefruit Avocado Cup
Stuffed Ham Slices*
Corn Pudding
Buttered Green Lima Beans
Hot Biscuits
Cranberry and Fig Jam*
Mocha Parfait*

———◆———

Melanzane alla Marinara
(Eggplant Marinara
Appetizer)*
Pollo alla Cacciatora
(Chicken Cacciatora)*
Spaghetti with Parmesan
Cheese   Bread Sticks
Instant Blender Lemon Ice*

Sarson Bhara Kekda
(Shrimps with Mustard)*
Murgha Kari (Chicken Curry
with Tomatoes)*
Rice   Raw Cauliflower
Salad with Sesame Seed
Banana Ice Cream*

———◆———

Chopped Chicken Livers*
Tongue with Sweet-and-
Sour Sauce*
Cabbage Strudel*
Waldorf Salad
Coffee Ice Cream with
Chocolate-Covered
Coffee Beans*

Cold Fresh Ham*
Sweet Pickled Peaches
Tejfeles Baffőzélek
(Dried Beans in Sour Cream)*
Hearts of Romaine or
Belgian Endive
Chakin Shibori
(Sweet-Potato Dessert)*

———◆———

Crabmeat Cocktail
Roast-Beef Hash Casserole*
Red-Pepper Jam*
Stewed Tomatoes
and Celery
Corn Muffins
Dutch Honey Cake*

Bárány Pörkölt Árpakásával
(Lamb and Barley Stew)*
Squash Baked in Shells*
Green Bean Salad
Sour Rye Bread
Applesauce   Huszárcsok
(Hussar's Kisses)*

———◆———

Broiled Haddock Fillets*
with Fresh Grapefruit
Sections
Peperoni con Patate
(Peppers and Potatoes)*
Watercress-Radish Salad
Jelly-Roll Sandwiches*
with Ice Cream

Clam and Tomato Juice
Cocktail
Roast Duck
Honey-Glazed Apples*
Onions with Peas
Red and Green Cabbage Salad
Poppy-Seed Strudel*

———◆———

Ham and Corn Potato Soup*
Jellied Chicken Mold*
Tomato, Cucumber, and
Avocado Salad
Peach Ice*
Brown-Sugar Hermits*

Celery and Sweet Pickles
Cock-a-Leekie Soup*
Haggerty*
Mince Pie   Tea

———◆———

Hamburger Princess*
Salt Pork, Beans,
and Hominy*
Shredded Carrot and
Cabbage Salad
Fruit-Juice Ice*
Hickory Nut Cake*

Hamburger Guacamole*
Mexican Hominy*
Fresh Pineapple and
Mixed Greens Salad
Crisp Toast
Cinnamon Chocolate Parfait*

———◆———

Chicken Hash à la Ritz*
Fresh Asparagus
Wild Rice
Tomatoes Stuffed with
Cucumbers and Green
Onion Salad
Garlic French Bread
Frozen Crêpes*

Turkey Noodle Soup
Jellied Meat Loaf*
Carrot Curls·
Toasted Split French Rolls
with Parmesan Cheese   Butter
Cherry Strudel*

———◆———

Cold Rusell Borscht*
Hot Sweet and Sour Fish*
Kartoffel Latkes
(Potato Pancakes)*
Toasted Bagels
Sweet Butter
Hickory Crescents*
Muscatel Ice*

Fruit Cup
Disznókaraj Magyarosan
(Hungarian Pork Chops)*
Kasha Varnishkas (Buckwheat
Groats with Noodles)*
Jerusalem Artichokes
with Tomatoes*
Nut Strudel*

———◆———

Ham-Lima Bean Soup*
Canadian Hamburger Pie*
Avocado-Melon Salad*
Chocolate Ice Cream Roll*
with Chocolate Fudge Sauce*

Jellied Consommé Madrilene*
Baked Ham with Spicy Sauce*
Baked Yams
Buttered Spinach
Pear, Cranberry, and Lettuce
Salad
Rolls   Butter
Chocolate Ice Cream*

———◆———

Ham-Stuffed Chicken*
Quince and Cranberry Jelly*
Baked Potatoes
Wilted Spinach Salad
Hot Buttermilk Biscuits
Margarine
Gajar Halwa (Carrot Dessert)*

Prosciutto with Fruits*
Cannelloni alla Parmigiana
(Stuffed Pancakes)*
Mixed Green Salad
with Plum Tomatoes
Italian Dressing
Wholewheat Italian Bread
Butter
Chocolate-Rum Sundae*

———◆———

Wild West Hamburger*
Potatoes Hashed in Cream*
Tomatoes, Green Peppers, and
Cucumbers in Vinegar
Sourdough or French Bread
Huckleberry Shortcake*

Knaidlach
(Matzo Balls)*
in Consommé
Pesce alla Siciliana
(Sicilian Fish)*
Cooked Mixed
Vegetable Salad
Hard Rolls
Orange Ice*   Cookies

⸻

Meatball Shepherd's Pie*
Kale, Country Style*
Lettuce Hearts and
French Dressing
Spanish Cream*
Mincemeat Hermits*

Kreplach* in Chicken Soup
Brisket of Beef*
with Lima Beans
Tomato and Watercress Salad
Sour Rye Bread
Meringues Glacées* with
Rhubarb Ice*

⸻

Juniper Pot Roast
in Burgundy*
Kartoffel Chremsel
(Potato Fritters)*
Zucchini al Burro
(Squash with Butter)*
Escarole-Beet Salad
Mocha Sundae*

Head Cheese*
Liffey Trout with Mushroom
Sauce*
Duchess Potatoes
Coleslaw
Blueberry Ice Cream*
Molasses Hermits*

⸻

Chicken Soup with Sherry*
Corned-Beef Hash Lyonnaise*
Tomato Ketchup*
Brussels Sprouts
Apple and Celery Salad
Ladyfinger Ice-Cream Cake*

Vegetable Juice Cocktail
Clam Pastries*
Creamed Hamburger
and Cabbage*
French-Fried Potatoes
Celery and Cucumber Sticks
Fresh Pineapple Ice*
Cookies

⸻

Ham Croquettes*
with Hazelnut
and Mushroom Sauce*
Whole Carrots with Honey
Glaze*   Brown Rice
Asparagus, Pimiento Salad
Raspberry Chiffon Pie*

Broiled Cod Steaks with
Salsa Verde Piccante
(Piquant Green Sauce)*
Shoestring Potatoes
Orange and Grapefruit Salad
Toasted Corn Bread
Vanilla Bavarian Cream*

⸻

Maiale Affogato
(Stewed Pork with Celery)*
Whipped Potatoes
Marinated Carrots and Peas
on Lettuce
Seeded Hard Rolls
Coffee-Banana Bavarian*
Salted Almonds

Barbecued Halibut Steaks*
New Potatoes in Cream
Peas and Mushrooms
Grape and Orange Salad
Buttered Parkerhouse Rolls
Harlequin Crinkle Cups*

⸻

Suimono (Clear Soup)*
Vegetable Tempura
and Sauce*
Chirinabe (Fish Sukiyaki)*
Kyuri-Momi
(Vinegared Cucumber)*
Chakin Shibori
(Sweet Potato Dessert)*
Green Tea

Miso Shiru
(Bean Paste Soup)*
Sashimi (Sliced Raw Fish)*
Jyuniku-Teriyaki
(Broiled Beef)*
Soba (Buckwheat Noodles)*
Oshitashi
(Spinach with Sesame)*
Awayuki-Kan (Snow Gelatin)*

⸻

Ham Baked in Claret*
Succotash   Baked Yams
Spinach-Red Onion Salad
Huckleberry Cream-Cheese
Pie*

Beef Loaf, Farmer Style*
Mushroom Ketchup*
Hominy au Gratin*
Panned Mixed Greens
Radishes   Green Onions
Strawberry Ice*
Chocolate-Diamonds
with Hazelnuts*

⸻

Beef and Rice Casserole*
Buttered Mixed Vegetables
Wholewheat Rolls
Pear and Mandarin Orange
Salad
Molasses Chip Sundae*

Melon Wedges Wrapped
in Prosciutto*
Lasagne con le Polpettine
(Lasagna with Meatballs)*
Tossed Green Salad with
Ripe Olives
Lemon Frappé*

⸻

Spicy Pork Kabobs*
Wheat or Rice Pilaf
Sesame Wafers
Apple, Olive and Celery
Salad
Hazelnut Cream*

Tennessee Hamburger*
Baked Hominy Grits*
Mustard Greens
or Swiss Chard
Hot Corn Sticks   Butter
Perfection Salad
Strawberry-Honey Bavarian*

⸻

Meatballs with Almond–
Mushroom Noodles*
Zucchini Fritte
(Fried Squash)*
Green Pepper, Pimiento and
Cabbage Salad
Plum Ice*   Poundcake

Tomato-Avocado
Hors-d'Oeuvre*
Dingle Mackerel*
Slieve na mBam Carrots*
Hard Rolls   Butter
Honey-Nut-Apple Pie*

⸻

Pumpkin Soup*
Pork Fricassee Filipino*
Curried Rice
Banana and Macadamia Nut
Salad
Coconut Cake

Pork and Veal Head Cheese*
Sweet Pickles
Mellanzane alla Parmigiana
(Eggplant Parmigiana)*
Chicory and Romaine Salad
Italian Bread Sticks
Fresh or Stewed Figs in
Tokay Wine

⸻

Watercress Soup*
Pot Roast*
Vegetable Cutlets*
Zeller Salatá (Celery-
Root Salad)* on Greens
Pumpernickel Toast
Cherry Strudel*

Petto di Vitello
(Veal Breast)*
Vermicelli alla Pastora
(Fine Noodles for the
Shepherdess)*
Marinated Tomatoes and
Cucumbers
Fresh Fruit Cup

⸻

Turkey Hash*
Shoestring Potatoes
Broccoli with Hollandaise
Sauce*
Tomato Aspic on Lettuce
Seeded Hard Rolls
Hazelnut Tarts*

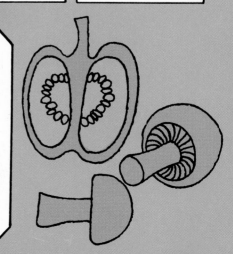

*Recipes for all starred dishes found in this volume.

GENERAL INFORMATION

The Ingredients and Measurements Used in Recipes

All recipes in this book have been tested in the Woman's Day Kitchens with standard American measuring cups (8 ounces = 16 tablespoons), measuring spoons (1 tablespoon = 3 teaspoons), and other standard kitchen equipment. All measurements are level. Liquids are measured in standard 8-ounce glass measuring cups, at eye level.

All sugar is granulated white sugar unless otherwise specified.

All flours, cake and all-purpose, are sifted before measuring unless otherwise specified. No self-rising flour is used.

All baking powder is double-acting baking powder.

All brown sugar is firmly packed when measured.

All confectioners' sugar is sifted before measuring.

All pepper is ground black pepper unless otherwise specified.

Fats and shortening are measured at room temperature, packed firmly into measuring cup and leveled with a straight knife. They are scraped out with a rubber spatula.

Salted butter or margarine, packed in ¼-pound sticks, is used unless otherwise specified. 1 stick = ½ cup = 8 tablespoons = ¼ pound.

1 tall can evaporated milk (14½ ounces) contains 1⅔ cups undiluted evaporated milk. Sweetened condensed milk is an entirely different product, and cannot be used interchangeably with evaporated milk.

⅓ to ½ teaspoon dried herbs can be substituted for each tablespoon fresh herbs. Crumble herbs before using to release flavor.

Before starting to cook or to bake, read the recipes carefully. Assemble all ingredients and equipment. Follow recipe exactly. Do not increase or decrease recipe unless you are a skilled enough cook to recognize what adjustments must be made as to ingredients, pan sizes, and/or cooking time.

Cooking Temperatures and Times

Cooking temperatures and times are approximate for meat. They depend not only on the weight and kind of meat, but also on its shape, temperature, and its bone and fat contents. A meat thermometer was used in testing.

Cooking times for meats are as recommended by the National Live Stock and Meat Board, 36 Wabash Avenue, Chicago, Illinois 60603.

Oven Temperatures

TEMPERATURES (Degree F.)	TERM
250 to 275	VERY SLOW
300 to 325	SLOW
350 to 375	MODERATE
400 to 425	HOT
450 to 475	VERY HOT
500 to 525	EXTREMELY HOT

Important—Preheat oven for 10 to 15 minutes before placing food in it. Many a cake has been spoiled by being placed in a barely heated oven. Baking times are based on the assumption that the oven is already at the stated temperature.

Check the oven temperature control frequently, especially if baking times vary from those given in recipes. (This can be done with a portable oven thermometer.) If a control is consistently off, call your public utility. They should be able to reset the oven temperature control.

Caloric Values

The caloric values, where mentioned, for each food are based on 100 grams, about 3½ ounces edible portion, as mentioned in Composition of Foods, Agriculture Handbook No. 8, Agricultural Service of the United States Department of Agriculture, Washington, D. C., revised December 1963.

MODELING AND ANALYSIS OF DYNAMIC SYSTEMS

MODELING AND ANALYSIS OF DYNAMIC SYSTEMS

Second Edition

Charles M. Close and Dean K. Frederick
Rensselaer Polytechnic Institute

JOHN WILEY & SONS, INC.
New York • Chichester • Brisbane • Toronto • Singapore

To my wife Margo

CMC

To my mother
Elizabeth Dean Frederick
and to the memory of my father
Charles Elder Frederick

DKF

▶ Contents

▶ Preface

The primary purpose of this edition remains the same as in the first edition: to provide an introductory treatment of dynamic systems that is suitable for all engineering students regardless of discipline. We have, however, made major changes as a result of experiences with many thousands of our students, comments from dozens of professors around the country, and the increasing educational use of standard computer packages. We have also arranged the contents to provide more flexibility in the selection and ordering of material.

The book can be adapted to several types of courses. One such use is for students who need a detailed treatment of modeling mechanical and electrical systems and of obtaining time-domain and Laplace-transform solutions before proceeding to more advanced concepts. For example, this text is the basis for a one-semester course at Rensselaer Polytechnic Institute taken by every engineering student in his or her sophomore or junior year. The course serves as a foundation for such subsequent courses as circuits and electronics, vehicular dynamics, chemical process control, linear systems, feedback systems, nuclear reactor control, and biocontrol systems.

The book also covers such general topics as transfer functions, the linearization of nonlinear models, computer solutions, block diagrams, feedback systems, state variables, and matrix methods. Hence it is very suitable for a general dynamic systems course for students who have completed a disciplinary course such as machine dynamics, electrical circuits, or chemical process dynamics.

This text can also be used for students with significant modeling and analysis experience who wish to emphasize computer techniques and feedback control systems. Topics include computer solutions for both linear and nonlinear models, as well as root-locus diagrams, Bode plots, block diagrams, and operational amplifiers. We explain some of the practical design criteria for control systems and illustrate the use of analytical and computer methods to meet those criteria. Finally, the book can provide a general introduction to dynamic systems for students in broad-based engineering programs or in programs (such as biomedical and materials engineering) that may have limited time for this subject.

We assume that the reader has had differential and integral calculus and basic college physics, including mechanics and electrical phenomena. A course in differential equations is recommended at least concurrently. We have been careful to present the mathematical results precisely (although without the rigorous proofs required for a mathematics book), so that the concepts learned will remain valid in subsequent courses. For example, the impulse has been treated in a manner that is consistent with distribution theory but is no more difficult to grasp than the usual approach taken in introductory engineering books.

Approach

The book reflects the approach we have used for over two decades in teaching basic courses in dynamic systems. Whether for a particular discipline or for a general engineering course, we have found it valuable to include systems from at least two disciplines in some depth. This illustrates the commonality of the modeling and analysis techniques, encourages students to avoid compartmentalizing their knowledge, and prepares them to work on projects as part of an interdisciplinary team.

Mechanical systems are examined first because of their greater familiarity. However, there are also chapters on electrical, electromechanical, thermal, and hydraulic systems. Each type of system is modeled in terms of its own fundamental laws and nomenclature.

We develop linear models in terms of state-variable equations, input-output differential equations, and transfer functions. We introduce both time-domain solutions and Laplace transforms fairly early. We give considerable emphasis to such concepts as time constants, damping ratios, transfer functions, poles and zeros, mode functions, and frequency-response functions. Although the use of matrices in undergraduate courses is increasing, we recognize that time limitations and possible gaps in the student's background might preclude their use. Accordingly, we have confined the analytical solution of models in matrix form to optional sections at the end of Chapters 3, 6, and 8.

We have always treated both linear and nonlinear models, although the book allows nonlinear systems to be deemphasized if desired. Students should realize that inherent nonlinearities generally cannot be ignored in the formulation of an accurate model. Techniques are introduced for approximating nonlinear systems by linear models. We also show that it is not difficult to write the equations needed for computer solutions for nonlinear models.

We believe that obtaining and interpreting computer solutions of both linear and nonlinear models constitute an important part of any course on dynamic systems. We employ MATLAB and ACSL, two computer packages that are widely used in both educational and industrial settings, although other equivalent packages can be used. Because individual instructors introduce numerical solutions at different points in a course, we have put the explanation of these programs in Chapter 15. However, some of the sections can be used as early as Chapter 3.

Organization

The majority of the material can be covered in a one-semester course, but the book can also be used as the basis for a two-quarter or year-long course. A number of chapters (including Chapters 10, 11, 12, and 14) and a number of individual sections (including Sections 3.3, 5.7, 6.5, 6.6, 8.6, and 8.7) can be omitted or abbreviated without any loss of continuity. As we have pointed out, the computer packages described in Chapter 15 can be used throughout the book. The remaining 14 chapters can be grouped into the following four blocks.

1. Modeling of mechanical and electrical systems: Chapters 1 through 5

2. Analytical solutions for linear systems and linearizing nonlinear models: Chapters 6 through 9

3. Modeling other types of systems: Chapters 10 through 12

4. Block diagrams, feedback systems, and design tools: Chapters 13 and 14

A core sequence for students without previous courses in dynamic systems might include Chapters 1 through 9 plus Chapter 13. Readers with prior modeling experience might find parts of the first five chapters to be review, although they should be sure to understand the state-variable and input-output models in Chapter 3. As an illustration of how to extend the modeling and analysis techniques to other types of systems, we suggest including one or more of Chapters 10, 11, and 12.

Chapters 13 and 14 can be used as an introduction to the modeling, analysis, and design of feedback control systems. In Chapter 14, we present root-locus and Bode diagrams. Rather than provide lengthy descriptions of how to draw such diagrams by hand, we emphasize interpreting computer-generated plots and using them in an iterative process to meet some practical design criteria.

The following table of prerequisites should be helpful in selecting material from the later chapters.

Topic	Chapter	Prerequisite Material
Linearization	9	Chapter 4 [1]
Electromechanical Systems	10	Chapters 4–8
Thermal Systems	11	Chapters 8, 9
Hydraulic Systems	12	Chapters 8, 9
Block Diagrams	13	Chapter 8
Feedback Modeling and Design	14	Chapter 13
Computer Analysis	15.1, 15.2	Chapter 8 [2]
	15.3, 15.4	Chapter 3 [3]

[1] Section 9.3 also requires Chapter 5.
[2] Parts of Sections 15.1 and 15.2 require Chapter 14.
[3] Parts of Sections 15.3 and 15.4 require Chapter 4.

New to this Edition

Many of the major changes in the content and organization of this edition resulted from a comprehensive series of surveys and in-depth reviews. These changes include the following.

1. Electrical systems and Laplace transform techniques are introduced earlier. Electrical systems now appear in the initial block of modeling chapters. Transform methods are treated immediately after the discussion of time-domain solutions.

2. Material on individual transistor and diode circuits has been replaced by optional sections on operational amplifiers and impedances.

3. We have merged the treatment of simulation and block diagrams and have extended the coverage of feedback systems and frequency-response functions.

4. We have also expanded the treatment of matrix methods and have regrouped it into several optional sections.

5. Instead of including the more abstract discussion of simulation and numerical methods contained in the first edition, we have shown how to apply specific computer packages to linear and nonlinear models.

In addition, we have provided increased motivation and guidance for the reader.

1. Summaries have been added to each chapter.

2. The majority of the examples have been modified or replaced, and the number of examples has been increased to nearly 200. Explicit statements about the points to be illustrated have been added before the examples. Where appropriate, comments about the significance of the results follow the examples.

3. The end-of-chapter problems have been heavily revised, and a large number of new problems have been added. There are now well over 400 problems.

4. The answers to selected problems are contained in an appendix at the back of the book.

Solutions Manual

A solutions manual containing detailed solutions to all the problems in the text can be obtained by contacting Houghton Mifflin Company. At the beginning of each chapter in the manual, a table lists the following information for each of the major topics: the section of the text in which it is covered, the examples in which it is illustrated, and the problems that relate to it.

Acknowledgments

Colleagues at Rensselaer who provided support and helpful comments for this edition include Kevin Craig, Edward Maby, Jonathan Newell, Gary Saulnier, Joseph Smith, Jr., and Henry Sneck. We are also indebted to those faculty members from a number of departments who have taught our dynamic systems course over the past 15 years. We thank Mario Rivera of Union College and Stuart Trembly of Dartmouth College for their constructive criticism and for detailed accuracy reviews. Among the many other external reviewers, we especially recognize Peter L. Balise, University of Washington; Peter Dorato, University of New Mexico, Albuquerque; Leslie R. Koval, University of Missouri, Rolla; Paul H. Lewis, Michigan Technological University; Frank W. Paul, Clemson University; Helen A. Ryaciotaki-Boussalis, California State University, Los Angeles; and John Youngblood, University of Alabama.

Conscientious secretarial assistance was provided by Joan Hayner, Charmaine Darmetko, and Shirley Broderick. One of our students, Erwin Himawan, helped collect the solutions for the homework problems. Dan Olson of Electronic Technical Publishing and Harriet Borton of Rensselaer's Information Technology Services gave valuable advice about the use of LaTeX. It was a pleasure to work with Raymond Deveaux, Rodger Klas, June Goldstein, and Jean Andon of Houghton Mifflin in the planning and production of the book. Finally and most importantly, we sincerely appreciate the patience, support, and encouragement of our wives throughout this project.

C.M.C.
D.K.F.

INTRODUCTION

In this chapter we present the rationale for the book, define several terms that will be used throughout, and describe various types of systems. The chapter concludes with a description of the particular types of systems to be considered and a summary of the techniques that the reader should be able to apply after finishing the book.

1.1 RATIONALE

The importance of understanding and being able to determine the dynamic response of physical systems has long been recognized. It has been traditional in engineering education to have separate courses in dynamic mechanical systems, circuit theory, chemical-process dynamics, and other areas. Such courses develop techniques of modeling, analysis, and design for the particular physical systems that are relevant to that specific discipline, even though many of the techniques taught in these courses have much in common. This approach tends to reinforce the student's view of such courses as isolated entities with little in common and to foster a reluctance to apply what has been learned in one course to a new situation.

Another justification for considering a wide variety of different types of systems in an introductory book is that the majority of systems that are of practical interest contain components of more than one type. In the design of electronic circuits, for example, attention must also be paid to mechanical structure and to dissipation of the heat generated. Hydraulic motors and pneumatic process controllers are other examples of useful combinations of different types of elements. Furthermore, the techniques in this book can

1

be applied not only to pneumatic, acoustical, and other traditional areas but also to systems that are quite different, such as sociological, physiological, economic, and transportation systems.

Because of the universal need for engineers to understand dynamic systems, and because there is a common methodology applicable to such systems regardless of their physical origin, it makes sense to present them all together. This book considers both the problem of obtaining a mathematical description of a physical system and the various analytical techniques that are widely used.

■ 1.2 ANALYSIS OF DYNAMIC SYSTEMS

Because the most frequently used key word in the text is likely to be *system*, it is appropriate to define it at the outset. A **system** is any collection of interacting elements for which there are cause-and-effect relationships among the variables. This definition is necessarily general, because it must encompass a broad range of systems. The most important feature of the definition is that it tells us we must take interactions among the variables into account in system modeling and analysis, rather than treating individual elements separately.

Our study will be devoted to **dynamic systems**, for which the variables are time-dependent. In nearly all our examples, not only will the excitations and responses vary with time but at any instant the derivatives of one or more variables will depend on the values of the system variables at that instant. The system's response will normally depend on initial conditions, such as stored energy, in addition to any external excitations.

In the process of analyzing a system, two tasks must be performed: modeling the system and solving for the model's response. The combination of these steps is referred to as **system analysis**.

Modeling the System

A **mathematical model**, or **model** for short, is a description of a system in terms of equations. The basis for constructing a model of a system is the physical laws (such as the conservation of energy and Newton's laws) that the system elements and their interconnections are known to obey.

The type of model sought will depend on both the objective of the engineer and the tools for analysis. If a pencil-and-paper analysis with parameters expressed in literal rather than numerical form is to be performed, a relatively simple model will be needed. To achieve this simplicity, the engineer should be prepared to neglect elements that do not play a dominant role in the system.

On the other hand, if a computer is available for carrying out simulations of specific cases with parameters expressed in numerical form, a comprehensive mathematical model that includes descriptions of both primary and secondary effects might be appropriate. In short, a variety of mathematical models are possible for a system, and the engineer must be prepared to decide what form and complexity are most consistent with the objectives and the available resources.

One example of a dynamic system that is familiar to everyone is the automobile. In order to limit the complexity of any model we wish to make of this system, we must omit some of its features. And, in fact, many of the parameters may be relatively unimportant for the objective of a particular study. Among many possible concerns are ease of handling on the straightaway or while turning a corner; comfort of the driver; the vehicle's fuel efficiency, stopping ability, and crash resistance; and the effect of wind gusts, potholes, and other obstacles.

Suppose that we limit our concern to the forces on the driver when the vehicle is traveling over a rough road. Some of the key characteristics of the system are represented in Figure 1.1(a) by masses, springs, and shock absorbers.[1] The chassis has by far the largest mass, but other masses that may be significant are the front and rear axles and wheels and the driver. Suspension systems between the chassis and the axles are designed to minimize the vertical motion of the chassis when the tires undergo sudden motion because of the road surface. The tires themselves have some elasticity, which is represented by additional springs between the wheels and the road. The driver is somewhat cushioned from the chassis motion by the characteristics of the seat, and there is also some friction between the driver and the seat back.

We assume that the vehicle is traveling at a constant speed and that the horizontal motion of the chassis does not concern us. We must certainly allow for the vertical motion caused by the uneven road surface. We may also wish to consider the pitching effect when the front tires hit a bump or depression, causing the front of the chassis to move up or down before the rear. This would require us to consider not only the vertical motion of the chassis but also rotation about its center of mass.

The complexity of a system model is sometimes measured by the number of independent energy-storing elements. For Figure 1.1(a), energy can be stored in four different masses and in five different springs. If we ignore the pitching effect, we might simplify the analysis by combining the front and rear axles into a single mass, as shown in part (b) of the figure, which has only three masses and three springs.

In the initial phase of the analysis, we might make other simplifying assumptions. Perhaps some of the elements remaining in Figure 1.1(b) could be omitted. Perhaps we would use a mathematical description of the individual elements that is simpler than that required for the final analysis.

---

[1] This figure is adapted from a drawing in Chapter 42 of *The Shock and Vibration Handbook*, third edition (1988), edited by Cyril M. Harris. It is used with the permission of the publisher, McGraw-Hill, Inc.

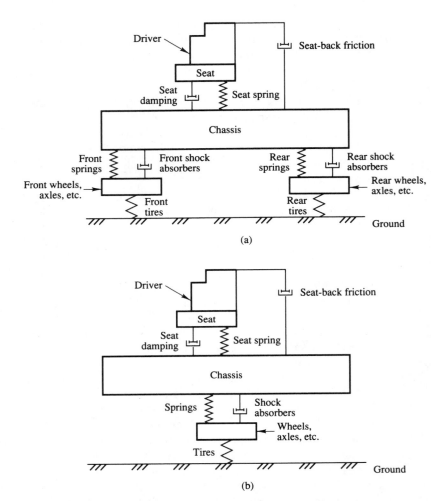

FIGURE 1.1   (a) One representation of an automobile. (b) A simplified representation.

On the other hand, for a more thorough study of the effect of a bumpy road on the driver, it might be necessary to add other characteristics to those represented in Figure 1.1(a). When one of the two wheels on the front axle encounters a bump or depression, the displacement and forces on it are different from those on its mate. Thus we might want to consider each of the four wheels as a separate mass and to allow for side-to-side rotation of the chassis, in addition to the vertical and pitching motions.

When devising models at various stages in the design process, engineers usually give considerable thought to how detailed the representation of the system's characteristics should be. Many of the remarks we have made about the automobile can be extended to airplanes, boats, rockets, motorcycles, and other vehicles. In the next few chapters, we shall show how to describe the important characteristics by sets of equations.

Solving the Model

The process of using the mathematical model to determine certain features of the system's cause-and-effect relationships is referred to as **solving the model**. For example, the responses to specific excitations may be desired for a range of parameter values, as guides in selecting design values for those parameters. As described in the discussion of modeling, this phase may include the analytical solution of simple models and the computer solution of more complex ones.

The type of equation involved in the model has a strong influence on the extent to which analytical methods can be used. For example, nonlinear differential equations can seldom be solved in closed form, and the solution of partial differential equations is far more laborious than that of ordinary differential equations. Computers can be used to generate the responses to specific numerical cases for complex models. However, using a computer to solve a complex model has its limitations. Models used for computer studies should be chosen with the approximations encountered in numerical integration in mind and should be relatively insensitive to system parameters whose values are uncertain or subject to change. Furthermore, it may be difficult to generalize results based only on computer solutions that must be run for *specific* parameter values, excitations, and initial conditions.

The engineer must not forget that the model being analyzed is only an approximate mathematical description of the system, not the physical system itself. Conclusions based on equations that required a variety of assumptions and simplifications in their development may or may not apply to the actual system. Unfortunately, the more faithful a model is in describing the actual system, the more difficult it is to obtain general results.

One procedure is to use a simple model for analytical results and design and then to use a different model to verify the design by means of computer simulation. In very complex systems, it may be feasible to incorporate actual hardware components into the simulation as they become available, thereby eliminating the corresponding parts of the mathematical model.

1.3 CLASSIFICATION OF VARIABLES

A system is often represented by a box (traditionally called a black box), as shown in Figure 1.2. The system may have several **inputs**, or **excitations**, each of which is a function of time. Typical inputs include a force applied to a mass, a voltage source applied to an electrical circuit, and a heat source applied to a vessel filled with a liquid. For the model of an automobile in Figure 1.1(a), the inputs might be the vertical displacements of the bottoms

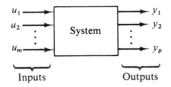

FIGURE 1.2   Black-box representation of a system.

of the springs representing the tires, as the tires move over the bumps in the road. In general discussions that are not related to specific systems, we shall use the symbols $u_1(t)$, $u_2(t)$, ..., $u_m(t)$ to denote the m inputs, shown by the arrows directed into the box.

Outputs are variables that are to be calculated or measured. Typical outputs include the velocity of a mass, the voltage across a resistor, and the rate at which a liquid flows through a pipe. For the model in Figure 1.1(a), one of the outputs might be the vertical acceleration of the driver. The p outputs are represented in Figure 1.2 by the arrows pointing away from the box representing the system. They are denoted by the symbols $y_1(t)$, $y_2(t)$, ..., $y_p(t)$. There is a cause-and-effect relationship between the outputs and inputs. To calculate any one of the outputs for all $t \geq t_0$, we must know the inputs for $t \geq t_0$ and also the accumulated effect of any previous inputs. One approach to constructing a mathematical model is to find equations that relate the outputs directly to the inputs by eliminating all the other variables that are internal to the system. If we are interested only in the input-output relationships, eliminating extraneous variables may seem appealing. However, by deleting information from the model, we may lose potentially important aspects of the system's behavior.

Another modeling technique is to introduce a set of **state variables**, which generally differs from the set of outputs but may include one or more of them. The state variables must be chosen so that a knowledge of their values at any reference time t_0 and a knowledge of the inputs for all $t \geq t_0$ is sufficient to determine the outputs and state variables for all $t \geq t_0$. An additional requirement is that the state variables must be independent; that is, it must not be possible to express one state variable as an algebraic function of the others. This approach is particularly convenient for working with multi-input, multi-output systems and for obtaining computer solutions. In Figure 1.3, the representation of the system has been modified to include the state variables denoted by the symbols $q_1(t)$, $q_2(t)$, ..., $q_n(t)$ within the box. The state variables can account for all important aspects of the system's internal behavior, regardless of the choice of output variables. Equations for the outputs are then written as algebraic functions of the state variables, the inputs, and time.

Whenever it is appropriate to indicate units for the variables and parameters, we shall use the International System of Units (abbreviated SI, from

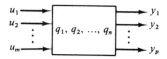

FIGURE 1.3 General system representation showing inputs, state variables, and outputs.

the French *Système International d'Unités*). A list of the units used in this book appears in Appendix A.

1.4 CLASSIFICATION OF SYSTEMS

Systems are grouped according to the types of equations that are used in their mathematical models. Examples include partial differential equations with time-varying coefficients, ordinary differential equations with constant coefficients, and difference equations. In this section we define and briefly discuss ways of classifying the models, and in the next section we indicate those categories that will be treated in this book. The classifications that we use are listed in Table 1.1.

TABLE 1.1   Criteria for Classifying Systems

Criterion	Classification
Spatial characteristics	Lumped Distributed
Continuity of the time variable	Continuous Discrete-time Hybrid
Quantization of the dependent variable	Nonquantized Quantized
Parameter variation	Fixed Time-varying
Superposition property	Linear Nonlinear

Spatial Characteristics

A **distributed system** does not have a finite number of points at which state variables can be defined. In contrast, a **lumped system** can be described by a finite number of state variables.

To illustrate these two types of systems, consider the flexible shaft shown in Figure 1.4(a) with one end embedded in a wall and with a torque applied to the other end. The angle through which a point on the surface of the shaft is twisted depends on both its distance from the wall and the applied

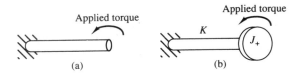

FIGURE 1.4   (a) A torsional shaft. (b) Its lumped approximation.

torque. Hence the shaft is inherently distributed and would be modeled by a partial differential equation. However, if we are interested only in the angle of twist at the right end of the shaft, we may account for the flexibility of the shaft by a rotational spring constant K and represent the effect of the distributed mass by the single moment of inertia J. Making these approximations results in the lumped system shown in Figure 1.4(b), which has the important property that its model is an ordinary differential equation. Because ordinary differential equations are far easier to solve than partial differential equations, converting from a distributed system to a lumped approximation is often essential if the resulting model is to be solved with the resources available.

Another example of a distributed system is an inductor that consists of a wire wound around a core, as shown in Figure 1.5(a). If an electrical excitation is applied across the terminals of the coil, then different values of voltage exist at all points along the coil, characteristic of a distributed system. To develop a lumped circuit whose behavior as calculated at the terminals closely approximates that of the distributed device, we might account for the resistance of the wire by a lumped resistance R and for the inductive effect related to the magnetic field by a single inductance L. The resulting lumped circuit is shown in Figure 1.5(b). Note that in these two examples (though not in all cases), the two elements in the lumped model do not correspond to separate physical parts of the actual system. The stiffness and moment of inertia of the flexible shaft cannot be separated into two physical pieces, nor can the resistance and inductance of the coil.

FIGURE 1.5   (a) An inductor. (b) Its lumped approximation.

Continuity of the Time Variable

A second basis for classifying dynamic systems is the independent-variable time. A **continuous system** is one for which the inputs, state variables, and outputs are defined over some continuous range of time (although the signals may have discontinuities in their waveshapes and not be continuous functions in the mathematical sense). A **discrete-time system** has variables that are determined at distinct instants of time and that are either not defined or not of interest between those instants. Continuous systems are described by differential equations, discrete-time systems by difference equations.

Examples of the variables associated with continuous and discrete-time systems are shown in Figure 1.6. In fact, the discrete-time variable $f_2(kT)$ shown in Figure 1.6(b) is the sequence of numbers obtained by taking the values of the continuous variable $f_1(t)$ at instants separated by T units of time. Hence $f_2(kT) = f_1(t)|_{t=kT}$, where k takes on integer values. In practice, a discrete-time variable may be composed of pulses of very short duration (much less than T) or numbers that reside in digital circuitry. In either case, the variable is assumed to be represented by a sequence of numbers, as indicated by the dots in Figure 1.6(b). There is no requirement that their spacing with respect to time be uniform, although this is often the case.

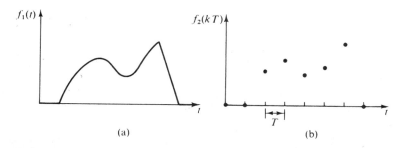

FIGURE 1.6 Sample variables. (a) Continuous. (b) Discrete-time.

A system that contains both discrete-time and continuous subsystems is referred to as a **hybrid system**. Many modern control and communication systems contain a digital computer as a subsystem. In such cases, those variables that are associated with the computer are discrete in time, whereas variables elsewhere in the system are continuous. In such systems, sampling equipment is used to form discrete-time versions of continuous variables, and signal reconstruction equipment is used to generate continuous variables from discrete-time ones.

Quantization of the Dependent Variable

In addition to possible restrictions on the values of the independent-variable time, the system variables may be restricted to certain distinct values. If within some finite range a variable may take on only a finite number of different values, it is said to be **quantized**. A variable that may have any value within some continuous range is **nonquantized**. Quantized variables may arise naturally, or they may be created by rounding or truncating the values of a nonquantized variable to the nearest quantization level.

The variables shown in Figure 1.7(a) and Figure 1.7(b) are both non-quantized, whereas those in the remaining parts of the figure are quantized. Although the variable in Figure 1.7(b) is restricted to the interval $-1 \le f_b \le 1$, it is nonquantized because it can take on a continuous set of values within that interval. The variable f_c shown in Figure 1.7(c) is restricted to the two values 0 and 1 and is representative of the signals found in devices that perform logical operations. The variable f_d is restricted to integer values and thus is quantized, although there need not be any other restriction on the magnitude of its values. The variable f_e is a discrete-time variable that is also quantized.

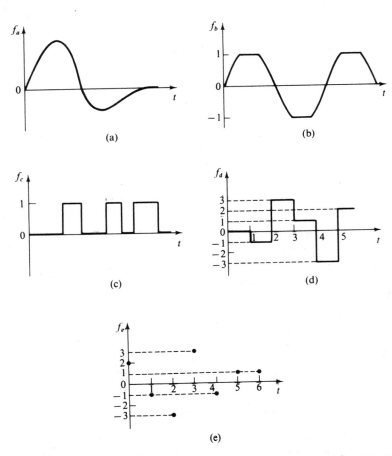

FIGURE 1.7   Sample variables. (a), (b) Nonquantized. (c), (d), (e) Quantized.

Because variables that are both discrete in time and quantized in amplitude, such as f_e, occur within a digital computer, they are referred to as **digital variables**. In contrast, the variable f_a in Figure 1.7(a) is both continuous and nonquantized and is representative of a signal within an analog computer. Hence continuous, nonquantized variables are often referred to as **analog variables**.

Parameter Variation

Systems may be classified according to properties of their parameters as well as of their variables. **Time-varying systems** are systems whose characteristics (such as the value of a mass or a resistance) change with time. Element values may change because of environmental factors such as temperature and radiation. Other examples of time-varying elements include the mass of a rocket, which decreases as fuel is burned, and the inductance of a coil, which increases as an iron slug is inserted into the core. In the differential equations describing time-varying systems, some of the coefficients are functions of time. Delaying the input to a time-varying system affects the size and shape of the response.

For **fixed** or **time-invariant systems**, whose characteristics do not change with time, the system model that describes the relationships between the inputs, state variables, and outputs is independent of time. If such a system is initially at rest, delaying the input by t_d units of time just delays the output by t_d units, without any change in its size or waveshape.

Superposition Property

A system can also be classified in terms of whether it obeys the **superposition property**, which requires that the following two tests be satisfied when the system is initially at rest with zero energy. (1) Multiplying the inputs by any constant α must multiply the outputs by α. (2) The response to several inputs applied simultaneously must be the sum of the individual responses to each input applied separately. **Linear systems** are those that satisfy the conditions for superposition; **nonlinear systems** are those for which superposition does not hold. For a linear system, the coefficients in the differential equations that make up the system model do not depend on the size of the excitation, whereas for nonlinear systems, at least some of the coefficients do. For a linear system initially at rest, multiplying all the inputs by a constant multiplies the output by the same constant. Likewise, replacing all the original inputs by their derivatives (or integrals) gives outputs that are the derivatives (or integrals) of the original outputs.

Nearly all systems are inherently nonlinear if no restrictions at all are placed on the allowable values of the inputs. If the values of the inputs are confined to a sufficiently small range, the originally nonlinear model of a system may often be replaced by a linear model whose response closely approximates that of the nonlinear model. This type of approximation is desirable because analytical solutions to linear models are more easily obtained.

In other applications, the nonlinear nature of an element may be an essential feature of the system and should not be avoided in the model. Examples include mechanical valves or electrical diodes designed to give completely different types of responses for positive and negative inputs. Devices used to produce constant-amplitude oscillations generally have the amplitude of the response determined by nonlinear elements in the system.

To illustrate the difference between linear and nonlinear models, consider a system with the single input $u(t)$ and the single output $y(t)$. If the input and output are related by the differential equation

$$a_1 \frac{dy}{dt} + a_0 y(t) = b_0 u(t)$$

where a_0, a_1, and b_0 may be functions of time but do not depend on $u(t)$ or $y(t)$ in any way, then the system is linear. However, if one or more of the coefficients is a function of the input or output, as in

$$\frac{dy}{dt} + u(t)y(t) = u(t)$$

or

$$\frac{dy}{dt} + |y(t)|y(t) = u(t)$$

then the system is nonlinear.

Analogous Systems

Different systems that are described by equations that are identical except for the use of different symbols are called **analogs**. Consider the four simple systems depicted in Figure 1.8. In the later chapters, we shall examine mechanical, electrical, and hydraulic systems in detail. For the systems in this figure, we shall give at this time only a very brief explanation of the variables, the symbols used, and the equations describing the systems.

Each type of system has two basic variables, both of which are functions of time t. For the translational mechanical system, the variables used in the figure are force $f(t)$ and velocity $v(t)$; for the rotational mechanical system, torque $\tau(t)$ and angular velocity $\omega(t)$; for the electrical system, voltage $e(t)$ and current $i(t)$; and for the hydraulic system, flow rate $q(t)$ and pressure difference $p(t)$. Instead of velocity, angular velocity, and current, the alternative variables of displacement, angular displacement, and charge could be used just as well. For simplicity, we assume for Figure 1.8 that all the elements are linear and that no energy is stored within the system before the input is applied.

In the translational system shown in part (a) of the figure, an external force $f(t)$ is applied to a mass M, whose motion is restrained by a spring K and a friction element B. For the rotational system in part (b), a torque $\tau(t)$ is exerted on a disk whose moment of inertia is J, which is restrained by the

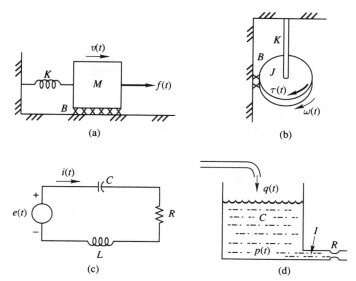

FIGURE 1.8 Analogous systems. (a) Translational mechanical.
(b) Rotational mechanical. (c) Electrical. (d) Hydraulic.

torsional bar K and the friction B. The electrical system in part (c) consists
of an inductor L, a resistor R, and a capacitor C excited by a voltage source
$e(t)$. In part (d), fluid with a known flow rate $q(t)$ enters a vessel that has
hydraulic capacitance C. The orifice in the outlet pipe is approximated by
the hydraulic resistance R. The inertia effect of the fluid mass can usually
be neglected, but in order to complete the analogy, we represent it here by
the inertance I.

The following equations, which describe the four systems in Figure 1.8,
are identical except for the symbols used. The inputs are on the right sides
of the equations, the output variables on the left.

$$M\frac{dv}{dt} + Bv(t) + K \int_0^t v(\lambda)d\lambda = f(t)$$

$$J\frac{d\omega}{dt} + B\omega(t) + K \int_0^t \omega(\lambda)d\lambda = \tau(t)$$

$$L\frac{di}{dt} + Ri(t) + \frac{1}{C} \int_0^t i(\lambda)d\lambda = e(t)$$

$$C\frac{dp}{dt} + \frac{1}{R}p(t) + \frac{1}{I} \int_0^t p(\lambda)d\lambda = q(t)$$

If the inputs are identical, then the respective responses will have the same
form. The expressions for the power supplied by each of the inputs in

the four parts of the figure are $f(t)v(t), \tau(t)\omega(t), e(t)i(t),$ and $p(t)q(t),$ respectively.

Other analogous components could have been included in our discussion. Levers, gears, transformers, and double-headed pistons constitute one set of analogous components. Brakes, diodes, and overflow valves are another. Our treatment of analogies could also be extended to other types of systems, such as thermal, pneumatic, and acoustical systems. We shall not overemphasize analogies, because it is generally better to treat each type of system separately. However, it is important to realize that the modeling and analysis tools that we shall develop are applicable to a very wide range of physical systems.

■ 1.5 SCOPE AND OBJECTIVES

This book is restricted to lumped, continuous, nonquantized systems that can be described by sets of ordinary differential equations. Because well-developed analytical techniques are available for solving linear ordinary differential equations with constant coefficients, we shall emphasize such methods. The majority of our examples will involve systems that are both fixed and linear. A method for approximating a nonlinear system by a fixed linear model will be developed. For time-varying or nonlinear systems that cannot be approximated by a fixed linear model, one can resort to computer solutions.

We list as **objectives** the following things that the reader should be able to do after finishing this book. These objectives are grouped in the two general categories of modeling and solving for the response.

After finishing this book, the reader should be able to do the following for dynamic systems composed of mechanical, electrical, thermal, and hydraulic components:

1. Given a description of the system, construct a simplified version using idealized elements and define a suitable set of variables.

2. Use the appropriate element and interconnection laws to obtain a mathematical model generally consisting of ordinary differential equations.

3. If the model is nonlinear, determine the equilibrium conditions and, where appropriate, obtain a linearized model in terms of incremental variables.

4. Arrange the equations that make up the model in a form suitable for solution. Construct and simplify block diagrams.

When a linear mathematical model has been determined or is given, the reader should be able to do the following:

1. For a first- or second-order system, solve directly for the time-domain response without transforming the functions of time into functions of other variables.

2. For a model of moderate order (of order four or less), use the Laplace transform to
   a. Find the complete time response.
   b. Determine the transfer function and its poles and zeros.
   c. Analyze stability and, where appropriate, evaluate time constants, damping ratios, and undamped natural frequencies.
3. Find from the transformed expression the steady-state response to a constant or sinusoidal input without requiring a general solution.
4. Use block diagrams, root-locus plots, and Bode diagrams as aids in analyzing and designing feedback systems.

In addition to using these analytical methods for obtaining the model's response, the reader should be able to use a computer to obtain the time response of a linear or nonlinear model in numerical form.

This book investigates all the foregoing procedures in detail. We illustrate the basic modeling approaches and introduce state variables first in the context of mechanical systems and then for electrical systems. There are several chapters about the analytical solution of mathematical models. In Chapter 6, we review and apply the classical procedures usually introduced in basic mathematics courses for solving the equations describing linear systems. Then we develop and use analytical techniques based on transforming functions of time into functions of a different variable.

The material in Chapter 9 and in much of Chapter 15 can be presented any time after Chapter 5, depending on the organization of a particular course of study. The first of these chapters gives procedures for approximating a nonlinear model by a linear one. The second considers the computer solution of both linear and nonlinear models, with an emphasis on the widely used MATLAB and ACSL programs.

Chapters 10 through 12 extend the procedures of the earlier chapters to electromechanical, thermal, and hydraulic systems. Chapters 13 and 14 present block and simulation diagrams and then introduce the modeling and design of feedback systems.

TRANSLATIONAL MECHANICAL SYSTEMS

The modeling techniques for translational and rotational mechanical systems are discussed in this and the next two chapters. Procedures for solving the mathematical models are developed in later chapters.

After introducing the variables to be used, we discuss the laws for the individual elements, the laws governing the interconnections of the elements, and the use of free-body diagrams as an aid in formulating the equations of the model. Inputs will consist of either the application of a known external force or the moving of some body with a known displacement.

The first examples will be systems that can have only horizontal or only vertical motion. For masses that can move vertically, the gravitational forces must be considered. If the system contains an ideal pulley, then some parts can move horizontally and other parts vertically. Special situations, such as free-body diagrams for massless junctions and rules for the series or parallel combination of similar elements, will be treated later in the chapter.

■ 2.1 VARIABLES

The symbols for the basic variables used to describe the dynamic behavior of translational mechanical systems are

x, displacement in meters (m)

v, velocity in meters per second (m/s)

a, acceleration in meters per second per second (m/s^2)

f, force in newtons (N)

All these variables are functions of time. In general, however, we shall add a t in parentheses immediately after the symbol only when it denotes an input or when we find doing so useful for clarity or emphasis.

Displacements are measured with respect to some reference condition, which is often the equilibrium position of the body or point in question. Velocities are normally expressed as the derivatives of the corresponding displacements. If the reference condition of a displacement is not indicated because it is not of interest, then the reference condition for the velocity needs to be given.

Two conventions used to define displacements are illustrated in Figure 2.1(a) and Figure 2.1(b). In Figure 2.1(a), the variable x represents the displacement of the left side of the body from the fixed vertical wall, whereas in Figure 2.1(b), the reference position corresponding to $x = 0$ is not specifically shown.

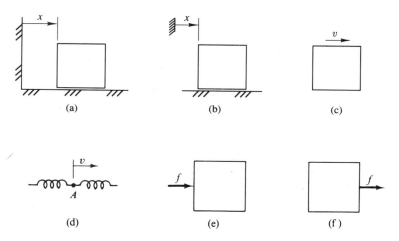

FIGURE 2.1   Conventions for designating variables.

Generally, the reference position will correspond to a co..dition of equilibrium for which the system inputs are constants and in which the net force on the body being considered is zero. Figure 2.1(c) and Figure 2.1(d) indicate two methods of defining a velocity. All points on the body in Figure 2.1(c) must move with the same velocity, so there is no possible ambiguity about which point has the velocity v. In Figure 2.1(d), the vertical line at the base of the arrow indicates that v is the velocity of the point labeled A. Forces can be represented by arrows pointing either into or away from a body, as depicted in Figure 2.1(e) and Figure 2.1(f), which are equivalent to one another.

Remember that the arrows only indicate an assumed positive sense for the displacement, velocity, or force being considered and by themselves do not imply anything about the actual direction of the motion or of the force at a given instant. If, for example, in Figure 2.1(e) and Figure 2.1(f), the force acting on the body is $f(t) = \sin t$, the force acts to the right for $0 < t < \pi$ and to the left for $\pi < t < 2\pi$, and it continues to change direction every π seconds. Note that an alternative way of describing the identical situation is to draw the arrow pointing to the left and then write $f(t) = -\sin t$. Reversing a reference arrow is equivalent to reversing the sign of the algebraic expression associated with it. There is no unique way of choosing reference directions on a diagram, but the equations must be consistent with whatever choice is made for the arrows.

Reference arrows for the displacement, velocity, and acceleration of a given point are invariably drawn in the same direction so that the equations

$$v = \frac{dx}{dt}$$

and

$$a = \frac{dv}{dt} = \frac{d^2x}{dt^2}$$

can be used. With this understanding, a reference arrow for acceleration is not shown explicitly on the diagrams, and for the same reason only the reference arrow for either the displacement or the velocity of a point (but not both) is shown in many examples.

Variables in addition to those defined at the beginning of this section include

w, energy in joules (J)

p, power in watts (W)

where 1 joule = 1 newton-meter and 1 watt = 1 joule per second. Because the arrows defining the positive senses of the velocity and the force point in the same direction, the power supplied to the mass in Figure 2.2(a) and to the spring in Figure 2.2(b) is

$$p = fv \tag{1}$$

Because power is defined to be the rate at which energy is supplied or dissipated, it follows that

$$p = \frac{dw}{dt} \tag{2}$$

and the energy supplied between time t_0 and t_1 is

$$\int_{t_0}^{t_1} p(t)dt$$

If $w(t_0)$ denotes the energy supplied up to time t_0, then the total energy supplied up to any later time t is

$$w(t) = w(t_0) + \int_{t_0}^{t} p(\lambda)d\lambda \tag{3}$$

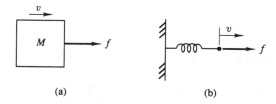

FIGURE 2.2 Reference arrows for (1).

In the last integrand, t has been replaced by the dummy variable λ in order to avoid confusion between the upper limit and the variable of integration.

2.2 ELEMENT LAWS

Physical devices are represented by one or more idealized elements that obey laws involving the variables associated with the elements. As we mentioned in Chapter 1, some degree of approximation is required in selecting the elements to represent a device, and the behavior of the combined elements may not correspond exactly to the behavior of the device. The elements that we include in translational systems are mass, friction, stiffness, and the lever. The element laws for the first three relate the external force to the acceleration, velocity, or displacement associated with the element. The lever is considered in Chapter 4.

Mass

Figure 2.2(a) shows a **mass** M, which has units of kilograms (kg), subjected to a force f. Newton's second law states that the sum of the forces acting on a body is equal to the time rate of change of the momentum:

$$\frac{d}{dt}(Mv) = f \tag{4}$$

which, for a constant mass, can be written as

$$M\frac{dv}{dt} = f \tag{5}$$

For (4) and (5) to hold, the momentum and acceleration must be measured with respect to an inertial reference frame. For ordinary systems at or near the surface of the earth, the earth's surface is a very close approximation to an inertial reference frame, so it is the one we use. The momentum, acceleration, and force are really vector quantities, but in this chapter the mass is constrained to move in a single direction, so we can write scalar equations.

We shall restrict our attention to constant masses and shall neglect relativistic effects so that we can use (5). Hence a mass can be modeled by an algebraic relationship between the acceleration dv/dt and the external force f. For (5) to hold, the positive senses of both dv/dt and f must be the same, because the force will cause the velocity to increase in the direction in which the force is acting.

Energy in a mass is stored as kinetic energy if the mass is in motion and as potential energy if the mass has a vertical displacement relative to its reference position. The kinetic energy is

$$w_k = \frac{1}{2}Mv^2 \tag{6}$$

and the potential energy, assuming a uniform gravitational field, is

$$w_p = Mgh \tag{7}$$

where g is the gravitational constant (approximately 9.807 m/s^2 at the surface of the earth) and h is the height of the mass above its reference position. In order to determine the response for $t \geq t_0$ of a dynamic system containing a mass, we must know its initial velocity $v(t_0)$ and, if vertical motion is possible, its initial height $h(t_0)$.

Friction

Forces that are algebraic functions of the relative velocity between two bodies are modeled by friction elements. A mass sliding on an oil film that has laminar flow, as depicted in Figure 2.3(a), is subject to **viscous friction** and obeys the linear relationship

$$f = B\Delta v \tag{8}$$

where B has units of newton-seconds per meter (N·s/m) and where $\Delta v = v_2 - v_1$. The direction of a frictional force will be such as to oppose the motion of the mass. For (8) to apply to Figure 2.3(a), the force f exerted on the mass M by the oil film is to the left. (By Newton's third law, the mass exerts an equal force f to the right on the oil film.) The friction coefficient B is proportional to the contact area and to the viscosity of the oil and inversely proportional to the thickness of the film.

Sometimes the frictional forces on adjacent bodies that have relative motion are small enough to be neglected. This might be the situation, for example, if the bodies are separated by bearings. The diagrams for such cases often show small wheels between the two bodies, as illustrated in Figure 2.3(b), in order to emphasize the lack of frictional forces.

Viscous friction may also be used to model a dashpot, such as the shock absorbers on an automobile. As indicated in Figure 2.4(a), a piston moves through an oil-filled cylinder, and there are small holes in the face of the piston through which the oil passes as the parts move relative to each other. The symbol often used for a dashpot is shown in Figure 2.4(b). Many dashpot devices involve high rates of fluid flow through the orifices and

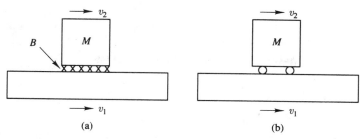

FIGURE 2.3 (a) Friction described by (8) with $\Delta v = v_2 - v_1$. (b) Adjacent bodies with negligible friction.

have nonlinear characteristics. If the flow is laminar, then the element is again described by (8). If the lower block in Figure 2.3(a) or the cylinder of the dashpot in Figure 2.4(a) is stationary, then $v_1 = 0$ and the element law reduces to $f = Bv_2$.

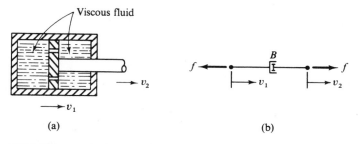

FIGURE 2.4 (a) A dashpot. (b) Its representation.

If the dashpot or oil film is assumed to be massless and if the accelerations are to remain finite, then when a force f is applied to one side, a retarding force of equal magnitude must be exerted on the other side (either by a wall or by some other component) as shown in Figure 2.4(b), again with $f = B(v_2 - v_1)$. This means that in the system shown in Figure 2.5, the force f is transmitted through the dashpot and exerted directly on the mass M.

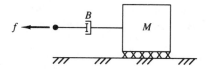

FIGURE 2.5 Force transmitted through a dashpot.

The viscous friction described by (8) is a linear element, for which the plot of f versus Δv is a straight line passing through the origin, as shown in Figure 2.6(a). Examples of friction that obey nonlinear relationships are **dry friction** and **drag friction**. The former is modeled by a force that is independent of the magnitude of the relative velocity, as indicated in Figure 2.6(b), and that can be described by the equation

$$f = \begin{cases} -A & \text{for } \Delta v < 0 \\ A & \text{for } \Delta v > 0 \end{cases}$$

Drag friction is caused by resistance to a body moving through a fluid (such as wind resistance) and can often be described by an equation of the form $f = D|\Delta v|\Delta v$, as depicted in Figure 2.6(c). Various other nonlinearities may be encountered in friction elements.

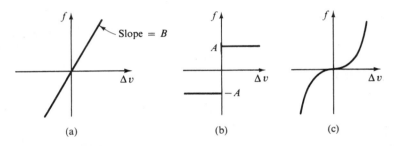

FIGURE 2.6   Friction characteristics. (a) Linear. (b) Dry. (c) Drag.

The power dissipated by friction is the product of the force exerted and the relative velocity of the two ends of the element. This power is immediately converted to heat and thus cannot be returned to the rest of the mechanical system at a later time. Accordingly, we do not usually need to know the initial velocities of the friction elements in order to solve the model of a system.

Stiffness

Any mechanical element that undergoes a change in shape when subjected to a force can be characterized by a **stiffness element**, provided only that an algebraic relationship exists between the elongation and the force. The most common stiffness element is the spring, although most mechanical elements undergo some deflection when stressed. For the spring sketched in Figure 2.7(a), we define d_0 to be the length of the spring when no force is applied and x to be the elongation caused by the force f. Then the total length at any instant is $d(t) = d_0 + x$, and the stiffness property refers to the algebraic relationship between x and f, as depicted in Figure 2.7(b). Because x has been defined as an elongation and the plot shows that f and x always have the same sign, it follows that the positive sense of f must be to the right in Figure 2.7(a); that is, f represents a tensile rather than

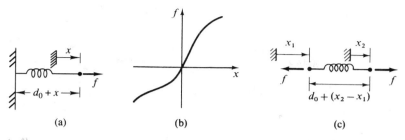

FIGURE 2.7   Characteristics of a spring.

a compressive force. For a linear spring, the curve in Figure 2.7(b) is a straight line and $f = Kx$, where K is a constant with units of newtons per meter (N/m).

Figure 2.7(c) shows a spring whose ends are displaced by the amounts x_1 and x_2 relative to their respective reference positions. If $x_1 = x_2 = 0$ corresponds to a condition when no force is applied to the spring, then the elongation at any instant is $x_2 - x_1$. For a linear spring,

$$f = K\Delta x \tag{9}$$

where $\Delta x = x_2 - x_1$. For small elongations of a structural shaft, K is proportional to the cross-sectional area and to Young's modulus and is inversely proportional to the length.

When a force f is applied to one side of a stiffness element that is assumed to have no mass, a force equal in magnitude but of opposite direction must be exerted on the other side. Thus for the system shown in Figure 2.8, the force f passes through the first spring and is exerted directly on the mass M. Of course, all physical devices have some mass, but to obtain a lumped model we assume either that it is negligible or that it is represented by a separate element.

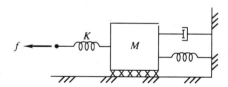

FIGURE 2.8   Force transmitted through a spring.

Potential energy is stored in a spring that has been stretched or compressed, and for a linear spring that energy is given by

$$w_p = \frac{1}{2}K(\Delta x)^2 \tag{10}$$

This energy may be returned to the rest of the mechanical system at some time in the future. Therefore, the initial elongation $\Delta x(t_0)$ is one of the initial conditions we need in order to find the complete response of a system.

■ 2.3 INTERCONNECTION LAWS

Having identified the individual elements in translational systems and having given equations describing their behavior, we next present the laws that describe the manner in which the elements are interconnected. These include D'Alembert's law, the law of reaction forces, and the law for displacement variables.

D'Alembert's Law

D'Alembert's law is just a restatement of Newton's second law governing the rate of change of momentum. For a constant mass, we can write

$$\sum_i (f_{\text{ext}})_i = M \frac{dv}{dt} \tag{11}$$

where the summation over the index i includes all the external forces $(f_{\text{ext}})_i$ acting on the body. The forces and velocity are in general vector quantities, but they can be treated as scalars provided that the motion is constrained to be in a fixed direction. Rewriting (11) as

$$\sum_i (f_{\text{ext}})_i - M \frac{dv}{dt} = 0 \tag{12}$$

suggests that the mass in question can be considered to be in equilibrium—that is, the sum of the forces is zero—provided that the term $-M dv/dt$ is thought of as an additional force. This fictitious force is called the **inertial force** or **D'Alembert force**, and including it along with the external forces allows us to write the force equation as one of equilibrium:

$$\sum_i f_i = 0 \tag{13}$$

This equation is known as **D'Alembert's law**. The minus sign associated with the inertial force in (12) indicates that when $dv/dt > 0$, the force acts in the negative direction.

In addition to applying (13) to a mass, we can apply it to any point in the system, such as the junction between components. Because a junction is considered massless, the inertial force is zero in such a case.

The Law of Reaction Forces

In order to relate the forces exerted by the elements of friction and stiffness to the forces acting on a mass or junction point, we need Newton's third law regarding reaction forces. Accompanying any force of one element on another, there is a **reaction force** on the first element of equal magnitude and opposite direction.

In Figure 2.9(a), for example, let f_k denote the force exerted by the mass on the right end of the spring, with the positive sense defined to be to the right. Newton's third law tells us that there acts on the mass a reaction force f_k of equal magnitude with its positive sense to the left, as indicated in Figure 2.9(b). Likewise, at the left end, the fixed surface exerts a force f_k on the spring with the positive sense to the left, while the spring exerts an equal and opposite force on the surface.

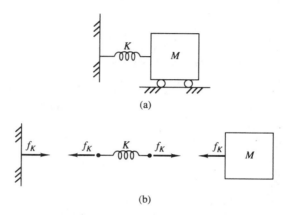

(a)

(b)

FIGURE 2.9 Example of reaction forces.

The Law for Displacements

If the ends of two elements are connected, those ends are forced to move with the same displacement and velocity. For example, because the dashpot and spring in Figure 2.10(a) are both connected between the wall and the mass, the right ends of both elements have the same displacement x and move with the same velocity v. In Figure 2.10(b), where B_2 and K are connected

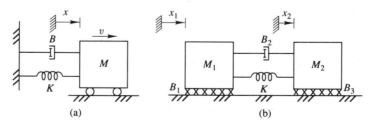

(a)   (b)

FIGURE 2.10 Two elements connected between the same endpoints.
(a) One endpoint fixed. (b) Both endpoints movable.

between two moving masses, the elongation of both elements is $x_2 - x_1$. An equivalent statement is that if we go from M_1 to M_2 and record the elongation of the dashpot B_2, and then return to M_1 and subtract the elongation of the spring K, the result is zero. In effect, we are saying that the difference between the displacements of any two points is the same regardless of which elements we are examining between those points. This statement is really a consequence of our being able to uniquely define points in space.

The discussion in the previous paragraph can be summarized by saying that at any instant the algebraic sum of the elongations around any closed path is zero; that is

$$\sum_i (\Delta x)_i = 0 \quad \text{around any closed path} \qquad (14)$$

It is understood that the left side of (14) is the algebraic sum of the elongations with signs that take into account the direction in which the path is being traversed. Furthermore, it is understood that for two elements connected between the same two points, such as B_2 and K in Figure 2.10(b), the elongations of both elements must be measured with respect to the same references. If for some reason the two elongations were measured with respect to different references, then the algebraic sum of the elongations around the closed path would be a constant but not zero.

In Figure 2.11, let x_1 and x_2 denote displacements measured with respect to reference positions that correspond to a single equilibrium condition of the system. Then the respective elongations of B_1, B_2, and K are x_1, $x_2 - x_1$, and x_2. When the elongations are summed going from the fixed surface to the mass by way of the friction elements B_1 and B_2 and going back by way of the spring K, (14) gives

$$x_1 + (x_2 - x_1) - x_2 = 0$$

This equation can be regarded as a justification for the statement that the elongation of B_2 is $x_2 - x_1$ and that an additional symbol for this elongation is not needed.

In the analysis of mechanical systems, (14) is normally used implicitly and automatically in the process of labeling the system diagram. For example, we use the same symbol for two elongations that are forced to be equal

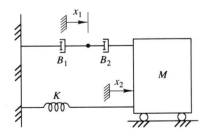

FIGURE 2.11   Illustration for the displacement law.

by the element interconnections, and we avoid using different symbols for displacements that are known to be identical.

Differentiating (14) would lead to a similar equation in terms of relative velocities. However, we shall use only a single symbol for the velocities of two points that are constrained to move together. It will therefore not be necessary to invoke (14) in a formal way.

2.4 OBTAINING THE SYSTEM MODEL

The system model must incorporate both the element laws and the interconnection laws. The element laws involve displacements, velocities, and accelerations. Because the acceleration of a point is the derivative of the velocity, which in turn is the derivative of the displacement, we could write all the element laws in terms of x and its derivatives or in terms of x, v, and dv/dt. It is important to indicate the assumed positive directions for displacements, velocities, and accelerations. We shall always choose the assumed positive directions for a, v, and x to be the same, so it will not be necessary to indicate all three positive directions on the diagram. Throughout this book, dots over the variables are used to denote derivatives with respect to time. For example, $\dot{x} = dx/dt$ and $\ddot{y} = d^2y/dt^2$.

Free-Body Diagrams

We normally need to apply D'Alembert's law, given by (13), to each mass or junction point in the system that moves with a velocity that is unknown beforehand. To do so, it is useful to draw a free-body diagram for each such mass or point, showing all external forces and the inertial force by arrows that define their positive senses. The element laws are used to express all forces except inputs in terms of displacements, velocities, and accelerations. We must be sure that the signs of these expressions are consistent with the directions of the reference arrows. After the free-body diagram is completed, we can apply (13) by summing the forces indicated on the diagram, again taking into account their assumed positive senses. Normally all forces must be added as vectors, but in our examples the forces in the free-body diagram will be collinear and can be summed by scalar equations. The following two examples illustrate the procedure in some detail. The first system contains a single mass; the second has two masses that can move with different velocities.

▶ *EXAMPLE 2.1*

Draw the free-body diagram and apply D'Alembert's law for the system shown in Figure 2.12(a). The mass is assumed to move horizontally on frictionless bearings, and the spring and dashpot are linear.

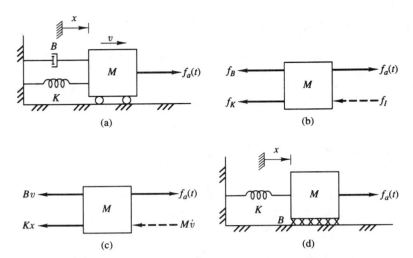

FIGURE 2.12 (a) Translational system for Example 2.1. (b) Free-body diagram. (c) Free-body diagram including element laws. (d) Additional system described by (15).

Solution

The free-body diagram for the mass is shown in Figure 2.12(b). The vertical forces on the mass (the weight Mg and the upward forces exerted by the frictionless bearings) have been omitted because these forces are perpendicular to the direction of motion. The horizontal forces, which are included in the free-body diagram, are

f_K, the force exerted by the spring

f_B, the force exerted by the dashpot

f_I, the inertial force

$f_a(t)$, the applied force

The choice of directions for the arrows representing f_K, f_B, and f_I is arbitrary and does not affect the final result. However, the expressions for these individual forces must agree with the choice of arrows. The use of a dashed arrow for the inertial force f_I emphasizes that it is not an external force like the other three.

We next use the element laws to express the forces f_K, f_B, and f_I in terms of the element values K, B, and M and the system variables x and v. In Figure 2.12(a), the positive direction of x and v is defined to be to the right, so the spring is stretched when x is positive and compressed when x is negative. If the spring undergoes an elongation x, then there must be a tensile force Kx on the right end of the spring directed to the right and a reaction force $f_K = Kx$ on the mass directed to the left. Because the arrow for f_K does point to the left in Figure 2.12(b), we may relabel this force as

Kx in Figure 2.12(c). Note that if x is negative at some instant of time, the spring will be compressed and will exert a force to the right on the mass. Under these conditions, Kx will be negative and the free-body diagram will show a negative force on the mass to the left, which is equivalent to a positive force to the right. Although the result is the same either way, it is customary to assume that all displacements are in the assumed positive directions when determining the proper expressions for the forces.

Similarly, when the right end of the dashpot moves to the right with velocity v, a force $f_B = Bv$ is exerted on the mass to the left. Finally, because of (12), the inertial force $f_I = M\dot{v}$ must have its positive direction opposite to that of dv/dt. After trying a few examples, the reader should be able to draw a free-body diagram such as the one in Figure 2.12(c) without first having to show explicitly the diagram in Figure 2.12(b).

D'Alembert's law can now be applied to the free-body diagram in Figure 2.12(c), with due regard for the assumed arrow directions. If forces acting to the right are regarded as positive, the law yields

$$f_a(t) - (M\dot{v} + Bv + Kx) = 0$$

Replacing v by $\dot{x}$ and $\dot{v}$ by $\ddot{x}$, and rearranging the terms, we can rewrite this equation as

$$M\ddot{x} + B\dot{x} + Kx = f_a(t) \tag{15}$$

In place of the dashpot between the mass and the wall in part (a) of Figure 2.12, part (d) shows viscous friction between the mass and the horizontal support. The free-body diagram for this system would remain the same as in Figure 2.12(c), and D'Alembert's law would again yield (15).

▶ *EXAMPLE 2.2*

Draw the free-body diagrams and write D'Alembert's law for the two-mass system shown in Figure 2.13(a).

Solution

Because there are two masses that can move with different unknown velocities, a separate free-body diagram should be drawn for each one. This is done in Figure 2.13(b) and Figure 2.13(c). In Figure 2.13(b), the forces K_1x_1 and $M_1\ddot{x}_1$ are similar to those in Example 2.1. As indicated in our earlier discussion of displacements, the net elongation of the spring and dashpot connecting the two masses is $x_2 - x_1$. Hence a positive value of $x_2 - x_1$ results in a reaction force by the spring to the right on M_1 and to the left on M_2, as indicated in the figure. Of course, the force on either free-body diagram could be labeled $K_2(x_1 - x_2)$, provided that the corresponding reference arrow was reversed. For a positive value of $\dot{x}_2 - \dot{x}_1$, the reaction force of the middle dashpot is to the right on M_1 and to the left on M_2.

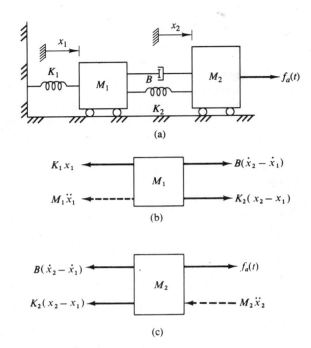

FIGURE 2.13 (a) Translational system for Example 2.2. (b), (c) Free-body diagrams.

As always, the inertial forces $M_1\ddot{x}_1$ and $M_2\ddot{x}_2$ are opposite to the positive directions of the accelerations.

Summing the forces on each free-body diagram separately and taking into account the directions of the reference arrows give the following pair of differential equations:

$$B(\dot{x}_2 - \dot{x}_1) + K_2(x_2 - x_1) - M_1\ddot{x}_1 - K_1 x_1 = 0$$
$$f_a(t) - M_2\ddot{x}_2 - B(\dot{x}_2 - \dot{x}_1) - K_2(x_2 - x_1) = 0$$

Rearranging, we have

$$M_1\ddot{x}_1 + B\dot{x}_1 + (K_1 + K_2)x_1 - B\dot{x}_2 - K_2 x_2 = 0 \tag{16a}$$
$$-B\dot{x}_1 - K_2 x_1 + M_2\ddot{x}_2 + B\dot{x}_2 + K_2 x_2 = f_a(t) \tag{16b}$$

Equations (16a) and (16b) constitute a pair of coupled second-order differential equations. In the next chapter, we shall discuss two alternative methods of presenting the information contained in such a set of equations.

In the force equation (16a) for the mass M_1 in the last example, note that all the terms involving the displacement x_1 and its derivatives have the

same sign. Similarly in (16b) for the mass M_2, all the terms with x_2 and
its derivatives have the same sign. This is generally true for systems where
the only permanent energy sources are associated with the external inputs.
The reason for this will become apparent from the discussion of stability in
Chapter 6, but the reader may wish to use this fact now as a check on the
work.

Suppose that D'Alembert's law is applied to any mass M_i and that terms
involving corresponding variables are collected together. Then all the terms
involving the displacement x_i of the mass M_i should be expected to have
the same sign. If they do not, the engineer should suspect that an error
has been made and should check the steps leading to that equation. In the
simplified equation for M_i no general statement can be made about the signs
of terms involving displacements other than x_i and its derivatives, because
the other signs depend on the reference directions used for the definition of
the variables.

Inputs are variables that are specified functions of time, which are completely known at the beginning of a problem rather than depending on the
values of the system's components. Inputs for translational mechanical systems may be either forces or displacements. A displacement input exists
when one part of a system is moved in a predetermined way. We assume
that the mechanism that provides the specified displacement has a sufficient
source of energy to carry out the motion regardless of any retarding forces
that might come from the system components.

▶ *EXAMPLE 2.3*

The system shown in Figure 2.14 is the same as that in Figure 2.13(a), except
that the excitation is the displacement input $x_2(t)$ instead of an applied force.
Write the equation governing the motion.

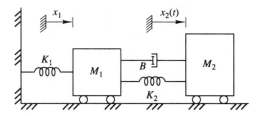

FIGURE 2.14 Translational system with displacement input for
Example 2.3.

Solution

We know the motion of mass M_2 in advance, so there is no need to draw
a free-body diagram for it. The free-body diagram for M_1 is still the one

shown in Figure 2.13(b), and D'Alembert's law again gives

$$M_1\ddot{x}_1 + B\dot{x}_1 + (K_1 + K_2)x_1 - B\dot{x}_2 - K_2x_2(t) = 0 \qquad (17)$$

Because $x_2(t)$ and $\dot{x}_2$ are known functions of time, x_1 is the only unknown variable in (17) and a second equation is not needed.

If we wished to determine the force f_2 that needs to be applied in order to move M_2 with the prescribed displacement, we could also draw a free-body diagram for M_2. This would be the same as the one in Figure 2.13(c), except that $f_a(t)$ would be replaced by the unknown force f_2, with its positive sense to the right. The corresponding equation is

$$f_2 = -B\dot{x}_1 - K_2x_1 + M_2\ddot{x}_2 + B\dot{x}_2 + K_2x_2(t) \qquad (18)$$

The quantities $x_2(t)$, $\dot{x}_2$, and $\ddot{x}_2$ are known. Once we have solved (17) for the unknown displacement $x_1(t)$ as a function of time, we can insert that result into (18) in order to calculate f_2.

A D'Alembert equation is not usually written for a body whose motion is known in advance. If, however, a free-body diagram is drawn for such a body, it is important to show the force associated with the displacement input. The quantity f_2 in (18) would then be regarded as one of the outputs in the system model.

Relative Displacements

In the previous examples, the displacement variable associated with each mass was expressed with respect to its own fixed reference position. However, the position of a mass is sometimes measured with respect to some other moving body, rather than from a fixed reference. Such a **relative displacement** is used as one of the variables in the following example.

▶ **EXAMPLE 2.4**

For the two-mass system shown in Figure 2.15(a), x denotes the position of mass M_1 with respect to a fixed reference, and z denotes the relative displacement of mass M_2 with respect to M_1. The positive direction for both displacements is to the right. Assume that the two springs are neither stretched nor compressed when $x = z = 0$. Find the equations describing the system.

Solution

The free-body diagrams for the two masses are shown in parts (b) and (c) of the figure. The force on mass M_1 through the viscous friction element B_2 is proportional to the relative velocity $\dot{z}$ of the two masses. If M_2 is moving to the right faster than M_1, so that $\dot{z}$ is positive, then the force on M_1 through B_2 tends to pull the mass to the right, as indicated in Figure 2.15(b).

2 negle of Frand
2 equation

$Z = pos$ of m_2 relative to m

$X = abs.$ pos of m

$X_2 = X + Z$

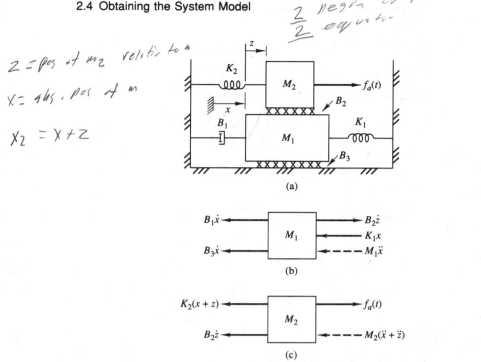

(a)

(b)

(c)

FIGURE 2.15 (a) Translational system for Example 2.4. (b), (c) Free-body diagrams.

To draw the free-body diagram for M_2, we note that the elongation of the spring K_2 is $x + z$. Furthermore, the inertial force is always proportional to the *absolute* acceleration $\ddot{x} + \ddot{z}$, not to the *relative* acceleration with respect to some other moving body. Thus only the force exerted through the friction element B_2 is expressed in terms of the *relative* motion of the two masses. Summing the forces on each of the free-body diagrams gives

$$B_2\dot{z} - K_1 x - M_1\ddot{x} - B_1\dot{x} - B_3\dot{x} = 0$$

$$f_a(t) - M_2(\ddot{x} + \ddot{z}) - K_2(x + z) - B_2\dot{z} = 0$$

or, after we rearrange the terms,

$$M_1\ddot{x} + (B_1 + B_3)\dot{x} + K_1 x - B_2\dot{z} = 0 \tag{19a}$$

$$M_2\ddot{x} + K_2 x + M_2\ddot{z} + B_2\dot{z} + K_2 z = f_a(t) \tag{19b}$$

The comments made after Example 2.2 about the signs in the force equations for M_1 and M_2 still apply when a relative displacement variable is used. In the force equation (19a) for M_1, all the terms with the displacement x of the mass M_1 and its derivatives have the same sign. Similarly in (19b), all the terms involving the relative displacement z of M_2 with respect to M_1 have the same sign.

The reader is encouraged to repeat this example when the displacement of each mass is expressed with respect to its own fixed reference position. If x_1 and x_2 denote the displacements of M_1 and M_2, respectively, with the positive senses to the right, we find that

$$M_1 \ddot{x}_1 + (B_1 + B_2 + B_3)\dot{x}_1 + K_1 x_1 - B_2 \dot{x}_2 = 0$$
$$-B_2 \dot{x}_1 + M_2 \ddot{x}_2 + B_2 \dot{x}_2 + K_2 x_2 = f_a(t)$$

(20)

When x_1 is replaced by x, and x_2 is replaced by $x + z$, this pair of equations reduces to those in (19). However, it is useful to be able to obtain (19) directly from the free-body diagrams in Figure 2.15.

Displacement variables must be expressed with respect to some reference position. These references are commonly chosen such that any springs are neither stretched nor compressed when the values of the displacement variables are zero. The following two examples show why this may not necessarily be the case for systems with vertical motion.

▶ **EXAMPLE 2.5**

Draw the free-body diagram, including the effect of gravity, and find the differential equation describing the motion of the mass shown in Figure 2.16(a).

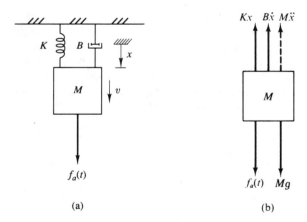

(a)   (b)

FIGURE 2.16 (a) Translational system with vertical motion. (b) Free-body diagram.

Solution

Assume that x is the displacement from the position corresponding to a spring that is neither stretched nor compressed. The gravitational force on the mass is Mg, and we include it in the free-body diagram shown in

Figure 2.16(b) because the mass moves vertically. By summing the forces on the free-body diagram, we obtain

$$M\ddot{x} + B\dot{x} + Kx = f_a(t) + Mg \tag{21}$$

Suppose that the applied force $f_a(t)$ is zero and that the mass is not moving. Then $x = x_0$, where x_0 is the constant displacement caused by the gravitational force. Because $\dot{x}_0 = \ddot{x}_0 = 0$, the foregoing differential equation reduces to the algebraic equation

$$Kx_0 = Mg \tag{22}$$

We can also see this directly from the free-body diagram by noting that all but two of the five forces vanish under these conditions.

We now reconsider the case where $f_a(t)$ is nonzero and where the mass is moving. Let

$$x = x_0 + z \tag{23}$$

This equation defines z as the displacement caused by the input $f_a(t)$, namely the additional displacement beyond that resulting from the constant weight Mg. Substituting (23) into (21) and again noting that $\dot{x}_0 = \ddot{x}_0 = 0$, we have

$$M\ddot{z} + B\dot{z} + K(x_0 + z) = f_a(t) + Mg$$

or, by using (22),

$$M\ddot{z} + B\dot{z} + Kz = f_a(t) \tag{24}$$

Comparison of (21) and (24) indicates that we can ignore the gravitational force Mg when drawing the free-body diagram and when writing the system equation, provided that the displacement is defined to be the displacement from the static position corresponding to no inputs except gravity.

This conclusion is valid for all cases where masses are suspended vertically by one or more linear springs. Under static-equilibrium conditions, there are no inertial or friction forces, and the force exerted by the spring has the form

$$f_K(t) = K(x_0 + z)$$
$$= Kx_0 + Kz$$

which is just the superposition of the static force caused by gravity and the force caused by additional inputs. For nonlinear springs, however, this conclusion is not valid because superposition does not hold.

Normally, a new symbol such as z is not introduced in problems involving gravitational forces. Instead, the symbol x can be redefined to be the additional displacement from the static position.

▶ *EXAMPLE 2.6*

For the system shown in Figure 2.17(a), x_1 and x_2 denote the elongations of K_1 and K_2, respectively. Note that x_1 is the displacement of mass M_1 with respect to a fixed reference but that x_2 is the relative displacement of M_2 with respect to M_1. When $x_1 = x_2 = 0$, all three springs shown in the figure are neither stretched nor compressed. Draw the free-body diagram for each mass, including the effect of gravity, and find the differential equations describing the system's behavior. Determine the values of x_1 and x_2 that correspond to the static-equilibrium position, when $f_a(t) = 0$ and when the masses are motionless.

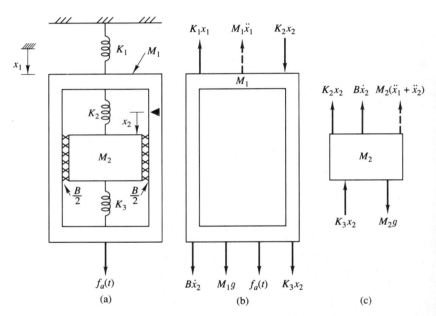

FIGURE 2.17   (a) Translational system for Example 2.6. (b), (c) Free-body diagrams.

Solution

The free-body diagrams are shown in parts (b) and (c) of the figure. Many of the comments made in Example 2.4 also apply to this problem. If x_1 and x_2 are positive, then K_1 and K_2 are stretched and K_3 is compressed. Under these circumstances, K_1 exerts an upward force on M_1, and K_2 and K_3 exert downward forces on M_1. The relative velocity of M_2 with respect to M_1 is $\dot{x}_2$, so frictional forces of $B\dot{x}_2$ are exerted downward on M_1 and upward on M_2. The inertial force on M_2 is proportional to its absolute acceleration, which is $\ddot{x}_1 + \ddot{x}_2$. Summing the forces on each of the free-body diagrams gives

$$M_1\ddot{x}_1 + K_1 x_1 - B\dot{x}_2 - (K_2 + K_3)x_2 = M_1 g + f_a(t)$$
$$M_2\ddot{x}_1 + M_2\ddot{x}_2 + B\dot{x}_2 + (K_2 + K_3)x_2 = M_2 g \tag{25}$$

This pair of coupled equations has two unknown variables. If the element values and $f_a(t)$ are known, and if the necessary initial conditions are given, then (25) can be solved for x_1 and x_2 as functions of time by the methods discussed in later chapters. Because x_2 is a relative displacement, the total displacement of M_2 is $x_1 + x_2$.

To find the displacements x_{1_0} and x_{2_0} that correspond to the static-equilibrium position, we replace $f_a(t)$ and all the displacement derivatives by zero. Then (25) reduces to

$$K_1 x_{1_0} - (K_2 + K_3)x_{2_0} = M_1 g$$
$$(K_2 + K_3)x_{2_0} = M_2 g \tag{26}$$

from which

$$x_{1_0} = \frac{(M_1 + M_2)g}{K_1}$$
$$x_{2_0} = \frac{M_2 g}{K_2 + K_3} \tag{27}$$

If we want the differential equations in terms of displacements z_1 and z_2 measured with respect to the equilibrium conditions given by (27), then we can write $x_1 = x_{1_0} + z_1$ and $x_2 = x_{2_0} + z_2$. Substituting these expressions into (25) and using (26), we find that

$$M_1\ddot{z}_1 + K_1 z_1 - B\dot{z}_2 - (K_2 + K_3)z_2 = f_a(t)$$
$$M_2\ddot{z}_1 + M_2\ddot{z}_2 + B\dot{z}_2 + (K_2 + K_3)z_2 = 0$$

As expected, these equations are similar to (25) except for the absence of the gravitational forces.

The Ideal Pulley

A pulley can be used to change the direction of motion in a translational mechanical system. Frequently, part of the system then moves horizontally and the rest vertically. The basic pulley consists of a cylinder that can rotate about its center and that has a cable resting on its surface. An ideal pulley has no mass and no friction associated with it. We assume that there is no slippage between the cable and the surface of the cylinder—that is, that they both move with the same velocity. We also assume that the cable is always in tension but that it cannot stretch. If we need to consider a cable that can stretch, we can approximate that effect by showing a separate spring leading to an ideal cable. If the pulley is not ideal, then its mass and any frictional effects must be considered, as will be discussed in Chapter 4. The action of an ideal pulley is illustrated in the following example.

▶ **EXAMPLE 2.7**

Find and compare the equations describing the systems shown in Figure 2.18(a) and Figure 2.19(a). Let $x_1 = x_2 = 0$ correspond to the condition when the springs are neither stretched nor compressed.

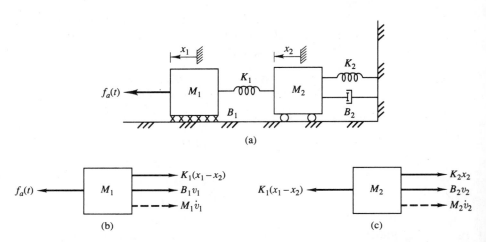

FIGURE 2.18 (a) Translational system for Example 2.7. (b), (c) Free-body diagrams.

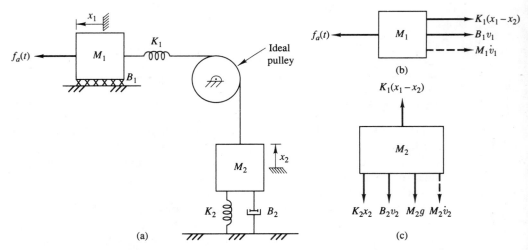

FIGURE 2.19 (a) Translational system with an ideal pulley added. (b), (c) Free-body diagrams.

Solution

Free-body diagrams for the system in part (a) of Figure 2.18 are shown in parts (b) and (c). Note that the spring K_1 exerts equal but opposite forces on M_1 and M_2. Summing the forces shown in the diagrams gives

$$M_1\dot{v}_1 + B_1v_1 + K_1(x_1 - x_2) = f_a(t)$$
$$M_2\dot{v}_2 + B_2v_2 + K_2x_2 = K_1(x_1 - x_2) \tag{28}$$

When an ideal pulley is added to give the system in Figure 2.19(a), the free-body diagram for M_1, which is repeated in part (b) of the figure, remains unchanged. To draw the diagram for M_2, we note that both ends of the cable move with the same motion because it cannot stretch. The force exerted by K_1 passes through the cable and is exerted directly on M_2. Hence the cable does not affect the magnitude of the forces exerted by K_1 but merely changes the direction of the force on M_2 to be upward. Because M_2 moves vertically, we also include the gravitational force in its free-body diagram, which is shown in Figure 2.19(c). Summing the forces shown in parts (b) and (c) of the figure gives

$$M_1\dot{v}_1 + B_1v_1 + K_1(x_1 - x_2) = f_a(t)$$
$$M_2\dot{v}_2 + B_2v_2 + K_2x_2 + M_2g = K_1(x_1 - x_2) \tag{29}$$

As expected, (28) and (29) are identical except for the presence of the gravitational force M_2g.

It is important to be aware of a significant difference between the models given by (28) and (29) for the last example. The difference involves their validity. Positive or negative values of the quantity $x_1 - x_2$ correspond to the elongation or compression, respectively, of the spring K_1. Equations (28) are valid for Figure 2.18(a) for all values of x_1 and x_2. For the system with the pulley, however, the free-body diagram in Figure 2.19(c) indicates that the cable would exert a downward force on M_2 for a negative value of $x_1 - x_2$. This implies that the cable would tend to push apart the bodies attached to its ends, which is not physically possible. In such a case the cable would buckle, become detached from the pulley, and exert no force at all on M_2. Thus (29) can be used only when $x_1 - x_2 \geq 0$. Although this condition is not normally written next to the corresponding equations, the engineer should always examine the analytical or computer solution to be sure that the results correspond to conditions for which the modeling equations are valid.

Parallel Combinations

In some cases, two or more springs or dashpots can be replaced by a single equivalent element. Two springs or dashpots are said to be in **parallel** if the first end of each is attached to the same body and if the remaining ends are also attached to a common body. We shall consider a specific example before formulating a general rule.

▶ **EXAMPLE 2.8**

The system shown in Figure 2.20(a) includes two linear springs between the wall and the mass M. Write the differential equation describing the motion of the mass. Find the spring constant K_{eq} for a single spring that could replace K_1 and K_2. Assume first that the springs have the same unstretched length. Then repeat the problem when the unstretched lengths of K_1 and K_2 are d_1 and d_2, respectively.

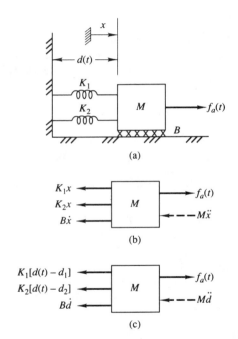

FIGURE 2.20 (a) Translational system for Example 2.8. (b) Free-body diagram when the springs have the same unstretched lengths. (c) Free-body diagram when the springs have different unstretched lengths.

Solution

If the unstretched lengths of the two springs are identical, then they will have the same elongation, denoted by x, when the mass is in motion. The free-body diagram is shown in Figure 2.20(b). Summing the forces gives

$$M\ddot{x} + B\dot{x} + (K_1 + K_2)x = f_a(t) \tag{30}$$

If the combination of K_1 and K_2 is replaced by a single equivalent spring, then the system reduces to that shown in Figure 2.12(d), which is described by (15). Comparing (30) and (15) reveals that

$$K_{eq} = K_1 + K_2 \tag{31}$$

Next suppose that the springs have different unstretched lengths, and let $d(t)$ denote the distance from the wall to the left side of the mass. The elongations of K_1 and K_2, which are no longer the same, are $d(t) - d_1$ and $d(t) - d_2$, respectively. The mass has velocity $\dot{d}$ and acceleration $\ddot{d}$. The new free-body diagram, with all the retarding forces expressed in terms of $d(t)$, is shown in Figure 2.20(c). By D'Alembert's law,

$$M\ddot{d} + B\dot{d} + K_1[d(t) - d_1] + K_2[d(t) - d_2] = f_a(t) \tag{32}$$

Let d_0 be the distance from the wall to the mass when $f_a(t) = 0$ and when the mass is motionless in a position of static equilibrium. The only forces on the mass will be those exerted by the two springs, which will be equal and opposite. From (32), or directly from Figure 2.20(c),

$$K_1(d_0 - d_1) + K_2(d_0 - d_2) = 0 \tag{33}$$

from which

$$d_0 = \frac{K_1 d_1 + K_2 d_2}{K_1 + K_2} \tag{34}$$

The respective static elongations of K_1 and K_2 are

$$d_0 - d_1 = \frac{K_2(d_2 - d_1)}{K_1 + K_2}$$

$$d_0 - d_2 = \frac{K_1(d_1 - d_2)}{K_1 + K_2}$$

If $d_1 \neq d_2$, one of these elongations will be negative. This means that one spring will be stretched and the other compressed, so that the net static force exerted by the two springs on the mass can be zero.

It is now reasonable to define the variable z as the distance of the mass beyond d_0 when a force input is applied—that is, as the displacement with respect to the reference position given by (34). Then

$$d(t) = d_0 + z$$

Substituting this expression into (32) and noting that $\dot{d} = \dot{z}$ and $\ddot{d} = \ddot{z}$, we have

$$M\ddot{z} + B\dot{z} + K_1(d_0 + z - d_1) + K_2(d_0 + z - d_2) = f_a(t)$$

Using (33) to cancel some of the terms in this equation, we obtain

$$M\ddot{z} + B\dot{z} + (K_1 + K_2)z = f_a(t)$$

which is identical to (30) except for the use of z in place of x. Thus (31) is valid for the equivalent spring constant even if the unstretched lengths of the springs are different, provided that x is interpreted as the displacement beyond the static-equilibrium position given by (34).

Two parallel springs or dashpots have their respective ends joined, as shown in Figure 2.21. From the last example, we see that for the parallel combination of two springs,

$$K_{eq} = K_1 + K_2 \qquad (35)$$

Similarly, it can be shown that for two dashpots in parallel, as in part (b) of the figure,

$$B_{eq} = B_1 + B_2 \qquad (36)$$

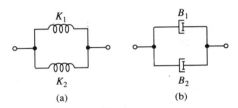

FIGURE 2.21   Parallel combinations. (a) $K_{eq} = K_1 + K_2$. (b) $B_{eq} = B_1 + B_2$.

The formulas for parallel stiffness or friction elements can be extended to situations that may seem somewhat different than those in Figure 2.21. The key requirement for parallel elements is that respective ends move with the same displacement. The individual ends need not be tied directly together in the figure depicting the system. Although one pair of ends may sometimes be connected to a fixed surface, in other cases both pairs of ends may be free to move.

▶ **EXAMPLE 2.9**

Find the equation describing the motion of the mass in the translational system shown in Figure 2.22(a). Show that the two springs can be replaced by a single equivalent spring, and the three friction elements by an equivalent element.

Solution

Note that each of the springs has one side attached to the mass and the other attached to the fixed surface on the perimeter of the diagram. When x is positive, K_1 is stretched and K_2 compressed. Thus the springs will exert forces of K_1x and K_2x on the mass to the left, as shown on the free-body diagram in Figure 2.22(b).

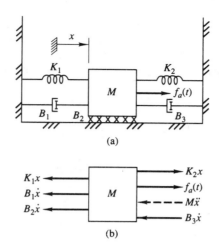

FIGURE 2.22 (a) Translational system with parallel stiffness and friction elements. (b) Free-body diagram.

For each of the three friction elements, one side moves with the velocity of the mass and the other side is stationary. When $\dot{x}$ is positive, each of these elements exerts a retarding force on the mass to the left. Summing the forces shown on the free-body diagram, we have

$$M\ddot{x} + (B_1 + B_2 + B_3)\dot{x} + (K_1 + K_2)x = f_a(t)$$

With $K_{eq} = K_1 + K_2$ and $B_{eq} = B_1 + B_2 + B_3$, this equation becomes

$$M\ddot{x} + B_{eq}\dot{x} + K_{eq}x = f_a(t)$$

When the parallel combinations of stiffness and friction elements in Figure 2.22(a) are replaced by equivalent elements, the system reduces to that shown in Figure 2.12(d), which is described by (15).

Series Combinations

Two springs or dashpots are said to be in **series** if they are joined at only one end of each element and if there is no other element connected to their common junction. The following example has a series combination of two springs and also illustrates the application of D'Alembert's law to a massless junction.

▶ *EXAMPLE 2.10*

When $x_1 = x_2 = 0$, the two springs shown in Figure 2.23(a) are neither stretched nor compressed. Draw free-body diagrams for the mass M and for the massless junction A, and then write the equations describing the system. Show that the motion of point A is not independent of that of the

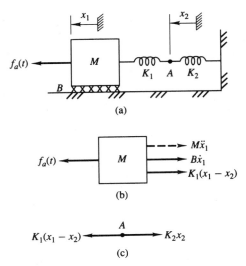

FIGURE 2.23   (a) Translational system with a massless junction. (b), (c) Free-body diagrams.

mass M and that x_1 and x_2 are directly proportional to one another. Finally, find K_{eq} for a single spring that could replace the combination of K_1 and K_2.

Solution

The free-body diagrams are shown in parts (b) and (c) of the figure. Because there is no mass at point A, there is no inertial force in its free-body diagram. Summing the forces for each diagram gives

$$M\ddot{x}_1 + B\dot{x}_1 + K_1(x_1 - x_2) = f_a(t)$$

$$K_2 x_2 = K_1(x_1 - x_2)$$

Solving the second equation for x_2 in terms of x_1 gives

$$x_2 = \left(\frac{K_1}{K_1 + K_2}\right) x_1$$

which shows that the two displacements are proportional to one another. Substituting this expression back into the first equation, we have

$$M\ddot{x}_1 + B\dot{x}_1 + K_1\left[1 - \frac{K_1}{K_1 + K_2}\right] x_1 = f_a(t)$$

from which

$$M\ddot{x}_1 + B\dot{x}_1 + \frac{K_1 K_2}{K_1 + K_2} x_1 = f_a(t)$$

This equation describes the system formed when the two springs in Figure 2.23(a) are replaced by a single spring for which $K_{eq} = K_1 K_2 / (K_1 + K_2)$.

Series combinations of stiffness and friction elements are shown in Figure 2.24. It is assumed that no other element is connected to the common junctions. For the two springs in part (a) of the figure, as in the last example,

$$K_{eq} = \frac{K_1 K_2}{K_1 + K_2} \tag{37}$$

For two dashpots in series, as in part (b) of the figure, it can be shown that

$$B_{eq} = \frac{B_1 B_2}{B_1 + B_2} \tag{38}$$

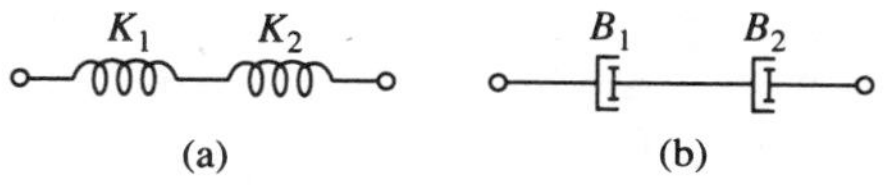

FIGURE 2.24   Series combinations. (a) $K_{eq} = K_1 K_2 / (K_1 + K_2)$. (b) $B_{eq} = B_1 B_2 / (B_1 + B_2)$.

In order to reduce certain combinations of springs or dashpots to a single equivalent element, we may have to use the rules for both parallel and series combinations. The following example illustrates the procedure for two different combinations of dashpots.

▶ *EXAMPLE 2.11*

Find B_{eq} for the single friction element that can replace the three dashpots in each part of Figure 2.25.

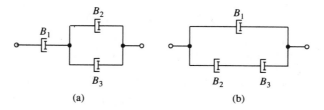

FIGURE 2.25   Parallel-series combinations.

Solution

In part (a) of the figure, the parallel combination of B_2 and B_3 can be replaced by a single element whose viscous friction coefficient is $B_2 + B_3$.

This is then in series with B_1, so that for the overall combination,

$$B_{eq} = \frac{B_1(B_2 + B_3)}{B_1 + B_2 + B_3}$$

In Figure 2.25(b), the series combination of B_2 and B_3 is in parallel with B_1. Thus

$$B_{eq} = B_1 + \frac{B_2 B_3}{B_2 + B_3}$$

SUMMARY

In this chapter we have introduced the variables, element laws, and interconnection laws for linear, lumped-element translational mechanical systems. Either force or displacement inputs can be applied to any part of the system. An applied force is a known function of time, but the motion of the body to which it is applied is not known at the outset of a problem. Conversely, a displacement input moves some part of the system with a specified motion, but the force exerted by the external mechanism moving that part is normally not known.

Displacements may be measured with respect to fixed reference positions or with respect to some other moving body. When relative displacements are used, it is important to keep in mind that the inertial force of a mass is always proportional to its absolute acceleration, not to its relative acceleration.

To model a system, we draw a free-body diagram and sum the forces for every mass or other junction point whose motion is unknown. The free-body diagram for a massless junction is drawn in the usual way, except that there is no inertial force. The modeling process can sometimes be simplified by replacing a series-parallel combination of stiffness or friction elements by a single equivalent element.

Special attention was given to linear systems that involve vertical motion. If displacements are measured from positions where the springs are neither stretched nor compressed, the gravitational forces must be included in the free-body diagrams for any masses that can move vertically. If, however, the displacements are measured with respect to the static-equilibrium positions when the system is motionless and when no other external inputs are applied, then the gravitational forces do not appear in the final equations of motion. Systems containing pulleys can have some parts of the system moving horizontally and other parts moving vertically.

Our basic task in this chapter was to draw free-body diagrams and to write the corresponding equations describing the system. In the next chapter we shall discuss how to present the information contained in these equations in ways that will facilitate the development of both computer and analytical solutions.

PROBLEMS

Throughout this book, answers to problems marked with an asterisk are given in Appendix E.

* **2.1** For the system shown in Figure P2.1, the springs are undeflected when $x_1 = x_2 = 0$. The input is $f_a(t)$. Draw free-body diagrams and write the modeling equations.

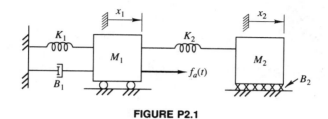

FIGURE P2.1

2.2 Repeat Problem 2.1 for the system shown in Figure P2.2.

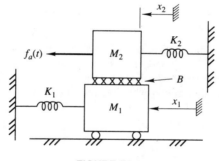

FIGURE P2.2

2.3 Repeat Problem 2.1 for the system shown in Figure P2.3.

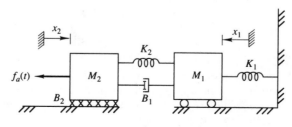

FIGURE P2.3

* 2.4 For the system shown in Figure P2.4, draw the free-body diagram for each mass and write the differential equations describing the system.

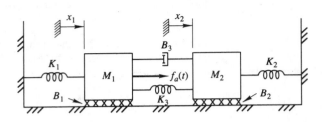

FIGURE P2.4

2.5 Repeat Problem 2.4 for the system shown in Figure P2.5.

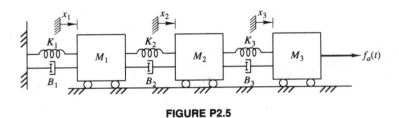

FIGURE P2.5

2.6 In the mechanical system shown in Figure P2.6, the spring forces are zero when $x_1 = x_2 = x_3 = 0$. Let the base be stationary so that $x_3(t) = 0$ for all values of t. Draw free-body diagrams and write a pair of coupled differential equations that govern the motion when the only input is $f_a(t)$.

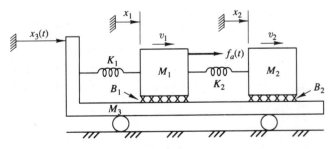

FIGURE P2.6

* 2.7 For the system shown in Figure P2.7, the springs are undeflected when $x_1 = x_2 = 0$. The input is $x_2(t)$, the displacement of the left edge of M_2.
   a) Write the equation governing the motion of M_1.
   b) Write an expression for the force f_2, positive sense to the right, that must be applied to M_2 in order to achieve the displacement $x_2(t)$.

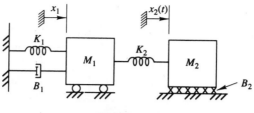

FIGURE P2.7

2.8 Repeat Problem 2.7 for the system shown in Figure P2.8.

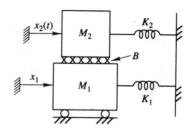

FIGURE P2.8

2.9 a) Repeat Problem 2.6 when the displacement $x_3(t)$ is the input and the applied force $f_a(t)$ is zero for all time.

b) Write an expression for the force f_3, positive sense to the right, that must be applied to M_3 in order to move M_3 with the specified displacement $x_3(t)$.

* 2.10 For the system shown in Figure P2.10, the distance between masses M_1 and M_2 is $A + x_2$, where A is a constant. The springs are undeflected when $x_1 = x_2 = 0$. Draw free-body diagrams and write the differential equations for the system.

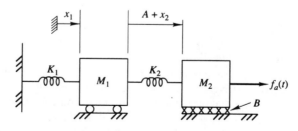

FIGURE P2.10

2.11 For the system shown in Figure P2.11, the input is the displacement $x_1(t)$. The springs are undeflected when $x_1 = x_2 = x_3 = 0$. The variable x_2 represents the displacement of M_2 with respect to M_1. Write the mathematical model to describe the

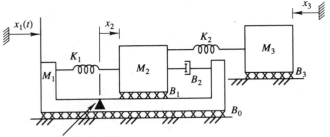

FIGURE P2.11

motion of the masses as a set of coupled differential equations. Include appropriate free-body diagrams.

* **2.12** The input to the translational mechanical system shown in Figure P2.12 is the displacement $x_3(t)$ of the right end of the spring K_1. The displacement of M_2 relative to M_1 is x_2. The forces exerted by the springs are zero when $x_1 = x_2 = x_3 = 0$. Draw the free-body diagrams and write the modeling equations.

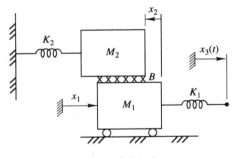

FIGURE P2.12

2.13 For the system shown in Figure P2.13, the displacement of M_1 relative to M_2 is x_1. The spring force is zero when $x_1 = x_2 = 0$. Draw free-body diagrams and write the modeling equations.

2.14 For the system shown in Figure P2.14, the displacements x_1 and x_2 are measured relative to M_3. Both springs are undeflected when $x_1 = x_2 = 0$. Draw free-body diagrams and write the modeling equations.

* **2.15** The mechanical system shown in Figure P2.15 is driven by the applied force $f_a(t)$. When $x_1 = x_2 = 0$, the springs are neither stretched nor compressed.

    a) Draw the free-body diagrams and write the differential equations of motion for the two masses in terms of x_1 and x_2.

    b) Find x_{1_0} and x_{2_0}, the constant displacements of the masses caused by the gravitational forces when $f_a(t) = 0$ and when the system is in static equilibrium.

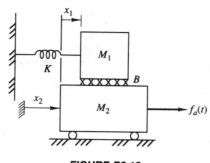

FIGURE P2.13

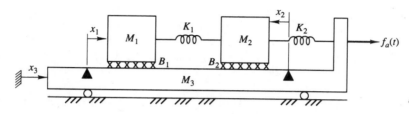

FIGURE P2.14

$$z_1 = x_1 - x_{01}$$

$$\dot{x}_1 = \dot{z}_1$$

$$\ddot{x}_1 = \ddot{z}_1$$

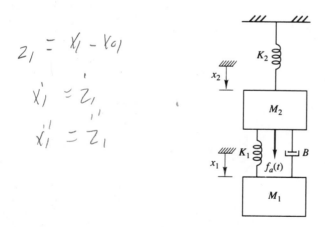

FIGURE P2.15

c) Rewrite the system equations in terms of z_1 and z_2, the relative displacements of the masses with respect to the static-equilibrium positions found in part (b).

2.16 Repeat all three parts of Problem 2.15 for the system shown in Figure P2.16. Each of the three springs has the same spring constant K.

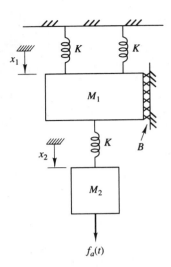

FIGURE P2.16

2.17 All the springs in Figure P2.17 are identical, each with spring constant K. The spring forces are zero when $x_1 = x_2 = x_3 = 0$.

    a) Draw the free body diagrams, including the gravitational forces, and write the differential equations describing the system.

    b) Determine the constant elongation of each spring caused by the gravitational forces when the masses are stationary in a position of static equilibrium and when $f_a(t) = 0$.

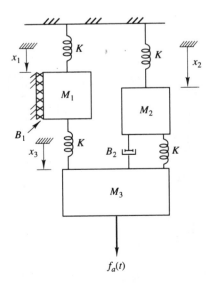

FIGURE P2.17

* 2.18 Repeat Problem 2.17 for the system shown in Figure P2.18.

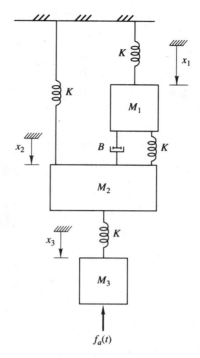

FIGURE P2.18

2.19 The system shown in Figure P2.19 has a nonlinear spring that obeys the expression $f_K = x^3$.

 a) Write the differential equation describing the system in terms of the displacement x.

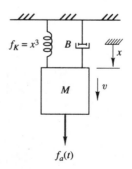

FIGURE P2.19

b) Let $x = x_0 + z$, where x_0 is the constant displacement caused by the gravitational force when the system is in static equilibrium. Rewrite the differential equation in terms of the variable z, canceling the gravitational term.

c) Comparison of (21) and (24) in Example 2.5 for a linear spring showed that the differential equation in z was the same as the one in x except for the deletion of the Mg term. Compare the results of parts (a) and (b) to show that such is not the case in this problem.

2.20 For the system shown in Figure P2.20, x_1 and x_2 are displacements relative to the undeflected spring lengths. The inputs are $f_a(t)$, $f_b(t)$, and gravity. Draw free-body diagrams and write the modeling equations.

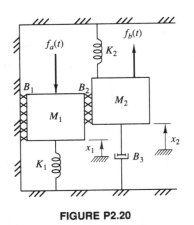

FIGURE P2.20

2.21 Repeat Problem 2.20 for the system shown in Figure P2.21.

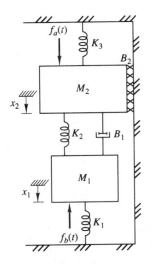

FIGURE P2.21

* **2.22** The pulley shown in Figure P2.22 is ideal. Draw free-body diagrams and write the modeling equations.

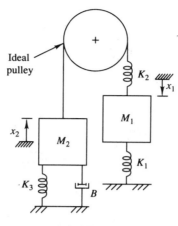

FIGURE P2.22

2.23 Repeat Problem 2.22 for the system shown in Figure P2.23.

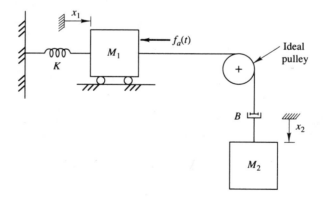

FIGURE P2.23

2.24 Repeat Problem 2.22 for the system shown in Figure P2.24.

* **2.25** For the system shown in Figure 2.11, draw the free-body diagrams for M and the junction of the dashpots. Apply D'Alembert's law and show that $\dot{x}_1$ is proportional to $\dot{x}_2$. Determine an equivalent coefficient B_{eq} for the combination of B_1 and B_2.

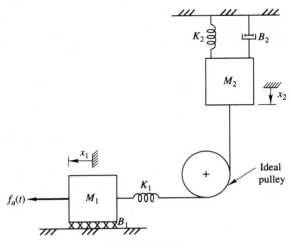

FIGURE P2.24

2.26 For the system shown in Figure P2.26, draw the free-body diagram and write a single differential equation. Determine an equivalent coefficient B_{eq} for the combination of B_1 and B_3.

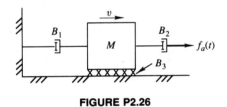

FIGURE P2.26

* **2.27** The input for the system shown in Figure P2.27 is the displacement $x_3(t)$. Draw the free-body diagrams for the mass M and for the massless point A. Write the differential equations describing the system.

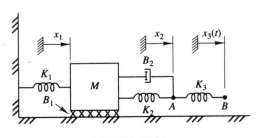

FIGURE P2.27

2.28 Repeat Problem 2.27 when the input is the force $f_a(t)$ applied to point B, with its positive sense to the right.

2.29 For the system shown in Figure P2.29, $x_1 = 0$ when the spring is undeflected. Draw free-body diagrams and write the modeling equations.

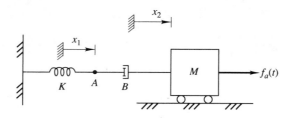

FIGURE P2.29

2.30 a) Write the equations describing the series combination of elements shown in Figure P2.30(a).

b) Find expressions for K_{eq} and B_{eq} in Figure P2.30(b) such that the motions of the ends of the combination are the same as those in part (a) of the figure.

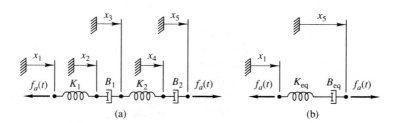

FIGURE P2.30

STANDARD FORMS
FOR SYSTEM MODELS

In Chapter 2, we introduced the element and interconnection laws for translational systems and the procedure for drawing free-body diagrams and applying D'Alembert's law. These are essential steps regardless of the final form of the equations.

Not only should the complete mathematical model contain as many independent equations as unknown variables, but it should also have a form that is convenient for its solution. The two most common forms for the model when a direct solution is contemplated are discussed, illustrated, and compared in this chapter. Although translational mechanical systems are used as examples, the same techniques are applied in subsequent chapters to other types of systems. Other important forms of the model, based on Laplace transform procedures, will be found later in the book.

■ 3.1 STATE-VARIABLE EQUATIONS

One procedure for formulating the system model is to begin by selecting a set of **state variables**. This set of variables must completely describe the effect of the past history of the system on its response in the future. Then, knowing the values of the state variables at a reference time t_0 and the values of the inputs for all $t \geq t_0$ is sufficient for evaluating the state variables and outputs for all $t \geq t_0$. It is further understood that the state variables must be independent; that is, it must be impossible to express any state variable as an algebraic function of the remaining state variables and the inputs.

Although the choice of state variables is not unique, the state variables for mechanical systems are usually related to the energy stored in each of the system's energy-storing elements. Because any energy that is initially stored in these elements can affect the response of the system at a later time, one state variable is normally associated with each of the energy-storing elements. Generally, this adequately summarizes the effect of the past history of the system. In some systems, the number of state variables is different from the number of energy-storing elements because a particular interconnection of elements causes redundant variables or because there is need for a state variable that is not related to the storage of energy.

Suppose the system has n state variables, m inputs, and p outputs. Let q_1, q_2, $\ldots$, q_n denote the state variables, let u_1, u_2, $\ldots$, u_m be the inputs, and let y_1, y_2, $\ldots$, y_p be the outputs. We must find a set of first-order differential equations having a particular form. Each equation must express the derivative of one of the state variables as an *algebraic* function of the state variables and inputs. For a linear system, these algebraic functions will consist of a sum of terms, each of which is just a state variable multiplied by a coefficient or an input multiplied by a coefficient. If, for example, there are three state variables and two inputs, the state-variable equations have the form

$$\dot{q}_1 = a_{11}q_1 + a_{12}q_2 + a_{13}q_3 + b_{11}u_1 + b_{12}u_2$$

$$\dot{q}_2 = a_{21}q_1 + a_{22}q_2 + a_{23}q_3 + b_{21}u_1 + b_{22}u_2 \tag{1}$$

$$\dot{q}_3 = a_{31}q_1 + a_{32}q_2 + a_{33}q_3 + b_{31}u_1 + b_{32}u_2$$

The outputs of interest are then expressed as algebraic functions of the state variables and inputs. If, for example, the linear system described by (1) happens to have two outputs, then the output equations normally have the form

$$y_1 = c_{11}q_1 + c_{12}q_2 + c_{13}q_3 + d_{11}u_1 + d_{12}u_2$$

$$y_2 = c_{21}q_1 + c_{22}q_2 + c_{23}q_3 + d_{21}u_1 + d_{22}u_2 \tag{2}$$

For fixed linear systems, all of the coefficients given by a_{ij}, b_{ij}, c_{ij}, and d_{ij} are constants. For linear systems whose parameters vary with time, some of these coefficients are functions of time. Only for nonlinear elements could some of the coefficients themselves become functions of the state variables or inputs. In the most general case of time-varying, nonlinear systems, the right sides of the state-variable and output equations can be quite complicated functions of the state variables, the inputs, and time. Even then, however, the right sides of these equations should still be algebraic functions, without any derivative or integral terms. An uncommon exception wherein derivatives of the input must appear in (2) will be illustrated in one of the examples.

In this chapter we shall deal almost entirely with fixed linear systems. The form of the equations will then be generally similar to (1) and (2), although there may be more state variables, inputs, or outputs. An output variable may be identical to a state variable, in which case (2) may contain one or more equations such as $y_i = q_i$. When all the outputs are identical to some of the state variables, (2) becomes trivial and can be omitted.

Solving (1) for $t \geq t_0$ requires knowledge of the inputs for $t \geq t_0$ and also of the initial values of the state variables, namely $q_1(t_0)$, $q_2(t_0)$, and $q_3(t_0)$. In general, we cannot solve the individual state-variable equations separately but must solve them as a group. For example, the equation $\dot{q}_1 = -q_1 + q_2$ cannot be solved for q_1 unless another equation exists that can be solved for q_2.

The energy stored in translational mechanical systems must be associated with the masses or springs. From (2.6)[1] the kinetic energy of a mass is $\frac{1}{2}Mv^2$, and from (2.10) the potential energy of a spring is $\frac{1}{2}K(\Delta x)^2$. Thus it is logical to consider as possible state variables the velocities of the masses and the elongations of the springs. In most problems, we can express the elongations of the springs in terms of the displacements of the masses.

When drawing free-body diagrams, we try to express the forces in terms of state variables and inputs and in a way that avoids unnecessary derivatives. Thus we normally label inertial and friction forces in the form $M\dot{v}$ and Bv, rather than $M\ddot{x}$ and $B\dot{x}$.

In the remainder of this section, a variety of examples illustrate the technique of deriving the mathematical model in state-variable form. The general approach is as follows:

1. Identify the state variables and write those state-variable equations that do not require a free-body diagram, such as equations of the form $\dot{x} = v$.

2. Draw free-body diagrams for each independent mass and junction point that can move with an unknown motion. Sum the forces on each free-body diagram separately to obtain a set of differential equations.

3. Manipulate the equations into state-variable form. For each of the state variables, there must be an equation that expresses its derivative as an algebraic function of the state variables, the inputs, and possibly time.

4. Express the output variables as algebraic functions of the state variables, the inputs, and possibly time. In some unusual cases, it may be necessary to have derivatives of the input on the right side of the output equations. However, input derivatives should be avoided wherever possible.

▶ **EXAMPLE 3.1**

Find the state-variable model for the system shown in Figure 3.1(a), which is identical to Figure 2.12(a). The outputs of interest are the tensile force for the spring K and the velocity and acceleration of the mass M.

Solution

We choose as state variables the elongation x of the spring, which is related to its potential energy, and the velocity v of the mass, which is related to its

---

[1]This denotes equation (6) in Chapter 2.

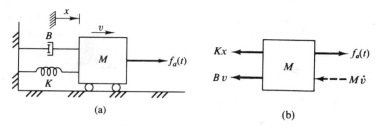

FIGURE 3.1   (a) Translational system for Example 3.1. (b) Free-body diagram.

kinetic energy. Having made this choice, we can write the first of the two state-variable equations by inspection:

$$\dot{x} = v$$

Summing the forces on the free-body diagram, which was drawn for Example 2.1 and which is repeated in Figure 3.1(b), gives

$$M\dot{v} + Bv + Kx = f_a(t)$$

Solving this equation for $\dot{v}$ results in the second state-variable equation, where the right side is a function of only the state variables x and v and the input $f_a(t)$, as required. Thus the state variable equations are

$$\dot{x} = v$$

$$\dot{v} = \frac{1}{M}[-Kx - Bv + f_a(t)]$$

Analytical and computer solutions of such a set of equations are treated in Chapters 6 and 15, respectively. In order to find the state variables x and v as functions of time for all $t \geq 0$, we would need to know the input $f_a(t)$ for $t \geq 0$ and also the initial values of the state variables at $t = 0$. Any outputs that are not also state variables are expressed as algebraic functions of the state variables and inputs, so they can be evaluated as soon as the state variables have been found.

The velocity of the mass is one of the state variables. The output equations for the tensile force f_K in the spring and the acceleration a_M of the mass are

$$f_K = Kx$$

$$a_M = \frac{1}{M}[-Kx - Bv + f_a(t)]$$

The system considered in the following three examples has four energy-storing elements and four state variables. The modeling is carried out for two different choices of state variables in order to illustrate that there are often several satisfactory choices. The examples also show that finding the state-variable equations is not made significantly more difficult when some of the system's elements are nonlinear.

▶ **EXAMPLE 3.2**

Find the state-variable equations for the system shown in Figure 3.2(a), which is identical to Figure 2.13(a). Write output equations for the tensile force f_{K_2} in the spring K_2 and for the total momentum m_T of the masses.

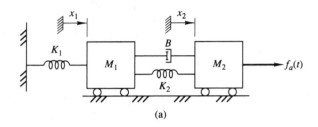

(a)

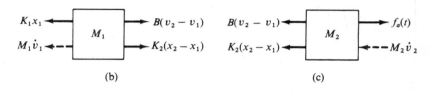

(b)   (c)

FIGURE 3.2   (a) Translational system for Example 3.2. (b), (c) Free-body diagrams.

Solution

An appropriate choice of state variables is x_1, v_1, x_2 and v_2, because we can express the velocity of each mass and the elongation of each spring in terms of these four variables and because none of these variables can be expressed in terms of the other three. Because $\dot{x}_1 = v_1$ and $\dot{x}_2 = v_2$, two of the four state-variable equations are available immediately.

The free-body diagrams for the two masses are repeated from Example 2.2 in Figure 3.2(b) and Figure 3.2(c), with all forces labeled in terms of the state variables and the input. By D'Alembert's law,

$$M_1\dot{v}_1 + K_1x_1 - K_2(x_2 - x_1) - B(v_2 - v_1) = 0$$

$$M_2\dot{v}_2 + K_2(x_2 - x_1) + B(v_2 - v_1) = f_a(t)$$

which may be solved for $\dot{v}_1$ and $\dot{v}_2$, respectively. The state-variable equations are

$$\dot{x}_1 = v_1 \tag{3a}$$

$$\dot{v}_1 = \frac{1}{M_1}[-(K_1 + K_2)x_1 - Bv_1 + K_2x_2 + Bv_2] \tag{3b}$$

$$\dot{x}_2 = v_2 \qquad (3c)$$

$$\dot{v}_2 = \frac{1}{M_2}[K_2 x_1 + B v_1 - K_2 x_2 - B v_2 + f_a(t)] \qquad (3d)$$

If we know the element values, the input $f_a(t)$ for $t \geq 0$, and the initial conditions $x_1(0)$, $v_1(0)$, $x_2(0)$, and $v_2(0)$, then we can solve this set of simultaneous first-order differential equations for x_1, v_1, x_2, and v_2 for all $t \geq 0$. The output equations are

$$f_{K_2} = K_2(x_2 - x_1)$$
$$m_T = M_1 v_1 + M_2 v_2 \qquad (4)$$

▶ *EXAMPLE 3.3*

As an alternative choice of state variables for the system in Figure 3.2(a), use the relative displacement x_R and the relative velocity v_R of mass M_2 with respect to M_1, in place of x_2 and v_2. Again find the state-variable and output equations.

Solution

We choose the four state variables x_1, v_1, x_R, and v_R, where

$$x_R = x_2 - x_1$$
$$v_R = v_2 - v_1$$

The free-body diagrams when the forces are labeled in terms of these variables are shown in Figure 3.3. Remember that the inertial forces depend on the absolute accelerations of the respective masses. By D'Alembert's law,

$$M_1 \dot{v}_1 + K_1 x_1 - K_2 x_R - B v_R = 0$$
$$M_2 \dot{v}_1 + M_2 \dot{v}_R + B v_R + K_2 x_R = f_a(t)$$

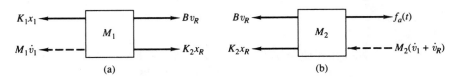

(a) (b)

FIGURE 3.3 Free-body diagrams for Example 3.3 using relative displacement and relative velocity.

from which

$$\dot{v}_1 = \frac{1}{M_1}(-K_1 x_1 + K_2 x_R + B v_R) \tag{5a}$$

$$\dot{v}_R = \frac{1}{M_2}[-M_2 \dot{v}_1 - B v_R - K_2 x_R + f_a(t)] \tag{5b}$$

Although (5a) is a satisfactory state-variable equation, (5b) is not because of the derivative on the right side. Thus we must substitute (5a) into (5b) in order to get an appropriate expression for $\dot{v}_R$. When this is done, we obtain for the complete set of state-variable equations

$$\begin{aligned}
\dot{x}_1 &= v_1 \\
\dot{v}_1 &= \frac{1}{M_1}(-K_1 x_1 + K_2 x_R + B v_R) \\
\dot{x}_R &= v_R \\
\dot{v}_R &= \frac{1}{M_1 M_2}[K_1 M_2 x_1 - K_2(M_1 + M_2)x_R \\
&\qquad - B(M_1 + M_2)v_R + M_1 f_a(t)]
\end{aligned} \tag{6}$$

To write the output equations in terms of the new state variables, we note that x_R is the elongation of K_2 and that the momentum of a mass depends on its absolute velocity. Thus

$$\begin{aligned}
f_{K_2} &= K_2 x_R \\
m_T &= M_1 v_1 + M_2(v_1 + v_R) \\
&= (M_1 + M_2)v_1 + M_2 v_R
\end{aligned} \tag{7}$$

▶ **EXAMPLE 3.4**

For the system shown in Figure 3.2(a), the forces exerted by the linear spring K_1 and the linear dashpot B were $K_1 x_1$ and $B v_R$, respectively. Now assume that these two elements are replaced by nonlinear elements. The expression relating the force f_{K_1} to the displacement x_1 is denoted by $f_{K_1}(x_1)$, whereas the force on the dashpot is denoted by $f_B(v_R)$. Also take as an additional output the energy stored in the linear spring K_2.

Solution

We again choose the state variables to be x_1, v_1, x_R, and v_R. The free-body diagrams are the same as those in Figure 3.3 except that $K_1 x_1$ is replaced by $f_{K_1}(x_1)$, and $B v_R$ by $f_B(v_R)$, respectively. The resulting state-variable equations are identical to (6) except for the contributions of the two nonlinear elements:

$$\dot{x}_1 = v_1$$

$$\dot{v}_1 = \frac{1}{M_1}[-f_{K_1}(x_1) + K_2 x_R + f_B(v_R)]$$

$$\dot{x}_R = v_R$$

$$\dot{v}_R = \frac{1}{M_1 M_2}[M_2 f_{K_1}(x_1) - K_2(M_1 + M_2)x_R$$

$$- (M_1 + M_2)f_B(v_R) + M_1 f_a(t)]$$

Note that the procedure for drawing the free-body diagrams and writing the state-variable equations is no more complicated than for the linear case. However, solving the differential equations analytically would be much more difficult, if not impossible.

The output equations for f_{K_2} and m_T remain the same as those in (7). The additional output equation for the energy stored in the linear spring K_2 is

$$w_{K_2} = \frac{1}{2}K_2 x_R^2$$

which has a squared variable on the right side. Even in the case of linear components, some possible outputs may require output equations that are not just linear combinations of the state variables and inputs. Even then, however, the output equation should normally be an algebraic function of the state variables and inputs.

Next we consider two modifications of Figure 3.2(a) that illustrate circumstances in which the number of state variables might be different from the number of energy-storing elements. In the first of these, the spring K_1 is removed; in the second, an additional spring is added between the mass M_2 and a wall at the right.

▶ **EXAMPLE 3.5**

Find the state-variable model for the linear system shown in Figure 3.2(a) when the spring K_1 is removed. Let the outputs again be the tensile force f_{K_2} in the spring K_2 and the total momentum m_T of the masses. Then reconsider the problem when the displacement x_1 of the mass M_1 is an additional output of interest.

Solution

The free-body diagrams will be the same as those in parts (b) and (c) of Figure 3.2, except that the force $K_1 x_1$ will be missing. Thus (3) and (4) will still be valid if we just let $K_1 = 0$.

Because there are only three energy-storing elements in the modified system, however, we would expect to need only three state variables, rather than the four that appear in (3). Two of the three state variables can be chosen to be v_1 and v_2, which are related to the kinetic energy stored in the masses. We choose the third to be the elongation of the spring K_2, which is related to the potential energy in that element and which is $x_R = x_2 - x_1$. One of the state-variable equations is $\dot{x}_R = v_2 - v_1$. The other two follow from (3b) and (3d), with $K_1 = 0$ and with $x_2 - x_1$ replaced by x_R:

$$
\begin{aligned}
\dot{x}_R &= v_2 - v_1 \\
\dot{v}_1 &= \frac{1}{M_1}[K_2 x_R - B v_1 + B v_2] \\
\dot{v}_2 &= \frac{1}{M_2}[-K_2 x_R + B v_1 - B v_2 + f_a(t)]
\end{aligned}
\tag{8}
$$

The only variables on the right side of these equations are state variables and the input $f_a(t)$, as is required. The output equations are

$$
\begin{aligned}
f_{K_2} &= K_2 x_R \\
m_T &= M_1 v_1 + M_2 v_2
\end{aligned}
\tag{9}
$$

An alternative form of the state-variable model can be found by letting $K_1 = 0$ in (6) and (7). Because the only state variables that are needed are v_1, x_R, and v_R, we can omit the first equation in (6). Then the state-variable and output equations become

$$
\begin{aligned}
\dot{v}_1 &= \frac{1}{M_1}(K_2 x_R + B v_R) \\
\dot{x}_R &= v_R \\
\dot{v}_R &= \frac{1}{M_1 M_2}[-K_2(M_1 + M_2)x_R - B(M_1 + M_2)v_R + M_1 f_a(t)]
\end{aligned}
\tag{10}
$$

and

$$
\begin{aligned}
f_{K_2} &= K_2 x_R \\
m_T &= (M_1 + M_2)v_1 + M_2 v_R
\end{aligned}
\tag{11}
$$

Finally, suppose that one of the outputs of interest is x_1. It is not possible to express x_1 as an algebraic function of only x_R, v_1, v_2, and $f_a(t)$. Thus we cannot construct a suitable output equation based on (8). Similarly, because x_1 cannot be expressed as an algebraic function of only v_1, x_R, v_R, and $f_a(t)$, we cannot write a suitable output equation based on (10). Hence, if x_1 is specified as one of the outputs of interest, three state variables are not sufficient. We would need to consider x_1 as an additional state variable and add the equation $\dot{x}_1 = v_1$ to either (8) or (10).

The previous example shows why an additional state variable that is not related to energy storage is sometimes needed. The following example illustrates how the number of state variables can be less than the number of energy-storing elements when the system's stored energy can be expressed by a reduced number of variables.

▶ **EXAMPLE 3.6**

Find a state-variable model for the linear system shown in Figure 3.4(a).

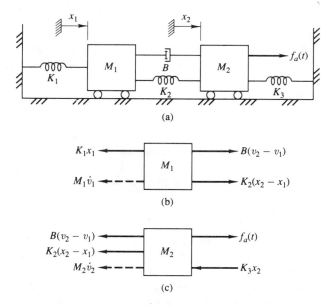

(a)

(b)

(c)

FIGURE 3.4 (a) Translational system with fewer state variables than energy-storing elements. (b), (c) Free-body diagrams.

Solution

Although there are three springs, their elongations are not all independent and can be specified in terms of the two displacement variables x_1 and x_2. The elongations of K_1, K_2, and K_3 are $x_1, x_2 - x_1$, and $-x_2$, respectively. The free-body diagrams for the two masses, which are shown in Figures 3.4(b) and 3.4(c), are the same as those in Figure 3.2 except for the additional force associated with K_3. By D'Alembert's law,

$$M_1\dot{v}_1 + (K_1 + K_2)x_1 + Bv_1 - K_2x_2 - Bv_2 = 0$$
$$M_2\dot{v}_2 - K_2x_1 - Bv_1 + (K_2 + K_3)x_2 + Bv_2 = f_a(t)$$

By solving these equations for $\dot{v}_1$ and $\dot{v}_2$, we can write the following four state-variable equations:

$$\dot{x}_1 = v_1$$
$$\dot{v}_1 = \frac{1}{M_1}[-(K_1 + K_2)x_1 - Bv_1 + K_2 x_2 + Bv_2]$$
$$\dot{x}_2 = v_2 \tag{12}$$
$$\dot{v}_2 = \frac{1}{M_2}[K_2 x_1 + Bv_1 - (K_2 + K_3)x_2 - Bv_2 + f_a(t)]$$

If the outputs of interest are the tensile force f_{K_2} and the total momentum m_T, then the output equations are again given by (4).

In the following example, two springs and a dashpot are attached to a massless junction. The system contains three energy-storing elements and normally requires three state variables. However, when the dashpot is removed from the massless junction, the number of state variables is reduced.

▶ **EXAMPLE 3.7**

Find the state-variable model for the system shown in Figure 3.5(a). The input is the force $f_a(t)$, and the output is the displacement x_2 of the massless junction A. Repeat the problem when the dashpot B_2 is removed.

Solution

A satisfactory choice of state variables is x_1, v_1, and x_2, because these three variables determine the elongations of the springs and the velocity of the mass. One of the three state-variable equations is $\dot{x}_1 = v_1$.

To obtain the other two equations, we draw free-body diagrams for both the mass and the junction point, as shown in Figure 3.5(b) and Figure 3.5(c). Because the point A is massless, no inertial force is present in its free-body diagram. Summing the forces shown in these diagrams gives

$$M\dot{v}_1 + B_1 v_1 + K_1(x_1 - x_2) = f_a(t) \tag{13a}$$
$$B_2 \dot{x}_2 + K_2 x_2 + K_1(x_2 - x_1) = 0 \tag{13b}$$

Solving (13) for $\dot{v}_1$ and $\dot{x}_2$, we arrive at the state-variable equations

$$\dot{x}_1 = v_1 \tag{14a}$$

$$\dot{v}_1 = \frac{1}{M}[-K_1 x_1 - B_1 v_1 + K_1 x_2 + f_a(t)] \tag{14b}$$

$$\dot{x}_2 = \frac{1}{B_2}[K_1 x_1 - (K_1 + K_2)x_2] \tag{14c}$$

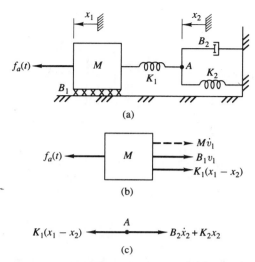

FIGURE 3.5 (a) Translational system containing a massless junction. (b), (c) Free-body diagrams.

Because the only output is one of the state variables, we shall not write a separate output equation.

Removing the dashpot corresponds to setting $B_2 = 0$. We cannot make this substitution in (14c), because division by zero is an invalid mathematical operation. However, replacing B_2 by zero in (13) gives

$$M\dot{v}_1 + B_1 v_1 + K_1(x_1 - x_2) = f_a(t) \tag{15a}$$

$$K_2 x_2 + K_1(x_2 - x_1) = 0 \tag{15b}$$

The second of these equations is purely algebraic and can be solved for x_2 in terms of x_1:

$$x_2 = \left(\frac{K_1}{K_1 + K_2}\right) x_1 \tag{16}$$

The displacements x_1 and x_2 are now proportional to each other, so they cannot both be state variables. If we choose x_1 and v_1 as the state variables, we still have $\dot{x}_1 = v_1$. To find the second state-variable equation, we substitute (16) into (15a) and solve for $\dot{v}_1$. Thus

$$\dot{x}_1 = v_1$$
$$\dot{v}_1 = \frac{1}{M}\left[-\left(\frac{K_1 K_2}{K_1 + K_2}\right) x_1 - B_1 v_1 + f_a(t)\right] \tag{17}$$

As required, the variables appearing on the right sides of these equations are either state variables or the input.

The system for $B_2 = 0$ is shown in Figure 3.6. From the discussion associated with Example 2.10 and Figure 2.23(a), we see that the two springs

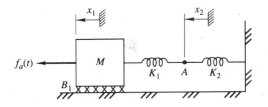

FIGURE 3.6   Translational system with springs in series.

---

are now in series and can be replaced by a single equivalent spring for which $K_{eq} = K_1 K_2/(K_1 + K_2)$. This is reflected by the corresponding term in (17) and by the fact that only two state variables are needed. Because the output x_2 is no longer a state variable, we need a separate output equation to accompany (17). It is given by (16).

Sometimes the proposed state-variable equations that are initially found contain the derivative of an input on the right side. It might be argued that because the input is presumably known completely, its derivative could be found. However, it is important for the standard methods of solution (whether the solution is to be carried out analytically or with a computer) to eliminate any derivatives on the right side of the state-variable equations.

It is also desirable to avoid input derivatives on the right side of the output equations. For some possible outputs, however, such derivatives may be unavoidable.

A general method for eliminating derivatives of the input whenever possible is discussed in Chapter 13, which uses Laplace-transform techniques. However, a basic approach is illustrated in the following example, which also has a displacement rather than an applied force as the specified input. An input derivative on the right side of the state-variable equations is removed by redefining one of the state variables. One of the output equations, however, has unavoidable derivatives on the right side.

▶ EXAMPLE 3.8

Find the state-variable model for the system shown in Figure 3.7(a), which is identical to Figure 2.14. The displacement $x_2(t)$ is a prescribed function of time that is the input of the system. The primary outputs of interest are the displacement and velocity of M_1. Consider as an additional output the force f_2 that must be applied to M_2 in order to move it with the prescribed displacement.

Solution

We know the motion of M_2 in advance, so there is no need to draw a free-body diagram for it unless it is needed for one of the output equations. The

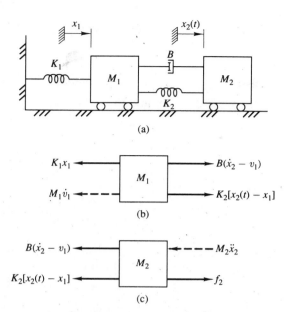

FIGURE 3.7   (a) Translational system with displacement input.
(b), (c) Free-body diagrams.

free-body diagram for M_1 is shown in Figure 3.7(b), and the corresponding
force equation is

$$M_1\dot{v}_1 + Bv_1 + (K_1 + K_2)x_1 = B_2\dot{x}_2 + K_2x_2(t)$$

We may choose x_1 and v_1 as the state variables, write $\dot{x}_1 = v_1$, and solve
the last equation for $\dot{v}_1$, which yields

$$\dot{x}_1 = v_1 \tag{18a}$$

$$\dot{v}_1 = \frac{1}{M_1}[-(K_1 + K_2)x_1 - Bv_1 + B\dot{x}_2 + K_2x_2(t)] \tag{18b}$$

Equation (18b) does not fit the required form for state-variable equations
given by (1) because its right side contains $\dot{x}_2$, the derivative of the input. In
order to eliminate $\dot{x}_2$ from the initial state-variable equations, we introduce
a new state variable q to be used in place of v_1. To determine how q must
be defined, we rewrite (18b) with the derivative of x_2 moved to the left side:

$$\dot{v}_1 - \frac{B}{M_1}\dot{x}_2 = \frac{1}{M_1}[-(K_1 + K_2)x_1 - Bv_1 + K_2x_2(t)] \tag{19}$$

If we select the new state variable q as

$$q = v_1 - \frac{B}{M_1}x_2(t) \tag{20}$$

then the left side of (19) can be written as $\dot{q}$. Rearranging (20), we see that the old state variable v_1 is given by

$$v_1 = q + \frac{B}{M_1}x_2(t) \tag{21}$$

Finally, we insert (21) into the right sides of (18a) and (19) to obtain

$$\dot{x}_1 = q + \frac{B}{M_1}x_2(t)$$

$$\dot{q} = \frac{1}{M_1}\left[-(K_1 + K_2)x_1 - Bq + \left(K_2 - \frac{B^2}{M_1}\right)x_2(t) \right] \tag{22}$$

which is in state-variable form. The output x_1 is a state variable, and the output v_1 is given by (21), which fits the standard form for an output equation.

To obtain an expression for the force f_2 applied to M_2, we draw the free-body diagram shown in Figure 3.7(c). By D'Alembert's law,

$$f_2 = -K_2 x_1 - B v_1 + M_2 \ddot{x}_2 + B\dot{x}_2 + K_2 x_2(t)$$

Using (21) for v_1, we rewrite this equation as

$$f_2 = -K_2 x_1 - Bq + M_2 \ddot{x}_2 + B\dot{x}_2 + \left(K_2 - \frac{B^2}{M_1}\right)x_2(t)$$

which contains derivatives of the input in addition to the input $x_2(t)$ and the state variables x_1 and q. For this particular output, however, there is no way to avoid input derivatives on the right side.

Systems may have several inputs. In the final state-variable example, a time-varying force $f_a(t)$ is applied to M_1, and there is a gravitational force on M_2.

▶ **EXAMPLE 3.9**

Find a state-variable model for the system that was shown in Figure 2.19(a) and considered in Example 2.7. The two inputs are $f_a(t)$ and the gravitational constant g. The outputs are x_{K_1} and f_{B_2}, defined as the elongation of K_1 and the upward force on the top of B_2, respectively.

Solution

The free-body diagrams for the two masses were shown in parts (b) and (c) of Figure 2.19. The four state variables can be chosen to be the displacements x_1 and x_2 and the velocities v_1 and v_2. In Example 2.7, the force equations were shown to be

$$M_1 \dot{v}_1 + B_1 v_1 + K_1(x_1 - x_2) = f_a(t)$$

$$M_2 \dot{v}_2 + B_2 v_2 + K_2 x_2 + M_2 g = K_1(x_1 - x_2)$$

We solve the first equation for $\dot{v}_1$, solve the second equation for $\dot{v}_2$, and then write the following four state-variable equations:

$$\dot{x}_1 = v_1$$
$$\dot{v}_1 = \frac{1}{M_1}[-K_1 x_1 - B_1 v_1 + K_1 x_2 + f_a(t)]$$
$$\dot{x}_2 = v_2 \tag{23}$$
$$\dot{v}_2 = \frac{1}{M_2}[K_1 x_1 - (K_1 + K_2)x_2 - B_2 v_2 - M_2 g]$$

The output equations are

$$x_{K_1} = x_1 - x_2$$
$$f_{B_2} = B_2 v_2 \tag{24}$$

The right sides of both sets of equations are algebraic functions of the four state variables and the two inputs, as required.

3.2 INPUT-OUTPUT EQUATIONS

In this section, we develop the system models in the form of input-output differential equations by eliminating all variables except the inputs and outputs and their derivatives. For a system with one input $u(t)$ and one output y, the input-output equation has the general form

$$a_n y^{(n)} + \cdots + a_2 \ddot{y} + a_1 \dot{y} + a_0 y = b_m u^{(m)} + \cdots + b_1 \dot{u} + b_0 u(t) \tag{25}$$

where $y^{(n)} = d^n y/dt^n$ and $u^{(m)} = d^m u/dt^m$, and where for systems of practical interest $m \leq n$. For fixed linear systems, all the coefficients in (25) are constants. In order to solve such an equation for y for all $t \geq t_0$, we need to know not only the input $u(t)$ for $t \geq t_0$ but also the n initial conditions $y(t_0)$, $\dot{y}(t_0)$, $\ddot{y}(t_0)$, $\ldots$, $y^{(n-1)}(t_0)$. Finding these initial conditions may be a difficult task.

For systems with more than one input, the right side of (25) will include additional input terms. If there are several outputs, we need a separate equation similar to (25) for each output. For example, the pair of equations

$$\ddot{y}_1 + 2\dot{y}_1 + 2y_1 = 3\dot{u}_1 + 2u_1(t) + u_2(t) + 3\dot{u}_3$$
$$\ddot{y}_2 + 2\dot{y}_2 + 2y_2 = u_1(t) + 2u_2(t) + u_3(t)$$

corresponds to a system with two outputs and three inputs. In the general case, each of the input-output equations involves only one unknown variable and its derivatives. Thus, unlike state-variable equations, each equation can be solved independently of the others.

An input-output equation can be constructed by combining the equations in a state-variable model, if such a model has already been found. A more direct method is to label the forces in the free-body diagrams in terms of the output variables and the minimum number of additional variables. For a translational system in which the outputs are displacements, for example, we would normally write the inertial and friction forces in the form $M\ddot{x}$ and $B\dot{x}$, rather than as $M\dot{v}$ and Bv.

▶ **EXAMPLE 3.10**

Write the input-output equation for the system shown in Figure 3.1(a) when the output is the displacement x.

Solution

In Example 3.1, the state-variable equations were found to be

$$\dot{x} = v$$
$$\dot{v} = \frac{1}{M}[-Kx - Bv + f_a(t)]$$

We can combine these equations by replacing v and $\dot{v}$ in the second equation by $\dot{x}$ and $\ddot{x}$, respectively, to obtain

$$M\ddot{x} + B\dot{x} + Kx = f_a(t)$$

The direct approach, which does not make use of the state-variable model, would be to label all the forces on the free-body diagram except $f_a(t)$ in terms of x and its derivatives. Then the foregoing input-output equation follows directly from D'Alembert's law.

▶ **EXAMPLE 3.11**

Find the input-output equations that relate the outputs x_1 and x_2 to the input $f_a(t)$ for the system shown in Figure 3.5(a).

Solution

The free-body diagrams for the mass M and the junction point A were shown in parts (b) and (c) of Figure 3.5, and the corresponding force equations were written in (13). When all forces except the input are expressed in terms of x_1 and x_2, these equations become

$$M\ddot{x}_1 + B_1\dot{x}_1 + K_1x_1 - K_1x_2 = f_a(t) \tag{26a}$$

$$B_2\dot{x}_2 + (K_1 + K_2)x_2 - K_1x_1 = 0 \tag{26b}$$

To obtain a single differential equation relating x_1 to $f_a(t)$ from this pair of coupled equations, we must eliminate x_2 and $\dot{x}_2$. If one of the equations contains an unwanted variable but none of its derivatives, we can solve for it in terms of the remaining variables and their derivatives. Then we can eliminate the unwanted variable from the model by substitution. Thus we rewrite (26a) as

$$x_2 = \frac{1}{K_1} [M\ddot{x}_1 + B_1\dot{x}_1 + K_1 x_1 - f_a(t)]$$

and, by differentiating once, we obtain

$$\dot{x}_2 = \frac{1}{K_1} (M\dddot{x}_1 + B_1\ddot{x}_1 + K_1\dot{x}_1 - \dot{f}_a)$$

Substituting these expressions for x_2 and $\dot{x}_2$ into (26b) gives

$$\frac{B_2}{K_1} (M\dddot{x}_1 + B_1\ddot{x}_1 + K_1\dot{x}_1 - \dot{f}_a)$$

$$+ \frac{K_1 + K_2}{K_1} [M\ddot{x}_1 + B_1\dot{x}_1 + K_1 x_1 - f_a(t)] - K_1 x_1 = 0$$

or

$$M B_2 \dddot{x}_1 + (B_1 B_2 + K_1 M + K_2 M)\ddot{x}_1$$
$$+ (B_2 K_1 + B_1 K_1 + B_1 K_2)\dot{x}_1 + K_1 K_2 x_1$$
$$= B_2 \dot{f}_a + (K_1 + K_2) f_a(t) \qquad (27)$$

which is the input-output equation for x_1. To obtain a differential equation with x_2 as the only unknown variable, we use (26b) to get an expression for x_1, which we then substitute into (26a). The result is

$$M B_2 \dddot{x}_2 + (B_1 B_2 + K_1 M + K_2 M)\ddot{x}_2$$
$$+ (B_2 K_1 + B_1 K_1 + B_1 K_2)\dot{x}_2 + K_1 K_2 x_2 = K_1 f_a(t) \qquad (28)$$

Note that the coefficients on the left sides of (27) and (28) are the same. Note also that the input-output equations are third-order and that the system has three state variables.

For the special case where $B_2 = 0$, which corresponds to removing the dashpot, (27) and (28) reduce to

$$M\ddot{x}_1 + B_1\dot{x}_1 + \left(\frac{K_1 K_2}{K_1 + K_2}\right) x_1 = f_a(t)$$

$$M\ddot{x}_2 + B_1\dot{x}_2 + \left(\frac{K_1 K_2}{K_1 + K_2}\right) x_2 = \left(\frac{K_1}{K_1 + K_2}\right) f_a(t)$$

The input-output equation for x_1 is now similar to that in Example 3.10, with K replaced by an equivalent constant $K_{eq} = K_1 K_2/(K_1 + K_2)$ for the two springs that are now in series. We also see that $x_2 = [K_1/(K_1 + K_2)]x_1$

and that our results are consistent with those in Example 3.7. Because the two springs can be replaced by a single equivalent spring, the input-output equations are only second-order.

Reduction of Simultaneous Differential Equations

As we have seen, it is often necessary to combine a set of differential equations involving more than one dependent variable into a single differential equation with a single dependent variable. We did this in Example 3.11 by straightforward substitution. However, when it is not obvious how to eliminate the unwanted variable easily, the following procedure is recommended.

Let p denote the differentiation operator d/dt such that $py = \dot{y}$, $p^2 y = \ddot{y}$, etc. Then, for example,

$$(p + 2)y = \dot{y} + 2y$$

$$[(p + 1)(p + 2)]\,y = (p^2 + 3p + 2)y$$

$$= \ddot{y} + 3\dot{y} + 2y$$

$$(a_n p^n + \cdots + a_2 p^2 + a_1 p + a_0)y = a_n y^{(n)} + \cdots + a_2 \ddot{y} + a_1 \dot{y} + a_0 y$$

where $y^{(k)} = d^k y/dt^k$ for any positive integer value of k. Remember that p must operate on the variable or expression that follows it and that it is not a variable or algebraic quantity itself.

Suppose that we have the pair of equations

$$\dot{y}_1 + 2y_1 + y_2 = 3u(t) \tag{29}$$

$$2\dot{y}_1 + 5y_1 - 2\dot{y}_2 + 2y_2 = 0$$

and want to find a single differential equation involving only the variables y_2 and $u(t)$. In terms of the p operator, we can rewrite (29) as

$$(p + 2)y_1 + y_2 = 3u(t)$$

$$(2p + 5)y_1 + (-2p + 2)y_2 = 0$$

We now premultiply the first equation by $(2p + 5)$, premultiply the second equation by $(p + 2)$, and then subtract the new second equation from the first. The result is

$$[(2p + 5) - (p + 2)(-2p + 2)]y_2 = (2p + 5)3u(t)$$

from which

$$(2p^2 + 4p + 1)y_2 = (6p + 15)u(t) \tag{30}$$

To return to a differential equation relating y_2 and $u(t)$, we observe that (30) is the operator form of

$$2\ddot{y}_2 + 4\dot{y}_2 + y_2 = 6\dot{u} + 15u(t)$$

which is indeed the correct input-output equation. This algebraic procedure provides a useful means of manipulating sets of differential equations with constant coefficients.

▶ **EXAMPLE 3.12**

For the system in Figure 3.2(a), which is identical to Figure 2.13(a), find the input-output equation relating x_1 and $f_a(t)$.

Solution

The free-body diagrams for the two masses were shown in Figure 2.13 (with all forces labeled in terms of displacements and the input) and in Figure 3.2 (with forces labeled in terms of state variables and the input). Repeating (2.16), where the force equations were written in terms of displacements, we have the pair of simultaneous second-order differential equations

$$M_1\ddot{x}_1 + B\dot{x}_1 + (K_1 + K_2)x_1 - B\dot{x}_2 - K_2x_2 = 0$$

$$-B\dot{x}_1 - K_2x_1 + M_2\ddot{x}_2 + B\dot{x}_2 + K_2x_2 = f_a(t)$$

In terms of the p operator, these equations become

$$[p^2M_1 + pB + (K_1 + K_2)]x_1 - (pB + K_2)x_2 = 0$$

$$-(pB + K_2)x_1 + (p^2M_2 + pB + K_2)x_2 = f_a(t)$$

When we combine this pair of operator equations algebraically to eliminate x_2, we find that

$$\{M_1M_2p^4 + (M_1 + M_2)Bp^3 + [M_1K_2 + M_2(K_1 + K_2)]p^2 + BK_1p + K_1K_2\}x_1 = (pB + K_2)f_a(t)$$

which is the operator form of the differential equation

$$M_1M_2x_1^{(iv)} + (M_1 + M_2)Bx_1^{(iii)} + [M_1K_2 + M_2(K_1 + K_2)]\ddot{x}_1 + BK_1\dot{x}_1 + K_1K_2x_1 = B\dot{f}_a + K_2f_a(t)$$

The symbols $x^{(iv)}$ and $x^{(iii)}$ are defined as $x^{(iv)} = d^4x/dt^4$ and $x^{(iii)} = d^3x/dt^3$. As expected for a system that has four state variables, the input-output differential equation is of order four.

Comparison with the State-Variable Method

The order of the input-output differential equation describing a system is usually the same as the number of state variables. Occasionally one or more of the state variables may have no effect on the output, in which case the order of the input-output equation is less than the number of state variables.

For a first-order system, both forms of the system model involve a single first-order differential equation and are essentially identical. For higher-order systems they are quite different. We must solve a set of n first-order differential equations in state-variable form as a group, and we must know the initial value of each state variable to solve the set of n equations. An input-output equation of order n contains only one dependent variable, but we need to know the initial values of that variable and its first $n - 1$ derivatives. In practice, finding the input-output equation and the associated initial conditions may require more effort than finding the information needed for a state-variable solution.

Using the state-variable equations has significant computational advantages when a computer solution is to be found, as is discussed in Chapter 15. In fact, standard methods for solving a high-order, possibly nonlinear input-output differential equation on a computer usually require decomposition into a set of simultaneous first-order equations anyway. The analytical solution of input-output equations and of sets of state-variable equations is considered in Chapter 6.

State-variable equations are particularly convenient for complex multi-input, multi-output systems. They are often written in matrix form, and, in addition to their computational advantages, they can be used to obtain considerable insight into system behavior. The state-variable concept has formed the basis for many of the recent theoretical developments in system analysis.

■ 3.3 MATRIX FORMULATION OF STATE-VARIABLE EQUATIONS

One of the characteristics of state-variable models is that they are suitable for matrix notation and for the techniques of linear algebra. For example, we can represent any number of first-order state-variable equations by a single matrix differential equation merely by making the appropriate definitions. Furthermore, when we are dealing with complex multi-input, multi-output systems, using matrix concepts and properties leads to an understanding of system behavior that would be difficult to achieve otherwise. An additional advantage of using matrices is that we can apply many of the theoretical properties of matrices that are taught in introductory linear algebra courses to the study of dynamic systems once we have put their models into matrix form.

We assume that the reader is somewhat familiar with matrix methods through an introductory course in linear algebra. Such basic matrix operations as multiplication, evaluation of determinants, and inversion are summarized in Appendix C.

The required form for the state-variable model was explained in Section 3.1. For a fixed linear system in which q_1, q_2, $\ldots$, q_n are the state variables, where u_1, u_2, ..., u_m are the inputs, and where y_1, y_2, ..., y_p are the outputs, the state-variables equations are

$$
\begin{aligned}
\dot{q}_1 &= a_{11}q_1 + a_{12}q_2 + \cdots + a_{1n}q_n + b_{11}u_1 + \cdots + b_{1m}u_m \\
\dot{q}_2 &= a_{21}q_1 + a_{22}q_2 + \cdots + a_{2n}q_n + b_{21}u_1 + \cdots + b_{2m}u_m \\
&\;\;\vdots \\
\dot{q}_n &= a_{n1}q_1 + a_{n2}q_2 + \cdots + a_{nn}q_n + b_{n1}u_1 + \cdots + b_{nm}u_m
\end{aligned}
\tag{31}
$$

and the output equations have the form

$$
\begin{aligned}
y_1 &= c_{11}q_1 + c_{12}q_2 + \cdots + c_{1n}q_n + d_{11}u_1 + \cdots + d_{1m}u_m \\
y_2 &= c_{21}q_1 + c_{22}q_2 + \cdots + c_{2n}q_n + d_{21}u_1 + \cdots + d_{2m}u_m \\
&\;\;\vdots \\
y_p &= c_{p1}q_1 + c_{p2}q_2 + \cdots + c_{pn}q_n + d_{p1}u_1 + \cdots + d_{pm}u_m
\end{aligned}
\tag{32}
$$

where the coefficients a_{ij}, b_{ij}, c_{ij}, and d_{ij} are constants. The initial conditions associated with (31) are the initial values of the state variables, $q_1(0)$, $q_2(0)$, ..., $q_n(0)$.

When dealing with the set of n state variables q_1, q_2, ..., q_n, we shall use the symbol $\mathbf{q}$ to denote the entire set.[2] Thus

$$
\mathbf{q} = \begin{bmatrix} q_1 \\ q_2 \\ \vdots \\ q_n \end{bmatrix}
$$

which is a matrix having n rows and a single column, with each of its elements being one of the state variables. As such, its elements are functions of time. Matrices having a single column are commonly referred to as **column vectors** or, for short, **vectors**. Hence the symbol $\mathbf{q}$ will be called the **state vector**, and it is understood that its ith element is the state variable q_i. The initial value of the state vector $\mathbf{q}$ is the vector

$$
\mathbf{q}(0) = \begin{bmatrix} q_1(0) \\ q_2(0) \\ \vdots \\ q_n(0) \end{bmatrix}
$$

---

[2] Boldface symbols are used to denote matrices. The symbols are generally capitals, but lowercase letters may be used for vectors. Variables written in italic type are scalars.

The vector $\dot{\mathbf{q}}$ is an n-element vector whose elements are the derivatives of the corresponding elements in $\mathbf{q}$:

$$\dot{\mathbf{q}} = \begin{bmatrix} \dot{q}_1 \\ \dot{q}_2 \\ \vdots \\ \dot{q}_n \end{bmatrix}$$

The m inputs $u_1, u_2, \ldots, u_m$ will be represented by $\mathbf{u}$, the **input vector**, which is defined as

$$\mathbf{u} = \begin{bmatrix} u_1 \\ u_2 \\ \vdots \\ u_m \end{bmatrix}$$

The p outputs $y_1, y_2, \ldots, y_p$ will be elements in $\mathbf{y}$, the **output vector**, which is given by

$$\mathbf{y} = \begin{bmatrix} y_1 \\ y_2 \\ \vdots \\ y_p \end{bmatrix}$$

The coefficients are put into the following four matrices. We define the $n \times n$ matrix

$$\mathbf{A} = \begin{bmatrix} a_{11} & a_{12} & \cdots & a_{1n} \\ a_{21} & a_{22} & \cdots & a_{2n} \\ \vdots & \vdots & & \vdots \\ a_{n1} & a_{n2} & \cdots & a_{nn} \end{bmatrix}$$

the $n \times m$ matrix

$$\mathbf{B} = \begin{bmatrix} b_{11} & b_{12} & \cdots & b_{1m} \\ b_{21} & b_{22} & \cdots & b_{2m} \\ \vdots & \vdots & & \vdots \\ b_{n1} & b_{n2} & \cdots & b_{nm} \end{bmatrix}$$

the $p \times n$ matrix

$$\mathbf{C} = \begin{bmatrix} c_{11} & c_{12} & \cdots & c_{1n} \\ c_{21} & c_{22} & \cdots & c_{2n} \\ \vdots & \vdots & & \vdots \\ c_{p1} & c_{p2} & \cdots & c_{pn} \end{bmatrix}$$

and the $p \times m$ matrix

$$\mathbf{D} = \begin{bmatrix} d_{11} & d_{12} & \cdots & d_{1m} \\ d_{21} & d_{22} & \cdots & d_{2m} \\ \vdots & \vdots & & \vdots \\ d_{p1} & d_{p2} & \cdots & d_{pm} \end{bmatrix}$$

Then we can write the state-variable and output equations for the fixed linear system described by (31) and (32) as

$$\dot{\mathbf{q}} = \mathbf{Aq} + \mathbf{Bu}$$
$$\mathbf{y} = \mathbf{Cq} + \mathbf{Du} \tag{33}$$

Reflecting for a moment, we note that $\dot{q}_i$ is the ith element of $\dot{\mathbf{q}}$ and is obtained by multiplying the ith row of $\mathbf{A}$ by the corresponding elements in the column vector $\mathbf{q}$ and adding to that product the product of the ith row of $\mathbf{B}$ and the column vector $\mathbf{u}$. Carrying out these operations gives

$$\dot{q}_i = a_{i1}q_1 + a_{i2}q_2 + \cdots + a_{in}q_n + b_{i1}u_1 + \cdots + b_{im}u_m$$

Likewise, we find the kth element of $\mathbf{y}$ by multiplying the kth row of $\mathbf{C}$ by $\mathbf{q}$ and adding to that product the product of the kth row of $\mathbf{D}$ and the vector $\mathbf{u}$, obtaining

$$y_k = c_{k1}q_1 + c_{k2}q_2 + \cdots + c_{kn}q_n + d_{k1}u_1 + \cdots + d_{km}u_m$$

▶ **EXAMPLE 3.13**

For the system shown in Figure 3.1(a) and modeled in Example 3.1, write the state-variable model in the form of (33) and identify the coefficient matrices $\mathbf{A}$, $\mathbf{B}$, $\mathbf{C}$, and $\mathbf{D}$.

Solution

From Example 3.1, the state-variable equations are

$$\dot{x} = v$$
$$\dot{v} = \frac{1}{M}[-Kx - Bv + f_a(t)] \tag{34}$$

and the output equations are

$$f_K = Kx$$
$$v = v$$
$$a_M = \frac{1}{M}[-Kx - Bv + f_a(t)] \tag{35}$$

Note that v is both a specified output and a state variable. Although the corresponding output equation may seem trivial, we should include it when writing the model in matrix form.

Because there are two state variables, one input, and three outputs, the state vector **q**, the input vector **u**, and the output vector **y** will have two, one, and three elements respectively. Let

$$\mathbf{q} = \begin{bmatrix} x_1 \\ v_1 \end{bmatrix}, \quad \mathbf{u} = [\, f_a(t) \,], \quad \text{and} \quad \mathbf{y} = \begin{bmatrix} f_K \\ v \\ a_M \end{bmatrix}$$

When a matrix contains only a single element, as is the case with **u**, the brackets around the matrix are usually omitted. With the above definitions of **q**, **u**, and **y**, we can write (34) and (35) as

$$\begin{bmatrix} \dot{x}_1 \\ \dot{v}_1 \end{bmatrix} = \underbrace{\begin{bmatrix} 0 & 1 \\ -K/M & -B/M \end{bmatrix}}_{\mathbf{A}} \begin{bmatrix} x \\ v \end{bmatrix} + \underbrace{\begin{bmatrix} 0 \\ 1/M \end{bmatrix}}_{\mathbf{B}} f_a(t)$$

and

$$\begin{bmatrix} f_K \\ v \\ a_M \end{bmatrix} = \underbrace{\begin{bmatrix} K & 0 \\ 0 & 1 \\ -K/M & -B/M \end{bmatrix}}_{\mathbf{C}} \begin{bmatrix} x \\ v \end{bmatrix} + \underbrace{\begin{bmatrix} 0 \\ 0 \\ 1/M \end{bmatrix}}_{\mathbf{D}} f_a(t)$$

which have the form of (33) and where the coefficient matrices **A**, **B**, **C**, and **D** are specifically identified. Because there is only one input, **B** and **D** have only one column. The reader should verify that carrying out the matrix operations in these equations gives (34) and (35).

▶ **EXAMPLE 3.14**

Write the state-variable model in matrix form for the system shown in Figure 3.5(a) and considered in Example 3.7. Let the only output be the tensile force f_{K_1} in the spring K_1.

Solution

From (14), the state-variable equations are

$$\dot{x}_1 = v_1$$

$$\dot{v}_1 = \frac{1}{M}[-K_1 x_1 - B_1 v_1 + K_1 x_2 + f_a(t)]$$

$$\dot{x}_2 = \frac{1}{B_2}[K_1 x_1 - (K_1 + K_2)x_2]$$

and the output equation is $f_{K_1} = K_1(x_1 - x_2)$. We take the state vector **q**, the input vector **u**, and the output vector **y** to be

$$\mathbf{q} = \begin{bmatrix} x_1 \\ v_1 \\ x_2 \end{bmatrix}, \quad \mathbf{u} = [\, f_a(t) \,], \quad \text{and} \quad \mathbf{y} = [\, f_{K_1} \,]$$

Then

$$
\dot{\mathbf{q}} = \begin{bmatrix} 0 & 1 & 0 \\ -\dfrac{K_1}{M} & -\dfrac{B_1}{M} & \dfrac{K_1}{M} \\ \dfrac{K_1}{B_2} & 0 & -\left(\dfrac{K_1+K_2}{B_2}\right) \end{bmatrix} \mathbf{q} + \begin{bmatrix} 0 \\ \dfrac{1}{M} \\ 0 \end{bmatrix} \mathbf{u}
$$

and

$$
\mathbf{y} = \begin{bmatrix} K_1 & 0 & -K_1 \end{bmatrix} \mathbf{q} + \begin{bmatrix} 0 \end{bmatrix} \mathbf{u}
$$

which have the form of (33). Because there is only one input, **B** and **D** have only one column. Because there is only one output, **C** and **D** have only one row. Thus **B** is a column vector, **C** a row vector, and **D** a scalar. Such systems are called single-input, single-output systems to distinguish them from the more general class of multi-input, multi-output systems.

▶ **EXAMPLE 3.15**

Rewrite in matrix form the state-variable and output equations for the system shown in Figure 2.19(a) and modeled in Example 3.9.

Solution

From Example 3.9, the state-variable equations are

$$\dot{x}_1 = v_1$$

$$\dot{v}_1 = \frac{1}{M_1}[-K_1 x_1 - B_1 v_1 + K_1 x_2 + f_a(t)]$$

$$\dot{x}_2 = v_2$$

$$\dot{v}_2 = \frac{1}{M_2}[K_1 x_1 - (K_1 + K_2)x_2 - B_2 v_2 - M_2 g]$$

and the output equations are

$$x_{K_1} = x_1 - x_2$$

$$f_{B_2} = B_2 v_2$$

The state vector has four elements and is taken to be

$$
\mathbf{q} = \begin{bmatrix} x_1 \\ v_1 \\ x_2 \\ v_2 \end{bmatrix}
$$

We take the input vector **u** and the output vector **y** to be

$$
\mathbf{u} = \begin{bmatrix} f_a(t) \\ g \end{bmatrix}
$$

and

$$y = \begin{bmatrix} x_{K_1} \\ f_{B_2} \end{bmatrix}$$

With these definitions, we can write the model in the form of (33) as

$$\dot{q} = \begin{bmatrix} 0 & 1 & 0 & 0 \\ -\dfrac{K_1}{M_1} & -\dfrac{B_1}{M_1} & \dfrac{K_1}{M_1} & 0 \\ 0 & 0 & 0 & 1 \\ \dfrac{K_1}{M_2} & 0 & -\dfrac{(K_1 + K_2)}{M_2} & -\dfrac{B_2}{M_2} \end{bmatrix} q + \begin{bmatrix} 0 & 0 \\ \dfrac{1}{M_1} & 0 \\ 0 & 0 \\ 0 & -1 \end{bmatrix} u$$

and

$$y = \begin{bmatrix} 1 & 0 & -1 & 0 \\ 0 & 0 & 0 & B_2 \end{bmatrix} q + \begin{bmatrix} 0 & 0 \\ 0 & 0 \end{bmatrix} u$$

For any fixed linear system, the elements in the coefficients matrices **A**, **B**, **C**, and **D** will all be constants. Equations (33) would also be valid for a time-varying linear system, with the understanding that some of the elements in **A**, **B**, **C**, and **D** would then be functions of time.

For the case of systems that can be time-varying and nonlinear, a more comprehensive form for the equations is necessary. For a general nth-order system having m inputs, the individual state-variable equations would have the form

$$\dot{q}_1 = f_1(q_1, q_2, \ldots, q_n, u_1, \ldots, u_m, t)$$
$$\dot{q}_2 = f_2(q_1, q_2, \ldots, q_n, u_1, \ldots, u_m, t)$$
$$\vdots$$
$$\dot{q}_n = f_n(q_1, q_2, \ldots, q_n, u_1, \ldots, u_m, t)$$

(36)

where $q_1, q_2, \ldots, q_n$ are the state variables and $u_1, u_2, \ldots, u_m$ are the inputs. The algebraic functions $f_1, f_2, \ldots, f_n$ express the state-variable derivatives $\dot{q}_1, \dot{q}_2, \ldots, \dot{q}_n$ in terms of the state variables, the inputs, and possibly the time t.[3] The initial conditions associated with (36) are the initial values of the state variables, $q_1(0), q_2(0), \ldots, q_n(0)$. If the system

---

[3] Note that the use of the symbol f in this very general context is not related to the use of f to denote forces in mechanical systems.

has p outputs, the individual output equations have the general form

$$y_1 = g_1(q_1, q_2, \ldots, q_n, u_1, u_2, \ldots, u_m, t)$$
$$y_2 = g_2(q_1, q_2, \ldots, q_n, u_1, u_2, \ldots, u_m, t)$$
$$\vdots \tag{37}$$
$$y_p = g_p(q_1, q_2, \ldots, q_n, u_1, u_2, \ldots, u_m, t)$$

where g_1, g_2, $\ldots$, g_p are again algebraic functions of the state variables, the inputs, and possibly time. The sets of equations in (36) and (37) can be represented by the two vector equations

$$\dot{\mathbf{q}} = \mathbf{f}(\mathbf{q}, \mathbf{u}, t)$$
$$\mathbf{y} = \mathbf{g}(\mathbf{q}, \mathbf{u}, t) \tag{38}$$

where $\mathbf{f}$ and $\mathbf{g}$ are vector functions having n and p elements, respectively.

SUMMARY

In this chapter we introduced the concept of state variables and showed how to write the mathematical model of a dynamic system in terms of these variables. Such a model consists of a set of coupled first-order differential equations, whose right-hand sides are algebraic functions of the state variables and inputs. Once the state variables have been found as known functions of time, the system outputs can be found easily as algebraic functions of the state variables and inputs.

In Section 3.2 we used a very different approach, eliminating from our equations all variables except the inputs and outputs and their derivatives. For an nth-order system, we obtain an nth-order differential equation for each output. These equations, which are not coupled together and which can be solved independently of each other, have only the inputs and their derivatives as variables on the right-hand side.

The final section showed how to write the state-variable equations in matrix form. The analytical solution of input-output differential equations and also of matrix state-variable equations is considered in Chapter 6. Computer solutions are discussed in Chapter 15.

PROBLEMS

3.1 Find the state-variable model for the system shown in Figure 2.16(a) and considered in Example 2.5:

    a) When x and $v = \dot{x}$ are state variables.
    b) When z and $w = \dot{z}$ are state variables.

The inputs are $f_a(t)$ and g. Take the energy stored in the spring as the output.

3.2 The mathematical model of a linear system with input $f_a(t)$ and output y is

$$\dddot{x} + \alpha\ddot{x} + \beta\dot{x} + \gamma x = f_a(t)$$

$$y = \ddot{x} + \dot{x}$$

Write the model in state-variable form, where the state variables are x, $v = \dot{x}$, and $a = \ddot{x}$.

* 3.3 The following pair of equations corresponds to a linear dynamic system having $f_a(t)$ as its input and y as its output.

$$\ddot{y} + 4\dot{y} + 2y = x$$

$$\dot{x} + x + y = f_a(t)$$

Derive the state-variable form of the model. Define any new symbols.

3.4 A mechanical system having input $f_a(t)$ and output $y = \dot{x}_1 - \dot{x}_2$ obeys the pair of differential equations

$$M_1\ddot{x}_1 + B(\dot{x}_1 - \dot{x}_2) + K_1x_1 = 0$$

$$M_2\ddot{x}_2 + B(\dot{x}_2 - \dot{x}_1) + K_2x_2 = f_a(t)$$

Write the model in state-variable form when the state variables are x_1, $v_1 = \dot{x}_1$, x_2, and $v_2 = \dot{x}_2$.

* 3.5 Write state-variable equations for the mechanical system shown in Figure 2.15(a) and modeled in Example 2.4 by (2.20). Take the state variables to be the absolute displacements x_1 and x_2 and their derivatives v_1 and v_2. Include algebraic output equations for y_1, the viscous force of M_2 on M_1 (positive to the right), and y_2, the tensile force in spring K_2.

3.6 Repeat Problem 3.5 using (2.19). Take the state variables to be the absolute displacement x, its derivative $v_x = \dot{x}$, the relative displacement z, and its derivative $v_z = \dot{z}$.

3.7 Write state-variable equations for the mechanical system shown in Figure 2.17(a) and modeled in Example 2.6 by (2.25). The inputs are the applied force $f_a(t)$ and the gravitational constant g. Include algebraic output equations for the tensile force in each of the three springs.

3.8 Find a set of state-variable equations for the system shown in Figure P2.5. The output is the total momentum of the system.

* 3.9 Find the state-variable model for the system shown in Figure P2.15 when the outputs are the elongation y_1 of the spring K_1 and the acceleration a_1 of the mass M_1. The inputs are $f_a(t)$ and the gravitational constant g.

3.10 Repeat Problem 3.5 when the spring K_1 in Figure 2.15(a) is removed. Keep the same outputs, but use x_2, v_1, and v_2 as the state variables. Explain why it is not necessary to have x_1 as a state variable.

* 3.11 Find the state-variable model for the system shown in Figure P2.16. The output is the elongation of the lower spring.

3.12 Find the state-variable model for the system shown in Figure P2.21. The output is the increase in the separation between M_1 and M_2.

* 3.13 Write the state-variable equations for the system shown in Figure P2.27, where the input is the displacement $x_3(t)$. The output is the force exerted by the dashpot B_2 on point A, with the positive sense to the left.

3.14 Repeat Problem 3.13 when $B_2 = 0$. Let the output be the displacement x_2 instead of the force exerted by the dashpot.

* **3.15** The model for a certain dynamic system is

$$\dot{x}_1 = -3x_1 + 2x_2 + u_1(t) + 2\dot{u}_2$$
$$\dot{x}_2 = 2x_1 + x_2 + \dot{u}_1$$
$$y = x_1 - x_2 + u_2(t)$$

where x_1 and x_2 are state variables, $u_1(t)$ and $u_2(t)$ the inputs, and y the output. Rewrite the model in state-variable form by avoiding derivatives on the right side of the equations. Define any new symbols and identify the state variables.

3.16 The input to the system shown in Figure P3.16 is the displacement $x_2(t)$ of M_2. Write a set of state-variable equations. The springs are relaxed when $x_1 = x_2 = 0$. Include an output equation for the downward force f_2 that must be applied to M_2 to achieve the specified motion.

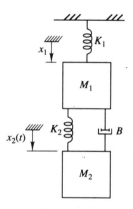

FIGURE P3.16

3.17 For the system shown in Figure P2.2, replace the force input $f_a(t)$ by the displacement $x_2(t)$ of M_2. The springs are relaxed when $x_1 = x_2 = 0$. Write a set of state-variable equations. Include an output equation for the force f_2 that must be applied to M_2 to achieve the specified motion, with the positive sense to the left.

* **3.18** Find a set of state-variable equations for the system shown in Figure P2.6 when the inputs are $x_3(t)$ and $f_a(t)$. The outputs are the velocities v_1 and v_2.

3.19 A linear dynamic system with input $u(t)$, output y, and state variables x_1 and x_2 is characterized by the equations

$$\dot{x}_1 + 2\dot{x}_2 = 3x_1 + 4x_2 - 5u(t)$$
$$\dot{x}_1 - \dot{x}_2 = 2x_1 + 2x_2$$
$$y = \dot{x}_1 + 2x_2$$

Find the state-variable and output equations.

3.20 Find the state-variable model for the system shown in Figure P2.22, when the energy stored in each spring is a separate output.

* 3.21 Find the state-variable model for the system shown in Figure P2.23. The outputs are the momentum of each mass and the tensile force in the cable.

3.22 Find the state-variable model for the system shown in Figure P2.24 when the elongation of each spring is a separate output.

3.23 Redo Example 3.11 by using the p operator to obtain
   a) The input-output equation for x_1.
   b) The input-output equation for x_2.

* 3.24 Use the p operator to obtain the input-output equation relating x_1 and $x_2(t)$ for the system shown in Figure 3.7(a), starting with
   a) The state-variable equations for x_1 and v_1 given in (18).
   b) The state-variable equations for x_1 and q given in (22).

3.25 **a)** Starting with (2.19) and using the p operator, obtain an input-output differential equation for x in the system model developed in Example 2.4. To simplify the calculations, let all parameters have values of unity in the appropriate units.
   b) Repeat part (a) by starting with (2.20) to find the input-output equation for x_1. Compare the answer to that which you obtained in part (a).

* 3.26 Set all of the parameters to unity in (2.25) and then use the p operator to obtain the input-output equation relating x_1 to the inputs $f_a(t)$ and g for the system shown in Figure 2.17(a).

3.27 **a)** Repeat Problem 3.26 for (2.29), describing the system shown in Figure 2.19(a).
   b) Obtain the input-output equation for x_2.

3.28 Write in matrix form the state-variable model developed in Example 3.8, with the input $x_2(t)$ and the outputs x_1 and v_1. Identify the matrices **A**, **B**, **C**, and **D**, the state vector **q**, the input vector **u**, and the output vector **y**. Also give the values of n, m, and p.

* 3.29 Repeat Problem 3.28 for the system modeled by (8) and (9) in Example 3.5, with the input $f_a(t)$ and the outputs f_{K_2} and m_T.

3.30 Repeat Problem 3.29 using (10) and (11) in place of (8) and (9).

3.31 Repeat Problem 3.28 for the system modeled by (3) and (4) in Example 3.2, with the input $f_a(t)$ and the outputs f_{K_2} and m_T.

3.32 Repeat Problem 3.28 for the state-variable model developed in Example 3.6, with the input $f_a(t)$ and the outputs f_{K_2}, m_T, and v_2.

ROTATIONAL MECHANICAL SYSTEMS

In Chapter 2 we presented the laws governing translational systems and introduced the use of free-body diagrams as an aid in writing equations describing the motion. In Chapter 3 we showed how to rearrange the equations and develop state-variable and input-output models.

Extending these procedures to rotational systems requires little in the way of new concepts. We first introduce the three rotational elements that are analogs of mass, friction, and stiffness in translational systems. Two other elements, levers and gears, are characterized in a somewhat different way. The use of interconnection laws and free-body diagrams is very similar to their use for translational systems. In the examples, we shall seek models consisting of sets of state-variable and output equations or else input-output equations that contain only a single unknown variable. The chapter closes with examples of combined translational and rotational systems.

4.1 VARIABLES

For rotational mechanical systems, the symbols used for the variables are

θ, angular displacement in radians (rad)

ω, angular velocity in radians per second (rad/s)

α, angular acceleration in radians per second per second (rad/s^2)

τ, torque in newton-meters (N·m)

all of which are functions of time. Angular displacements are measured with respect to some specified reference angle, often the equilibrium orientation of the body or point in question. We shall always choose the reference arrows for the angular displacement, velocity, and acceleration of a body to be in the same direction so that the relationships

$$\omega = \dot{\theta}$$

$$\alpha = \dot{\omega} = \ddot{\theta}$$

hold. The conventions used are illustrated in Figure 4.1, where τ denotes an external torque applied to the rotating body by means of some unspecified mechanism, such as by a gear on the supporting shaft. Because of the convention that the assumed positive directions for θ, ω, and α are the same, it is not necessary to show all three reference arrows explicitly.

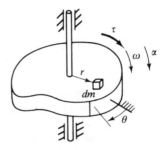

FIGURE 4.1   Conventions for designating rotational variables.

The power supplied to the rotating body in Figure 4.1 is

$$p = \tau\omega \tag{1}$$

The power is the derivative of the energy w, and the energy supplied to the body up to time t is

$$w(t) = w(t_0) + \int_{t_0}^{t} p(\lambda)d\lambda$$

■ 4.2 ELEMENT LAWS

The elements used to represent physical devices in rotational systems are moment of inertia, friction, stiffness, levers, and gears. We shall restrict our consideration to elements that rotate about fixed axes in an inertial reference frame.

Moment of Inertia

When Newton's second law is applied to the differential mass element dm in Figure 4.1 and the result is integrated over the entire body, we obtain

$$\frac{d}{dt}(J\omega) = \tau \tag{2}$$

where $J\omega$ is the angular momentum of the body and where τ denotes the net torque applied about the fixed axis of rotation. The symbol J denotes the **moment of inertia** in kilogram-meters^2 (kg·m^2). We can obtain it by carrying out the integration of $r^2 \, dm$ over the entire body.

The moment of inertia for a body whose mass M can be considered to be concentrated at a point is ML^2, where L is the distance from the point to the axis of rotation. Figure 4.2 shows a slender bar and a solid disk, each of which has a total mass M that is uniformly distributed throughout the body. In parts (a) and (b) of the figure, expressions for J are given for the case where the axis of rotation passes through the center of mass. The results for other common shapes can be found in basic physics and mechanics books. If we have an axis that does not pass through the center of mass, we can use the **parallel-axis theorem**. Let J_0 denote the moment of inertia about the parallel axis that passes through the center of mass, and let a be the distance between the two axes. Then the desired moment of inertia is

$$J = J_0 + Ma^2 \tag{3}$$

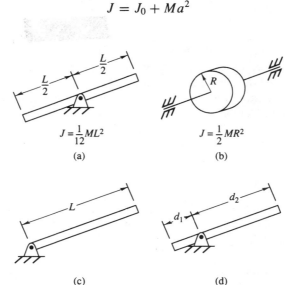

FIGURE 4.2 Moments of inertia. (a) Slender bar. (b) Disk. (c), (d) Slender bar where axis of rotation does not pass through the center of mass.

For the slender bar shown in Figure 4.2(c) with the axis of rotation at one end, (3) gives

$$J = \frac{1}{12}ML^2 + M\left(\frac{L}{2}\right)^2 = \frac{1}{3}ML^2 \tag{4}$$

For two or more components rotating about the same axis, we can find the total moment of inertia by summing the individual contributions. If the uniform bar shown in Figure 4.2(d) has a total mass M, then the masses for the sections of length d_1 and d_2 will be $M_1 = d_1 M/(d_1 + d_2)$ and $M_2 = d_2 M/(d_1 + d_2)$. Using (4), we see that the total moment of inertia is

$$J = \frac{1}{3}M_1 d_1^2 + \frac{1}{3}M_2 d_2^2 = \frac{M(d_1^3 + d_2^3)}{3(d_1 + d_2)} \tag{5}$$

We consider only nonrelativistic systems and constant moments of inertia, so (2) reduces to

$$J\dot{\omega} = \tau \tag{6}$$

where $\dot{\omega}$ is the angular acceleration. As is the case for a mass having translational motion, a rotating body can store energy in both kinetic and potential forms. The kinetic energy is

$$w_k = \frac{1}{2}J\omega^2 \tag{7}$$

and for a uniform gravitational field, the potential energy is

$$w_p = Mgh \tag{8}$$

where M is the mass, g the gravitational constant, and h the height of the center of mass above its reference position. If the fixed axis of rotation is vertical or passes through the center of mass, there is no change in the potential energy as the body rotates, and (8) is not needed. To find the complete response of a dynamic system containing a rotating body, we must know its initial angular velocity $\omega(t_0)$. If its potential energy can vary or if we want to find $\theta(t)$, then we must also know $\theta(t_0)$.

Friction

A **rotational friction** element is one for which there is an algebraic relationship between the torque and the relative angular velocity between two surfaces. **Rotational viscous friction** arises when two rotating bodies are separated by a film of oil. Figure 4.3(a) shows two concentric rotating cylinders separated by a thin film of oil, where the angular velocities of the cylinders are ω_1 and ω_2 and the relative angular velocity is $\Delta\omega = \omega_2 - \omega_1$. The torque

$$\tau = B\Delta\omega \tag{9}$$

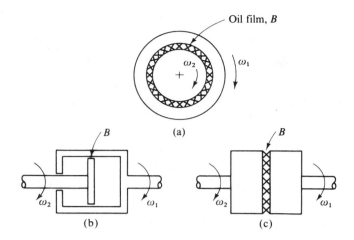

FIGURE 4.3 Rotational devices characterized by viscous friction.

will be exerted on each cylinder, in directions that tend to reduce the relative angular velocity $\Delta\omega$. Hence the positive sense of the frictional torque must be counterclockwise on the inner cylinder and clockwise on the outer cylinder. The friction coefficient B has units of newton-meter-seconds. Note that the same symbol is used for translational viscous friction, where it has units of newton-seconds per meter.

Equation (9) also applies to a rotational dashpot that might be used in modeling a fluid drive system, such as shown in Figure 4.3(b) or Figure 4.3(c). The inertia of the parts is assumed to be negligible or else is accounted for in the mathematical model by separate moments of inertia. If the rotational friction element is assumed to have no inertia, then when a torque τ is applied to one side, a torque of equal magnitude but opposite direction must be exerted on the other side (by a wall, the air, or some other component), as shown in Figure 4.4(a), where $\tau = B(\omega_2 - \omega_1)$. Thus in Figure 4.4(b), the torque τ passes through the first friction element and is exerted directly on the moment of inertia J.

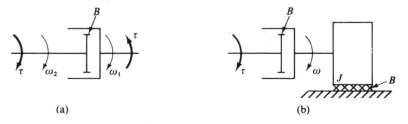

FIGURE 4.4 (a) Dashpot with negligible inertia. (b) Torque transmitted through a friction element.

Other types of friction, such as the damping vanes shown in Figure 4.5(a), may exert a retarding torque that is not directly proportional to the angular velocity but that may be described by a curve of τ versus $\Delta\omega$, as shown in Figure 4.5(b). For a linear element, the curve must be a straight line passing through the origin. The power supplied to the friction element, $\tau\Delta\omega$, is immediately lost to the mechanical system in the form of heat.

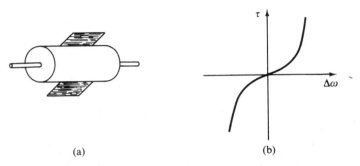

(a)   (b)

FIGURE 4.5   (a) Rotor with damping vanes. (b) Nonlinear friction characteristic.

Stiffness

Rotational stiffness is usually associated with a torsional spring, such as the mainspring of a clock, or with a relatively thin shaft. It is an element for which there is an algebraic relationship between τ and θ, and it is generally represented as shown in Figure 4.6(a). The angle θ is the relative angular displacement of the ends of the element from the positions corresponding to no applied torque. If both ends of the device can move as shown in Figure 4.6(b), then the element law relates τ and $\Delta\theta$, where $\Delta\theta = \theta_2 - \theta_1$. For a linear torsional spring or flexible shaft,

$$\tau = K\Delta\theta \tag{10}$$

where K is the spring constant with units of newton-meters (N·m), in contrast to newtons per meter for the parameter K in translational systems. For a thin shaft, K is directly proportional to the shear modulus of the material and to the square of the cross-sectional area and is inversely proportional to the length of the shaft.

Because we assume that the moment of inertia of a stiffness element either is negligible or is represented by a separate element, the torques exerted on the two ends of a stiffness element must be equal in magnitude and opposite in direction, as was indicated in Figure 4.6(b). Thus for the system shown in Figure 4.7, the applied torque τ passes through the first shaft and is exerted directly on the body that has moment of inertia J.

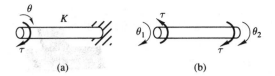

(a)

(b)

FIGURE 4.6 (a) Rotational stiffness element with one end fixed. (b) Rotational stiffness element with $\Delta\theta = \theta_2 - \theta_1$.

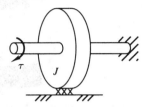

FIGURE 4.7 Torque transmitted through a shaft.

Potential energy is stored in a twisted stiffness element and can affect the response of the system at later times. For a linear spring or shaft, the potential energy is

$$w_p = \frac{1}{2}K(\Delta\theta)^2 \tag{11}$$

The relative angular displacement at time t_0 is one of the initial conditions we need in order to find the response of a system for $t \geq t_0$.

The Lever

An **ideal lever** is assumed to be a rigid bar pivoted at a point and having no mass, no friction, no momentum, and no stored energy. In all our examples the pivot point will be fixed. If the magnitude of the angle of rotation is small (say less than 0.25 rad), the motion of the ends can be considered strictly translational. In Figure 4.8, let θ denote the angular displacement of the lever from the horizontal position. For a rigid lever with a fixed pivot,

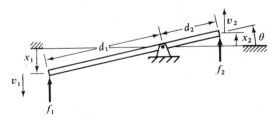

FIGURE 4.8 The lever.

the displacements of the ends are given by $x_1 \simeq d_1\theta$ and $x_2 \simeq d_2\theta$, where θ is in radians. Thus for small displacements we have

$$x_2 = \left(\frac{d_2}{d_1}\right) x_1 \tag{12}$$

and, by differentiating the foregoing equation, we find

$$v_2 = \left(\frac{d_2}{d_1}\right) v_1 \tag{13}$$

Because the sum of the moments about the pivot point vanishes, as required by the assumed absence of mass, it follows that $f_2 d_2 - f_1 d_1 = 0$, or

$$f_2 = \left(\frac{d_1}{d_2}\right) f_1 \tag{14}$$

The pivot exerts a downward force of $f_1 + f_2$ on the lever, but this does not enter into the derivation of (14), because this force exerts no moment about the pivot. The lever differs from the mass, friction, and stiffness elements in that the algebraic relationships given by (12) through (14) involve pairs of the same types of variables: two displacements, two velocities, or two forces.

If the lever's mass cannot be neglected, then we must include its moment of inertia when summing moments about the pivot point, and (14) is no longer valid. If the bar in Figure 4.8 has mass M, then its moment of inertia is given by (5). The examples in Section 4.4 include a system with a massless lever and one in which the lever's mass is not negligible.

Gears

Consider next the pair of gears shown in Figure 4.9. In order to develop the basic geometric and torque relationships, we shall assume **ideal gears**, which have no moment of inertia, no stored energy, no friction, and a perfect meshing of the teeth. Any inertia or bearing friction in an actual pair of gears can be represented by separate lumped elements in the free-body diagrams.

The relative sizes of the two gears result in a proportionality constant for the angular displacements, angular velocities, and transmitted torques of the respective shafts. For purposes of analysis, it is convenient to visualize the pair of ideal gears as two circles, shown in Figure 4.10(a), that are tangent at the contact point and rotate without slipping. The spacing between teeth must be equal for each gear in a pair, so the radii of the gears are proportional to the number of teeth. Thus if r and n denote the radius and number of teeth, respectively, then

$$\frac{r_2}{r_1} = \frac{n_2}{n_1} = N \tag{15}$$

where N is called the **gear ratio**.

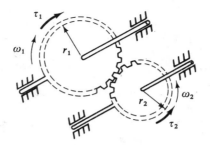

FIGURE 4.9 A pair of gears.

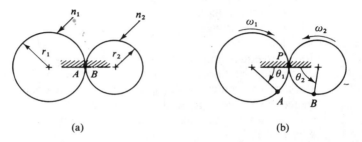

FIGURE 4.10 Ideal gears. (a) Reference position. (b) After rotation.

Let points A and B in Figure 4.10(a) denote points on the circles that are in contact with each other at some reference time t_0. At some later time, points A and B will have moved to the positions shown in Figure 4.10(b), where θ_1 and θ_2 denote the respective angular displacements from their original positions. Because the arc lengths PA and PB must be equal,

$$r_1\theta_1 = r_2\theta_2 \tag{16}$$

which we can rewrite as

$$\frac{\theta_1}{\theta_2} = \frac{r_2}{r_1} = N \tag{17}$$

By differentiating (16) with respect to time, we see that the angular velocities are also related by the gear ratio:

$$\frac{\omega_1}{\omega_2} = \frac{r_2}{r_1} = N \tag{18}$$

Note that the positive directions of θ_1 and θ_2, and likewise of ω_1 and ω_2, are taken in opposite directions in the figure. Otherwise a negative sign would be introduced into (16), (17), and (18).

We can derive the torque relationship for a pair of gears by drawing a free-body diagram for each gear, as shown in Figure 4.11. The external torques applied to the gear shafts are denoted by τ_1 and τ_2. The force

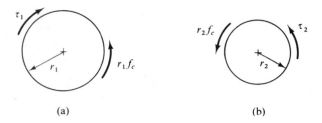

(a)   (b)

FIGURE 4.11   Free-body diagrams for a pair of ideal gears.

exerted by each gear at the point of contact by its mate is f_c. By the law of reaction forces, the arrows must be in opposite directions for the two gears. The corresponding torques $r_1 f_c$ and $r_2 f_c$ are shown on the diagram. In addition to the contact force f_c, each gear must be supported by a bearing force of equal magnitude and opposite direction, because the gears have no translational motion. However, because the bearing support forces act through the center of the gear, they do not contribute to the torque and hence have been omitted from the figure. Because the gears have no inertia, the sum of the torques on each of the gears must be zero. Thus, from Figure 4.11,

$$f_c r_1 - \tau_1 = 0$$
$$f_c r_2 + \tau_2 = 0$$

(19)

Eliminating the contact force f_c, the value of which is seldom of interest, we obtain

$$\frac{\tau_2}{\tau_1} = -\frac{r_2}{r_1} = -N$$

(20)

The minus sign in (20) should be expected, because both τ_1 and τ_2 in Figure 4.11 are shown as driving torques; that is, the reference arrows indicate that positive values of τ_1 and τ_2 both tend to make the gears move in the positive direction. The gears are assumed to have no inertia, so the two torques must actually be in opposite directions, and either τ_1 or τ_2 must be negative at any instant.

An alternative derivation of (20) makes use of the fact that the power supplied to the first gear is $p_1 = \tau_1 \omega_1$ and the power supplied to the second gear is $p_2 = \tau_2 \omega_2$. Since no energy can be stored in the ideal gears and since no power can be dissipated as heat due to the assumed absence of friction, conservation of energy requires that $p_1 + p_2 = 0$. Thus

$$\tau_1 \omega_1 + \tau_2 \omega_2 = 0$$

or

$$\frac{\tau_2}{\tau_1} = -\frac{\omega_1}{\omega_2} = -N$$

which agrees with (20).

4.3 INTERCONNECTION LAWS

The interconnection laws for rotational systems involve laws for torques and angular displacements that are analogous to (2.13) and (2.14) for translational mechanical systems. The law governing reaction torques has an important modification when compared to the one governing reaction forces.

D'Alembert's Law

For a body with constant moment of inertia rotating about a fixed axis, we can write (6) as

$$\sum_i (\tau_{\text{ext}})_i - J\dot{\omega} = 0 \tag{21}$$

where the summation over i includes all the torques acting on the body. Like the translational version of D'Alembert's law, the term $-J\dot{\omega}$ can be considered an **inertial torque**. When it is included along with all the other torques acting on the body, (21) reduces to the form appropriate for a body in equilibrium:

$$\sum_i \tau_i = 0 \tag{22}$$

In the application of (22), the torque $J\dot{\omega}$ is directed opposite to the positive sense of θ, ω, and α. D'Alembert's law can also be applied to a junction point that has no moment of inertia, in which case the $J\dot{\omega}$ term vanishes.

The Law of Reaction Torques

For bodies that are rotating about the same axis, any torque exerted by one element on another is accompanied by a **reaction torque** of equal magnitude and opposite direction on the first element. In Figure 4.12, for example, a counterclockwise torque $K_1\theta_1$ exerted by the shaft K_1 on the right disk is accompanied by a clockwise torque $K_1\theta_1$ exerted by the disk on the shaft. However, for bodies not rotating about the same axis, the magnitudes of the two torques are not necessarily equal. For the pair of gears shown in Figure 4.9, Figure 4.10, and Figure 4.11, the contact forces where the gears

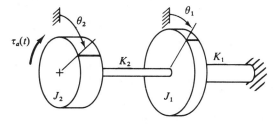

FIGURE 4.12 Rotational system to illustrate the laws for reaction torques and angular displacements.

mesh are equal and opposite, but because the gears have different radii, the torque exerted by the first gear on the second has a different magnitude from the torque exerted by the second on the first.

The Law for Angular Displacements

When examining the interconnection of elements in a system, we automatically use the fact that we can express the motions of some of the elements in terms of the motions of other elements. In Figure 4.12, the angular velocity of the left end of the shaft K_1 is identical to the angular velocity of the disk labeled J_1. Suppose that, in the same figure, the reference marks on the rims are at the top of the two disks when no torque is applied, but make the angles θ_1 and θ_2 with the vertical reference when the torque $\tau_a(t)$ is applied to the left disk. Then the net angular displacement for the shaft K_2 with respect to its unstressed condition is $\theta_2 - \theta_1$.

One way to summarize these facts in the form of a general interconnection law is to say that at any instant the algebraic sum of the differences in angular displacement around any closed path is zero. The equation

$$\sum_i (\Delta\theta)_i = 0 \quad \text{around any closed path} \tag{23}$$

is analogous to (2.14) for translational systems. It is understood that the signs in the summation take into account the direction in which the path is being traversed and that all measurements are with respect to reference positions that correspond to a single equilibrium condition for the system. If in Figure 4.12, for example, the relative differences in angular displacement are summed going from the vertical reference to disk 1, then to disk 2, and finally back to the vertical reference, (23) gives

$$(\theta_1 - 0) + (\theta_2 - \theta_1) + (0 - \theta_2) = 0$$

Although this is a rather trivial result, it does provide a formal basis for stating that the relative angular displacements for the shafts K_1 and K_2 are θ_1 and $\theta_2 - \theta_1$, respectively. If for some reason the references for the angular displacements did not correspond to a single equilibrium condition, then the summation in (23) would be a constant other than zero.

In formulating the system equations, we normally use (23) automatically to reduce the number of displacement variables that must be shown on the diagram. Equation (23) could be differentiated to yield a comparable equation governing the relative velocities.

■ 4.4 OBTAINING THE SYSTEM MODEL

The methods for using the element and interconnection laws to develop an appropriate mathematical model for a rotational system are the same as those discussed in Chapter 2 and Chapter 3 for translational systems. We indicate the assumed positive directions for the variables, and the assumed senses for the angular displacement, velocity, and acceleration of a body are chosen to be the same. We automatically use (23) to avoid introducing more symbols than are necessary to describe the motion. For each mass or junction point whose motion is unknown beforehand, we normally draw a free-body diagram showing all torques, including the inertial torque. We express all the torques except inputs in terms of angular displacements, velocities, or accelerations by means of the element laws. Then we apply D'Alembert's law, as given in (22), to each free-body diagram.

If we seek a set of state-variable equations, we identify the state variables and write those equations (such as $\dot\theta = \omega$) that do not require a free-body diagram. We write the equations obtained from the free-body diagrams by D'Alembert's law in terms of the state variables and inputs and manipulate them into the standard form of (3.31) or (3.36). Each of the state-variable equations should express the derivative of a different state variable as an *algebraic* function of the state variables, inputs, and possibly time. For any output of the system that is not one of the state variables, we need a separate algebraic equation.

If, on the other hand, we seek an input-output differential equation, we normally write the equations from the free-body diagrams in terms of only angular displacements or only angular velocities. Then we combine the equations to eliminate all variables except the input and output, which can be done by the p operator described in Section 3.2. For single-input, single-output systems, the equation has the form of (3.25).

We shall now consider a number of examples involving free-body diagrams, state-variable equations, and input-output equations for rotational systems. Although these examples involve linear friction and stiffness elements, it is a simple matter to replace the appropriate terms by the nonlinear element laws when we encounter a nonlinear system. For example, a linear frictional torque $B\omega$ would become $\tau_B(\omega)$, which is a single-valued algebraic function that describes the nonlinear relationship.

▶ *EXAMPLE 4.1*

Derive the state-variable model for the rotational system shown in Figure 4.13(a) when the outputs are the angular acceleration of the disk and the counterclockwise torque exerted on the disk by the flexible shaft. Also find the input-output equation relating θ and $\tau_a(t)$.

Solution

The first step is to draw a free-body diagram of the disk. This is done in Figure 4.13(b), where the left face of the disk is shown. The torques acting on the disk are the spring torque $K\theta$, the viscous-frictional torque $B\omega$, and the applied torque $\tau_a(t)$. In addition, the inertial torque $J\dot\omega$ is indicated by

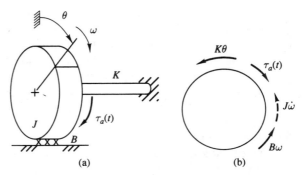

FIGURE 4.13   (a) Rotational system for Example 4.1.
(b) Free-body diagram.

the dashed arrow. By D'Alembert's law,

$$J\dot{\omega} + B\omega + K\theta = \tau_a(t) \tag{24}$$

The normal choices for the state variables are θ and ω, which are related to the energy stored in the shaft and in the disk, respectively. One state-variable equation is $\dot{\theta} = \omega$, and the other can be found by solving (24) for $\dot{\omega}$. Thus

$$
\begin{aligned}
\dot{\theta} &= \omega \\
\dot{\omega} &= \frac{1}{J}[-K\theta - B\omega + \tau_a(t)]
\end{aligned}
\tag{25}
$$

The output equations are

$$
\begin{aligned}
\alpha_M &= \frac{1}{J}[-K\theta - B\omega + \tau_a(t)] \\
\tau_K &= K\theta
\end{aligned}
$$

For the input-output equation with θ designated as the output, we merely rewrite (24) with all terms on the left side expressed in terms of θ and its derivatives. Then the desired result is

$$J\ddot{\theta} + B\dot{\theta} + K\theta = \tau_a(t)$$

▶ *EXAMPLE 4.2*

In the system shown in Figure 4.14(a), the two shafts are assumed to be flexible, with stiffness constants K_1 and K_2. The two disks, with moments of inertia J_1 and J_2, are supported by bearings whose friction is negligible compared with the viscous-friction elements denoted by the coefficients B_1 and B_2. The reference positions for θ_1 and θ_2 are the positions of the reference marks on the rims of the disks when the system contains no stored

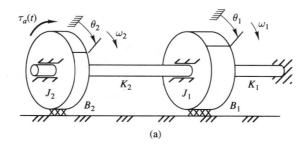

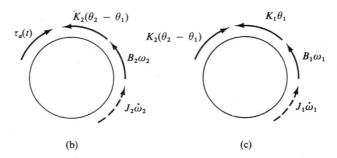

FIGURE 4.14 (a) Rotational system for Example 4.2. (b), (c) Free-body diagrams.

energy. Find a state-variable model when the outputs are the counterclockwise torque exerted on J_2 by the shaft K_2 and the total angular momentum of the disks. Also find an input-output equation relating θ_2 and $\tau_a(t)$.

Solution

The system has two inertia elements with independent angular velocities and two shafts with independent angular displacements, so four state variables are required. We choose θ_1, θ_2, ω_1, and ω_2, because they reflect the potential energy stored in each of the shafts and the kinetic energy stored in each disk.

The resulting free-body diagrams are shown in Figure 4.14(b) and Figure 4.14(c), where only the torque $K_2(\theta_2 - \theta_1)$, which is the reaction torque on the left disk by the shaft connecting the two disks, should require an explanation. The corresponding reference arrow has arbitrarily been drawn counterclockwise in Figure 4.14(b), implying that the torque is being treated as a retarding torque on disk 2. The actual torque will act in the counterclockwise direction only when $\theta_2 > \theta_1$, so the torque must be labeled $K_2(\theta_2 - \theta_1)$ and not $K_2(\theta_1 - \theta_2)$. By the law of reaction torques, the effect of the connecting shaft on disk 1 is a torque $K_2(\theta_2 - \theta_1)$ with its positive sense in the clockwise direction. We can reach the same conclusion by first selecting a clockwise sense for the arrow in Figure 4.14(c), thereby treating that torque as a driving torque on disk 1, and then noting that disk 2 will tend to drive disk 1 in the positive direction only if $\theta_2 > \theta_1$. Thus the correct expression is $K_2(\theta_2 - \theta_1)$. Of course, if we had selected a counterclockwise arrow in Figure 4.14(c), we would have labeled the arrow either $-K_2(\theta_2 - \theta_1)$ or $K_2(\theta_1 - \theta_2)$.

For each of the free-body diagrams, the algebraic sum of the torques may be set equal to zero by D'Alembert's law, giving the pair of equations

$$\begin{aligned}
J_1\dot{\omega}_1 + B_1\omega_1 + K_1\theta_1 - K_2(\theta_2 - \theta_1) &= 0 \\
J_2\dot{\omega}_2 + B_2\omega_2 + K_2(\theta_2 - \theta_1) - \tau_a(t) &= 0
\end{aligned} \tag{26}$$

Two of the state-variable equations are $\dot{\theta}_1 = \omega_1$ and $\dot{\theta}_2 = \omega_2$, and we can find the other two by solving the two equations in (26) for $\dot{\omega}_1$ and $\dot{\omega}_2$, respectively. Thus

$$\begin{aligned}
\dot{\theta}_1 &= \omega_1 \\
\dot{\omega}_1 &= \frac{1}{J_1}[-(K_1 + K_2)\theta_1 - B_1\omega_1 + K_2\theta_2] \\
\dot{\theta}_2 &= \omega_2 \\
\dot{\omega}_2 &= \frac{1}{J_2}[K_2\theta_1 - K_2\theta_2 - B_2\omega_2 + \tau_a(t)]
\end{aligned} \tag{27}$$

The output equations are

$$\begin{aligned}
\tau_{K_2} &= K_2(\theta_2 - \theta_1) \\
m_T &= J_1\omega_1 + J_2\omega_2
\end{aligned}$$

where m_T is the total angular momentum.

To obtain an input-output equation, we rewrite (26) in terms of the angular displacements θ_1 and θ_2. A slight rearrangement of terms yields

$$J_1\ddot{\theta}_1 + B_1\dot{\theta}_1 + (K_1 + K_2)\theta_1 - K_2\theta_2 = 0 \tag{28a}$$

$$-K_2\theta_1 + J_2\ddot{\theta}_2 + B_2\dot{\theta}_2 + K_2\theta_2 = \tau_a(t) \tag{28b}$$

Neither of the equations in (28) can be solved separately, but we want to combine them into a single differential equation that does not contain θ_1. Because θ_1 appears in (28b) but none of its derivatives do, we rearrange that equation to solve for θ_1 as

$$\theta_1 = \frac{1}{K_2}[J_2\ddot{\theta}_2 + B_2\dot{\theta}_2 + K_2\theta_2 - \tau_a(t)]$$

Substituting this result into (28a) gives

$$\begin{aligned}
J_1 J_2\theta_2^{(iv)} + (J_1 B_2 + J_2 B_1)\theta_2^{(iii)} &+ (J_1 K_2 + J_2 K_1 + J_2 K_2 + B_1 B_2)\ddot{\theta}_2 \\
+ (B_1 K_2 + B_2 K_1 + B_2 K_2)\dot{\theta}_2 &+ K_1 K_2\theta_2 \\
&= J_1\ddot{\tau}_a + B_1\dot{\tau}_a + (K_1 + K_2)\tau_a(t)
\end{aligned} \tag{29}$$

which is the desired result. Equation (29) is a fourth-order differential equation relating θ_2 and $\tau_a(t)$, in agreement with the fact that four state variables appear in (27).

In the last example, note the signs when like terms are gathered together in the torque equations corresponding to the free-body diagrams. In (28a) for J_1, all the terms involving θ_1 and its derivatives have the same sign. Similarly in (28b) for J_2, the signs of all the terms with θ_2 and its derivatives are the same. This is consistent with the comments made after Example 2.2 and can be used as a check on the work. Some insight into the reason for this can be obtained from the discussion of stability in Chapter 6.

▶ **EXAMPLE 4.3**

Find state-variable and input-output models for the system shown in Figure 4.14(a) and studied in Example 4.2, but with the shaft connecting disk 1 to the wall removed.

Solution

This example is analogous to Example 3.5. Because there are now only three energy-storing elements, we expect to need only three state variables. Two of these are chosen to be ω_1 and ω_2, which are related to the kinetic energy stored in the disks. The relative displacement of the ends of the connecting shaft is $\theta_2 - \theta_1$, which is related to the potential energy in that element. Hence we select as the third state variable

$$\theta_R = \theta_2 - \theta_1$$

although $\theta_1 - \theta_2$ would have been an equally good choice.

The free-body diagrams for each of the disks, with torques labeled in terms of the state variables and input, are shown in Figure 4.15. By D'Alembert's law,

$$J_1\dot{\omega}_1 + B_1\omega_1 - K_2\theta_R = 0$$
$$J_2\dot{\omega}_2 + B_2\omega_2 + K_2\theta_R = \tau_a(t) \tag{30}$$

We obtain one of the state-variable equations by noting that $\dot{\theta}_R = \dot{\theta}_2 - \dot{\theta}_1 = \omega_2 - \omega_1$, and we find the other two by rearranging the last two equations. Thus the third-order state-variable model is

$$\dot{\theta}_R = \omega_2 - \omega_1 \tag{31a}$$

$$\dot{\omega}_1 = \frac{1}{J_1}(-B_1\omega_1 + K_2\theta_R) \tag{31b}$$

$$\dot{\omega}_2 = \frac{1}{J_2}[-K_2\theta_R - B_2\omega_2 + \tau_a(t)] \tag{31c}$$

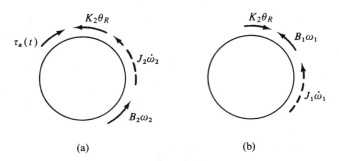

FIGURE 4.15   Free-body diagrams for Example 4.3.

The output equations for τ_{K_2} and m_T are

$$\tau_{K_2} = K_2\theta_R$$

$$m_T = J_1\omega_1 + J_2\omega_2$$

If one of the outputs were the angular displacement θ_2, it would not be possible to write an output equation for θ_2 as an algebraic function of θ_R, ω_1, ω_2, and $\tau_a(t)$. In that case we would need four state variables. For the state-variable equations, we could either use (27) with $K_1 = 0$ or add to (31) the equation $\dot{\theta}_2 = \omega_2$.

The input-output differential equation relating θ_2 and $\tau_a(t)$ can be obtained by letting $K_1 = 0$ in (29):

$$J_1 J_2\theta_2^{(iv)} + (J_1 B_2 + J_2 B_1)\theta_2^{(iii)} + (J_1 K_2 + J_2 K_2 + B_1 B_2)\ddot{\theta}_2$$
$$+ (B_1 + B_2)K_2\dot{\theta}_2 = J_1\ddot{\tau}_a + B_1\dot{\tau}_a + K_2\tau_a(t)$$

Although this could be viewed as a third-order differential equation in the variable $\dot{\theta}_2$, which is the angular velocity ω_2, we would need four initial conditions if we wanted to determine θ_2 rather than ω_2. This is consistent with the fact that four state variables are needed when the output is θ_2.

We would expect the input-output equation relating θ_R and $\tau_a(t)$ to be strictly third-order, because only three state variables are needed for the output θ_R. We see from (31a) that $\omega_1 = \omega_2 - \dot{\theta}_R$. Substituting this expression into (30), we obtain

$$J_1\dot{\omega}_2 + B_1\omega_2 - (J_1\ddot{\theta}_R + B_1\dot{\theta}_R + K_2\theta_R) = 0$$

$$J_2\dot{\omega}_2 + B_2\omega_2 + K_2\theta_R = \tau_a(t)$$

We can eliminate the variable ω_2 from this pair of equations by using the p-operator method described in Section 3.2. When this is done, we find that

$$J_1 J_2\dddot{\theta}_R + (J_1 B_2 + J_2 B_1)\ddot{\theta}_R + (J_1 K_2 + J_2 K_2 + B_1 B_2)\dot{\theta}_R$$
$$+ (B_1 + B_2)K_2\theta_R = J_1\dot{\tau}_a + B_1\tau_a(t)$$

▶ *EXAMPLE 4.4*

The shaft supporting the disk in the system shown in Figure 4.16 is composed of two sections that have spring constants K_1 and K_2. Show how to replace the two sections by an equivalent stiffness element, and derive the state-variable model. The outputs of interest are the angular displacements θ and θ_A.

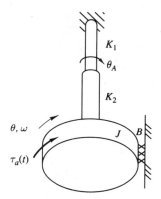

FIGURE 4.16 Rotational system for Example 4.4.

Solution

Free-body diagrams for each of the sections of the support shaft and for the inertia element J are shown in Figure 4.17. No inertial torques are included on the shafts, because their moments of inertia are assumed to be negligible. The quantity τ_r is the reaction torque applied by the support on the top of

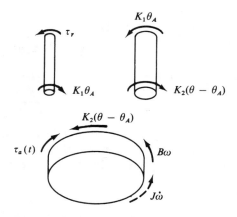

FIGURE 4.17 Free-body diagrams for Example 4.4.

the shaft. Summing the torques on each of the free-body diagrams gives

$$K_1\theta_A - \tau_r = 0 \tag{32a}$$

$$K_2(\theta - \theta_A) - K_1\theta_A = 0 \tag{32b}$$

$$J\dot{\omega} + B\omega + K_2(\theta - \theta_A) - \tau_a(t) = 0 \tag{32c}$$

We need the first of these equations only if we wish to find τ_r, which is not normally the case. Equations (32b) and (32c) can also be obtained by considering the free-body diagrams for just the disk and the massless junction of the two shafts. The corresponding free-body diagrams are shown in Figure 4.18. Applying D'Alembert's law to them yields (32b) and (32c).

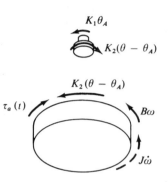

FIGURE 4.18   Alternative free-body diagrams for Example 4.4.

We see from (32b) that θ_A and θ are proportional to each other. Specifically,

$$\theta_A = \left(\frac{K_2}{K_1 + K_2}\right)\theta \tag{33}$$

Substituting (33) into (32c) yields

$$J\dot{\omega} + B\omega + K_{eq}\theta = \tau_a(t) \tag{34}$$

where

$$K_{eq} = \frac{K_1 K_2}{K_1 + K_2}$$

The parameter K_{eq} can be regarded as an equivalent spring constant for the series combination of the two shafts. Selecting θ and ω as the state variables and using (34), we can write the state-variable model as

$$\dot{\theta} = \omega$$
$$\dot{\omega} = \frac{1}{J}[-K_{eq}\theta - B\omega + \tau_a(t)] \tag{35}$$

The output θ is one of the state variables. The output equation for θ_A is given by (33).

▶ *EXAMPLE 4.5*

The system shown in Figure 4.19 consists of a moment of inertia J_1 corresponding to the rotor of a motor or a turbine, which is coupled to the moment of inertia J_2 representing a propeller. Power is transmitted through a fluid coupling with viscous-friction coefficient B and a shaft with spring constant K. A driving torque $\tau_a(t)$ is exerted on J_1, and a load torque $\tau_L(t)$ is exerted on J_2. If the output is the angular velocity ω_2, find the state-variable model and also the input-output differential equation.

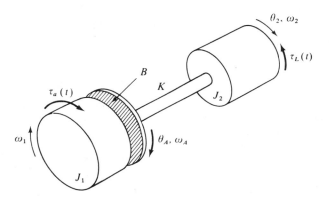

FIGURE 4.19   Rotational system for Example 4.5.

Solution

There are three independent energy-storing elements, so we select as state variables ω_1, ω_2, and the relative displacement θ_R of the two ends of the shaft, where

$$\theta_R = \theta_A - \theta_2 \tag{36}$$

Note that the equation

$$\dot{\theta}_R = \omega_A - \omega_2 \tag{37}$$

is not yet a state-variable equation because of the symbol ω_A on the right side.

   Next we draw the free-body diagrams for the two inertia elements and for the shaft, as shown in Figure 4.20. Note that the moment of inertia of the right side of the fluid coupling element is assumed to be negligible. The directions of the arrows associated with the torque $B(\omega_1 - \omega_A)$ are consistent with the law of reaction torques and also indicate that the frictional torque tends to retard the relative motion

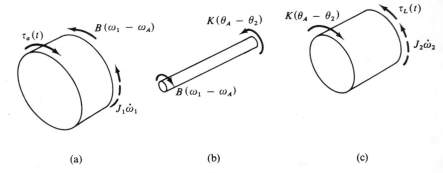

(a)   (b)   (c)

FIGURE 4.20   Free-body diagrams for Example 4.5.

Setting the algebraic sum of the torques on each diagram equal to zero yields the three equations

$$J_1\dot{\omega}_1 + B(\omega_1 - \omega_A) - \tau_a(t) = 0 \tag{38a}$$

$$B(\omega_1 - \omega_A) - K(\theta_A - \theta_2) = 0 \tag{38b}$$

$$J_2\dot{\omega}_2 - K(\theta_A - \theta_2) + \tau_L(t) = 0 \tag{38c}$$

Using (36), we can rewrite (38) as

$$J_1\dot{\omega}_1 + B(\omega_1 - \omega_A) - \tau_a(t) = 0 \tag{39a}$$

$$B(\omega_1 - \omega_A) = K\theta_R \tag{39b}$$

$$J_2\dot{\omega}_2 - K\theta_R + \tau_L(t) = 0 \tag{39c}$$

Substituting (39b) into (39a) and repeating (39c) give

$$J_1\dot{\omega}_1 + K\theta_R - \tau_a(t) = 0$$
$$J_2\dot{\omega}_2 - K\theta_R + \tau_L(t) = 0 \tag{40}$$

Also from (39b),

$$\omega_A = \omega_1 - \frac{K}{B}\theta_R \tag{41}$$

Substituting (41) into (37) and rearranging (40) give the three state-variable equations

$$\dot{\theta}_R = -\frac{K}{B}\theta_R + \omega_1 - \omega_2 \tag{42a}$$

$$\dot{\omega}_1 = \frac{1}{J_1}[-K\theta_R + \tau_a(t)] \tag{42b}$$

$$\dot{\omega}_2 = \frac{1}{J_2}[K\theta_R - \tau_L(t)] \tag{42c}$$

Because the specified output is one of the state variables, a separate output equation is not needed as part of the state-variable model.

To obtain the input-output equation, we first rewrite (38) in terms of the angular velocities ω_1, ω_2, and ω_A and the torques $\tau_A(t)$ and $\tau_L(t)$. Differentiating (38b) and (38c) and noting that $\dot\theta_2 = \omega_2$ and $\dot\theta_A = \omega_A$, we have

$$J_1\dot\omega_1 + B(\omega_1 - \omega_A) = \tau_a(t)$$

$$B(\dot\omega_1 - \dot\omega_A) - K(\omega_A - \omega_2) = 0$$

$$J_2\ddot\omega_2 - K(\omega_A - \omega_2) + \dot\tau_L = 0$$

By using the p-operator technique to eliminate ω_A and ω_1 from these equations, we can obtain the input-output equation

$$\dddot\omega_2 + \frac{K}{B}\ddot\omega_2 + K\left(\frac{1}{J_1} + \frac{1}{J_2}\right)\dot\omega_2$$

$$= \frac{K}{J_1 J_2}\tau_a(t) - \frac{1}{J_2}\ddot\tau_L - \frac{K}{B J_2}\dot\tau_L - \frac{K}{J_1 J_2}\tau_L(t) \qquad (43)$$

Although this result can be viewed as a second-order differential equation in $\dot\omega_2$, we will need three initial conditions if we are to determine ω_2 rather than the acceleration $\dot\omega_2$. Note that if the load torque $\tau_L(t)$ were given as an algebraic function of ω_2, as it would be in practice, ω_2 would appear in (43). Then the input-output equation would be strictly third-order.

The next three examples contain either a lever or a pendulum that does not rotate about its midpoint. In Example 4.6 the mass of the lever is assumed to be negligible. The pendulum in the next example is approximated by a point mass at the end of a rigid bar. The final example includes a lever whose mass is uniformly distributed along the bar.

▶ **EXAMPLE 4.6**

Find the state-variable equations for the system shown in Figure 4.21(a). Also find the output equation when the output is defined to be the force exerted on the pivot by the lever. The input is the displacement $x_4(t)$ of the right end of the spring K_2; it affects the mass M through the lever. The lever has a fixed pivot and is assumed to be massless yet rigid. Its angular rotation θ is small so that only horizontal motion need be considered. In a practical situation, the springs K_1 and K_2 might represent the stiffness of the lever and of associated linkages that have a certain degree of flexibility.

Solution

The displacements x_2 and x_3 are directly proportional to the angle θ and hence to one another. Furthermore, the two springs appear to form a series

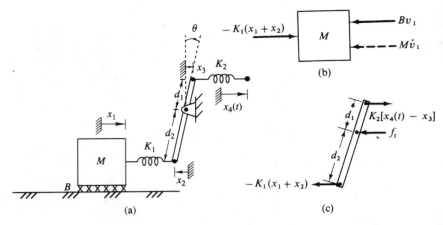

FIGURE 4.21   (a) Translational system containing a lever. (b), (c) Free-body diagrams.

combination somewhat similar to the one shown in Figure 2.24(a), because
the lever has no mass. Hence we can express x_2, x_3, and θ as algebraic
functions of x_1 and $x_4(t)$. Thus we will select only x_1 and v_1 as state
variables, with $x_4(t)$ being the input. By inspection, we determine that one
of the required state-variable equations is $\dot{x}_1 = v_1$.

The next step is to draw free-body diagrams for the mass M and the
lever, as shown in Figure 4.21(b) and Figure 4.21(c). We must pay particular
attention to the signs of the force arrows and to the expressions for the
elongations of the springs. For example, the elongation of spring K_1 is
$-(x_1 + x_2)$ because of the manner in which the displacements have been
defined. Summing the forces on the mass M yields

$$M\dot{v}_1 + Bv_1 + K_1(x_1 + x_2) = 0 \qquad (44)$$

The forces on the lever are those exerted by the springs and the reaction
force f_r of the pivot. Because the lever's angle of rotation θ is small, the
motion of the lever ends can be considered to be translational, obeying the
relationships $\theta = x_2/d_2 = x_3/d_1$ and

$$x_3 = \left(\frac{d_1}{d_2}\right)x_2 \qquad (45)$$

To obtain a second lever equation that involves x_1 and x_2 but not f_r, we
sum moments about the pivot point, getting

$$K_2[x_4(t) - x_3]d_1 - K_1(x_1 + x_2)d_2 = 0 \qquad (46$$

Equations (45) and (46) can also be obtained directly from (12) and (14)
In order to solve (44) for $\dot{v}_1$ as a function of only the state variables and the
input, we must first express x_2 in terms of x_1 and $x_4(t)$. Substituting (45

into (46) and solving for x_2, we obtain the algebraic expression

$$x_2 = \frac{(d_1/d_2)K_2x_4(t) - K_1x_1}{K_1 + (d_1/d_2)^2 K_2} \tag{47}$$

We find the second of the two state-variable equations by substituting (47) into (44) and rearranging terms so as to solve for $\dot{v}_1$. Doing this, we find that the state-variable equations are

$$\dot{x}_1 = v_1$$
$$\dot{v}_1 = -\frac{1}{M}\left[Bv_1 + \alpha K_1 x_1 + \alpha \left(\frac{d_2}{d_1}\right) K_1 x_4(t) \right] \tag{48}$$

where

$$\alpha = \frac{1}{1 + \dfrac{K_1}{K_2}\left(\dfrac{d_2}{d_1}\right)^2} \tag{49}$$

To develop the output equation expressing f_r as an algebraic function of the state variables and the input, we first sum the forces on the lever in Figure 4.21(c) to obtain

$$f_r = K_2[x_4(t) - x_3] + K_1(x_1 + x_2) \tag{50}$$

Substituting (45) and (47) into (50) gives

$$f_r = \left[K_1 + \left(K_2 - \frac{d_2}{d_1}K_1\right)\left(\frac{\alpha d_2 K_1}{d_1 K_2}\right) \right]x_1 + \left[K_2 + \alpha\left(\frac{d_2}{d_1}K_1 - K_2\right) \right]x_4(t)$$

which has the desired form.

In the last example it is instructive to consider the special case where $d_1 = d_2$, which corresponds to having the lever pivoted at its midpoint. From (49), $\alpha K_1 = K_1 K_2/(K_1 + K_2)$, which is the equivalent spring constant for a series connection of the two springs, as in (2.37). Furthermore, the reader can readily verify that (48) reduces to the equations describing the system shown in Figure 4.22(a), in which the massless junction A replaces the lever. In turn, this system is equivalent to that shown in Figure 4.22(b), where a single spring with the coefficient $K_{eq} = K_1 K_2/(K_1 + K_2)$ replaces the series spring connection. Note, in determining the motion of M, that the lever changes the effective direction of the displacement input $x_4(t)$.

In each of the next two examples, an object with mass M rotates about an axis that does not pass through the center of mass. In order to obtain a complete description of all the forces acting on such an object, we would have to consider the motion of its center of mass. The acceleration of this point has one component tangential to the direction of motion and another component perpendicular to it, directed toward the pivot point. The force corresponding to the tangential acceleration is accounted for by the

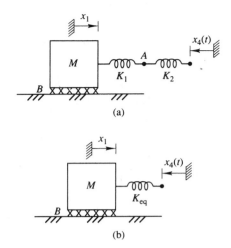

FIGURE 4.22   Systems equivalent to Figure 4.21(a) when $d_1 = d_2$.

D'Alembert torque $J\dot{\omega}$. Corresponding to the perpendicular component of acceleration, there is a centrifugal force directed away from the pivot point. However, this centrifugal force does not result in a torque about the pivot. Similarly, the forces exerted by the fixed pivot do not contribute to such a torque.

Obtaining expressions for the forces corresponding to the acceleration of the center of mass can become cumbersome, and the interested reader should consult a book on mechanics. When drawing free-body diagrams for rotating bodies, we shall generally consider only those forces that yield a torque about the axis of rotation and shall not include the centrifugal and pivot forces. We shall not seek expressions for the pivot forces except when the mass of the rotating body is negligible or when the acceleration of the center of mass is zero. The first of these special cases was illustrated by Example 4.6 and Figure 4.21(c). The second occurs when the axis of rotation passes through the center of mass.

▶ **EXAMPLE 4.7**

The pendulum sketched in Figure 4.23(a) can be considered a point mass M attached to a rigid massless bar of length L, which rotates about a pivot at the other end. An external torque $\tau_a(t)$ is applied to the bar by a mechanism that is not shown. Let B denote the rotational viscous friction at the pivot point. Derive the input-output differential equation relating the angular displacement θ to the applied torque $\tau_a(t)$. Also write a set of state-variable equations. Simplify the expressions for the case where $|\theta|$ is restricted to small values.

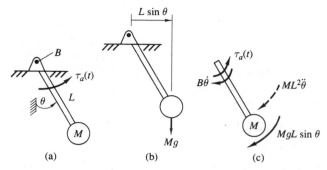

FIGURE 4.23 (a) Pendulum for Example 4.7. (b) Partial diagram to determine the torque produced by the weight. (c) Free-body diagram showing all torques about the pivot.

Solution

As can be seen from Figure 4.23(b), the weight of the mass results in a clockwise torque $MgL \sin \theta$ on the bar. Because of the assumption of a point mass, its moment of inertia about the pivot is $J = ML^2$. Applying D'Alembert's law to the free-body diagram in Figure 4.23(c) yields the input-output equation

$$ML^2\ddot{\theta} + B\dot{\theta} + MgL \sin \theta = \tau_a(t) \tag{51}$$

In order to write a set of state-variable equations, we note that $\dot{\theta} = \omega$ and $\ddot{\theta} = \dot{\omega}$, where ω is the angular velocity. Then from (51) we have

$$\dot{\theta} = \omega$$
$$\dot{\omega} = \frac{1}{ML^2}[-MgL \sin \theta - B\omega + \tau_a(t)] \tag{52}$$

Equations (51) and (52) are nonlinear because of the factor $\sin \theta$. In Chapter 9 we shall discuss methods for approximating nonlinear systems by linear models. For the present, we note that $\sin \theta \simeq \theta$ for small values of θ. The quality of this approximation is reasonably good for $|\theta| \leq 0.5$ rad. This is indicated by the fact that when $\theta = 0.5$ rad, the deviation of θ from $\sin \theta$ is only 4.2%. Thus for small values of θ, we can approximate (51) and (52) by the linear models

$$ML^2\ddot{\theta} + B\dot{\theta} + MgL\theta = \tau_a(t)$$

and

$$\dot{\theta} = \omega$$
$$\dot{\omega} = \frac{1}{ML^2}[-MgL\theta - B\omega + \tau_a(t)]$$

▶ **EXAMPLE 4.8**

Find the state-variable equations for the system shown in Figure 4.21(a) when the lever's moment of inertia cannot be neglected. Continue to assume that the friction at the pivot point can be neglected and also that the angular rotation θ is small, so that the ends of the lever move essentially horizontally.

Solution

Let J denote the lever's moment of inertia about the pivot point. There are now four independent energy-storing elements: M, K_1, J, and K_2. We choose the state variables to be x_1, v_1, θ, and ω, where ω denotes the clockwise angular velocity of the lever. Two of the four state-variable equations are $\dot{x}_1 = v_1$ and $\dot{\theta} = \omega$. The other two equations can be obtained from the free-body diagrams in Figure 4.24. The diagram for the mass is the same as in the previous example, but the lever is labeled with torques rather than forces.

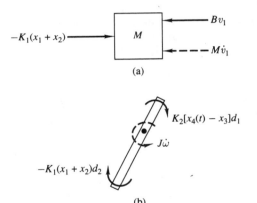

(a)

(b)

FIGURE 4.24 Free-body diagrams for Example 4.8. (a) Forces on M. (b) Torques on the lever.

Summing forces on the mass M, we again have

$$M\dot{v}_1 + Bv_1 + K_1(x_1 + x_2) = 0$$

Summing torques about the lever's pivot point gives

$$J\dot{\omega} = K_2 d_1[x_4(t) - x_3] - K_1 d_2(x_1 + x_2)$$

With the substitutions $x_2 = d_2\theta$ and $x_3 = d_1\theta$, these two equations become

$$M_1\dot{v}_1 + Bv_1 + K_1 x_1 + K_1 d_2\theta = 0$$
$$J\dot{\omega} + K_2 d_1^2\theta + K_1 d_2^2\theta + K_1 d_2 x_1 = K_2 d_1 x_4(t)$$

Thus the state-variable equations are

$$\dot{x}_1 = v_1$$

$$\dot{v}_1 = \frac{1}{M_1}[-K_1 x_1 - B v_1 - K_1 d_2 \theta]$$

$$\dot{\theta} = \omega$$

$$\dot{\omega} = \frac{1}{J}[-K_1 d_2 x_1 - (K_1 d_2^2 + K_2 d_1^2)\theta + K_2 d_1 x_4(t)]$$

Each of the following two examples involves a pair of gears. The first example shows how gears can change the magnitude of the torque applied to a rotating body. When gears are used to couple two rotational subsystems, as in the second example, the parameters J, B, and K are sometimes reflected in an appropriate manner from one side of the pair of gears to the other.

▶ **EXAMPLE 4.9**

Derive the state-variable equations for the gear-driven disk shown in Figure 4.25(a). The torque $\tau_a(t)$ is applied to a gear with radius r_1. The mating

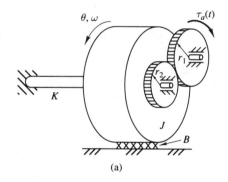

(a)

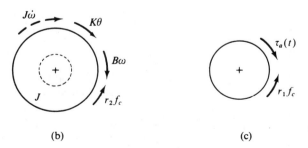

(b)   (c)

FIGURE 4.25 (a) System for Example 4.9. (b), (c) Free-body diagrams.

gear with radius r_2 is rigidly connected to the moment of inertia J, which in turn is restrained by the flexible shaft K and viscous damping B.

Solution

The free-body diagram for the disk and the gear attached to it is shown in Figure 4.25(b), and the diagram for the other gear is shown in Figure 4.25(c). The contact force where the gears mesh is denoted by f_c, and the corresponding torques are included on the diagrams. Rather than drawing a separate free-body diagram for the shaft, we show the torque $K\theta$ that it exerts on the disk in Figure 4.25(b). By D'Alembert's law,

$$J\dot{\omega} + B\omega + K\theta - r_2 f_c = 0 \tag{53a}$$

$$r_1 f_c = \tau_a(t) \tag{53b}$$

Solving (53b) for f_c and substituting the result into (53a), we have

$$J\dot{\omega} + B\omega + K\theta = N\tau_a(t)$$

where $N = r_2/r_1$. If θ and ω are chosen as the state variables, we write

$$\begin{aligned} \dot{\theta} &= \omega \\ \dot{\omega} &= \frac{1}{J}[-K\theta - B\omega + N\tau_a(t)] \end{aligned} \tag{54}$$

Note that (25), which describes a system identical to this one except for the gears, is identical to (54) with $N = 1$. Hence, as expected, the only effect of the gears is to multiply the applied torque $\tau_a(t)$ by the gear ratio N and to reverse its direction on the disk.

▶ **EXAMPLE 4.10**

Find the state-variable equations for the system shown in Figure 4.26(a), in which the pair of gears couples two similar subsystems.

Solution

Because of the two moments of inertia and the two shafts, it might appear that we could choose ω_1, ω_2, θ_1, and θ_2 as state variables. However, θ_1 and θ_2 are related by the gear ratio, as are ω_1 and ω_2. Because the state variables must be independent, either θ_1 and ω_1 or θ_2 and ω_2 constitute a suitable set.

The free-body diagrams for each of the moments of inertia are shown in Figure 4.26(b) and Figure 4.26(c). As in Example 4.9, f_c represents the contact force between the two gears. Summing the torques on each of the

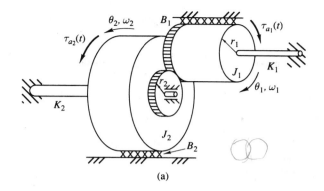

(a)

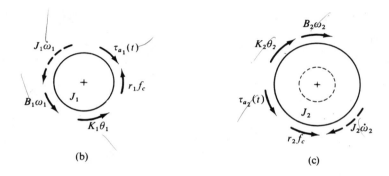

(b)   (c)

FIGURE 4.26   (a) System for Example 4.10. (b), (c) Free-body diagrams.

free-body diagrams gives

$$J_1\dot{\omega}_1 + B_1\omega_1 + K_1\theta_1 + r_1 f_c = \tau_{a_1}(t) \tag{55a}$$

$$J_2\dot{\omega}_2 + B_2\omega_2 + K_2\theta_2 - r_2 f_c = \tau_{a_2}(t) \tag{55b}$$

By the geometry of the gears,

$$\begin{aligned} \theta_1 &= N\theta_2 \\ \omega_1 &= N\omega_2 \end{aligned} \tag{56}$$

where $N = r_2/r_1$.

Selecting θ_2 and ω_2 as the state variables, we can write $\dot{\theta}_2 = \omega_2$ as the first state-variable equation and combine (55) and (56) to obtain the required equation for $\dot{\omega}_2$ in terms of θ_2, ω_2, $\tau_{a_1}(t)$, and $\tau_{a_2}(t)$. We first solve (55b) for f_c and substitute that expression into (55a). Then, substituting (56) into the result gives

$$(J_2 + N^2 J_1)\dot{\omega}_2 + (B_2 + N^2 B_1)\omega_2 + (K_2 + N^2 K_1)\theta_2 - N\tau_{a_1}(t) - \tau_{a_2}(t) = 0 \tag{57}$$

At this point, it is convenient to define the parameters

$$
\begin{aligned}
J_{2_{eq}} &= J_2 + N^2 J_1 \\
B_{2_{eq}} &= B_2 + N^2 B_1 \\
K_{2_{eq}} &= K_2 + N^2 K_1
\end{aligned}
\tag{58}
$$

which can be viewed as the combined moment of inertia, damping co-efficient, and spring constant, respectively, when the combined system is described in terms of the variables θ_2 and ω_2. For example, it is common to say that $N^2 J_1$ is the equivalent inertia of disk 1 when that inertia is reflected to shaft 2. Similarly, $N^2 B_1$ and $N^2 K_1$ are the reflected viscous-friction co-efficient and spring constant, respectively. Hence the parameters $J_{2_{eq}}$, $B_{2_{eq}}$, and $K_{2_{eq}}$ defined in (58) are the sums of the parameters associated with shaft 2 and the corresponding parameters reflected from shaft 1.

With the new notation, we can rewrite (57) as

$$
J_{2_{eq}} \dot{\omega}_2 + B_{2_{eq}} \omega_2 + K_{2_{eq}} \theta_2 - N \tau_{a_1}(t) - \tau_{a_2}(t) = 0
\tag{59}
$$

and the state-variable equations are

$$
\begin{aligned}
\dot{\theta}_2 &= \omega_2 \\
\dot{\omega}_2 &= \frac{1}{J_{2_{eq}}} \left[-K_{2_{eq}} \theta_2 - B_{2_{eq}} \omega_2 + N \tau_{a_1}(t) + \tau_{a_2}(t) \right]
\end{aligned}
\tag{60}
$$

Note that the driving torque $\tau_{a_1}(t)$ applied to shaft 1 has the value $N \tau_{a_1}(t)$ when reflected to shaft 2.

If we wanted the system model in terms of θ_1 and ω_1, straightforward substitutions would lead to the equations

$$
\begin{aligned}
\dot{\theta}_1 &= \omega_1 \\
\dot{\omega}_1 &= \frac{1}{J_{1_{eq}}} \left[-K_{1_{eq}} \theta_1 - B_{1_{eq}} \omega_1 + \tau_{a_1}(t) + \frac{1}{N} \tau_{a_2}(t) \right]
\end{aligned}
$$

where the combined parameters with the elements associated with shaft 2 reflected to shaft 1 are

$$
J_{1_{eq}} = J_1 + \frac{1}{N^2} J_2
$$

$$
B_{1_{eq}} = B_1 + \frac{1}{N^2} B_2
$$

$$
K_{1_{eq}} = K_1 + \frac{1}{N^2} K_2
$$

With the experience we have gained in deriving the mathematical models for separate translational and rotational systems, it is a straightforward matter to treat systems that combine both types of elements. The next example uses a rack and a pinion gear to convert rotational motion to translational motion. The final example combines translational and rotational systems via a cable attached to a disk.

▶ **EXAMPLE 4.11**

Derive the state-variable model for the system shown in Figure 4.27. The moment of inertia J represents the rotor of a motor on which an applied torque $\tau_a(t)$ is exerted. The rotor is connected by a flexible shaft to a pinion gear of radius R that meshes with the linear rack. The rack is rigidly attached to the mass M, which might represent the bed of a milling machine. The outputs of interest are the displacement and velocity of the rack and the contact force between the rack and the pinion.

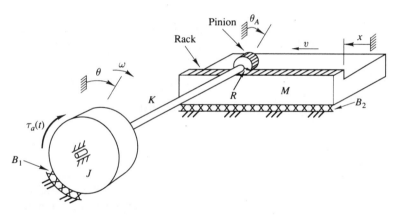

FIGURE 4.27   System for Example 4.11 with rack and pinion gear.

Solution

The free-body diagrams for the moment of inertia J, the pinion gear, and the mass M are shown in Figure 4.28. The contact force between the rack and the pinion is denoted by f_c. Forces and torques that will not appear in the equations of interest (such as the vertical force on the mass and the bearing forces on the rotor and pinion gear) have been omitted. Summing the torques in Figure 4.28(a) and Figure 4.28(b) and the forces in Figure 4.28(c) yields the three equations

$$J\dot{\omega} + B_1\omega + K(\theta - \theta_A) - \tau_a(t) = 0 \qquad (61a)$$

$$Rf_c - K(\theta - \theta_A) = 0 \qquad (61b)$$

$$M\dot{v} + B_2 v - f_c = 0 \qquad (61c)$$

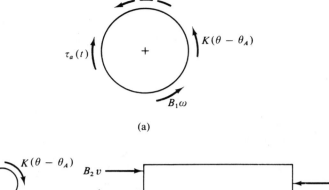

(a)

(b)   (c)

FIGURE 4.28 Free-body diagrams for Example 4.11. (a) Rotor. (b) Pinion
gear. (c) Mass.

In addition, the geometric relationship

$$R\theta_A = x \tag{62}$$

must hold because of the contact between the rack and the pinion gear.

The fact that there are three energy-storing elements corresponding to
the parameters J, M, and K suggests that the three variables ω, v, and
$\theta_R = \theta - \theta_A$ might constitute a satisfactory set of state variables. However,
the displacement x of the mass, which is usually of interest and which is
one of the specified outputs, cannot be expressed as an algebraic function of
ω, v, θ_R, and the input. Thus we need four state variables, which we choose
to be θ, ω, x, and v. Using (62) to eliminate θ_A in (61a) gives

$$J\dot{\omega} + B_1\omega + K\theta - \frac{K}{R}x - \tau_a(t) = 0$$

and using (62) and (61b) to eliminate f_c in (61c) results in

$$M\dot{v} + B_2v + \frac{K}{R^2}x - \frac{K}{R}\theta = 0$$

Thus the desired state-variable equations are

$$\dot{\theta} = \omega$$
$$\dot{\omega} = \frac{1}{J}\left[-K\theta - B_1\omega + \frac{K}{R}x + \tau_a(t)\right]$$
$$\dot{x} = v$$
$$\dot{v} = \frac{1}{M}\left(\frac{K}{R}\theta - \frac{K}{R^2}x - B_2v\right)$$

(63)

The outputs x and v are also state variables. The output equation for f_c can be found by substituting (62) into (61b). It is

$$f_c = \frac{K}{R}\left(\theta - \frac{x}{R}\right)$$

▶ **EXAMPLE 4.12**

In the system shown in Figure 4.29, the mass and spring are connected to the disk by a flexible cable. Actually, the spring might be used to represent the stretching of the cable. The mass M is subjected to the external force

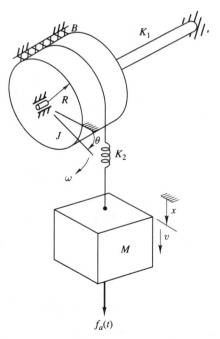

FIGURE 4.29 System for Example 4.12 with translational and rotational elements.

$f_a(t)$ in addition to the gravitational force. Let θ and x be measured from references corresponding to the position where the shaft K_1 is not twisted and the spring K_2 is not stretched. Find the state-variable model, treating $f_a(t)$ and the weight of the mass as inputs and the angular displacement θ and the tensile force in the cable as outputs.

Solution

The free-body diagrams for the disk and the mass are shown in Figure 4.30, where f_2 denotes the force exerted by the spring. The downward displacement of the top end of the spring is $R\theta$, so

$$f_2 = K_2(x - R\theta) \tag{64}$$

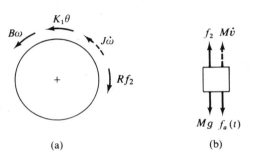

(a)   (b)

FIGURE 4.30   Free-body diagrams for Example 4.12. (a) Disk.
(b) Mass.

Because of the four energy-storing elements corresponding to the parameters K_1, J, K_2, and M, we select θ, ω, x, and v as the state variables. From the free-body diagrams and with (64), we can write

$$J\dot{\omega} + B\omega + K_1\theta - RK_2(x - R\theta) = 0 \tag{65a}$$

$$M\dot{v} + K_2(x - R\theta) = f_a(t) + Mg \tag{65b}$$

Note that the reaction force $f_2 = K_2(x - R\theta)$ of the cable on the mass is not the same as the total external force $f_a(t) + Mg$ on the mass. As indicated by (65b), the difference is the inertial force $M\dot{v}$. Only if the mass were negligible would the external force be transmitted directly through the spring. From (65) and the identities $\dot{\theta} = \omega$ and $\dot{x} = v$, we can write the state-variable equations

$$\begin{aligned}
\dot{\theta} &= \omega \\
\dot{\omega} &= \frac{1}{J}\left[-(K_1 + K_2R^2)\theta - B\omega + K_2Rx\right] \\
\dot{x} &= v \\
\dot{v} &= \frac{1}{M}[K_2R\theta - K_2x + f_a(t) + Mg]
\end{aligned} \tag{66}$$

The only output that is not a state variable is the tensile force in the cable, for which the output equation is given by (64).

In order to emphasize the effect of the weight Mg, suppose that $f_a(t) = 0$ and that the mass and disk are not moving. Let θ_0 denote the constant angular displacement of the disk and x_0 the constant displacement of the mass under these conditions. Then (65) becomes

$$K_1\theta_0 = RK_2(x_0 - R\theta_0)$$
$$K_2(x_0 - R\theta_0) = Mg$$

(67)

from which

$$\theta_0 = \frac{RMg}{K_1}$$
$$x_0 = \frac{Mg}{K_2} + \frac{R^2Mg}{K_1}$$

(68)

These expressions represent the constant displacements caused by the gravitational force Mg.

Now reconsider the case where $f_a(t)$ is nonzero and where the system is in motion. Let

$$\theta = \theta_0 + \phi$$
$$x = x_0 + z$$

(69)

so that ϕ and z represent the additional angular and vertical displacements caused by the input $f_a(t)$. Note that $\omega = \dot{\theta} = \dot{\phi}$ and $v = \dot{x} = \dot{z}$. Substituting (69) into (65) gives

$$J\dot{\omega} + B\omega + K_1(\theta_0 + \phi) - RK_2(x_0 + z - R\theta_0 - R\phi) = 0$$
$$M\dot{v} + K_2(x_0 + z - R\theta_0 - R\phi) = f_a(t) + Mg$$

Using (67) to cancel those terms involving θ_0, x_0, and Mg, we are left with

$$J\dot{\omega} + B\omega + K_1\phi - RK_2(z - R\phi) = 0$$
$$M\dot{v} + K_2(z - R\phi) = f_a(t)$$

so the corresponding state-variable equations are

$$\dot{\phi} = \omega$$
$$\dot{\omega} = \frac{1}{J}[-(K_1 + K_2R^2)\phi - B\omega + K_2Rz]$$
$$\dot{z} = v$$
$$\dot{v} = \frac{1}{M}[K_2R\phi - K_2z + f_a(t)]$$

(70)

We see that (66) and (70) have the same form, except that in the latter case the term Mg is missing and θ and x have been replaced by ϕ and z. As long as the stiffness elements are linear, we can ignore the gravitational force Mg if we measure all displacements from the static-equilibrium positions corresponding to no inputs except gravity. This agrees with the conclusion reached in Examples 2.5 and 2.6. Note that if one of the desired outputs is the total tensile force in the cable, we must substitute (69) into (64) to get

$$f_2 = K_2(x_0 - R\theta_0) + K_2(z - R\phi) \qquad (71)$$

where x_0 and θ_0 are given by (68). The first of the two terms in (71) is the constant tensile force resulting only from the weight of the mass. The second term is the additional tensile force caused by the input $f_a(t)$.

SUMMARY

In this chapter we extended the techniques of Chapters 2 and 3 to include bodies that rotate about fixed axes. Moment of inertia, friction, and stiffness elements are characterized by an algebraic relationship between the torque and the angular acceleration, velocity, or displacement, respectively. In contrast, levers and gears are described by algebraic equations that relate two variables of the same type (two displacements, for example, or two velocities). We showed how systems with levers, gears, or pulleys can have both rotational and translational motion.

As in Chapter 2, we drew free-body diagrams to help us obtain the basic equations governing the motion of the system. We then combined these equations into sets of state-variable equations or input-output equations. The same general modeling procedures are used for other types of systems in later chapters.

PROBLEMS

4.1 Write a differential equation for the system shown in Figure P4.1 and determine the equivalent spring constant.

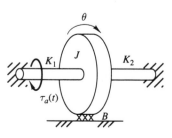

FIGURE P4.1

* 4.2 The left side of the fluid drive element denoted by B in Figure P4.2 moves with the angular velocity $\omega_a(t)$. Find the input-output differential equation relating ω_2 and $\omega_a(t)$.

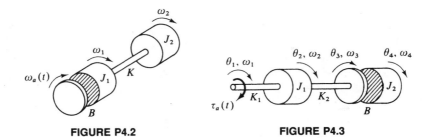

FIGURE P4.2   FIGURE P4.3

4.3 a) Choose a set of state variables for the system shown in Figure P4.3, assuming that the values of the individual angular displacements $\theta_1, \theta_2, \theta_3$, and θ_4 with respect to a fixed reference are not of interest. Then write the state-variable equations describing the system.
   b) Find the input-output differential equation relating ω_4 and $\tau_a(t)$.

4.4 Repeat part (a) of Problem 4.3 if the torque input $\tau_a(t)$ is replaced by the angular velocity input $\omega_1(t)$.

4.5 a) Find a state-variable model for the system shown in Figure P4.5. The input is the applied torque $\tau_a(t)$, and the output is the viscous torque on J_2, with the positive sense counterclockwise.
   b) Write the input-output differential equation relating ω_2 and $\tau_a(t)$ when $K_1 = K_2 = B = J_1 = J_2 = 1$ in a consistent set of units.

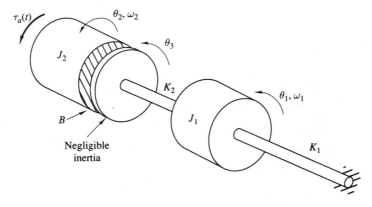

FIGURE P4.5

* 4.6 a) For the system shown in Figure P4.6, select state variables and write the model in state-variable form. The input is the applied torque $\tau_a(t)$, and the

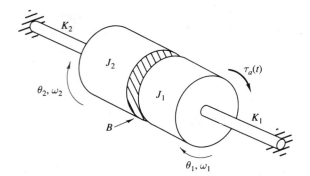

FIGURE P4.6

output is the viscous torque acting on J_2 through the fluid drive element, with the positive sense counterclockwise.

b) Write the input-output differential equation relating θ_2 and $\tau_a(t)$ when $K_1 = K_2 = B = J_1 = J_2 = 1$ in a consistent set of units.

* 4.7 Find the value of K_{eq} in Figure P4.7(b) such that the relationship between $\tau_a(t)$ and θ is the same as for Figure P4.7(a).

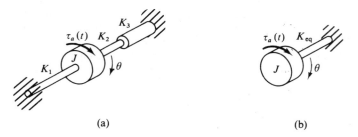

(a)   (b)

FIGURE P4.7

4.8 Use the *p*-operator technique to derive (43).

4.9 For the system shown in Figure P4.9, the angular motion of the ideal lever from the vertical position is small, so the motion of the top and midpoint can be regarded as horizontal. The input is the force $f_a(t)$ applied at the top of the lever, and the output is the support force on the lever, taking the positive sense to the right.

    a) Select a suitable set of state variables and write the corresponding state-variable model.

    b) Find the input-output differential equation relating x and $f_a(t)$.

* 4.10 In the mechanical system shown in Figure P4.10, the input is the applied force $f_a(t)$, and the output is the tensile force in the spring K_2. The lever is ideal and is horizontal when the system is in static equilibrium with $f_a(t) = 0$ and M supported by the spring K_1. The displacements x_1, x_2, x_3, and θ are measured with respect to this equilibrium position. The lever angle θ remains small.

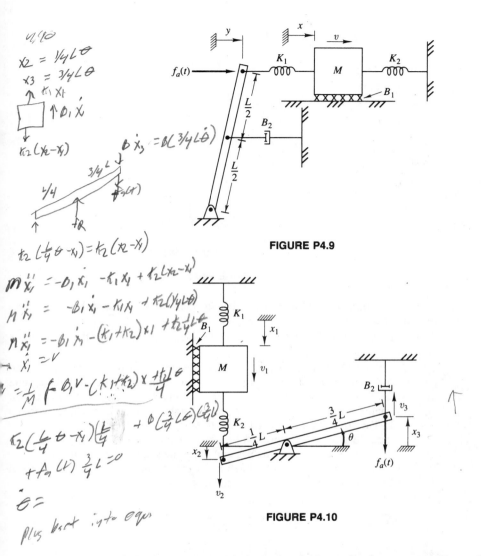

FIGURE P4.9

FIGURE P4.10

a) Taking x_1, v_1, and θ as state variables, write the state-variable model.

b) Also write the algebraic output equation for the reaction force of the pivot on the lever, taking the positive sense upward.

4.11 For the system shown in Figure P4.11, the input is the force $f_a(t)$, and the output is x_1. Assume that the lever is ideal and that $|\theta|$ is small.

a) Select a suitable set of state variables and write the corresponding state-variable model.

b) Find the input-output differential equation when $a = 2$ and $b = K_1 = K_2 = B = M_1 = M_2 = 1$ in a consistent set of units.

4.12 Repeat part (a) of Problem 4.9 when the moment of inertia of the lever cannot be neglected and the output is the displacement x.

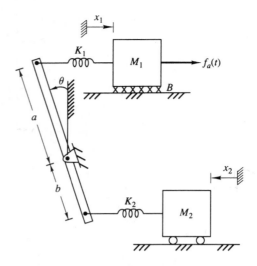

FIGURE P4.11

* 4.13 Repeat part (a) of Problem 4.10 when the moment of inertia of the lever cannot be neglected.

4.14 Repeat part (a) of Problem 4.11 when the moment of inertia of the lever cannot be neglected.

4.15 Figure P4.15 shows two pendulums suspended from frictionless pivots and connected at their midpoints by a spring. Each pendulum may be considered a point mass M at the end of a rigid, massless bar of length L. Assume that $|\theta_1|$ and $|\theta_2|$ are sufficiently small to allow use of the small-angle approximations $\sin\theta \simeq \theta$ and $\cos\theta \simeq 1$. The spring is unstretched when $\theta_1 = \theta_2$.
   a) Draw a free-body diagram for each pendulum.
   b) Define a set of state variables and write the state-variable equations.
   c) Write an algebraic output equation for the spring force. Consider the force to be positive when the spring is in tension.

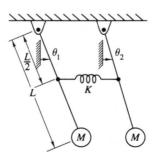

FIGURE P4.15

4.16 Find the equivalent stiffness constant K_{eq} such that the algebraic model of the gears and shafts shown in Figure P4.16 can be written as $\theta_1 = (1/K_{eq})\tau_a(t)$.

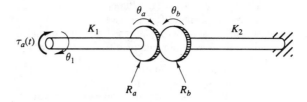

FIGURE P4.16

4.17 In the system shown in Figure P4.17, a torque $\tau_a(t)$ is applied to the cylinder J_1. The gears are ideal with gear ratio $N = R_2/R_1$.

    a) Write the input-output differential equation when the inertia J_1 is reflected to J_2 and ω_2 is the output.

    b) Write the equation when J_2 is reflected to J_1 and ω_1 is the output.

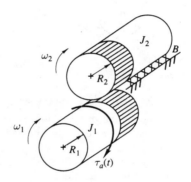

FIGURE P4.17

* 4.18 A torque input $\tau_a(t)$ is applied to the lower gear shown in Figure P4.18. There are two outputs: the total angular momentum and the viscous torque acting on J_1, with the positive sense clockwise.

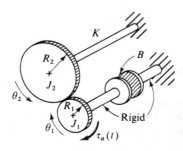

FIGURE P4.18

a) Write a pair of simultaneous differential equations describing the system, where the contact force between the gears is included.

b) Select state variables and write the model in state-variable form.

c) Derive an input-output differential equation relating θ_1 and $\tau_a(t)$.

* 4.19 The input to the rotational system shown in Figure P4.19 is the applied torque $\tau_a(t)$ and the output is θ_3. The gear ratio is $N = R_2/R_3$. Using θ_1, ω_1, θ_2, and ω_2 as the state variables, write the model in state-variable form.

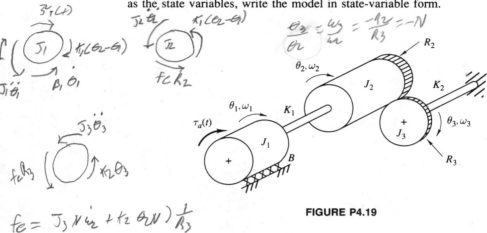

FIGURE P4.19

4.20 Repeat Problem 4.19 when the state variables are $\theta_R = \theta_1 - \theta_2$, ω_1, θ_3, and ω_3.

4.21 The input for the drive system shown in Figure P4.21 is the applied torque $\tau_a(t)$, and a load attached to the moment of inertia J_2 produces the load torque $\tau_L = A|\omega_2|\omega_2$.

a) Taking as state variables ω_1, ω_2, ω_a, $\phi_a = \theta_1 - \theta_a$ and $\phi_b = \theta_2 - \theta_b$, write the state-variable equations.

b) Write an algebraic output equation for the contact force on gear a, with the positive sense upward.

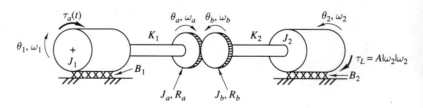

FIGURE P4.21

4.22 The input to the combined translational and rotational system shown in Figure P4.22 is the force $f_a(t)$ applied to the mass M. The elements K_1 and K_2 are undeflected when $x = 0$ and $\theta = 0$.

a) Write a single input-output differential equation for x.

b) Write a single input-output differential equation for θ.

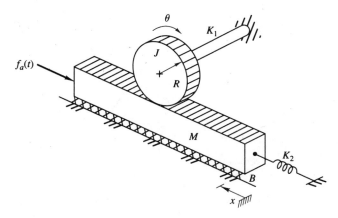

FIGURE P4.22

4.23 Starting with (63), find the input-output differential equation for the system shown in Figure 4.27, taking $\tau_a(t)$ as the input and x as the output.

4.24 In the mechanical system shown in Figure P4.24, the cable is wrapped around the disk and does not slip or stretch. The input is the force $f_a(t)$, and the output is the displacement x. The springs are undeflected when $\theta = x = 0$.

    a) Write the system model as a pair of differential equations involving only the variables x, θ, $f_a(t)$, and their derivatives.

    b) Select state variables and write the model in state-variable form.

    c) Find an input-output differential equation relating x and $f_a(t)$ when $K_1 = K_2 = K_3 = B_1 = B_2 = M = J = R = 1$ in a consistent set of units.

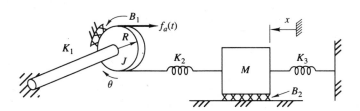

FIGURE P4.24

4.25 A mass and a translational spring are suspended by cables wrapped around two sections of a drum as shown in Figure P4.25. The cables are assumed not to stretch, and the moment of inertia of the drum is J. The viscous-friction coefficient between the drum and a fixed surface is denoted by B. The spring is neither stretched nor compressed when $\theta = 0$.

    a) Write a differential equation describing the system in terms of the variable θ.

    b) For what value of θ will the rotational element remain motionless?

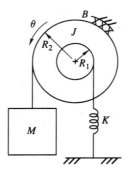

FIGURE P4.25

c) Rewrite the system's differential equation in terms of ϕ, the relative angular displacement with respect to the static-equilibrium position you found in part (b).

* **4.26** In the system shown in Figure P4.26, the cable around the cylinder J does not stretch and does not slip. The input is the applied force $f_a(t)$ and the outputs are θ and z, the additional elongation of K from its static-equilibrium position due to $f_a(t)$. The spring is undeflected when $x_1 = x_2 = \theta = 0$. Select a set of state variables and write the model in state-variable form.

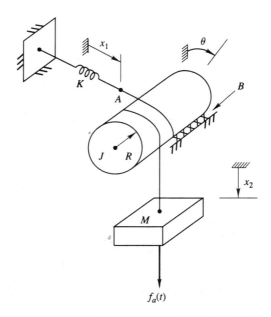

FIGURE P4.26

4.27 In the system shown in Figure P4.27, the two masses are equal and the cable neither stretches nor slips. The springs are undeflected when $\theta = x_1 = x_2 = 0$. The input is the force $f_a(t)$ applied to the right mass, and the output is x_1. Select a set of state variables and write the model in state-variable form.

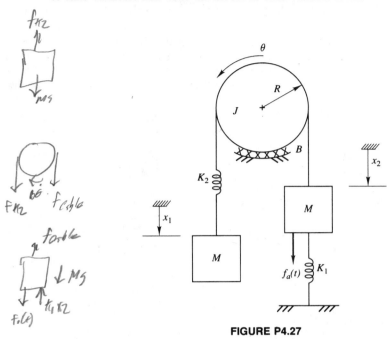

FIGURE P4.27

4.28 The input to the system in Figure P4.28 is the applied torque $\tau_a(t)$. The shaft K_1 and the spring K_2 are undeflected when $\theta_1 = \theta_2 = x = 0$.

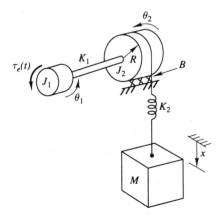

FIGURE P4.28

a) Write a set of differential equations describing the system in terms of $\theta_1, \theta_2, x,$ and $\tau_a(t)$.

b) Select a set of state variables and write the state-variable equations.

c) Find the constant value of $\tau_a(t)$ for which the system will reach an equilibrium position with the mass remaining motionless. Determine the corresponding deflections of K_1 and K_2.

* 4.29 The input to the combined translational and rotational system shown in Figure P4.29 is the displacement $x_1(t)$. The output is the torque applied to the gear by the shaft, with the positive sense clockwise. The springs are undeflected when $\theta = x_1 = x_2 = 0$. Select an appropriate set of state variables and write the model in state-variable form.

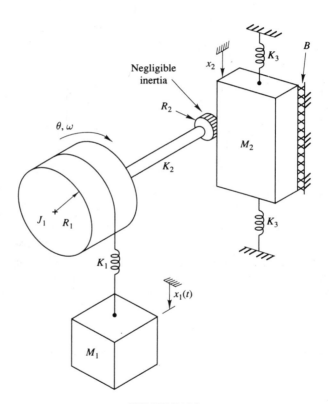

FIGURE P4.29

4.30 Starting with (66), find the input-output differential equation for the system shown in Figure 4.29, taking $f_a(t)$ and the gravitational force as inputs and θ as the output.

4.31 a) For the rotational mechanical system discussed in Example 4.3, write the state-variable equations (31) in matrix form. Show why we cannot obtain either θ_1 or θ_2 from this model.

   b) Add θ_1 as the fourth state variable and write the state-variable equations in matrix form.

* **4.32** For the combined translational and rotational system modeled in Example 4.12, write (66) in matrix form. Note that the system has two inputs, the gravitational constant g and the applied force $f_a(t)$.

   4.33 For the combined translational and rotational system modeled in Example 4.12, write (70) in matrix form. Also write a matrix output equation for the displacements θ and x defined in (69).

ELECTRICAL SYSTEMS

Except at quite high frequencies, electrical circuits can usually be considered an interconnection of lumped elements. In such cases, which include a large and very important portion of the applications of electrical phenomena, we can model a circuit by using ordinary differential equations and apply the solution techniques discussed in this book.

In this chapter, we shall consider fixed linear circuits using the same approach we used for mechanical systems. We shall introduce the element and interconnection laws and then combine them to form procedures for finding the model of a circuit. After developing a general technique for finding the input-output model, we shall present several specialized results for the important case of resistive circuits. We shall then discuss systematic procedures for obtaining the model as a set of state-variable equations. A discussion of controlled sources, with an emphasis on the operational amplifier, concludes the chapter.

■ 5.1 VARIABLES

The variables most commonly used to describe the behavior of electrical circuits are

e, voltage in volts (V)

i, current in amperes (A)

The related variables

q, charge in coulombs (C)

ϕ, flux in webers (Wb)

Λ, flux linkage in weber-turns

may be used on occasion. Current is the time derivative of charge, so i and q are related by the expressions

$$i = \frac{dq}{dt} \tag{1}$$

and

$$q(t) = q(t_0) + \int_{t_0}^{t} i(\lambda)d\lambda \tag{2}$$

Flux and flux linkage are related by the number of turns N in a coil of wire, such that if all the turns are linked by all the flux, then $\Lambda = N\phi$.

We represent the current into and out of a circuit element by arrows drawn on the circuit diagram as shown in Figure 5.1. The arrows point in the direction in which positive charge—that is, positive ions—flows when the current has a positive value. Equivalently, a positive current can also correspond to electrons (which have a negative charge) flowing in the opposite direction.

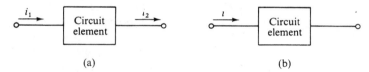

(a)   (b)

FIGURE 5.1 Conventions for denoting current. (a) Acceptable. (b) Preferred.

Because a net charge cannot exist within any circuit element, the current entering one end of a two-terminal element must leave the other end. Hence $i_1 = i_2$ in Figure 5.1(a) at all times, so only one current arrow need be shown, as in Figure 5.1(b).

The voltage at a point in a circuit is a measure of the difference between the electrical potential of that point and the potential of an arbitrarily established reference point called the **ground node,** or **ground** for short. The ground associated with a circuit is denoted by the symbol shown in the lower part of Figure 5.2(a). Any point in the circuit that has the same potential as the ground has a voltage of zero, by definition. The voltage e_1 shown in Figure 5.2(a) is positive if the point with which it is associated is at a higher potential than the ground; it is negative if the potential of the point with which it is associated is lower than that of the ground.

We can define the voltages of the two terminals of a circuit element individually with respect to ground by writing appropriate symbols next to the terminals, as shown in Figure 5.2(b). We define the voltage between the terminals of an element by placing a symbol next to the element and plus

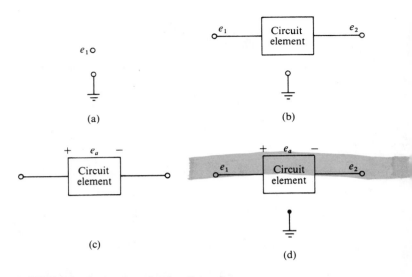

FIGURE 5.2   Conventions for denoting voltages.

and minus signs on either side of the element or at the terminals, as shown in Figure 5.2(c). When the element voltage e_a is positive, the terminal marked with the plus sign is at a higher potential than the other terminal.

In Figure 5.2(d), e_1 and e_2 denote the terminal voltages with respect to ground, and e_a is the voltage across the element, with its positive sense indicated by the plus and minus signs. These three voltages are related by the equation

$$e_a = e_1 - e_2$$

Interchanging the plus and minus signs reverses the sign of the voltage e_a in any equation in which it appears.

When we define the positive senses of the current and voltage associated with a circuit element as shown in Figure 5.3, such that a positive current is assumed to enter the element at the terminal designated by the plus sign, then the power supplied to the element is

$$p = ei \tag{3}$$

which has units of watts. If at some instant p is negative, then the circuit element is supplying power to the rest of the circuit at that instant. Because

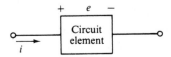

FIGURE 5.3   Positive senses of voltage and current for (3).

power is the time derivative of energy, the energy supplied to the element over the interval t_0 to t_1 is

$$\int_{t_0}^{t_1} p(t)dt$$

which has units of joules, where 1 joule = 1 volt-ampere-second.

5.2 ELEMENT LAWS

The elements in the electrical circuits that we shall consider are resistors, capacitors, inductors, and sources. The first three of these are referred to as **passive elements** because, although they can store or dissipate energy that is present in the circuit, they cannot introduce additional energy. They are analogous to the dashpot, mass, and spring for mechanical systems. In contrast, sources are **active elements** that can introduce energy into the circuit and that serve as the inputs. They are analogous to the force or displacement inputs for mechanical systems.

Resistor

A **resistor** is an element for which there is an algebraic relationship between the voltage across its terminals and the current through it—that is, an element that can be described by a curve of e versus i. A linear resistor is one for which the voltage and current are directly proportional to each other—that is, one described by **Ohm's law**:

$$e = Ri \tag{4}$$

or

$$i = \frac{1}{R}e \tag{5}$$

where R is the **resistance** in ohms (Ω). A resistor and its current and voltage are denoted as shown in Figure 5.4. If we reversed either the current arrow or the voltage polarity (but not both) in the figure, we would introduce a minus sign into (4) and (5). The resistance of a body of length ℓ and constant cross-sectional area A made of a material with resistivity ρ is $R = \rho\ell/A$.

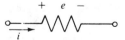

FIGURE 5.4 A resistor and its variables.

A resistor dissipates any energy supplied to it by converting it into heat (in this it is analogous to the frictional element of mechanical systems). We can write the power ei dissipated by a linear resistor as

$$p = Ri^2 = \frac{1}{R}e^2$$

Capacitor

A **capacitor** is an element that obeys an algebraic relationship between the voltage and the charge, where the charge is the integral of the current. We use the symbol shown in Figure 5.5 to represent a capacitor. For a linear capacitor, the charge and voltage are related by

$$q = Ce \tag{6}$$

where C is the **capacitance** in farads (F). For a fixed linear capacitor, the capacitance is a constant. If (6) is differentiated and $\dot{q}$ replaced by i, the element law for a fixed linear capacitor becomes

$$i = C\frac{de}{dt} \tag{7}$$

To express the voltage across the terminals of the capacitor in terms of the current, we solve (7) for de/dt and then integrate, getting

$$e(t) = e(t_0) + \frac{1}{C}\int_{t_0}^{t} i(\lambda)d\lambda \tag{8}$$

where $e(t_0)$ is the voltage corresponding to the initial charge, and where the integral is the charge delivered to the capacitor between the times t_0 and t.

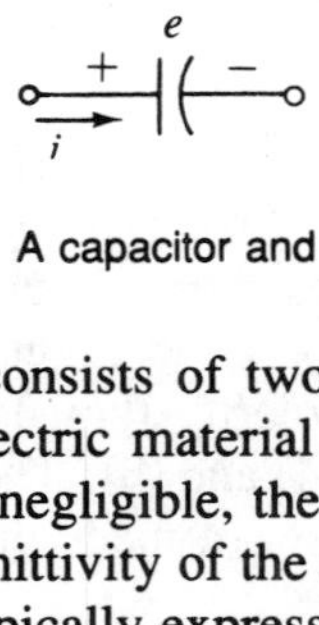

FIGURE 5.5   A capacitor and its variables.

One form of a capacitor consists of two parallel metallic plates, each of area A, separated by a dielectric material of thickness d. Provided that fringing of the electric field is negligible, the capacitance of this element is $C = \varepsilon A/d$, where ε is the permittivity of the dielectric material. The values of practical capacitances are typically expressed in microfarads (μF), where $1\mu F = 10^{-6}$ F. However, for numerical convenience we may use farads in our examples.

The energy supplied to a capacitor is stored in its electrical field and can affect the response of the circuit at future times. For a fixed linear capacitor, the stored energy is

$$w = \frac{1}{2}Ce^2$$

Because the energy stored is a function of the voltage across its terminals, the initial voltage $e(t_0)$ of a capacitor is one of the conditions we need in order to find the complete response of a circuit for $t \geq t_0$.

Inductor

An **inductor** is an element for which there is an algebraic relationship between the voltage across its terminals and the derivative of the flux linkage. The symbol for an inductor and the convention for defining its current and voltage are shown in Figure 5.6. For a linear inductor,

$$e = \frac{d}{dt}(Li)$$

where L is the **inductance** with units of henries (H). For a fixed linear inductor, L is constant and we can write the element law as

$$e = L\frac{di}{dt} \tag{9}$$

We can find an expression for the current through the inductor by using (9) to integrate di/dt, giving

$$i(t) = i(t_0) + \frac{1}{L}\int_{t_0}^{t} e(\lambda)d\lambda \tag{10}$$

where $i(t_0)$ is the initial current through the inductor.

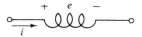

FIGURE 5.6 An inductor and its variables.

For a linear inductor made by winding N turns of wire around a toroidal core of a material having a constant permeability μ, cross-sectional area A, and mean circumference ℓ, the inductance is $L = \mu N^2 A/\ell$. Typical values of inductance are usually less than 1 henry and are often expressed in millihenries (mH).

The energy supplied to an inductor is stored in its magnetic field, and for a fixed linear inductor this energy is given by

$$w = \frac{1}{2}Li^2$$

To find the complete response of a circuit for $t \geq t_0$, we need to know the initial current $i(t_0)$ for each inductor.

Sources

The inputs for electrical circuit models are provided by ideal voltage and current sources. A **voltage source** is any device that causes a specified voltage to exist between two points in a circuit, regardless of the current that may flow. A **current source** causes a specified current to flow through the branch containing the source, regardless of the voltage that may be required. The symbols used to represent general voltage and current sources are shown in Figure 5.7(a) and Figure 5.7(b). We often represent physical sources by the combination of an ideal source and a resistor, as shown in parts (c) and (d) of the figure.

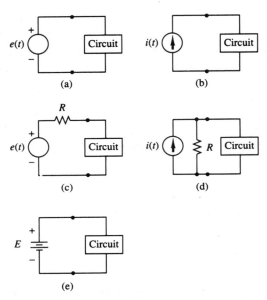

FIGURE 5.7   Sources. (a) Voltage. (b) Current. (c), (d) Possible representations of non-ideal sources. (e) Constant voltage source.

A voltage source that has a constant value for all time is often represented as shown in Figure 5.7(e). The symbol E denotes the value of the voltage, and the terminal connected to the longer line is the positive terminal. A battery is often represented in this fashion.

Open and Short Circuits

An **open circuit** is any element through which current cannot flow. For example, a switch in the open position provides an open circuit, as shown in Figure 5.8(a). Likewise, we can consider a current source that has a value of $i(t) = 0$ over a nonzero time interval an open circuit and can draw it as shown in Figure 5.8(b).

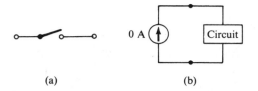

(a)   (b)

FIGURE 5.8 Examples of open circuits. (a) Open switch. (b) Zero current source.

A **short circuit** is any element across which there is no voltage. A switch in the closed position, as shown in Figure 5.9(a), is an example of a short circuit. Another example is a voltage source with $e(t) = 0$, as indicated in Figure 5.9(b).

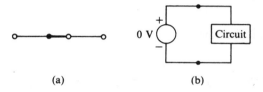

(a)   (b)

FIGURE 5.9 Examples of short circuits. (a) Closed switch. (b) Zero voltage source.

5.3 INTERCONNECTION LAWS

Two interconnection laws are used in conjunction with the appropriate element laws in modeling electrical circuits. These laws are known as Kirchhoff's voltage law and Kirchhoff's current law.

Kirchhoff's Voltage Law

When a closed path—that is, a loop—is traced through any part of a circuit, the algebraic sum of the voltages across the elements that make up the loop must equal zero. This property is known as **Kirchhoff's voltage law**. It may be written as

$$\sum_j e_j = 0 \qquad \text{around any loop} \tag{11}$$

where e_j denotes the voltage across the jth element in the loop.

It follows that summing the voltages across individual elements in any two different paths from one point to another will give the same result. For instance, in the portion of a circuit sketched in Figure 5.10(a), summing the voltages around the loop, going in a counterclockwise direction, and taking

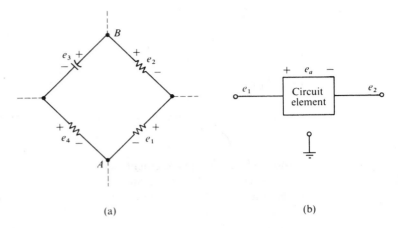

FIGURE 5.10 Partial circuits to illustrate Kirchhoff's voltage law.

into account the polarities indicated on the diagram give

$$e_1 + e_2 - e_3 - e_4 = 0$$

Reversing the direction in which the loop is traversed yields

$$e_4 + e_3 - e_2 - e_1 = 0$$

Likewise, going from point A to point B by each of the two paths shown gives

$$e_1 + e_2 = e_4 + e_3$$

which is, of course, equivalent to both of the foregoing loop equations. In fact, we invoked (11) for the circuit element shown in Figure 5.2(d), which is repeated in Figure 5.10(b), when we stated that $e_a = e_1 - e_2$, because it follows from the voltage law that $e_2 + e_a - e_1 = 0$.

Kirchhoff's Current Law

When the terminals of two or more circuit elements are connected together, the common junction is referred to as a **node**. All the joined terminals are at the same voltage and can be considered part of the node. Because it is not possible to accumulate any net charge at a node, the algebraic sum of the currents at any node must be zero at all times. This property is known as **Kirchhoff's current law**. It may be written as

$$\sum_j i_j = 0 \qquad \text{at any node} \qquad (12)$$

where the summation is over the currents through all the elements joined to the node.

In applying (12), we must take into account the directions of the current arrows. We shall use a plus sign in (12) for a current arrow directed away from the node being considered and a minus sign for a current arrow directed toward the node. This is consistent with the fact that the current i entering a node is equivalent to the current $-i$ leaving the node.[1] For the partial circuit shown in Figure 5.11, applying (12) at the node to which the three elements are connected gives $i_1 + i_2 + i_3 = 0$. If we wish, we can also use Kirchhoff's current law in (12) for any closed surface that surrounds part of the circuit.

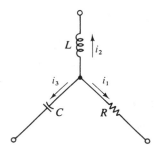

FIGURE 5.11   Partial circuit to illustrate Kirchhoff's current law.

It is a common practice to write the current-law equation directly in terms of the element values and the voltages of the nodes. Consider, for example, the circuit segment shown in Figure 5.12, where e_A, e_B, e_D, and e_F

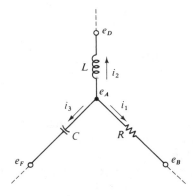

FIGURE 5.12   Partial circuit to illustrate Kirchhoff's current law written in terms of node voltages.

---

[1]Instead of interpreting the left side of (12) as the algebraic sum of the currents leaving the node, it would also be correct to use the algebraic sum of the currents entering the node.

represent the voltages of the nodes with respect to ground. By Kirchhoff's voltage law, the voltage across the resistor is $e_A - e_B$; and by the element law, the current through the resistor is $i_1 = (e_A - e_B)/R$. Similarly, the current through the inductor is

$$i_2 = i_2(0) + \frac{1}{L} \int_0^t (e_A - e_D) d\lambda$$

and that through the capacitor is $i_3 = C(\dot{e}_A - \dot{e}_F)$. Thus we can write the current law in terms of the node voltages and the initial inductor current as

$$\frac{1}{R}(e_A - e_B) + i_2(0) + \frac{1}{L} \int_0^t (e_A - e_D) d\lambda + C(\dot{e}_A - \dot{e}_F) = 0$$

In the following two examples, Kirchhoff's voltage law and current law are used to derive a circuit model.

▶ **EXAMPLE 5.1**

Derive the model for the circuit shown in Figure 5.13.

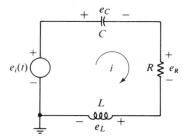

FIGURE 5.13 Series a *RLC* circuit with a voltage source.

Solution

By a trivial application of Kirchhoff's current law, the same current must flow through each of the four elements in the circuit. This current is denoted by i and its positive sense is taken as clockwise, as indicated in Figure 5.13. Because they have the same current flowing through them, the four elements are said to be connected in **series**.

The voltages across the three passive elements are e_L, e_R, and e_C, and we have assigned them the polarities indicated in the diagram. Starting at the ground node and proceeding counterclockwise around the single loop, we have, by Kirchhoff's voltage law,

$$e_L + e_R + e_C - e_i(t) = 0 \tag{13}$$

The element laws (4), (8), and (9) give expressions for e_R, e_C, and e_L:

$$e_R = Ri$$
$$e_C = e_C(0) + \frac{1}{C}\int_0^t i(\lambda)d\lambda \tag{14}$$
$$e_L = L\frac{di}{dt}$$

where the initial time has been taken as $t_0 = 0$ in (8). Substituting (14) into (13) and rearranging give the circuit model as the integral-differential equation

$$L\frac{di}{dt} + Ri + \frac{1}{C}\int_0^t i(\lambda)d\lambda = e_i(t) - e_C(0) \tag{15}$$

To eliminate the constant term and the integral, we differentiate (15) term by term, which yields

$$L\frac{d^2i}{dt^2} + R\frac{di}{dt} + \frac{1}{C}i = \dot{e}_i$$

a second-order differential equation for the current i with the derivative of the applied voltage acting as the forcing function.

▶ *EXAMPLE 5.2*

Obtain the input-output differential equation relating the input $i_i(t)$ to the output e_o for the circuit shown in Figure 5.14.

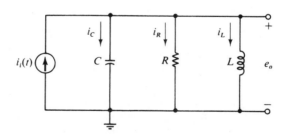

FIGURE 5.14 Parallel *RLC* circuit with a current source.

Solution

Each of the four circuit elements in Figure 5.14 has one terminal connected to the ground node and the other terminal connected to another common node. By a trivial application of Kirchhoff's voltage law, we see that the voltage across each element is e_o. Hence we say that the elements are connected in **parallel**.

Because the circuit has a single node whose voltage is unknown, we shall apply Kirchhoff's current law at that node in order to obtain the circuit model. We could also apply the current law at the ground node, but we would obtain no new information. The currents through the three passive elements are i_C, i_R, and i_L. As indicated by the arrows in Figure 5.14, each of these currents is considered positive when it flows from the upper node to the ground node.

Applying Kirchhoff's current law by summing the currents leaving the upper node, we write

$$i_C + i_R + i_L - i_i(t) = 0 \qquad (16)$$

From the element laws given by (5), (7), and (10), we have

$$
\begin{aligned}
i_R &= \frac{1}{R}e_o \\
i_C &= C\dot{e}_o \\
i_L &= i_L(0) + \frac{1}{L}\int_0^t e_o(\lambda)d\lambda
\end{aligned}
\qquad (17)
$$

where the initial time has been taken as $t_0 = 0$.

Substituting (17) into (16) and rearranging the result give the model as

$$C\dot{e}_o + \frac{1}{R}e_o + \frac{1}{L}\int_0^t e_o(\lambda)d\lambda = i_i(t) - i_L(0) \qquad (18)$$

Differentiating (18) term by term eliminates the constant term and the integral, resulting in the input-output differential equation

$$C\ddot{e}_o + \frac{1}{R}\dot{e}_o + \frac{1}{L}e_o = \frac{di_i}{dt}$$

■ 5.4 OBTAINING THE INPUT-OUTPUT MODEL

Two general procedures for developing input-output models of electrical circuits are the node-equation method and the loop-equation method. Example 5.1 was actually a simple illustration of the loop-equation method, and Example 5.2 used the node-equation method. In the **loop-equation method**, a rather trivial application of the current law enables us to express the current through every element in terms of one or more loop currents. We then write an appropriate set of simultaneous equations by using the voltage law and the element laws. In the **node-equation method**, we use Kirchhoff's voltage law in a trivial way to express the voltage across every element in terms of node voltages. Then we write a set of simultaneous equations by using Kirchhoff's current law and the element laws.

We shall emphasize the node-equation method, partly because in some circuits the loop-equation method requires us to use fictitious loop currents that do not correspond to measurable currents through individual elements. Furthermore, the node-equation method is well suited to handling the current sources that appear in models of transistor circuits. (References that cover both methods in detail are listed in Appendix D.)

When we use the node-equation method, we start by labeling the voltage of each node with respect to the ground node. If a voltage source is connected between a particular node and ground, the voltage of that node is the known source voltage. Where they are needed, we introduce symbols to define the voltages of the other nodes with respect to ground. Once we have done this, we can express the voltage across each passive element in terms of the node voltages by a trivial application of Kirchhoff's voltage law, as illustrated by the discussion of Figure 5.2(d) and Figure 5.12. We write a current-law equation for each of the nodes whose voltage is unknown, using the element laws to express the currents through the passive elements in terms of the node voltages. We need only combine the resulting set of equations into input-output form to complete the model.

▶ **EXAMPLE 5.3**

Derive the input-output equation for the circuit shown in Figure 5.15(a), using the node-equation method. The input and output voltages are $e_i(t)$ and e_o, respectively.

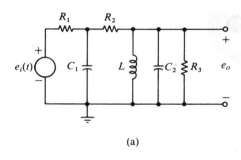

(a)

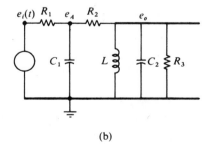

(b)

FIGURE 5.15 (a) Circuit for Example 5.3. (b) Circuit with node voltages shown.

Solution

The first step is to define all unknown node voltages and redraw the circuit diagram with all node voltages shown, as in Figure 5.15(b). We use the heavy lines to emphasize that the ground node extends across the bottom of the entire circuit and that the node whose voltage is e_o extends from L to R_3. We show the source voltage $e_i(t)$ at the upper left node and denote the voltage of the remaining node with respect to ground by e_A. Because e_A and e_o are unknown node voltages, we shall write a current-law equation at each of these nodes, using the appropriate element laws.

To assist in writing the equations, we can draw separate sketches for each node, as shown in Figure 5.16 (analogous to the free-body diagrams drawn for mechanical systems). For each element, the voltage across its terminals is shown in terms of the node voltages, with the plus sign placed at the node in question. Then we use the appropriate element law to write an expression for the current leaving the node.

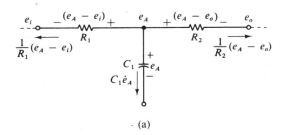

(a)

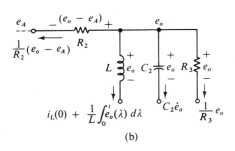

(b)

FIGURE 5.16 Nodes with currents expressed by element laws for Example 5.3.

We can apply Kirchhoff's current law to each of the nodes shown in Figure 5.16 by setting the algebraic sum of the currents leaving each node equal to zero. The result is the pair of equations

$$\frac{e_A - e_i(t)}{R_1} + C_1 \dot{e}_A + \frac{e_A - e_o}{R_2} = 0 \qquad (19a)$$

$$\frac{e_o - e_A}{R_2} + i_L(0) + \frac{1}{L}\int_0^t e_o(\lambda)d\lambda + C_2\dot{e}_o + \frac{e_o}{R_3} = 0 \qquad (19b)$$

With a bit of experience, the reader should be able to write these equations directly from the circuit diagram, without drawing the sketches shown in Figure 5.16. It is worthwhile to note that the current through R_2 is labeled $(e_A - e_o)/R_2$ in the sketch for node A and is labeled $(e_o - e_A)/R_2$ in Figure 5.16(b). However, the reference arrows for this current are also reversed on the two parts of the figure, so there is no inconsistency in the expressions.

We can now differentiate (19b) to eliminate the constant term and the integral. Doing this and rearranging terms give the circuit model as the following pair of coupled differential equations for the node voltages e_A and e_o:

$$C_1\dot{e}_A + \left(\frac{1}{R_1} + \frac{1}{R_2}\right)e_A - \frac{1}{R_2}e_o = \frac{1}{R_1}e_i(t) \qquad (20a)$$

$$-\frac{1}{R_2}\dot{e}_A + C_2\ddot{e}_o + \left(\frac{1}{R_2} + \frac{1}{R_3}\right)\dot{e}_o + \frac{1}{L}e_o = 0 \qquad (20b)$$

By combining these equations to eliminate e_A, we can obtain the input-output differential equation relating $e_i(t)$ and e_o. To simplify the calculations, assume that the passive elements have the numerical values $R_1 = R_2 = 2\ \Omega$, $R_3 = 4\ \Omega$, $C_1 = 1$ F, $C_2 = 4$ F, and $L = \frac{1}{2}$ H. With these parameter values, (20) becomes

$$\dot{e}_A + e_A - \frac{1}{2}e_o = \frac{1}{2}e_i(t)$$

$$-\frac{1}{2}\dot{e}_A + 4\ddot{e}_o + \frac{3}{4}\dot{e}_o + 2e_o = 0$$

By using the p-operator method described in Section 3.2 or by using a combination of substitution and differentiation, we can show that the circuit obeys the third-order equation

$$16\dddot{e}_o + 19\ddot{e}_o + 10\dot{e}_o + 8e_o = \dot{e}_i \qquad (21)$$

for the prescribed element values. In order to solve (21) for e_o for all $t \geq 0$, we would need to know the three initial conditions $e_o(0)$, $\dot{e}_o(0)$, and $\ddot{e}_o(0)$, as well as the input $e_i(t)$ for $t \geq 0$.

Several results in the last example should be specifically noted. The order of an input-output equation is generally the same as the number of energy-storing elements—that is, it is the number of capacitors plus the number of inductors. Thus we could have anticipated that (21) would be third-order. In unusual cases, the order of the input-output equation might be less than the number of energy-storing elements. This can happen when the specified output does not depend on the values of some of the passive elements or when the capacitor voltages or inductor currents are not all independent. An illustration of this will be considered in Example 5.10.

In order to avoid drawing partial circuits like those in Figure 5.16, we can use the following rule for the current leaving a node through a passive element. The voltage that appears in the basic element law is replaced by the voltage of the node being considered minus the voltage at the other end of the passive element. The reader should examine (19a) for node A and (19b) for node O to see how the terms can be written down directly from Figure 5.15(b). If a current source is attached to the node, we can easily include the known source when writing Kirchhoff's current law. If, however, a voltage source is connected directly to the node, its current will not be known until after the circuit has been completely solved. To prevent introducing an additional unknown, we try to avoid summing currents at nodes to which voltage sources are attached. Thus, in the last example, we would not write a current-law equation at the junction of R_1 and $e_i(t)$.

Finally, consider the simplified node equations that remain after any integral signs have been eliminated by differentiation and after like terms have been collected together. In (20a) for node A, all the terms involving e_A and its derivatives have the same sign. Similarly in (20b) for node O, all the terms with e_o and its derivatives have the same sign. Some insight into the reason for this can be found in Chapter 6, but the reader may wish to use this general property now as a check on the work.

The next example involves a voltage source neither end of which is connected to ground. In such cases, we must take special care when labeling the node voltages and writing the current-law equations.

▶ **EXAMPLE 5.4**

Find the input-output differential equation for the circuit shown in Figure 5.17(a) where the inputs are the two voltage sources $e_1(t)$ and $e_2(t)$ and the output is the voltage e_o.

Solution

The voltage of each node with respect to the ground is shown in Figure 5.17(b). Two of the nodes are labeled $e_1(t)$ and e_o to correspond to the left voltage source and the output voltage, respectively. In labeling the node to the right of L and R_1, we do not introduce a new symbol (such as e_A) but take advantage of the fact that $e_2(t)$ is a source voltage. By Kirchhoff's voltage law, this remaining node voltage is $e_o + e_2(t)$, as shown on the diagram. This approach avoids the introduction of unnecessary variables whenever there is a voltage source not connected to ground.

The directions of the current reference arrows included in Figure 5.17(b) are arbitrary, but our equations must be consistent with the directions selected. Applying Kirchhoff's current law to the upper right node, we have

$$i_C + i_{R_2} + i_2 = 0 \tag{22}$$

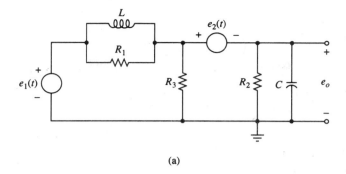

(a)

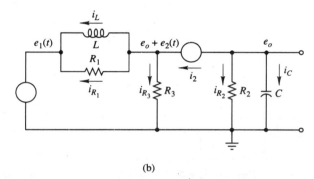

(b)

FIGURE 5.17 Circuit for Example 5.4. (a) As specified by the example statement. (b) With currents and node voltages defined.

Although we can express i_C and i_{R_2} in terms of the node voltage e_o by the element laws, the current i_2 through the voltage source cannot be directly related to $e_2(t)$. However, by applying the current law to the node labeled $e_o + e_2(t)$, we see that

$$i_2 = i_{R_3} + i_{R_1} + i_L$$

which, when inserted into (22), gives

$$i_C + i_{R_2} + i_{R_3} + i_{R_1} + i_L = 0 \qquad (23)$$

Using the element laws in the forms given by (5), (7), and (10), we write

$$i_{R_1} = \frac{1}{R_1}[e_o + e_2(t) - e_1(t)] \qquad (24a)$$

$$i_{R_2} = \frac{1}{R_2}e_o \qquad (24b)$$

$$i_{R_3} = \frac{1}{R_3}[e_o + e_2(t)] \qquad (24c)$$

$$i_C = C\dot{e}_o \tag{24d}$$

$$i_L = i_L(0) + \frac{1}{L}\int_0^t (e_o + e_2 - e_1)d\lambda \tag{24e}$$

Substituting (24) into (23) and rearranging terms give the integral-differential equation

$$C\dot{e}_o + \left(\frac{1}{R_1} + \frac{1}{R_2} + \frac{1}{R_3}\right)e_o + \frac{1}{L}\int_0^t e_o d\lambda$$

$$= \frac{1}{R_1}e_1(t) - \left(\frac{1}{R_1} + \frac{1}{R_3}\right)e_2(t) + \frac{1}{L}\int_0^t (e_1 - e_2)d\lambda - i_L(0)$$

By differentiating this expression term-by-term, we obtain the desired input-output model:

$$C\ddot{e}_o + \left(\frac{1}{R_1} + \frac{1}{R_2} + \frac{1}{R_3}\right)\dot{e}_o + \frac{1}{L}e_o$$

$$= \frac{1}{R_1}\dot{e}_1 - \left(\frac{1}{R_1} + \frac{1}{R_3}\right)\dot{e}_2 + \frac{1}{L}[e_1(t) - e_2(t)] \tag{25}$$

which is a second-order differential equation. To solve it, we must know the two initial conditions $e_o(0)$ and $\dot{e}_o(0)$, in addition to the source voltages $e_1(t)$ and $e_2(t)$.

The solution of a circuit model, such as the one in (25), is discussed in the next chapter. We may sometimes wish to see how the nature of the response changes when a source branch is disconnected. Even with all the sources disconnected, there will still be some output due to any energy that has been previously stored in the capacitors and inductors. The circuit in the following example contains only one energy storing element, so we should expect that it will be described by a first-order input-output equation.

▶ **EXAMPLE 5.5**

Find the differential equation for the output voltage e_o in Figure 5.18(a) when the switch is closed. Numerical values are given for the resistors but not for the capacitor. Repeat the problem when the left branch is disconnected by opening the switch.

Solution

The node voltages with respect to ground, with the switch closed, are labeled in Figure 5.18(b). Summing currents at nodes A and O gives the following pair of equations:

$$C(\dot{e}_A - \dot{e}_o) + \frac{1}{3}(e_A - e_o) + \frac{1}{4}e_A + \frac{3}{4}[e_A - e_i(t)] = 0 \tag{26a}$$

$$C(\dot{e}_o - \dot{e}_A) + \frac{1}{3}(e_o - e_A) + \frac{1}{2}e_o = 0 \tag{26b}$$

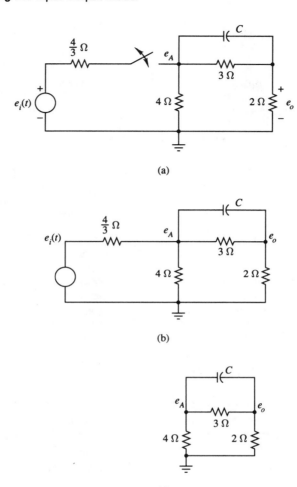

FIGURE 5.18 (a) Circuit for Example 5.5. (b) With the switch closed. (c) With the switch open.

We could collect like terms in each of these equations and then use the p-operator method to eliminate e_A and to obtain an equation in e_o and its derivatives. However, by adding (26a) and (26b) we see that

$$\frac{1}{2}e_o + e_A - \frac{3}{4}e_i(t) = 0$$

Replacing e_A in (26b) by $-\frac{1}{2}e_o + \frac{3}{4}e_i(t)$, we have

$$C\left[\dot{e}_o + \frac{1}{2}\dot{e}_o - \frac{3}{4}\dot{e}_i\right] + \frac{1}{3}\left[e_o + \frac{1}{2}e_o - \frac{3}{4}e_i(t)\right] + \frac{1}{2}e_o = 0$$

from which

$$\frac{3}{2}C\dot{e}_o + e_o = \frac{3}{4}C\dot{e}_i + \frac{1}{4}e_i(t)$$

With the switch open, the circuit reduces to the one shown in Figure 5.18(c). Once again summing currents at nodes A and O, we obtain

$$C(\dot{e}_A - \dot{e}_o) + \frac{1}{3}(e_A - e_o) + \frac{1}{4}e_A = 0$$

$$C(\dot{e}_o - \dot{e}_A) + \frac{1}{3}(e_o - e_A) + \frac{1}{2}e_o = 0$$

Following the same procedure as before, we find that for part (c) of the figure,

$$2C\dot{e}_o + e_o = 0$$

Note that, as is the case in most examples, disconnecting the source has not only caused the input terms to disappear but has also changed the coefficients on the left side of the differential equation.

■ 5.5 RESISTIVE CIRCUITS

There are many useful circuits that contain only resistors and sources, with no energy-storing elements. Such circuits are known as **resistive circuits** and are modeled by algebraic rather than differential equations. In this section we shall develop rules for finding the voltages and currents in such circuits and for replacing certain combinations of resistors by a single equivalent resistor.

The analysis of resistive circuits is important for other reasons as well. Even for circuits with energy-storing elements, we are often interested primarily in the steady-state response to a constant input, after any initial transients have died away. In the next chapter, we shall see how any circuit reduces to a resistive one under these circumstances.

Even when we need to find the complete response of a general electrical system, a combination of two or more resistors will frequently be connected to the remainder of the circuit by a single pair of terminals, as shown in Figure 5.19(a). In such situations, it is possible to replace the entire combination of resistors by a single equivalent resistor R_{eq}, as shown in Figure 5.19(b). Provided that R_{eq} is selected such that $e = R_{eq}i$ is satisfied, the response of the remainder of the circuit is identical in both cases. Once we have found R_{eq}, it is easier to analyze the complete circuit because there are fewer nodes and thus fewer equations. The two most important cases of combinations of resistors are the series and parallel connections.

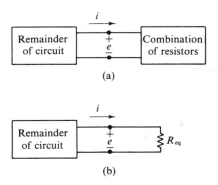

(a)

(b)

FIGURE 5.19 Replacement of a combination of resistors by an equivalent resistance.

Resistors in Series

Two resistors are in series when a single terminal of each resistor is connected to a single terminal of the other with no other element connected to the common node, as shown in Figure 5.20(a). Obviously, two resistors in series must have the same current flowing through them.

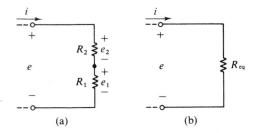

(a)   (b)

FIGURE 5.20 (a) Two resistors in series. (b) Equivalent resistance.

It follows from Ohm's law that $e_1 = R_1 i$ and $e_2 = R_2 i$ and from Kirchhoff's voltage law that $e = e_1 + e_2$. Thus

$$e = (R_1 + R_2)i \tag{27}$$

Because $e = R_{eq}i$, we know from (27) that the equivalent resistance shown in Figure 5.20(b) for the series combination shown in Figure 5.20(a) is

$$R_{eq} = R_1 + R_2 \tag{28}$$

Using (27) with the expressions for e_1 and e_2, we see that

$$e_1 = \left(\frac{R_1}{R_1 + R_2} \right) e \tag{29a}$$

$$e_2 = \left(\frac{R_2}{R_1 + R_2} \right) e \tag{29b}$$

which is known as the **voltage-divider rule**. From (29), the ratio of the individual resistor voltages is

$$\frac{e_1}{e_2} = \frac{R_1}{R_2} \tag{30}$$

Resistors in Parallel

Two resistors are in parallel when each terminal of one resistor is connected to a separate terminal of the other resistor, as shown in Figure 5.21(a). It is apparent that two resistors in parallel must have the same voltage across their terminals.

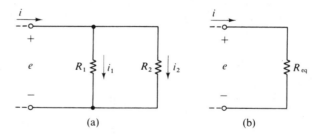

(a)   (b)

FIGURE 5.21   (a) Two resistors in parallel. (b) Equivalent resistance.

From Ohm's law, the individual currents are $i_1 = (1/R_1)e$ and $i_2 = (1/R_2)e$. From Kirchhoff's current law, $i = i_1 + i_2$. Thus

$$i = \left(\frac{1}{R_1} + \frac{1}{R_2} \right) e \tag{31}$$

For the equivalent resistance shown in Figure 5.21(b), we have $i = (1/R_{eq})e$. From (31), we see that for the parallel combination in Figure 5.21(a),

$$\frac{1}{R_{eq}} = \frac{1}{R_1} + \frac{1}{R_2}$$

or

$$R_{eq} = \frac{R_1 R_2}{R_1 + R_2} \tag{32}$$

To relate i_1 to the total current, we can write $i_1 = (1/R_1)e = (R_{eq}/R_1)i$. Doing this for i_2 and then using (32) to express R_{eq} in terms of R_1 and R_2, we obtain

$$i_1 = \left(\frac{R_2}{R_1 + R_2} \right) i \qquad (33a)$$

$$i_2 = \left(\frac{R_1}{R_1 + R_2} \right) i \qquad (33b)$$

which is known as the **current-divider rule**. From (33), the ratio of the individual resistor currents is $i_1/i_2 = R_2/R_1$.

Calculating equivalent resistances and solving for the currents and voltages in most types of resistive networks can be simplified by using these rules for series and parallel combinations, as demonstrated in the following example.

▶ *EXAMPLE 5.6*

The resistive circuit shown in Figure 5.22(a) consists of a voltage source connected to a combination of seven resistors. The output is the voltage e_o. Find the equivalent resistance R_{eq} of the seven-resistor combination and evaluate e_o.

Solution

To obtain R_{eq}, we use (28) and (32) repeatedly to combine series or parallel combinations of resistors into single equivalent resistors. Starting with the original circuit in Figure 5.22(a), we replace the 6-Ω and 3-Ω resistors that are in parallel by a single 2-Ω resistor. We also combine the 10-Ω and 2-Ω resistors in series into a 12-Ω resistor, which yields the intermediate circuit diagram shown in Figure 5.22(b). Note that the output voltage e_o does not appear on this diagram. Next we replace the parallel combination of the 4-Ω and 12-Ω resistors by a 3-Ω resistor, and obtain Figure 5.22(c). The series combination of 2 Ω and 3 Ω gives a 5-Ω resistor, which is in parallel with another 5-Ω branch, yielding the resistor of $\frac{5}{2}\Omega$ that is shown in Figure 5.22(d). Thus the equivalent resistance connected across the voltage source is

$$R_{eq} = \frac{1}{2} + \frac{5}{2} = 3 \ \Omega$$

To find the output voltage e_o, we make repeated use of the voltage-divider rule given by (29a) to obtain, in turn, e_A, e_B, and finally e_o. From Figure 5.22(d),

$$e_A = \left(\frac{5/2}{1/2 + 5/2} \right) e_i(t) = \frac{5}{6} e_i(t)$$

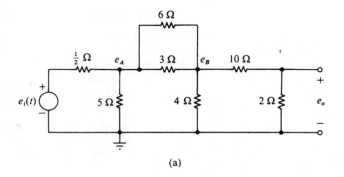

(a)

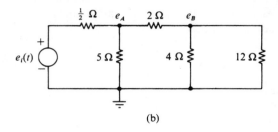

(b)

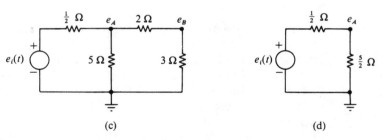

(c)   (d)

FIGURE 5.22 Circuits for Example 5.6. (a) Original circuit. (b), (c), (d) Equivalent circuits.

and from Figure 5.22(c),

$$e_B = \left(\frac{3}{2+3} \right) e_A = \frac{1}{2} e_i(t)$$

Then, from the original circuit diagram,

$$e_o = \left(\frac{2}{2+10} \right) e_B = \frac{1}{12} e_i(t)$$

Although the rules for combining series and parallel resistors often simplify the process of modeling a circuit, there are circuits in which the resistances do not occur in series or parallel combinations. In such situations, we can find an equivalent resistance by writing and solving the appropriate node equations, which will be strictly algebraic when only resistors and sources are involved.

5.6 OBTAINING THE STATE-VARIABLE MODEL

To obtain the model of a circuit in state-variable form, we define an appropriate set of state variables and then derive an equation for the derivative of each state variable in terms of only the state variables and inputs. The choice of state variables is not unique, but they are normally related to the energy in each of the circuit's energy-storing elements. Recalling that the energy stored in a capacitor is $\frac{1}{2}Ce^2$ and for an inductor is $\frac{1}{2}Li^2$, we generally select the capacitor voltages and inductor currents as the state variables. For fixed linear circuits, exceptions occur only when there are capacitor voltages or inductor currents that are not independent of one another. This unusual situation will be illustrated in Example 5.10.

For each capacitor or inductor, we want to express $\dot{e}_c$ or di_L/dt as an algebraic function of state variables and inputs. We do this by writing the capacitor and inductor element laws in their derivative forms as

$$\dot{e}_C = \frac{1}{C}i_C$$
$$\frac{di_L}{dt} = \frac{1}{L}e_L$$

(34)

and then obtaining algebraic expressions for i_C and e_L in terms of the state variables and inputs. To find these expressions, we use the resistor element laws and Kirchhoff's voltage and current laws.

All the techniques we have discussed can still be used. The only basic difference is that we want to retain the variables e_C and i_L wherever they appear in our equations and to express other variables in terms of them. For example, in applying Kirchhoff's current law to node A in the partial circuit shown in Figure 5.23(a), we would write

$$\frac{1}{R_1}(e_A - e_B) + \frac{1}{R_2}(e_A - e_D) + i_L = 0$$

instead of

$$\frac{1}{R_1}(e_A - e_B) + \frac{1}{R_2}(e_A - e_D) + i_L(0) + \frac{1}{L}\int_0^t (e_A - e_F)d\lambda = 0$$

In the partial circuit of Figure 5.23(b), we do not use both e_A and e_B when summing the currents at nodes A and B. If the symbol e_B is used,

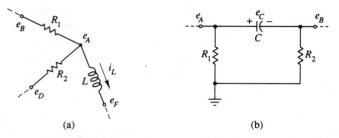

(a)   (b)

FIGURE 5.23   Partial circuits to illustrate writing Kirchhoff's current law in terms of state variables.

the voltage at node A is written as $e_B + e_C$. If e_A is used, the voltage at node B is expressed as $e_A - e_C$.

▶ *EXAMPLE 5.7*

Write the state-variable equations for the circuit shown in Figure 5.24, for which we found the input-output equation in Example 5.2.

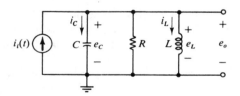

FIGURE 5.24   Parallel *RLC* circuit for Example 5.7.

Solution

Because the circuit contains an inductor and a capacitor, we select i_L and e_C as the state variables, with the positive senses indicated on the circuit diagram. Starting with the inductor element law in the form $di_L/dt = (1/L)e_L$, we note that e_L is the same as the capacitor voltage e_C because the two elements are in parallel. Thus we obtain the first state-variable equation by replacing e_L by e_C, getting

$$\frac{di_L}{dt} = \frac{1}{L}e_C \tag{35}$$

For the second equation, we write the capacitor element law as $\dot{e}_C = (1/C)i_C$. To express the capacitor current i_C in terms of the state variables and input, we apply Kirchhoff's current law at the upper node, getting

$$i_C + \frac{1}{R}e_C + i_L - i_i(t) = 0 \tag{36}$$

where we have written the resistor current in terms of the state variable e_C. Solving (36) for i_C gives

$$i_C = -i_L - \frac{1}{R}e_C + i_i(t) \tag{37}$$

the right side of which is written entirely in terms of the state variables and input. Substituting (37) into the capacitor element law, we find the second state-variable equation to be

$$\dot{e}_C = \frac{1}{C}\left[-i_L - \frac{1}{R}e_C + i_i(t)\right] \tag{38}$$

Finally, we find the voltage e_o from the algebraic output equation

$$e_o = e_C \tag{39}$$

To solve the state-variable equations in (35) and (38), we must know the input and the initial values of the state variables. Note also that once we have the state-variable and output equations, we can always combine them into an input-output differential equation. In this example, we could differentiate (38), substitute (35) into it, and finally use (39) to replace e_C by e_o. The result would be the answer to Example 5.2.

There are several ways of summarizing a general procedure for constructing a state-variable model. We assume here that each capacitor voltage and inductor current is chosen to be a state variable. The unusual case where the number of state variables is less than the number of energy-storing elements will be treated later in this section.

1. We show the positive senses for each e_C and i_L on the circuit diagram, and then label i_C and e_L so that each current reference arrow enters the capacitor or inductor at the positive end of the voltage reference. Insofar as possible, we label the voltages of the nodes with respect to ground in terms of the state variables and inputs. We can then use additional symbols for any remaining node voltages, but we try to minimize the use of new variables.

2. We need to find algebraic expressions for each capacitor current i_C and each inductor voltage e_L. We make use of Kirchhoff's laws and Ohm's law, but at this time do not use the element laws for the capacitors and inductors. We require algebraic equations in this step, and the laws for the energy-storing elements will be used in the next step. In general, we may have to solve a set of simultaneous algebraic equations in order to get individual equations for each i_C and e_L in terms of the state variables and inputs.

3. For the state-variable equations, we substitute the expressions for i_C and e_L into the capacitor and inductor element laws, as given by (34). Finally, for each output that is not a state variable, we write an algebraic expression in terms of state variables and inputs.

The next two examples illustrate this general procedure for circuits of moderate complexity.

▶ **EXAMPLE 5.8**

Derive the state-variable model for the circuit shown in Figure 5.25. The outputs of interest are e_B, i_{C_2}, and i_1.

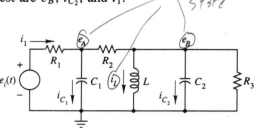

FIGURE 5.25   Circuit for Example 5.8.

Solution

We choose as state variables the inductor current i_L and the capacitor voltages e_A and e_B. We need algebraic equations for the voltage across the inductor and the current through each capacitor. The inductor voltage is identical to the state variable e_B. Thus, by the element law for the inductor, one of the state-variable equations is

$$\frac{di_L}{dt} = \frac{1}{L}e_B$$

The current i_{C_1} will appear in a Kirchhoff current-law equation for node A, namely

$$i_{C_1} = \frac{1}{R_1}[e_i(t) - e_A] - \frac{1}{R_2}(e_A - e_B) \qquad (40)$$

For i_{C_2} we consider node B, getting

$$i_{C_2} = \frac{1}{R_2}(e_A - e_B) - i_L - \frac{1}{R_3}e_B \qquad (41)$$

Substituting (40) and (41) into the respective element-law equations gives the final two state-variable equations. The complete set of three equations is

$$\frac{di_L}{dt} = \frac{1}{L}e_B$$

$$\dot{e}_A = \frac{1}{C_1}\left[-\left(\frac{1}{R_1} + \frac{1}{R_2}\right)e_A + \frac{1}{R_2}e_B + \frac{1}{R_1}e_i(t)\right] \qquad (42)$$

$$\dot{e}_B = \frac{1}{C_2}\left[-i_L + \frac{1}{R_2}e_A - \left(\frac{1}{R_2} + \frac{1}{R_3}\right)e_B\right]$$

As required, we have expressed the derivative of each of the state variables as an algebraic function of the state variables and the input $e_i(t)$. The output voltage e_B is the same as one of the state variables, and the output current i_{C_2} is given by (41). The output equation for i_1 is

$$i_1 = \frac{1}{R_1}[e_i(t) - e_A] \tag{43}$$

The next example has only two energy-storing elements and hence only two state variables. However, not all of the node voltages can be immediately expressed in terms of state variables and inputs.

▶ **EXAMPLE 5.9**

Find the state-variable model for the circuit shown in Figure 5.26(a), when e_o is the output.

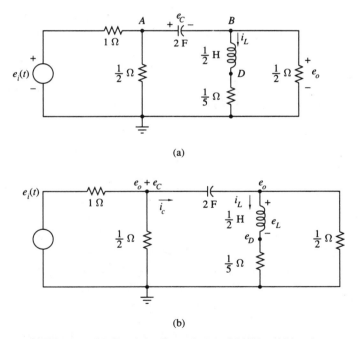

(a)

(b)

FIGURE 5.26 (a) Circuit for Example 5.9. (b) With additional variables added.

Solution

We make the usual choice of e_C and i_L as state variables, with the positive senses shown on the diagram. The voltage at node D is $e_D = \frac{1}{5}i_L$, and node B corresponds to the output voltage e_o. Because we want to retain e_C in our equations, we use Kirchhoff's voltage law to express the voltage at node A as $e_o + e_C$. These symbols, as well as the reference directions for i_C and e_L, are added to the diagram in Figure 5.26(b). Applying Kirchhoff's current law to nodes B and A, we have

$$2e_o + i_L - i_C = 0$$
$$[e_o + e_C - e_i(t)] + 2(e_o + e_C) + i_C = 0 \tag{44}$$

The quantity inside the brackets is the current through the 1-Ω resistor—that is, it is the voltage at node A minus the source voltage all divided by 1 Ω. We now solve (44) simultaneously for e_o and i_C in terms of the state variables and the input. Doing this gives the algebraic equations

$$e_o = \frac{1}{5}[-i_L - 3e_C + e_i(t)] \tag{45a}$$

$$i_C = \frac{1}{5}[3i_L - 6e_C + 2e_i(t)] \tag{45b}$$

We also note that

$$e_L = e_o - e_D = \frac{1}{5}[-2i_L - 3e_C + e_i(t)] \tag{46}$$

To obtain the state-variable equations, we substitute (45b) and (46) into the element laws, as given by (34) and with $C = 2$ F and $L = \frac{1}{2}$ H. We also repeat the output equation (45a) to obtain the complete state-variable model:

$$\dot{e}_C = \frac{1}{10}[3i_L - 6e_C + 2e_i(t)]$$

$$\frac{di_L}{dt} = \frac{2}{5}[-2i_L - 3e_C + e_i(t)] \tag{47}$$

$$e_o = \frac{1}{5}[-i_L - 3e_C + e_i(t)]$$

In the previous three examples, we took as state variables the voltage across each capacitor and the current through each inductor. Figure 5.27 illustrates two exceptions to this procedure. For part (a) of the figure, we might first try to choose both e_A and e_B as state variables. However, by applying Kirchhoff's voltage law to the left loop, we see that

$$e_A + e_B - e_i(t) = 0 \tag{48}$$

Equation (48) is an algebraic relationship between the proposed state variables and the input, which is not allowed. In other words, the capacitor voltages e_A and e_B are not independent and thus cannot both be chosen as state variables. The basic problem is that the circuit contains a loop composed of only capacitors and voltage sources.

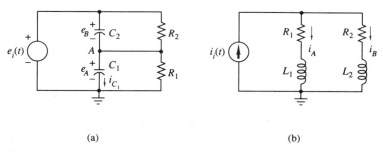

FIGURE 5.27 Circuits having fewer state variables than energy-storing elements.

An analogous situation occurs when a circuit has a node to which only inductors and current sources are connected. For Figure 5.27(b), suppose that we try to choose both i_A and i_B as state variables. By Kirchhoff's current law,

$$-i_i(t) + i_A + i_B = 0$$

Again we have an algebraic relationship between the proposed state variables and the input. Because i_A and i_B are not independent, only one of them should be chosen as a state variable.

The situations illustrated in Figure 5.27 are relatively rare and may even be caused by starting with a circuit diagram that does not correspond closely enough to the physical devices. In part (a), for example, a better model of a physical source might be an ideal voltage source in series with a resistor, which could represent the "internal resistance" of the device. If the diagram were changed in this way, then there would no longer be a loop composed of only capacitors and voltage sources, and both e_A and e_B would be suitable state variables.

A state-variable model for Figure 5.27(a) is developed in Example 5.10. The treatment of Figure 5.27(b) is left for a problem at the end of the chapter. In such cases, we may need to redefine a state variable in order to avoid having the derivative of the input appear on the right-hand side of the state-variable equation. For certain outputs, however, it may not always be possible to avoid an input derivative on the right-hand side of the output equation.

▶ **EXAMPLE 5.10**

Find the state-variable model for the circuit shown in Figure 5.27(a). Take the outputs to be e_A, e_B, and i_{C_1}.

Solution

Because both e_A and e_B cannot be chosen as state variables, suppose we select e_A as the single state variable. Then we need an equation for $\dot{e}_A$ in terms of e_A and $e_i(t)$. First we write the element law for C_1 as

$$\dot{e}_A = \frac{1}{C_1} i_{C_1} \tag{49}$$

where the positive sense of i_{C_1} is downward. Then we apply Kirchhoff's current law at node A, obtaining

$$C_2(\dot{e}_A - \dot{e}_i) + \frac{1}{R_2}[e_A - e_i(t)] + \frac{1}{R_1}e_A + i_{C_1} = 0 \tag{50}$$

Solving (50) for i_{C_1} and substituting the result into (49), we find

$$\dot{e}_A = \frac{1}{C_1}\left[-C_2\dot{e}_A - \left(\frac{1}{R_1} + \frac{1}{R_2}\right)e_A + C_2\dot{e}_i + \frac{1}{R_2}e_i(t)\right]$$

which can be rearranged to yield

$$\dot{e}_A = \left(\frac{1}{C_1 + C_2}\right)\left[-\left(\frac{1}{R_1} + \frac{1}{R_2}\right)e_A + C_2\dot{e}_i + \frac{1}{R_2}e_i(t)\right] \tag{51}$$

Equation (51) would be in state-variable form were it not for the term involving $\dot{e}_i$ on the right side. The derivative of the input should not appear in the final equation, so we define a new state variable, denoted by x, using the same procedure as for the mechanical system in Example 3.8. Transferring the term involving $\dot{e}_i$ to the left side of (51), we have

$$\frac{d}{dt}\left[e_A - \left(\frac{C_2}{C_1 + C_2}\right)e_i(t)\right]$$
$$= \left(\frac{1}{C_1 + C_2}\right)\left[-\left(\frac{1}{R_1} + \frac{1}{R_2}\right)e_A + \frac{1}{R_2}e_i(t)\right] \tag{52}$$

We define the bracketed term on the left to be the new state variable

$$x = e_A - \left(\frac{C_2}{C_1 + C_2}\right)e_i(t) \tag{53}$$

Then e_A is given by the output equation

$$e_A = x + \left(\frac{C_2}{C_1 + C_2}\right)e_i(t) \tag{54}$$

and, when we substitute (53) and (54) into (52), the state-variable equation becomes

$$\dot{x} = \left(\frac{1}{C_1 + C_2}\right)\left\{-\left(\frac{1}{R_1} + \frac{1}{R_2}\right)x \right.$$
$$\left. + \left[\frac{1}{R_2} - \left(\frac{1}{R_1} + \frac{1}{R_2}\right)\left(\frac{C_2}{C_1 + C_2}\right)\right]e_i(t)\right\} \tag{55}$$

Note that the circuit is first-order and can be modeled by a single state-variable equation. However, we did find that the state variable had to be a linear combination of the voltage across C_1 and the input. We can obtain the capacitor voltage e_A from the algebraic output equation (54) after solving the state-variable equation. For the output equation for e_B, we combine (48) and (54) to obtain

$$e_B = \left(\frac{C_1}{C_1 + C_2}\right) e_i(t) - x$$

For the final output, we substitute (54) into the element law for C_1:

$$i_{C_1} = C_1 \dot{e}_A = C_1 \left[\dot{x} + \left(\frac{C_2}{C_1 + C_2}\right)\dot{e}_i\right]$$

and then, by (55), we write

$$i_{C_1} = \left(\frac{C_1}{C_1 + C_2}\right)\left\{-\left(\frac{1}{R_1} + \frac{1}{R_2}\right)x\right.$$
$$\left. + \left[\frac{1}{R_2} - \left(\frac{1}{R_1} + \frac{1}{R_2}\right)\left(\frac{C_2}{C_1 + C_2}\right)\right] e_i(t) + C_2\dot{e}_i\right\}$$

The output equations in a state-variable model should be purely algebraic whenever possible. This is an example of the unusual case where we cannot avoid a derivative of the input on the right-hand side.

5.7 CONTROLLED SOURCES AND OPERATIONAL AMPLIFIERS

Some important types of electrical elements, unlike those in earlier sections, have more than two terminals to which external connections can be made. Controlled sources are considered in this section, and the frequently used operational amplifier receives special attention.

Controlled sources arise in the models of transistors and other electronic devices. Rather than being independently specified, the values of such sources are proportional to the voltage or current somewhere else in the circuit. One purpose for which such devices are used is to amplify electrical signals, giving them sufficient power, for example, to drive loudspeakers, instrumentation, or various electromechanical systems. Ideal voltage and current amplifiers are shown in parts (a) and (b), respectively, of Figure 5.28.

The models for many common devices have the two bottom terminals connected together. They may also include the added resistors shown in parts (c) and (d) of the figure in order to represent some of the imperfections of the device. For part (c) of the figure to approach part (a), R_n must be very large and R_o very small. In order for part (d) of the figure to approach part (b), R_n must be very small and R_o very large.

As is the case with any source in a circuit diagram, we assume that a controlled source can supply as much power as is required by the passive elements connected to it. Although we do not discuss in detail the internal

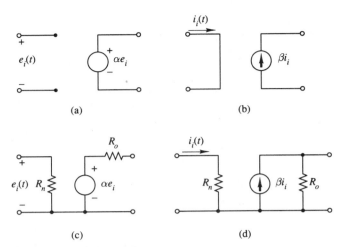

FIGURE 5.28   (a), (b) Ideal voltage and current amplifiers.
(c), (d) Amplifiers with internal resistances causing non-ideal
behavior.

mechanism responsible for the behavior of any element, a brief comment
here should be helpful for those who encounter devices that are represented
by controlled sources. The drawings in Figure 5.28 do not show all of the
external connections to the physical device. In addition to the time-varying
input $e_i(t)$ or $i_i(t)$, there is a constant voltage source that normally is not
explicitly shown. This additional voltage, which is usually a battery called
the bias supply, has two primary purposes. One is to supply any needed
power for the time-varying output signal. The other is to make the electronic
device, which usually is inherently nonlinear, operate in its linear region so
that the models in Figure 5.28 can be used. Chapter 9 contains a general
discussion of how to make a device operate about a particular point in its
linear region. The bias voltages that are needed are usually given in the
specifications for the device to be used. Also specified are the maximum
values of input voltage or current for which the operation of the device can
be expected to remain in its linear region.

   We shall assume that the values of our controlled sources are directly
proportional to the signals controlling them. In addition to the sources
represented in Figure 5.28, we can also have a voltage source controlled
by a *current* somewhere else in the circuit, as well as a current source
controlled by a *voltage*. The problems given at the end of the chapter include
these various types of controlled sources. However, we shall emphasize the
voltage-controlled voltage source, because that will lead to the concept of
the operational amplifier.

   Electronic devices can do much more than simply amplify an input
signal. In order to accomplish other objectives, additional passive elements
are connected around the controlled source. In the following two examples,

the controlled source is modeled by the simple circuit in Figure 5.28(a). In the first example, two external resistors are added; in the second, a resistor and a capacitor.

▶ **EXAMPLE 5.11**

Find e_o for the circuit shown in Figure 5.29(a).

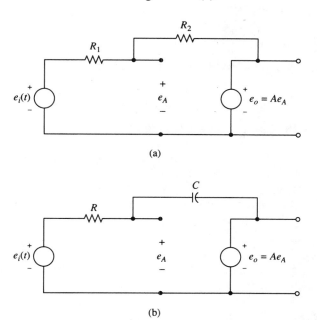

(a)

(b)

FIGURE 5.29 (a) Circuit for Example 5.11. (b) Circuit for Example 5.12.

Solution

Summing the currents at node A gives

$$\frac{1}{R_1}[e_A - e_i(t)] + \frac{1}{R_2}(e_A - e_o) = 0$$

Because $e_o = Ae_A$,

$$\left(\frac{1}{R_1} + \frac{1}{R_2} - \frac{A}{R_2}\right)e_A = \frac{1}{R_1}e_i(t)$$

Multiplying both sides of this equation by $R_1 R_2$, solving for e_A, and then setting $e_o = Ae_A$, we obtain

$$e_o = Ae_A = \left[\frac{AR_2}{R_2 + (1 - A)R_1}\right]e_i(t) = \left[\frac{R_2}{-R_1 + \frac{1}{A}(R_1 + R_2)}\right]e_i(t)$$

Note that for very large values of A, $e_o = -(R_2/R_1)e_i(t)$. Under these conditions, the size of the voltage gain is determined solely by the ratio of the two resistors.

▶ **EXAMPLE 5.12**

Find an expression for e_o for the circuit shown in Figure 5.29(b).

Solution

Summing the currents at node A gives

$$\frac{1}{R}[e_A - e_i(t)] + C(\dot{e}_A - \dot{e}_o) = 0$$

Because $e_o = Ae_A$, we replace e_A by e_o/A to obtain

$$\frac{1}{AR}e_o + \frac{C}{A}\dot{e}_o - C\dot{e}_o = \frac{1}{R}e_i(t)$$

Dividing both sides of this equation by C and rearranging terms, we obtain the input-output differential equation

$$\left(1 - \frac{1}{A}\right)\dot{e}_o - \frac{1}{ARC}e_o = \frac{-1}{RC}e_i(t)$$

For very large values of A, this reduces to

$$\dot{e}_o = -\left(\frac{1}{RC}\right)e_i(t)$$

If there is no initial stored energy, then $e_o(0) = 0$, and

$$e_o = \frac{-1}{RC}\int_0^t e_i(\lambda)d\lambda$$

The circuit is then called an integrator, because its output is proportional to the integral of the input.

The **operational amplifier** (often called an **op-amp**) is a particularly important building block in the electrical part of many modern systems. The device typically contains over twenty transistors plus a number of resistors and capacitors, and it may have ten or more external terminals. However, its basic behavior is reasonably simple. There are two input terminals for time-varying signals and one output terminal. The symbol for the device is shown in Figure 5.30(a), and a basic circuit model is given in part (b) of the figure.

Complete physical descriptions can be found in undergraduate electronics books. However, before considering any applications, we shall list

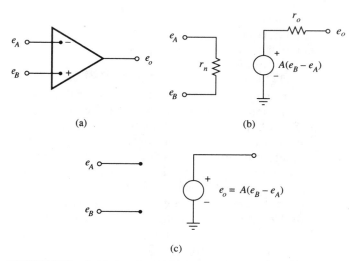

FIGURE 5.30 Operational amplifier. (a) Schematic representation. (b) Equivalent circuit. (c) Idealized equivalent circuit.

without detailed explanations some practical features that users of op-amps should know about.

The input terminals marked with the minus and plus signs are called the inverting and noninverting terminals, respectively. We have denoted their voltages with respect to the ground point (which is the zero-volt reference) by e_A and e_B, although e_1 and e_2 are frequently used. One of the input terminals is often connected to the ground point, but this is not necessary.

Typical values for r_n exceed 10^6 Ω, and r_o is normally less than 100 Ω. In most applications, the resistance r_n can be replaced by an open circuit, and r_o by a short circuit, leading to the simplified model in Figure 5.30(c). Then no current can flow into the device from the left, and the output voltage is $e_o = A(e_B - e_A)$. The voltage amplification A is extremely large, typically exceeding 10^5.

Note that the symbol in Figure 5.30(a) does not show the ground point. In fact, the device itself does not have an external terminal that can be connected directly to ground. There are, however, terminals for the attachment of positive and negative bias voltages. The other ends of these constant bias voltages are connected to a common junction, which is the ground point that appears in parts (b) and (c) of the figure. Circuit diagrams involving op-amps must always show which of the other elements are connected to this external ground. Sometimes ground symbols appear in several different places on the diagram, in which case they can all be connected together. However, the diagrams for our examples will already have had this done.

Because our interest is in the time-varying signals, the constant bias voltages are not normally shown on the circuit diagram. In addition to establishing an external ground point for the op-amp, they provide whatever power is needed for the output signal. Although there may also be other terminals on a practical op-amp, we need be concerned only with those shown in Figure 5.30.

For the examples in this section, we shall use Figure 5.30(c) as the equivalent circuit for the op-amp. When doing so, we shall avoid summing the currents at the output of the op-amp, because the current coming out of that terminal from the controlled voltage source would be an additional unknown. After a little practice, many people prefer not to bother to formally replace the original op-amp symbol in Figure 5.30(a) by the equivalent circuit. In this case, the reader must remember that there is no current into terminals A and B but that an unknown current leaves the output terminal. When we are dealing directly with the op-amp symbol, which does not show all the terminals, it might seem at first glance that the sum of the currents leaving the device is not zero, an apparent violation of Kirchhoff's current law. However, when the symbol in part (a) of Figure 5.30 is replaced by an equivalent circuit that includes the ground point, as in part (c), this apparent contradiction disappears.

▶ **EXAMPLE 5.13**

Find the input-output equation for the two circuits shown in Figure 5.31.

Solution

With the op-amp replaced by the ideal model in Figure 5.30(c), the circuits are equivalent to those in Figure 5.29, except that $e_o = -Ae_A$ rather than $e_o = Ae_A$. Therefore, the results are the same as those in Examples 5.11 and 5.12, except that A is replaced by $-A$. For part (a) of the figure,

$$e_o = \left(\frac{-R_2}{R_1 + \dfrac{1}{A}(R_1 + R_2)} \right) e_i(t)$$

which for very large values of A becomes $e_o = -(R_2/R_1)e_i(t)$. For part (b),

$$\left(1 + \frac{1}{A} \right) \dot{e}_o + \frac{1}{ARC} e_o = \frac{-1}{RC} e_i(t)$$

which for very large values of A becomes

$$\dot{e}_o = -\frac{1}{RC} e_i(t)$$

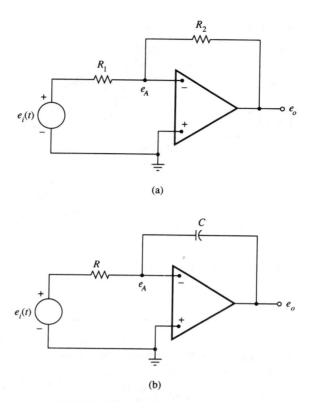

(a)

(b)

FIGURE 5.31   Circuits for Example 5.13.

▶ *EXAMPLE 5.14*

Find an expression for the output voltage e_o for the circuit in Figure 5.32.

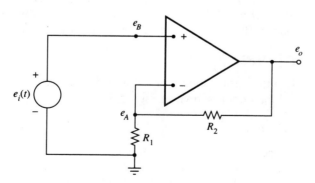

FIGURE 5.32   Circuit for Example 5.14.

Solution

Because no current can flow into the input terminals of the op-amp, we can use the voltage-divider rule to write

$$e_A = \frac{R_1}{R_1 + R_2} e_o$$

Then

$$e_o = A[e_i(t) - e_A] = Ae_i(t) - \left(\frac{AR_1}{R_1 + R_2}\right)e_o$$

from which

$$e_o = \left(\frac{R_1 + R_2}{R_1 + \dfrac{1}{A}(R_1 + R_2)}\right)e_i(t)$$

which for very large values of A becomes

$$e_o = \left(1 + \frac{R_2}{R_1}\right)e_i(t)$$

In the foregoing examples, note how the elements connected around the op-amp completely determine the behavior when we use the simple model with $A \rightarrow \infty$. We first found a general input-output equation in terms of A and then let $A \rightarrow \infty$ in order to get a simpler expression. Because A is so very large in practice, people often use an easier method to get the simpler expression directly. The output voltage of the device, given by $e_o = A(e_B - e_A)$, must be finite, so the voltage $e_B - e_A$ between the input terminals must approach zero when A is very large. In practice, this voltage really is only a tiny fraction of one volt, such as 0.1 mV.

Assuming that the voltage difference $e_B - e_A$ is virtually zero is sometimes called the **virtual-short** concept, because the voltage across a short circuit is zero. However, unlike a physical short circuit represented by an ideal wire (through which current could flow), we must still assume that no current flows into either of the input terminals.

▶ EXAMPLE 5.15

Use the virtual-short concept to determine directly the input-output behavior for the circuit shown in Figure 5.33 when A is very large.

Solution

Because $e_A = 0$, $i_1 = e_i(t)/R$ and $i_C = -C\dot{e}_o$. No current can flow into the input terminals of the op-amp, so $i_1 = i_C$ and $\dot{e}_o = -(1/RC)e_i(t)$, which agrees with the answer to Example 5.13.

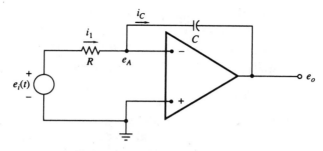

FIGURE 5.33 Circuit for Example 5.15.

▶ *EXAMPLE 5.16*

Find the input-output differential equation describing the circuit shown in Figure 5.34.

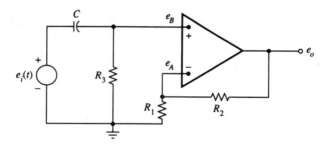

FIGURE 5.34 Circuit for Example 5.16.

Solution

Summing the currents at node B gives

$$C(\dot{e}_B - \dot{e}_i) + \frac{1}{R_3}e_B = 0$$

By the virtual-short concept, $e_B = e_A$, which according to the voltage-divider rule can be written as $e_B = [R_1/(R_1 + R_2)]e_o$. Substituting this into the previous equation gives

$$\frac{R_1 C}{R_1 + R_2}\dot{e}_o - C\dot{e}_i + \frac{R_1}{(R_1 + R_2)R_3}e_o = 0$$

from which

$$R_1 R_3 C\dot{e}_o + R_1 e_o = (R_1 + R_2)R_3 C\dot{e}_i$$

or

$$\dot{e}_o + \frac{1}{R_3 C}e_o = \left(1 + \frac{R_2}{R_1}\right)\dot{e}_i$$

The final example illustrates finding the state-variable model for circuits containing an op-amp. The choice of state variables and the procedure for deriving the model are essentially the same as for the examples in Section 5.6.

▶ **EXAMPLE 5.17**

Find a state-variable model for the circuit shown in Figure 5.35. Assume that the op-amp is ideal, with a gain large enough to allow use of the virtual-short concept. Let the output be e_o, and take as state variables the capacitor voltages e_{C_1} and e_{C_2}.

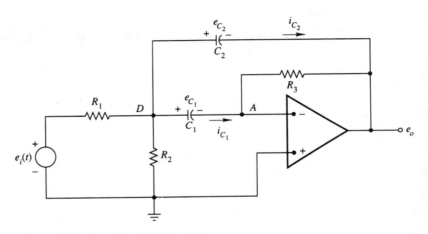

FIGURE 5.35   Circuit for Example 5.17.

Solution

By the virtual-short concept, $e_A = 0$. Then the voltage at point D is e_{C_1}, and

$$e_o = e_{C_1} - e_{C_2} \tag{56}$$

which is the output equation. Because there is no current flowing into the input terminals of the op-amp, and because the voltage at node A is zero, $i_{C_1} = -(1/R_3)e_o$. Using (56), we see that

$$i_{C_1} = -\frac{1}{R_3}(e_{C_1} - e_{C_2}) \tag{57}$$

Summing currents at node D gives

$$i_{C_1} + i_{C_2} + \frac{1}{R_2}e_{C_1} + \frac{1}{R_1}\left[e_{C_1} - e_i(t)\right] = 0$$

Inserting (57) into this equation yields

$$i_{C_2} = \left(\frac{1}{R_3} - \frac{1}{R_1} - \frac{1}{R_2}\right) e_{C_1} - \frac{1}{R_3} e_{C_2} + \frac{1}{R_1} e_i(t) \qquad (58)$$

Finally, substituting (57) and (58) into the element law for a capacitor, we have the state-variable equations

$$\dot{e}_{C_1} = -\frac{1}{R_3 C_1} \left(e_{C_1} - e_{C_2}\right)$$

$$\dot{e}_{C_2} = \frac{1}{C_2}\left[\left(\frac{1}{R_3} - \frac{1}{R_1} - \frac{1}{R_2}\right) e_{C_1} - \frac{1}{R_3} e_{C_2} + \frac{1}{R_1} e_i(t)\right]$$

Other op-amp circuits appear in the problems at the end of this chapter and also in Chapters 8 and 14. They include applications involving isolation, summing, inverting, integrating, and filtering of signals.

SUMMARY

After introducing the element and interconnection laws for electrical circuits, we developed systematic procedures for obtaining both the input-output differential equation and the set of state-variable equations. For the general node-equation method, we select a ground node and label the voltages of the other nodes with respect to ground. We then write current-law equations at the nodes whose voltages are unknown, using the element laws to express the currents through the passive elements in terms of the node voltages. If it becomes necessary to sum currents at a node to which a voltage source is connected, keep in mind that the current through such a source is another unknown variable.

For a state-variable model, we normally choose as state variables the voltage across each capacitor and the current through each inductor. Two types of exceptions to this choice were illustrated in Figure 5.27. As far as possible, unknown variables are labeled on the diagram in terms of state variables and inputs. By using Ohm's law and Kirchhoff's laws, we then express the capacitor currents, the inductor voltages, and any other outputs as algebraic functions of the state variables and inputs. Inserting these expressions into the element laws $\dot{e}_C = (1/C)i_C$ and $di_L/dt = (1/L)e_L$ yields the state-variable model.

The important special case of resistive circuits, including the rules for series-parallel combinations, was treated in Section 5.5. Controlled sources, with an emphasis on op-amp applications, were explained in Section 5.7. For an ideal op-amp, no current flows into the input terminals, but the output current is unknown. The op-amp gain is usually large enough so that the voltage between the two input terminals can be assumed to be zero.

PROBLEMS

5.1 Find the input-output differential equation relating e_o and $i_i(t)$ for the circuit shown in Figure P5.1.

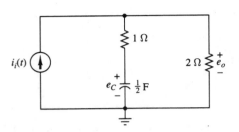

FIGURE P5.1

5.2 Find the input-output differential equation relating e_o and $e_i(t)$ for the circuit shown in Figure P5.2.

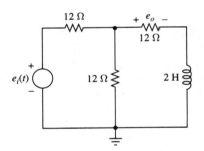

FIGURE P5.2

* 5.3 Repeat Problem 5.2 for the circuit shown in Figure P5.3.

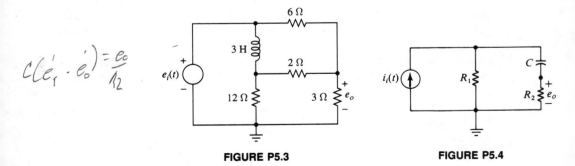

$$C\left(\dot{e}_1 - \dot{e}_o\right) = \frac{e_o}{12}$$

FIGURE P5.3

FIGURE P5.4

5.4 Find the input-output differential equation for the circuit shown in Figure P5.4.

$$i_i = \frac{e_1}{R_1} + C\left(\dot{e}_1 - \dot{e}_o\right) \;\Rightarrow\; i_i\left(C_1 + \frac{1}{R_1}\right)e_1 - C_1 e_o$$

5.5 For the circuit shown in Figure P5.5, use the node-equation method to find the input-output differential equation.

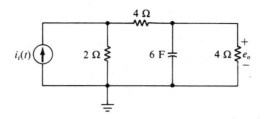

FIGURE P5.5

5.6 Repeat Problem 5.5 for the circuit shown in Figure P5.6.

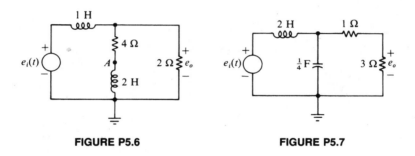

FIGURE P5.6   **FIGURE P5.7**

* 5.7 Repeat Problem 5.5 for the circuit shown in Figure P5.7.

5.8 Repeat Problem 5.5 for the circuit shown in Figure P5.8.

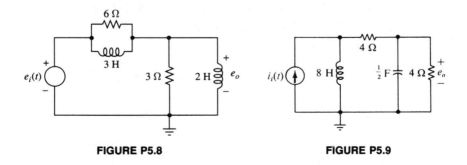

FIGURE P5.8   **FIGURE P5.9**

* 5.9 Repeat Problem 5.5 for the circuit shown in Figure P5.9.

5.10 Find the input-output differential equation relating e_o to $e_i(t)$ and $i_a(t)$ for the circuit shown in Figure P5.10.

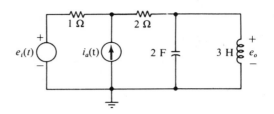

FIGURE P5.10

5.11 a) For the circuit shown in Figure P5.11, write current-law equations at nodes A and B to obtain a pair of coupled differential equations in the variables e_A, e_o, and $e_i(t)$.
b) Find the input-output differential equation relating e_o and $e_i(t)$.

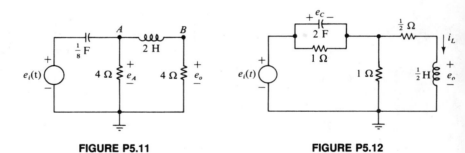

FIGURE P5.11   **FIGURE P5.12**

* **5.12** For the circuit shown in Figure P5.12, use the node-equation method to find the input-output differential equation relating e_o and $e_i(t)$.

5.13 Repeat Example 5.5 with the capacitor C replaced by an inductor L.

5.14 For the circuit shown in Figure P5.14, use the rules for series and parallel combinations of resistors to find i_o and the equivalent resistance connected across the source.

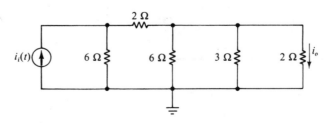

FIGURE P5.14

5.15 For the circuit shown in Figure P5.15, use the rules for series and parallel resistors to find e_o and the equivalent resistance connected across the source.

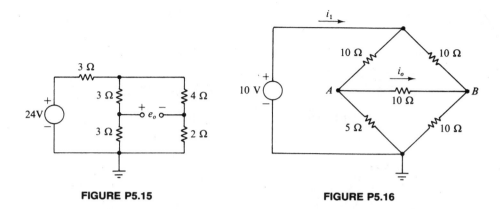

FIGURE P5.15   **FIGURE P5.16**

5.16 a) Explain why the rules for series and parallel resistors cannot be used for the circuit shown in Figure P5.16.
b) Use the node-equation method to find the voltages of nodes A and B with respect to the ground node.
c) Find the currents i_o and i_1 and the equivalent resistance connected across the source.

* 5.17 Find e_o for the circuit shown in Figure P5.17.

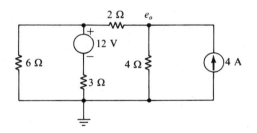

FIGURE P5.17

* 5.18 a) Find a set of state-variable equations describing the circuit shown in Figure P5.18. Define the variables and show their positive senses on the diagram.
b) Write an algebraic output equation for i_o, which is the current through the 6-V source.

5.19 For the circuit shown in Figure P5.6, find a set of state-variable equations and an algebraic output equation for e_o.

5.20 Repeat Problem 5.19 for the circuit shown in Figure P5.7.

* 5.21 Repeat Problem 5.19 for the circuit shown in Figure P5.9.

$i_L = i_L$

$i_L = \dfrac{e_c - e_L}{R_2}$

$e_L = e_c - R_2 i_L$

$i_i = i_{R_1} + i_e + i_L$

$i_i = \dfrac{e_e + 6}{R_1} + i_e + i_L$

$i_e = i_i - \dfrac{e_e + 6}{R_1} - i_L$

$\dot{e}_c = \dfrac{1}{c}\left[i_i - \left(\dfrac{e_c + 6}{R_1}\right) - i_L \right]$

$\dot{i}_L = \dfrac{1}{L}\left(e_c - R_2 i_L \right)$

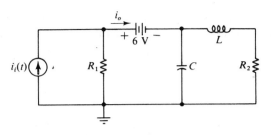

FIGURE P5.18

5.22 Repeat Problem 5.19 for the circuit shown in Figure P5.22.

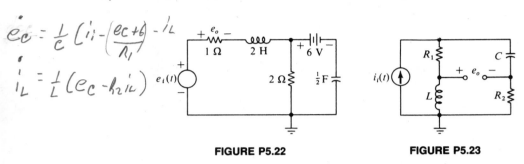

FIGURE P5.22   **FIGURE P5.23**

5.23 Repeat Problem 5.19 for the circuit shown in Figure P5.23.

* 5.24 Repeat Problem 5.19 for the circuit shown in Figure P5.24.

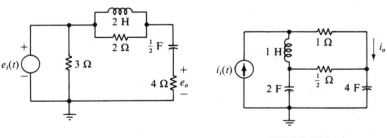

FIGURE P5.24   **FIGURE P5.25**

5.25 For the circuit shown in Figure P5.25, find a set of state-variable equations and write an algebraic output equation for i_o. Define the variables and show their positive senses on the diagram.

5.26 Repeat Problem 5.25 for the circuit shown in Figure P5.26.

* 5.27 Find a set of state-variable equations for the circuit shown in Figure P5.27. Write the algebraic output equation for i_o.

5.28 Find the state-variable equation for the circuit shown in Figure 5.27(a) when the initial choice of the state variable is e_B rather than e_A. Write an algebraic output equation for e_A.

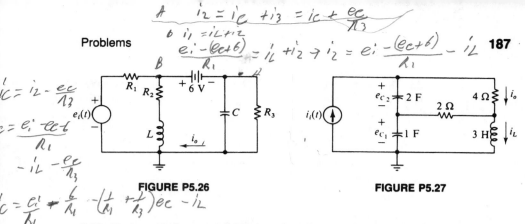

Handwritten annotations:

$A \quad i_2 = i_e + i_3 = i_c + \dfrac{e_c}{R_3}$

$b \quad i_1 = i_L + i_2$

$e_i - (e_c + 6) = i_L + i_2 \rightarrow i_2 = e_i - \dfrac{(e_c + 6)}{R_1} - i_L$

$i_C = i_2 - \dfrac{e_c}{R_3}$

$i_2 = \dfrac{e_i - e_c - 6}{R_1}$

$= e_i - e_c - 6$

$\overline{R_1}$

$- i_L - \dfrac{e_c}{R_3}$

$i_C = \dfrac{e_i}{R_1} + \dfrac{6}{R_1} - \left(\dfrac{1}{R_1} + \dfrac{1}{R_3}\right)e_c - i_L$

FIGURE P5.26   **FIGURE P5.27**

5.29 Find a set of state-variable equations for the circuit shown in Figure 5.27(a) when the voltage source is replaced by the current source $i_i(t)$ with its reference arrow directed upward. Write an algebraic output equation for i_{C_1}.

5.30 a) Find the state-variable model for the circuit shown in Figure 5.27(b).
  b) Write an algebraic output equation for the voltage across the current source.

* 5.31 The circuit shown in Figure P5.31 contains two current sources, one of which is voltage-controlled. Find the input-output differential equation relating e_o and $i_i(t)$.

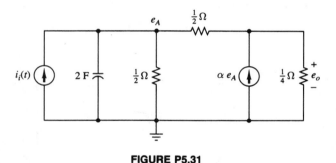

FIGURE P5.31

5.32 The circuit shown in Figure P5.32 contains an independent current source and a current-controlled voltage source. Find the input-output differential equation relating e_o and $i_i(t)$.

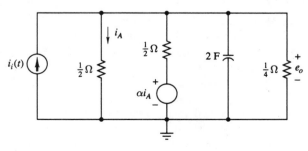

FIGURE P5.32

5.33 The circuit shown in Figure P5.33 contains an independent voltage source and a current-controlled current source. Find the input-output differential equation relating e_o and $e_i(t)$.

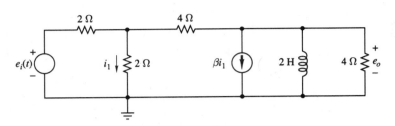

FIGURE P5.33

* **5.34** For the op-amp circuit shown in Figure P5.34, derive the algebraic expression for the output voltage e_o in terms of the two input voltages, $e_1(t)$ and $e_2(t)$. Indicate what mathematical operation the circuit performs.

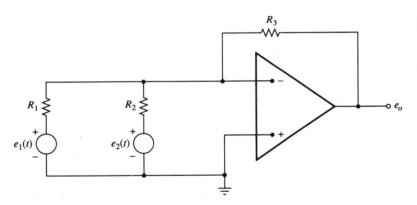

FIGURE P5.34

5.35 Repeat Problem 5.34 for the circuit shown in Figure P5.35.

5.36 For the op-amp circuit shown in Figure P5.36, derive the input-output differential equation relating the output voltage e_o and the input voltage $e_i(t)$.

* **5.37** For the op-amp circuit shown in Figure P5.37, derive the input-output differential equation relating the output voltage e_o and the input voltage $e_i(t)$.

5.38 a) For the op-amp circuit shown in Figure P5.38, derive the input-output differential equation relating the output voltage e_o and the input voltage $e_i(t)$.
b) Derive the state-variable model, taking the output to be the current through R_3, with the positive sense to the right.

5.39 Write in matrix form the circuit model developed in Example 5.7. Identify the matrices **A**, **B**, **C**, and **D**.

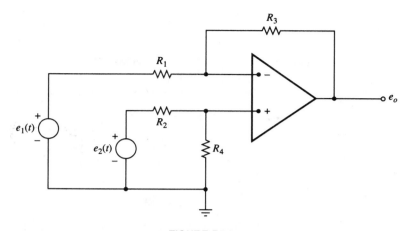

FIGURE P5.35

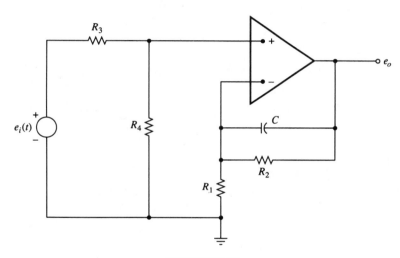

FIGURE P5.36

5.40 Repeat Problem 5.39 for the state-variable model derived in Example 5.8 for the circuit shown in Figure 5.25.

* 5.41 Repeat Problem 5.39 for the state-variable model derived in Example 5.9 for the circuit shown in Figure 5.26(a).

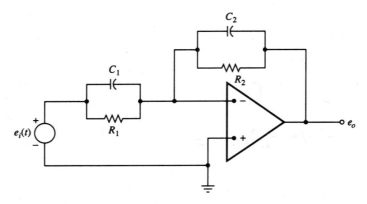

FIGURE P5.37

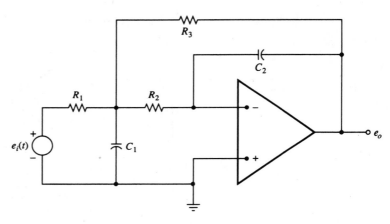

FIGURE P5.38

ANALYTICAL SOLUTION OF LINEAR MODELS

The first several chapters of this book presented methods for formulating the mathematical model for a system and illustrated them with many mechanical and electrical examples. The same techniques will be used for other types of systems in some of the later chapters. The mathematical model can be solved analytically or with the aid of a digital computer. Analytical solutions, which in general are feasible only for fixed linear models, are examined in this chapter.

Section 6.1 summarizes the basic procedures that will be needed in later sections for solving differential equations. For many readers, this will be a review. Throughout the chapter, we assume that we have fixed linear differential equations with real coefficients. Furthermore, the methods we describe are not sufficient for all possible inputs, though they are satisfactory for the inputs that are commonly encountered. Proofs and detailed justifications are omitted, but some general references are included in Appendix D. In the rest of the chapter, we consider in detail the solution of first- and second-order models, examine some specific inputs that are useful in system analysis, and define a number of important terms. Some comments are also made about systems of arbitrary order. In the final section, we present methods of solving models that are in state-variable form, using a number of techniques from linear algebra.

6.1 THE COMPLETE SOLUTION OF DIFFERENTIAL EQUATIONS

We assume that the system model has been put into input-output form with all other variables eliminated, as discussed in Section 3.2. The model for an nth-order system with input $u(t)$ and output $y(t)$ can be written, as in (3.25), as

$$a_n y^{(n)} + \cdots + a_2 \ddot{y} + a_1 \dot{y} + a_0 y = b_m u^{(m)} + \cdots + b_1 \dot{u} + b_0 u(t) \quad (1)$$

where $y^{(n)} = d^n y / dt^n$, etc. The collection of terms on the right side of (1), which involves the input and its derivatives, is represented by

$$F(t) = b_m u^{(m)} + \cdots + b_1 \dot{u} + b_0 u(t) \quad (2)$$

where $F(t)$ is called the **forcing function**. With this definition, we may rewrite (1) as

$$a_n y^{(n)} + \cdots + a_2 \ddot{y} + a_1 \dot{y} + a_0 y = F(t) \quad (3)$$

The desired solution, $y(t)$ for $t \geq 0$, must satisfy the differential equation for $t \geq 0$ and also n specified initial conditions, which are usually $y(0)$, $\dot{y}(0), \ldots, y^{(n-1)}(0)$.

Homogeneous Differential Equations

If $F(t)$ is replaced by zero, (3) reduces to the **homogeneous differential equation**

$$a_n y_H^{(n)} + \cdots + a_2 \ddot{y}_H + a_1 \dot{y}_H + a_0 y_H = 0 \quad (4)$$

where the subscript H has been added to emphasize that $y_H(t)$ is the solution to the homogeneous equation. Assume that a solution of (4) has the form

$$y_H(t) = K \epsilon^{rt}$$

where we must determine the constant r such that (4) is satisfied. Multiplying y_H by a constant just multiplies the entire left side of (4) by that constant, so any nonzero value will be satisfactory for the constant K. Substituting the assumed solution into (4) gives

$$(a_n r^n + \cdots + a_2 r^2 + a_1 r + a_0) K \epsilon^{rt} = 0$$

Because $K \epsilon^{rt} \neq 0$ for a nontrivial solution, we must have

$$a_n r^n + \cdots + a_2 r^2 + a_1 r + a_0 = 0 \quad (5)$$

which is called the **characteristic equation.** Note that the coefficients in this algebraic equation are identical to those on the left side of the differential equation, so we can write (5) by inspection. An nth-order algebraic equation has n roots, which we denote by $r_1, r_2, \ldots, r_n$. Not only are $K_1 \epsilon^{r_1 t}$, $K_2 \epsilon^{r_2 t}$, $\ldots, K_n \epsilon^{r_n t}$ all solutions of (4) for arbitrary K_i, but

$$y_H(t) = K_1 \epsilon^{r_1 t} + K_2 \epsilon^{r_2 t} + \cdots + K_n \epsilon^{r_n t} \quad (6)$$

is a solution for any values of the arbitrary constants K_1 through K_n. If all the roots of the characteristic equation are different, then (6) is the most general solution.

If two or more of the characteristic roots are identical—that is, if there is a repeated root of (5)—then we must modify the form of (6) to contain n independent terms and to represent the most general solution. If $r_1 = r_2$ with the remaining roots being distinct, the solution is

$$y_H(t) = K_1 \epsilon^{r_1 t} + K_2 t \epsilon^{r_1 t} + K_3 \epsilon^{r_3 t} + \cdots + K_n \epsilon^{r_n t}$$

If $r_1 = r_2 = r_3$, the most general solution to the homogeneous differential equation is

$$y_H(t) = (K_1 + K_2 t + K_3 t^2) \epsilon^{r_1 t} + K_4 \epsilon^{r_4 t} + \cdots + K_n \epsilon^{r_n t}$$

If any of the roots of the characteristic equation are complex numbers, they must occur in complex conjugate pairs because the coefficients in the characteristic equation are real. Suppose that $r_1 = \alpha + j\beta$ and $r_2 = \alpha - j\beta$, where $j = \sqrt{-1}$,[1] and that the characteristic equation has no other roots. Then

$$y_H(t) = K_1 \epsilon^{(\alpha + j\beta)t} + K_2 \epsilon^{(\alpha - j\beta)t}$$

However, because the solution is a real function of time, we should rewrite this equation by using suitable trigonometric identities. Factoring out $\epsilon^{\alpha t}$ from the right side, then using the first two entries in Table 6.1 with $\theta = \beta t$, and finally collecting like terms, we have

$$
\begin{aligned}
y_H(t) &= \epsilon^{\alpha t} [K_1 \epsilon^{j\beta t} + K_2 \epsilon^{-j\beta t}] \\
&= \epsilon^{\alpha t} [K_1 (\cos \beta t + j \sin \beta t) + K_2 (\cos \beta t - j \sin \beta t)] \\
&= \epsilon^{\alpha t} [(K_1 + K_2) \cos \beta t + j (K_1 - K_2) \sin \beta t]
\end{aligned}
$$

With $K_3 = K_1 + K_2$ and $K_4 = j(K_1 - K_2)$, the equation becomes

$$y_H(t) = \epsilon^{\alpha t} (K_3 \cos \beta t + K_4 \sin \beta t) \tag{7}$$

By using the last entry in Table 6.1, we can rewrite (7) in the alternative form

$$y_H(t) = K \epsilon^{\alpha t} \cos(\beta t + \phi) \tag{8}$$

where the constants K and ϕ depend on K_3 and K_4. In these expressions involving complex roots, K_1 and K_2 are complex numbers, with K_2 the complex conjugate of K_1; but K_3, K_4, K, and ϕ are real constants. Either of the two forms given by (7) and (8) should be used.

We treat repeated complex characteristic roots much like repeated real roots. For a fourth-order characteristic equation with $r_1 = r_3 = \alpha + j\beta$ and $r_2 = r_4 = \alpha - j\beta$, the most general solution to the homogeneous differential equation has the form

$$y_H(t) = K_A \epsilon^{\alpha t} \cos(\beta t + \phi_A) + K_B t \epsilon^{\alpha t} \cos(\beta t + \phi_B)$$

---

[1] The symbol i is also used for $\sqrt{-1}$, but we reserve i for electrical current.

TABLE 6.1   Useful Trigonometric Identities

$$\epsilon^{j\theta} = \cos\theta + j\sin\theta$$

$$\epsilon^{-j\theta} = \cos\theta - j\sin\theta$$

$$\cos\theta = \tfrac{1}{2}(\epsilon^{j\theta} + \epsilon^{-j\theta})$$

$$\sin\theta = \frac{1}{2j}(\epsilon^{j\theta} - \epsilon^{-j\theta})$$

$$\sin(\theta \pm \phi) = \sin\theta\cos\phi \pm \cos\theta\sin\phi$$

$$\cos(\theta \pm \phi) = \cos\theta\cos\phi \mp \sin\theta\sin\phi$$

$$A\cos\theta + B\sin\theta = \sqrt{A^2 + B^2}\sin\left(\theta + \tan^{-1}\frac{A}{B}\right)$$

$$A\cos\theta + B\sin\theta = \sqrt{A^2 + B^2}\cos\left(\theta - \tan^{-1}\frac{B}{A}\right)$$

Nonhomogeneous Differential Equations

We now consider the nonhomogeneous differential equation, where the forcing function $F(t)$ in (3) is nonzero. For mathematical convenience, we express the solution as the sum of two parts, namely

$$y(t) = y_H(t) + y_P(t) \tag{9}$$

where $y_H(t)$ and $y_P(t)$ are known as the complementary and the particular solutions, respectively. The **complementary solution** $y_H(t)$ is the solution to the homogeneous differential equation in (4); examples are given by (6) through (8). The **particular solution** $y_P(t)$ must satisfy the entire original differential equation, so

$$a_n y_P^{(n)} + \cdots + a_2 \ddot{y}_P + a_1 \dot{y}_P + a_0 y_P = F(t) \tag{10}$$

A general procedure for finding $y_P(t)$ is the variation-of-parameters method. When the forcing function $F(t)$ has only a finite number of different derivatives, however, the method of undetermined coefficients is satisfactory. Some examples of functions possessing only a finite number of independent derivatives are given in the left-hand column of Table 6.2. Others include $\cosh\omega t$ and $t^2\epsilon^{\alpha t}\cos(\omega t + \phi)$. An example of a forcing function that does *not* fall into this category is $1/t$.

In using the **method of undetermined coefficients**, we normally assume that the form of $y_P(t)$ consists of terms similar to those in $F(t)$ and its derivatives, with each term multiplied by a constant to be determined. We find the values of these constants by substituting the assumed $y_P(t)$ into the differential equation and then equating corresponding coefficients. The particular solution to be assumed for some common forcing functions is shown in Table 6.2.

TABLE 6.2   Usual Form of the Particular Solution

$F(t)$	$y_P(t)$
α	A
$\alpha_1 t + \alpha_0$	$At + B$
$\epsilon^{\alpha t}$	$A\epsilon^{\alpha t}$
$\cos \omega t$	$A \cos \omega t + B \sin \omega t$
$\sin \omega t$	$A \cos \omega t + B \sin \omega t$

If $F(t)$ or one of its derivatives contains a term identical to a term in $y_H(t)$, the corresponding terms in the right-hand column of Table 6.2 should be multiplied by t. Thus if $y_H(t) = K_1\epsilon^{-t} + K_2\epsilon^{-2t}$ and $F(t) = 3\epsilon^{-t}$, then $y_P(t) = At\epsilon^{-t}$ should be used. If a term in $F(t)$ corresponds to a double root of the characteristic equation, the normal form for $y_P(t)$ is multiplied by t^2. If, for example, $y_H(t) = K_1\epsilon^{-t} + K_2 t\epsilon^{-t}$ and $F(t) = \epsilon^{-t}$, then $y_P(t) = At^2\epsilon^{-t}$.

In the **general solution** $y(t) = y_H(t) + y_P(t)$ for an nth-order nonhomogeneous differential equation, the complementary solution $y_H(t)$ contains n arbitrary constants, which we earlier denoted by K_1 through K_n. The original differential equation in (3) will be satisfied regardless of the values of these constants, so their evaluation requires n separately specified initial conditions: $y(0), \dot{y}(0), \ldots, y^{(n-1)}(0)$. Because these initial values are associated with the entire solution and not just with the complementary solution, we cannot evaluate the arbitrary constants until we have found both $y_H(t)$ and $y_P(t)$.

▶ **EXAMPLE 6.1**

If $\dot{y} + 2y = F(t)$ and $y(0) = 2$, find $y(t)$ for $t \geq 0$ for each of the following forcing functions:

1. $F(t) = 10$
2. $F(t) = 10 \cos 2t$
3. $F(t) = 10 + 10 \cos 2t$

Solution

By inspection of the left-hand side of the differential equation, we find that the characteristic equation is $r + 2 = 0$, which has a single root at $r = -2$. Thus the complementary solution has the form

$$y_H(t) = K\epsilon^{-2t}$$

Because the value of K depends on $F(t)$ as well as $y(0)$, we shall use subscripts on K to distinguish among the three cases.

To find the particular solution for case 1, wherein $F(t) = 10$, we assume that $y_P(t) = A$. Substituting these expressions into the original differential equation gives $0 + 2A = 10$, so $A = 5$, and for $t \geq 0$,

$$y(t) = y_H(t) + y_P(t)$$
$$= K_1 \epsilon^{-2t} + 5$$

We replace t by zero in the last equation and use $y(0) = 2$ to obtain

$$2 = K_1 + 5$$

Thus $K_1 = -3$, and the response for $t \geq 0$ to $F(t) = 10$ is

$$y(t) = -3\epsilon^{-2t} + 5$$

In case 2, the forcing function is $F(t) = 10\cos 2t$, so we assume that $y_P(t) = A\cos 2t + B\sin 2t$. Substituting these expressions into $\dot{y}_P + 2y_P = F(t)$, we have

$$(-2A\sin 2t + 2B\cos 2t) + 2(A\cos 2t + B\sin 2t) = 10\cos 2t$$

or, collecting like terms,

$$(2A + 2B - 10)\cos 2t + (-2A + 2B)\sin 2t = 0$$

Because this must be an identity for all $t \geq 0$, we require that $2A + 2B - 10 = 0$ and that $-2A + 2B = 0$. Solving these equations gives $A = B = \frac{5}{2}$, so

$$y(t) = K_2\epsilon^{-2t} + \frac{5}{2}(\cos 2t + \sin 2t)$$

Replacing t by zero and $y(t)$ by 2, we have $2 = K_2 + \frac{5}{2}$. Thus $K_2 = -\frac{1}{2}$, and for all $t \geq 0$ the solution is

$$y(t) = -\frac{1}{2}\epsilon^{-2t} + \frac{5}{2}(\cos 2t + \sin 2t)$$

Finally, for case 3, $F(t) = 10 + 10\cos 2t$ and the particular solution is the sum of the particular solutions for the individual terms in $F(t)$. Thus

$$y(t) = K_3\epsilon^{-2t} + 5 + \frac{5}{2}(\cos 2t + \sin 2t)$$

For the right side to reduce to 2 when t is replaced by zero, we require that $K_3 = -\frac{11}{2}$. Hence for $t \geq 0$,

$$y(t) = -\frac{11}{2}\epsilon^{-2t} + 5 + \frac{5}{2}(\cos 2t + \sin 2t)$$

Although $y_P(t)$ for case 3 is the sum of the particular solutions for the first two cases, note that $K_3 \neq K_1 + K_2$. This is because the constants in $y_H(t)$ cannot be evaluated until after the *entire* particular solution has been found.

▶ *EXAMPLE 6.2*

Find the solution to the differential equation $\ddot{y} + 2\dot{y} + 5y = t$ for $t \geq 0$ if $y(0) = 0$ and $\dot{y}(0) = 2$.

Solution

The characteristic equation is $r^2 + 2r + 5 = 0$, which by the quadratic formula has roots at

$$r = \frac{-2 \pm \sqrt{4 - 20}}{2} = -1 \pm j2$$

As in (7), we can write the complementary solution as

$$y_H(t) = \epsilon^{-t}[K_1 \cos 2t + K_2 \sin 2t]$$

The particular solution is assumed to have the form $y_P(t) = At + B$. Substituting this expression into the differential equation gives

$$0 + 2A + 5(At + B) = t$$

or

$$(5A - 1)t + (2A + 5B) = 0$$

which requires that $5A = 1$ and $2A + 5B = 0$. Thus $A = \frac{1}{5}$, $B = -\frac{2}{25}$, and the general solution for $t \geq 0$ is

$$y(t) = \epsilon^{-t}[K_1 \cos 2t + K_2 \sin 2t] + \frac{1}{5}t - \frac{2}{25}$$

The derivative of this general solution is

$$\dot{y}(t) = \epsilon^{-t}[(2K_2 - K_1) \cos 2t - (K_2 + 2K_1) \sin 2t] + \frac{1}{5}$$

At $t = 0$ and with the given initial conditions, the last two equations reduce to

$$0 = K_1 - \frac{2}{25}$$

$$2 = 2K_2 - K_1 + \frac{1}{5}$$

from which $K_1 = \frac{2}{25}$ and $K_2 = \frac{47}{50}$. For $t \geq 0$,

$$y(t) = \epsilon^{-t}\left[\frac{2}{25} \cos 2t + \frac{47}{50} \sin 2t\right] + \frac{1}{5}t - \frac{2}{25}$$

■ 6.2 FIRST-ORDER SYSTEMS

In this section, we consider the solution of first-order systems, which usually consist of one energy-storing element and any number of dissipative elements. We also introduce some definitions that will be used throughout the rest of the book. Although they are illustrated in the context of first-order systems, we shall define the terms in a general way to make their extension to systems of arbitrary order obvious.

A first-order system is described by a single differential equation of the form

$$\dot{y} + \frac{1}{\tau}y = F(t) \tag{11}$$

where τ is a real, nonzero constant. To find the response for $t \geq 0$, we must know the forcing function $F(t)$ for all positive values of time and the initial condition $y(0)$. Because the characteristic equation $r + (1/\tau) = 0$ has one root at $r = -1/\tau$, the complementary solution is

$$y_H(t) = K\epsilon^{-t/\tau} \tag{12}$$

Stability

Typical curves for the complementary solution are shown in Figure 6.1. If $y_H(t)$ decays to zero as t approaches infinity, the system is said to be **stable**. If, on the other hand, $y_H(t)$ increases without limit as t becomes large, the system is **unstable**. A first-order system is stable if $\tau > 0$ and unstable if $\tau < 0$. If the magnitude of τ approaches infinity, $y_H(t)$ becomes constant, as shown in Figure 6.1(c). Such a system is said to be **marginally stable**.

Parts of the Complete Solution

A variety of names are used to identify the terms in the response of a fixed linear system, and these names can be easily confused. We shall explain the general terminology and relate the new terms to the complementary and particular solutions.

We have seen that we can find the form of the complementary solution by letting $F(t) = 0$ and solving for the roots of the characteristic equation. Thus the form of $y_H(t)$ does not depend on the input, but only on the system elements and their interconnections. The form of $y_H(t)$ represents the natural behavior of the system when the external input is removed and the system is excited by some initial stored energy. Thus $y_H(t)$ is also called the **free response**.

The size of the terms in the free response is given by the arbitrary constants, such as K in (12). In Section 6.1, we saw that the values of such constants depend on $y_P(t)$ and hence on the input. The constants also

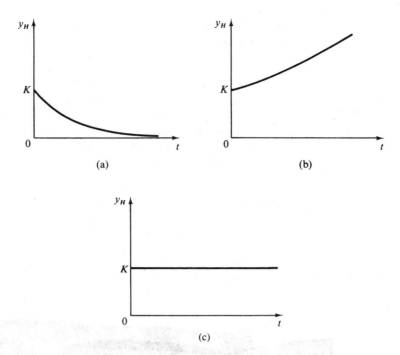

FIGURE 6.1 The complementary solution for a first-order system.
(a) $\tau > 0$. (b) $\tau < 0$. (c) τ infinite.

depend on the initial conditions, which in turn represent the effect of the history of the system prior to the initial instant.

Studying the method of undetermined coefficients, we saw that the particular solution depends on the form of the forcing function. For this reason, $y_P(t)$ is called the **forced response**. In summary, the free and forced responses are identical to the complementary and particular solutions, respectively.

An alternative way of dividing the total response into two parts is to regard it as the sum of the zero-state response and the zero-input response. The **zero-state response** $y_{zs}(t)$ is the complete response to the input when the initial values of the state variables are zero. It includes both the particular solution and the complementary solution, where the arbitrary constants in the complementary solution are found for initial conditions that correspond to zero initial values for the state variables. For a first-order system, we can write

$$y_{zs}(t) = y_P(t) + K_{zs}\epsilon^{-t/\tau}$$

where K_{zs} is the arbitrary constant evaluated for zero-state conditions.

The **zero-input response** $y_{zi}(t)$ corresponds to specified initial values of the state variables and a forcing function of zero. Hence it consists of the complementary solution but ,iot the particular solution, and for a first-order system we can denote it by

$$y_{zi}(t) = K_{zi}\epsilon^{-t/\tau}$$

where K_{zi} is the arbitrary constant evaluated for zero input. Note that although both y_{zs} and y_{zi} contain a term of the form $\epsilon^{-t/\tau}$, the constants in front of the terms are not the same.

A linear system with a specified input and specified initial values for its state variables has a response that we can find by superposition of the zero-state and zero-input responses. Thus

$$y(t) = y_{zs}(t) + y_{zi}(t)$$

Combining these expressions for a first-order system gives

$$y(t) = y_P(t) + (K_{zs} + K_{zi})\epsilon^{-t/\tau}$$

By comparing this equation to (9), we see that the two terms $K_{zs}\epsilon^{-t/\tau}$ and $K_{zi}\epsilon^{-t/\tau}$ combine to give the free response $y_H(t)$.

It is often convenient to decompose the total response into transient and steady-state components. The **transient response** $y_t(t)$ consists of those terms that decay to zero as t approaches infinity. The **steady-state response** $y_{ss}(t)$ is the part of the solution that remains after the transient terms have disappeared. For a first-order system, $y_H(t) = K\epsilon^{-t/\tau}$ will be part of the transient response if τ is positive—that is, if the system is stable. If $y_P(t)$ has a form such as A, $A\cos\omega t + B\sin\omega t$, or $At + B$, then $y_P(t)$ will constitute the steady-state response. On the other hand, if $y_P(t) = At\epsilon^{-t} + B\epsilon^{-t}$, then $y_P(t)$ will be part of the transient response. For systems that are stable and for which the terms in y_P do not decay to zero, the transient and steady-state components are identical to the free and the forced responses, respectively.

The Complete Response to a Constant Input

If $F(t)$ has a constant value of A, then the forced response to the first-order differential equation

$$\dot{y} + \frac{1}{\tau}y = F(t)$$

is $y_P(t) = \tau A$, as discussed in Example 6.1. Assume that $\tau > 0$, so that the free response

$$y_H(t) = K\epsilon^{-t/\tau}$$

decays to zero. Then $y_P(t) = y_{ss}$ and we can write the complete solution as

$$y(t) = y_{ss} + K\epsilon^{-t/\tau} \qquad (13)$$

If $y(0)$ is known, we can evaluate this solution at $t = 0$, giving $y(0) = y_{ss} + K$ or $K = y(0) - y_{ss}$. Thus for $t \geq 0$,

$$y(t) = y_{ss} + [y(0) - y_{ss}]\epsilon^{-t/\tau} \qquad (14)$$

which is shown in Figure 6.2(a). Special cases of this result are shown in Figure 6.2(b) and Figure 6.2(c).

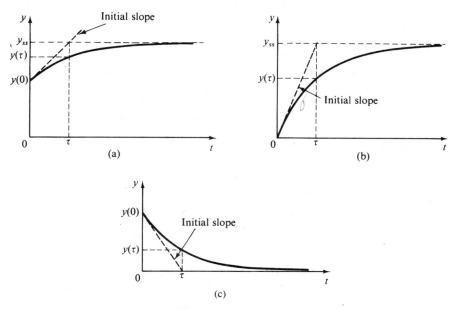

FIGURE 6.2 Response of a stable first-order system to a constant input. (a) y_{ss} and $y(0)$ both nonzero. (b) $y(0) = 0$. (c) $y_{ss} = 0$.

To give significance to the value of $y(\tau)$ shown in Figure 6.2(a), first note from (14) that, for $t = \tau$, we have

$$y(\tau) = y_{ss} + [y(0) - y_{ss}]\epsilon^{-1}$$

Because $\epsilon^{-1} = 0.3679$,

$$y(\tau) = y(0) + 0.6321[y_{ss} - y(0)]$$

Thus after τ seconds, the response to a constant input is approximately 63% of the way from the initial value to the steady-state value. Because $\epsilon^{-4} = 0.0183$, the response after 4τ seconds is approximately 98% of the way from the initial value to the steady-state value. We see that the system parameter τ, which is called the **time constant**, is a measure of the system's speed of response. Another interpretation of the time constant results from considering the initial slope of the response. Differentiation of (14) gives

$$\dot{y}(t) = \frac{1}{\tau}[y_{ss} - y(0)]\epsilon^{-t/\tau}$$

and setting $t = 0$ yields

$$y_{ss} = y(0) + \tau\dot{y}(0)$$

Thus if the slope of the response curve were maintained at its initial value of $\dot{y}(0)$, it would take τ seconds, instead of an infinite time, for the response to reach its steady-state value.

▶ **EXAMPLE 6.3**

Find the response of each of the first-order systems shown in Figure 6.3. The systems are at rest with no stored energy at $t = 0$, and for $t > 0$ the respective inputs are $f_a(t) = A$ and $\omega_a(t) = A$. In Figure 6.3(a), the output x is the elongation of the spring from its unstretched position. The output for Figure 6.3(b) is the angular velocity ω_1.

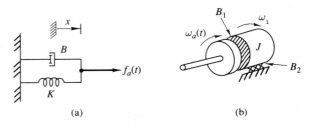

(a)   (b)

FIGURE 6.3   First-order mechanical systems for Example 6.3.
(a) Translational. (b) Rotational.

Solution

The translational system shown in Figure 6.3(a) is described by the differential equation

$$B\dot{x} + Kx = f_a(t)$$

or

$$\dot{x} + \frac{K}{B}x = \frac{1}{B}f_a(t)$$

Comparing this equation to (11), we see that the time constant is

$$\tau = \frac{B}{K} \tag{15}$$

Note that if the friction coefficient B is increased, τ increases and the system takes a longer time to approach its steady-state value. Because $f_a(t) = A$ for all positive values of time, $x_P = x_{ss} = A/K$. Although we can get this result by setting the derivative in the differential equation equal to zero, we can also see this by looking at Figure 6.3(a). When the applied force is a constant, the right ends of B and K will eventually become stationary. Then no force will be exerted by the friction element. The only steady-state forces will be those exerted by the input and the spring, so $A = Kx_{ss}$. Finally, because there is no initial energy stored in the spring, $x(0) = 0$. Thus by

(14), the complete response is

$$x = \frac{A}{K}(1 - \epsilon^{-t/\tau}) \tag{16}$$

where τ is given by (15).

For the rotational system shown in Figure 6.3(b),

$$J\dot{\omega}_1 + (B_1 + B_2)\omega_1 = B_1\omega_a(t)$$

or

$$\dot{\omega}_1 + \frac{B_1 + B_2}{J}\omega_1 = \frac{B_1}{J}\omega_a(t)$$

The time constant is

$$\tau = \frac{J}{B_1 + B_2} \tag{17}$$

With $\omega_a(t) = A$ for all positive time, $(\omega_1)_{ss} = AB_1/(B_1 + B_2)$. Because $\omega_1(0) = 0$,

$$\omega_1 = \frac{AB_1}{B_1 + B_2}(1 - \epsilon^{-t/\tau}) \tag{18}$$

As should be expected for the rotational system, the time needed to approach steady-state conditions is directly proportional to the inertia of the disk. However, once the disk reaches a constant speed, the only torques on it are those from the friction elements. Thus the steady-state angular velocity is determined by the relative sizes of B_1 and B_2.

An electrical circuit consisting of one capacitor or one inductor, together with any number of resistors and sources, can also be described by a first-order differential equation. If the sources are constant for $t > 0$, the response of any output voltage or current will have the form shown in (14). The steady-state response y_{ss} and the time constant τ can be determined from inspection of the circuit's differential equation. The quantity $y(0)$ will depend on the energy contained in the circuit at $t = 0$ and on the input.

It is possible for the output to undergo, at $t = 0$, an instantaneous change caused by the sudden application of a source or the opening or closing of a switch. An output having a discontinuity at $t = 0$ is relatively rare in mechanical systems but fairly common in electrical ones. Recall that the energy stored in a passive element cannot change instantaneously unless there is an infinitely large power flow. Hence, as long as all voltages and currents remain finite, neither the voltage across a capacitor nor the current through an inductor can change instantaneously.

Other electrical variables, however, are not directly related to the stored energy and thus can have discontinuities. Included in this category are resistor voltages and currents, capacitor currents, and inductor voltages. When we must consider functions that have a discontinuity at $t = 0$, it is customary to use the notations $y(0-)$ and $y(0+)$ for the limiting values of $y(t)$ as t approaches zero through negative and positive values, respectively. The function $y(t)$ shown in Figure 6.4 has a discontinuity at $t = 0$, where it jumps instantaneously from $y(0-)$ to $y(0+)$. This is typical for the responses of first-order circuits. To account for the possibility of discontinuous behavior, we modify (14) slightly to read

$$y(t) = y_{ss} + [y(0+) - y_{ss}]\epsilon^{-t/\tau} \tag{19}$$

This change is consistent with the fact that in computing the response for $t > 0$, we must use $y(0+)$, the value of $y(t)$ immediately following any discontinuity.

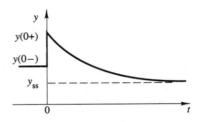

FIGURE 6.4 Typical response of a first-order circuit.

▶ **EXAMPLE 6.4**

The voltage source shown in Figure 6.5(a) is zero for $t < 0$ but has a constant value of A for all $t > 0$. Find and sketch the output voltage e_o.

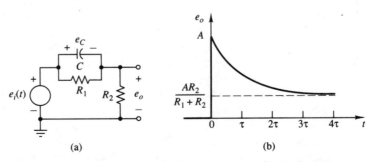

(a)   (b)

FIGURE 6.5 First-order circuit for Example 6.4. (a) Circuit diagram.
(b) Zero-state response when $e_i(t) = A$ for $t > 0$.

Solution

Setting the sum of the currents that are leaving the upper right-hand node equal to zero, we have

$$C(\dot{e}_o - \dot{e}_i) + \frac{1}{R_1}[e_o - e_i(t)] + \frac{1}{R_2}e_o = 0$$

which gives the first-order input-output equation

$$C\dot{e}_o + \left(\frac{1}{R_1} + \frac{1}{R_2}\right)e_o = C\dot{e}_i + \frac{1}{R_1}e_i(t) \tag{20}$$

In order to obtain an expression for $e_o(t)$ for $t > 0$, we first evaluate the terms in the forcing function on the right-hand side of this equation for $t > 0$. The general solution will contain one arbitrary constant. To evaluate this constant, we will need $e_o(0+)$, the value of the output at the beginning of the interval $0 < t < \infty$.

Because $e_i(t) = A$ and $\dot{e}_i = 0$ for all $t > 0$, (20) reduces to

$$C\dot{e}_o + \left(\frac{1}{R_1} + \frac{1}{R_2}\right)e_o = \frac{A}{R_1} \quad \text{for } t > 0$$

or

$$\dot{e}_o + \left(\frac{R_1 + R_2}{R_1 R_2 C}\right)e_o = \frac{A}{R_1 C} \quad \text{for } t > 0 \tag{21}$$

By inspection of this equation, we see that

$$\tau = \frac{R_1 R_2 C}{R_1 + R_2} \tag{22a}$$

$$(e_o)_{\text{ss}} = \frac{R_2}{R_1 + R_2}A \tag{22b}$$

Then by (19),

$$e_o(t) = \frac{R_2 A}{R_1 + R_2} + K\epsilon^{-t/\tau} \quad \text{for } t > 0 \tag{23}$$

where

$$K = e_o(0+) - (e_o)_{\text{ss}} \tag{24}$$

Because e_o is the voltage across a resistor, it can change instantaneously when $e_i(t)$ changes from 0 to A at $t = 0$. However, the voltage across the capacitor, denoted by e_C in Figure 6.5(a), must be continuous at $t = 0$ because it is related to the energy stored in the capacitor, which cannot change instantaneously. By applying Kirchhoff's voltage law to a loop consisting of the voltage source, the capacitor, and the resistor R_2, we have

$$e_i(t) - e_C(t) - e_o(t) = 0 \tag{25}$$

In order to find $e_o(0+)$, we apply (25) at $t = 0+$. We know that $e_i(0+) = A$. Because the capacitor contains no energy at $t = 0-$ and because its energy cannot change instantaneously, $e_C(0+) = e_C(0-) = 0$. Thus for $t = 0+$, (25) gives

$$e_o(0+) = e_i(0+) - e_C(0+) = A \tag{26}$$

Substituting (22b) and (26) into (24), we find that the complete response for $t > 0$ is

$$e_o(t) = \frac{A}{R_1 + R_2}(R_2 + R_1\epsilon^{-t/\tau})$$

where τ is given by (22a). The response is sketched in Figure 6.5(b).

Although the steady-state response to a constant input can always be obtained from the circuit's differential equation, it can also be found directly from the circuit diagram. For a constant input, the steady-state values of all currents and voltages are constants. Under these conditions, $di_L/dt = 0$ and $de_C/dt = 0$. Then from the respective element laws, we see that the voltage across any inductor and the current through any capacitor must be zero. Hence in the steady state, an inductor acts like a short circuit, and a capacitor becomes an open circuit.

When finding the steady-state response to a constant input, we may redraw the circuit with any inductor replaced by a short circuit and any capacitor replaced by an open circuit. The original circuit then reduces to a purely resistive one. In the case of Figure 6.5(a), we can draw the steady-state equivalent circuit shown in Figure 6.6. The resistances R_1 and R_2 now form a series combination directly across the source, so we can use the voltage-divider rule to write

$$(e_o)_{ss} = \frac{R_2}{R_1 + R_2}A$$

which agrees with (22b).

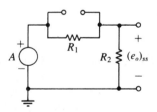

FIGURE 6.6 Steady-state equivalent circuit for Figure 6.5(a).

In the final first-order example, a source branch is disconnected from the rest of the circuit. We shall note that the time constant changes when the branch is removed. We shall replace the original circuit by a resistive one in order to calculate the voltage across the capacitor just before the source is disconnected. Because the capacitor voltage cannot change instantaneously, we know that $e_C(0+) = e_C(0-)$. Once again, however, the output voltage has a discontinuity at $t = 0$.

▶ **EXAMPLE 6.5**

Find the time constant for the circuit shown in Figure 6.7(a) when the switch is closed and when the switch is open. Let the source voltage have a constant value of 24 volts. Assume that the switch has been closed for a long time for $t < 0$, so that the circuit is in the steady state at $t = 0-$. If the switch opens at $t = 0$, find and sketch e_o versus t for $t > 0$.

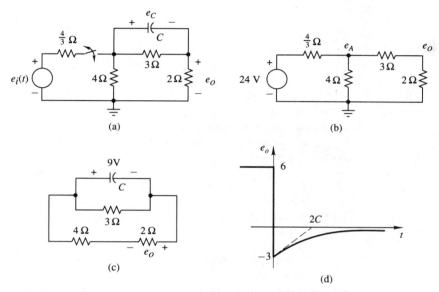

(a)

(b)

(c)

(d)

FIGURE 6.7 (a) Circuit for Example 6.5. (b) Circuit at $t = 0-$. (c) Circuit at $t = 0+$. (d) Sketch of e_o versus t.

Solution

From Example 5.5, the input-output equation with the switch closed is

$$\dot{e}_o + \frac{2}{3C}e_o = \frac{1}{2}\dot{e}_i + \frac{1}{6C}e_i(t)$$

so the time constant is $\tau = 3C/2$. Again from Example 5.5, when the switch is open,

$$\dot{e}_o + \frac{1}{2C}e_o = 0 \tag{27}$$

which corresponds to a time constant $\tau = 2C$.

To find the response for $t > 0$ with the switch open, we first note that the general solution to (27) is

$$e_o(t) = K\epsilon^{-t/2C} \tag{28}$$

As the first step in determining the initial condition $e_o(0+)$, we shall find the capacitor voltage at $t = 0-$, when the circuit is in the steady state with the switch closed. Replacing the capacitor by an open circuit, we obtain Figure 6.7(b). The parallel combination of 4 Ω and 5 Ω is 20/9 Ω. By the voltage-divider rule,

$$e_A(0-) = \frac{20/9}{4/3 + 20/9}(24) = 15 \text{ V}$$

$$e_o(0-) = \frac{2}{3+2}e_A(0-) = 6 \text{ V}$$

so

$$e_C(0-) = e_A(0-) - e_o(0-) = 9 \text{ V}$$

which must also be the value of $e_C(0+)$.

The circuit at $t = 0+$ is shown in Figure 6.7(c), with $e_C(0+) = 9\text{V}$, with the source branch removed, and with the 4-Ω and 2-Ω resistors positioned slightly differently for increased clarity. Again using the voltage-divider rule, we see that

$$e_o(0+) = \frac{2}{4+2}(-9) = -3 \text{ V}$$

With this initial condition, we can rewrite (28) as

$$e_o(t) = -3\epsilon^{-t/2C} \quad \text{for } t > 0$$

which is sketched in part (d) of the figure. Note the discontinuity in the output voltage at $t = 0$.

■ 6.3 THE STEP FUNCTION AND IMPULSE

Two of the most important inputs we encounter in the analysis of dynamic systems are the unit step function and the unit impulse.

The Unit Step Function

One frequently encounters inputs that are zero before some reference time and that have a nonzero constant value thereafter. To treat such inputs mathematically, we define the **unit step function**, which is denoted by $U(t)$. This function is defined to be zero for $t \leq 0$ and unity for $t > 0$; it is shown in Figure 6.8(a).[2] If the step discontinuity occurs at some later time t_1, as

---

[2]Note that a capital U is used for the unit step function $U(t)$, in contrast to the lowercase letter in the symbol $u(t)$ for a general input. The value of the unit step function at time zero could be defined to be unity, or its value could be left undefined at this instant. Defining $U(0) = 0$ will be convenient in Chapter 7.

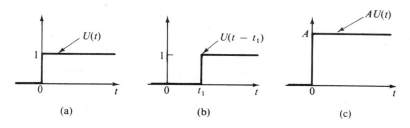

FIGURE 6.8 Step functions. (a) $U(t)$. (b) $U(t - t_1)$. (c) $AU(t)$.

shown in Figure 6.8(b), the function is defined by

$$U(t - t_1) = \begin{cases} 0 \text{ for } t \leq t_1 \\ 1 \text{ for } t > t_1 \end{cases} \tag{29}$$

This notation is consistent with the fact that when any function $f(t)$ is plotted versus t, replacing every t in $f(t)$ by $t - t_1$ shifts the curve t_1 units to the right. If the height of the step is A rather than unity, we simply have A times the unit step function, as shown in Figure 6.8(c).

From the definition of $U(t - t_1)$, we note that

$$f(t)U(t - t_1) = \begin{cases} 0 \quad \text{ for } t \leq t_1 \\ f(t) \text{ for } t > t_1 \end{cases} \tag{30}$$

Thus the output of a system that was at rest for $t \leq 0$ is often written in the form $f(t)U(t)$, where the multiplying factor $U(t)$ is used in place of the phrase "for $t > 0$."

We define the **unit step response** of a system, denoted by $y_U(t)$, as the output that occurs when the input is the unit step function $U(t)$ and when the system contains no initial stored energy—that is, $y_U(t)$ is the zero-state response to the input $U(t)$. For the translational system shown in Figure 6.3(a),

$$y_U(t) = \frac{1}{K}[1 - \epsilon^{-Kt/B}] \quad \text{for } t \geq 0$$

whereas for the rotational system shown in Figure 6.3(b),

$$y_U(t) = \frac{B_1}{B_1 + B_2}[1 - \epsilon^{-(B_1 + B_2)t/J}] \quad \text{for } t \geq 0$$

We can represent any function that consists of horizontal and vertical lines as the sum of step functions. Consider, for example, the pulse shown in Figure 6.9(a). This function is the sum of the two functions shown in Figure 6.9(b) and Figure 6.9(c), so

$$f_1(t) = AU(t) - AU(t - t_1) \tag{31}$$

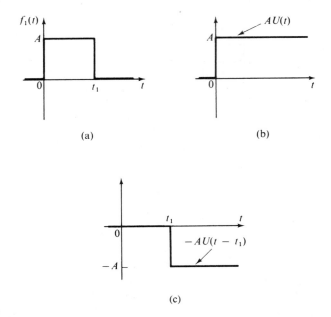

FIGURE 6.9   (a) Rectangular pulse. (b), (c) Formation of the
rectangular pulse by the sum of two step functions.

Suppose that the pulse in (31) is the input to a linear first-order system
described by the differential equation

$$\dot{y} + \frac{1}{\tau}y = u(t) \tag{32}$$

and for which $y(0) = 0$. From Section 6.2, we know that the response
to $AU(t)$ is $A\tau(1 - \epsilon^{-t/\tau})$ for $t \geq 0$, and this is also the response for
$0 \leq t \leq t_1$ to the input in (31). For $t > t_1$, we may use superposition and
sum the responses to the components $AU(t)$ and $-AU(t - t_1)$ to obtain

$$y(t) = A\tau[1 - \epsilon^{-t/\tau}] - A\tau[1 - \epsilon^{-(t-t_1)/\tau}]$$
$$= A\tau(-1 + \epsilon^{t_1/\tau})\epsilon^{-t/\tau}$$

Hence we may write

$$y(t) = \begin{cases} A\tau(1 - \epsilon^{-t/\tau}) & \text{for } 0 \leq t \leq t_1 \\ A\tau(\epsilon^{t_1/\tau} - 1)\epsilon^{-t/\tau} & \text{for } t > t_1 \end{cases} \tag{33}$$

which is shown in Figure 6.10(a). As expected, the response for the first t_1
seconds is the same as in Figure 6.2(b), whereas for $t > t_1$ the output decays
exponentially to zero with a time constant τ. The output is the superposition
of the two functions shown in Figure 6.10(b) and Figure 6.10(c). It can also

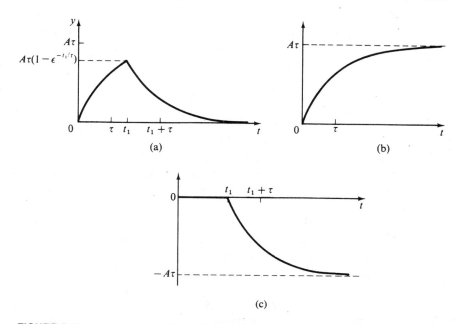

FIGURE 6.10 Responses of a first-order system to the inputs shown in Figure 6.9.

be written in the alternative form

$$y(t) = A\tau(1 - \epsilon^{-t/\tau})U(t) - A\tau(1 - \epsilon^{-(t-t_1)/\tau})U(t - t_1)$$

It is instructive to rewrite the pulse response for $t > t_1$ in (33) with $\epsilon^{t_1/\tau}$ replaced by its Taylor-series expansion

$$\epsilon^{t_1/\tau} = 1 + \frac{t_1}{\tau} + \frac{1}{2!}\left(\frac{t_1}{\tau}\right)^2 + \cdots$$

Then, for $t > t_1$,

$$y(t) = A\tau\left[\frac{t_1}{\tau} + \frac{1}{2!}\left(\frac{t_1}{\tau}\right)^2 + \cdots\right]\epsilon^{-t/\tau}$$

Suppose that the pulse width is small compared to the time constant of the system, so that $t_1 \ll \tau$. Then we can neglect all the terms inside the brackets except the first and write

$$y(t) \simeq At_1\epsilon^{-t/\tau} \quad \text{for } t > t_1 \tag{34}$$

where At_1 is the area underneath the input pulse. We could also consider input pulses that have somewhat different shapes but have the same area underneath the curve. We would find that as long as the width t_1 of any pulse that is the input to a first-order system is small compared to the system's time constant, the response for $t > t_1$ depends on the area underneath the pulse but not on its shape.

As background for another important property, note that the response of the system modeled by (32) to a step function of height At_1, with $y(0) = 0$, is At_1 times the unit step response:

$$At_1 y_U(t) = At_1 \tau (1 - \epsilon^{-t/\tau}) \quad \text{for } t \geq 0$$

Note that

$$\frac{d}{dt}[At_1 y_U(t)] = At_1 \epsilon^{-t/\tau} \tag{35}$$

for all positive values of t. Because the right side of (35) is identical to (34), we see that if $t_1 \ll \tau$, the response for $t > t_1$ to a pulse of area At_1 is the derivative of the response to a step function of height At_1.

The Unit Impulse

The response of a first-order system to a pulse of given area appears to be independent of the pulse shape as long as the pulse width t_1 is small compared to the time constant τ, so it is reasonable to try to define an idealized pulse function whose width is small compared to the time constant of all first-order systems. However, in order to have $t_1 \ll \tau$ for all nonzero values of τ, t_1 must be infinitesimally small; and to have a nonzero pulse area, the height of the pulse must become infinitely large. Although such an idealized pulse creates conceptual and mathematical difficulties, let us reconsider the rectangular input pulse that is shown in Figure 6.11(a). Note that $f_1(t)$ in part (a) of the figure is the derivative of the function $f_2(t)$ shown in part (b).

Let us specify $A = 1/t_1$ in Figure 6.11 such that the area underneath $f_1(t)$ is unity and such that the value of $f_2(t)$ for $t > t_1$ is also unity. If we continually decrease the value of t_1, then the height of the pulse $f_1(t)$ increases in order to maintain unit area, while $f_2(t)$ rises to its final value more rapidly. The dashed lines in Figure 6.12 show the changes in $f_1(t)$ and $f_2(t)$ when t_1 is halved.

As t_1 approaches zero, $f_1(t)$ approaches a pulse of infinitesimal width, infinite height, and unit area. The limit of this process is called the **unit impulse**, denoted by the symbol $\delta(t)$. It is represented graphically as shown in Figure 6.13(a). The number 1 next to the head of the arrow indicates the area underneath the function that approached the impulse. In the limit, as t_1 approaches zero, $f_2(t)$ becomes the unit step function $U(t)$, shown in Figure 6.13(b). Because $f_1(t)$ in Figure 6.11 is the time derivative of $f_2(t)$, it appears that in the limit,

$$\delta(t) = \frac{d}{dt}U(t) \tag{36}$$

The arguments we used in the preceding paragraph are heuristic and not mathematically rigorous. Questions can be raised about (36) because differentiation is a limiting process and we introduced $\delta(t)$ as the result

$\delta(t) = \frac{d}{dt} y_U(t) =$

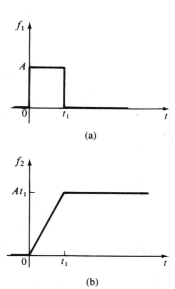

FIGURE 6.11 (a) Rectangular pulse with area At_1.
(b) $f_2(t) = \int_0^t f_1(\lambda)d\lambda$.

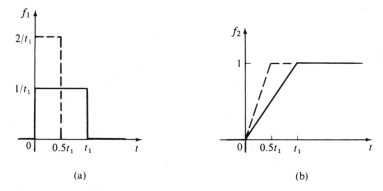

FIGURE 6.12 The functions $f_1(t)$ and $f_2(t)$ shown in Figure 6.11 when $A = 1/t_1$.

of another limiting process. Then, without mathematical justification, we interchanged the order of the two limiting processes. Furthermore, if we were to put our description of the unit impulse into equations, we might write

$$\delta(t) = 0 \quad \text{for } t \neq 0 \tag{37a}$$

$$\int_{-\varepsilon}^{\varepsilon} \delta(t)dt = 1 \quad \text{for } \varepsilon > 0 \tag{37b}$$

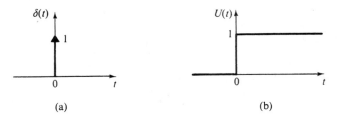

FIGURE 6.13 (a) The unit impulse. (b) The unit step function.

where (37b) suggests that the unit impulse has unit area. Although we shall not discuss the matter in detail here, it happens that (37) violates the axioms of real-function theory and is an impermissible way of defining a function. In fact, $\delta(t)$ is not a function in the usual sense, and we have purposely avoided calling it the unit impulse "function." However, results obtained in this section can be justified by rigorous mathematical arguments.[3]

We can define the unit impulse formally in terms of an integral and in a way that is consistent with distribution theory. For any function $f(t)$ that is continuous at $t = 0$, the unit impulse $\delta(t)$ must satisfy the integral expression

$$\int_{-a}^{b} f(t)\delta(t)dt = f(0) \quad \text{for } a > 0, b > 0 \tag{38}$$

Note that (37b) is a special case of this equation, with $f(t) = 1$ for all values of t.

A unit impulse that occurs at time t_a rather than at $t = 0$ is denoted by $\delta(t - t_a)$ and is shown in Figure 6.14(a). Furthermore, for any function $f(t)$ that is continuous at $t = t_a$, we can replace (38) by

$$\int_{b}^{c} f(t)\delta(t - t_a)dt = f(t_a) \quad \text{for } b < t_a < c \tag{39}$$

which is referred to as the **sampling property** of the impulse. The product $A\delta(t)$, which is shown in Figure 6.14(b), is called an impulse of weight A. We can visualize it as the limit of a high, narrow pulse of area A. Equation (36) may be replaced by the more general relationship

$$A\delta(t - t_a) = \frac{d}{dt}[AU(t - t_a)] \tag{40}$$

In other words, differentiating a step function of height A occurring at t_a gives rise to an impulse of weight A at $t = t_a$, which is indicated in Figure 6.14(c).

---

[3]The unit impulse is also called the **Dirac delta function** and is used in many areas of science and engineering. Both the unit impulse and ordinary functions can be regarded as special cases of generalized functions or distributions.

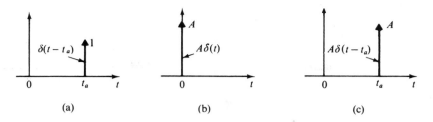

FIGURE 6.14 Impulses. (a) $\delta(t - t_a)$. (b) $A\delta(t)$. (c) $A\delta(t - t_a)$.

The **unit impulse response** $h(t)$ is defined as the output that occurs when the input is $\delta(t)$ and when the system contains no stored energy before the impulse is applied. Thus $h(t)$ is the zero-state response to $\delta(t)$. The zero-state response for $t > t_1$ to a pulse of any shape is approximately equal to $h(t)$ times the area underneath the original pulse, as long as the pulse width t_1 is small compared to the time constant of the system.

Because a unit impulse applied to a system can cause an infinite power flow that instantaneously changes the energy stored in the system, the initial conditions we would need in order to calculate $h(t)$ directly are often hard to find. For this reason, the property described in the following paragraph often proves useful.

Assume that we know the response to a certain input for a linear system that contains no initial stored energy. Then, if we substitute a new input that is the derivative of the original input, the new response will be the derivative of the old response. A formal proof of this property will be found in Section 8.2. Because $\delta(t)$ is the derivative of $U(t)$, the unit impulse response and the unit step response for a linear system are related by

$$h(t) = \frac{d}{dt} y_U(t) \tag{41}$$

Thus once the unit step response $y_U(t)$ is known, we can obtain $h(t)$ from it by using (41).

▶ **EXAMPLE 6.6**

For the translational system shown in Figure 6.15, find $y_U(t)$ and $h(t)$ when the output is the velocity $v(t)$.

Solution

The system is described by the differential equation

$$M\dot{v} + Bv = f_a(t)$$

or

$$\dot{v} + \frac{B}{M}v = \frac{1}{M}f_a(t)$$

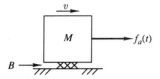

FIGURE 6.15   Translational system for Example 6.6.

Because the system's time constant is $\tau = M/B$, and $v_{ss} = 1/B$ if $f_a(t) = 1$ for all $t > 0$, the unit step response is

$$y_U(t) = \frac{1}{B}(1 - \epsilon^{-Bt/M}) \quad \text{for } t > 0 \tag{42}$$

From (41), the unit impulse response can be found by differentiating $y_U(t)$. It is

$$h(t) = \frac{1}{M}\epsilon^{-Bt/M} \quad \text{for } t > 0 \tag{43}$$

These responses are shown in Figure 6.16.

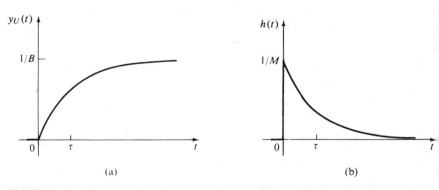

(a)

(b)

FIGURE 6.16   Responses for the system shown in Figure 6.15 when the output is the velocity. (a) Unit step response. (b) Unit impulse response.

Note in Figure 6.16(a) that when $f_a(t)$ is a step function, the velocity of the mass does not change instantaneously at $t = 0$. When $f_a(t)$ is an impulse, however, the velocity of the mass does undergo an instantaneous change. In the first case, there is no change in the kinetic energy of the mass at $t = 0$. In the latter case, the impulse causes an instantaneous increase in the energy of the mass.

[handwritten margin notes: undamped $\xi = 0$, $r_1, r_2 = \pm \omega_n \sqrt{-1} = \pm \omega_n j$, $y_H = k_1 \cos \omega_n t + k_2 \sin \omega_n t$ (marginal stable), underdamped $0 < \xi < 1$]

6.4 SECOND-ORDER SYSTEMS

[handwritten: critical damped $\xi = 1$, overdamped $\xi > 1$]

We can write the differential equation for a fixed linear second-order system as

$$\ddot{y} + a_1 \dot{y} + a_0 y = F(t) \tag{44}$$

where, without loss of generality, the coefficient of $\ddot{y}$ has been made unity and where a_0 and a_1 are real constants. To find the response, as in Example 6.2, we need to know $F(t)$ for $t \geq 0$ and also the initial conditions $y(0)$ and $\dot{y}(0)$.

If the forcing function $F(t)$ has a finite number of independent derivatives, we can find the forced response by the method of undetermined coefficients. The free response $y_H(t)$ contains two terms instead of the one that is present for first-order systems. If the roots r_1 and r_2 of the characteristic equation

$$r^2 + a_1 r + a_0 = 0$$

are real and distinct, then

$$y_H(t) = K_1 \epsilon^{r_1 t} + K_2 \epsilon^{r_2 t} \tag{45}$$

For $r_1 = r_2$, the two roots are not distinct, and we must replace (45) by

$$y_H(t) = K_1 \epsilon^{r_1 t} + K_2 t \epsilon^{r_1 t} \tag{46}$$

If the roots are complex, they must have the form $r_1 = \alpha + j\beta$ and $r_2 = \alpha - j\beta$, and we write the free response as

$$y_H(t) = \epsilon^{\alpha t}[K_1 \cos \beta t + K_2 \sin \beta t]$$

or, equivalently,

$$y_H(t) = K \epsilon^{\alpha t} \cos(\beta t + \phi) \tag{47}$$

Examples of $y_H(t)$ are shown in Figure 6.17 for the three cases represented by (45) through (47) when r_1, r_2, and α are negative numbers. The light lines in Figure 6.17(a) and Figure 6.17(b) indicate the two individual functions that are added to give $y_H(t)$, which is the heavy curve. In Figure 6.17(c), dashed lines labeled $K\epsilon^{\alpha t}$ and $-K\epsilon^{\alpha t}$ form the envelope of the damped oscillations. The values of the arbitrary constants K_1, K_2, K, and ϕ in (45) through (47) depend on $y_P(t)$ and the initial conditions $y(0)$ and $\dot{y}(0)$.

The Complex Plane

When the roots of the characteristic equation are plotted in a complex plane, inspection of the plot reveals the nature of the system's free response. The root locations corresponding to the typical free responses shown in Figure 6.17 are indicated by the crosses in the respective parts of Figure 6.18.

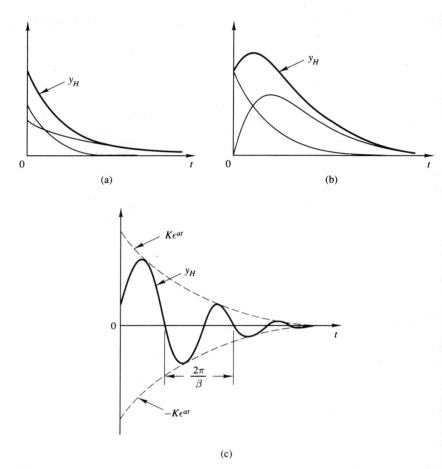

FIGURE 6.17 Typical curves for the free response of a second-order system. (a) Real distinct negative roots of the characteristic equation. (b) Identical negative roots. (c) Complex roots with $\alpha < 0$.

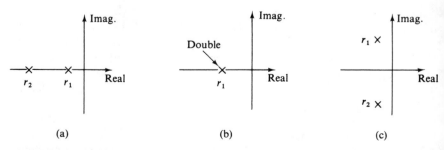

FIGURE 6.18 Roots of the characteristic equation corresponding to Figure 6.17. (a) Real distinct negative roots. (b) Identical negative roots. (c) Complex roots with $\alpha < 0$.

Recall from Section 6.2 that a stable system is one for which the free response $y_H(t)$ decays to zero as t approaches infinity. All the examples in Figure 6.17 fall into this category. Examples of unstable systems, where $y_H(t)$ increases without bound, are shown in Figure 6.19. The characteristic-root locations appear directly under the corresponding sketches of the free response. Figure 6.19(a) and Figure 6.19(b) correspond to a positive value of r_1 in (45), Figure 6.19(c) and Figure 6.19(d) correspond to a positive value of α in (47), and Figure 6.19(e) and Figure 6.19(f) correspond to $r_1 = 0$ in (46).

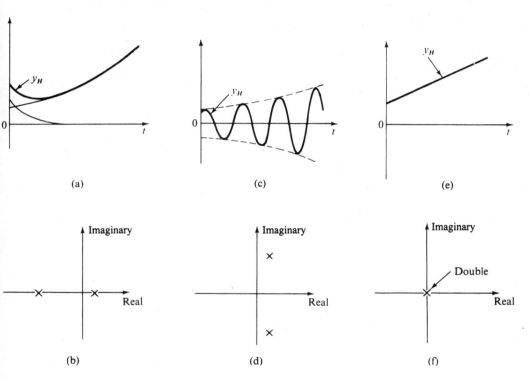

FIGURE 6.19 Examples of unstable second-order systems. (a), (b) One real root in the right half-plane. (c), (d) Complex roots in the right half-plane. (e), (f) Double root at the origin of the complex plane.

In addition to these stable and unstable classes of systems, it is possible (at least in an idealized case) for a linear system to be marginally stable and have a free response that neither decays to zero nor grows without bound. For second-order systems, such a response occurs when the characteristic equation has either a single root at $r_1 = 0$ with the remaining root in the left half-plane or a pair of imaginary roots at $r_1 = j\beta$ and $r_2 = -j\beta$. The first case corresponds to the characteristic equation $r^2 + a_1 r = 0$ and to the free response

$$y_H(t) = K_1 + K_2 \epsilon^{-a_1 t}$$

where $a_1 > 0$. The second case corresponds to the characteristic equation $r^2 + \beta^2 = 0$ and to the free response

$$y_H(t) = K \cos(\beta t + \phi)$$

A system whose free response is a constant-amplitude sine or cosine function is often called a **simple harmonic oscillator**. Sample root locations and typical free-response curves for the two types of marginally stable second-order systems are shown in Figure 6.20.

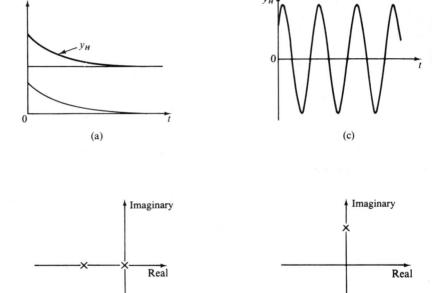

FIGURE 6.20 Examples of marginally stable second-order systems. (a), (b) One root at the origin of the complex plane. (c) (d) A pair of complex roots on the imaginary axis.

We can summarize the discussion about stability in a way that is applicable to fixed linear systems of any order as follows. If all the roots of the characteristic equation are inside the left half-plane, the system is stable. If there are any roots inside the right half-plane or repeated roots on the imaginary axis, the system is unstable. If all the roots are inside the left half-plane except for one or more distinct roots on the imaginary axis, the system is marginally stable.

The following property of polynominals can be useful when we are considering stability. If the signs of the coefficients in the characteristic equation are not all the same, then there is at least one root inside the right half-plane and the system is unstable. However, if all the signs are the same, we can be sure that there are no right half-plane roots only in the case of first- and second-order systems; for higher-order systems, all the signs being the same is not sufficient to guarantee the absence of right half-plane roots.

In Chapters 2, 4, and 5 we noted a property that can be used as a check on the equations obtained by examining the free-body diagrams for a mechanical system or the nodes of an electrical circuit. Suppose we sum the forces at a mass M_i and collect like terms. Then all the terms involving the displacement of M_i and its derivatives must have the same sign. We can make a similar statement when summing torques for a rotational system. For an electrical circuit, suppose we sum the currents that leave a node whose voltage is e_A and then collect like terms. All the terms involving e_A and its derivatives must have the same sign.

Although we shall not prove this property, we do now provide an explanation for it. All the systems that we have considered, except for those in Section 5.7, were excited by external independent inputs and consisted only of passive elements (such as M, J, B, K, C, R, and L). Systems composed of passive elements cannot be unstable, because there are no permanent sources of energy inside them. Thus all the coefficients in the characteristic equation, which are identical to those on the left-hand side of the input-output differential equation, must have the same sign. Let us first write and combine the system equations in literal form, with the element values represented by letters rather than numbers. Then the coefficients on the left-hand side of the input-output equation must have the same sign for all combinations of positive numbers that might be substituted for the element values. If, however, the property described in the previous paragraph were not satisfied, then we would find that we can make the signs of the coefficients different merely by choosing some of the element values sufficiently large.

▶ *EXAMPLE 6.7*

Consider the following pair of coupled first-order differential equations:

$$a_1 \dot{v}_1 + a_0 v_1 - b v_2 = f_1(t) \tag{48a}$$

$$-c v_1 + d_1 \dot{v}_2 + d_0 v_2 = f_2(t) \tag{48b}$$

which describe several simple systems. Two such systems will be presented immediately after this example. Assume, without loss of generality, that a_1 and d_1 are positive. If this were not the case for either of the original equations, we could make it so by multiplying that equation by -1. The magnitudes of a_0 and d_0 can be made arbitrarily large by an appropriate choice of element values.

Find the input-output equation relating v_2 to the inputs $f_1(t)$ and $f_2(t)$. Show that a_0 and d_0 must be positive in order for the system described by (48) to be stable.

Solution

From (48b),

$$v_1 = \frac{1}{c}[d_1 \dot{v}_2 + d_0 v_2 - f_1(t)]$$

Substituting this expression into (48a) and collecting terms, we obtain

$$a_1 d_1 \ddot{v}_2 + (a_1 d_0 + a_0 d_1)\dot{v}_2 + (a_0 d_0 - bc)v_2 = cf_1(t) + a_1 \dot{f}_2 + a_0 f_2(t)$$

For a stable system, the coefficient of $\dot{v}_2$ must be positive. Because this must be true regardless of the magnitudes of a_0 and d_0, we require that a_0 and d_0 be positive. We also require that $a_0 d_0 > bc$, which will be satisfied for passive systems, as illustrated by the two cases that are considered next.

For the mechanical system shown in Figure 6.21(a), it is easy to show that (48a) and (48b) are the D'Alembert-law equations written for M_1 and M_2, respectively, where

$$a_1 = M_1, \quad a_0 = B_1 + B_3, \quad b = c = B_3$$
$$d_1 = M_2, \quad d_0 = B_2 + B_3$$

Thus we should be able to anticipate that a_1 and a_0 must have the same sign, as must d_1 and d_0. Similarly, for the electrical circuit in Figure 6.21(b), we

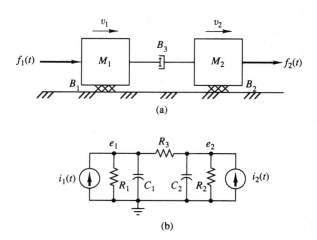

FIGURE 6.21   Two systems that can be described by (48).

can show that (48a) and (48b) are the current-law equations at nodes 1 and 2, with the following change of symbols:

$$v_1 = e_1, \quad v_2 = e_2, \quad f_1(t) = i_1(t), \quad f_2(t) = i_2(t)$$

$$a_1 = C_1, \quad a_0 = \frac{1}{R_1} + \frac{1}{R_3}, \quad b = c = \frac{1}{R_3}$$

$$d_1 = C_2, \quad d_0 = \frac{1}{R_2} + \frac{1}{R_3}$$

Even though we have not justified the sign rule for the general case, it is helpful to use it as a partial check on the equations for any passive system.

Damping Ratio and Undamped Natural Frequency

When the roots of the characteristic equation are complex, the parameter a_0 in (44) is positive, and it is useful to rewrite the differential equation in the standard form

$$\ddot{y} + 2\zeta\omega_n\dot{y} + \omega_n^2 y = F(t) \tag{49}$$

The parameter ω_n is called the **undamped natural frequency** and has units of radians per second. The parameter ζ is dimensionless and is known as the **damping ratio**. The characteristic equation is

$$r^2 + 2\zeta\omega_n r + \omega_n^2 = 0 \tag{50}$$

For $\zeta > 1$, the roots are distinct negative numbers, and $y_H(t)$ consists of two decaying exponentials. For $\zeta = 1$, there is a repeated root at $r = -\omega_n$, and $y_H(t)$ consists of terms having the form $\epsilon^{-\omega_n t}$ and $t\epsilon^{-\omega_n t}$. For $0 \leq \zeta < 1$, the roots are complex and are

$$r_1 = -\zeta\omega_n + j\omega_n\sqrt{1 - \zeta^2}$$

$$r_2 = -\zeta\omega_n - j\omega_n\sqrt{1 - \zeta^2}$$

Then by (47), the free response is

$$y_H(t) = K\epsilon^{-\zeta\omega_n t}\cos(\omega_n\sqrt{1 - \zeta^2}\, t + \phi) \tag{51}$$

For $\zeta < 0$, the system is unstable.

The advantage of introducing the parameters ζ and ω_n becomes apparent when the characteristic roots are complex and are plotted in the complex plane, as indicated in Figure 6.22(a). Their distances from the origin are the same and are denoted by d. The distance d is the square root of the sum of the squares of the real and imaginary parts of the root. For the upper root,

$$d = \sqrt{(-\zeta\omega_n)^2 + \omega_n^2(1 - \zeta^2)} = \omega_n$$

damped natural frequency $= \omega_n\sqrt{1-\zeta^2}$

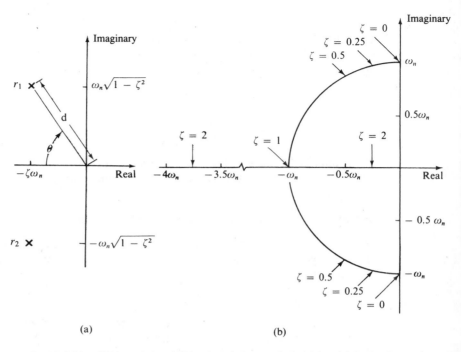

FIGURE 6.22 Characteristic-root locations in terms of ζ and ω_n. (a) General complex roots. (b) Locations for constant ω_n and varying ζ.

Hence, when $0 \leq \zeta < 1$, the complex characteristic roots lie on a circle of radius ω_n centered at the origin. It is easy to show that their locations on the circle depend only on the damping ratio ζ. Specifically, the angle θ between the negative real axis and the line from the origin to r_1 in Figure 6.22(a) satisfies the relationship $\cos\theta = \zeta\omega_n/\omega_n = \zeta$. Thus

$$\theta = \cos^{-1}\zeta \tag{52}$$

The geometric relationships between ζ, ω_n, and the roots of (50) are summarized in Figure 6.22(b) for $\zeta \geq 0$.

It is instructive to observe the effect of the damping ratio ζ on the responses of a system described by the equation

$$\ddot{y} + 2\zeta\omega_n\dot{y} + \omega_n^2 y = \omega_n^2 u(t) \tag{53}$$

The unit step response is shown in Figure 6.23 for several values of ζ, with ω_n held constant. For $\zeta > 0$, the steady-state response is unity. Note that the value of ζ determines to what extent, if any, the response will overshoot its steady-state value. The overshoot is 100% for $\zeta = 0$ and decreases to zero when the damping ratio is unity. For $\zeta > 1$, the response approaches its steady-state value monotonically.

The case $\zeta = 1$ is the boundary between responses that oscillate and those that do not, and the system is said to have **critical damping**. Second-order systems for which $\zeta > 1$ have more than critical damping; those for which $0 < \zeta < 1$ are less than critically damped. When $\zeta = 0$ the system is **undamped**. Figure 6.24 shows the unit impulse response of the general second-order system described by (53) for the values of ζ used in Figure 6.23. Note that the steady-state response is zero for $\zeta > 0$ and that the value of the damping ratio establishes the character of the response.

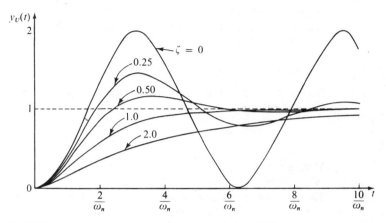

FIGURE 6.23   The unit step response for a second-order system described by (53).

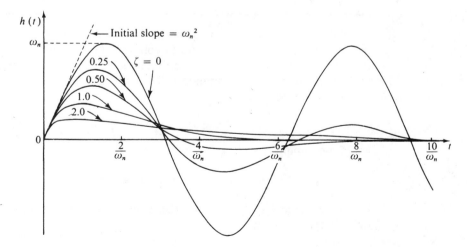

FIGURE 6.24   The unit impulse response for a second-order system described by (53).

We consider next an example in numerical form. Then we discuss briefly the role of friction and resistance in determining the damping ratio. We conclude by examining two approximations of a nonlinear second-order system that exhibit quite different behaviors.

▶ **EXAMPLE 6.8**

The differential equation describing a certain fixed linear system is

$$2\ddot{y} + \alpha\dot{y} + 50y = F(t)$$

Determine ω_n and ζ for $\alpha = 12$ and for $\alpha = 52$. Write the form of the free response for each case. For what values of α does the free response consist of decaying oscillations?

Solution

Dividing by 2 to put the left-hand side of the differential equation in the form of (49) gives

$$\ddot{y} + \frac{\alpha}{2}\dot{y} + 25y = \frac{1}{2}F(t)$$

Thus $\omega_n^2 = 25$ and $2\zeta\omega_n = \alpha/2$, from which $\omega_n = 5$ rad/s and $\zeta = \alpha/20$. When $\alpha = 12$, $\zeta = 3/5$, which corresponds to less than critical damping. The roots of the characteristic equation $r^2 + 6r + 25 = 0$ are at $-3 \pm j4$, so $y_H(t) = K\epsilon^{-3t}\cos(4t + \phi)$.

When $\alpha = 52$, $\zeta = 13/5$, showing that the system is more than critically damped. The characteristic equation for this case is $r^2 + 26r + 25 = 0$, which has roots at $r_1 = -1$ and $r_2 = -25$, so $y_H(t) = K_1\epsilon^{-t} + K_2\epsilon^{-25t}$. The free response will contain decaying oscillations when $0 < \zeta < 1$, which requires $0 < \alpha < 20$.

Although the damping ratio normally depends on the values of all the passive elements, it is instructive to consider the role of friction and resistance for the four systems shown in Figure 6.25. For the translational system in part (a), which was examined in Example 2.1, the differential equation was shown to be

$$\ddot{x} + \frac{B}{M}\dot{x} + \frac{K}{M}x = \frac{1}{M}f_a(t)$$

and the damping ratio is

$$\zeta = \frac{B}{2\sqrt{MK}} \tag{54}$$

For the rotational system in part (b), which was modeled in Example 4.1, the differential equation is

$$\ddot{\theta} + \frac{B}{J}\dot{\theta} + \frac{K}{J}\theta = \frac{1}{J}\tau_a(t)$$

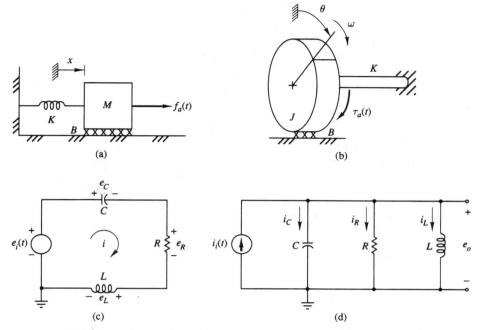

FIGURE 6.25 Second-order systems illustrating the role of friction and resistance in determining ζ.

and the damping ratio is

$$\zeta = \frac{B}{2\sqrt{JK}} \tag{55}$$

The series circuit in part (c) of the figure was treated in Example 5.1 and is described by

$$\frac{d^2i}{dt^2} + \frac{R}{L}\frac{di}{dt} + \frac{1}{LC}i = \frac{1}{L}\dot{e}_i$$

The damping ratio is

$$\zeta = \frac{R}{2}\sqrt{\frac{C}{L}} \tag{56}$$

Finally, for the parallel circuit in part (d), we have from Example 5.2,

$$\ddot{e}_o + \frac{1}{RC}\dot{e}_o + \frac{1}{LC}e_o = \frac{1}{C}\frac{di_i}{dt}$$

and the damping ratio is

$$\zeta = \frac{1}{2R}\sqrt{\frac{L}{C}} \tag{57}$$

If there is no friction in the two mechanical cases, then we see from (54) and (55) that $\zeta = 0$. The free response will consist of a constant-amplitude oscillation. Because there is no element that can dissipate energy in the form of heat, any initial stored energy will be interchanged undiminished between potential energy in K and kinetic energy in M or J. For positive values of B that do not exceed $2\sqrt{MK}$ or $2\sqrt{JK}$, $y_H(t)$ will contain decaying oscillations. If B is increased still further, $y_H(t)$ will have two decaying exponential terms.

When $R = 0$ in part (c) of the figure—that is, when the resistor is replaced by a short circuit—we see from (56) that $\zeta = 0$. Then any initial stored energy is continually swapped back and forth between the capacitor and inductor, and the free response does not die out. When R takes on positive values, energy is lost from the circuit in the form of heat, and $y_H(t)$ decays to zero.

For the circuit in part (d), the undamped case of no energy loss in the form of heat occurs when R is replaced by an open circuit—that is, when $R \to \infty$. Then $y_H(t)$ will again be a constant-amplitude sinusoidal oscillation. As R takes on smaller positive values, ζ increases.

▶ **EXAMPLE 6.9**

The pendulum shown in Figure 6.26(a) was considered in Example 4.7. From (4.51), its input-output differential equation is

$$\ddot{\theta} + \frac{B}{ML^2}\dot{\theta} + \frac{g}{L}\sin\theta = \frac{1}{ML^2}\tau_a(t) \qquad (58)$$

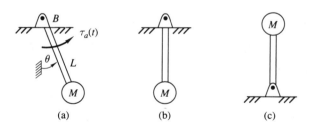

(a)   (b)   (c)

FIGURE 6.26   (a) Pendulum for Example 6.9. (b) Stable equilibrium position. (c) Unstable equilibrium position.

Discuss the motion of the pendulum for small variations about each of the two equilibrium positions shown in Figure 6.26(b) and Figure 6.26(c).

Solution

For the positions shown in parts (b) and (c) of the figure, $\theta = 0$ and $\theta = \pi$ rad, respectively. Note that (58) is satisfied if $\tau_a(t) = 0$ and if θ has a constant value of either zero or π rad. This indicates that if the pendulum is stationary in either of these two positions, it will not move unless there is an applied torque.

Equation (58) is nonlinear because of the factor $\sin\theta$. In Example 4.7, we noted that $\sin\theta \simeq \theta$ for small values of θ. Thus for small deviations about the vertical position shown in Figure 6.26(b), we can approximate (58) by the linear equation

$$\ddot{\theta} + \frac{B}{ML^2}\dot{\theta} + \frac{g}{L}\theta = \frac{1}{ML^2}\tau_a(t) \tag{59}$$

The free response $\theta_H(t)$ will then have the form of (51) with

$$\omega_n = \sqrt{\frac{g}{L}}$$

$$\zeta = \frac{B}{2Mg^{1/2}L^{3/2}}$$

As expected, the system is stable as long as the pendulum remains close to the position shown in Figure 6.26(b). Decreasing the friction coefficient B decreases the damping ratio ζ. If $B = 0$, then (59) becomes

$$\ddot{\theta} + \frac{g}{L}\theta = \frac{1}{ML^2}\tau_a(t)$$

for which

$$\theta_H(t) = K\cos\left(\sqrt{\frac{g}{L}}\,t + \psi\right)$$

where K and ψ are arbitrary constants that depend on the initial conditions. Such a system is marginally stable. If $\tau_a(t) = 0$ for $t > 0$ but if the pendulum is given some initial angular displacement θ_0, then it will have a sinusoidal oscillation with an angular frequency of $\sqrt{g/L}$ radians per second.

Finally, we consider small displacements about the position shown in Figure 6.26(c). If $\phi(t)$ represents the deviation from that position, then $\theta(t) = \phi(t) + \pi$. We note that $\dot{\theta} = \dot{\phi}$ and $\ddot{\theta} = \ddot{\phi}$, and we also use the mathematical identity $\sin(\phi + \pi) = -\sin\phi \simeq -\phi$. Thus for motion close to the position shown in Figure 6.26(c), (58) reduces to

$$\ddot{\phi} + \frac{B}{ML^2}\dot{\phi} - \frac{g}{L}\phi = \frac{1}{ML^2}\tau_a(t) \tag{60}$$

This linearized model is unstable, because one root of the characteristic equation is in the right half-plane. For the case where $B = 0$,

$$\ddot{\phi} - \frac{g}{L}\phi = \frac{1}{ML^2}\tau_a(t)$$

and

$$\phi_H(t) = K_1\epsilon^{\sqrt{g/L}\,t} + K_2\epsilon^{-\sqrt{g/L}\,t}$$

This agrees with our expectation that the equilibrium position in Figure 6.26(c) would be unstable. Even a very small initial displacement away from the upright position would cause the pendulum to fall.

■ 6.5 SYSTEMS OF ORDER THREE AND HIGHER

Except for situations involving repeated characteristic roots, the free response of third- and higher-order systems is composed of those functions that comprise the free response of first- and second-order systems. The basis for this property is the fact that all the characteristic roots must either be real or occur in complex-conjugate pairs. For example, the third-order differential equation

$$\dddot{y} + a_2\ddot{y} + a_1\dot{y} + a_0 y = F(t)$$

has as its characteristic equation

$$r^3 + a_2 r^2 + a_1 r + a_0 = 0 \tag{61}$$

If two of its roots are complex, we may write this equation in factored form as

$$(r - \alpha - j\beta)(r - \alpha + j\beta)(r - \gamma) = 0$$

where the roots are $r_1 = \alpha + j\beta$, $r_2 = \alpha - j\beta$, and $r_3 = \gamma$. The general form of the free response is

$$y_H(t) = K_1 \epsilon^{r_1 t} + K_2 \epsilon^{r_2 t} + K_3 \epsilon^{r_3 t}$$

which, by using (47) for the terms corresponding to the complex roots, we can write as

$$y_H(t) = K_4 \epsilon^{\alpha t} \cos(\beta t + \phi) + K_3 \epsilon^{\gamma t}$$

Figure 6.27 shows a typical set of characteristic roots in the complex plane and a sample free response for such a third-order system. Figure 6.27(b) shows the individual response curves, with the response associated with the roots r_1 and r_2 designated as y_{12}. Note that the term $y_3 = K_3 \epsilon^{\gamma t}$ decays more slowly than the envelope of y_{12}, because $|\alpha| > |\gamma|$ in Figure 6.27(a). In graphical terms, r_3 is further to the right in the complex plane than r_1 and r_2. Figure 6.27(c) shows the free response, which is the sum of the two individual responses.

We find the forced response $y_P(t)$ of a third- or higher-order system just as we found it for first- and second-order systems. Although it requires no

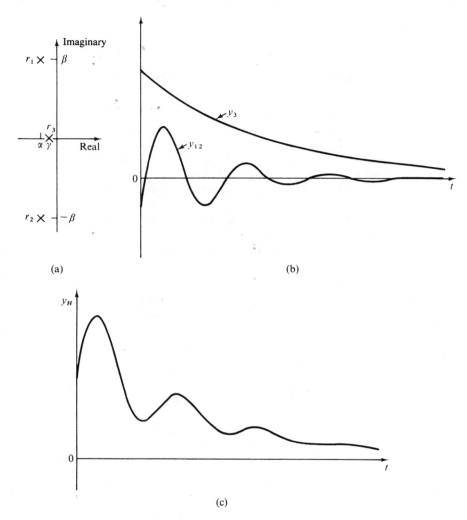

FIGURE 6.27　(a) Characteristic roots for a third-order system with $\alpha = -2$, $\beta = 10$, and $\gamma = -1$. (b) Components of the free response. (c) The free response.

new concepts or techniques, the solution is more cumbersome than that for the lower-order cases.

6.6 TIME-DOMAIN SOLUTION OF MATRIX STATE-VARIABLE EQUATIONS

For fixed linear systems, the state-variable and output equations have the forms shown in (3.31) and (3.32). The matrix form of these equations, which was given in (3.33), is

$$\dot{\mathbf{q}} = \mathbf{A}\mathbf{q} + \mathbf{B}\mathbf{u} \tag{62a}$$

$$\mathbf{y} = \mathbf{C}\mathbf{q} + \mathbf{D}\mathbf{u} \tag{62b}$$

where the elements in the coefficient matrices $\mathbf{A}$, $\mathbf{B}$, $\mathbf{C}$, and $\mathbf{D}$ are constants. The matrix $\mathbf{A}$ is always square, but this is not necessarily the case for the other coefficient matrices. To solve (62a) for $\mathbf{q}(t)$ for $t \geq t_0$, we must know the input vector $\mathbf{u}(t)$ for $t \geq t_0$ and the initial state vector $\mathbf{q}(t_0)$. We shall normally take t_0 to be zero. Once $\mathbf{q}(t)$ has been found, it is relatively easy to find the output vector $\mathbf{y}(t)$ from (62b).

Although (62a) is a set of first-order differential equations, the individual equations are generally coupled together; that is, more than one state variable appears in each of the equations. Thus the individual differential equations that make up (62a) cannot be solved independently of one another. One approach is to try to find a change of variables that will uncouple the individual equations, so that each of the new equations contains only one unknown variable. This is equivalent to converting $\mathbf{A}$ into a diagonal matrix. Ways of finding what change of variables is needed are discussed in books on linear algebra, often under the topic of similarity transformations or diagonalizing a matrix. One limitation of this approach is that it is sometimes impossible to diagonalize the matrix $\mathbf{A}$.

In this section, we shall develop procedures for solving the state-variable equations as a group without resorting to a substitution of variables. We shall draw upon a number of linear algebra results, some of which may be unfamiliar. For proofs and further details, consult the references in Appendix D.

The Zero-Input Response

We consider first the case where the inputs are zero for $t > 0$, in which case (62) reduces to

$$\dot{\mathbf{q}} = \mathbf{A}\mathbf{q} \tag{63a}$$

$$\mathbf{y} = \mathbf{C}\mathbf{q} \tag{63b}$$

Recall that the solution to the first-order scalar equation $\dot{q} = aq$ is $q(t) = \epsilon^{at} q(0)$ and that the infinite series for the exponential factor is

$$\epsilon^{at} = 1 + at + \frac{1}{2!}a^2 t^2 + \frac{1}{3!}a^3 t^3 + \cdots$$

Thus it is reasonable to try, as a solution to (63a),

$$\mathbf{q}(t) = \epsilon^{\mathbf{A}t} \mathbf{q}(0) \tag{64}$$

Because $\mathbf{A}$ is a matrix, the proper interpretation of $\epsilon^{\mathbf{A}t}$ is not obvious. However, most functions of a matrix can be represented by an infinite series in powers of $\mathbf{A}$. As might be expected from the series for the scalar exponential function,

$$\epsilon^{\mathbf{A}t} = \mathbf{I} + \mathbf{A}t + \frac{1}{2!}\mathbf{A}^2 t^2 + \frac{1}{3!}\mathbf{A}^3 t^3 + \cdots \tag{65}$$

If $\mathbf{A}$ is a square matrix of order n, each of the terms in this series, and hence $\epsilon^{\mathbf{A}t}$ itself, is also a square matrix of order n.

It can be proved by direct substitution that (64), with $\epsilon^{\mathbf{A}t}$ defined by (65), does indeed satisfy the matrix differential equation in (63a). However, we want solutions in closed form whenever possible, rather than as an infinite series. By using the Cayley–Hamilton theorem, we can also express most matrix functions as a series of finite length. If $\mathbf{A}$ is a square matrix of order n, then

$$\epsilon^{\mathbf{A}t} = \alpha_0 \mathbf{I} + \alpha_1 \mathbf{A} + \alpha_2 \mathbf{A}^2 + \cdots + \alpha_{n-1} \mathbf{A}^{n-1} \tag{66}$$

The standard method for finding the coefficients α_0 through α_{n-1} for a particular matrix $\mathbf{A}$ starts by finding the characteristic values of $\mathbf{A}$. As illustrated in Appendix C, $|s\mathbf{I} - \mathbf{A}|$ is a polynomial of degree n in the scalar quantity s. The **characteristic values** (or **eigenvalues**) of $\mathbf{A}$ are the values of s for which

$$|s\mathbf{I} - \mathbf{A}| = 0 \tag{67}$$

Many mathematics books use the symbol λ for the scalar quantity in (67). However, we have reserved λ for a dummy variable of integration. Furthermore, using the symbol s is consistent with the alternative treatment of matrix state-variable equations in Section 8.7.

If we replace the matrix $\mathbf{A}$ in (66) by the scalar quantity s, then the corresponding scalar equation

$$\epsilon^{st} = \alpha_0 + \alpha_1 s + \alpha_2 s^2 + \cdots + \alpha_{n-1} s^{n-1} \tag{68}$$

can be shown to be valid for each of the characteristic values of $\mathbf{A}$. We first assume that all n of the characteristic values are distinct, and we denote them by $s_1, s_2, \ldots, s_n$. Then

$$\epsilon^{s_1 t} = \alpha_0 + \alpha_1 s_1 + \alpha_2 s_1^2 + \cdots + \alpha_{n-1} s_1^{n-1}$$
$$\epsilon^{s_2 t} = \alpha_0 + \alpha_1 s_2 + \alpha_2 s_2^2 + \cdots + \alpha_{n-1} s_2^{n-1}$$
$$\vdots \tag{69}$$
$$\epsilon^{s_n t} = \alpha_0 + \alpha_1 s_n + \alpha_2 s_n^2 + \cdots + \alpha_{n-1} s_n^{n-1}$$

For distinct characteristic values, these n equations are linearly independent and can be solved simultaneously for the coefficients α_o through α_{n-1}. The functions $\epsilon^{s_1 t}$, $\epsilon^{s_2 t}$, $\ldots$, $\epsilon^{s_n t}$ are called the **mode functions** for the matrix $\mathbf{A}$. The α's will be linear combinations of these mode functions.

▶ **EXAMPLE 6.10**

Find ϵ^{At} in the form of (66) when

$$A = \begin{bmatrix} 0 & 1 \\ -6 & -5 \end{bmatrix}$$

Solution

We first evaluate the determinant of $sI - A$ and factor the resulting characteristic polynomial.

$$\begin{aligned} |sI - A| &= \begin{vmatrix} s & -1 \\ 6 & s+5 \end{vmatrix} \\ &= s^2 + 5s + 6 \\ &= (s+2)(s+3) \end{aligned} \tag{70}$$

By (67), we see that the characteristic values of A are $s_1 = -2$ and $s_2 = -3$. Because the order of A is $n = 2$, the power series for ϵ^{At} in (66) contains only two terms:

$$\epsilon^{At} = \alpha_0 I + \alpha_1 A \tag{71}$$

Replacing A by s_1 and then by s_2, we have the two scalar equations

$$\epsilon^{-2t} = \alpha_0 - 2\alpha_1$$
$$\epsilon^{-3t} = \alpha_0 - 3\alpha_1$$

Solving these simultaneously yields

$$\begin{aligned} \alpha_0 &= 3\epsilon^{-2t} - 2\epsilon^{-3t} \\ \alpha_1 &= \epsilon^{-2t} - \epsilon^{-3t} \end{aligned} \tag{72}$$

Inserting (72) into (71) gives

$$\begin{aligned} \epsilon^{At} &= \begin{bmatrix} \alpha_0 & \alpha_1 \\ -6\alpha_1 & \alpha_0 - 5\alpha_1 \end{bmatrix} \\ &= \begin{bmatrix} 3\epsilon^{-2t} - 2\epsilon^{-3t} & \epsilon^{-2t} - \epsilon^{-3t} \\ -6\epsilon^{-2t} + 6\epsilon^{-3t} & -2\epsilon^{-2t} + 3\epsilon^{-3t} \end{bmatrix} \end{aligned} \tag{73}$$

If the characteristic values of A are not all distinct, then not all the equations in (69) are independent. Suppose that the characteristic value s_1 has multiplicity p. Then we can use not only (68) but also the first $p - 1$ derivatives of this equation with respect to s, if s is then replaced by s_1. For example, suppose the order of A is four, such that

$$\epsilon^{At} = \alpha_0 I + \alpha_1 A + \alpha_2 A^2 + \alpha_3 A^3$$

If s_1 is a characteristic value of multiplicity three, and s_2 is a characteristic value of multiplicity one, we may write

$$\begin{aligned}
\epsilon^{s_1 t} &= \alpha_0 + \alpha_1 s_1 + \alpha_2 s_1^2 + \alpha_3 s_1^3 \\
t\epsilon^{s_1 t} &= \alpha_1 + 2\alpha_2 s_1 + 3\alpha_3 s_1^2 \\
t^2\epsilon^{s_1 t} &= 2\alpha_2 + 6\alpha_3 s_1 \\
\epsilon^{s_2 t} &= \alpha_0 + \alpha_1 s_2 + \alpha_2 s_2^2 + \alpha_3 s_2^3
\end{aligned}$$

which can be solved simultaneously for the coefficients α_0 through α_3 in terms of the four mode functions $\epsilon^{s_1 t}$, $t\epsilon^{s_1 t}$, $t^2\epsilon^{s_1 t}$, and $\epsilon^{s_2 t}$.

▶ **EXAMPLE 6.11**

Find ϵ^{At} when

$$\mathbf{A} = \begin{bmatrix} -1 & 1 \\ -1 & -3 \end{bmatrix}$$

Solution

To find the characteristic values of $\mathbf{A}$, we examine

$$\begin{aligned}
|s\mathbf{I} - \mathbf{A}| &= \begin{vmatrix} s+1 & -1 \\ 1 & s+3 \end{vmatrix} \\
&= s^2 + 4s + 4 \\
&= (s+2)^2
\end{aligned}$$

from which $s_1 = s_2 = -2$. We know that

$$\begin{aligned}
\epsilon^{At} &= \alpha_0 \mathbf{I} + \alpha_1 \mathbf{A} \\
&= \begin{bmatrix} \alpha_0 - \alpha_1 & \alpha_1 \\ -\alpha_1 & \alpha_0 - 3\alpha_1 \end{bmatrix}
\end{aligned} \tag{74}$$

The scalar equations

$$\epsilon^{st} = \alpha_0 + \alpha_1 s$$

$$t\epsilon^{st} = \alpha_1$$

are valid when s is replaced by -2. Thus

$$\epsilon^{-2t} = \alpha_0 - 2\alpha_1$$

$$t\epsilon^{-2t} = \alpha_1$$

from which $\alpha_0 = \epsilon^{-2t} + 2t\epsilon^{-2t}$. Substituting the expressions for α_0 and α_1 into (74) gives

$$\epsilon^{At} = \begin{bmatrix} (1+t)\epsilon^{-2t} & t\epsilon^{-2t} \\ -t\epsilon^{-2t} & (1-t)\epsilon^{-2t} \end{bmatrix}$$

The quantity ϵ^{At}, which plays a key role in many aspects of system analysis, is called the **state-transition matrix** and is usually given the special symbol $\phi(t)$. With ϵ^{At} replaced by the new symbol $\phi(t)$ in (64), the solution to $\dot{\mathbf{q}} = \mathbf{Aq}$ can be written as

$$\mathbf{q}(t) = \phi(t)\mathbf{q}(0) \tag{75}$$

Once $\phi(t)$ has been found, the state vector $\mathbf{q}(t)$ and the output vector $\mathbf{y}$ can be found in terms of the initial state vector $\mathbf{q}(0)$ by straightforward substitution into (75) and (63b). Because $\mathbf{q}$ is the product of an $n \times n$ matrix of time functions, $\phi(t)$, and an $n \times 1$ vector of constants, $\mathbf{q}(0)$, it follows that the elements of $\mathbf{q}$ are given by

$$q_i = \phi_{i1}(t)q_1(0) + \phi_{i2}(t)q_2(0) + \cdots + \phi_{in}(t)q_n(0) \quad i = 1, 2, \ldots, n$$

From this expression, we see that q_i is a linear combination of the n functions of time $\phi_{ij}(t)$, $j = 1, 2, \ldots, n$, where the weightings of these functions are the corresponding initial values of the state variables, $q_1(0), q_2(0), \ldots, q_n(0)$. Furthermore, we have previously seen that the functions $\phi_{ij}(t)$ are themselves linear combinations of the n mode functions. Hence it follows that each of the state variables $q_i(t)$ is merely a linear combination of the system's mode functions, with the relative weightings dependent on the initial state vector $\mathbf{q}(0)$ and the coefficients $\alpha_0, \alpha_1, \ldots, \alpha_{n-1}$ in (66).

Once we have found the state vector $\mathbf{q}$, it is a straightforward matter to determine the response of the output variables. Because $\mathbf{y} = \mathbf{Cq}$ when the input is zero, the kth output is a linear combination of all the state variables, the weightings being given by the elements in the kth row of the $\mathbf{C}$ matrix. Specifically,

$$y_k = c_{k1}q_1 + c_{k2}q_2 + \cdots + c_{kn}q_n \quad k = 1, 2, \ldots, p$$

Before discussing some of the properties of the state-transition matrix, we shall illustrate its use in evaluating both the state and output vectors for a second-order example in numerical form

▶ *EXAMPLE 6.12*

Determine the zero-input responses of the state and output vectors for the system described by the matrix equations

$$\dot{\mathbf{q}} = \begin{bmatrix} 0 & 1 \\ -6 & -5 \end{bmatrix} \mathbf{q} \tag{76a}$$

$$\mathbf{y} = \begin{bmatrix} 2 & -1 \\ 0 & 1 \end{bmatrix} \mathbf{q} \tag{76b}$$

Give the responses in terms of the elements of the initial state vector $\mathbf{q}(0)$.

Solution

From inspection of (76a) and (76b), we see that the matrices $\mathbf{A}$ and $\mathbf{C}$ characterizing the system are

$$\mathbf{A} = \begin{bmatrix} 0 & 1 \\ -6 & -5 \end{bmatrix}$$

and

$$\mathbf{C} = \begin{bmatrix} 2 & -1 \\ 0 & 1 \end{bmatrix}$$

The state-transition matrix corresponding to $\mathbf{A}$ was evaluated in Example 6.10 and is given by (73). Hence to find $\mathbf{q}$ in terms of the initial states $q_1(0)$ and $q_2(0)$, we need only substitute (73) into (75) and carry out the matrix multiplication. For the first state variable, we find that

$$q_1 = (3\epsilon^{-2t} - 2\epsilon^{-3t})q_1(0) + (\epsilon^{-2t} - \epsilon^{-3t})q_2(0)$$

which can be rewritten in terms of the mode functions ϵ^{-2t} and ϵ^{-3t} as

$$q_1 = [3q_1(0) + q_2(0)]\epsilon^{-2t} + [-2q_1(0) - q_2(0)]\epsilon^{-3t}$$

Similarly, you may verify that the response of the second state variable is

$$q_2 = [-6q_1(0) - 2q_2(0)]\epsilon^{-2t} + [6q_1(0) + 3q_2(0)]\epsilon^{-3t}$$

Finally, we can obtain the response of the output variable $\mathbf{y}$ by substituting these expressions for q_1 and q_2 into the output equation given by (76b). For y_1, we get

$$y_1 = 2q_1 - q_2$$

which simplifies to

$$y_1 = [12q_1(0) + 4q_2(0)]\epsilon^{-2t} - [10q_1(0) + 5q_2(0)]\epsilon^{-3t} \tag{77}$$

The second element of the output vector is just q_2, so

$$y_2 = [-6q_1(0) - 2q_2(0)]\epsilon^{-2t} + [6q_1(0) + 3q_2(0)]\epsilon^{-3t} \tag{78}$$

Properties of the State-Transition Matrix

Starting with (75), which states that

$$\mathbf{q}(t) = \phi(t)\mathbf{q}(0) \tag{79}$$

we can develop several properties of $\phi(t)$ that are useful in the analysis of dynamic systems. First, by setting t equal to zero in (79), we have

$$\mathbf{q}(0) = \phi(0)\mathbf{q}(0)$$

which implies that

$$\phi(0) = \mathbf{I} \tag{80}$$

Thus the state-transition matrix reduces to the $n \times n$ identity matrix when its argument equals zero.

The initial time in (79) need not be restricted to $t = 0$. More generally, we can rewrite (79) in terms of the initial time t_0 as

$$\mathbf{q}(t) = \phi(t - t_0)\mathbf{q}(t_0) \tag{81}$$

which reduces to (79) if $t_0 = 0$. Using (81), we can express the state vector at some time t_2 in terms of $\mathbf{q}(t_0)$ as

$$\mathbf{q}(t_2) = \phi(t_2 - t_0)\mathbf{q}(t_0)$$

or in terms of $\mathbf{q}(t_1)$ as

$$\mathbf{q}(t_2) = \phi(t_2 - t_1)\mathbf{q}(t_1)$$

By using (81) again to express $\mathbf{q}(t_1)$ in terms of $\mathbf{q}(t_0)$, we can write the second expression for $\mathbf{q}(t_2)$ as

$$\mathbf{q}(t_2) = \phi(t_2 - t_1)\phi(t_1 - t_0)\mathbf{q}(t_0)$$

Now, comparing the two expressions for $\mathbf{q}(t_2)$, we see that

$$\phi(t_2 - t_1)\phi(t_1 - t_0) = \phi(t_2 - t_0) \tag{82}$$

Hence the product of two state-transition matrices (for the same $\mathbf{A}$ matrix, of course) is merely the state-transition matrix with its argument set equal to the sum of the arguments of the two matrices being multiplied.

If we write (82) with $t_0 = t_2 = 0$, we see that

$$\phi(-t_1)\phi(t_1) = \phi(0)$$

But we know from (80) that $\phi(0)$ is the identity matrix, so

$$\phi(-t_1)\phi(t_1) = \mathbf{I}$$

which implies that

$$\phi^{-1}(t) = \phi(-t) \tag{83}$$

Thus the state-transition matrix is nonsingular for all values of its argument, and we can obtain its inverse by merely changing the sign of its argument.

One way of gaining some insight into the physical significance of the state-transition matrix is to consider (79) for some very specific values of $\mathbf{q}(0)$. For instance, suppose $q_1(0) = 1$ and all the other elements of $\mathbf{q}(0)$ are zero. It follows from the definition of matrix multiplication that the resulting response for the state vector $\mathbf{q}$ will be the first column of $\phi(t)$. In similar fashion, setting the ith initial state to unity and the rest to zero will result in a response for q that consists of the ith column of $\phi(t)$. Hence we could use a computer simulation of a system repetitively to compute and plot each element of the state-transition matrix, one column at a time, until we had determined all n^2 time functions.

▶ *EXAMPLE 6.13*

For the state-transition matrix found in Example 6.10 and given by (73), verify that (80) and (83) are true in general and show that (82) holds for $t_0 = 0$, $t_1 = 1$, and $t_2 = 2$.

Solution

Setting t equal to zero in (73) gives

$$\phi(0) = \begin{bmatrix} 3\epsilon^0 - 2\epsilon^0 & \epsilon^0 - \epsilon^0 \\ -6\epsilon^0 + 6\epsilon^0 & -2\epsilon^0 + 3\epsilon^0 \end{bmatrix} = \begin{bmatrix} 1 & 0 \\ 0 & 1 \end{bmatrix}$$

which agrees with (80).

To check (83), we shall show that $\phi(-t)\phi(t) = I$, where I is the 2×2 identity matrix. From (73), we have

$$\phi(t) = \begin{bmatrix} 3\epsilon^{-2t} - 2\epsilon^{-3t} & \epsilon^{-2t} - \epsilon^{-3t} \\ -6\epsilon^{-2t} + 6\epsilon^{-3t} & -2\epsilon^{-2t} + 3\epsilon^{-3t} \end{bmatrix}$$

so

$$\phi(-t) = \begin{bmatrix} 3\epsilon^{2t} - 2\epsilon^{3t} & \epsilon^{2t} - \epsilon^{3t} \\ -6\epsilon^{2t} + 6\epsilon^{3t} & -2\epsilon^{2t} + 3\epsilon^{3t} \end{bmatrix}$$

For example, the 2,2 element[4] of $\phi(-t)\phi(t)$ is the product of the second row of $\phi(-t)$ and the second column of $\phi(t)$:

$$[-6\epsilon^{2t} + 6\epsilon^{3t} \quad -2\epsilon^{2t} + 3\epsilon^{3t}] \begin{bmatrix} \epsilon^{-2t} - \epsilon^{-3t} \\ -2\epsilon^{-2t} + 3\epsilon^{-3t} \end{bmatrix}$$

$$= (-6\epsilon^{2t} + 6\epsilon^{3t})(\epsilon^{-2t} - \epsilon^{-3t}) + (-2\epsilon^{2t} + 3\epsilon^{3t})(-2\epsilon^{-2t} + 3\epsilon^{-3t})$$

$$= 1$$

In similar fashion, you can verify that the 1,1 element is also unity and that the 1,2 and 2,1 elements are zero, giving the 2×2 identity matrix.

To verify (82) for the specified values of t_0, t_1, and t_2, we must show that

$$\phi(2 - 1)\phi(1 - 0) = \phi(2 - 0)$$

---

[4]The i, j element of a matrix is the one in the ith row and the jth column.

which is equivalent to

$$\phi(1)\phi(1) = \phi(2) \tag{84}$$

For example, we can write the 1,1 element of the left-hand side of (84) as the matrix product

$$[3\epsilon^{-2} - 2\epsilon^{-3} \quad \epsilon^{-2} - \epsilon^{-3}] \begin{bmatrix} 3\epsilon^{-2} - 2\epsilon^{-3} \\ -6\epsilon^{-2} + 6\epsilon^{-3} \end{bmatrix}$$

$$= (3\epsilon^{-2} - 2\epsilon^{-3})^2 + (\epsilon^{-2} - \epsilon^{-3})(-6\epsilon^{-2} + 6\epsilon^{-3})$$

$$= 3\epsilon^{-4} - 2\epsilon^{-6}$$

which is indeed equal to the 1,1 element of $\phi(2)$. By evaluating the remaining three elements that make up the left-hand and right-hand sides of (84), you can show that (82) does hold for the values of t_0, t_1, and t_2 selected. It would be possible to verify (82) for arbitrary t_0, t_1, and t_2, but the process would be more tedious than it is when specific values are selected.

The Complete Response

Finally, we consider the response for the case where the input vector is nonzero. The special case of the zero-state response corresponds to setting $\mathbf{q}(0) = \mathbf{0}$ in the following presentation.

In the solution of scalar differential equations earlier in this chapter, we regarded the response as the sum of a complementary and particular solution. Moreover, we had to know the form of the input before starting to find the particular solution. A different approach would have been necessary in order to obtain an explicit formula that would be valid for all inputs. It can be shown, however, that the solution to the scalar equation $\dot{q} = aq + bu$ can be written as

$$q(t) = \underbrace{\epsilon^{at} q(0)}_{q_{zi}(t)} + \underbrace{\int_0^t \epsilon^{a(t-\lambda)} bu(\lambda) d\lambda}_{q_{zs}(t)} \tag{85}$$

for $t > 0$. The symbols $q_{zi}(t)$ and $q_{zs}(t)$ denote the zero-input and zero-state portions, respectively, of the general expression. The development of such equations as (85) can be found not only in books on differential equations but also in books on circuits and systems, often under the heading of convolution. An even more general result for the zero-state response, which is valid for a scalar differential equation of any order, is

$$q_{zs}(t) = \int_0^t h(t - \lambda) bu(\lambda) d\lambda$$

where $h(t)$ is the response of $q(t)$ to a unit impulse in $u(t)$ when the system has no stored energy for $t < 0$.

We return now to the general matrix equations in (62), which are repeated here:

$$\dot{\mathbf{q}} = \mathbf{Aq} + \mathbf{Bu} \tag{86a}$$

$$\mathbf{y} = \mathbf{Cq} + \mathbf{Du} \tag{86b}$$

As expected by analogy to (85), the solution to (86a) is

$$\mathbf{q}(t) = \underbrace{\boldsymbol{\phi}(t)\mathbf{q}(0)}_{\mathbf{q}_{zi}(t)} + \underbrace{\int_0^t \boldsymbol{\phi}(t - \lambda)\mathbf{Bu}(\lambda)d\lambda}_{\mathbf{q}_{zs}(t)} \tag{87}$$

where $\boldsymbol{\phi}(t)$ is the state-transition matrix, and where $\boldsymbol{\phi}(t - \lambda)$ is $\boldsymbol{\phi}(t)$ with every t replaced by $t - \lambda$. The symbols $\mathbf{q}_{zi}(t)$ and $\mathbf{q}_{zs}(t)$ denote the zero-input and zero-state parts of the state vector. Once (87) has been evaluated, the output vector can be easily obtained via the algebraic equation (86b). To illustrate the evaluation of the integral in (87) and to show the general procedure, the following example examines the zero-state response for a system that has the same $\mathbf{A}$ and $\mathbf{C}$ matrices as in Example 6.12.

▶ **EXAMPLE 6.14**

Find the state and output vectors for the system described by (86) when

$$\mathbf{A} = \begin{bmatrix} 0 & 1 \\ -6 & -5 \end{bmatrix}, \quad \mathbf{B} = \begin{bmatrix} 2 & 1 \\ -1 & 0 \end{bmatrix}, \quad \mathbf{C} = \begin{bmatrix} 2 & -1 \\ 0 & 1 \end{bmatrix}, \quad \text{and } \mathbf{D} = \begin{bmatrix} 0 & 0 \\ 0 & 0 \end{bmatrix}$$

and when $\mathbf{q}(0) = \mathbf{0}$. Let the input vector be

$$\mathbf{u} = \begin{bmatrix} u_1(t) \\ u_2(t) \end{bmatrix} = \begin{bmatrix} 0 \\ U(t) \end{bmatrix}$$

That is, let $u_1(t)$ be zero, and let $u_2(t)$ be the unit step function.

Solution

The state-transition matrix $\boldsymbol{\phi}(t)$ for the given matrix $\mathbf{A}$ was found in (73). Thus

$$\boldsymbol{\phi}(t)\mathbf{B} = \begin{bmatrix} 3\epsilon^{-2t} - 2\epsilon^{-3t} & \epsilon^{-2t} - \epsilon^{-3t} \\ -6\epsilon^{-2t} + 6\epsilon^{-3t} & -2\epsilon^{-2t} + 3\epsilon^{-3t} \end{bmatrix} \begin{bmatrix} 2 & 1 \\ -1 & 0 \end{bmatrix}$$

$$= \begin{bmatrix} 5\epsilon^{-2t} - 3\epsilon^{-3t} & 3\epsilon^{-2t} - 2\epsilon^{-3t} \\ -10\epsilon^{-2t} + 9\epsilon^{-3t} & -6\epsilon^{-2t} + 6\epsilon^{-3t} \end{bmatrix}$$

Replacing t by $t - \lambda$ and postmultiplying by the column vector $\mathbf{u}(\lambda)$ give

$$\boldsymbol{\phi}(t - \lambda)\mathbf{Bu}(\lambda)$$

$$= \begin{bmatrix} \left(5\epsilon^{-2(t-\lambda)} - 3\epsilon^{-3(t-\lambda)}\right) u_1(\lambda) + \left(3\epsilon^{-2(t-\lambda)} - 2\epsilon^{-3(t-\lambda)}\right) u_2(\lambda) \\ \left(-10\epsilon^{-2(t-\lambda)} + 9\epsilon^{-3(t-\lambda)}\right) u_1(\lambda) + \left(-6\epsilon^{-2(t-\lambda)} + 6\epsilon^{-3(t-\lambda)}\right) u_2(\lambda) \end{bmatrix}$$

Substituting $u_1(\lambda) = 0$ and $u_2(\lambda) = 1$ for all $\lambda > 0$ yields

$$\phi(t - \lambda)\mathbf{B}u(\lambda) = \begin{bmatrix} 3\epsilon^{-2t}\epsilon^{2\lambda} - 2\epsilon^{-3t}\epsilon^{3\lambda} \\ -6\epsilon^{-2t}\epsilon^{2\lambda} + 6\epsilon^{-3t}\epsilon^{3\lambda} \end{bmatrix}$$

Integrating each row of this matrix and inserting the limits of 0 and t, we see that (86a) reduces to

$$\mathbf{q}(t) = \begin{bmatrix} \frac{3}{2}\epsilon^{-2t}\epsilon^{2\lambda} - \frac{2}{3}\epsilon^{-3t}\epsilon^{3\lambda} \\ -3\epsilon^{-2t}\epsilon^{2\lambda} + 2\epsilon^{-3t}\epsilon^{3\lambda} \end{bmatrix}_0^t = \begin{bmatrix} \frac{5}{6} - \frac{3}{2}\epsilon^{-2t} + \frac{2}{3}\epsilon^{-3t} \\ -1 + 3\epsilon^{-2t} - 2\epsilon^{-3t} \end{bmatrix}$$

The output matrix $\mathbf{y}$ is, according to (86b),

$$\mathbf{y}(t) = \begin{bmatrix} 2q_1 - q_2 \\ q_2 \end{bmatrix} = \begin{bmatrix} \frac{8}{3} - 6\epsilon^{-2t} + \frac{10}{3}\epsilon^{-3t} \\ -1 + 3\epsilon^{-2t} - 2\epsilon^{-3t} \end{bmatrix}$$

Note that the two outputs become constants in the steady state, because the inputs have constant values for $t > 0$. As expected, the transient terms are linear combinations of the two mode functions ϵ^{-2t} and ϵ^{-3t}.

SUMMARY

After a review of procedures for solving differential equations, this chapter emphasized first- and second-order systems. Among the important general concepts were the definitions of the free response (usually the same as the transient response), the forced response (usually the same as the steady-state response), the zero-input and zero-state responses, and system stability. The nature of the free response is characterized by the time constant τ for a first-order system and by the damping ratio ζ and the undamped natural frequency ω_n for a second-order system.

Inputs of special importance include the unit step function and the unit impulse. The steady-state response to a constant input can always be determined from the differential equations, but it can also be found directly from the figures representing the systems.

The state-variable model of a first-order system is not essentially different from an input-output model. However, for systems of order two and higher, the state-variable equations are usually coupled together and cannot be solved individually. A systematic way of solving a state-variable model was presented in Section 6.6. The key step is finding the state-transition matrix $\phi(t)$, which is the same as the matrix function ϵ^{At}.

PROBLEMS

6.1 Find and sketch the response of the system described by the equation

$$\dot{y} + 4y = F(t)$$

a) When the input is $F(t) = 3$ for $t \geq 0$ and $y(0) = 2$.
b) When $F(t) = t$ for $t \geq 0$ and $y(0) = 0$.

r + ½ = 0   r = -½ $yp(t) = 21\cos t + 2b \sin t$
$y_H(t) = Ke^{-\frac{1}{2}t}$ $\dot{y}p = -21\sin t + 20\cos t$

* 6.2 Find the response $y(t)$ for $t \geq 0$ for a linear first-order system described by $\dot{y} + 0.5y = F(t)$ for each of the following conditions.
   a) $F(t) = \sin t + \cos t$ and $y(0) = 0$
   b) $F(t) = \epsilon^{-t/2}$ and $y(0) = 1$

6.3 Find and sketch the response of the system described by the equation

$$3\dot{y} + y = F(t)$$

with the initial condition $y(0) = 4$ when the input is
   a) $F(t) = 5$
   b) $F(t) = 4\epsilon^{-t/2}$
   c) $F(t) = 5 + 4\epsilon^{-t/2}$

6.4 Find the response $y(t)$ for $t \geq 0$ for a linear first-order system described by $2\dot{y} + 6y = F(t)$ for each of the following conditions.
   a) $F(t) = 4\epsilon^{-t}$ and $y(0) = 8$
   b) $F(t) = \sin 3t$ and $y(0) = 0$

* 6.5 Find the response of the system described by

$$\ddot{y} + 3\dot{y} + 2y = \dot{u} + 2u(t)$$

when $u(t) = t$ for $t \geq 0$, $y(0) = 0$, and $\dot{y}(0) = 1$.

6.6 Consider the differential equation $\ddot{y} + 7\dot{y} + 6y = F(t)$.
   a) Find the complete response for $t \geq 0$ when $F(t) = 3$, $y(0) = 0$, and $\dot{y}(0) = -2$.
   b) Repeat part (a) when the initial conditions are changed to $y(0) = 2$, $\dot{y}(0) = 0$.

6.7 Repeat Problem 6.5 when $u(t) = t\epsilon^{-t}$ for $t \geq 0$ and $y(0) = \dot{y}(0) = 0$.

* 6.8 Find the response of the first-order system described by

$$3\dot{y} + 2y = A$$

when $y(0) = 0$ and A is a constant. Give the values of the time constant and the steady-state response. Identify the transient response and sketch the complete response.

6.9 Repeat Problem 6.8 for the equation

$$\frac{1}{2}\dot{y} + 4y = A$$

6.10 Repeat Problem 6.8 for the equation

$$2\dot{y} + 5y = A$$

6.11 A velocity input $v_a(t)$ is applied to point A in the mechanical system shown in Figure P6.11.
   a) Write the system's differential equation in terms of the velocity v_1.
   b) What is the time constant τ for the system?
   c) Sketch the response when $v_a(t) = 0$ for $t \geq 0$ and $v_1(0) = 10$.

$$\dot{v}_1 - \frac{r_1(-B_3 - B_2 - B_2)}{M} = \frac{V_s B_3}{M}$$

$$3 = \frac{M}{B_3 + B_2 + B_1}$$

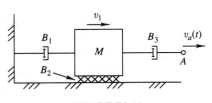

FIGURE P6.11

d) Repeat parts (a), (b), and (c) when the velocity input is replaced by a force $f_a(t)$ applied at point A, with the positive sense to the right. Explain why the expression for τ differs from the answer to part (b).

* 6.12 Assume that the circuit shown in Figure P5.1 contains no stored energy for $t < 0$ and that the input is the unit step function. The input-output differential equation, found in Problem 5.1, is

$$\frac{3}{4}\dot{e}_o + \frac{1}{2}e_o = \frac{1}{2}\frac{di_i}{dt} + i_i(t)$$

a) Verify the differential equation and determine the time constant.
b) For $t > 0$, let $i_i(t)$ have a constant value of unity. Then write the general solution for $t > 0$.
c) Find $e_o(0+)$ and evaluate the arbitrary constant in the answer to part (b).
d) Find and sketch e_o versus t for all $t > 0$.
e) Check the steady-state response by replacing the capacitor by an open circuit.

6.13 Repeat Problem 6.12 for the circuit shown in Figure P5.4, for which the input-output differential equation, found in Problem 5.4, is

$$C(R_1 + R_2)\dot{e}_o + e_o = CR_1R_2\frac{di_i}{dt}$$

6.14 Assume that the circuit shown in Figure P5.2 contains no stored energy for $t < 0$ and that the input is the unit step function. The input-output differential equation, found in Problem 5.2, is

$$\dot{e}_o + 9e_o = 3e_i(t)$$

$-kre^{rt} + 9Ke^{rt}$
$(r+9)\,ke^{rt}$
$r = -9$

a) Verify the differential equation and determine the time constant.
b) Find $e_o(0+)$.
c) Find and sketch e_o versus t for all $t > 0$.
d) Check the steady-state response by replacing the inductor by a short circuit.

6.15 The switch shown in Figure P6.15 has been closed for a long time, so the circuit is in the steady state at $t = 0-$. If the switch opens at $t = 0$, find and sketch e_o versus t. Show on the same scale the curves for $R_o = 5\,\Omega$ and for $R_o = 10\,\Omega$. What would be the circuit's response if R_o were to approach infinity?

* 6.16 Consider a first-order system with input $u(t)$ and output y that is described by
$\dot{y} + 0.5y = u(t)$.
a) Find and sketch the unit step response $y_U(t)$.
b) Find and sketch the response to $u(t) = 2$ for $t > 0$ and with $y(0) = -1$.
c) Find and sketch the response to $u(t) = U(t) - U(t - 2)$ with $y(0) = 0$.

$e_o u(t) = ke^{-9t}$
$r = \frac{1}{9}$

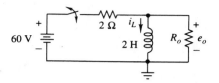

FIGURE P6.15

d) Find and sketch the unit impulse response $h(t)$.

6.17 Figure P6.17 shows the unit step responses of three first-order systems that have the same steady-state value but different time constants. The characteristic-equation root of system A is $r_A = -0.2$, that of system B is $r_B = -1.0$, and that of system C is $r_C = -0.5$. Determine which system generated each response, give the time constant, and state your reasoning.

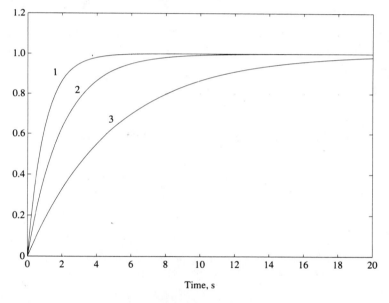

FIGURE P6.17

6.18 The unit step responses of four second-order systems are shown in Figure P6.18, and four pairs of characteristic roots are listed below. Match each pair of roots with the corresponding step-response curve.

A	$r = -0.5 \pm j2$
B	$r = -0.5 \pm j4$
C	$r = -1 \pm j4$
D	$r = -2 \pm j4$

$-1 \pm j4$

$-.5 \pm j2$

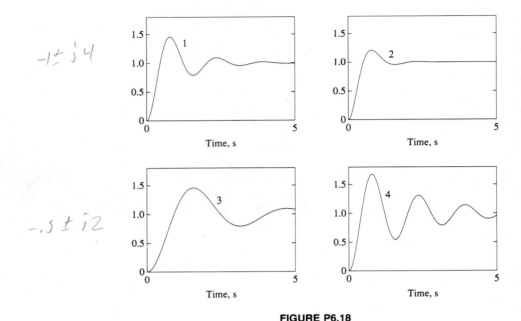

FIGURE P6.18

6.19 The unit impulse responses of four second-order systems are shown in Figure P6.19, and four pairs of characteristic roots are listed below. Match each pair of roots with the corresponding impulse-response curve.

A	$r = -0.2 \pm j1$
B	$r = -0.2 \pm j3$
C	$r = -0.2, -0.3$
D	$r = -0.5 \pm j1$

* 6.20 If the spring K_1 in Figure 2.19 is replaced by a cable that does not stretch, the system can be shown to obey the differential equation

$$(M_1 + M_2)\ddot{x} + (B_1 + B_2)\dot{x} + K_2x = f_a(t) - M_2g$$

where $x_1 = x_2 = x$.

a) Verify that the differential equation is correct.

b) Find expressions for the damping ratio ζ and the undamped natural frequency ω_n.

c) Find the steady-state response when the applied force is the unit step function.

6.21 The input-output differential equation for the mechanical system shown in Figure P4.22 is

$$(M + J/R^2)\ddot{x} + B\dot{x} + (K_2 + K_1/R^2)x = -f_a(t)$$

a) Verify that the differential equation is correct.

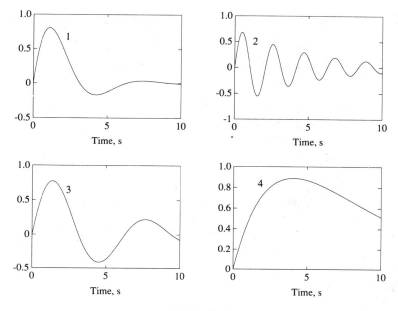

FIGURE P6.19

b) Find expressions for the damping ratio ζ and the undamped natural frequency ω_n.

c) Find the steady-state response when the applied force is the unit step function. Check your answer by examining Figure P4.22 directly in the steady state.

6.22 The input-output differential equation for the circuit shown in Figure P6.22 is

$$C\ddot{e}_o + \left(\frac{1}{R_1} + \frac{1}{R_2}\right)\dot{e}_o + \frac{1}{L}e_o = \frac{1}{R_1}\dot{e}_i$$

a) Verify that the differential equation is correct.

b) Find expressions for the damping ratio ζ and the undamped natural frequency ω_n.

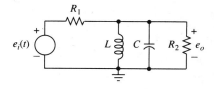

FIGURE P6.22

6.23 For the differential equation $\ddot{y} + 5\dot{y} + 4y = u(t)$, find and sketch the unit step response $y_U(t)$ and the unit impulse response $h(t)$.

6.24 A second-order system is described by the equation $\ddot{y} + 4\dot{y} + 25y = 50u(t)$.
a) Find the damping ratio ζ and the undamped natural frequency ω_n.
b) Find and sketch the unit step response $y_U(t)$ and the unit impulse response $h(t)$.

* 6.25 Repeat Problem 6.24 for the differential equation $\ddot{y} + 2\dot{y} + 2y = u(t)$.

6.26 A second-order system is described by $\ddot{y} + 2\dot{y} + 4y = 4u(t)$.
a) Find the damping ratio ζ and the undamped natural frequency ω_n.
b) Find and sketch the response when $u(t) = 2$ for $t > 0$ and when the initial conditions are $y(0) = 0$ and $\dot{y}(0) = 1$.

* 6.27 The unit step response of a certain linear system is

$$y_U(t) = [2 + 2\epsilon^{-t} \cos(2t + \pi/4)]U(t)$$

a) Find the numerical values of the damping ratio ζ and the undamped natural frequency ω_n.
b) Find the unit impulse response $h(t)$. Sketch $y_U(t)$ and $h(t)$.

* 6.28 A certain third-order system is described by the differential equation

$$\ddot{y} + 2\ddot{y} + \dot{y} + 2y = 4.$$

Find $y(t)$ when $y(0) = 0$, $\dot{y}(0) = 5$, and $\ddot{y}(0) = -3$. The roots of the system's characteristic equation are $r_1 = -2, r_2 = j1$, and $r_3 = -j1$.

6.29 The input-output equation for the translational mechanical system shown in Figure 3.5(a) was found in (3.27). When, in a consistent set of units, the parameter values $M = B_1 = B_2 = K_1 = K_2 = 1$ are used and the input $f_a(t)$ is the unit step function, the equation becomes

$$\dddot{x}_1 + 3\ddot{x}_1 + 3\dot{x}_1 + x_1 = 2 \quad \text{for } t > 0$$

a) Verify that the differential equation is correct.
b) By examining the figure, show that $x_1(0+) = \dot{x}_1(0+) = 0$ and $\ddot{x}_1(0+) = 1$.
c) Find $x_1(t)$ for all $t > 0$.

6.30 A linear fourth-order system is described by the input-output equation

$$a_4 y^{(iv)} + a_3 y^{(iii)} + a_2 \ddot{y} + a_1 \dot{y} + a_0 y = F(t)$$

Write the form of the complete response when $F(t) = A$ for each of the following sets of characteristic-root locations. Do not evaluate the multiplying constants in front of the individual terms. Identify the transient and steady-state responses.
a) $0, -2, -2, -5$
b) $-1, -2, \pm j3$
c) $-2, -2, -2 \pm j3$
d) $-2 \pm j3, -2 \pm j3$

6.31 Repeat Problem 6.30 when $F(t) = \cos 3t$.

6.32 A system obeying the state-variable equations $\dot{\mathbf{q}} = \mathbf{Aq}$ and $\mathbf{y} = \mathbf{Cq}$ has

$$\mathbf{A} = \begin{bmatrix} 0 & 1 \\ 0 & -2 \end{bmatrix} \quad \text{and} \quad \mathbf{C} = \begin{bmatrix} 2 & -1 \end{bmatrix}$$

a) Calculate the state-transition matrix $\phi(t)$.
b) Write $\mathbf{y}_{zi}(t)$ in terms of the initial states $q_i(0)$.

  c) Verify that

    i. $\phi(0) = \mathbf{I}$

    ii. $\phi^{-1}(t) = \phi(-t)$

    iii. $\phi(1)\,\phi(2) = \phi(3)$

6.33 Repeat Problem 6.32 when

$$\mathbf{A} = \begin{bmatrix} -2 & 1 \\ 0 & -2 \end{bmatrix} \qquad \text{and} \qquad \mathbf{C} = \begin{bmatrix} 4 & 1 \end{bmatrix}$$

* 6.34 Repeat parts (a) and (b) of Problem 6.32 when

$$\mathbf{A} = \begin{bmatrix} 0 & 1 \\ -2 & -3 \end{bmatrix} \qquad \text{and} \qquad \mathbf{C} = \begin{bmatrix} -1 & -2 \end{bmatrix}$$

* 6.35 Find the zero-state response of the output vector $\mathbf{y}(t)$ for the multi-input multi-output system discussed in Example 6.14 when the inputs are $u_1(t) = \epsilon^{-t}U(t)$ and $u_2(t) = 0$.

6.36 Using the results of Examples 6.12 and 6.14, find the complete response of the system output vector $\mathbf{y}(t)$ when the initial states are $q_1(0) = -1$ and $q_2(0) = 1$ and the inputs are $u_1(t) = 0$ and $u_2(t) = 1$ for $t > 0$.

THE LAPLACE TRANSFORM

Frequently, we can transform a mathematical problem that is difficult to solve as it stands into an equivalent problem whose solution is much easier. If the solution of the transformed problem can be converted back to the framework of the original problem, then going through the process of transformation, solution, and conversion of the solution may be more attractive than attempting to solve the original problem directly.

A familiar example of such a process is the use of logarithms. Logarithms transform numbers into other numbers, but there are also procedures for transforming functions of one variable into functions of another variable. Among these procedures are the Fourier series, the Fourier transform, and the Laplace transform. Because the Laplace transform converts fixed linear differential equations into algebraic equations, it is of considerable value in analyzing the response of a dynamic system whose model is fixed and linear.

In this chapter, we first define the Laplace transform and derive the transforms of several common functions of time. We then develop properties that are useful in finding the transforms of specific time functions and in transforming the equations that describe dynamic models. We complete the initial mathematical development by showing how to convert a transform back to the corresponding time function. In the next section, we use Laplace transforms to solve for the response of a variety of models. We conclude the chapter by introducing and illustrating several additional transform properties.

250

7.1 TRANSFORMS OF FUNCTIONS

The **Laplace transform** converts a function of a real variable, which will always be time t in our applications, into a function of a complex variable that is denoted by s. The transform of $f(t)$ is represented symbolically by either $\mathscr{L}[f(t)]$ or $F(s)$, where the symbol $\mathscr{L}$ stands for "the Laplace transform of." One can think of the Laplace transform as providing a means of transforming a given problem from the **time domain**, where all variables are functions of t, to the **complex-frequency domain**, where all variables are functions of s.

The defining equation for the Laplace transform[1] is

$$F(s) = \int_0^\infty f(t)\epsilon^{-st}dt \tag{1}$$

Some authors take the lower limit of integration at $t = 0-$ rather than at $t = 0$. Either convention is acceptable provided that the transform properties are developed in a manner consistent with the defining integral.

The integration in (1) with respect to t is carried out between the limits of zero and infinity, so the resulting transform is not a function of t. In the factor ϵ^{-st} appearing in the integrand, we treat s as a constant in carrying out the integration.

The variable s is a complex quantity, which we can write as

$$s = \sigma + j\omega$$

where σ and ω are the real and imaginary parts of s, respectively. We can write the factor ϵ^{-st} in (1) as

$$\epsilon^{-st} = \epsilon^{-\sigma t}\epsilon^{-j\omega t}$$

Because the magnitude of $\epsilon^{-j\omega t}$ is always unity, $|\epsilon^{-st}| = \epsilon^{-\sigma t}$. By placing appropriate restrictions on σ, we can ensure that the the integral converges in most cases of practical interest, even if the function $f(t)$ becomes infinite as t approaches infinity. For all time functions considered in this book, convergence of the transform integral can be achieved.

To gain familiarity with the use of the transform definition and to begin the development of a table of transforms, we shall derive the Laplace transforms of several common functions. The results, along with others, are included in Appendix B.

---

[1]Equation (1) defines the one-sided Laplace transform. There is a more general, two-sided Laplace transform, which is useful for theoretical work but is seldom used for solving for system responses.

Step Function

The unit step function $U(t)$ is unity for all $t > 0$, so it follows from (1) that

$$\mathcal{L}[U(t)] = \int_0^\infty \epsilon^{-st} dt$$

$$= \frac{\epsilon^{-st}}{-s}\bigg|_{t=0}^{t \to \infty} \tag{2}$$

In order for the integral to converge, $|\epsilon^{-st}|$ must approach zero as t approaches infinity. Because $|\epsilon^{-st}| = \epsilon^{-\sigma t}$, the integral will converge provided that $\sigma > 0$. Hence the expression for the transform of the unit step function converges for all values of s in the right half of the complex plane, and (2) becomes

$$\mathcal{L}[U(t)] = \frac{1}{s} \tag{3}$$

Note that the variable t has disappeared in the integration process and that the result is strictly a function of s.

For all functions of time with which we shall be concerned, the transform definition will converge for all values of s to the right of some vertical line in the complex s-plane. Although knowledge of the region of convergence is required in some advanced applications, we do not need such knowledge for the applications in this book. When evaluating Laplace transforms, we shall assume that σ, the real part of s, is sufficiently large to ensure convergence. If you are interested in regions of convergence, you should consult one of the more advanced references on system theory cited in Appendix D.

Because $U(t) = 1$ for all $t > 0$, the constant 1 is equivalent to $U(t)$ over the interval $t > 0$ and has the same transform as the unit step function. Thus

$$\mathcal{L}[1] = \frac{1}{s} \tag{4}$$

Exponential Function

Depending on the value of the parameter a, the function $f(t) = \epsilon^{-at}$ represents an exponentially decaying function, a constant, or an exponentially growing function for $t > 0$, as shown in Figure 7.1. In any case, the Laplace transform of the exponential function is

$$\mathcal{L}[\epsilon^{-at}] = \int_0^\infty \epsilon^{-at} \epsilon^{-st} dt$$

$$= \int_0^\infty \epsilon^{-(s+a)t} dt$$

$$= \frac{\epsilon^{-(s+a)t}}{-(s+a)}\bigg|_{t=0}^{t \to \infty}$$

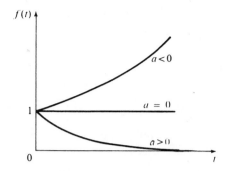

FIGURE 7.1 The exponential function ϵ^{-at} for various values of a.

The upper limit vanishes when σ, the real part of s, is greater than $-a$, so

$$\mathscr{L}[\epsilon^{-at}] = \frac{1}{s+a} \tag{5}$$

Note that if $a = 0$, the exponential function ϵ^{-at} reduces to the constant value of 1. Likewise, (5) reduces to (4), as it must for this value of a.

Ramp Function

The unit ramp function is defined to be $f(t) = t$ for $t > 0$. Substituting for $f(t)$ in (1), we have

$$\mathscr{L}[t] = \int_0^\infty t\epsilon^{-st} dt \tag{6}$$

To evaluate the integral in (6), we use the formula for integration by parts:

$$\int_a^b u \, dv = uv \Big|_a^b - \int_a^b v \, du \tag{7}$$

where the limits a and b apply to the variable t. Making the identifications $u = t$ and $v = \epsilon^{-st}/(-s)$, $a = 0$, and $b \to \infty$, we can rewrite (6) as

$$\mathscr{L}[t] = \frac{t\epsilon^{-st}}{(-s)} \Big|_0^\infty - \frac{1}{(-s)} \int_0^\infty \epsilon^{-st} dt \tag{8}$$

It can be shown that

$$\lim_{t \to \infty} t\epsilon^{-st} = 0 \tag{9}$$

provided that σ, the real part of s, is positive. Thus

$$\mathscr{L}[t] = 0 - 0 + \frac{1}{s} \int_0^\infty \epsilon^{-st} dt \tag{10}$$

Because the integral in (10) is $\mathcal{L}[U(t)]$, which from (3) has the value $1/s$, (10) simplifies to

$$\mathcal{L}[t] = \frac{1}{s^2} \tag{11}$$

Rectangular Pulse

The rectangular pulse shown in Figure 7.2 has unit height and a duration of L. Its Laplace transform is

$$F(s) = \int_0^L \epsilon^{-st} dt + \int_L^\infty 0\,\epsilon^{-st} dt$$

$$= \frac{1}{(-s)} \epsilon^{-st} \Big|_0^L + 0$$

$$= \frac{1}{s}(1 - \epsilon^{-sL}) \tag{12}$$

As the pulse duration L becomes infinite, the pulse approaches the unit step function $U(t)$, and the term ϵ^{-sL} in (12) approaches zero for all values of s having a positive real part. Thus as L approaches infinity, $F(s)$ given by (12) approaches $1/s$, which is $\mathcal{L}[U(t)]$.

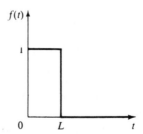

FIGURE 7.2   The rectangular pulse of unit height and duration L.

The Impulse

From (1), we can write the transform of the unit impulse as

$$\mathcal{L}[\delta(t)] = \int_0^\infty \delta(t)\epsilon^{-st} dt$$

This expression presents a dilemma because when the impulse was introduced in Section 6.3, we adopted the convention that $\delta(t)$ is an impulse at $t = 0$, which is the lower limit of integration in (1). To avoid this problem, we shall now adopt the convention that when we are working with Laplace transforms, the unit impulse $\delta(t)$ occurs just after $t = 0$, namely at $t = 0+$.

With this stipulation, (6.39) is applicable with $t_a = 0+, b = 0$, and $c \to \infty$, and we can say that

$$\int_0^\infty \delta(t)\epsilon^{-st}dt = \epsilon^{-st}\Big|_{t=0+} = 1$$

so

$$\mathcal{L}[\delta(t)] = 1 \tag{13}$$

In books wherein the lower limit of the transform integral in (1) is taken to be $t = 0-$, the impulse can be considered to occur at $t = 0$. This convention also yields (13).

Trigonometric Functions

When $f(t)$ is replaced by $\sin \omega t$ or $\cos \omega t$ in the definition of the Laplace transform, we can evaluate the resulting integral by using the identities given in Table 6.1, by performing integration by parts, or by consulting a table of integrals. Using an integral table, we find that

$$\mathcal{L}[\sin \omega t] = \int_0^\infty \sin \omega t \; \epsilon^{-st}dt$$

$$= \frac{\epsilon^{-st}}{(-s)^2 + \omega^2}(-s \sin \omega t - \omega \cos \omega t)\Big|_0^\infty$$

$$= \frac{\omega}{s^2 + \omega^2} \tag{14}$$

By a similar procedure, we can show that

$$\mathcal{L}[\cos \omega t] = \frac{s}{s^2 + \omega^2} \tag{15}$$

7.2 TRANSFORM PROPERTIES

The Laplace transform has a number of properties that are useful in finding the transforms of functions in terms of known transforms and in solving for the responses of dynamic models. We shall state, illustrate, and in most cases derive those properties that will be useful in later work. They are tabulated in Appendix B.

Throughout this section, the symbols $F(s)$ and $G(s)$ denote the Laplace transforms of the arbitrary time functions $f(t)$ and $g(t)$, and a and b denote arbitrary constants. Our object is to express the transforms of various functions of $f(t)$ and $g(t)$ in terms of $F(s) = \int_0^\infty f(t)\epsilon^{-st}dt$ and $G(s) = \int_0^\infty g(t)\epsilon^{-st}dt$.

Multiplication by a Constant

To express $\mathcal{L}[af(t)]$ in terms of $F(s)$, where a is a constant and where $F(s) = \mathcal{L}[f(t)]$, we use (1) to write

$$\mathcal{L}[af(t)] = \int_0^\infty af(t)\epsilon^{-st}dt$$

$$= a\int_0^\infty f(t)\epsilon^{-st}dt$$

$$= aF(s) \tag{16}$$

Thus multiplying a function of time by a constant multiplies its transform by the same constant.

Superposition

The transform of the sum of the two functions $f(t)$ and $g(t)$ is

$$\mathcal{L}[f(t) + g(t)] = \int_0^\infty [f(t) + g(t)]\epsilon^{-st}dt$$

$$= \int_0^\infty f(t)\epsilon^{-st}dt + \int_0^\infty g(t)\epsilon^{-st}dt$$

$$= F(s) + G(s) \tag{17}$$

Using (16) and (17), we have the general superposition property

$$\mathcal{L}[af(t) + bg(t)] = aF(s) + bG(s) \tag{18}$$

for any constants a and b and any transformable functions $f(t)$ and $g(t)$. As an illustration of the superposition property, we can evaluate $\mathcal{L}[2 + 3\sin 4t]$ by using (18) with (4) and (14) to write

$$\mathcal{L}[2 + 3\sin 4t] = \frac{2}{s} + 3\left(\frac{4}{s^2 + 4^2}\right)$$

$$= \frac{2s^2 + 12s + 32}{s^3 + 16s}$$

Multiplication by an Exponential

If we replace $f(t)$ in (1) by the function $f(t)\epsilon^{-at}$, we have

$$\mathcal{L}[f(t)\epsilon^{-at}] = \int_0^\infty f(t)\epsilon^{-at}\epsilon^{-st}dt$$

$$= \int_0^\infty f(t)\epsilon^{-(s+a)t}dt$$

$$= F(s + a) \tag{19}$$

In words, (19) states that multiplying a function $f(t)$ by ϵ^{-at} is equivalent to replacing the variable s by the quantity $s + a$ wherever it occurs in $F(s)$.

With this property, we can derive several of the transforms in Appendix B rather easily from other entries in the table. Specifically, because $\mathcal{L}[\cos \omega t] = s/(s^2 + \omega^2)$ and $\mathcal{L}[\sin \omega t] = \omega/(s^2 + \omega^2)$, we can write

$$\mathcal{L}[\epsilon^{-at} \cos \omega t] = \frac{s + a}{(s + a)^2 + \omega^2}$$

$$\mathcal{L}[\epsilon^{-at} \sin \omega t] = \frac{\omega}{(s + a)^2 + \omega^2}$$

Also, because $\mathcal{L}[t] = 1/s^2$, it follows that

$$\mathcal{L}[t\epsilon^{-at}] = \frac{1}{(s + a)^2}$$

Multiplication by Time

We obtain the transform of the product of $f(t)$ and the variable t by differentiating the transform $F(s)$ with respect to the complex variable s and then multiplying by -1:

$$\mathcal{L}[tf(t)] = -\frac{d}{ds} F(s) \tag{20}$$

To prove (20), we note that

$$\frac{d}{ds} F(s) = \frac{d}{ds} \left[\int_0^\infty f(t)\epsilon^{-st} dt \right]$$

$$= -\int_0^\infty tf(t)\epsilon^{-st} dt$$

$$= -\mathcal{L}[tf(t)] \tag{21}$$

Multiplying both sides of (21) by -1 results in (20).

We can illustrate the use of this property by deriving the entry in Appendix B for $\mathcal{L}[t^n]$, where n is any positive integer. Because $\mathcal{L}[1] = \mathcal{L}[U(t)] = 1/s$, it follows that

$$\mathcal{L}[t] = -\frac{d}{ds}\left(\frac{1}{s}\right) = \frac{1}{s^2}$$

$$\mathcal{L}[t^2] = -\frac{d}{ds}\left(\frac{1}{s^2}\right) = \frac{2}{s^3}$$

$$\mathcal{L}[t^3] = -\frac{d}{ds}\left(\frac{2}{s^3}\right) = \frac{2 \cdot 3}{s^4}$$

and, for the general case,

$$\mathcal{L}[t^n] = \frac{n!}{s^{n+1}} \tag{22}$$

Differentiation

Because we shall need to take the Laplace transform of each term in a differential equation when solving system models for their responses, we must derive expressions for the transforms of derivatives of arbitrary order. We shall first develop and illustrate the formula for obtaining the transform of df/dt in terms of $F(s) = \mathcal{L}[f(t)]$. Then we shall use this result to derive expressions for the transforms of higher derivatives.

First Derivative.   From the transform definition (1), we can write the transform of df/dt as

$$\mathcal{L}[\dot{f}] = \int_0^\infty \left(\frac{df}{dt}\right) \epsilon^{-st} dt \tag{23}$$

We can rewrite (23) by using the formula for integration by parts given by (7), with $a = 0$ and $b \to \infty$. The result is

$$\int_0^\infty u\, dv = uv \Big|_0^\infty - \int_0^\infty v\, du$$

If we let $u = \epsilon^{-st}$ and $dv = (df/dt)dt$, then $du = -s\epsilon^{-st}dt$, $v = f(t)$, and (23) becomes

$$\mathcal{L}[\dot{f}] = \epsilon^{-st} f(t) \Big|_0^\infty - \int_0^\infty f(t)(-s\epsilon^{-st})dt$$

For all the functions we shall encounter, there will be values of s for which $\epsilon^{-st} f(t)$ approaches zero as t approaches infinity, so

$$\mathcal{L}[\dot{f}] = [0 - f(0)] + s\int_0^\infty f(t)\epsilon^{-st}dt$$
$$= sF(s) - f(0) \tag{24}$$

To illustrate the application of (24), let $f(t) = \sin \omega t$. Then $F(s) = \omega/(s^2 + \omega^2)$ from (14) and $f(0) = \sin 0 = 0$, so

$$\mathcal{L}[\dot{f}] = s\left(\frac{\omega}{s^2 + \omega^2}\right) - 0 = \frac{s\omega}{s^2 + \omega^2} \tag{25}$$

We can verify this result by noting that $\dot{f} = \omega \cos \omega t$ and that

$$\mathcal{L}[\omega \cos \omega t] = \omega\mathcal{L}[\cos \omega t] = \omega\left(\frac{s}{s^2 + \omega^2}\right)$$

which agrees with (25).

Deriving and using (24) are straightforward when $f(t)$ is continuous at $t = 0$. However, when $f(t)$ is discontinuous at $t = 0$, we must take care in applying (24) because of the potential ambiguity in evaluating $f(0)$. To avoid such problems, we shall adopt the convention that $f(0) = f(0-)$, which is equivalent to saying that any discontinuity at the time origin is considered to occur just after $t = 0$. In such cases $f(0) \neq f(0+)$, and

df/dt will contain an impulse of weight $f(0+) - f(0)$ occurring at $t = 0+$. This impulse is within the integration interval $0 \le t < \infty$ that we used for (1), and thus it will contribute to the expression for $\mathcal{L}[f]$. This approach is consistent with our definition of the unit step function in Chapter 6 as

$$U(t) = \begin{cases} 0 \text{ for } t \le 0 \\ 1 \text{ for } t > 0 \end{cases}$$

and with our derivation of the transform of $\delta(t)$.

To illustrate the application of (24) when $f(t)$ has a discontinuity at $t = 0+$, consider the product of $\cos \omega t$ and the unit step function $U(t)$:

$$f(t) = [\cos \omega t] U(t)$$

$$= \begin{cases} 0 & \text{for } t \le 0 \\ \cos \omega t & \text{for } t > 0 \end{cases} \tag{26}$$

which is shown in Figure 7.3(a). Because $f(t)$ differs from $\cos \omega t$ only at the point $t = 0$ within the interval $0 \le t < \infty$, its transform is the same[2] as that of $\cos \omega t$:

$$F(s) = \frac{s}{s^2 + \omega^2} \tag{27}$$

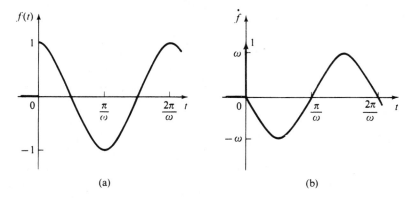

(a)   (b)

FIGURE 7.3   The function $f(t) = [\cos \omega t] U(t)$ and its derivative.

We see from (26), however, that $f(0) = 0$ because of the presence of the unit step function. Thus (24) gives

$$\mathcal{L}[\dot{f}] = s \left(\frac{s}{s^2 + \omega^2} \right) - 0$$

$$= \frac{s^2}{s^2 + \omega^2} \tag{28}$$

---

[2]The value of a definite integral, and hence the result of using (1), is not affected if the value of the integrand at a single point is changed to another finite value.

To check this result, consider $\dot{f}$, the derivative of (26), which is shown in Figure 7.3(b). Because of the discontinuity in $f(t)$ at $t = 0+$, the function $\dot{f}$ contains a unit impulse at $t = 0+$. Consistent with the facts that $\dot{f}(t) = 0$ for all $t < 0$ and that the impulse occurs at $t = 0+$, we define $\dot{f}(0) = 0$. Thus

$$\dot{f} = \begin{cases} 0 & \text{for } t \le 0 \\ \delta(t) - \omega \sin \omega t & \text{for } t > 0 \end{cases} \tag{29}$$

Transforming (29) gives

$$\mathscr{L}[\dot{f}] = 1 - \omega \left(\frac{\omega}{s^2 + \omega^2} \right)$$

$$= \frac{s^2}{s^2 + \omega^2}$$

which is in agreement with (28).

For comparison, consider the related function

$$g(t) = \cos \omega t \qquad \text{for all } t$$

which is continuous for all t and for which $g(0) = 1$. From (24), the transform of its derivative is

$$\mathscr{L}[\dot{g}] = s \left(\frac{s}{s^2 + \omega^2} \right) - 1$$

$$= -\frac{\omega^2}{s^2 + \omega^2}$$

The derivative of $g(t)$ is $\dot{g} = -\omega \sin \omega t$ for all t. Taking the transform of this expression gives $-\omega^2/(s^2 + \omega^2)$, which agrees with the foregoing result.

In summary, whenever we use (24) we shall consider any discontinuities in $f(t)$ at the time origin to occur at $t = 0+$. We shall now develop formulas for finding the transforms of second and higher derivatives of $f(t)$ in terms of $F(s)$.

Second and Higher Derivatives.   If we write (24) in terms of the function $g(t)$, it becomes

$$\mathscr{L}[\dot{g}] = sG(s) - g(0) \tag{30}$$

Now let $g(t) = \dot{f}(t)$. Then $\dot{g}(t) = \ddot{f}(t)$, and it follows from (30) and (24) that

$$\mathscr{L}[\ddot{f}] = s\mathscr{L}[\dot{f}(t)] - \dot{f}(0)$$

$$= s[sF(s) - f(0)] - \dot{f}(0)$$

$$= s^2 F(s) - sf(0) - \dot{f}(0) \tag{31}$$

If $\dot{f}$ is discontinuous at the time origin, we must use for $\dot{f}(0)$ in (31) the limit of $\dot{f}$ as t approaches zero from the left. Consider, for example,

$$f(t) = [\sin \omega t]U(t)$$

which is shown in Figure 7.4(a). The first and second derivatives of this function are

$$\dot{f} = [\omega \cos \omega t]U(t) \tag{32a}$$

$$\ddot{f} = \omega\delta(t) - [\omega^2 \sin \omega t]U(t) \tag{32b}$$

which are shown in Figure 7.4(b) and Figure 7.4(c). To be consistent with our previous development, we consider the discontinuity in $\dot{f}$ to occur at $t = 0+$ and assume that $\dot{f}(0) = 0$. Then (31) gives

$$\mathcal{L}[\ddot{f}] = s^2\left(\frac{\omega}{s^2 + \omega^2}\right) - s \cdot 0 - 0$$

$$= \frac{\omega s^2}{s^2 + \omega^2}$$

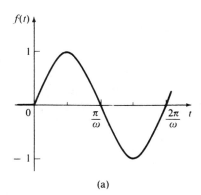

(a)

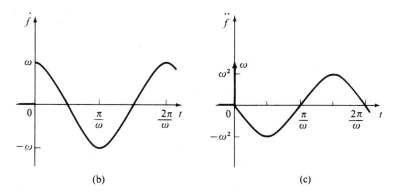

(b)   (c)

FIGURE 7.4   The function $f(t) = [\sin \omega t]U(t)$ and its first two derivatives.

By a direct transformation of the right side of (32b), we obtain

$$\mathcal{L}[\ddot{f}] = \omega - \omega^2 \left(\frac{\omega}{s^2 + \omega^2} \right)$$

$$= \frac{\omega s^2}{s^2 + \omega^2}$$

which is the same result.

Equation (31) can be generalized to give the formula for the transform of the nth derivative of $f(t)$. The result is

$$\mathcal{L}\left[\frac{d^n f}{dt^n} \right] = s^n F(s) - s^{n-1} f(0) - \cdots - f^{(n-1)}(0) \tag{33}$$

where $f^{(n-1)}(0)$ denotes $d^{n-1} f/dt^{n-1}$ evaluated at $t = 0$. If any of the derivatives of $f(t)$ has a discontinuity at the time origin, we use its value at $t = 0-$ in the corresponding initial-condition term in (33).

Integration

The definite integral $\int_0^t f(\lambda)d\lambda$ will be a function of t because of the upper limit. From the transform definition given by (1), we can write

$$\mathcal{L}\left[\int_0^t f(\lambda)d\lambda \right] = \int_0^\infty \left[\int_0^t f(\lambda)d\lambda \right] \epsilon^{-st} dt$$

To evaluate the double integral on the right side of this expression, we use integration by parts with $u = \int_0^t f(\lambda)d\lambda$ and $dv = \epsilon^{-st}dt$. Then $du = f(t)dt$, $v = \epsilon^{-st}/(-s)$, and

$$\mathcal{L}\left[\int_0^t f(\lambda)d\lambda \right] = \left[\left(\frac{\epsilon^{-st}}{-s} \right) \int_0^t f(\lambda)d\lambda \right]\Big|_{t=0}^{t \to \infty} - \int_0^\infty \left(\frac{\epsilon^{-st}}{-s} \right) f(t)dt$$

$$= [0 - 0] + \frac{1}{s} \int_0^\infty f(t)\epsilon^{-st}dt$$

$$= \frac{1}{s} F(s) \tag{34}$$

For example, if $f(t) = \cos \omega t$, then $F(s) = s/(s^2 + \omega^2)$, so

$$\mathcal{L}\left[\int_0^t \cos \omega\lambda \, d\lambda \right] = \frac{1}{s} \left(\frac{s}{s^2 + \omega^2} \right)$$

$$= \frac{1}{s^2 + \omega^2}$$

To check this result, we note that

$$\int_0^t \cos \omega\lambda \, d\lambda = \frac{1}{\omega} \sin \omega t$$

and

$$\mathscr{L}\left[\frac{1}{\omega}\sin\omega t\right] = \frac{1}{\omega}\left(\frac{\omega}{s^2+\omega^2}\right) = \frac{1}{s^2+\omega^2}$$

which agrees with the result we obtained by using (34).

When solving dynamic models, we may need to transform a term such as $g(t) = g(0) + \int_0^t f(\lambda)d\lambda$. To do this, we note that $g(0)$ is a constant and thus has the transform $g(0)/s$, whereas we can transform the integral part of the term by using (34). The result is

$$G(s) = \frac{g(0)}{s} + \frac{F(s)}{s} \tag{35}$$

7.3 TRANSFORM INVERSION

When we use Laplace transforms to solve for the response of a system, we find the transform $F(s)$ of a particular variable, such as the output, first. The final step in the process, known as **transform inversion**, is to determine the corresponding time function $f(t)$ where $f(t) = \mathscr{L}^{-1}[F(s)]$, which is read "$f(t)$ is the inverse transform of $F(s)$."

For the types of problems encountered in this book, we do not need a completely general method of transform inversion. In this section, we present and illustrate a method that uses a partial-fraction expansion of $F(s)$. An extension of this method that permits handling an additional category of transformed functions appears in Section 7.5.

Assume that we can write the transform $F(s)$ as the ratio of two polynomials $N(s)$ and $D(s)$, such that

$$F(s) = \frac{N(s)}{D(s)} = \frac{b_m s^m + \cdots + b_0}{s^n + a_{n-1}s^{n-1} + \cdots + a_0} \tag{36}$$

Functions that can be written in the form of (36) are called **rational functions**. A **proper rational function** is one for which $m \le n$; while a **strictly proper rational function** is one for which $m < n$.

The equation $D(s) = 0$ will have n roots denoted by $s_1, s_2, \ldots, s_n$, and $D(s)$ can be written in factored form as

$$D(s) = (s - s_1)(s - s_2)\cdots(s - s_n) \tag{37}$$

Note that the coefficient of the highest power of s in the denominator polynomial $D(s)$ has been assumed to be unity. If this is not the case for a given $F(s)$, we can always make the coefficient unity by dividing both $N(s)$ and $D(s)$ by a constant. The quantities $s_1, s_2, \ldots, s_n$ are called the **poles** of $F(s)$ and are those values of s for which $F(s)$ becomes infinite.[3]

---

[3]It is assumed that $N(s) \ne 0$ at any of the poles.

The **method of partial-fraction expansion** is applicable to any strictly proper rational function. Briefly, it allows us to express a known transform $F(s)$ as the sum of less complicated transforms. Using the table in Appendix B, we can identify the time functions that correspond to the individual transforms in the expansion and then use the superposition theorem to write $f(t)$.

We consider first the case where all the poles of $F(s)$ are distinct. We next modify the procedure to include repeated poles, where two or more of the quantities s_1, s_2, ..., s_n are equal. Then we examine the case where the poles are complex numbers and discuss what to do if the degree of $N(s)$ is not less than that of $D(s)$. Throughout the section, we assume that the polynomial $D(s)$ has been factored, so that the values of the n poles are known.

Distinct Poles

The partial-fraction expansion theorem states that if $F(s)$ is a strictly proper rational function with distinct poles, it can be written as

$$F(s) = \frac{A_1}{s - s_1} + \frac{A_2}{s - s_2} + \cdots + \frac{A_n}{s - s_n} \tag{38}$$

where $A_1, A_2, \ldots, A_n$ are constants. We can write (38) with a summation sign as follows:

$$F(s) = \sum_{i=1}^{n} A_i \left(\frac{1}{s - s_i} \right) \tag{39}$$

From (5), the term $1/(s - s_i)$ is the transform of the time function $\epsilon^{s_i t}$. Then, from the superposition formula given in (18), it follows that for $t > 0$,

$$f(t) = A_1 \epsilon^{s_1 t} + A_2 \epsilon^{s_2 t} + \cdots + A_n \epsilon^{s_n t}$$

$$= \sum_{i=1}^{n} A_i \epsilon^{s_i t} \tag{40}$$

We can find the n poles s_i by factoring the denominator of $F(s)$ or, more generally, by finding the roots of $D(s) = 0$. We shall now develop a procedure for evaluating the n coefficients A_i so that we can write $f(t)$ as a sum of exponential time functions by using (40).

Multiplying both sides of (38) by the term $(s - s_1)$ yields

$$(s - s_1)F(s) = A_1 + A_2 \frac{(s - s_1)}{(s - s_2)} + \cdots + A_n \frac{(s - s_1)}{(s - s_n)}$$

Because this equation must be a mathematical identity for all values of the variable s, we can set s equal to s_1 throughout the equation. The poles are distinct, so $s_1 \neq s_j$ for $j = 2, 3, \ldots, n$. Thus each term on the right side will vanish except the term A_1, and we can write

$$A_1 = (s - s_1)F(s)|_{s=s_1} \tag{41}$$

To make it clear why (41) does not give a value of zero, we write $F(s)$ as $N(s)/D(s)$ with $D(s)$ in factored form. Then

$$A_1 = \frac{(s-s_1)N(s)}{(s-s_1)(s - s_2) \cdots (s - s_n)}\Big|_{s=s_1}$$

The term $(s - s_1)$ in the numerator will be canceled by the corresponding term in $D(s)$ before s is replaced by s_1.

Repeating the above process with s_1 replaced by s_2, we have

$$A_2 = (s - s_2)F(s)|_{s=s_2}$$

The general expression for the coefficients is

$$A_i = (s - s_i)F(s)|_{s=s_i} \qquad i = 1, 2, \ldots, n \tag{42}$$

In a numerical problem we can check the calculation of A_1, A_2, ..., A_n by combining the terms on the right side of (38) over a common denominator, which should give the original function $F(s)$.

▶ **EXAMPLE 7.1**

Find the inverse transform of

$$F(s) = \frac{-s + 5}{(s + 1)(s + 4)}$$

Solution

Comparing $F(s)$ to (36), we see that $N(s) = -s + 5$ so $m = 1$, and $D(s) = (s + 1)(s + 4)$ so $n = 2$. Because $D(s)$ is already in factored form, we see by inspection that the poles are $s_1 = -1$ and $s_2 = -4$. Thus we can rewrite the transform $F(s)$ in the form of (38) as

$$F(s) = \frac{A_1}{s + 1} + \frac{A_2}{s + 4}$$

Using (42) with $i = 1$ and 2, we find the coefficients of the partial-fraction expansion to be

$$A_1 = \frac{(s+1)(-s + 5)}{(s+1)(s + 4)}\Big|_{s=-1} = \frac{6}{3} = 2$$

$$A_2 = \frac{(s+4)(-s + 5)}{(s + 1)(s+4)}\Big|_{s=-4} = \frac{9}{-3} = -3$$

Hence the partial-fraction expansion of the transform is

$$F(s) = \frac{2}{s + 1} - \frac{3}{s + 4}$$

and, from (40), the time function $f(t)$ is

$$f(t) = 2\epsilon^{-t} - 3\epsilon^{-4t} \qquad \text{for } t > 0$$

Repeated Poles

If two or more of the n roots of $D(s) = 0$ are identical, these roots, which are poles of $F(s)$, are said to be **repeated**. When $F(s)$ contains repeated poles, (38) and (40) no longer hold. If $s_1 = s_2$, for example, the first two terms in (40) become $A_1 \epsilon^{s_1 t}$ and $A_2 \epsilon^{s_1 t}$, which are identical except for the multiplying constant, and (40) is not valid. If $s_1 = s_2$ and if the remaining poles are distinct, then (38) must be modified to be

$$F(s) = \frac{A_{11}}{(s - s_1)^2} + \frac{A_{12}}{s - s_1} + \frac{A_3}{s - s_3} + \cdots + \frac{A_n}{s - s_n} \tag{43}$$

Referring to Appendix B, we see that the first term on the right-hand side of (43) is the transform of $A_{11} t \epsilon^{s_1 t}$, whereas the second term has the same form as the remaining ones. Thus the inverse transform is

$$f(t) = A_{11} t \epsilon^{s_1 t} + A_{12} \epsilon^{s_1 t} + A_3 \epsilon^{s_3 t} + \cdots + A_n \epsilon^{s_n t} \tag{44}$$

Note that the repeated pole at $s = s_1$ introduces into the time function a term of the form $t \epsilon^{s_1 t}$.

In order to evaluate any of the $n - 2$ coefficients $A_3, \ldots, A_n$ we can use the procedure given by (42). This formula cannot be used to find A_{11} and A_{12} because of the term $(s - s_1)^2$ in the denominator of $F(s)$. However, multiplying both sides of (43) by $(s - s_1)^2$ gives

$$(s - s_1)^2 F(s) = A_{11} + A_{12}(s - s_1) + A_3 \frac{(s - s_1)^2}{(s - s_3)} + \cdots + A_n \frac{(s - s_1)^2}{(s - s_n)} \tag{45}$$

Setting s equal to s_1 throughout (45) results in

$$A_{11} = (s - s_1)^2 F(s)|_{s = s_1} \tag{46}$$

To find A_{12}, we note that the right-hand side of (45) has the terms $A_{11} + A_{12}(s - s_1)$ and that all the remaining terms contain $(s - s_1)^2$ in their numerators. Thus if we differentiate both sides of (45) with respect to s, we have

$$\frac{d}{ds}[(s - s_1)^2 F(s)] = A_{12} + (s - s_1)G(s) \tag{47}$$

where $G(s)$ is a rational function without a pole at $s = s_1$. Note that in (47) the coefficient A_{11} is not present, A_{12} stands alone, and the function $G(s)$ that contains all the other coefficients is multiplied by the quantity $s - s_1$.

Hence setting s equal to s_1 in (47) gives

$$A_{12} = \left\{ \frac{d}{ds}[(s - s_1)^2 F(s)] \right\} \Bigg|_{s=s_1} \tag{48}$$

where the differentiation must be performed before s is set equal to s_1.

If $F(s)$ has two or more pairs of identical poles, then each pair of poles contributes terms of the form $\epsilon^{s_i t}$ and $t\epsilon^{s_i t}$, and we can evaluate the coefficients of these terms by using (46) and (48) with the appropriate indices. If $F(s)$ has three or more identical poles, (43) must be modified further. For example, if $s_1 = s_2 = s_3$ and if the remaining poles are distinct, the partial-fraction expansion has the form

$$F(s) = \frac{A_{11}}{(s - s_1)^3} + \frac{A_{12}}{(s - s_1)^2} + \frac{A_{13}}{s - s_1} + \frac{A_4}{s - s_4} + \cdots + \frac{A_n}{s - s_n} \tag{49}$$

By a procedure similar to that used in the derivation of (46) and (48), we find that

$$A_{11} = (s - s_1)^3 F(s)|_{s=s_1}$$

$$A_{12} = \left\{ \frac{d}{ds}[(s - s_1)^3 F(s)] \right\} \Bigg|_{s=s_1} \tag{50}$$

$$A_{13} = \frac{1}{2!} \left\{ \frac{d^2}{ds^2}[(s - s_1)^3 F(s)] \right\} \Bigg|_{s=s_1}$$

and

$$A_i = (s - s_i) F(s)|_{s=s_i} \quad \text{for } i = 4, 5, \ldots, n.$$

The time function corresponding to (49) and (50) is

$$f(t) = \left(\frac{1}{2!} A_{11} t^2 + A_{12} t + A_{13} \right) \epsilon^{s_1 t} + A_4 \epsilon^{s_4 t} + \cdots + A_n \epsilon^{s_n t} \tag{51}$$

▶ **EXAMPLE 7.2**

Find the inverse Laplace transform of

$$F(s) = \frac{5s + 16}{(s + 2)^2 (s + 5)}$$

Solution

The denominator of $F(s)$ is given in factored form, so we note that the poles are $s_1 = s_2 = -2$ and $s_3 = -5$. Because of the repeated pole, the partial-fraction expansion of $F(s)$ has the form

$$F(s) = \frac{A_{11}}{(s + 2)^2} + \frac{A_{12}}{s + 2} + \frac{A_3}{s + 5}$$

Using (46), (48), and (42) in order, we find that the coefficients are

$$A_{11} = (s + 2)^2 F(s)\big|_{s=-2} = \frac{5s + 16}{s + 5}\bigg|_{s=-2} = 2$$

$$A_{12} = \left\{ \frac{d}{ds} \left[\frac{5s + 16}{s + 5} \right] \right\}\bigg|_{s=-2} = \frac{9}{(s + 5)^2}\bigg|_{s=-2} = 1$$

$$A_3 = (s + 5) F(s)\big|_{s=-5} = \frac{5s + 16}{(s + 2)^2}\bigg|_{s=-5} = -1$$

Using numerical values for the coefficients gives the partial-fraction expansion of the transform as

$$F(s) = \frac{2}{(s + 2)^2} + \frac{1}{s + 2} - \frac{1}{s + 5}$$

The corresponding time function is

$$f(t) = 2t\epsilon^{-2t} + \epsilon^{-2t} - \epsilon^{-5t} \quad \text{for } t > 0$$

Complex Poles

The form of $f(t)$ given by (40) is valid for complex poles as well as for real poles. When (40) is used directly with complex poles, however, it has the disadvantage that the functions $\epsilon^{s_i t}$ and the coefficients A_i are complex. Hence, further developments are necessary in order to write $f(t)$ directly in terms of real functions and real coefficients. We shall present two methods for finding $f(t)$ that lead to slightly different but equivalent forms. First we show how mathematical identities are used to combine any complex terms in the partial-fraction expansion of $F(s)$ into real functions of time. Then we present the alternative method known as completing the square.

For simplicity, we shall first assume that $F(s)$ has only two complex poles and that the order of its numerator is less than the order of its denominator. Any other poles, whether real or complex, will lead to additional terms in the partial-fraction expansion. With these restrictions, we can write the transform as

$$F(s) = \frac{Bs + C}{(s + a - j\omega)(s + a + j\omega)} \qquad (52)$$

which has poles at $s_1 = -a + j\omega$ and $s_2 = -a - j\omega$.

Partial-Fraction Expansion. As indicated in (52), the complex poles of $F(s)$ always occur in complex conjugate pairs. Using the partial-fraction expansion of (38) for distinct poles, we can write $F(s)$ as

$$F(s) = \frac{K_1}{s + a - j\omega} + \frac{K_2}{s + a + j\omega} \qquad (53)$$

where

$$K_1 = (s + a - j\omega)F(s)|_{s=-a+j\omega} \tag{54a}$$

$$K_2 = (s + a + j\omega)F(s)|_{s=-a-j\omega} \tag{54b}$$

Because (54a) is identical to (54b) except for the sign of the imaginary term $j\omega$ wherever it appears, the coefficient K_2 is the complex conjugate of K_1; that is, $K_2 = K_1^*$. Hence we can write K_1 and K_2 in polar form as $K_1 = K\epsilon^{j\phi}$ and $K_2 = K\epsilon^{-j\phi}$, where K and ϕ are the magnitude and angle, respectively, of the complex number K_1. Thus both K and ϕ are real quantities, and $K \geq 0$.

Rewriting (53) with K_1 and K_2 in polar form, we have

$$F(s) = \frac{K\epsilon^{j\phi}}{s+a-j\omega} + \frac{K\epsilon^{-j\phi}}{s+a+j\omega} \tag{55}$$

which has the form of (39), although the coefficients and poles are complex. From (40) with $n = 2$ and with the appropriate values substituted for A_i and s_i, the complex form of the time function is

$$f(t) = K\epsilon^{j\phi}\epsilon^{(-a+j\omega)t} + K\epsilon^{-j\phi}\epsilon^{(-a-j\omega)t}$$

To obtain $f(t)$ as a real function of time, we factor the term $2K\epsilon^{-at}$ out of each term on the right-hand side of this equation and combine the remaining complex exponentials. This yields

$$f(t) = 2K\epsilon^{-at}\left[\frac{\epsilon^{j(\omega t+\phi)} + \epsilon^{-j(\omega t+\phi)}}{2}\right]$$

Recognizing from Table 6.1 that the term in the brackets is $\cos(\omega t + \phi)$, we can write

$$f(t) = 2K\epsilon^{-at}\cos(\omega t + \phi) \qquad \text{for } t > 0 \tag{56}$$

where the parameters a, ω, K, and ϕ are all real. Note that (55) and (56) constitute one of the entries in Appendix B.

Completing the Square. To develop the second of the two forms of $f(t)$ when $F(s)$ has complex poles, we multiply the denominator factors in (52) to get

$$F(s) = \frac{Bs + C}{s^2 + 2as + a^2 + \omega^2}$$

Next we write the denominator as the sum of the perfect square $(s + a)^2$ and the constant ω^2, so that

$$F(s) = \frac{Bs + C}{(s + a)^2 + \omega^2} \tag{57}$$

Now we rearrange the numerator of $F(s)$ to have the term $(s + a)$ appear:

$$F(s) = \frac{B(s + a) + (C - aB)}{(s + a)^2 + \omega^2}$$

$$= B\left[\frac{s + a}{(s + a)^2 + \omega^2}\right] + \left(\frac{C - aB}{\omega}\right)\left[\frac{\omega}{(s + a)^2 + \omega^2}\right]$$

Referring to Appendix B, we see that the quantities within the brackets are the transforms of $\epsilon^{-at}\cos\omega t$ and $\epsilon^{-at}\sin\omega t$, respectively. Thus

$$f(t) = B\epsilon^{-at}\cos\omega t + \left(\frac{C - aB}{\omega}\right)\epsilon^{-at}\sin\omega t \qquad (58)$$

Equations (57) and (58) form another one of the entries in Appendix B. Although (56) and (58) look somewhat different, we can always use Table 6.1 to show that they are equivalent functions of time.

▶ **EXAMPLE 7.3**

Use each of the two methods that we have described to find $f(t)$ when

$$F(s) = \frac{4s + 8}{s^2 + 2s + 5}$$

Solution

The poles of $F(s)$ are the roots of $s^2 + 2s + 5 = 0$, namely $s_1 = -1 + j2$ and $s_2 = -1 - j2$. Hence $a = 1$, $\omega = 2$, and the partial-fraction expansion of $F(s)$ is

$$F(s) = \frac{K_1}{s + 1 - j2} + \frac{K_2}{s + 1 + j2}$$

Solving for K_1 according to (54a), we find

$$K_1 = \left.\frac{\cancel{(s + 1 - j2)}(4s + 8)}{\cancel{(s + 1 - j2)}(s + 1 + j2)}\right|_{s = -1 + j2}$$

$$= 2 - j1$$

$$= \sqrt{5}\,\epsilon^{-j0.4636}$$

Thus $K = \sqrt{5}$ and $\phi = -0.4636$ rad. Substituting the known values of a, ω, K and ϕ into (56) yields

$$f(t) = 2\sqrt{5}\,\epsilon^{-t}\cos(2t - 0.4636) \qquad \text{for } t > 0 \qquad (59)$$

Having found $f(t)$ from the partial-fraction expansion of $F(s)$, we repeat the problem by the method of completing the square. Because the denominator of $F(s)$ is $s^2 + 2s + 5$, we can obtain a perfect-square term by adding and subtracting 1 to give

$$(s^2 + 2s + 1) + (5 - 1) = (s + 1)^2 + 4$$

so

$$F(s) = \frac{4s + 8}{(s + 1)^2 + 2^2}$$

By comparison with (57), we see that $B = 4, C = 8, a = 1$, and $\omega = 2$. With these values, (58) gives

$$f(t) = 4\epsilon^{-t} \cos 2t + 2\epsilon^{-t} \sin 2t \quad \text{for } t > 0$$

which we can convert to the form given by (59) by using the appropriate entry in Table 6.1.

Comparison of the two methods for finding $f(t)$ indicates that the partial-fraction expansion requires the manipulation of complex numbers. It is frequently employed, however, and we shall need it for a derivation in the next chapter. The method of completing the square has the advantage of avoiding the use of complex numbers. The following example illustrates the two methods when $F(s)$ has more than the two poles specified by (52) and (57).

▶ **EXAMPLE 7.4**

Find the inverse transform of

$$F(s) = \frac{5s^2 + 8s - 5}{s^2(s^2 + 2s + 5)}$$

$$= \frac{5s^2 + 8s - 5}{s^2(s + 1 - j2)(s + 1 + j2)}$$

Solution

In order to use (56), we write the partial-fraction expansion as

$$F(s) = \frac{A_{11}}{s^2} + \frac{A_{12}}{s} + \frac{K_1}{s + 1 - j2} + \frac{K_1^*}{s + 1 + j2} \qquad (60)$$

where

$$A_{11} = \frac{5s^2 + 8s - 5}{s^2 + 2s + 5}\bigg|_{s=0} = -1$$

$$A_{12} = \left\{ \frac{d}{ds} \left[\frac{5s^2 + 8s - 5}{s^2 + 2s + 5} \right] \right\}\bigg|_{s=0} = \frac{2s^2 + 60s + 50}{(s^2 + 2s + 5)^2}\bigg|_{s=0} = 2$$

$$K_1 = \frac{5s^2 + 8s - 5}{s^2(s + 1 + j2)}\bigg|_{s=-1+j2} = \frac{-28 - j4}{16 - j12} = \frac{-7 - j1}{4 - j3}$$

Although it is possible to evaluate the quotient of two complex numbers directly on many hand calculators, an alternative procedure is to rationalize the fraction by multiplying both halves by the complex conjugate of the denominator. Then

$$K_1 = \frac{-7 - j1}{4 - j3} \cdot \frac{4 + j3}{4 + j3} = \frac{1}{25}(-25 - j25)$$

$$= -1 - j1 = \sqrt{2}\epsilon^{-j2.356}$$

Inserting the values of A_{11}, A_{12}, and K_1 into (60) and then using (11), (4) and (56), we obtain

$$f(t) = -t + 2 + 2\sqrt{2}\epsilon^{-t} \cos(2t - 2.356) \quad \text{for } t > 0 \qquad (61)$$

In order to avoid complex numbers, we may choose not to factor the quadratic $s^2 + 2s + 5$ that appears in the denominator of $F(s)$. For the corresponding term in a partial-fraction expansion, however, we must then assume a numerator of the form $Bs + C$. Thus, for an alternative solution to this example, we write

$$F(s) = \frac{5s^2 + 8s - 5}{s^2(s^2 + 2s + 5)}$$

$$= \frac{A_{11}}{s^2} + \frac{A_{12}}{s} + \frac{Bs + C}{s^2 + 2s + 5}$$

Recombining the terms on the right side of this equation over a common denominator gives

$$F(s) = \frac{(A_{12} + B)s^3 + (A_{11} + 2A_{12} + C)s^2 + (2A_{11} + 5A_{12})s + 5A_{11}}{s^2(s^2 + 2s + 5)}$$

By equating corresponding coefficients in the numerators, we have

$$A_{12} + B = 0$$

$$A_{11} + 2A_{12} + C = 5$$

$$2A_{11} + 5A_{12} = 8$$

$$5A_{11} = -5$$

from which $A_{11} = -1$, $A_{12} = 2$, $B = -2$, and $C = 2$. If we also complete the square in the factor $s^2 + 2s + 5$, we may write the partial-fraction expansion as

$$F(s) = \frac{-1}{s^2} + \frac{2}{s} + \frac{-2s + 2}{(s + 1)^2 + (2)^2}$$

From (11), (4), and (58), the corresponding function of time is

$$f(t) = -t + 2 - 2\epsilon^{-t} \cos 2t + 2\epsilon^{-t} \sin 2t \quad \text{for } t > 0 \qquad (62)$$

It is easy to show by Table 6.1 that (61) and (62) are equivalent.

Preliminary Step of Long Division

Remember that the techniques discussed so far are subject to the restriction that $F(s)$ is a strictly proper rational function—in other words, that m, the degree of the numerator polynomial $N(s)$, is less than n, the degree of the denominator polynomial $D(s)$. Otherwise, the partial-fraction expansion given for distinct poles by (39) or for a pair of repeated poles by (43) is not valid. In order to find the inverse transform of $F(s)$ when $m = n$, we must first write $F(s)$ as the sum of a constant[4] and a fraction whose numerator is of degree $n - 1$ or less. We can accomplish this by dividing the numerator by the denominator so that the remainder is of degree $n - 1$ or less. Then we may write

$$F(s) = A + F'(s) \tag{63}$$

where A is a constant and is the transform of $A\delta(t)$. The function $F'(s)$ is a ratio of polynomials having the same denominator as $F(s)$ but a numerator of degree less than n. We can find the inverse transform of $F'(s)$ by using the techniques described previously. Thus

$$f(t) = A\delta(t) + \mathcal{L}^{-1}[F'(s)] \tag{64}$$

▶ **EXAMPLE 7.5**

Find $f(t)$ when

$$F(s) = \frac{2s^2 + 7s + 8}{s^2 + 3s + 2}$$

Solution

Both the numerator and the denominator of $F(s)$ are quadratic in s, so we have $m = n = 2$. Before carrying out the partial-fraction expansion, we must rewrite $F(s)$ in the form of (63) by dividing its numerator by its denominator, as follows:

$$
\begin{array}{r}
2 \\
s^2 + 3s + 2 \overline{)\, 2s^2 + 7s + 8} \\
2s^2 + 6s + 4 \\
\hline
s + 4
\end{array}
$$

Because the poles of $F(s)$ are $s_1 = -1$ and $s_2 = -2$, we can write

$$F(s) = 2 + \frac{s + 4}{(s + 1)(s + 2)}$$

$$= 2 + \frac{A_1}{s + 1} + \frac{A_2}{s + 2}$$

---

[4]When $m > n$, we can write $F(s)$ as the sum of a polynomial in s and a strictly proper rational function, but we shall not encounter such cases here.

where

$$A_1 = \frac{\cancel{(s+1)}(s+4)}{\cancel{(s+1)}(s+2)}\Bigg|_{s=-1} = 3$$

$$A_2 = \frac{(s+2)(s+4)}{(s+1)\cancel{(s+2)}}\Bigg|_{s=-2} = -2$$

Thus

$$F(s) = 2 + \frac{3}{s+1} - \frac{2}{s+2}$$

and

$$f(t) = 2\delta(t) + 3\epsilon^{-t} - 2\epsilon^{-2t} \quad \text{for } t > 0$$

which is the sum of an impulse at $t = 0+$ and two decaying exponentials.

■ 7.4 SOLVING FOR THE RESPONSE

The preceding sections of this chapter have laid the groundwork for an efficient means of solving for the responses of fixed linear systems. The analysis of first-order systems is not difficult enough to warrant transform methods. However, for second- and higher-order systems, using transform methods is generally easier than using the methods discussed in Chapter 6. In addition, acquaintance with the transform approach will enable us to develop important concepts in Chapter 8. Before outlining the general technique, we shall consider a simple, first-order example, which we would not normally solve by transform methods.

▶ **EXAMPLE 7.6**

The capacitor in the circuit shown in Figure 7.5(a) is uncharged for $t < 0$, and the switch closes at $t = 0$. Using Laplace transforms, find $e_C(t)$ for $t > 0$.

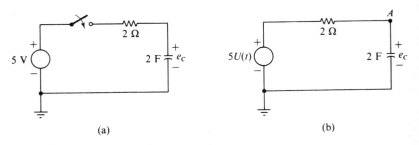

(a)   (b)

FIGURE 7.5   (a) Circuit for Example 7.6. (b) Equivalent circuit without the switch.

Solution

For convenience of analysis, we can redraw the original circuit as shown in Figure 7.5(b), where the switch and constant voltage source have been replaced by the step-function input $5\,U(t)$. Summing the currents leaving node A gives the first-order differential equation

$$\frac{1}{2}[e_C - 5U(t)] + 2\dot{e}_C = 0$$

Transforming this equation term by term, we have

$$\frac{1}{2}\{\mathcal{L}[e_C(t)] - \mathcal{L}[5U(t)]\} + 2\mathcal{L}[\dot{e}_C(t)] = 0$$

From Appendix B, we see that $\mathcal{L}[5U(t)] = 5/s$. Because $e_C(t)$ is unknown, we cannot write down its transform explicitly, so we use $E_C(s)$ to denote $\mathcal{L}[e_C(t)]$.[5] Using the expression for the transform of a derivative, we rewrite the transformed equation as

$$\frac{1}{2}\left[E_C(s) - \frac{5}{s}\right] + 2[sE_C(s) - e_C(0)] = 0$$

Note that the original differential equation has been converted into an algebraic equation. Because the capacitor is uncharged for $t < 0$, $e_C(0) = (0)$. Solving this equation algebraically for $E_C(s)$ gives

$$E_C(s) = \frac{2.5/s}{2s + 0.5}$$

$$= \frac{1.25}{s(s + 0.25)}$$

To find the output voltage $e_C(t)$, we take the inverse transform by expanding $E_C(s)$ in its partial-fraction expansion and using Appendix B to identify the individual time functions. The expansion is

$$E_C(s) = \frac{A_1}{s} + \frac{A_2}{s + 0.25}$$

where

$$A_1 = sE_C(s)|_{s=0} = 5$$

$$A_2 = (s + 0.25)E_C(s)|_{s=-0.25} = -5$$

Thus

$$E_C(s) = \frac{5}{s} - \frac{5}{s + 0.25}$$

---

[5] As a rule, functions of time are denoted by lowercase letters and their Laplace transforms by the corresponding capital letters followed by the transform variable s in parentheses.

and

$$e_C(t) = 5 - 5\epsilon^{-0.25t} \quad \text{for } t > 0$$

Because $e_C(t) = 0$ for all $t \leq 0$, we can write the solution in the alternative form

$$e_C(t) = 5[1 - \epsilon^{-0.25t}]U(t)$$

which is valid for all t. We can check this answer by solving the differential equation by the classical method of Chapter 6.

General Procedure

Application of the Laplace transform to solve for the response of dynamic systems of any order consists of the following three steps:

1. Write and immediately transform the differential or integral-differential equations describing the system for $t > 0$, evaluating all the initial-condition terms that appear in the transformed equations.

2. Solve these algebraic equations for the transform of the output.

3. Evaluate the inverse transform to obtain the output as a function of time.

The first step transforms the original equations into a set of algebraic equations in the variable s. Then we may solve the algebraic equations by any convenient method to obtain the transform of the response. The inverse transform includes both the steady-state and the transient components and, unlike the classical approach, contains no unknown constants that must still be evaluated. Any necessary initial-condition terms will automatically appear in step 1.

If we transform immediately the equations obtained by summing forces or torques shown on the free-body diagrams or by summing currents at the nodes of a circuit, the only initial-condition terms normally encountered are for variables that cannot change instantaneously. However, if any variable or one of its derivatives does have a discontinuity at the origin, we define its value at time zero to be the value approached through negative values of time. Thus $f(0) = f(0-)$ and $\dot{f}(0) = \dot{f}(0-)$, where the value at $t = 0-$ is the value at the left side of any discontinuity. This is consistent with the treatment in previous sections; examples include our definition of $U(0) = 0$ and our interpretation of $\delta(t)$ as a unit impulse occurring at $t = 0+$. Any initial-condition terms, such as $f(0)$ and $\dot{f}(0)$, that appear in the transformed equations are due entirely to conditions for $t < 0$ and are not affected by a discontinuity in the input at time zero.

The remainder of this section contains a variety of examples. The next two examples illustrate the application of the foregoing general procedure for a mechanical and an electrical system.

▶ **EXAMPLE 7.7**

The mechanical system shown in Figure 7.6 has the parameter values $M = 1$ kg, $B = 4$ N·s/m, and $K = 3$ N/m, and the applied force is $f_a(t) = 9$ N for all $t > 0$. The mass has no initial velocity, but it is released from a position 1 m to the right of its equilibrium position at the instant the force is applied. Find the displacement $x(t)$ for all $t > 0$.

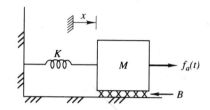

FIGURE 7.6   Mechanical system for Example 7.7.

Solution

The differential equation describing the system for $t > 0$ is $M\ddot{x} + B\dot{x} + Kx = f_a(t)$, which becomes

$$\ddot{x} + 4\dot{x} + 3x = 9$$

when the parameter and input values are substituted. Transforming the equation term by term gives

$$[s^2 X(s) - sx(0) - \dot{x}(0)] + 4[sX(s) - x(0)] + 3X(s) = \frac{9}{s}$$

Substituting the specified initial conditions $x(0) = 1$ and $\dot{x}(0) = 0$, we solve algebraically to obtain

$$X(s) = \frac{s + 4 + 9/s}{s^2 + 4s + 3} = \frac{s^2 + 4s + 9}{s(s + 1)(s + 3)}$$

Noting that $X(s)$ has three distinct real poles and that $m < n$, we write $X(s)$ in the form

$$X(s) = \frac{A_1}{s} + \frac{A_2}{s + 1} + \frac{A_2}{s + 3}$$

where

$$A_1 = sX(s)|_{s=0} = 3$$

$$A_2 = (s + 1)X(s)|_{s=-1} = -3$$

$$A_3 = (s + 3)X(s)|_{s=-3} = 1$$

Thus

$$X(s) = \frac{3}{s} - \frac{3}{s+1} + \frac{1}{s+3}$$

and the displacement is

$$x(t) = 3 - 3\epsilon^{-t} + \epsilon^{-3t} \quad \text{for } t > 0$$

The response $x(t)$ reduces to the specified initial condition $x(0) = 1$ m and approaches a steady-state value of $x_{ss} = 3$ m. The two transient terms decay exponentially with time constants of 1 s and $\frac{1}{3}$ s.

▶ **EXAMPLE 7.8**

After steady-state conditions have been reached, the switch in Figure 7.7(a) opens at $t = 0$. Find the voltage e_o across the capacitor for all $t > 0$.

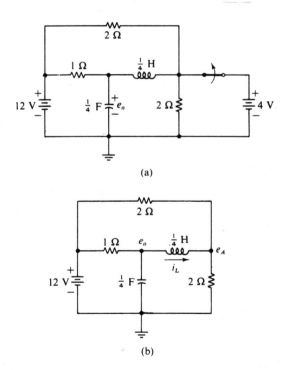

(a)

(b)

FIGURE 7.7 Circuit for Example 7.8 (a) Original circuit.
(b) Circuit valid for $t > 0$.

Solution

The circuit for $t > 0$ is shown in Figure 7.7(b), with the switch open and with the node voltages e_o and e_A shown. The current-law equations at these two nodes are

$$e_o - 12 + \frac{1}{4}\dot{e}_o + i_L(0) + 4\int_0^t (e_o - e_A)d\lambda = 0$$

$$\frac{1}{2}(e_A - 12) - i_L(0) + 4\int_0^t (e_A - e_o)d\lambda + \frac{1}{2}e_A = 0$$

Transforming these equations, we have

$$E_o(s) - \frac{12}{s} + \frac{1}{4}[sE_o(s) - e_o(0)] + \frac{i_L(0)}{s} + \frac{4}{s}[E_o(s) - E_A(s)] = 0$$

$$\frac{1}{2}\left[E_A(s) - \frac{12}{s}\right] - \frac{i_L(0)}{s} + \frac{4}{s}[E_A(s) - E_o(s)] + \frac{1}{2}E_A(s) = 0$$

We must find the numerical values of the initial conditions $e_o(0)$ and $i_L(0)$ that appear in these transformed equations. Because e_o and i_L are measures of the energy stored in the capacitor and inductor, respectively, they cannot change instantaneously and do not have discontinuities at the time origin.

When the circuit is in the steady state with the switch closed, the capacitor and inductor may be replaced by open and short circuits, respectively. This is done in Figure 7.8(a), from which we find that $e_o(0) = 4$ V and $i_L(0) = 8$ A. Substituting these initial conditions into the transformed equations and collecting like terms, we get

$$\left[\frac{1}{4}s + 1 + \frac{4}{s}\right]E_o(s) - \frac{4}{s}E_A(s) = 1 + \frac{4}{s} \tag{65a}$$

$$-\frac{4}{s}E_o(s) + \left[1 + \frac{4}{s}\right]E_A(s) = \frac{14}{s} \tag{65b}$$

We want to find the capacitor voltage $e_o(t)$, so the next step is to solve (65) for $E_o(s)$ by eliminating $E_A(s)$. Noting from (65b) that

$$E_A(s) = \frac{4E_o(s) + 14}{s + 4}$$

and substituting this expression into (65a), we find that

$$E_o(s) = \frac{4(s^2 + 8s + 72)}{s^3 + 8s^2 + 32s}$$

One pole of $E_o(s)$ is $s = 0$, and the remaining two are the roots of $s^2 + 8s + 32 = 0$. Hence the poles are $s_1 = 0$, $s_2 = -4 + j4$, and $s_3 = -4 - j4$, and we can expand the transformed output into the form

$$E_o(s) = \frac{A_1}{s} + \frac{A_2}{s + 4 - j4} + \frac{A_3}{s + 4 + j4} \tag{66}$$

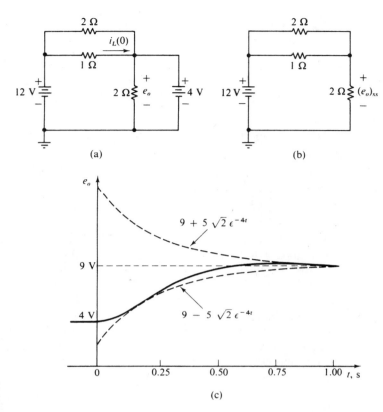

FIGURE 7.8 (a) Equivalent circuit for Example 7.8 just before the switch opens. (b) Equivaient circuit valid as t approaches infinity. (c) Complete response.

where the coefficients are

$$A_1 = sE_o(s)|_{s=0} = \frac{(4)(72)}{32} = 9$$

$$A_2 = (s + 4 - j4)E_o(s)|_{s=-4+j4}$$

$$= \frac{4[(-4 + j4)^2 + 8(-4 + j4) + 72]}{(-4 + j4)(-4 + j4 + 4 + j4)}$$

$$= \frac{4(40)}{(-4 + j4)(j8)} = \frac{5}{-(1 + j1)} = \frac{5}{\sqrt{2}}\epsilon^{j3\pi/4}$$

and

$$A_3 = A_2^* = \frac{5}{\sqrt{2}}\epsilon^{-j3\pi/4}$$

Comparing the second and third terms on the right side of (66) to (55), we see that $a = 4$, $\omega = 4$, $K = 5/\sqrt{2}$, and $\phi = \frac{3}{4}\pi$ rad. Using (56) to write the part of the response that corresponds to the pair of complex poles, we have

$$e_o(t) = 9 + 5\sqrt{2}\epsilon^{-4t} \cos\left(4t + \frac{3}{4}\pi\right) \qquad \text{for } t > 0$$

As a check on the work, note that as t approaches infinity, this expression gives a constant value of 9. We can also find the steady-state behavior with the switch open from Figure 7.8(b), where the capacitor and inductor have again been replaced by open and short circuits, respectively. The parallel combination of the 2-Ω and 1-Ω resistors is equivalent to $(2)(1)/(2+1) = \frac{2}{3}$ Ω. By the voltage-divider rule,

$$e_o(\infty) = \frac{2}{2 + \frac{2}{3}}(12) = 9 \text{ V}$$

which agrees with the general equation for $t > 0$.

The complete response is shown in Figure 7.8(c). The transient component has an envelope that decays with a time constant of 0.25 s and has a period of $\frac{1}{2}\pi$ s.

When the input is an impulse, it can instantaneously change the energy stored within the system. Because of this, when finding the unit impulse response in Chapter 6, we first found and then differentiated the unit step response. With the Laplace transform, however, there is no difficulty in finding the impulse response directly.

▶ **EXAMPLE 7.9**

Find the unit impulse response $h(t)$ for the system shown in Figure 7.6 when $M = 1$ kg, $B = 4$ N·s/m, and $K = 4$ N/m. The differential equation relating the displacement x to the applied force $f_a(t)$ is $\ddot{x} + 4\dot{x} + 4x = f_a(t)$.

Solution

Recall that the impulse response $h(t)$ is the zero-state response when $u(t) = \delta(t)$. If we rewrite the system equation as $\ddot{h} + 4\dot{h} + 4h = \delta(t)$ and assume that the impulse occurs at $t = 0+$, it follows that we should take $h(0)$ and $\dot{h}(0)$ as zero in evaluating the transforms of $\ddot{h}$ and $\dot{h}$.

Transforming both sides of the differential equation, using $\mathcal{L}[\delta(t)] = 1$ and denoting $\mathcal{L}[h(t)]$ by $H(s)$, we find that

$$[s^2 H(s) - sh(0) - \dot{h}(0)] + 4[sH(s) - h(0)] + 4H(s) = 1$$

which reduces to

$$(s^2 + 4s + 4)H(s) = 1$$

when the initial conditions are set equal to zero. Hence

$$H(s) = \frac{1}{s^2 + 4s + 4} = \frac{1}{(s+2)^2}$$

Referring to Appendix B and noting that $h(t) = 0$ for all $t \leq 0$, we can write

$$h(t) = \begin{cases} 0 & \text{for } t \leq 0 \\ t\epsilon^{-2t} & \text{for } t > 0 \end{cases} \tag{67}$$

which is shown in Figure 7.9.

Inspection of Figure 7.9 reveals that $\dot{h}(t)$ undergoes a discontinuity at $t = 0$. This means that the velocity of the mass changes instantaneously. You can verify from (67) that $\dot{h}(0+) = 1$, whereas we used $\dot{h}(0) = 0$ in taking the transform of the original differential equation. This distinction between the initial slopes is consistent with our assertion that the impulse occurs at $t = 0+$.

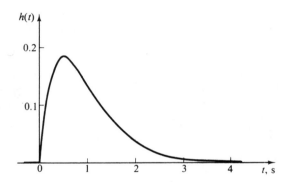

FIGURE 7.9   Impulse response found in Example 7.9.

The final three examples illustrate three different methods of finding a system's response to a given input. First, using the procedure recommended in most cases, we transform the original equations immediately. In the other two methods, we find either the state-variable model or the input-output model before applying the Laplace transform.

▶ *EXAMPLE 7.10*

The translational system shown in Figure 7.10(a) was modeled in Example 3.7 and in Example 3.11. Let $M_1 = 1$ kg, $B_1 = B_2 = 1$ N·s/m, and $K_1 = K_2 = 1$ N/m. The springs are undeflected when $x_1 = x_2 = 0$. Take the output to be the displacement x_1. Find the unit step response by transforming the equations obtained from the free-body diagrams.

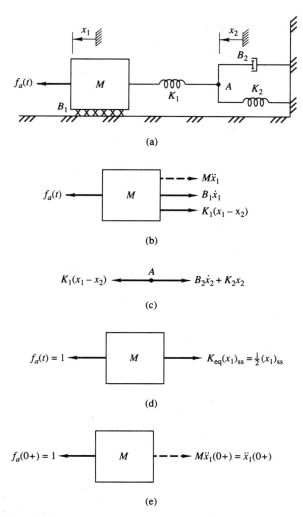

FIGURE 7.10 (a) Translational system for Example 7.10. (b), (c) General free-body diagrams. (d) Free-body diagram for the steady state. (e) Free-body diagram for $t = 0+$.

Solution

The free-body diagrams for the mass M and for the massless junction A are shown in parts (b) and (c) of the figure, respectively. Summing the forces on these diagrams gives

$$M\ddot{x}_1 + B_1\dot{x}_1 + K_1(x_1 - x_2) = f_a(t)$$

$$B_2\dot{x}_2 + K_2x_2 + K_1(x_2 - x_1) = 0$$

Transforming these equations, with all the element values equal to unity and with $\mathcal{L}[f_a(t)] = F_a(s)$, we have

$$[s^2 X_1(s) - s x_1(0) - \dot{x}_1(0)] + [s X_1(s) - x_1(0)] + X_1(s) - X_2(s) = F_a(s)$$

$$[s X_2(s) - x_2(0)] + 2 X_2(s) - X_1(s) = 0$$

$$\text{(68)}$$

Because we assume that the initial stored energy is zero when finding the unit step response, the initial elongations of the springs and the initial velocity of the mass must be zero. Thus $x_1(0) = x_2(0) = 0$ and $\dot{x}_1(0) = 0$, so (68) becomes

$$(s^2 + s + 1)X_1(s) - X_2(s) = F_a(s)$$

$$-X_1(s) + (s + 2)X_2(s) = 0$$

Eliminating $X_2(s)$ from these equations, we obtain

$$X_1(s) = \left[\frac{s+2}{s^3 + 3s^2 + 3s + 1} \right] F_a(s) \qquad \text{(69)}$$

Factoring the denominator, noting that $F_a(s) = \mathcal{L}[U(t)] = 1/s$, and th... writing a partial-fraction expansion, we have

$$X_1(s) = \frac{s+2}{s(s+1)^3} = \frac{A_0}{s} + \frac{A_{11}}{(s+1)^3} + \frac{A_{12}}{(s+1)^2} + \frac{A_{13}}{s+1} \qquad \text{(70)}$$

where

$$A_0 = \frac{s+2}{(s+1)^3}\bigg|_{s=0} = 2$$

$$A_{11} = \frac{s+2}{s}\bigg|_{s=-1} = -1$$

$$A_{12} = \left[\frac{d}{ds}\frac{s+2}{s} \right]_{s=-1} = -2$$

$$A_{13} = \frac{1}{2}\left[\frac{d^2}{ds^2}\frac{s+2}{s} \right]_{s=-1} = -2$$

To find the output as a function of time, we insert these numbers into (70) and take the inverse transform of each term. This gives us

$$x_1(t) = 2 - (\tfrac{1}{2}t^2 + 2t + 2)\epsilon^{-t} \qquad \text{for } t > 0 \qquad \text{(71)}$$

This equation reveals that the steady-state response is $(x_1)_{ss} = 2$ m, which we can check by referring to Figure 7.10(a). When $f_a(t)$ has a constant value of 1, the mass will eventually become motionless and there will be no inertial or friction forces. Because the friction elements can be disregarded, the two springs are then in series and can be replaced by single equivalent spring for which $K_{eq} = \tfrac{1}{2}$ N/m. The only forces acting on the mass are those shown in Figure 7.10(d), so we can again conclude that $(x_1)_{ss} = 2$ m.

By differentiating (71), we can show that the velocity and acceleration of the mass are

$$\begin{aligned} \dot{x}_1 &= (\tfrac{1}{2}t^2 + t)\epsilon^{-t} \qquad \text{for } t > 0 \\ \ddot{x}_1 &= (-\tfrac{1}{2}t^2 + 1)\epsilon^{-t} \qquad \text{for } t > 0 \end{aligned} \tag{72}$$

Replacing t by zero in (71) and (72), we see that

$$x_1(0+) = 0 \tag{73a}$$

$$\dot{x}_1(0+) = 0 \tag{73b}$$

$$\ddot{x}_1(0+) = 1 \tag{73c}$$

The fact that x_1 and $\dot{x}_1$ remain zero at $t = 0+$ is expected; the elongations of the springs and the velocity of the mass cannot change instantaneously. Because of this, we also know that at $t = 0+$ there is no force on the mass from K_1 or B_1. Thus the only forces on the mass at $t = 0+$ are the applied and inertial forces, as shown in Figure 7.10(e). From that figure, we see that the initial acceleration must be $\ddot{x}_1(0+) = 1$ m/s^2, which serves as a check on (73c).

▶ *EXAMPLE 7.11*

Repeat Example 7.10 by transforming the state-variable equations.

Solution

The state-variable model for Figure 7.10(a) was found in Example 3.7. From (3.14), with all the element values set equal to unity, we have

$$\begin{aligned} \dot{x}_1 &= v_1 \\ \dot{v}_1 &= -x_1 - v_1 + x_2 + f_a(t) \\ \dot{x}_2 &= x_1 - 2x_2 \end{aligned}$$

Transforming these equations gives

$$sX_1(s) - x_1(0) = V_1(s) \tag{74a}$$

$$sV_1(s) - v_1(0) = -X_1(s) - V_1(s) + X_2(s) + F_a(s) \tag{74b}$$

$$sX_2(s) - x_2(0) = X_1(s) - 2X_2(s) \tag{74c}$$

where we can again set the initial-condition terms equal to zero. Then, by substituting (74a) into (74b) and rearranging the last two equations, we obtain

$$(s^2 + s + 1)X_1(s) - X_2(s) = F_a(s)$$

$$-X_1(s) + (s + 2)X_2(s) = 0$$

from which

$$X_1(s) = \left[\frac{s+2}{s^3 + 3s^2 + 3s + 1}\right] F_a(s)$$

which agrees with (69).

▶ **EXAMPLE 7.12**

Repeat Example 7.10 by transforming the input-output differential equation.

Solution

The input-output equation for Figure 7.10(a) was derived in Example 3.11. From (3.27) with the element values set equal to unity, we have

$$\ddot{x}_1 + 3\ddot{x}_1 + 3\dot{x}_1 + x_1 = \dot{f}_a + 2f_a(t)$$

We transform this equation, getting

$$[s^3 X_1(s) - s^2 x_1(0) - s\dot{x}_1(0) - \ddot{x}_1(0)] + 3[s^2 X_1(s) - sx_1(0) - \dot{x}_1(0)]$$

$$+ 3[s X_1(s) - x_1(0)] + X_1(s) = s F_a(s) - f_a(0) + 2F_a(s) \quad (75)$$

We note that (75) involves four different initial conditions: $x_1(0)$, $\dot{x}_1(0)$, $\ddot{x}_1(0)$, and $f_a(0)$. Because there is zero initial stored energy and because the step-function input is assumed to occur just after $t = 0$ (that is, at $t = 0+$), each of these initial conditions is zero. Then (75) reduces to

$$(s^3 + 3s^2 + 3s + 1)X_1(s) = (s + 2)F_a(s)$$

which is equivalent to (69).

Although somewhat different, the methods used in the last three examples gave the same equations for the transformed output $X_1(s)$ and for $x_1(t)$ for all $t > 0$. When the equations from the free-body diagrams were transformed immediately or when the state-variable equations were transformed, the only initial conditions needed were for functions that did not change instantaneously.

This was not the case, however, when we obtained the input-output equation before applying the Laplace transform. In this method, it is not unusual for one or more of the initial conditions to involve functions that have discontinuities. For the acceleration $\ddot{x}_1$ in the last example, $\ddot{x}_1(0-) = 0$ but it was found that $\ddot{x}_1(0+) = 1$ m/s^2. Whenever there is a discontinuity at the time origin, we use the value at $t = 0-$ for the initial-condition term, for the reasons explained earlier in this section. This is in contrast to the classical solution of an input-output differential equation outlined in Section 6.1, which requires the values of the initial conditions at $t = 0+$. One advantage of the transform method is that evaluating the initial-condition terms is often easier.

   In the last three examples, we chose to denote the transform of the unit step input $f_a(t)$ by $F_a(s)$ rather than to immediately replace it by $\mathcal{L}[U(t)] = 1/s$. Thus the expression for $X_1(s)$ in (69) was a somewhat more general result than necessary. Equation (69) holds for any input, provided only that the input has a Laplace transform and that the initial stored energy is zero. The quantity inside the brackets is called the transfer function and will become important in the next chapter. When finding the response to a particular input, however, we more often replace its transform immediately by the appropriate expression from Appendix B .

7.5 ADDITIONAL TRANSFORM PROPERTIES

We now introduce several useful transform properties that were not needed for the examples in Section 7.4. The first two of these concern functions that are shifted in time. The others provide certain information about the time function directly from its transform, without our having to carry out the transform inversion.

Time Delay

If the function $f(t)$ is delayed by a units of time, we denote the delayed function as $f(t-a)$, where $a > 0$. In order to develop a general expression for the transform of the delayed function $f(t-a)$ in terms of the transform of $f(t)$, we must ensure that any part of $f(t)$ that is nonzero for $t < 0$ does not fall within the range $0 < t < \infty$ for the delayed function. Otherwise, a portion of the original time function will contribute to the transform of $f(t-a)$ but not to that of $f(t)$. To illustrate this point, consider the functions $f(t)$ and $f(t-a)$ shown in Figure 7.11. The shaded portion of $f(t)$ that is nonzero for $t < 0$ does not affect $\mathcal{L}[f(t)]$, because it is outside the limits of integration in (1). It does affect $\mathcal{L}[f(t-a)]$, however, because for $a > 0$, at least part of it falls within the interval $0 < t < \infty$, as shown in Figure 7.11(b).

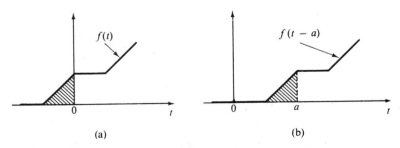

(a) (b)

FIGURE 7.11 A function for which the time-delay theorem is not applicable.

We shall consider functions of the form

$$f_1(t) = f(t)U(t)$$

which are the product of any transformable function $f(t)$ and the unit step function $U(t)$. Because $U(t) = 0$ for all $t \leq 0$, the function $f_1(t)$ will be zero for all $t \leq 0$, and the delayed function

$$f_1(t - a) = f(t - a)U(t - a)$$

will be zero for all $t \leq a$. The functions $f_1(t)$ and $f_1(t - a)$ corresponding to the $f(t)$ defined in Figure 7.11(a) are shown in Figure 7.12.

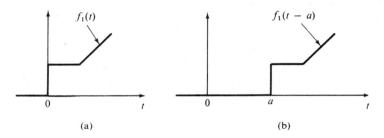

(a)   (b)

FIGURE 7.12   A function for which the time-delay theorem is applicable.

To express the transform of $f(t - a)U(t - a)$, where $a > 0$, in terms of $F(s) = \mathcal{L}[f(t)]$, we start with the transform definition in (1) and write

$$\mathcal{L}[f(t - a)U(t - a)] = \int_0^\infty f(t - a)U(t - a)\epsilon^{-st}dt$$

Because

$$U(t - a) = \begin{cases} 0 \text{ for } t \leq a \\ 1 \text{ for } t > a \end{cases}$$

we can rewrite the transform as

$$\mathcal{L}[f(t - a)U(t - a)] = \int_a^\infty f(t - a)\epsilon^{-st}dt$$

$$= \epsilon^{-sa}\int_a^\infty f(t - a)\epsilon^{-s(t-a)}dt$$

$$= \epsilon^{-sa}\int_0^\infty f(\lambda)\epsilon^{-s\lambda}d\lambda$$

$$= \epsilon^{-sa}F(s) \tag{76}$$

where $F(s)$ is the transform of $f(t)$ and where $a > 0$. This theorem is one of the entries in Appendix B.

▶ *EXAMPLE 7.13*

Use the time-delay theorem to derive the transform of the triangular pulse shown in Figure 7.13(a) and defined by the equation

$$f(t) = \begin{cases} 0 & \text{for } t \leq 0 \\ At & \text{for } 0 < t \leq L \\ 0 & \text{for } t > L \end{cases}$$

Solution

Any pulse that consists of straight lines can be decomposed into a sum of step functions and ramp functions. The triangular pulse shown in Figure 7.13(a) can be regarded as the superposition of the three functions shown in Figure 7.13(b), Figure 7.13(c), and Figure 7.13(d). These are a ramp starting at $t = 0$, a delayed ramp starting at $t = L$, and a delayed step function starting

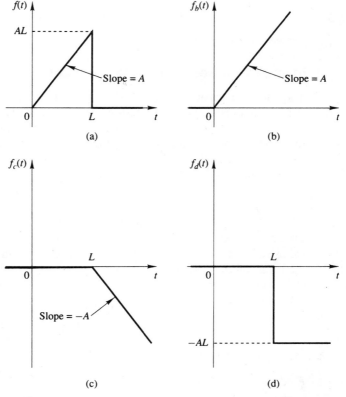

FIGURE 7.13   (a) Triangular pulse. (b), (c), (d) Its ramp and step components.

at $t = L$. Thus

$$f(t) = AtU(t) - A(t - L)U(t - L) - ALU(t - L) \tag{77}$$

From Appendix B, we note that

$$\mathscr{L}[AtU(t)] = \frac{A}{s^2} \tag{78}$$

Using (76) with (78), we have

$$\mathscr{L}[-A(t - L)U(t - L)] = -\frac{A\epsilon^{-sL}}{s^2}$$

From (76) and the fact that $\mathscr{L}[U(t)] = 1/s$,

$$\mathscr{L}[-ALU(t - L)] = -\frac{AL\epsilon^{-sL}}{s}$$

Using the superposition theorem, we obtain the transform of the triangular pulse as

$$F(s) = \frac{A}{s^2}(1 - \epsilon^{-sL}) - \frac{AL}{s}\epsilon^{-sL} \tag{79}$$

Inversion of Some Irrational Transforms

The use of a partial-fraction expansion to find an inverse transform is restricted to transforms that are rational functions of s. However, the transform given by (79) is not a rational function because of the factor ϵ^{-sL}. For transforms that would be rational functions except for multiplicative factors in the numerator such as ϵ^{-sL}, we may use the time-delay theorem in (76).

Assume that an irrational transform can be written as

$$F(s) = F_1(s) + F_2(s)\epsilon^{-sa} \tag{80}$$

where $F_1(s)$ and $F_2(s)$ are rational functions and where a is a positive constant. Then we can find the inverse transforms of $F_1(s)$ and $F_2(s)$ by using partial-fraction expansions and, if the order of the numerator is not less than that of the denominator, a preliminary step of long division. Denote the inverse transforms of $F_1(s)$ and $F_2(s)$ by $f_1(t)$ and $f_2(t)$, respectively. Then, by (76),

$$f(t) = f_1(t) + f_2(t - a)U(t - a) \tag{81}$$

▶ **EXAMPLE 7.14**

Find the inverse transform of

$$F(s) = \frac{A}{s^2}(1 - \epsilon^{-sL}) - \frac{AL}{s}\epsilon^{-sL}$$

Solution

We can rewrite the transform $F(s)$ in the form of (80) as

$$F(s) = \frac{A}{s^2} - \left(\frac{A}{s^2} + \frac{AL}{s}\right) \epsilon^{-sL}$$

Hence $F_1(s) = A/s^2$ and $f_1(t) = At$ for $t > 0$. The rational portion of the remaining term is

$$F_2(s) = -\left(\frac{A}{s^2} + \frac{AL}{s}\right)$$

which has as its inverse transform

$$f_2(t) = -At - AL \qquad \text{for } t > 0$$

Using (81) with $a = L$, we can write the complete inverse transform as

$$f(t) = At - A(t - L)U(t - L) - ALU(t - L) \qquad \text{for } t > 0$$

which agrees with (77) and Figure 7.13(a).

Initial-Value and Final-Value Theorems

It is possible to determine the limits of $f(t)$ as time approaches zero and infinity directly from its transform $F(s)$ without having to find $f(t)$ for all $t > 0$. First we consider the limit of $f(t)$ as time approaches zero through positive values (that is, from the right). This limit of $f(t)$ is denoted by $f(0+)$. To evaluate this limit directly from $F(s)$, we use the **initial-value theorem**, which states that

$$f(0+) = \lim_{s \to \infty} sF(s) \tag{82}$$

where the limit exists.

If $F(s)$ is a rational function, (82) will yield a finite value provided that the degree of the numerator polynomial is less than that of the denominator—in other words, provided that $m < n$. If we attempt to use (82) when $m = n$, the result will be infinite. Recall from Section 7.3 that to find $f(t)$ when $m = n$, we must use a preliminary step of long division to write $F(s)$ as the sum of a constant and a transform for which $m < n$. Because the inverse transform of the constant is an impulse at $t = 0+$, the value of $f(0+)$ is undefined when $m = n$.

The **final-value theorem** states that

$$f(\infty) = \lim_{s \to 0} sF(s) \tag{83}$$

provided that $F(s)$ has no poles in the right half of the complex plane and, with the possible exception of a single pole at the origin, has no poles on the imaginary axis. The symbol $f(\infty)$ denotes the limit of $f(t)$ as t approaches infinity.

To gain some insight into the effect of this restriction on the use of the final-value theorem, we recall that the forms of the terms in a partial-fraction expansion are dictated by the locations of the poles of $F(s)$. Suppose, for example, that

$$F(s) = \frac{A_1}{s} + \frac{A_2(s + \alpha)}{(s + \alpha)^2 + \beta^2} + \frac{A_3}{s - b} + \frac{A_4\omega}{s^2 + \omega^2}$$

where α, β, b, and ω are positive real constants. The expansion implies that the poles of $F(s)$ are $s_1 = 0$, $s_2 = -\alpha + j\beta$, $s_3 = -\alpha - j\beta$, $s_4 = b$, $s_5 = j\omega$, and $s_6 = -j\omega$. The corresponding time function for $t > 0$ is

$$f(t) = A_1 + A_2\epsilon^{-\alpha t} \cos \beta t + A_3\epsilon^{bt} + A_4 \sin \omega t$$

The limits of the first two terms as t approaches infinity are A_1 and zero, respectively. However, $A_3\epsilon^{bt}$ increases without limit, whereas $A_4 \sin \omega t$ oscillates continually without approaching a constant value. Thus, because of the poles of $F(s)$ at $s_4 = b$, $s_5 = j\omega$, and $s_6 = -j\omega$, the function $f(t)$ does not approach a limit as t approaches infinity. As another example, double poles of $F(s)$ at the origin will cause the partial-fraction expansion to have terms of the form

$$F(s) = \frac{A_{11}}{s^2} + \frac{A_{12}}{s} + \cdots$$

The corresponding time function for $t > 0$ is

$$f(t) = A_{11}t + A_{12} + \cdots$$

which again does not approach a limit.

The use of the initial-value and final-value theorems is illustrated in the following example and in the next chapter. In Example 7.16 we consider a transform for which neither theorem is applicable.

▶ **EXAMPLE 7.15**

Use the initial-value and final-value theorems to find $f(0+)$ and $f(\infty)$ when

$$F(s) = \frac{s^2 + 2s + 4}{s^3 + 3s^2 + 2s} \tag{84}$$

Solution

From (82), the initial value of $f(t)$ is

$$f(0+) = \lim_{s \to \infty} \frac{s(s^2 + 2s + 4)}{s^3 + 3s^2 + 2s}$$

$$= \lim_{s \to \infty} \frac{s^3 + 2s^2 + 4s}{s^3 + 3s^2 + 2s} \tag{85}$$

Because $f(0+)$ is the limit of a ratio of polynomials in s as s approaches infinity, we need consider only the highest powers in s in both the numerator and denominator. Hence (85) reduces to

$$f(0+) = \lim_{s \to \infty} \frac{s^3}{s^3} = 1$$

Before applying the final-value theorem, we must verify that the conditions necessary for it to be valid are satisfied. In this case, we can rewrite (84) with its denominator in factored form as

$$F(s) = \frac{s^2 + 2s + 4}{s(s+1)(s+2)} \tag{86}$$

which has distinct poles at $s = 0$, -1, and -2. The function $F(s)$ has a single pole at the origin with the remaining poles inside the left half of the s-plane, so we can apply the final-value theorem. Using (83), we find that

$$f(\infty) = \lim_{s \to 0} \frac{s(s^2 + 2s + 4)}{s(s^2 + 3s + 2)}$$

$$= \lim_{s \to 0} \frac{s^2 + 2s + 4}{s^2 + 3s + 2} = 2$$

In this example, it is a simple task to evaluate $f(t)$ for all $t > 0$ by writing $F(s)$ as given by (86) in its partial-fraction expansion. The result is

$$f(t) = 2 - 3\epsilon^{-t} + 2\epsilon^{-2t} \qquad \text{for } t > 0$$

and it is apparent that the values we found for $f(0+)$ and $f(\infty)$ are correct.

▶ *EXAMPLE 7.16*

Explain why the initial-value and final-value theorems are not applicable to the transform

$$F(s) = \frac{s^3 + 2s^2 + 6s + 8}{s^3 + 4s} \tag{87}$$

Solution

Attempting to apply the initial-value theorem, we would write

$$f(0+) = \lim_{s \to \infty} \frac{s(s^3 + 2s^2 + 6s + 8)}{s^3 + 4s}$$

$$= \lim_{s \to \infty} \frac{s^4 + 2s^3 + 6s^2 + 8s}{s^3 + 4s}$$

which is infinite. This is expected, because $m = n = 3$ in (87).

As for the final-value theorem, we see from (87) that we can write the denominator of $F(s)$ as $s(s^2 + 4) = s(s - j2)(s + j2)$. Hence $F(s)$ has a pair of imaginary poles at $s_2 = j2$ and $s_3 = -j2$ and violates the requirements for the final-value theorem. If we carry out the partial-fraction expansion of $F(s)$, we find that

$$F(s) = 1 + \frac{2}{s} + \frac{2}{s^2 + 4}$$

which is the transform of the time function

$$f(t) = \delta(t) + 2 + \sin 2t \quad \text{for } t > 0$$

The initial-value theorem is invalid because of the impulse at $t = 0+$, and the final-value theorem is invalid because of the constant-amplitude sinusoidal term.

SUMMARY

The Laplace transform can be used to convert the integral-differential equations that describe fixed, linear dynamic systems into algebraic equations. The general procedure consists of three steps: transforming the system equations, solving the resulting algebraic equations for the transform of the output, and taking the inverse transform. Any initial conditions that need to be evaluated automatically appear in the first step. These initial conditions are often easier to find than those that are needed for a time-domain solution of the input-output equation.

Although the basic definition can be used to find the Laplace transform of a given function of time, transforms of the most common functions are tabulated in Appendix B. The inverse transform, which should be expressed as a real function of time, can usually be found by writing a partial-fraction expansion and by again using the table in Appendix B. The appendix also summarizes the properties and theorems developed throughout this chapter.

In addition to being an important tool for finding the response of a system to specified inputs, the Laplace transform can be used to develop a number of important general concepts. This further development will be carried out in the next chapter.

PROBLEMS

7.1 Using the definition of the Laplace transform in (1), evaluate the transforms of the following functions.

    a) $f_1(t) = t^2$
    b) $f_2(t) = \epsilon^{-at} \cos \omega t$
    c) $f_3(t) = t\epsilon^{-at}$
    d) $f_4(t) = \sin 2t$ for $0 < t < \pi$ and zero elsewhere

7.2 a) Derive the expressions given in (14) and (15) for the transforms of $\sin \omega t$ and $\cos \omega t$ by using the identities in Table 6.1 and then applying (5).
b) Using (14) and (15) with Table 6.1, derive expressions for the transforms of $\sin(\omega t + \phi)$ and $\cos(\omega t + \phi)$.

* 7.3 Use the properties tabulated in Appendix B to find the Laplace transform of each of the following functions of time.

    a) $f_1(t) = te^{-2t} \cos 3t$

    b) $f_2(t) = t^2 \sin 2t$

    c) $f_3(t) = \dfrac{d}{dt}(t^2 \epsilon^{-t})$

    d) $f_4(t) = \displaystyle\int_0^t \lambda^2 \epsilon^{-\lambda} d\lambda$

7.4 a) Prove that $\mathcal{L}[f(t/a)] = aF(as)$.
b) Apply this property with $f(t) = \cos \omega t$ to find $\mathcal{L}[\cos 2\omega t]$.

For Problems 7.5 through 7.7, find $f(t)$ for the given $F(s)$.

7.5 a) $F(s) = \dfrac{2s^3 + 3s^2 + s + 4}{s^3}$

    b) $F(s) = \dfrac{3s^2 + 9s + 24}{(s-1)(s+2)(s+5)}$

    c) $F(s) = \dfrac{4}{s^2(s+1)}$

    d) $F(s) = \dfrac{3s}{s^2 + 2s + 26}$

7.6 a) $F(s) = \dfrac{s}{s^2 + 8s + 16}$

    b) $F(s) = \dfrac{1}{s(s^2 + \omega^2)}$

    c) $F(s) = \dfrac{8s^2 + 20s + 74}{s(s^2 + s + 9.25)}$

    d) $F(s) = \dfrac{2s^2 + 11s + 16}{(s+2)^2}$

* 7.7 a) $F(s) = \dfrac{s^3 + 2s + 4}{s(s+1)^2(s+2)}$

    b) $F(s) = \dfrac{4s^2 + 10s + 10}{s^3 + 2s^2 + 5s}$

    c) $F(s) = \dfrac{3(s^3 + 2s^2 + 4s + 1)}{s(s+3)^2}$

    d) $F(s) = \dfrac{s^3 - 4s}{(s+1)(s^2 + 4s + 4)}$

(handwritten annotation):
$= \dfrac{A_1}{s} + \dfrac{A_2}{(s+1)^2} + \dfrac{A_3}{s+1} + \dfrac{A_4}{s+2}$

$\dfrac{A_1}{s} + \dfrac{A_2(s+1) + A_3}{(s+1)^2(+4)}$

* 7.8 a) Find the inverse transform of

$$F(s) = \dfrac{3s^2 + 2s + 2}{(s+2)(s^2 + 2s + 5)}$$

by writing a partial-fraction expansion and using (56).
b) Repeat part (a) by completing the square and using (58).

7.9 Find the inverse transform of $E_o(s)$ in Example 7.8 by first finding the constants A, B, and C in the expansion

$$E_o(s) = \frac{A}{s} + \frac{Bs + C}{s^2 + 8s + 32}$$

and then completing the square to evaluate the inverse transform of the term having complex poles.

* 7.10 Use (34) and the results of Example 7.1 to find the inverse transform of

$$F(s) = \frac{-s + 5}{s(s + 1)(s + 4)}$$

Check your answer by writing a partial-fraction expansion for $F(s)$.

7.11 Use (24) and the results of Example 7.1 to find the inverse transform of

$$F(s) = \frac{s(-s + 5)}{(s + 1)(s + 4)}$$

Check your answer by writing a partial-fraction expansion for $F(s)$.

7.12 Repeat all three parts of Example 6.1 using the Laplace transform.

7.13 Use the Laplace transform to solve for the response for $t > 0$ in Example 6.2.

* 7.14 For a given system described by the equation $\ddot{y} + 3\dot{y} + 2y = u(t)$, use the Laplace transform to find $y(t)$ for $t > 0$ when the input is $u(t) = 5t$ for $t > 0$ and the initial conditions are $y(0) = 1$ and $\dot{y}(0) = -1$. Sketch $y(t)$.

7.15 Repeat both parts of Example 6.3 using the Laplace transform.

7.16 Repeat Example 6.4 using the Laplace transform.

* 7.17 a) Find and sketch the unit step response for the circuit shown in Figure P5.1 by writing and transforming two node equations.
b) Repeat part (a) by transforming the input-output differential equation given in Problem 6.12.

7.18 Do part (d) of Problem 6.13 by using the Laplace transform.

7.19 Do part (c) of Problem 6.14 by using the Laplace transform.

7.20 Repeat Example 6.6 using the Laplace transform.

* 7.21 The mechanical system described in Problem 6.20 has two inputs, the gravitational force $M_2 g$ and the force $f_a(t)$ applied to M_1.
a) Solve for x_0, the constant displacement caused by gravity when the applied force $f_a(t)$ is zero.
b) Find the transformed output $X(s)$ when $x(0) = x_0$ and $f_a(t)$ is the unit step function.
c) Find $x(t)$ for the conditions in part (b) when $M_1 = M_2 = B_1 = B_2 = K_2 = 1$ in a consistent set of units. Check your answer by evaluating x_{ss} and $x(0+)$.

7.22 Use the Laplace transform to solve for the unit step response of the mechanical system described in Problem 6.21 when the parameter values are $M = J = R = K_1 = K_2 = 1$ and $B = 5$ in a consistent set of units.

* 7.23 Use the Laplace transform to find the zero-input responses of the pendulum modeled in Example 6.9 when there is no damping—that is, when $B = 0$. Give an expression for $\theta(t)$ in terms of $\theta(0)$ and $\dot{\theta}(0)$ that is valid about the equilibrium condition $\theta = 0$. Also give an expression for $\phi(t)$ in terms of $\phi(0)$ and $\dot{\phi}(0)$ that is valid about the equilibrium condition $\phi = 0$, which corresponds to $\theta = \pi$.

7.24 For the rotational system shown in Figure 4.19 and discussed in Example 4.5, let $J_1 = J_2 = 0.5$, $B = 1$, and $K = 2$ in a consistent set of units.

 a) Find a general expression for $\Omega_2(s) = \mathcal{L}[\omega_2(t)]$ by transforming (4.42).

 b) If the system is initially at rest and the inputs are $\tau_L(t) = 0$ and $\tau_a(t) = \epsilon^{-2t}$ for $t > 0$, find and sketch ω_2 for $t > 0$.

* 7.25 Find and sketch e_o versus t for the circuit shown in Figure 5.17 and discussed in Example 5.4. The parameter values are $C = 0.5$ F, $R_1 = 2\ \Omega$, $R_2 = R_3 = 1\ \Omega$, and $L = 0.5$ H. The inputs are $e_1(t) = 2$ V for all t and $e_2(t) = U(t)$ V. Steady-state conditions exist at $t = 0 -$.

7.26 Use the Laplace transform to solve for the unit step response of the circuit described in Problem 6.22 when the parameter values are $C = L = R_1 = R_2 = 1$ in a consistent set of units.

7.27 a) For the circuit shown in Figure P7.27, verify that the application of Kirchhoff's current law to nodes A and O leads to the following pair of coupled equations.

$$\frac{1}{2}[e_A - e_i(t)] + \frac{1}{2}e_A + 2(\dot{e}_A - \dot{e}_o) = 0$$

$$2(\dot{e}_o - \dot{e}_A) + i_L(0) + 4\int_0^t e_o(\lambda)d\lambda + 2e_o = 0$$

b) Use the Laplace transform to find the unit impulse response when e_o is the output.

c) Use the Laplace transform to solve for the unit step response.

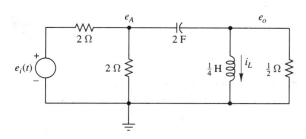

FIGURE P7.27

* 7.28 Consider the electrical circuit shown in Figure 5.15 and discussed in Example 5.3.

 a) Verify that, for the parameter values given in the example, (5.19) can be written as

$$2\dot{e}_A + 2e_A - e_o = e_i(t)$$

$$-2e_A + 16\dot{e}_o + 3e_o + 8\int_0^t e_o(\lambda)d\lambda = -4i_L(0)$$

b) Find the Laplace transform of the zero-input response of the output e_o to an initial voltage $e_A(0)$ on the capacitor C_1. Give your answer as a ratio of polynomials.

7.29 Consider the circuit shown in Figure P7.29.

a) Verify that $E_o(s)$, the transform of the output voltage, can be written as

$$E_o(s) = \frac{-se_C(0) - 2i_L(0) + (s^2 + 2s/R)E_i(s)}{s^2 + (1 + 2/R)s + 16}$$

b) Determine the poles of $E_o(s)$ for $R = 2/9 \ \Omega$, $2/7 \ \Omega$, and $2/3 \ \Omega$.

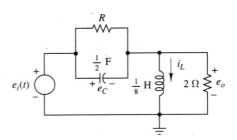

FIGURE P7.29

7.30 Consider the circuit shown in Figure 5.26(a) and modeled in Example 5.9.

a) Show that the Laplace transform of the zero-input response of $e_C(t)$ is

$$E_C(s) = \frac{15i_L(0) + (50s + 40)e_C(0)}{50s^2 + 70s + 42}$$

b) Find the Laplace transform of the zero-input response of $i_L(t)$.

c) Repeat part (b) for the output voltage e_o.

7.31 a) Use the time-delay theorem in (76) to derive the Laplace transform of the rectangular pulse shown in Figure 7.2.

b) Find the Laplace transform of the triangular pulse shown in Figure 7.13(a) by using (1) directly, rather than by decomposing the pulse into ramp and step components. Compare your results to (79).

* 7.32 Using the definition of the Laplace transform in (1), evaluate the transforms of the following functions.

a) The function $f_1(t)$ shown in Figure P7.32(a).

b) The function $f_2(t)$ shown in Figure P7.32(b).

7.33 Repeat Problem 7.32 by decomposing the functions into step functions and ramp functions, as appropriate.

7.34 Sketch the time functions corresponding to each of the following Laplace transforms.

a) $F(s) = \dfrac{1}{s^2 + 1} \left(1 + \epsilon^{-\pi s}\right)$

b) $F(s) = \dfrac{1}{s^2} \left(1 - 2\epsilon^{-s} + \epsilon^{-2s}\right)$

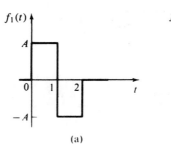

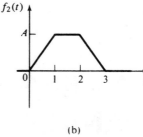

(a)

(b)

FIGURE P7.32

* 7.35 Apply the initial-value and final-value theorems to find $f(0+)$ and $f(\infty)$ for each of the four transforms in Problem 7.7. If either theorem is not applicable to a particular transform, explain why this is so.

7.36 Repeat Problem 7.35 for the following transforms.

    a) $E_o(s)$ in Example 7.8.

    b) The functions in part (c) and part (d) of Problem 7.6.

    c) $F(s) = \dfrac{4s^3}{(5s^2 + 3)^2}$

7.37 a) Using (24) and the initial-value theorem, show that

$$\dot{f}(0+) = \lim_{s \to \infty} [s^2 F(s) - sf(0)]$$

provided that the limit exists.

    b) Use the property derived in part (a) to find $\dot{f}(0+)$ for the transform $F(s)$ given in (84). Assume that $f(t) = 1$ for $t \le 0$. If this property is not applicable, explain why this is so.

    c) Repeat part (b), assuming that $f(t) = 0$ for $t \le 0$.

    d) Check your answers to part (b) and part (c) by differentiating the expression given for $f(t)$ in Example 7.15.

TRANSFER-FUNCTION ANALYSIS

We showed in Chapter 7 how to use the Laplace transform to obtain the responses of fixed linear systems. Now we shall consider in some detail two important special cases: the zero-input response, where the system's excitation consists only of some initial stored energy, and the response to a given input when the initial stored energy is zero. From the second case, we shall develop and illustrate the important concept of the transfer function.

Following a discussion of the transform solution for the complete response, we examine in some detail the responses to the unit impulse, the unit step function, and sinusoidal functions. We also show that finding the transfer function for electrical systems can be simplified by introducing the concept of impedances. Finally, we discuss the application of the Laplace transform to any fixed linear system that is described by a state-variable model in matrix form.

■ 8.1 THE ZERO-INPUT RESPONSE

In Section 6.2, we defined the zero-input response to be the output when the input $u(t)$ is zero for all $t > 0$ and when the initial conditions are nonzero. Hence the zero-input response of a fixed linear nth-order system satisfies a homogeneous nth-order differential equation of the form

$$a_n y^{(n)} + a_{n-1} y^{(n-1)} + \cdots + a_1 \dot{y} + a_0 y = 0 \tag{1}$$

which is similar to (6.4) and where $y^{(n)}$ denotes $d^n y/dt^n$. The solution to (1) will involve the n initial conditions $y(0), \dot{y}(0), \ldots, y^{(n-1)}(0)$. Using the expressions for the transforms of derivatives given in Appendix B, we can transform (1) term by term to obtain

$$a_n[s^n Y(s) - s^{n-1}y(0) - \cdots - y^{(n-1)}(0)]$$
$$+ a_{n-1}[s^{n-1}Y(s) - s^{n-2}y(0) - \cdots - y^{(n-2)}(0)]$$
$$+ \cdots + a_1[sY(s) - y(0)] + a_0 Y(s) = 0 \tag{2}$$

where $Y(s) = \mathcal{L}[y(t)]$. If we retain the terms involving $Y(s)$ on the left-hand side and collect those involving the initial conditions on the right-hand side, (2) becomes

$$(a_n s^n + a_{n-1}s^{n-1} + \cdots + a_1 s + a_0)Y(s)$$
$$= a_n y(0)s^{n-1} + [a_n \dot{y}(0) + a_{n-1}y(0)]s^{n-2} + \cdots$$
$$+ [a_n y^{(n-1)}(0) + a_{n-1}y^{(n-2)}(0) + \cdots + a_1 y(0)]$$

Thus the transform of the zero-input response is

$$Y(s) = \frac{F(s)}{P(s)} \tag{3}$$

where

$$F(s) = a_n y(0)s^{n-1} + [a_n \dot{y}(0) + a_{n-1}y(0)]s^{n-2} + \cdots$$
$$+ [a_n y^{(n-1)}(0) + a_{n-1}y^{(n-2)}(0) + \cdots + a_1 y(0)] \tag{4}$$

and

$$P(s) = a_n s^n + a_{n-1}s^{n-1} + \cdots + a_1 s + a_0 \tag{5}$$

Because $P(s)$ is of degree n and $F(s)$ is at most of degree $n - 1$, $Y(s)$ is a strictly proper rational function. The numerator polynomial $F(s)$ depends on the initial conditions. The denominator polynomial $P(s)$ is identical to the characteristic polynomial in (6.5), except that it is written in terms of the complex variable s rather than r. When $P(s)$ is factored, it will have the form

$$P(s) = a_n(s - s_1)(s - s_2) \cdots (s - s_n)$$

As we discussed in Section 7.3, the quantities $s_1, s_2, \ldots, s_n$ are the poles of the transformed output; hence they determine the form of the zero-input response. They are also the roots of the characteristic equation given by (6.5). Thus the discussion in Chapter 6 about the roots of the characteristic equation applies equally well to the poles of the transformed output when the input is zero for $t > 0$.

For a first-order system, where $n = 1$,

$$P(s) = a_1 s + a_0$$
$$= a_1(s + 1/\tau)$$

where τ is the time constant. The zero-input response will have one of the forms shown in Figure 6.1.

For a second-order system, where $n = 2$,

$$P(s) = a_2 s^2 + a_1 s + a_0$$

Possible pole positions and the corresponding typical zero-input responses are shown in Figure 6.17 through Figure 6.20. When a_0 and a_2 have the same sign, we can rewrite $P(s)$ as

$$P(s) = a_2(s^2 + 2\zeta\omega_n s + \omega_n^2)$$

where ζ and ω_n are the damping ratio and the undamped natural frequency, respectively. We pointed out the significance of these two parameters in the discussion associated with Figure 6.22.

Mode Functions

The transformed output $Y(s)$ is a strictly proper rational function, so we can expand it in partial fractions by the methods of Section 7.3. If the characteristic equation $P(s) = 0$ has the distinct roots $s_1, s_2, \ldots, s_n$, then

$$Y(s) = \frac{F(s)}{a_n(s - s_1)(s - s_2)\cdots(s - s_n)}$$

$$= \frac{A_1}{s - s_1} + \frac{A_2}{s - s_2} + \cdots + \frac{A_n}{s - s_n} \tag{6}$$

where the coefficients $A_1, A_2, \ldots, A_n$ depend on the initial conditions $y(0), \dot{y}(0), \ldots, y^{(n-1)}(0)$. Because $A_i/(s - s_i) = \mathcal{L}[A_i \epsilon^{s_i t}]$, the inverse transform of (6) is

$$y(t) = A_1 \epsilon^{s_1 t} + A_2 \epsilon^{s_2 t} + \cdots + A_n \epsilon^{s_n t} \tag{7}$$

The exponential functions $\epsilon^{s_i t}$ that make up $y(t)$ are referred to as the **mode functions** or **modes** of the system's zero-input response. The s_i are the roots of the characteristic equation, so the mode functions are properties of the system. However, the coefficients A_i in (7) are the weightings of the individual mode functions, and they depend on the particular initial conditions. In fact, we can select specific initial conditions so as to eliminate any of the mode functions in the zero-input response by forcing the corresponding A_i to be zero. The following three examples illustrate the manner in which we can use the Laplace transform to solve for a system's zero-input response and the manner in which the initial conditions affect the weighting of the system's modes.

▶ *EXAMPLE 8.1*

The rotational mechanical system shown in Figure 4.13(a) is redrawn in Figure 8.1. For the parameter values $J = 1$ kg·m², $B = 5$ N·m·s/rad, and

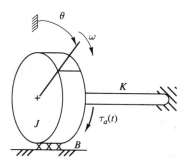

FIGURE 8.1 Rotational system for Example 8.1.

$K = 6$ N·m/rad, and for no applied torque, find and sketch the zero-input responses for the following sets of initial conditions.

1. $\theta(0) = \theta_0$ and $\dot{\theta}(0) = 0$
2. $\theta(0) = 0$ and $\dot{\theta}(0) = \dot{\theta}_0$

Solution

As derived in Example 4.1, the system model is

$$J\ddot{\theta} + B\dot{\theta} + K\theta = \tau_a(t)$$

which, for the given parameter values and no applied torque, becomes

$$\ddot{\theta} + 5\dot{\theta} + 6\theta = 0$$

Transforming each term in the differential equation and collecting on the right-hand side those terms not involving $\Theta(s)$, we get

$$(s^2 + 5s + 6)\Theta(s) = s\theta_0 + \dot{\theta}_0 + 5\theta_0$$

Dividing through by the characteristic polynomial

$$P(s) = s^2 + 5s + 6$$

gives $\Theta(s)$ for any combination of initial conditions:

$$\Theta(s) = \frac{s\theta_0 + \dot{\theta}_0 + 5\theta_0}{s^2 + 5s + 6} \tag{8}$$

The characteristic polynomial is quadratic and has a damping ratio $\zeta > 1$, so $\Theta(s)$ has two real distinct poles. To carry out the partial-fraction expansion in a general form before substituting specific values for θ_0 and $\dot{\theta}_0$, we write

$$\Theta(s) = \frac{s\theta_0 + \dot{\theta}_0 + 5\theta_0}{(s + 2)(s + 3)}$$

$$= \frac{A_1}{s + 2} + \frac{A_2}{s + 3}$$

where

$$A_1 = (s+2)\Theta(s)|_{s=-2} = 3\theta_0 + \dot{\theta}_0$$
$$A_2 = (s+3)\Theta(s)|_{s=-3} = -(2\theta_0 + \dot{\theta}_0)$$

Hence the transform of the response is

$$\Theta(s) = \frac{3\theta_0 + \dot{\theta}_0}{s+2} - \frac{2\theta_0 + \dot{\theta}_0}{s+3}$$

and the corresponding time function is

$$\theta(t) = (3\theta_0 + \dot{\theta}_0)\epsilon^{-2t} - (2\theta_0 + \dot{\theta}_0)\epsilon^{-3t} \quad \text{for } t > 0 \qquad (9)$$

From an examination of (9), it is evident that the zero-input response is composed of the two exponentially decaying mode functions ϵ^{-2t} and ϵ^{-3t}, with the weighting of each mode function dependent on the initial angle θ_0 and the initial angular velocity $\dot{\theta}_0$. Specifically, the two desired responses are

1. $\theta(t) = \theta_0(3\epsilon^{-2t} - 2\epsilon^{-3t})$ for $\theta_0 \neq 0$ and $\dot{\theta}_0 = 0$
2. $\theta(t) = \dot{\theta}_0(\epsilon^{-2t} - \epsilon^{-3t})$ for $\theta_0 = 0$ and $\dot{\theta}_0 \neq 0$

The responses are shown in Figure 8.2, along with the respective mode functions.

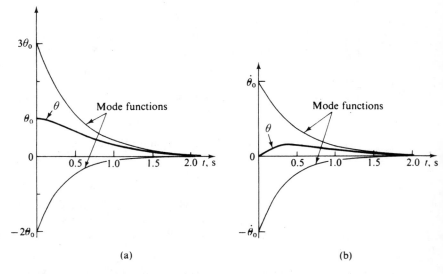

(a)   (b)

FIGURE 8.2 Responses of the rotational system in Example 8.1 to specified initial conditions. (a) $\theta_0 \neq 0$ and $\dot{\theta}_0 = 0$. (b) $\theta_0 = 0$ and $\dot{\theta}_0 \neq 0$.

From inspection of (9), we can determine for the last example the relative values of θ_0 and $\dot{\theta}_0$ that will suppress either of the two modes in the zero-input response. For example, if $2\theta_0 + \dot{\theta}_0 = 0$, the response given by (9) reduces to

$$\theta(t) = (3\theta_0 + \dot{\theta}_0)\epsilon^{-2t}$$
$$= \theta_0\epsilon^{-2t}$$

which would appear as the response of a first-order system having a time constant of $\tau = \frac{1}{2}$ s. Likewise, initial conditions satisfying $3\theta_0 + \dot{\theta}_0 = 0$ result in

$$\theta(t) = \theta_0\epsilon^{-3t}$$

which is the response of a first-order system with $\tau = \frac{1}{3}$ s. Hence one should not attempt to deduce the order of a system or the character of its mode functions solely on the basis of a single sample of the zero-input response. Rather, one should be certain that each of the mode functions appears in the observed responses.

▶ **EXAMPLE 8.2**

Find and sketch the zero-input response of the rotational system discussed in Example 8.1 for the parameter values $J = 1$ kg·m², $B = 2$ N·m·s/rad, and $K = 5$ N·m/rad and the initial conditions $\theta(0) = \theta_0$, $\dot{\theta}(0) = \dot{\theta}_0$.

Solution

Substituting the given parameter values into the model and transforming the resulting equation in terms of the arbitrary initial conditions θ_0 and $\dot{\theta}_0$ give

$$\Theta(s) = \frac{s\theta_0 + \dot{\theta}_0 + 2\theta_0}{s^2 + 2s + 5} \tag{10}$$

which is similar to (8) but has different coefficients in both numerator and denominator. A check of the damping ratio indicates that $\zeta = 1/\sqrt{5}$, which is less than unity, implying that the two roots of the characteristic equation are complex. Because the mode functions ϵ^{s_it} are themselves complex in such a case, it is preferable to leave the denominator in its quadratic form, rather than to expand $\Theta(s)$ into partial fractions with first-order denominators. Recalling that

$$\mathcal{L}[\epsilon^{-at}\cos\omega t] = \frac{s + a}{(s + a)^2 + \omega^2}$$
$$\mathcal{L}[\epsilon^{-at}\sin\omega t] = \frac{\omega}{(s + a)^2 + \omega^2} \tag{11}$$

we rewrite (10) as

$$\Theta(s) = \frac{\theta_0(s+1) + \dot{\theta}_0 + \theta_0}{(s+1)^2 + 2^2}$$

$$= \theta_0 \left[\frac{s+1}{(s+1)^2 + 2^2} \right] + \frac{\dot{\theta}_0 + \theta_0}{2} \left[\frac{2}{(s+1)^2 + 2^2} \right] \qquad (12)$$

From a comparison of (11) and (12), it is apparent that the zero-input response is

$$\theta(t) = \theta_0 \epsilon^{-t} \cos 2t + \frac{1}{2}(\dot{\theta}_0 + \theta_0)\epsilon^{-t} \sin 2t \quad \text{for } t > 0 \qquad (13)$$

The responses for the two sets of initial conditions $\theta_0 \neq 0, \dot{\theta}_0 = 0$ and $\theta_0 = 0, \dot{\theta}_0 \neq 0$ are shown in Figure 8.3.

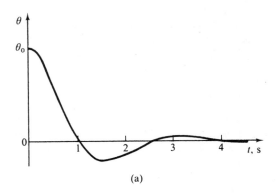

(a)

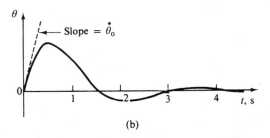

(b)

FIGURE 8.3   Responses of the rotational system in Example 8.2 to specified initial conditions. (a) $\theta_0 \neq 0$ and $\dot{\theta}_0 = 0$. (b) $\theta_0 = 0$ and $\dot{\theta}_0 \neq 0$.

Examination of (13) suggests that in place of the complex mode functions $\epsilon^{(-1+j2)t}$ and $\epsilon^{(-1-j2)t}$ corresponding to the poles of $\Theta(s)$ at $s_1 = -1 + j2$ and $s_2 = -1 - j2$, it is appropriate to consider the functions

$\epsilon^{-t}\cos 2t$ and $\epsilon^{-t}\sin 2t$. In more general terms, if a system has a pair of complex poles at $s_1 = \alpha + j\beta$ and $s_2 = \alpha - j\beta$, we can take the mode functions as either the complex functions $\epsilon^{(\alpha+j\beta)t}$ and $\epsilon^{(\alpha-j\beta)t}$ or the real functions $\epsilon^{\alpha t}\cos\beta t$ and $\epsilon^{\alpha t}\sin\beta t$.

▶ **EXAMPLE 8.3**

The two-inertia rotational system modeled in Example 4.2 is shown in Figure 8.4, with the viscous damping in the original version omitted. Find and sketch the zero-input response $\theta_1(t)$ for the parameter values $J_1 = J_2 = 1$ kg·m², $K_1 = 1$ N·m/rad, and $K_2 = 2$ N·m/rad, with the initial conditions $\theta_1(0) = \theta_2(0) = 0.5$ rad and $\dot\theta_1(0) = \dot\theta_2(0) = 0$.

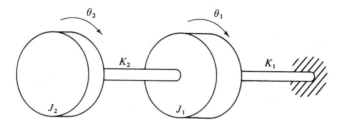

FIGURE 8.4 Rotational system for Example 8.3.

Solution

By substituting numerical values for J_1, J_2, K_1, and K_2 into (4.26) and setting $B_1 = B_2 = \tau_a(t) = 0$, we obtain the system model

$$\ddot\theta_1 + 3\theta_1 - 2\theta_2 = 0$$
$$\ddot\theta_2 + 2\theta_2 - 2\theta_1 = 0 \tag{14}$$

At this point, we could combine the pair of equations into a single homogeneous fourth-order differential equation for θ_1 and then transform the result to obtain $\Theta_1(s)$. However, that approach would require knowledge of $\ddot\theta_1(0)$ and $\dddot\theta_1(0)$. When we are working with coupled equations, including state-variable equations, it is more convenient to transform the differential equations immediately and then to solve the transformed equations for the transform of the desired output.

When transformed with the specified initial conditions, (14) becomes

$$(s^2 + 3)\Theta_1(s) - 2\Theta_2(s) = 0.5s$$
$$-2\Theta_1(s) + (s^2 + 2)\Theta_2(s) = 0.5s$$

Solving these two simultaneous algebraic equations for $\Theta_1(s)$ yields

$$\Theta_1(s) = \frac{0.5s^3 + 2s}{s^4 + 5s^2 + 2} \tag{15}$$

Although the denominator of $\Theta_1(s)$ is a polynomial of degree four in s, it contains only even powers of s and can be factored into the product $(s^2 + 0.4384)(s^2 + 4.562)$ by means of the quadratic formula. Thus we can decompose $\Theta_1(s)$ into the sum of two terms having quadratic denominators. The expansion of $\Theta_1(s)$ is

$$\Theta_1(s) = \frac{A_1 s + B_1}{s^2 + 0.4384} + \frac{A_2 s + B_2}{s^2 + 4.562} \qquad (16)$$

To evaluate the coefficients A_1, A_2, B_1, and B_2, we put the right-hand side of (16) over a common denominator and compare the numerator coefficients to those of (15). Doing this, we obtain the following four equations:

$$A_1 + A_2 = 0.5$$
$$B_1 + B_2 = 0$$
$$4.562A_1 + 0.4384A_2 = 2$$
$$4.562B_1 + 0.4384B_2 = 0$$

Solving these equations and substituting the results into (16), we find that

$$\Theta_1(s) = \frac{0.4319s}{s^2 + 0.6622^2} + \frac{0.0681s}{s^2 + 2.136^2}$$

Referring to Appendix B, we see that the response is

$$\theta_1(t) = 0.4319 \cos 0.6622t + 0.0681 \cos 2.136t \quad \text{for } t > 0$$

which is plotted in Figure 8.5. The figure indicates that the disk in question responds in a rather complicated fashion, which is the superposition of undamped oscillations at the two frequencies $\omega = 0.6622$ and 2.136 rad/s. These cosine functions and the corresponding sine functions having the same frequencies can be considered the mode functions of the system. Any other

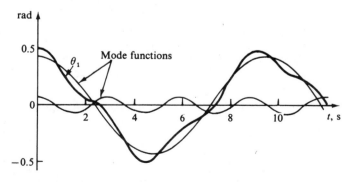

FIGURE 8.5 Response of the rotational system shown in Figure 8.4 to the initial conditions $\theta_1(0) = \theta_2(0) = 0.5$ rad and $\dot{\theta}_1(0) = \dot{\theta}_2(0) = 0$.

combination of initial conditions would result in a response that is a weighted sum of these four mode functions.

8.2 THE ZERO-STATE RESPONSE

As defined in Section 6.2, the zero-state response is the response to a nonzero input when the initial stored energy is zero. We assume that the input starts at $t = 0+$ and that $y(0)$, $\dot{y}(0)$, ..., $y^{(n-1)}(0)$, $u(0)$, $\dot{u}(0)$, ..., $u^{(m-1)}(0)$ are zero. The zero-state response will consist of both the forced response $y_P(t)$ and the free response $y_H(t)$. We shall consider the system model to be in the form of the general nth-order input-output equation:

$$a_n y^{(n)} + a_{n-1} y^{(n-1)} + \cdots + a_1 \dot{y} + a_0 y = b_m u^{(m)} + \cdots + b_0 u(t) \qquad (17)$$

The Transfer Function

Transforming both sides of (17) and collecting terms, we obtain the algebraic equation

$$(a_n s^n + a_{n-1} s^{n-1} + \cdots + a_1 s + a_0) Y(s) = (b_m s^m + \cdots + b_0) U(s)$$

which can be rearranged to give the transform of the output as

$$Y(s) = \left(\frac{b_m s^m + \cdots + b_0}{a_n s^n + a_{n-1} s^{n-1} + \cdots + a_1 s + a_0} \right) U(s) \qquad (18)$$

Hence the output transform $Y(s)$ is the product of the input transform $U(s)$ and a rational function of the complex variable s whose coefficients are the coefficients in the input-output differential equation. This rational function of s is known as the system's **transfer function**. It plays a key role in the analysis of linear systems. Denoting the transfer function by $H(s)$, we rewrite (18) as

$$Y(s) = H(s)U(s) \qquad (19)$$

Note that when we know a system's input-output differential equation, we can write its transfer function directly as

$$H(s) = \frac{b_m s^m + \cdots + b_0}{a_n s^n + a_{n-1} s^{n-1} + \cdots + a_1 s + a_0} \qquad (20)$$

Even if the system model is in a form other than the input-output differential equation, the transfer function can be found from (19) or from its equivalent,

$$H(s) = \frac{Y(s)}{U(s)} \qquad (21)$$

We denote the input by a general symbol, rather than using a specific function of time. We can then transform any version of the modeling equations, replace all of the initial-condition terms by zero, and solve for the transformed output. This was done in Chapter 7 for the mechanical system shown in Figure 7.10(a). In Example 7.10 we transformed the equations that were written directly from the free-body diagrams. The transfer function was the quantity inside the brackets in (7.69). In Example 7.11, we obtained the same result by transforming the state-variable model. Finally, in Example 7.12, we started with the input-output equation. An example of finding the transfer function for an electrical system will be given in Section 8.5.

Poles and Zeros

When the two polynomials in s that constitute $H(s)$ are factored, the transfer function will have the form

$$H(s) = K \frac{(s - z_1)(s - z_2) \cdots (s - z_m)}{(s - p_1)(s - p_2) \cdots (s - p_n)} \tag{22}$$

The quantities z_1, z_2, ..., z_m are those values of s for which the numerator of $H(s)$ is zero, and they are called the **zeros** of the transfer function.[1] The quantities p_1, p_2, ..., p_n are those values of s for which the denominator of $H(s)$ vanishes and for which $H(s)$ becomes infinite. They are the **poles** of the transfer function. From a comparison of (20) and (22), it follows that $K = b_m/a_n$, where we have assumed that neither b_m nor a_n may be zero. In the following discussion, we shall assume that none of the zeros coincides with any of the poles—that is, that $z_i \neq p_j$ for all $1 \leq i \leq m$ and all $1 \leq j \leq n$. If a pole and a zero of $H(s)$ were coincident, some of the factors in (22) could be canceled, in which case we could not reconstruct the input-output differential equation from $H(s)$. Then it would not be possible to find the response of all the system's modes from the transfer function.

From (22), it is apparent that a transfer function can be completely specified by its poles, its zeros, and the multiplying constant K. The poles and zeros may be complex numbers and can be represented graphically by points in a complex plane. This plane is called the s-**plane** or the **complex-frequency plane**, and because $s = \sigma + j\omega$, its real and imaginary axes are labeled σ and ω, respectively. The poles of $H(s)$ are indicated by crosses and the zeros by circles placed at the appropriate points.

Referring to (5), we see that the denominator of $H(s)$ in (20) is the characteristic polynomial of the system. Thus the poles p_1, p_2, ..., p_n of $H(s)$ are identical to the characteristic roots that appear in the zero-input response. As a consequence, we can write down the form of the zero-input response as soon as we know the poles of $H(s)$.

---

[1] If $m < n$, which is often the case, $H(s)$ will have a zero of multiplicity $n - m$ at infinity. However, one is usually interested in only the numerator zeros z_1, z_2, ..., z_m.

To lend further significance to the transfer-function concept, recall that the stability of a system is determined by the roots of its characteristic equation. Hence the stability can also be characterized by the locations of the poles of the transfer function. If all the poles are inside the left half of the s-plane ($\sigma < 0$), the system is stable; if at least one pole is in the right half of the s-plane ($\sigma > 0$), the system is unstable. If all the poles of $H(s)$ are in the left half of the s-plane except for distinct poles on the imaginary axis ($\sigma = 0$), the system is marginally stable. In addition, a system is unstable if its transfer function has repeated poles on the imaginary axis. Before discussing the zero-state response in more detail, we shall illustrate some of these notions in the following example.

▶ **EXAMPLE 8.4**

Find the transfer function and draw the corresponding pole-zero plot in the s-plane for the system described by the input-output equation

$$\dddot{y} + 7\ddot{y} + 15\dot{y} + 25y = 2\ddot{u} + 6\dot{u}$$

Also comment on the stability of the system and give the form of its zero-input response.

Solution

Transforming the input-output equation with zero initial conditions and with $u(0) = \dot{u}(0) = 0$, we have

$$(s^3 + 7s^2 + 15s + 25)Y(s) = (2s^2 + 6s)U(s)$$

which, when we solve for the ratio $Y(s)/U(s)$, gives

$$H(s) = \frac{2s^2 + 6s}{s^3 + 7s^2 + 15s + 25}$$

Alternatively, we could have used (20) to write $H(s)$ by inspection of the input-output equation.

In order to draw the pole-zero plot representing $H(s)$, we must factor its numerator and denominator. Although the numerator is readily factored, the denominator is a cubic in s. It turns out that

$$H(s) = \frac{2s(s+3)}{(s+5)(s^2+2s+5)} \tag{23a}$$

$$= 2\left[\frac{s(s+3)}{(s+5)(s+1-j2)(s+1+j2)}\right] \tag{23b}$$

Thus $H(s)$ has two real zeros (at $s = 0$ and $s = -3$) and three poles (a real one at $s = -5$ and a complex pair at $s = -1 + j2$ and $s = -1 - j2$), all of which can be represented by the pole-zero plot shown in Figure 8.6. In addition, the multiplying constant is $K = 2$.

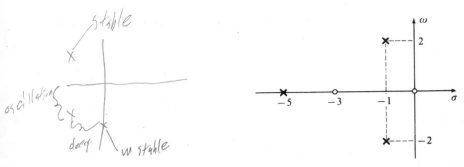

FIGURE 8.6 Pole-zero plot for $H(s)$ in Example 8.4.

Because the transfer function has all three of its poles in the left half of the s-plane, the system is stable. The fact that one of the zeros (at $s = 0$) is not inside the left half-plane has no bearing on the system's stability. For that matter, $H(s)$ can have zeros in the right half-plane and still correspond to a stable system. Knowing the three poles of the transfer function, we can immediately write down the form of the zero-input response in either of the following two equivalent forms:

$$y_{zi}(t) = K_1 \epsilon^{-5t} + \epsilon^{-t}(K_2 \cos 2t + K_3 \sin 2t)$$
$$y_{zi}(t) = K_1 \epsilon^{-5t} + K_4 \epsilon^{-t} \cos(2t + \phi) \tag{24}$$

Transient and Steady-State Components

Equation (19) is an expression for the transform of the system's zero-state response—that is, the output when there is no initial stored energy. Recall from Chapter 6 that the transient response consists of those terms that decay to zero as t becomes large, whereas the remaining terms constitute the steady-state response. For a stable system and for an input that does not decay to zero, the steady-state response is the forced response[2] $y_P(t)$. We now show how this relationship is manifested in (19) and how to interpret it in terms of poles and zeros.

Assume that the transform of the input $u(t)$ can be written as a rational function of s:

$$U(s) = \frac{N(s)}{D(s)} \tag{25}$$

where $N(s)$ and $D(s)$ are polynomials. For cases where the input contains a term delayed by a units of time, $N(s)$ will contain a factor ϵ^{-as}, which

---

[2]If a system is marginally stable, it can exhibit a steady-state response due to initial stored energy, even without an input. An unstable system can yield an unbounded response without an input. Hence the designations *transient* and *steady-state* are most useful for stable systems.

can be treated as in Example 7.14. Other inputs, such as $u(t) = 1/t$, that have Laplace transforms that do not fit (25) are beyond the scope of our consideration.

Rewriting (19) using (22) for $H(s)$ and (25) for $U(s)$, we have

$$Y(s) = K \frac{(s - z_1) \cdots (s - z_m)}{(s - p_1)(s - p_2) \cdots (s - p_n)} \cdot \frac{N(s)}{D(s)} \qquad (26)$$

Recognizing that $U(s)$ has its own poles and zeros, we see that the poles and zeros of $Y(s)$ are the combination of those of $H(s)$ and those of $U(s)$. If we expand $Y(s)$ in a partial-fraction expansion and all of its poles are distinct, the expansion will have the form

$$Y(s) = \frac{A_1}{s - p_1} + \frac{A_2}{s - p_2} + \cdots + \frac{A_n}{s - p_n} + \frac{A_{n+1}}{s - p_{n+1}} + \cdots + \frac{A_q}{s - p_q} \qquad (27)$$

where the poles $p_1, p_2, \ldots, p_n$ are the poles of $H(s)$ and the poles $p_{n+1}, \ldots, p_q$ are the poles of $U(s)$. Taking the inverse transform of each term, we have

$$y(t) = A_1 \epsilon^{p_1 t} + A_2 \epsilon^{p_2 t} + \cdots + A_n \epsilon^{p_n t} + A_{n+1} \epsilon^{p_{n+1} t} + \cdots + A_q \epsilon^{p_q t} \qquad (28)$$

where the first n terms are the free response $y_H(t)$ and the last $q - n$ terms are the forced response $y_P(t)$. Hence

$$y(t) = y_H(t) + y_P(t)$$

where

$$y_H(t) = A_1 \epsilon^{p_1 t} + \cdots + A_n \epsilon^{p_n t}$$

$$y_P(t) = A_{n+1} \epsilon^{p_{n+1} t} + \cdots + A_q \epsilon^{q t}$$

When the system is stable, the term $y_H(t)$ consists of the transients induced in having $y(t)$ start from zero initial conditions and reach the steady-state solution represented by $y_P(t)$. Keep in mind that when complex poles are present, it may be more efficient to include the corresponding second-order term (quadratic denominator and linear numerator) in the partial-fraction expansion, as in (7.57), rather than to factor it.

▶ **EXAMPLE 8.5**

Find the form of the zero-state response of a system for which

$$H(s) = \frac{9s + 14}{3(s + 1)(s + 3)}$$

when the input is $u(t) = 6 \cos 2t$ for $t > 0$. Identify the transient and steady-state terms.

Solution

The transform of the input is

$$U(s) = \frac{6s}{s^2 + 4}$$

When $H(s)$ and $U(s)$ are substituted into (19), it follows that

$$Y(s) = \frac{9s + 14}{3(s + 1)(s + 3)} \cdot \frac{6s}{(s^2 + 4)} \tag{29}$$

Referring to the procedures in Section 7.3, we can write the partial-fraction expansion for $Y(s)$ in either of the following two equivalent forms:

$$Y(s) = \frac{A_1}{s + 1} + \frac{A_2}{s + 3} + \frac{A_3}{s - j2} + \frac{A_3^*}{s + j2} \tag{30a}$$

$$Y(s) = \frac{A_1}{s + 1} + \frac{A_2}{s + 3} + \frac{A_4 s + A_5}{s^2 + 4} \tag{30b}$$

where A_3 is a complex number and A_3^* denotes the complex conjugate. Using the methods of Section 7.3 to evaluate the constants, we find that $A_1 = -1$, $A_2 = -3$, $A_3 = 2\sqrt{2}\epsilon^{-j\pi/4}$, $A_4 = 4$, and $A_5 = 8$. Then, by the entries in Appendix B, we obtain the following expressions for the inverse transform for $t > 0$.

$$y(t) = -\epsilon^{-t} - 3\epsilon^{-3t} + 4\sqrt{2}\cos(2t - \pi/4) \tag{31a}$$

$$y(t) = -\epsilon^{-t} - 3\epsilon^{-3t} + 4\cos 2t + 4\sin 2t \tag{31b}$$

By using Table 6.1, it is easy to show that these two forms for $y(t)$ are equivalent. For either form, the first two terms constitute the transient response. These terms come from the poles of $H(s)$, which are entirely within the left half of the s-plane. The rest of the expressions represent the steady-state response, which is a constant-amplitude oscillation resulting from the poles of $U(s)$, which are on the imaginary axis of the s-plane.

Differentiating the Input

We now consider a property that we used without a complete proof in Section 6.3. For a linear system that contains no initial stored energy, suppose that we know the response to a certain input. If we substitute a new input that is the derivative of the old input, then the new response is the derivative of the old response.

To prove this statement, we denote the original input and output by $u_1(t)$ and $y_1(t)$, respectively. Because we are dealing with the zero-state response, we can assume that $u_1(t)$, $y_1(t)$, and all their derivatives are zero for $t \le 0$. Any discontinuities are assumed to occur at $t = 0+$. By (19),

$$Y_1(s) = H(s)U_1(s)$$

Let the new input and output be $u_2(t)$ and $y_2(t)$, where $u_2(t) = \dot{u}_1$. Then with zero initial conditions, $U_2(s) = sU_1(s) - u_1(0) = sU_1(s)$, so

$$Y_2(s) = H(s)U_2(s) = sH(s)U_1(s) = sY_1(s)$$

Comparing this result with

$$\mathcal{L}[\dot{y}_1] = sY_1(s) - y_1(0) = sY_1(s)$$

we see that

$$y_2(t) = \dot{y}_1 \tag{32}$$

which confirms that the new output is the derivative of the old output.

8.3 THE COMPLETE RESPONSE

When we are to evaluate the response of a fixed linear system to the combination of nonzero initial conditions and a nonzero input for $t > 0$, the principle of superposition enables us to add the zero-input and zero-state responses to give the complete response. Likewise, we can evaluate the Laplace transforms of the two responses separately and add them to give the transform of the complete response.

For the nth-order system described by (17), (3) gives the transform of the zero-input response, that portion due to the initial conditions. The transform of the zero-state response, that portion due to the input, is given by (19). Thus the transform of the total response is

$$Y(s) = \frac{F(s)}{P(s)} + H(s)U(s) \tag{33}$$

where $F(s)$ is the polynomial given by (4) and involves the initial conditions, and where $P(s)$ is the characteristic polynomial given by (5). If we write $H(s)$ and $U(s)$ as ratios of polynomials, then (33) becomes

$$Y(s) = \frac{F(s)}{P(s)} + \frac{G(s)}{P(s)} \cdot \frac{N(s)}{D(s)} \tag{34}$$

where $G(s)$ is the numerator of $H(s)$ and where $U(s) = N(s)/D(s)$. The first term in (34) is the transform of the zero-input response; the second is the transform of the zero-state response.

Let p_1, p_2, $\ldots$, p_n denote the poles of $H(s)$, which are the roots of $P(s) = 0$. Let p_{n+1}, $\ldots$, p_q denote the poles of the transformed input—that is, the roots of $D(s) = 0$. If the poles are distinct, we can write the partial-fraction expansion of $Y(s)$ as

$$Y(s) = \left[\frac{K_1}{s - p_1} + \frac{K_2}{s - p_2} + \cdots + \frac{K_n}{s - p_n} \right]$$
$$+ \left[\frac{A_1}{s - p_1} + \frac{A_2}{s - p_2} + \cdots + \frac{A_n}{s - p_n} + \frac{A_{n+1}}{s - p_{n+1}} + \cdots + \frac{A_q}{s - p_q} \right]$$

where the expression in the first set of brackets is the transformed zero-input response, and the expression in the second set is the transformed zero-state response. Only the constants K_1, K_2, ..., K_n depend on the initial conditions. The complete time response is

$$y(t) = y_H(t) + y_P(t)$$

where

$$y_H(t) = (K_1 + A_1)\epsilon^{P_1 t} + \cdots + (K_n + A_n)\epsilon^{P_n t}$$

$$y_P(t) = A_{n+1}\epsilon^{P_{n+1} t} + \cdots + A_q\epsilon^{P_q t}$$

Comparing these expressions with (28), we see that the complete response is the same as the zero-state response, except that the terms in $y_H(t)$ have different coefficients. For a stable system with an input that does not decay to zero, $y_P(t)$ is the steady-state response, which is unaffected by the initial conditions.

We can rewrite (34) with a common denominator as

$$Y(s) = \frac{F(s)D(s) + G(s)N(s)}{P(s)D(s)} \tag{35}$$

The poles of $Y(s)$, the transform of the complete response, are the combined poles of the transfer function and the transformed input. The zeros of $Y(s)$ depend on the four polynomials $F(s)$, $D(s)$, $G(s)$, and $N(s)$.

▶ **EXAMPLE 8.6**

The system we discussed in Example 8.5 obeys the differential equation

$$3\ddot{y} + 12\dot{y} + 9y = 9\dot{u} + 14u(t) \tag{36}$$

Find the complete response when the initial conditions are $y(0) = 2$, $\dot{y}(0) = 0$ and when the input is $u(t) = 3\epsilon^{-2t}$ for $t > 0$ and zero otherwise.

Solution

Transforming (36) with the specified initial conditions and taking $u(0) = 0$, we obtain

$$3s^2 Y(s) - 6s + 12s Y(s) - 24 + 9Y(s) = (9s + 14)U(s)$$

where $U(s) = 3/(s + 2)$. Solving for $Y(s)$, the transform of the complete response, and writing the result in the form of (33), we find that

$$Y(s) = \frac{6s + 24}{P(s)} + \frac{9s + 14}{P(s)} \cdot \frac{3}{s + 2}$$

where the characteristic polynomial is

$$P(s) = 3s^2 + 12s + 9 = 3(s + 1)(s + 3)$$

Combining terms over a common denominator, we have

$$Y(s) = \frac{2s^2 + 21s + 30}{(s + 1)(s + 2)(s + 3)}$$

Carrying out the partial-fraction expansion gives

$$Y(s) = \frac{11/2}{s+1} + \frac{4}{s+2} - \frac{15/2}{s+3}$$

so for $t > 0$,

$$y(t) = \frac{11}{2}\epsilon^{-t} + 4\epsilon^{-2t} - \frac{15}{2}\epsilon^{-3t}$$

Note that each term in $y(t)$ decays to zero as t approaches infinity. This is because all the poles of $H(s)$ are in the left half of the s-plane and because the input $u(t)$ decays to zero with increasing time. Hence the steady-state response is zero.

▶ **EXAMPLE 8.7**

Repeat Example 8.6 when $y(0) = 2$ and $\dot{y}(0) = 0$ and when $u(t) = 6\cos 2t$ for $t > 0$ and zero otherwise.

Solution

Transforming (36) with the specified conditions and then solving for the transform of the output, we obtain

$$Y(s) = \frac{6s + 24}{3(s+1)(s+3)} + \frac{9s + 14}{3(s+1)(s+3)} \cdot \frac{6s}{s^2 + 4}$$

We could combine these terms over a common denominator. However, we recognize the second of the two terms as the transformed zero-state response, whose inverse transform we found in Example 8.5. The partial-fraction expansion for the first of the two terms is found to be

$$\frac{2s + 8}{(s+1)(s+3)} = \frac{3}{s+1} - \frac{1}{s+3}$$

whose inverse transform is

$$3\epsilon^{-t} - \epsilon^{-3t}$$

By adding this expression to the answer for Example 8.5, we obtain for the complete response

$$y(t) = 2\epsilon^{-t} - 4\epsilon^{-3t} + 4\cos 2t + 4\sin 2t$$

This is, of course, the same as the response in Example 8.5, except that the transient terms have different coefficients.

■ 8.4 STEP AND IMPULSE RESPONSES

In the analysis and design of dynamic systems, it is helpful to specify an evaluate the response of a system to a specific input in order to have common point of reference. Three inputs that stand out because of thei usefulness and acceptance are (1) the unit impulse $\delta(t)$, (2) the unit ste function $U(t)$, and (3) the sinusoidal function $\sin \omega t$. We shall examine th responses of fixed linear systems to these three functions by using Laplac transforms and the system transfer function $H(s)$. In the case of the impuls and the step function, we shall be interested in the zero-state response including both the transient and the steady-state portions, for both stabl and unstable systems. For the sinusoidal input, which will be considered i the next section, we shall limit our attention to the steady-state response o stable systems.

The basis for our study of the responses to these special inputs will be (19), which is

$$Y(s) = H(s)U(s) \qquad (37)$$

where $Y(s)$ is the transform of the zero-state response, $H(s)$ is the system's transfer function, and $U(s)$ is the transform of the input.

Impulse Response

The transform of the unit impulse is unity, so $U(s) = 1$ and (37) reduces to

$$Y(s) = H(s)$$

In words, the transform of the unit impulse response is merely the system's transfer function $H(s)$. In addition, $h(t)$ must be zero for all $t \leq 0$, because it is the zero-state response and the impulse does not occur until $t = 0+$. Using the symbol $h(t)$ to denote the response to the unit impulse, we can write

$$h(t) = \begin{cases} 0 & \text{for } t \leq 0 \\ \mathcal{L}^{-1}[H(s)] & \text{for } t > 0 \end{cases} \qquad (38)$$

which is a significant result in spite of its simplicity. In particular, (38) serves to tie together the system's time-domain characterization in terms of $h(t)$ and its complex-frequency-domain characterization $H(s)$. For example, one can relate the locations in the s-plane of the poles and zeros of the transfer function to the character of the system's impulse response. Furthermore, although the subject is beyond the scope of this book, the impulse response can be related to the response to arbitrary inputs by an integral expression known as the convolution integral.

In Section 6.3, we stated that the unit impulse response could be found by either (1) finding the appropriate initial conditions and solving the homogeneous differential equation or (2) finding the response to a unit step function and differentiating the result. Now an easier and more direct method is available. We can find the transfer function and then take its inverse transform. From (17) and (20), we know that we can write $H(s)$ by inspection of the system's input-output differential equation, although we may encounter some computational difficulties in factoring its denominator if the system is of third or higher order. In the event that the system model is available as two or more simultaneous equations (for example, as a set of state-variable equations and an output equation), we can find the transfer function by first transforming the simultaneous equations with zero initial conditions and then solving algebraically for the ratio $Y(s)/U(s)$, which is the transfer function.

▶ *EXAMPLE 8.8*

Find the unit impulse response of the first-order system described by $\dot{y} + (1/\tau)y = u(t)$.

Solution

The transfer function $Y(s)/U(s)$ is

$$H(s) = \frac{1}{s + 1/\tau}$$

Recalling that $\mathcal{L}[\epsilon^{-at}] = 1/(s+a)$, we can write

$$h(t) = \begin{cases} 0 & \text{for } t \leq 0 \\ \epsilon^{-t/\tau} & \text{for } t > 0 \end{cases} \tag{39}$$

which is shown in Figure 8.7.

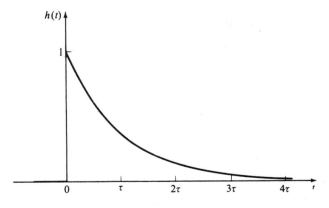

FIGURE 8.7   Impulse response for $\dot{y} + (1/\tau)y = u(t)$.

It is instructive to apply the initial-value theorem to $H(s)$ to evaluate $h(0+)$, getting

$$h(0+) = \lim_{s \to \infty} \frac{s}{s + 1/\tau} = 1$$

which agrees with (39) and Figure 8.7. It is easy to verify that the final-value theorem yields a value of zero.

▶ **EXAMPLE 8.9**

Find and sketch the unit impulse response of the system whose input-output equation is

$$\ddot{y} + 4\ddot{y} + 3\dot{y} = 2\dot{u} + u(t)$$

Solution

By inspection of the input-output differential equation, we see that the transfer function is

$$H(s) = \frac{2s + 1}{s^3 + 4s^2 + 3s}$$

$$= \frac{2s + 1}{s(s + 1)(s + 3)}$$

Carrying out the partial-fraction expansion, we find that

$$H(s) = \frac{\frac{1}{3}}{s} + \frac{\frac{1}{2}}{s + 1} - \frac{\frac{5}{6}}{s + 3}$$

Thus the unit impulse response is

$$h(t) = \begin{cases} 0 & \text{for } t \leq 0 \\ \frac{1}{3} + \frac{1}{2}\epsilon^{-t} - \frac{5}{6}\epsilon^{-3t} & \text{for } t > 0 \end{cases}$$

which is shown in Figure 8.8. In this case,

$$h(0+) = \lim_{s \to \infty} \frac{s(2s + 1)}{s(s^2 + 4s + 3)} = 0$$

and

$$\lim_{t \to \infty} h(t) = \lim_{s \to 0} \frac{s(2s + 1)}{s(s^2 + 4s + 3)} = \frac{1}{3}$$

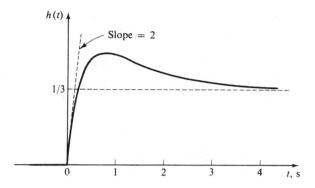

FIGURE 8.8   Impulse response for the system in Example 8.9.

both of which agree with the sketch of $h(t)$. Here $h(t)$ approaches a nonzero constant value because of the single pole at $s = 0$ in $H(s)$.

Step Response

Because the transform of the unit step function is $1/s$, it follows from (37) that the transform of $y_U(t)$, the zero-state response of a system to a unit step-function input, is

$$Y_U(s) = H(s) \cdot \frac{1}{s} \qquad (40)$$

Thus the unit step response $y_U(t)$ is zero for $t \leq 0$, and for $t > 0$ it is the inverse transform of $H(s)/s$. The poles of $Y_U(s)$ consist of the poles of $H(s)$ and a pole at $s = 0$. Provided that $H(s)$ has no pole at $s = 0$, the time functions that make up $y_U(t)$ will be the mode functions of the system's zero-input response and a constant term resulting from the pole of $Y_U(s)$ at $s = 0$. In fact, if the system is stable, all the mode functions will decay to zero as t approaches infinity, and the steady-state portion of the step response will be due entirely to the pole at $s = 0$. The coefficient in the partial-fraction expansion of this steady-state term, and thus $(y_U)_{ss}$ itself, will be

$$(y_U)_{ss} = sY_U(s)|_{s=0} = H(0)$$

We can also get this result by applying the final-value theorem to $Y_U(s)$ as given by (40):

$$y_U(\infty) = \lim_{s \to 0} sY_U(s) = H(0)$$

Because the initial conditions do not affect the steady-state response of a stable system, the result applies even when the initial stored energy is not zero. If $H(s)$ has a single pole at $s = 0$, then $Y_U(s)$ as given by (40) will have a double pole at $s = 0$, and the step response will contain a ramp function in addition to a constant term. Then $y_U(t)$ will grow without bound as t approaches infinity.

To show that a system's unit step response is the integral of its unit impulse response, we use the theorem for the transform of an integral to write

$$\frac{1}{s}H(s) = \mathcal{L}\left[\int_0^t h(\lambda)d\lambda\right]$$

where λ is a dummy variable of integration. Because $\mathcal{L}[y_U(t)] = H(s)/s$, it follows that

$$y_U(t) = \int_0^t h(\lambda)d\lambda \qquad (41)$$

In graphical terms, (41) states that the unit step response $y_U(t)$ is the area under the curve of the unit impulse response $h(t)$. By the same token, the impulse response is the derivative of the step response—that is,

$$h(t) = \frac{d}{dt}y_U(t) \qquad (42)$$

which agrees with (6.41) and (32).

▶ **EXAMPLE 8.10**

Evaluate the unit step response of the first-order system $\dot{y} + (1/\tau)y = u(t)$.

Solution

From Example 8.8, the system's transfer function is $H(s) = 1/(s + 1/\tau)$. Thus (40) indicates that the transform of the unit step response is

$$Y_U(s) = \frac{1}{s(s + 1/\tau)}$$

$$= \frac{\tau}{s} - \frac{\tau}{s + 1/\tau}$$

Evaluating the inverse transform of $Y_U(s)$ and noting that the step response must be zero for $t \leq 0$, we find that

$$y_U(t) = \begin{cases} 0 & \text{for } t \leq 0 \\ \tau(1 - \epsilon^{-t/\tau}) & \text{for } t > 0 \end{cases} \qquad (43)$$

which is shown in Figure 8.9. You should verify that (43) is indeed the integral of the unit impulse response, which was given by (39) and is repeated in Figure 8.9. Finally, we note that the steady-state value of the unit step response is

$$(y_U)_{ss} = H(0) = \tau$$

which agrees with (43) and Figure 8.9.

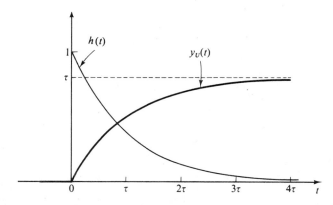

FIGURE 8.9 Step response for $\dot{y} + (1/\tau)y = u(t)$.

▶ *EXAMPLE 8.11*

Use Laplace transforms to find the unit step response of the system described by $\ddot{y} + 4\ddot{y} + 3\dot{y} = 2\dot{u} + u(t)$, for which we found the impulse response in Example 8.9.

Solution

Inspection of the system's differential equation reveals the transfer function to be

$$H(s) = \frac{2s + 1}{s^3 + 4s^2 + 3s}$$

Hence the transform of the unit step response is

$$Y_U(s) = \frac{2s + 1}{s^2(s^2 + 4s + 3)}$$

whose partial-fraction expansion can be shown to be

$$Y_U(s) = \frac{\frac{1}{3}}{s^2} + \frac{\frac{2}{9}}{s} - \frac{\frac{1}{2}}{s + 1} + \frac{\frac{5}{18}}{s + 3}$$

Thus

$$y_U(t) = \frac{1}{3}t + \frac{2}{9} - \frac{1}{2}\epsilon^{-t} + \frac{5}{18}\epsilon^{-3t} \quad \text{for } t > 0$$

As shown in Figure 8.10, the steady-state portion of the unit step response contains a ramp component with a slope of $\frac{1}{3}$, in addition to the constant of $\frac{2}{9}$. This is because $H(s)$ has a pole at $s = 0$. This pole combines with the pole at $s = 0$ that is due to the step-function input to give a double pole of $Y(s)$ at $s = 0$.

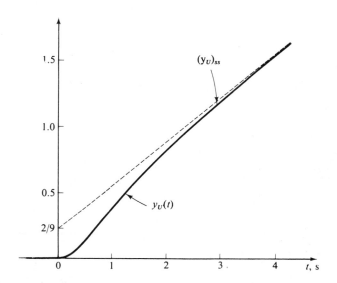

FIGURE 8.10   Step response for Example 8.11.

As an aid in sketching the unit step response, we note that in addition to $y_U(0+) = 0$, the initial slope is zero, because $h(t)$ is the derivative of the step response and (from Figure 8.8) $h(0+) = 0$.

■ 8.5 FREQUENCY RESPONSE

In discussing the impulse and step responses, we were interested in both the transient and steady-state components. However, when considering the sinusoidal input

$$u(t) = \sin \omega t \tag{44}$$

we are normally interested only in the forced response. From our discussion of the particular solution in Section 6.1, we know that the forced response will have the same frequency as the input but that, in general, its amplitude and phase will differ from those of the input. For stable systems with a sinusoidal input, the forced response is also the steady-state response. Denoting the amplitude and phase angle of the steady-state response by A

and ϕ, respectively, we can write

$$y_{ss}(t) = A \sin(\omega t + \phi) \tag{45}$$

which is referred to as the **sinusoidal-steady-state response**. It plays a key role in many aspects of system analysis, including electronic circuits and feedback control systems. We shall now show how we can express A and ϕ in terms of the transfer function $H(s)$.

The initial conditions do not affect the steady-state response of a stable system, so we start with the transform of the zero-state response as given by (37). Because $\mathscr{L}[\sin \omega t] = \omega/(s^2 + \omega^2)$, the transformed response to (44) is

$$Y(s) = H(s) \left[\frac{\omega}{s^2 + \omega^2} \right] \tag{46}$$

Hence the poles of $Y(s)$ will be the poles of $H(s)$ plus the two imaginary poles of $U(s)$ at $s = j\omega$ and $s = -j\omega$. Provided that the system is stable, all the poles of $H(s)$ will be in the left half of the complex plane, and all the terms in the response corresponding to these poles will decay to zero as time increases. Thus the steady-state response will result from the imaginary poles of $U(s)$ and will be a sinusoid at the frequency ω. To determine the steady-state component of the response, we can write (46) as

$$Y(s) = H(s) \left[\frac{\omega}{(s - j\omega)(s + j\omega)} \right]$$

$$= \frac{C_1}{s - j\omega} + \frac{C_2}{s + j\omega} + [\text{terms corresponding to poles of } H(s)] \tag{47}$$

where

$$C_1 = (s - j\omega)Y(s)|_{s=j\omega}$$

$$= H(s) \frac{\omega}{(s + j\omega)} \bigg|_{s=j\omega}$$

$$= \frac{H(j\omega)}{2j}$$

The constant C_2 is the complex conjugate of C_1; that is,

$$C_2 = -\frac{H(-j\omega)}{2j}$$

Because all the terms in (47) corresponding to the poles of $H(s)$ will decay to zero if the system is stable, the transform of the steady-state response is

$$Y_{ss}(s) = \frac{H(j\omega)/2j}{s - j\omega} - \frac{H(-j\omega)/2j}{s + j\omega} \tag{48}$$

In general, $H(j\omega)$ is a complex quantity and may be written in polar form as

$$H(j\omega) = M(\omega)\epsilon^{j\theta(\omega)} \qquad (49)$$

where $M(\omega)$ is the magnitude of $H(j\omega)$ and $\theta(\omega)$ is its angle. Both M and θ depend on the value of ω, as is emphasized by the ω within the parentheses. The quantity $H(-j\omega)$ is the complex conjugate of $H(j\omega)$, and we can write it as

$$H(-j\omega) = M(\omega)\epsilon^{-j\theta(\omega)} \qquad (50)$$

Substituting (49) and (50) into (48) gives

$$Y_{ss}(s) = \frac{M}{2j}\left(\frac{\epsilon^{j\theta}}{s - j\omega} - \frac{\epsilon^{-j\theta}}{s + j\omega}\right)$$

Taking the inverse transforms of the two terms in $Y_{ss}(s)$, we find that

$$y_{ss}(t) = \frac{M}{2j}(\epsilon^{j\theta}\epsilon^{j\omega t} - \epsilon^{-j\theta}\epsilon^{-j\omega t})$$

$$= \frac{M}{2j}[\epsilon^{j(\omega t+\theta)} - \epsilon^{-j(\omega t+\theta)}]$$

Using the exponential form of the sine function, as in Table 6.1, we obtain

$$y_{ss}(t) = M\sin(\omega t + \theta) \qquad (51)$$

which has the form predicted in (45), where $A = M(\omega)$ and $\phi = \theta(\omega)$. One can use a similar derivation to show that for a stable system, the steady-state response to $u(t) = B\sin(\omega t + \phi_1)$ is

$$y_{ss}(t) = BM\sin(\omega t + \phi_1 + \theta) \qquad (52)$$

Likewise, the steady-state response to $u(t) = B\cos(\omega t + \phi_2)$ is

$$y_{ss}(t) = BM\cos(\omega t + \phi_2 + \theta) \qquad (53)$$

In summary, the sinusoidal-steady-state response of a stable linear system is a sinusoid having the same frequency as the input, an amplitude that is $M(\omega)$ times that of the input, and a phase angle that is $\theta(\omega)$ plus the input angle, where $M(\omega)$ and $\theta(\omega)$ are the magnitude and angle of $H(j\omega)$, respectively. As a consequence, the function $H(j\omega)$, which is the transfer function evaluated for $s = j\omega$, is known as the **frequency-response function**.

Calculating and interpreting the frequency-response function are illustrated in the following examples. In the first example, we find the steady-state response to a sinusoidal input that has a specified frequency. In the next two examples, we sketch curves of $M(\omega)$ and $\theta(\omega)$ as functions of ω. Such curves indicate how the magnitude and angle of the sinusoidal steady-state response change as the frequency of the input is changed.

▶ **EXAMPLE 8.12**

Use (49) and (53) to find the steady-state response of the system described by the transfer function

$$H(s) = \frac{9s + 14}{3(s^2 + 4s + 3)}$$

to the input $u(t) = 6 \cos 2t$, and compare the result to that from Example 8.5.

Solution

We replace s by $j\omega$ with $\omega = 2$ rad/s, the frequency of the input, to form

$$H(j2) = \frac{j18 + 14}{3(-4 + j8 + 3)} = \frac{14 + j18}{3(-1 + j8)}$$

The magnitude of $H(j2)$ is the magnitude of its numerator divided by the magnitude of its denominator:

$$M = \frac{|14 + j18|}{3|-1 + j8|} = \frac{22.80}{3(8.062)} = 0.9427$$

The angle of $H(j2)$ is the angle of its numerator minus the angle of its denominator:

$$\theta = \tan^{-1}(18/14) - \tan^{-1}(-8)$$

$$= 0.9098 - 1.695 = -0.7853 \text{ rad}$$

Thus, by (53),

$$y_{ss}(t) = 6(0.9427) \cos(2t - 0.7853)$$

$$= 5.656 \cos(2t - 0.7853)$$

which agrees with the steady-state portion of the response found in Example 8.5.

▶ **EXAMPLE 8.13**

Evaluate and sketch the magnitude and phase angle of the frequency-response function for the system described by the first-order equation $\dot{y} + (1/\tau)y = u(t)$.

Solution

The system transfer function is $H(s) = 1/(s + 1/\tau)$. When we replace s by $j\omega$, we find the system's frequency-response function to be

$$H(j\omega) = \frac{1}{j\omega + 1/\tau} \tag{54}$$

In order to identify the magnitude $M(\omega)$ and angle $\theta(\omega)$ for (54), we convert it to polar form. To find $M(\omega)$, we divide the magnitude of the numerator of (54) by the magnitude of the denominator, obtaining

$$M(\omega) = \frac{1}{[\omega^2 + (1/\tau)^2]^{1/2}}$$

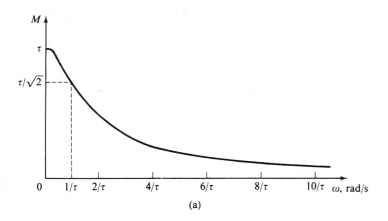

(a)

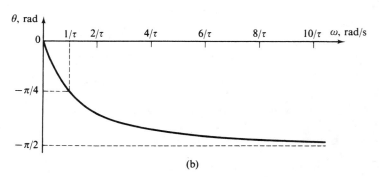

(b)

FIGURE 8.11   Frequency-response function for $\dot{y} + (1/\tau)y = u(t)$.
(a) Magnitude $M(\omega)$. (b) Phase angle $\theta(\omega)$.

Subtracting the angle of the denominator from the numerator angle, we find that the phase angle[3] of $H(j\omega)$ is

$$\theta(\omega) = \arg[1] - \arg[j\omega + 1/\tau]$$

$$= 0 - \tan^{-1}\omega\tau$$

$$= -\tan^{-1}\omega\tau$$

To assist us in sketching M versus ω and θ versus ω, we note that at $\omega = 0$ we have $M = \tau$ and $\theta = 0$. As ω approaches infinity, M diminishes monotonically to zero, and θ decreases to $-\frac{1}{2}\pi$ rad. At $\omega = 1/\tau$, $M = \tau/\sqrt{2}$ and $\theta = -\frac{1}{4}\pi$ rad. The actual functions are shown in Figure 8.11.

▶ **EXAMPLE 8.14**

The output for the circuit shown in Figure 8.12 is i_o. Find the frequency-response function $H(j\omega)$ and sketch its magnitude versus frequency.

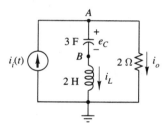

FIGURE 8.12   Circuit for Example 8.14.

Solution

We start by evaluating the circuit's transfer function $H(s)$, which is the ratio $I_o(s)/I_i(s)$ when the initial stored energy is zero. Applying Kirchhoff's current law at nodes A and B gives

$$3(\dot{e}_A - \dot{e}_B) + \frac{1}{2}e_A - i_i(t) = 0$$

$$3(\dot{e}_B - \dot{e}_A) + i_L(0) + \frac{1}{2}\int_0^t e_B(\lambda)d\lambda = 0$$

The output current is given by

$$i_o = \frac{1}{2}e_A$$

---

[3]The notation arg[z] denotes the angle of the complex quantity z. It is expressed in radians.

Transforming these equations with zero initial voltage across the capacitor and zero initial current through the inductor gives

$$(3s + \frac{1}{2})E_A(s) - 3s E_B(s) = I_i(s)$$

$$-3s E_A(s) + \left(3s + \frac{1}{2s}\right) E_B(s) = 0$$

$$I_o(s) = \frac{1}{2}E_A(s)$$

We can solve this set of three transformed equations for $H(s) = I_o(s)/I_i(s)$. The result is

$$H(s) = \frac{6s^2 + 1}{6s^2 + 6s + 1}$$

We find the system's frequency-response function by setting s equal to $j\omega$ in $H(s)$. Noting that $(j\omega)^2 = -\omega^2$, we get

$$H(j\omega) = \frac{-6\omega^2 + 1}{-6\omega^2 + j6\omega + 1}$$

The magnitude function is

$$M(\omega) = \frac{|1 - 6\omega^2|}{|1 - 6\omega^2 + j6\omega|}$$

$$= \frac{|1 - 6\omega^2|}{[(1 - 6\omega^2)^2 + (6\omega)^2]^{1/2}}$$

which is plotted versus ω in Figure 8.13. The phase angle $\theta(\omega)$ is given by

$$\theta(\omega) = \arg[1 - 6\omega^2] - \arg[1 - 6\omega^2 + j6\omega]$$

which could also be plotted versus frequency.

Note that when $\omega = 0$, $M(\omega)$ is unity. A sinusoidal function for which $\omega = 0$ reduces to a constant, so $H(0)$ is the steady-state response to the unit step function, which is consistent with our earlier discussion. We can check the fact that $H(0) = 1$ for Figure 8.12 by noting from Section 6.2 that when finding the steady-state response to a constant input, we can replace the inductor and capacitor by short and open circuits, respectively.

We see from Figure 8.13 that the sinusoidal-steady-state response is zero at a frequency of $\omega_1 = 1/\sqrt{6}$ rad/s. Because of the shape of the plot of $M(\omega)$ versus ω, such a circuit is often called a *notch filter*. For sinusoidal inputs with frequencies $\omega \ll \omega_1$ or $\omega \gg \omega_1$, the magnitude of the frequency-response function is approximately unity, which means that the amplitude of $(i_o)_{ss}$ will be close to that of $i_i(t)$. For inputs with $\omega \simeq 1/\sqrt{6}$ rad/s, however, the amplitude of $(i_o)_{ss}$ will be much less than that of $i_i(t)$. Hence sinusoidal inputs in this frequency range are substantially attenuated

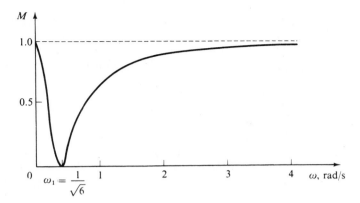

FIGURE 8.13 Frequency-response magnitude for the circuit in Example 8.14.

by the circuit. Such a circuit can be used to filter out unwanted signals that have frequencies close to ω_1 without significantly affecting signals at other frequencies.

Curves showing how the magnitude and angle of $H(j\omega)$ change with frequency constitute one of the important tools for the analysis and design of feedback control systems and will be used extensively in Chapter 14. It will become convenient to plot the curves somewhat differently, in the form of Bode diagrams, but the basic procedure is illustrated by the previous two examples.

8.6 IMPEDANCES

To find the transfer function for any linear system, we can transform the system's equations while assuming that there is no initial energy in the energy-storing elements. We can then solve for the transform of the output and after that, write the transfer function down by (21). However, when this needs to be done for the electrical part of a system, an easier method can be developed.

Consider the element laws for the resistor, inductor, and capacitor:

$$e(t) = Ri(t)$$

$$e(t) = L\frac{di}{dt} \tag{55}$$

$$i(t) = C\frac{de}{dt}$$

Transforming these equations, using the symbols $E(s) = \mathcal{L}[e(t)]$ and $I(s) = \mathcal{L}[i(t)]$, gives

$$E(s) = RI(s)$$
$$E(s) = L[sI(s) - i(0)] \tag{56}$$
$$I(s) = C[sE(s) - e(0)]$$

When determining the transfer function, we always assume that there is no initial stored energy. In the case of an inductor, this means that $i(0) = 0$; for a capacitor, it means that $e(0) = 0$. Under these circumstances, the previous transformed equations for the resistor, inductor, and capacitor reduce to

$$E(s) = RI(s) \tag{57a}$$

$$E(s) = sLI(s) \tag{57b}$$

$$E(s) = \frac{1}{sC}I(s) \tag{57c}$$

Equation (57a) looks exactly like Ohm's law for a resistor, except that transformed quantities are used for the voltage and current. Note that (57b) and (57c) have this same form, except that R is replaced by sL and $1/sC$, respectively. Thus we are led to define the **impedance** $Z(s)$ as the ratio of the transformed voltage to the transformed current when there is no initial stored energy. For the three types of passive circuit elements,

$$Z_R(s) = R \tag{58a}$$

$$Z_L(s) = sL \tag{58b}$$

$$Z_C(s) = \frac{1}{sC} \tag{58c}$$

Note that the impedance depends on the element value and on s. However, (57) and (58) are *algebraic* equations, with no derivative or integral signs and with no initial-condition terms. Furthermore, transforming the algebraic equations given by the interconnection laws (Kirchhoff's voltage and current laws) yields the same equations, but with the variables replaced by their Laplace transforms. When finding the transfer function, therefore, we can use all the rules for resistive circuits, even if the elements are not of the same type. This includes the procedures in Section 5.5 for series and parallel combinations, such as equivalent resistance and the voltage-divider and current-divider rules. For this reason, the impedance $Z(s)$ is sometimes viewed as a generalized resistance. It can be treated as a resistance, even though it is a function of s.

In order to avoid writing any time-domain equations, we redraw the circuit with the passive elements characterized by their impedances and the voltages and currents characterized by their Laplace transforms. The result is called the s-domain circuit. We can obtain the transfer function directly from it, using only the techniques for resistive circuits.

▶ **EXAMPLE 8.15**

Find the transfer function $H(s) = E_o(s)/E_i(s)$ for the circuit shown in Figure 8.14(a).

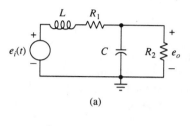

(a)

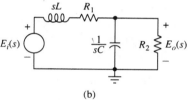

(b)

FIGURE 8.14 Circuit for Example 8.15. (a) Time-domain circuit. (b) s-domain circuit.

Solution

The s-domain circuit is drawn in Figure 8.14(b). The passive elements have been characterized by their impedances, as given in (58), and the input and output voltages by their Laplace transforms. The two right-hand elements are in parallel and can be replaced by the equivalent impedance

$$Z_2(s) = \frac{R_2/sC}{R_2 + 1/sC} = \frac{R_2}{1 + sCR_2}$$

Then, by the voltage-divider rule,

$$E_o(s) = \frac{Z_2(s)}{sL + R_1 + Z_2(s)} E_i(s)$$

$$= \frac{R_2}{(1 + sCR_2)(sL + R_1) + R_2} E_i(s)$$

$$= \left[\frac{R_2}{LCR_2s^2 + (L + R_1R_2C)s + (R_1 + R_2)} \right] E_i(s) \quad (59)$$

The quantity inside the brackets in (59) is the transfer function $H(s)$.

We saw from (17) and (20) how the transfer function and the input-output differential equation are directly related to one another. In the last example, the input-output equation for the transfer function in (59) would be

$$LCR_2\ddot{e}_o + (L + R_1 R_2 C)\dot{e}_o + (R_1 + R_2)e_o = R_2 e_i(t)$$

Note that for a constant input voltage $e_i(t) = A$, we can find the steady-state response by setting the derivatives of the output equal to zero, which yields

$$(e_0)_{ss} = \frac{R_2}{R_1 + R_2} A \tag{60}$$

This same result is achieved by replacing s by zero for the transfer function in (59). Alternatively, if we look at the original circuit in Figure 8.14(a) with the inductor and capacitor replaced by short and open circuits, respectively, we see that (60) follows immediately from the voltage-divider rule.

In the design of electrical networks, it is sometimes convenient to represent individual subnetworks by their impedances. Once a general expression for the transfer function has been found, we can then decide what to put inside the subnetworks in order to obtain a specific result. We conclude this section with two such examples involving an operational amplifier.

▶ **EXAMPLE 8.16**

Find the transfer function $H(s)$ for the s-domain circuit shown in Figure 8.15.

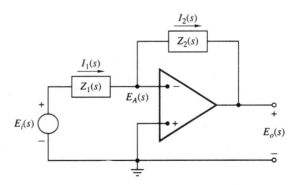

FIGURE 8.15   Circuit for Example 8.16.

Solution

From the virtual short concept discussed near the end of Section 5.7 for the ideal op-amp, we know that $E_A(s) = 0$ and that $I_1(s) = I_2(s)$. Thus

$$\frac{1}{Z_1(s)} E_i(s) = -\frac{1}{Z_2(s)} E_o(s)$$

from which the transfer function is seen to be

$$H(s) = \frac{E_o(s)}{E_i(s)} = -\frac{Z_2(s)}{Z_1(s)}$$

If, in the last example, we wanted $H(s) = K/s$, corresponding to an integrator, we could put a resistor R in the first subnetwork and a capacitor C in the second one. Then $Z_1(s) = R$, $Z_2(s) = 1/sC$, and $H(s) = -1/RCs$. The basic configuration in Figure 8.15 can be used to obtain a variety of useful transfer functions, as illustrated by some of the problems at the end of the chapter.

▶ **EXAMPLE 8.17**

Find the transfer function $H(s) = E_o(s)/E_i(s)$ for the s-domain circuit shown in Figure 8.16. Let $K = (R_1 + R_2)/R_1$.

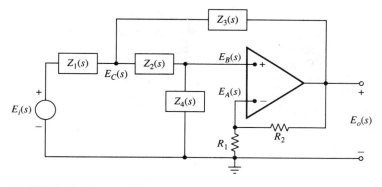

FIGURE 8.16   Circuit for Example 8.17.

Solution

This circuit can be relatively complex, with perhaps several elements inside each of the four boxes, but the general analysis is simplified by the use of impedances. Because no current flows into the input terminals of the op-amp, we can use the voltage-divider rule to write

$$E_A(s) = \frac{R_1}{R_1 + R_2} E_o(s) = \frac{1}{K} E_o(s)$$

$$E_B(s) = \frac{Z_4(s)}{Z_2(s) + Z_4(s)} E_C(s)$$

Using the virtual-short concept for the ideal op-amp, we know that $E_A(s) = E_B(s)$, so

$$E_C(s) = \frac{Z_2(s) + Z_4(s)}{K Z_4(s)} E_o(s) \tag{61}$$

Summing the currents at node C yields

$$\frac{1}{Z_1(s)}[E_C(s) - E_i(s)]$$

$$+ \frac{1}{Z_3(s)}[E_C(s) - E_o(s)] + \left[\frac{1}{Z_2(s) + Z_4(s)}\right] E_C(s) = 0 \quad (62)$$

Inserting (61) into (62), solving for $E_0(s)$, and simplifying, we obtain (after a little algebra) the following result:

$$H(s) = \frac{E_o(s)}{E_i(s)}$$

$$= \frac{K Z_3(s) Z_4(s)}{Z_1(s) Z_2(s) + (1 - K) Z_1(s) Z_4(s) + Z_3(s)[Z_1(s) + Z_2(s) + Z_4(s)]} \quad (63)$$

Even by considering very simple subnetworks for the blocks labeled $Z_1(s)$ through $Z_4(s)$ in Figure 8.16, we can obtain a number of useful results. Suppose, for example, that we want the denominator of the transfer function to be a quadratic in s and the numerator to be just a constant. We can put a single resistor inside blocks 1 and 2 and a single capacitor inside blocks 3 and 4. For simplicity, let $Z_1(s) = Z_2(s) = R$ and $Z_3(s) = Z_4(s) = 1/sC$. Then the general expression for the transfer function in (63) becomes

$$H(s) = \frac{\dfrac{K}{(RC)^2}}{s^2 + \dfrac{1}{RC}(3 - K)s + \left(\dfrac{1}{RC}\right)^2}$$

We can control the position of the poles of $H(s)$ by varying the parameter K. If, for example, $K = 3$ (corresponding to $R_2 = 2R_1$), the poles are on the imaginary axis of the complex plane. If $K = 1$ (corresponding to $R_2 = 0$), both the poles are on the negative real axis at $s = -1/RC$. Examples of the importance of controlling the pole and zero positions will be given in Chapter 14.

■ 8.7 TRANSFORM SOLUTION OF MATRIX STATE-VARIABLE EQUATIONS

For fixed linear systems, the matrix form of the state-variable and output equations is given by (6.62):

$$\dot{\mathbf{q}} = \mathbf{Aq} + \mathbf{Bu} \quad (64a)$$

$$\mathbf{y} = \mathbf{Cq} + \mathbf{Du} \quad (64b)$$

where the elements in the coefficient matrices **A**, **B**, **C**, and **D** are constants. Methods for solving these equations in the time domain were developed in Section 6.6. In this section, we use the Laplace transform to obtain a solution.

The Zero-Input Response

We start with the **zero-input response** for which $\mathbf{u} = \mathbf{0}$ for all $t > 0$ and for which the initial state $\mathbf{q}(0)$ has at least one nonzero element. Then the matrix form of the system model given by (64) reduces to

$$\dot{\mathbf{q}} = \mathbf{A}\mathbf{q} \tag{65a}$$

$$\mathbf{y} = \mathbf{C}\mathbf{q} \tag{65b}$$

where $\mathbf{q}(0)$ is specified and **A** and **C** are constant. Because (65a) represents a set of simultaneous linear differential equations, we can use the Laplace transform to solve them for $\mathbf{q}$. Once we have found the state vector, we need only premultiply it by the matrix **C** to find the output vector **y**.

The transform of a vector is defined to be that vector whose elements are the Laplace transforms of the corresponding time functions in the original vector.[4] For example, we denote the transform vector $\mathcal{L}[\mathbf{q}(t)]$ by $\mathbf{Q}(s)$ and define it to be

$$\mathbf{Q}(s) = \begin{bmatrix} Q_1(s) \\ Q_2(s) \\ \vdots \\ Q_n(s) \end{bmatrix}$$

where $Q_i(s) = \mathcal{L}[q_i(t)]$ for $i = 1, 2, \ldots, n$.

To transform the state-variable equation (65a), we first note that because the matrix **A** is constant, the transform of the right side is just $\mathbf{A}\mathbf{Q}(s)$. As for the left side of the equation, $\mathcal{L}[\dot{\mathbf{q}}]$ is a vector whose elements are the transforms of the corresponding state-variable derivatives. Recalling from Chapter 7 that $\mathcal{L}[\dot{q}_i] = sQ_i(s) - q_i(0)$, we can write

$$\mathcal{L}[\dot{\mathbf{q}}] = s\mathbf{Q}(s) - \mathbf{q}(0)$$

where $\mathbf{q}(0)$ is the vector of initial conditions. Thus, when transformed, (65a) becomes

$$s\mathbf{Q}(s) - \mathbf{q}(0) = \mathbf{A}\mathbf{Q}(s)$$

which can be rearranged to give

$$s\mathbf{Q}(s) - \mathbf{A}\mathbf{Q}(s) = \mathbf{q}(0) \tag{66}$$

---

[4]Capital letters followed by (s) are used for Laplace transforms, even when the time function is a vector.

To combine the two terms on the left side of (66), we note that $s\mathbf{Q}(s)$ can be written as $s\mathbf{IQ}(s)$, where $\mathbf{I}$ is the identity matrix of order n. Hence we can rewrite (66) as

$$(s\mathbf{I} - \mathbf{A})\mathbf{Q}(s) = \mathbf{q}(0) \tag{67}$$

where

$$s\mathbf{I} - \mathbf{A} = \begin{bmatrix} s - a_{11} & -a_{12} & \cdots & -a_{1n} \\ -a_{21} & s - a_{22} & \cdots & -a_{2n} \\ \vdots & \vdots & & \vdots \\ -a_{n1} & -a_{n2} & \cdots & s - a_{nn} \end{bmatrix}$$

We can find the transform of the state vector, $\mathbf{Q}(s)$, from (67) by pre-multiplying both of its sides by the inverse of the matrix $s\mathbf{I} - \mathbf{A}$, provided that this inverse exists—that is, provided that the matrix $s\mathbf{I} - \mathbf{A}$ is not singular. A square matrix is nonsingular if its determinant is nonzero, so we can solve for $\mathbf{Q}(s)$ provided that $|s\mathbf{I} - \mathbf{A}| \neq 0$. Hence the inverse of the matrix $s\mathbf{I} - \mathbf{A}$ will exist for all points in the complex s-plane except those points that coincide with the characteristic values (eigenvalues) of the matrix $\mathbf{A}$. This restriction is of no consequence in our solution for $\mathbf{q}$ because, as we shall see, these points (there are at most n of them) are the poles of the transform vector $\mathbf{Q}(s)$. A Laplace transform is infinite when s equals one of its poles, so we should not expect to obtain finite values for $\mathbf{Q}(s)$ at its poles by matrix inversion or any other method.

Except for values of s that coincide with a characteristic value of $\mathbf{A}$, we can write

$$\mathbf{Q}(s) = (s\mathbf{I} - \mathbf{A})^{-1}\mathbf{q}(0)$$

where $(s\mathbf{I} - \mathbf{A})^{-1}$ is an $n \times n$ matrix known as the **resolvent matrix**, each element of which is a function of s. Denoting the resolvent matrix by the symbol $\boldsymbol{\Phi}(s)$, we have

$$\mathbf{Q}(s) = \boldsymbol{\Phi}(s)\mathbf{q}(0) \tag{68}$$

where

$$\boldsymbol{\Phi}(s) = (s\mathbf{I} - \mathbf{A})^{-1} \tag{69}$$

All that remains is to take the inverse Laplace transform of $\mathbf{Q}(s)$, which gives

$$\mathbf{q}(t) = \mathcal{L}^{-1}\{\mathbf{Q}(s)\}$$
$$= \mathcal{L}^{-1}\{\boldsymbol{\Phi}(s)\mathbf{q}(0)\}$$

Because the vector $\mathbf{q}(0)$ does not involve the variable s, we may calculate the inverse transform of $\boldsymbol{\Phi}(s)$ first and then multiply it by $\mathbf{q}(0)$, obtaining

$$\mathbf{q}(t) = \mathcal{L}^{-1}\{\boldsymbol{\Phi}(s)\}\mathbf{q}(0)$$

When we denote the inverse transform of $\mathbf{\Phi}(s)$ by $\phi(t)$, which will be an $n \times n$ matrix, the desired expression for the zero-input response is

$$\mathbf{q}(t) = \phi(t)\mathbf{q}(0) \tag{70}$$

where

$$\phi(t) = \mathcal{L}^{-1}\{\mathbf{\Phi}(s)\}$$

The State-Transition Matrix

The matrix $\phi(t)$ is known as the **state-transition matrix**. The inverse of a matrix can be written as its adjoint matrix divided by its determinant (see Appendix C), so we can write the resolvent matrix from (69) as

$$\mathbf{\Phi}(s) = \frac{1}{|s\mathbf{I} - \mathbf{A}|} \, \text{adj} \, [s\mathbf{I} - \mathbf{A}] \tag{71}$$

where $\text{adj} \, [s\mathbf{I} - \mathbf{A}]$ denotes the adjoint matrix of $s\mathbf{I} - \mathbf{A}$. Thus the state-transition matrix $\phi(t)$ can be written as

$$\phi(t) = \mathcal{L}^{-1}\left[\frac{1}{|s\mathbf{I} - \mathbf{A}|} \, \text{adj} \, [s\mathbf{I} - \mathbf{A}]\right] \tag{72}$$

Evaluating $(s\mathbf{I} - \mathbf{A})^{-1}$ is difficult computationally because the matrix to be inverted is a function of s. Methods exist that are better suited for this task than using the adjoint matrix. However, our principal objective is to develop certain theoretical properties and to show the form of $\phi(t)$. For these tasks and for computational problems with matrices of order three or less, the adjoint method is acceptable.

As summarized in Appendix C, the adjoint of an $n \times n$ matrix is itself an $n \times n$ matrix that is the transposed matrix of cofactors, where the cofactor of an element is a determinant of order $n - 1$. It follows that $\text{adj} \, [s\mathbf{I} - \mathbf{A}]$ will be an $n \times n$ matrix whose elements are polynomials in s of degree $n - 1$ or less. Furthermore, the determinant of $s\mathbf{I} - \mathbf{A}$ is

$$|s\mathbf{I} - \mathbf{A}| = \begin{vmatrix} s - a_{11} & -a_{12} & \cdots & -a_{1n} \\ -a_{21} & s - a_{22} & \cdots & -a_{2n} \\ \vdots & \vdots & & \vdots \\ -a_{n1} & -a_{n2} & \cdots & s - a_{nn} \end{vmatrix}$$

which will always reduce to a polynomial in s of degree n. This polynomial is the **characteristic polynomial** of the matrix $\mathbf{A}$. Hence the matrix $\mathbf{\Phi}(s)$ defined by (71) is an $n \times n$ matrix whose elements are rational functions of s having numerators of lower degree than that of the denominator. Specifically, a general element of $\mathbf{\Phi}(s)$ will be of the form

$$\frac{\beta_{n-1}s^{n-1} + \cdots + \beta_0}{s^n + \alpha_{n-1}s^{n-1} + \cdots + \alpha_0}$$

where the numerator coefficients $\beta_{n-1}, \ldots, \beta_0$ depend on the specific row and column of the element. The denominator, however, which comes from the evaluation of $|s\mathbf{I} - \mathbf{A}|$, will be the characteristic polynomial and thus will be the same for each element of $\boldsymbol{\Phi}(s)$.

In principle, at least, the characteristic polynomial can be factored into the form

$$|s\mathbf{I} - \mathbf{A}| = s^n + \alpha_{n-1}s^{n-1} + \cdots + \alpha_0$$
$$= (s - s_1)(s - s_2) \cdots (s - s_n) \tag{73}$$

where the quantities $s_1, s_2, \ldots, s_n$ are known as the **characteristic values (eigenvalues)** of the matrix $\mathbf{A}$ (see Appendix C). Having factored the characteristic polynomial, we can evaluate the inverse transform of $\boldsymbol{\Phi}(s)$ by performing a partial-fraction expansion of each of its elements. If the characteristic values of $\mathbf{A}$ are distinct, a typical element of the resolvent matrix will have as its expansion

$$\Phi_{ij}(s) = \frac{\gamma_1}{s - s_1} + \frac{\gamma_2}{s - s_2} + \cdots + \frac{\gamma_n}{s - s_n}$$

and the corresponding term in the state-transition matrix will be

$$\phi_{ij}(t) = \gamma_1 \epsilon^{s_1 t} + \gamma_2 \epsilon^{s_2 t} + \cdots + \gamma_n \epsilon^{s_n t} \tag{74}$$

where, of course, the values of $\gamma_1, \gamma_2, \ldots, \gamma_n$ depend on the element being considered. Thus the state-transition matrix $\boldsymbol{\phi}(t)$ is an $n \times n$ matrix each of whose elements is a linear combination of the n mode functions $\epsilon^{s_1 t}, \ldots, \epsilon^{s_n t}$, where the s_i are the characteristic values of the matrix $\mathbf{A}$.

▶ **EXAMPLE 8.18**

Evaluate the state-transition matrix for a system that obeys the state-variable equation $\dot{\mathbf{q}} = \mathbf{A}\mathbf{q}$, where

$$\mathbf{A} = \begin{bmatrix} 0 & 1 \\ -6 & -5 \end{bmatrix}$$

and identify the corresponding mode functions.

Solution

First we write the matrix $s\mathbf{I} - \mathbf{A}$ in numerical form and evaluate its determinant and inverse. Thus

$$s\mathbf{I} - \mathbf{A} = \begin{bmatrix} s & -1 \\ 6 & s + 5 \end{bmatrix}$$

and

$$|s\mathbf{I} - \mathbf{A}| = s^2 + 5s + 6 = (s + 2)(s + 3)$$

Before taking the inverse of $s\mathbf{I} - \mathbf{A}$, we note that the characteristic polynomial associated with $\mathbf{A}$ is $P(s) = (s + 2)(s + 3)$. Hence the characteristic values, which must satisfy $P(s) = 0$, are $s_1 = -2$ and $s_2 = -3$. This means that the mode functions of which the zero-input response is composed are ϵ^{-2t} and ϵ^{-3t}.

The next step is to find the resolvent matrix $\mathbf{\Phi}(s) = (s\mathbf{I} - \mathbf{A})^{-1}$. Following the steps outlined here and illustrated in Appendix C for taking the inverse of a matrix, we find the adjoint of $s\mathbf{I} - \mathbf{A}$ to be

$$\text{adj}\,[s\mathbf{I} - \mathbf{A}] = \begin{bmatrix} s+5 & 1 \\ -6 & s \end{bmatrix}$$

Dividing each element of the adjoint matrix by $|s\mathbf{I} - \mathbf{A}|$, we find that

$$\mathbf{\Phi}(s) = \begin{bmatrix} \dfrac{s+5}{(s+2)(s+3)} & \dfrac{1}{(s+2)(s+3)} \\[2ex] \dfrac{-6}{(s+2)(s+3)} & \dfrac{s}{(s+2)(s+3)} \end{bmatrix} \tag{75}$$

Carrying out a partial-fraction expansion of each of the four elements on the right side of (75), we get

$$\mathbf{\Phi}(s) = \begin{bmatrix} \dfrac{3}{s+2} - \dfrac{2}{s+3} & \dfrac{1}{s+2} - \dfrac{1}{s+3} \\[2ex] -\dfrac{6}{s+2} + \dfrac{6}{s+3} & -\dfrac{2}{s+2} + \dfrac{3}{s+3} \end{bmatrix} \tag{76}$$

By taking the inverse transform of each element of $\mathbf{\Phi}(s)$, we find the state-transition matrix to be

$$\phi(t) = \begin{bmatrix} 3\epsilon^{-2t} - 2\epsilon^{-3t} & \epsilon^{-2t} - \epsilon^{-3t} \\ -6\epsilon^{-2t} + 6\epsilon^{-3t} & -2\epsilon^{-2t} + 3\epsilon^{-3t} \end{bmatrix} \tag{77}$$

The state-transition matrix corresponding to the matrix $\mathbf{A}$ used in the last example was also obtained in Example 6.10, where the solution was carried out entirely in the time domain. The expression for $\phi(t)$ in (77) is identical to that for $\epsilon^{\mathbf{A}t}$ in (6.73). A number of important properties of the state-transition matrix were discussed in Section 6.6, including the fact that $\phi(t) = \epsilon^{\mathbf{A}t}$.

Once $\phi(t)$ is known, the state vector $\mathbf{q}(t)$ can be found from (70) in terms of the initial state vector $\mathbf{q}(0)$. Each of the state variables $q_i(t)$ will be a linear combination of the system's mode functions, with the relative weightings dependent on the initial state vector $\mathbf{q}(0)$ and on the partial fraction coefficients $\gamma_1, \gamma_2, \ldots, \gamma_n$ in (74). The output vector $\mathbf{y}(t)$ then follows directly from (65b). This procedure was illustrated in some detail in Example 6.12.

Solution for the Zero-State Response

Having analyzed the zero-input response of a fixed linear system described in state-variable form, we now consider the **zero-state response** for which $\mathbf{q}(0) = \mathbf{0}$ but the input $\mathbf{u}$ is not zero. The system model is given by (64), which is repeated here:

$$\dot{\mathbf{q}} = \mathbf{Aq} + \mathbf{Bu} \tag{78a}$$

$$\mathbf{y} = \mathbf{Cq} + \mathbf{Du} \tag{78b}$$

If (78a) is transformed with $\mathbf{q}(0) = \mathbf{0}$, we get

$$s\mathbf{Q}(s) = \mathbf{A}\mathbf{Q}(s) + \mathbf{B}\mathbf{U}(s)$$

where $\mathbf{U}(s) = \mathscr{L}[\mathbf{u}(t)]$. As we did for the zero-input response, we solve the transformed equation for $\mathbf{Q}(s)$, obtaining

$$\mathbf{Q}(s) = (s\mathbf{I} - \mathbf{A})^{-1}\mathbf{B}\mathbf{U}(s)$$

$$= \mathbf{\Phi}(s)\mathbf{B}\mathbf{U}(s) \tag{79}$$

where $(s\mathbf{I} - \mathbf{A})^{-1}$ is the resolvent matrix $\mathbf{\Phi}(s)$. Hence we can write the zero-state response of $\mathbf{q}$ as

$$\mathbf{q}(t) = \mathscr{L}^{-1}[\mathbf{\Phi}(s)\mathbf{B}\mathbf{U}(s)]$$

As we shall see, the zero-state response consists of a combination of the free response and the forced response. Rather than proceed further with the response of the state vector $\mathbf{q}$, we shall obtain $\mathbf{Y}(s)$, the transform of the output vector. Transforming the output equation (78b) and substituting (79) give

$$\mathbf{Y}(s) = \mathbf{C}\mathbf{\Phi}(s)\mathbf{B}\mathbf{U}(s) + \mathbf{D}\mathbf{U}(s)$$

$$= [\mathbf{C}\mathbf{\Phi}(s)\mathbf{B} + \mathbf{D}]\mathbf{U}(s) \tag{80}$$

Recall that the system transfer function $H(s)$ was defined as the ratio $Y(s)/U(s)$, where $Y(s)$ is the transform of the zero-state response. As a consequence of this definition, we could write $Y(s) = H(s)U(s)$. When dealing with matrices as we are here, we cannot divide $Y(s)$ by $U(s)$. However, we can define the **transfer-function matrix** $\mathbf{H}(s)$ to be the quantity in brackets on the right side of (80), which when multiplied by $\mathbf{U}(s)$ gives $\mathbf{Y}(s)$.

Thus the transfer-function matrix is

$$\mathbf{H}(s) = \mathbf{C}\mathbf{\Phi}(s)\mathbf{B} + \mathbf{D} \tag{81}$$

and the Laplace transform of the zero-state output vector is

$$\mathbf{Y}(s) = \mathbf{H}(s)\mathbf{U}(s) \tag{82}$$

Often the output $\mathbf{y}$ is a function of only the state vector $\mathbf{q}$, in which case $\mathbf{D} = \mathbf{0}$ and (81) simplifies to

$$\mathbf{H}(s) = \mathbf{C}\mathbf{\Phi}(s)\mathbf{B} \tag{83}$$

We now define the **impulse-response matrix h**(t) as the inverse Laplace transform of the transfer-function matrix **H**(s). Thus

$$\mathbf{h}(t) = \mathcal{L}^{-1}[\mathbf{H}(s)] \tag{84}$$

is a $p \times m$ matrix of time functions such that $h_{ij}(t)$ is the response of y_i when u_j is a unit impulse, when all other inputs are zero, and when the initial value of the state vector is $\mathbf{q}(0) = \mathbf{0}$.

▶ *EXAMPLE 8.19*

Evaluate the transfer-function matrix **H**(s) for the system described by the matrix equations

$$\dot{\mathbf{q}} = \begin{bmatrix} 0 & 1 \\ -6 & -5 \end{bmatrix} \mathbf{q} + \begin{bmatrix} 2 & 1 \\ -1 & 0 \end{bmatrix} \mathbf{u}$$

$$\mathbf{y} = \begin{bmatrix} 2 & -1 \\ 0 & 1 \end{bmatrix} \mathbf{q} \tag{85}$$

Then use **H**(s) to find the zero-state response to the input vector

$$\mathbf{u} = \begin{bmatrix} \epsilon^{-t} U(t) \\ U(t) \end{bmatrix} \tag{86}$$

Solution

The system described by (85) has the same matrix **A** for which we found **Φ**(s) in Example 8.18. Using (75) for **Φ**(s), identifying **B** and **C** from (85), and noting that **D** = **0**, we can write (83) as

$$\mathbf{H}(s) = \begin{bmatrix} 2 & -1 \\ 0 & 1 \end{bmatrix} \begin{bmatrix} \dfrac{s+5}{(s+2)(s+3)} & \dfrac{1}{(s+2)(s+3)} \\ \dfrac{-6}{(s+2)(s+3)} & \dfrac{s}{(s+2)(s+3)} \end{bmatrix} \begin{bmatrix} 2 & 1 \\ -1 & 0 \end{bmatrix}$$

$$= \begin{bmatrix} 2 & -1 \\ 0 & 1 \end{bmatrix} \begin{bmatrix} \dfrac{2s+9}{(s+2)(s+3)} & \dfrac{s+5}{(s+2)(s+3)} \\ \dfrac{-s-12}{(s+2)(s+3)} & \dfrac{-6}{(s+2)(s+3)} \end{bmatrix}$$

$$= \begin{bmatrix} \dfrac{5s+30}{(s+2)(s+3)} & \dfrac{2s+16}{(s+2)(s+3)} \\ \dfrac{-s-12}{(s+2)(s+3)} & \dfrac{-6}{(s+2)(s+3)} \end{bmatrix} \tag{87}$$

As indicated by (87), **H**(s) is a 2×2 matrix, each element of which is a transfer function having the same two poles (at $s_1 = -2$ and $s_2 = -3$) and zeros that depend on its position in the matrix.

To find $\mathbf{Y}(s)$, we transform the input vector defined by (86), getting

$$\mathbf{U}(s) = \begin{bmatrix} \dfrac{1}{s+1} \\ \dfrac{1}{s} \end{bmatrix} \tag{88}$$

and then use (82) and (87) to write

$$\mathbf{Y}(s) = \begin{bmatrix} \dfrac{5s+30}{(s+2)(s+3)} & \dfrac{2s+16}{(s+2)(s+3)} \\ \dfrac{-s-12}{(s+2)(s+3)} & \dfrac{-6}{(s+2)(s+3)} \end{bmatrix} \begin{bmatrix} \dfrac{1}{s+1} \\ \dfrac{1}{s} \end{bmatrix}$$

$$= \begin{bmatrix} \dfrac{7s^2+48s+16}{s(s+1)(s+2)(s+3)} \\ \dfrac{-(s^2+18s+6)}{s(s+1)(s+2)(s+3)} \end{bmatrix}$$

We can now evaluate the zero-state responses of the two outputs y_1 and y_2 by performing a partial-fraction expansion of each element of $\mathbf{Y}(s)$. You can verify that the expansions of the two elements of $\mathbf{Y}(s)$ are

$$Y_1(s) = \frac{8/3}{s} + \frac{25/2}{s+1} - \frac{26}{s+2} + \frac{65/6}{s+3}$$

$$Y_2(s) = -\frac{1}{s} - \frac{11/2}{s+1} + \frac{13}{s+2} - \frac{13/2}{s+3}$$

Thus the zero-state response of the output vector is

$$\mathbf{y}(t) = \begin{bmatrix} \dfrac{8}{3} + \dfrac{25}{2}\epsilon^{-t} - 26\epsilon^{-2t} + \dfrac{65}{6}\epsilon^{-3t} \\ -1 - \dfrac{11}{2}\epsilon^{-t} + 13\epsilon^{-2t} - \dfrac{13}{2}\epsilon^{-3t} \end{bmatrix} \tag{89}$$

which holds for $t > 0$. Actually, (89) is valid for $t \geq 0$, because $\mathbf{y}(0) = \mathbf{y}(0+) = \mathbf{0}$.

Solution for the Complete Response

By the superposition property, the response of a linear system to a nonzero initial state vector $\mathbf{q}(0)$ and a nonzero input vector $\mathbf{u}$ is the sum of the zero-input and zero-state responses. It is known as the **complete response**. As an alternative to finding the zero-input and zero-state responses as functions of time and adding them, we can add their respective Laplace transforms to give the transform of the complete response. We shall develop this approach for the case when $\mathbf{D} = \mathbf{0}$ and then apply the result to the system considered in Example 8.19.

The transform of the zero-input state vector is given by (68) as

$$\mathbf{Q}(s) = \mathbf{\Phi}(s)\mathbf{q}(0)$$

With $\mathbf{D} = \mathbf{0}$, the output vector is

$$\mathbf{y} = \mathbf{Cq}$$

so the transform of the zero-input response, denoted here by $\mathbf{Y}_{zi}(s)$, is

$$\mathbf{Y}_{zi}(s) = \mathbf{C}\mathbf{\Phi}(s)\mathbf{q}(0) \tag{90}$$

For the transform of the zero-state response, denoted here by $\mathbf{Y}_{zs}(s)$, we can use (82) and (83) to write

$$\mathbf{Y}_{zs}(s) = \mathbf{C}\mathbf{\Phi}(s)\mathbf{B}\mathbf{U}(s) \tag{91}$$

Because of the superposition property for linear systems and the superposition theorem for Laplace transforms, the transform of the complete response is

$$\mathbf{Y}(s) = \mathbf{Y}_{zi}(s) + \mathbf{Y}_{zs}(s)$$
$$= \mathbf{C}\mathbf{\Phi}(s)\mathbf{q}(0) + \mathbf{C}\mathbf{\Phi}(s)\mathbf{B}\mathbf{U}(s)$$
$$= \mathbf{C}\mathbf{\Phi}(s)[\mathbf{q}(0) + \mathbf{B}\mathbf{U}(s)] \tag{92}$$

Having found $\mathbf{Y}(s)$ in numerical form by using (92), we can take its inverse Laplace transform element by element.

▶ *EXAMPLE 8.20*

Evaluate $\mathbf{y}$ for the system defined in Example 8.19 for the initial state vector

$$\mathbf{q}(0) = \begin{bmatrix} -1 \\ 1 \end{bmatrix}$$

and the input vector

$$\mathbf{u} = \begin{bmatrix} \epsilon^{-t}U(t) \\ U(t) \end{bmatrix}$$

Solution

Although the zero-input response of this system was found in general terms in Example 6.12, and the zero-state response for the specified input was found in Example 8.19, we shall use (92) to find $\mathbf{Y}(s)$ and take its inverse transform. You can use the functions of time found in Example 6.12 and Example 8.19 to verify that the result obtained here is correct.

Using (75) for $\mathbf{\Phi}(s)$ and transforming $\mathbf{u}$, we can substitute the appropriate matrices into (92) to write

$$\mathbf{Y}(s) = \begin{bmatrix} 2 & -1 \\ 0 & 1 \end{bmatrix} \begin{bmatrix} \dfrac{s+5}{(s+2)(s+3)} & \dfrac{1}{(s+2)(s+3)} \\ \dfrac{-6}{(s+2)(s+3)} & \dfrac{s}{(s+2)(s+3)} \end{bmatrix}$$

$$\times \left\{ \begin{bmatrix} -1 \\ 1 \end{bmatrix} + \begin{bmatrix} 2 & 1 \\ -1 & 0 \end{bmatrix} \begin{bmatrix} \dfrac{1}{s+1} \\ \dfrac{1}{s} \end{bmatrix} \right\}$$

$$= \begin{bmatrix} \dfrac{2s+16}{(s+2)(s+3)} & \dfrac{-s+2}{(s+2)(s+3)} \\ \dfrac{-6}{(s+2)(s+3)} & \dfrac{s}{(s+2)(s+3)} \end{bmatrix} \begin{bmatrix} \dfrac{-s^2+2s+1}{s(s+1)} \\ \dfrac{s^2}{s(s+1)} \end{bmatrix}$$

$$= \begin{bmatrix} \dfrac{-3s^3 - 10s^2 + 34s + 16}{s(s+1)(s+2)(s+3)} \\ \dfrac{s^3 + 6s^2 - 12s - 6}{s(s+1)(s+2)(s+3)} \end{bmatrix} \tag{93}$$

Using partial-fraction expansions of the two elements of $\mathbf{Y}(s)$ leads to the complete response $\mathbf{y}$:

$$\mathbf{y}(t) = \begin{bmatrix} \frac{8}{3} + \frac{25}{2}\epsilon^{-t} - 34\epsilon^{-2t} + \frac{95}{6}\epsilon^{-3t} \\ -1 - \frac{11}{2}\epsilon^{-t} + 17\epsilon^{-2t} - \frac{19}{2}\epsilon^{-3t} \end{bmatrix} \tag{94}$$

This result is valid for $t > 0$. If we set $t = 0$ in (94), we get -3 and 1 for the two elements of $\mathbf{y}$, which is also the result of the matrix product $\mathbf{Cq}(0)$. The fact that these results are the same indicates that, in this example, $\mathbf{y}$ is continuous at $t = 0$.

In closing, it is worthwhile to comment on the computational task of evaluating the response of a multi-input, multi-output system. The second-order model used in the examples in this section is simple enough to permit us to evaluate the response in analytical form by hand. To do the same operations by hand for a third- or higher-order system would probably not be feasible. In such cases, we must usually resort to the digital computer. A direct solution can apply the methods described here or other algorithms that are better suited for computation. Alternatively, we can obtain a numerical simulation of the system's differential equation by using the methods presented in Chapter 15.

SUMMARY

The transform of the zero-input response has the form $Y(s) = F(s)/P(s)$, where $F(s)$ is a polynomial that depends on the initial conditions. The mode functions, which characterize the form of the zero-input response, are determined from the roots of the characteristic equation $P(s) = 0$. The weighting of the mode functions depends on the initial energy in each of the energy-storing elements.

When the initial stored energy is zero, the transform of the output is given by $Y(s) = H(s)U(s)$, where $H(s)$ is the transfer function and $U(s)$ is the transform of the input. The transfer function can be written down by inspection of the input-output differential equation, can be found by transforming the system equations with the initial condition terms set equal to zero, or (in the case of electrical systems) can be found by using impedances. The poles and zeros are the values of s for which $H(s)$ becomes infinite or vanishes, respectively. The poles of $H(s)$ are identical to the roots of the characteristic equation $P(s) = 0$.

Two important special cases of the zero-state response are the unit impulse response $h(t)$ and the unit step response $y_U(t)$. Because they are found when the system is initially at rest, they are both zero for $t \leq 0$. For $t > 0$, $h(t) = \mathcal{L}^{-1}[H(s)]$ and $y_U(t) = \mathcal{L}^{-1}[H(s)/s]$.

For a stable system with an input that does not decay to zero, the steady-state response does not depend on the initial conditions. For the steady-state response to sinusoidal inputs, we can use the frequency-response function $H(j\omega)$. If $M(\omega)$ and $\theta(\omega)$ denote the magnitude and angle of $H(j\omega)$, then the steady-state response to $u(t) = B \sin(\omega t + \phi_1)$ is $y_{ss}(t) = BM \sin(\omega t + \phi_1 + \theta)$.

The time-domain solution of the matrix form of the state-variable model was included in Chapter 6. The corresponding transform solution is discussed in the final section of this chapter.

PROBLEMS

8.1 a) Repeat Example 8.1 for the parameter values $J = 1$ kg·m², $B = 4$ N·m·s/rad, and $K = 4$ N·m/rad and for no applied torque.
b) Identify the mode functions. For each mode function, give the restrictions on the initial conditions needed to eliminate it from the zero-input response.

* 8.2 Repeat Example 8.3 for the initial conditions $\theta_1(0) = \theta_2(0) = 0$ and $\dot{\theta}_1(0) = \dot{\theta}_2(0) = 0.5$ rad/s.

8.3 Use the expression for $E_o(s)$ in the statement of Problem 7.29 to obtain the zero-input response of the circuit shown in Figure P7.29 when $R = 2/9\ \Omega$. Identify the mode functions. For each mode function, give the restrictions on the initial conditions needed to eliminate it from the zero-input response.

8.4 Repeat Problem 8.3 when $R = 2/7\ \Omega$.

* 8.5 Repeat Problem 8.3 when $R = 2/3\ \Omega$.

8.6 a) Find the transfer function $H(s)$ for the circuit shown in Figure P7.29.
b) Find expressions for the damping ratio ζ and the undamped natural frequency ω_n in terms of the resistance R.
c) Find the zero-state response to the input $e_i(t) = 1 + \epsilon^{-2t}$ for $t > 0$ when $R = 2/7\ \Omega$. Explain why there is no steady-state response even though there

$E_o(s) = \dfrac{-5\, e_c(0) - 2 i_L(0) + (s^2 + 9s)\, E_i(s)}{s^2 + 10s + 16}$

$E_o(s) = \dfrac{A}{s+2} + \dfrac{A_2}{s+8}$, $\qquad A_1 = \tfrac{1}{3}(e_c(0) - i_L(0))$

$\qquad\qquad\qquad\qquad\qquad A_2 = \tfrac{1}{3}(4 e_c(0) - i_L(0))$

is a constant term in the input.

* **8.7** Find the transfer function $X_R(s)/F_a(s)$ for the third-order mechanical system modeled in Example 3.5.

8.8 **a)** For the translational mechanical system described in Problem 2.4, let $M_1 = M_2 = B_1 = B_2 = B_3 = K_1 = K_2 = K_3 = 1$ in a consistent set of units. Verify that the system can be modeled by the pair of differential equations

$$\ddot{x}_1 + 2\dot{x}_1 + 2x_1 - \dot{x}_2 - x_2 = f_a(t)$$
$$-\dot{x}_1 - x_1 + \ddot{x}_2 + 2\dot{x}_2 + 2x_2 = 0$$

b) Find the transfer function when the output is x_1.
c) Repeat part (b) when the output is x_2. Comment on the similarities and dissimilarities between the two transfer functions.

8.9 **a)** Find the transfer function for the translational system modeled in Example 2.6 when the output is z_1, the displacement of the frame M_1 relative to its equilibrium position when the applied force is zero. Take the parameter values to be $M_1 = M_2 = B = K_1 = K_2 = K_3 = 1$ in a consistent set of units.
b) Repeat part (a) when the output is z_2.

* **8.10** Find the transfer function of the rotational mechanical system modeled in Example 4.11 when the output is x.

8.11 Find the transfer function of the mechanical system modeled in Example 4.12, which has both translational and rotational elements, when the output is z.

* **8.12** **a)** Find the Laplace transform of the zero-input response of the circuit modeled in Example 5.9.
b) Find the transfer function $E_o(s)/E_i(s)$.

8.13 **a)** Plot the pole-zero pattern for the transfer function

$$H(s) = \frac{s+1}{s^2 + 5s + 6}$$

b) Write the general form of the zero-input response and find the system's input-output differential equation.
c) Use the initial-value and final-value theorems, if they are applicable, to determine the values of the unit step response at $t = 0+$ and when t approaches infinity.
d) Find the unit step response $y_U(t)$ and the unit impulse response $h(t)$ using $H(s)$.

* **8.14** Repeat Problem 8.13 for

$$H(s) = \frac{s^2 + 2s + 2}{s^2 + 4s + 4}$$

8.15 Repeat Problem 8.13 for

$$H(s) = \frac{s+3}{s^3 + 7s^2 + 10s}$$

8.16 Repeat Problem 8.13 for

$$H(s) = \frac{12}{s(s^2 + 2s + 4)}$$

* 8.17 Repeat Problem 8.13 for

$$H(s) = \frac{s^2}{(2s + 1)(s^2 + 4)}$$

8.18 Solve the differential equation in Problem 6.23 for the unit impulse response and the unit step response by using (38) and (41). Sketch both responses on the same axes.

8.19 Repeat Problem 8.18 for the differential equation in Problem 6.25.

* 8.20 Repeat Problem 8.18 for the differential equation in Problem 6.24.

8.21 a) Find the transfer function for a system that obeys the equation

$$\ddot{y} + 4\dot{y} + 4y = u(t)$$

and use it to evaluate the unit step response.

b) Differentiate the answer to part (a) and compare the result to the unit impulse response found in Example 7.9.

8.22 Find the zero-state response of a system described by the transfer function in Problem 8.13 to the input $t\epsilon^{-t}$ for $t > 0$. Identify the free response $y_H(t)$, the forced response $y_P(t)$, and the transient terms.

* 8.23 a) Verify that the transfer function for the circuit shown in Figure P8.23 is

$$H(s) = \frac{s^2 + 2s + 1}{s^2 + 4s + 4}$$

b) Find the unit impulse response.
c) Find the unit step response.

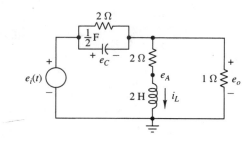

FIGURE P8.23

8.24 By a derivation similar to the one used to obtain (51), show that the steady-state response of a stable system to the input $u(t) = B \cos \omega t$ is $y_{ss}(t) = BM \cos(\omega t + \theta)$, where M and θ are given by (49).

8.25 Derive the expression given in (52) for the steady-state response to $u(t) = B \sin(\omega t + \phi_1)$.

8.26 For each of the following transfer functions, plot the pole-zero pattern, draw curves of $M(\omega)$ versus ω and $\theta(\omega)$ versus ω, and comment briefly on your results.

For the function in part (c), include the numerical values for $\omega = 9.9$, 10.0, and 10.1 rad/s.

a) $H(s) = \dfrac{2}{s^2 + 2s + 1}$

[handwritten:] $H(j\omega) = \dfrac{2}{-\omega^2 + 2\omega j + 1} = \dfrac{2}{(1-\omega^2) + 2\omega j}$

b) $H(s) = \dfrac{2s^2}{s^2 + 2s + 1}$

[handwritten:] $M = \dfrac{2}{\sqrt{(1-\omega^2)^2 + 4\omega^2}} = \dfrac{2}{\sqrt{1 - 2\omega^2 + \omega^4 + 4\omega^2}}$

c) $H(s) = \dfrac{s}{s^2 + 0.2s + 100}$

[handwritten:] $= \dfrac{2}{\sqrt{1 + 2\omega^2 + \omega^4}} = \dfrac{2}{\sqrt{(1+\omega^2)^2}}$

* 8.27 Repeat Problem 8.26 for the following transfer functions.

a) $H(s) = \dfrac{s - 1}{s + 1}$

[handwritten:] $M = \dfrac{2}{1 + \omega^2}$

b) $H(s) = \dfrac{(s + 1)^2}{s(s + 5)}$

[handwritten:] $\theta = 0° + \tan^{-1}\left(\dfrac{2\omega}{1-\omega^2}\right)$

c) $H(s) = \dfrac{s}{(s^2 + 0.2s + 100)^2}$

8.28 For the differential equation given in Example 6.1, find $H(j\omega)$ and $H(0)$. Also use (53) to verify the steady-state response to each of the inputs given in the example.

* 8.29 The steady-state response of a stable system to the input

$$u(t) = \sin 5t + \sin 10t + \sin 15t$$

has the form

$$y_{ss}(t) = A \sin(5t + \theta_1) + B \sin(10t + \theta_2) + C \sin(15t + \theta_3)$$

For a system described by the transfer function in part (c) of Problem 8.26, use (51) to find the values of A, B, and C, and calculate the ratios A/B and C/B.

8.30 The steady-state response of a system described by the transfer function in part (a) of Problem 8.26 to the input

$$u(t) = 1 + \sin t + \sin 10t$$

has the form

$$y_{ss}(t) = A + B \sin(t + \theta_2) + C \sin(10t + \theta_3)$$

Calculate A, B, and C, and comment on the ratios B/A and C/A.

* 8.31 a) For the series RLC circuit shown in Figure 5.13, find the transfer function $H(s) = I(s)/E_i(s)$.
b) By examining $H(j\omega)$, determine the value of ω such that the steady-state response to $e_i(t) = \sin \omega t$ is $i_{ss}(t) = (1/R) \sin \omega t$.

8.32 a) Find the transfer function $H(s) = E_o(s)/I_i(s)$ for the parallel RLC circuit shown in Figure 5.14.
b) By examining $H(j\omega)$, determine the value of ω for which the steady-state response to $i_i(t) = \sin \omega t$ is $e_o(t) = R \sin \omega t$.

8.33 a) Verify that when $\alpha \leq 1$, the transfer function

$$H(s) = \dfrac{K}{s^2 + 2\alpha s + 100}$$

can be approximated by

$$H^*(s) = \frac{K}{(s + \alpha - j10)(s + \alpha + j10)}$$

b) Plot the pole-zero pattern for $H^*(s)$.

c) Using $H^*(j\omega)$, sketch to scale a curve of $M(\omega)/K$ versus ω, where M is defined by (49), when $\alpha = 0.2$ and $\alpha = 1.0$.

d) The transfer function $H^*(s)$ represents a band-pass filter having a center frequency of 10 rad/s and a bandwidth of 2α. Explain the appropriateness of these names in relation to your answers to part (c).

e) Discuss the behavior of $M(\omega)$ as α approaches zero.

f) Show that the circuit in Figure 5.13 has $H(s)$ as its transfer function with $K = 100$ if the output is e_C. Find the value of α in terms of the circuit elements.

8.34 Find the transfer function for the circuit shown in Figure 8.12 by characterizing the passive elements by their impedances.

* 8.35 a) Draw the s-domain version of the circuit shown in Figure P8.23 using impedances.

b) Using the circuit drawn in part (a), determine the transfer function $E_o(s)/E_i(s)$.

8.36 a) Draw the s-domain circuit for Figure P5.1, with the passive elements characterized by their impedances.

b) Use the result of part (a) to determine the circuit's transfer function.

c) From the answer to part (b), write the input-output differential equation.

8.37 Repeat Problem 8.36 for the circuit shown in Figure P5.6.

* 8.38 Repeat Problem 8.36 for the circuit shown in Figure P5.12.

8.39 a) Use impedances and the results of Example 8.16 to find the transfer function for the op-amp circuit shown in Figure P8.39.

b) Plot the pole-zero pattern.

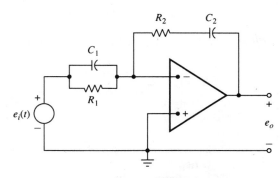

FIGURE P8.39

8.40 Repeat Problem 8.39 for the circuit shown in Figure P5.37.

In Problems 8.41 through 8.44, a system obeying the state-variable equation $\dot{\mathbf{q}} = \mathbf{A}\mathbf{q}$ has the given matrix $\mathbf{A}$.

a) Evaluate the resolvent matrix $\Phi(s)$.

b) Calculate the state-transition matrix $\phi(t)$.

c) Express each element of $\mathbf{q}$ in terms of the arbitrary initial state vector $\mathbf{q}(0)$.

8.41 $\mathbf{A} = \begin{bmatrix} 0 & 1 \\ 0 & -2 \end{bmatrix}$

* 8.42 $\mathbf{A} = \begin{bmatrix} 0 & 1 \\ -2 & -3 \end{bmatrix}$

8.43 $\mathbf{A} = \begin{bmatrix} -2 & 1 \\ 0 & -2 \end{bmatrix}$

8.44 $\mathbf{A} = \begin{bmatrix} 0 & 1 & 0 \\ 0 & 0 & 1 \\ 0 & -2 & -3 \end{bmatrix}$

8.45 Consider the dynamic system defined by the matrices

$$\mathbf{A} = \begin{bmatrix} 0 & 1 \\ 0 & -2 \end{bmatrix} \quad \mathbf{B} = \begin{bmatrix} 1 \\ -1 \end{bmatrix} \quad \mathbf{C} = \begin{bmatrix} 1 & -2 \end{bmatrix} \quad \mathbf{D} = 0$$

a) Indicate the numbers of state variables, inputs, and outputs.

b) Using $\phi(t)$ as found in Problem 8.41, evaluate the state vector $\mathbf{q}(t)$ and the output vector $\mathbf{y}(t)$ for the initial state vector $\mathbf{q}(0) = [2 \ 1]^T$ and zero input.

c) Find the transfer-function matrix $\mathbf{H}(s)$.

d) Evaluate and sketch the output $\mathbf{y}$ when $\mathbf{q}(0) = [2 \ 1]^T$ and $\mathbf{u}(t) = U(t)$.

* 8.46 Consider the dynamic system defined by the matrices

$$\mathbf{A} = \begin{bmatrix} 0 & 1 \\ -2 & -3 \end{bmatrix} \quad \mathbf{B} = \begin{bmatrix} 1 & 0 \\ 0 & 1 \end{bmatrix} \quad \mathbf{C} = \begin{bmatrix} 1 & 0 \end{bmatrix} \quad \mathbf{D} = \begin{bmatrix} 0 & 0 \end{bmatrix}$$

a) Indicate the numbers of state variables, inputs, and outputs.

b) Using $\Phi(s)$ as found in Problem 8.42, determine the transfer-function matrix $\mathbf{H}(s)$.

c) Evaluate the impulse-response matrix $\mathbf{h}(t)$ and sketch each element versus time.

8.47 Consider the dynamic system defined by the matrices

$$\mathbf{A} = \begin{bmatrix} -2 & 1 \\ 0 & -2 \end{bmatrix} \quad \mathbf{B} = \begin{bmatrix} 2 \\ 1 \end{bmatrix} \quad \mathbf{C} = \begin{bmatrix} -1 & 2 \\ 3 & 1 \end{bmatrix} \quad \mathbf{D} = \begin{bmatrix} 0 \\ 0 \end{bmatrix}$$

a) Indicate the numbers of state variables, inputs, and outputs.

b) Using $\Phi(s)$ as found in Problem 8.43, determine the transfer-function matrix $\mathbf{H}(s)$.

c) Evaluate the zero-input response when $\mathbf{q}(0) = \begin{bmatrix} 4 & -1 \end{bmatrix}^T$ and sketch each element versus time.

d) Evaluate the zero-state response when

$$\mathbf{u}(t) = \begin{cases} 0 & \text{for } t \le 0 \\ 5\epsilon^{-t} & \text{for } t > 0 \end{cases}$$

DEVELOPING A LINEAR MODEL

In nearly all the examples used in earlier chapters, the elements were assumed to be linear. In practice, however, many elements are inherently nonlinear and may be considered linear over only a limited range of operating conditions.

When confronted with a mathematical model that contains nonlinearities, the analyst has essentially three choices: (1) to attempt to solve the differential equations directly, (2) to derive a fixed linear approximation that can be analyzed, or (3) to obtain computer solutions of the response for specific numerical cases. The first alternative is possible only in specialized cases and will not be pursued. We present the linearization approach in this chapter and discuss computer solutions in Chapter 15.

We first develop a method for linearizing an element law where the two variables, such as force and displacement, are not directly proportional. We then show how to incorporate the linearized element law into the system model. We consider mechanical systems with nonlinear stiffness or friction elements, and we then discuss nonlinear electrical systems.

9.1 LINEARIZATION OF AN ELEMENT LAW

The object of linearization is to derive a linear model whose response will agree closely with that of the nonlinear model. Although the responses of the linear and nonlinear models will not agree exactly and may differ significantly under some conditions, there will generally be a set of inputs and initial conditions for which the agreement will be satisfactory. In this section, we consider the linearization of a single element law that is a nonlinear

353

function of a single variable. We can express such an element law as an algebraic function $f(x)$. If x represents the total length of a nonlinear spring and $f(x)$ the force on the spring, the function $f(x)$ might appear as shown in Figure 9.1(a), where x_0 denotes the free or unstretched length.

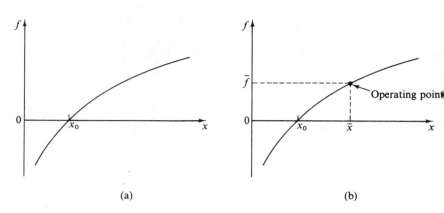

(a)   (b)

FIGURE 9.1   (a) A nonlinear spring characteristic. (b) Nonlinear spring characteristic with operating point.

We shall carry out the linearization of the element law with respect to an **operating point**, which is a specific point on the nonlinear characteristic denoted by $\bar{x}$ and $\bar{f}$. A sample operating point is shown in Figure 9.1(b). We discuss the procedure for determining the operating point in the following section; for now, we shall assume that the values of $\bar{x}$ and $\bar{f}$ are known.

We can write $x(t)$ as the sum of a constant portion, which is its value at the operating point, and a time-varying portion $\hat{x}(t)$ such that

$$x(t) = \bar{x} + \hat{x}(t) \tag{1}$$

The constant term $\bar{x}$ is called the **nominal value** of x, and the time-varying term $\hat{x}(t)$ is the **incremental variable** corresponding to x. Likewise, we can write $f(t)$ as the sum of its nominal value $\bar{f}$ and the incremental variable $\hat{f}(t)$:

$$f(t) = \bar{f} + \hat{f}(t) \tag{2}$$

where the dependence of $\hat{f}$ on time is shown explicitly. Because $\bar{x}$ and $\bar{f}$ always denote a point that lies on the curve for the nonlinear element law,

$$\bar{f} = f(\bar{x}) \tag{3}$$

Having defined the necessary terms, we shall develop two equivalent methods of linearizing the element law to relate the incremental variables $\hat{x}$ and $\hat{f}$. The first uses a graphical approach; the second is based on a Taylor-series expansion.

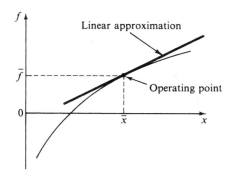

FIGURE 9.2 Nonlinear spring characteristic with linear approximation.

Graphical Approach

Figure 9.2 shows the nonlinear element law $f(x)$ with the tangent to the curve at the operating point appearing as the straight line. For the moment, we note that the tangent line will be a good approximation to the nonlinear curve provided that the independent variable x does not deviate greatly from its nominal value $\bar{x}$ and that the curvature of the curve $f(x)$ is small in the vicinity of the operating point. The slope of the tangent line is

$$k = \frac{df}{dx}\bigg|_{x=\bar{x}}$$

or, written more concisely,

$$k = \frac{df}{dx}\bigg|_{\bar{x}} \tag{4}$$

where the subscript $\bar{x}$ after the vertical line indicates that the derivative must be evaluated at $x = \bar{x}$. The tangent passes through the operating point that has the coordinates $(\bar{x}, \bar{f})$ and is described by the equation

$$f = \bar{f} + k(x - \bar{x})$$

which can be written as

$$f - \bar{f} = k(x - \bar{x}) \tag{5}$$

Noting from (1) and (2) that the incremental variables are

$$\hat{x} = x - \bar{x} \tag{6a}$$

$$\hat{f} = f - \bar{f} \tag{6b}$$

we see that (5) reduces to

$$\hat{f} = k\hat{x} \tag{7}$$

where k is given by (4).

We can represent (7) in graphical form by redrawing the nonlinear func-tion $f(x)$ with a coordinate system whose axes are $\hat{x}$ and $\hat{f}$ and whose origin is located at the operating point, as depicted in Figure 9.3. The incremental variables $\hat{x}$ and $\hat{f}$ are linearly related, the constant of proportionality k being the slope of the tangent line at the operating point.

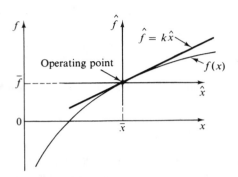

FIGURE 9.3 Nonlinear spring characteristic with incremental-variable coordinates.

Obviously, the accuracy of the linear approximation depends on the cur-vature of $f(x)$ in the vicinity of the operating point $(\bar{x}, \bar{f})$ and on the extent to which x deviates from $\bar{x}$ as the system responds to its excitations. We expect that the linearized model should be a good approximation for those values of x for which the straight line closely approximates the original curve. If the nonlinear spring is part of a larger system, we are unlikely to know in advance what range of values we will encounter for x. The problem is further complicated by the fact that usually we are primarily interested in how well certain responses of the overall system are approxi-mated by calculations made on the linearized model. For example, we can expect some of the elements in a particular system to play a more crit-ical role than others in determining the response of interest. Generally, the only way to assess with certainty the quality of the approximations is to compare computer solutions for the nonlinear model and the linearized model.

Series-Expansion Approach

As an alternative to the geometric arguments just presented, we can de-rive the linearized approximation in (7) by expressing $f(x)$ in terms of its **Taylor-series expansion** about the operating point $(\bar{x}, \bar{f})$. This expansion is

$$f(x) = f(\bar{x}) + \frac{df}{dx}\bigg|_{\bar{x}} (x - \bar{x}) + \frac{1}{2!} \frac{d^2 f}{dx^2}\bigg|_{\bar{x}} (x - \bar{x})^2 + \cdots$$

where the subscript $\bar{x}$ after the vertical line indicates that the associated derivative is evaluated at $x = \bar{x}$. We can find the first two terms of this expansion provided that f and its first derivative exist for $x = \bar{x}$. We seek a linear approximation to the actual curve, so we shall neglect subsequent terms, which are higher-order in $x - \bar{x}$. The justification for truncating the series after the first two terms is that if x is sufficiently close to $\bar{x}$, then the higher-order terms are negligible compared to the constant and linear terms. Hence we write

$$f(x) \simeq f(\bar{x}) + \frac{df}{dx}\bigg|_{\bar{x}} (x - \bar{x}) \tag{8}$$

Because $\bar{f} = f(\bar{x})$ and $k = [df/dx]|_{\bar{x}}$, this equation is equivalent to (5), which reduces to (7).

The accuracy of the linearized approximation in (8) depends on the extent to which the higher-order terms we have omitted from the Taylor-series expansion are truly negligible. This in turn depends on the magnitude of $x - \bar{x}$, which is the incremental independent variable, and on the values of the higher-order derivatives of $f(x)$ at the operating point. Before addressing the linearization of the complete model, we shall consider two numerical examples that illustrate the linearization of a nonlinear element law.

▶ **EXAMPLE 9.1**

A nonlinear translational spring obeys the force-displacement relationship $f(x) = |x|x$, where x is the elongation of the spring from its unstretched length. Determine the linearized element law in numerical form for each of the operating points corresponding to the nominal spring elongations $\bar{x}_1 = -1, \bar{x}_2 = 0, \bar{x}_3 = 1$, and $\bar{x}_4 = 2$.

Solution

We can rewrite $f(x)$ as

$$f(x) = \begin{cases} -x^2 & \text{for } x < 0 \\ x^2 & \text{for } x \geq 0 \end{cases} \tag{9}$$

The slope of the tangent at the operating point is

$$k = \frac{df}{dx}\bigg|_{\bar{x}} = \begin{cases} -2\bar{x} & \text{for } \bar{x} < 0 \\ 2\bar{x} & \text{for } \bar{x} \geq 0 \end{cases}$$

$$= 2|\bar{x}| \qquad \text{for all } \bar{x} \tag{10}$$

Thus the linear approximation to the spring characteristic is

$$\hat{f} = 2|\bar{x}|\hat{x}$$

where the coefficient $k = 2|\bar{x}|$ can be thought of as an effective spring constant whose numerical value depends on the nominal value of the spring's elongation $\bar{x}$. Substituting the four specified values of $\bar{x}$ into (9) and (10) gives the values of $\bar{f}$ and k that appear in Table 9.1. Figure 9.4 shows the four linear approximations superimposed on the nonlinear spring characteristic. Note that the value of the effective spring constant k is strongly dependent on the location of the operating point. In fact, k vanishes for $\bar{x} = 0$, which implies that the spring would not appear in the linearized model of a system having $\bar{x} = 0$ as its operating point. It is also interesting to note that k is the same for $\bar{x} = -1$ and $\bar{x} = +1$, although the values of $\bar{f}$ differ.

TABLE 9.1 Nominal Elongations, Nominal Forces, and Effective Spring Constants

i	$\bar{x}_i$	$\bar{f}_i$	k_i
1	−1	−1	2
2	0	0	0
3	1	1	2
4	2	4	4

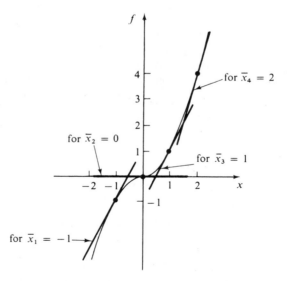

FIGURE 9.4 Nonlinear spring characteristic and linear approximations for four values of $\bar{x}$.

Concerning the accuracy of the approximation, one might say that for deviations in x up to 0.25 from the operating point, the approximation seems to be quite good; for deviations exceeding 1.0 it would be poor. It is difficult to make a definitive statement, however, without knowing the system in which the element is to appear.

▶ **EXAMPLE 9.2**

A torque τ_M exerted on a body that can rotate with an angular displacement θ is given by the equation $\tau_M = D \sin \theta$. Determine the linearized element law relating $\hat{\tau}_M$ and $\hat{\theta}$. Consider the five operating points corresponding to $\bar{\theta}_1 = 0$, $\bar{\theta}_2 = \pi/4$, $\bar{\theta}_3 = \pi/2$, $\bar{\theta}_4 = 3\pi/4$, and $\bar{\theta}_5 = \pi$.

Solution

The Taylor-series expansion for τ_M is

$$\tau_M = D \sin \bar{\theta} + \frac{d}{d\theta} D \sin \theta \bigg|_{\bar{\theta}} (\theta - \bar{\theta}) + \cdots$$

$$= D \sin \bar{\theta} + D(\cos \bar{\theta})\hat{\theta} + \cdots$$

Using the first two terms in this series, and noting that $\bar{\tau}_M = D \sin \bar{\theta}$, we can write

$$\hat{\tau}_M = D(\cos \bar{\theta})\hat{\theta} = k\hat{\theta}$$

where $k = D \cos \bar{\theta}$ is the linearized stiffness constant. In Table 9.2, the values of $\bar{\theta}, \bar{\tau}_M$, and k are listed for each of the five specified operating points.

TABLE 9.2 Operating Points and Effective Stiffness Constants for Example 9.2

i	$\bar{\theta}_i$	$\bar{\tau}_{M_i}$	k_i
1	0	0	D
2	$\pi/4$	$D/\sqrt{2}$	$D/\sqrt{2}$
3	$\pi/2$	D	0
4	$3\pi/4$	$D/\sqrt{2}$	$-D/\sqrt{2}$
5	π	0	$-D$

The values of k_i, which were found from $k_i = D \cos \bar{\theta}_i$, are also the slopes of the tangents to the characteristic curve drawn at the operating points. The tangent lines at three of these operating points are shown in Figure 9.5.

In the free-body diagram for the pendulum shown in Figure 4.23, one of the torques was $\tau_M = MgL \sin \theta$. In Examples 4.7 and 6.9, we used the small-angle approximation for θ and a trigonometric identity to obtain

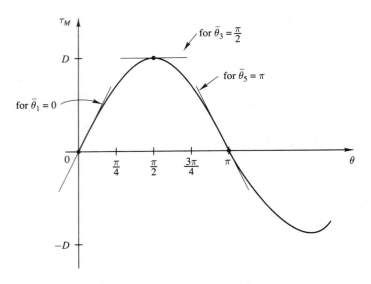

FIGURE 9.5   Nonlinear characteristic curve and linear approximations for Example 9.2.

a linearized element law for small variations about the operating points $\bar{\theta} = 0$ and $\bar{\theta} = \pi$. We found that $\hat{\tau}_M = (MgL)\hat{\theta}$ for $\bar{\theta} = 0$ and that $\hat{\tau}_M = -(MgL)\hat{\theta}$ for $\bar{\theta} = \pi$. In Example 9.2, these same results were obtained by a more general linearization method.

■ 9.2 LINEARIZATION OF THE MODEL

We shall now consider the process of incorporating one or more linearized element laws into a system model. Starting with a given nonlinear model, we need to do the following:

1. Determine the operating point of the model by writing and solving the appropriate nonlinear algebraic equations. Select the proper operating-point value if extraneous solutions also appear.

2. Rewrite all linear terms in the mathematical model as the sum of their nominal and incremental variables, noting that the derivatives of constant terms are zero.

3. Replace all nonlinear terms by the first two terms of their Taylor-series expansions—that is, the constant and linear terms.

4. Using the algebraic equation(s) defining the operating point, cancel the constant terms in the differential equations, leaving only linear terms involving incremental variables.

5. Determine the initial conditions of all incremental variables in terms of the initial conditions of the variables in the nonlinear model.

For all situations we shall consider, the operating point of the system will be a condition of equilibrium in which each variable will be constant and equal to its nominal value and in which all derivatives will be zero. Inputs will take on their nominal values, which are typically selected to be their average values. For example, if a system input were $u(t) = A + B \sin \omega t$, then the nominal value of the input would be taken as $\bar{u} = A$. Under these conditions, the differential equations reduce to algebraic equations that we can solve for the operating point, using a computer if necessary.

Upon completion of step 4, the terms remaining in the model should involve only incremental variables and they should all be linear with constant coefficients. In general, the coefficients involved in those terms that came from the expansion of nonlinear terms depend on the equilibrium conditions. Hence we must find a specific operating point before we can express the linearized model in numerical form. The entire procedure will be illustrated by several examples.

▶ **EXAMPLE 9.3**

Derive a linearized model of the translational mechanical system shown in Figure 9.6(a), where the nonlinear spring characteristic $f_K(x)$ is given in Figure 9.6(b) and where the average value of the applied force $f_a(t)$ is zero.

Solution

First we derive the nonlinear model by drawing the free-body diagram shown in Figure 9.6(c) and summing forces. This yields

$$M\ddot{x} + B\dot{x} + f_k(x) = f_a(t) \tag{11}$$

To find the operating point, we replace $f_a(t)$ by its average value $\bar{f}_a$ and x by $\bar{x}$:

$$M\ddot{\bar{x}} + B\dot{\bar{x}} + f_K(\bar{x}) = \bar{f}_a$$

Noting that $\dot{\bar{x}} = \ddot{\bar{x}} = 0$ because $\bar{x}$ is a constant and that $\bar{f}_a$ was specified to be zero, we see that

$$\bar{f}_K = f_K(\bar{x}) = 0$$

Thus the operating point is at $\bar{x} = 0$, $\bar{f}_K = 0$, which corresponds to the origin of the spring characteristic in Figure 9.6(b).

The next step is to rewrite the linear terms in (11) in terms of the incremental variables $\hat{x} = x - \bar{x}$ and $\hat{f}_a(t) = f_a(t) - \bar{f}_a$. This yields

$$M(\ddot{\bar{x}} + \ddot{\hat{x}}) + B(\dot{\bar{x}} + \dot{\hat{x}}) + f_K(x) = \bar{f}_a + \hat{f}_a(t)$$

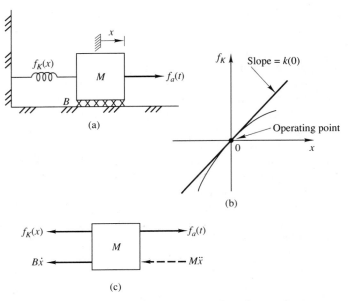

FIGURE 9.6 (a) Nonlinear system for Example 9.3. (b) Nonlinear spring characteristic. (c) Free-body diagram.

Because $\dot{\bar{x}} = \ddot{\bar{x}} = 0$, we can rewrite the equation as

$$M\ddot{\hat{x}} + B\dot{\hat{x}} + f_K(x) = \bar{f}_a + \hat{f}_a(t) \tag{12}$$

Expanding the spring force $f_K(x)$ about $\bar{x} = 0$ gives

$$f_K(x) = f_K(0) + \left.\frac{df_K}{dx}\right|_{x=0} \hat{x} + \cdots$$

Substituting the first two terms into (12) yields the approximate equation

$$M\ddot{\hat{x}} + B\dot{\hat{x}} + f_K(0) + k(0)\hat{x} = \bar{f}_a + \hat{f}_a(t)$$

The constant $k(0)$ denotes the derivative df_K/dx evaluated at $x = 0$ and is the slope of the tangent to the spring characteristic at the operating point, as indicated in Figure 9.6(b).

The spring force at the operating point is $f_K(0) = \bar{f}_a = 0$, so the linearized model is

$$M\ddot{\hat{x}} + B\dot{\hat{x}} + k(0)\hat{x} = \hat{f}_a(t) \tag{13}$$

which is a fixed linear differential equation in the incremental variable $\hat{x}$ with the incremental input $\hat{f}_a(t)$. The coefficients are the constants M, B, and $k(0)$. To solve (13), we must know the initial values $\hat{x}(0)$ and $\dot{\hat{x}}(0)$, which we find from the initial values $x(0)$ and $\dot{x}(0)$. Because $\hat{x}(t) = x(t) - \bar{x}$

and $\dot{\hat{x}}(t) = \dot{x}(t) - \dot{\bar{x}}$ for all values of t,

$$\hat{x}(0) = x(0) - \bar{x}$$

$$\dot{\hat{x}}(0) = \dot{x}(0) - \dot{\bar{x}}$$

In this example, $\bar{x} = \dot{\bar{x}} = 0$, so $\hat{x}(0) = x(0)$ and $\dot{\hat{x}}(0) = \dot{x}(0)$. Once we have solved the linearized model, we find the approximate solution of the nonlinear model by adding the nominal value $\bar{x}$ to the incremental solution $\hat{x}(t)$. Remember that the sum of the terms, $\bar{x} + \hat{x}(t)$, is only an approximation to the actual solution of the nonlinear model.

Should we want to put the linearized model given by (13) into state-variable form, we need only define the incremental velocity $\hat{v} = v - \bar{v}$, where $\bar{v} = 0$. Then $\hat{v} = \dot{\hat{x}}$, and we can write the pair of first-order equations

$$\dot{\hat{x}} = \hat{v}$$

$$\dot{\hat{v}} = \frac{1}{M}[-k(0)\hat{x} - B\hat{v} + \hat{f}_a(t)]$$

Because $\bar{x} = \bar{v} = 0$, the appropriate initial conditions are $\hat{x}(0) = x(0)$ and $\hat{v}(0) = v(0)$.

▶ **EXAMPLE 9.4**

Repeat Example 9.3 with the applied force $f_a(t)$ having a nonzero average value of $\bar{f}_a$ for positive time, as shown in Figure 9.7(a).

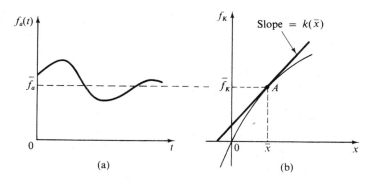

FIGURE 9.7   (a) Applied force for Example 9.4. (b) Nonlinear spring characteristic with new operating point.

Solution

The form of the nonlinear model given by (11) is unaffected by the value of $\bar{f}_a$. However, a new operating point will exist that is defined by the equation

$$f_K(\bar{x}) = \bar{f}_K = \bar{f}_a \tag{14}$$

For the spring characteristic shown in Figure 9.7(b) and the value of $\bar{f}_a$ shown in part (a) of the figure, the operating point is point A. In graphical terms, the straight line $\bar{f}_a$ in Figure 9.7(a) is projected horizontally onto the curve of the spring characteristic in part (b) of the figure, intersecting it at the operating point, the coordinates of which are $x = \bar{x}$, $f_K = \bar{f}_K$.

Upon substituting $x = \bar{x} + \hat{x}$ and $f_a(t) = \bar{f}_a + \hat{f}_a(t)$ into (11) and using $\dot{\bar{x}} = \ddot{\bar{x}} = 0$, we obtain

$$M\ddot{\hat{x}} + B\dot{\hat{x}} + f_K(x) = \bar{f}_a + \hat{f}_a(t) \tag{15}$$

which is identical to (12). The first two terms in the Taylor series for the spring force are

$$f_K(\bar{x}) + \left.\frac{df_K}{dx}\right|_{\bar{x}} \hat{x} \tag{16}$$

where $f_K(\bar{x}) = \bar{f}_K$ and where $\bar{x}$ must satisfy (14). Substituting (16) for $f_K(x)$ into (15) and invoking (14) yield the desired linear model:

$$M\ddot{\hat{x}} + B\dot{\hat{x}} + k(\bar{x})\hat{x} = \hat{f}_a(t) \tag{17}$$

where $k(\bar{x}) = [df_K/dx]|_{\bar{x}}$ and is the slope of the straight line in Figure 9.7(b). Note that the form of the model given by (17) with $\bar{f}_a \neq 0$ is the same as that with $\bar{f}_a = 0$, which is given by (13). The only difference between the two equations is the value of the effective spring constant. The value of $k(\bar{x})$ depends on the value of $\bar{x}$ at which the slope of $f_K(x)$ is measured. Hence the responses of the two linearized models could be rather different, even for the same incremental applied force $\hat{f}_a(t)$.

▶ **EXAMPLE 9.5**

Derive a linear model for the mechanical system and spring characteristic shown in Figure 9.8, where $x = 0$ corresponds to an unstretched spring.

Solution

We obtain the nonlinear model of the system by drawing the free-body diagram shown in Figure 9.9(a) and setting the sum of the vertical forces equal to zero. Because the mass is constrained to move vertically, we must include its weight Mg in the free-body diagram. The resulting nonlinear model is

$$M\ddot{x} + B\dot{x} + f_K(x) = f_a(t) + Mg$$

Note that its form is similar to that given by (11), the nonlinear model for the two preceding examples. By setting $x = \bar{x}$ and $f_a(t) = \bar{f}_a$ and by noting that $\dot{\bar{x}} = \ddot{\bar{x}} = 0$, we find the algebraic equation for the operating point to be

$$f_K(\bar{x}) = \bar{f}_a + Mg$$

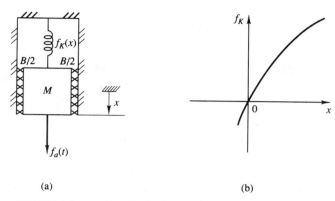

(a)   (b)

FIGURE 9.8 (a) Mechanical system for Example 9.5.
(b) Nonlinear spring characteristic.

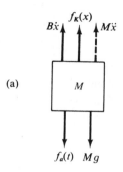

(a)

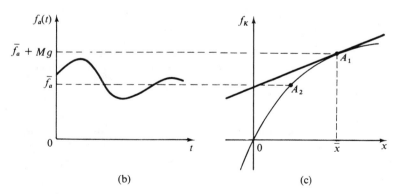

(b)   (c)

FIGURE 9.9 (a) Free-body diagram for Example 9.5. (b) Input.
(c) Nonlinear spring characteristic with two operating points.

which is the same as (14) except for inclusion of the force Mg on the right side.

The nonlinear spring characteristic in Figure 9.8(b) is repeated in Figure 9.9(c). Figure 9.9(b) shows $f_a(t)$ and $\bar{f}_a$ as in Example 9.4, but it also shows the total nominal force $\bar{f}_a + Mg$ that must be projected onto the characteristic curve in Figure 9.9(c) to establish the operating point A_1. The point A_2, which is obtained by projecting the force $\bar{f}_a$ from Figure 9.9(b), would be the operating point if the motion of the mass were horizontal, as it is in Example 9.4. For applied forces having the same average values, the two systems will have different linearized spring characteristics if the curve of $f_K(x)$ does not have the same slope at points A_1 and A_2. If the spring were linear, however, the slope of the characteristic in Figure 9.9(c) would be constant and the presence of the weight would have no influence on the effective spring constant, as was observed in Example 2.5. With the provision that $k(\bar{x})$ is the slope of $f_K(x)$ measured at the point A_1 rather than at point A_2, the resulting linearized model is again given by (17).

▶ **EXAMPLE 9.6**

A high-speed vehicle of mass M moves along a horizontal track and is subject to a linear retarding force Bv caused by viscous friction associated with the bearings and a nonlinear retarding force $D|v|v$ caused by air drag. Obtain a linear model that is valid when the driving force $f_a(t)$ undergoes variations about a positive nominal value $\bar{f}_a$.

Solution

The nonlinear differential equation governing the vehicle's velocity is

$$M\dot{v} + Bv + D|v|v = f_a(t) \tag{18}$$

Setting $v = \bar{v}$ and $f_a(t) = \bar{f}_a$ and noting that $\dot{\bar{v}} = 0$, we have

$$B\bar{v} + D|\bar{v}|\bar{v} = \bar{f}_a$$

for the operating-point equation. Because $\bar{f}_a$ is positive, we know that $\bar{v}$ is positive and we can replace $D|\bar{v}|\bar{v}$ by $D(\bar{v})^2$. Then

$$D(\bar{v})^2 + B\bar{v} - \bar{f}_a = 0 \tag{19}$$

By inspection we see that (19) will have two real roots, one positive and the other negative. However, we are interested only in the positive root, which is

$$\bar{v} = \frac{-B + \sqrt{B^2 + 4\bar{f}_a D}}{2D} \tag{20}$$

The negative root was introduced when we replaced $|\bar{v}|\bar{v}$ by $(\bar{v})^2$ and is not a root of the original operating-point equation.

Provided that v always remains positive, we can replace $D|\bar{v}|\bar{v}$ in (18) by Dv^2. Then, using $v = \bar{v} + \hat{v}$ and $f_a(t) = \bar{f}_a + \hat{f}_a(t)$ and noting that

$\dot{\bar{v}} = 0$, we can rewrite (18) as

$$M\dot{\hat{v}} + B(\bar{v} + \hat{v}) + Dv^2 = \bar{f}_a + \hat{f}_a(t) \tag{21}$$

To linearize the term v^2, we replace it by the constant and linear terms in its Taylor series:

$$(\bar{v})^2 + \frac{d}{dv}(v^2)\Big|_{\bar{v}} (v - \bar{v}) = (\bar{v})^2 + 2\bar{v}\hat{v} \tag{22}$$

Substituting (22) for v^2 into (21) and regrouping, we have

$$M\dot{\hat{v}} + (B + 2D\bar{v})\hat{v} + B\bar{v} + D(\bar{v})^2 = \bar{f}_a + \hat{f}_a(t)$$

The constant terms cancel because of (19), the operating-point equation. Thus the desired linearized model, which holds for $\bar{f}_a > 0$ and $v > 0$, is

$$M\dot{\hat{v}} + b\hat{v} = \hat{f}_a(t)$$

where b denotes the effective damping coefficient

$$b = B + 2D\bar{v}$$

with $\bar{v}$ given by (20) as a function of the average driving force $\bar{f}_a$.

It is worthwhile to observe that in this particular case the Taylor series of the nonlinearity has only three terms, and we could have obtained it without differentiation by writing

$$v^2 = (\bar{v} + \hat{v})^2 = (\bar{v})^2 + 2\bar{v}\hat{v} + (\hat{v})^2$$

In this example, we can see that $(\hat{v})^2$ is the error introduced by replacing v^2 by $(\bar{v})^2 + 2\bar{v}\hat{v}$. Provided that $\bar{v} \gg |\hat{v}|$, the error will be small compared to the two terms that are retained.

▶ *EXAMPLE 9.7*

A nonlinear system obeys the state-variable equations

$$\dot{x} = y \tag{23a}$$

$$\dot{y} = -|x|x - 2x - 2y^3 - 3 + 0.2\cos t \tag{23b}$$

Find the operating point and develop the linearized model in numerical form.

Solution

The operating point, described by $\bar{x}$ and $\bar{y}$, must satisfy the conditions $\dot{\bar{x}} = \dot{\bar{y}} = 0$ with the incremental portion of the input set to zero. Hence the operating-point equations reduce to

$$\bar{y} = 0$$
$$|\bar{x}|\bar{x} + 2\bar{x} + 3 = 0 \tag{24}$$

which have the solution $\bar{x} = -1$, $\bar{y} = 0$. We replace the two nonlinear elements in (23b) by the first two terms in their respective Taylor-series expansions. For $|x|x$, we write

$$|\bar{x}|\bar{x} + 2|\bar{x}|\hat{x}$$

and we replace y^3 by

$$(\bar{y})^3 + 3(\bar{y})^2 \hat{y}$$

By substituting these approximations into (23) and using $x = \bar{x} + \hat{x}$ and $y = \bar{y} + \hat{y}$, we obtain

$$\dot{\hat{x}} = \bar{y} + \hat{y}$$
$$\dot{\hat{y}} = -(|\bar{x}|\bar{x} + 2|\bar{x}|\hat{x}) - 2(\bar{x} + \hat{x}) - 2[(\bar{y})^3 + 3(\bar{y})^2 \hat{y}] - 3 + 0.2 \cos t$$

$$(25)$$

With $\bar{x} = -1$ and $\bar{y} = 0$, (25) reduces to

$$\dot{\hat{x}} = \hat{y}$$
$$\dot{\hat{y}} = -4\hat{x} + 0.2 \cos t$$

$$(26)$$

which is the linearized model in state-variable form. Comparing (26) with (25), we note that (1) all the constant terms have been canceled, (2) the coefficient of $\hat{y}$ in the second equation is zero because $\bar{y} = 0$, and (3) the coefficient of $\hat{x}$ reflects the combined effects of the linear and nonlinear terms.

■ 9.3 CIRCUITS WITH NONLINEAR RESISTORS

We have defined resistors, capacitors, and inductors as elements for which there is an algebraic relationship between the voltage and current, voltage and charge, and current and flux linkage, respectively. If the two variables involved in the algebraic relationship are directly proportional to one another, then the element is linear, as was the case in all the examples in Chapter 5.

In this section, we consider circuits with nonlinear resistors. The general procedure for obtaining a linearized model is the same as that used for the mechanical examples. As in Section 9.1, we express the variables as the sum of a constant portion and a time-varying portion. For example, we write a voltage e_o as

$$e_o = \bar{e}_o + \hat{e}_o$$

where the constant term $\bar{e}_o$ is the nominal value, corresponding to a particular operating point, and where $\hat{e}_o$ is the incremental time-varying component. In the circuit diagrams, we indicate the fact that a resistor is nonlinear by drawing a curved line through its symbol. The procedure is illustrated by three examples of increasing complexity.

▶ **EXAMPLE 9.8**

The circuit shown in Figure 9.10(a) contains a nonlinear resistor that obeys the element law $i_o = 2e_o^3$. Write the differential equation relating e_o and $e_i(t)$. If $e_i(t) = 18 + A \cos \omega t$, find the operating point and derive the linearized input-output differential equation. Also determine the time constant of the linearized model.

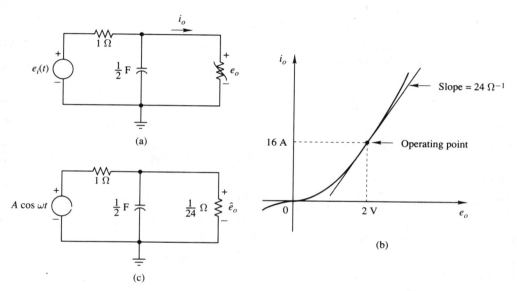

FIGURE 9.10 (a) Circuit for Example 9.8. (b) Characteristic curve for the nonlinear resistor. (c) Linearized equivalent circuit.

Solution

The right-hand resistor is nonlinear because the current i_o is not directly proportional to the voltage e_o. Summing the currents leaving the node at the upper right gives

$$\frac{1}{2}\dot{e}_o + [e_o - e_i(t)] + 2e_o^3 = 0$$

Thus the input-output equation is

$$\frac{1}{2}\dot{e}_o + 2e_o^3 + e_0 = e_i(t) \tag{27}$$

To determine the operating point, we replace $e_i(t)$ by $\bar{e}_i = 18$ V, e_o by $\bar{e}_o$, and $\dot{e}_o$ by zero to obtain

$$2\bar{e}_o^3 + \bar{e}_o = 18$$

The only real value of $\bar{e}_o$ that satisfies this algebraic equation is

$$\bar{e}_o = 2 \text{ V} \tag{28}$$

From the nonlinear element law, we see that $\bar{i}_o = 16$ A, which gives the operating point shown in Figure 9.10(b).

To develop a linearized model, we let

$$e_i(t) = 18 + A \cos \omega t$$
$$e_o = 2 + \hat{e}_o \tag{29}$$

As in (8), we write the first two terms in the Taylor series for the nonlinear term $2e_o^3$, which are

$$\bar{i}_o + \left. \frac{di_o}{de_o} \right|_{\bar{e}_o} (e_o - \bar{e}_o) = \bar{i}_o + (6\bar{e}_o^2)\hat{e}_o$$
$$= 16 + 24\hat{e}_o \tag{30}$$

This approximation describes the tangent to the characteristic curve at the operating point, as shown in Figure 9.10(b). Substituting (29) and (30) into (27) gives

$$\tfrac{1}{2}(\dot{\bar{e}}_o + \dot{\hat{e}}_o) + (16 + 24\,\hat{e}_o) + (2 + \hat{e}_o) = 18 + A \cos \omega t$$

Because $\dot{\bar{e}}_o = 0$ and because the constant terms cancel (as is always the case), we have for the linearized model

$$\tfrac{1}{2}\dot{\hat{e}}_o + 25\hat{e}_o = A \cos \omega t$$

or

$$\dot{\hat{e}}_o + 50\hat{e}_o = 2A \cos \omega t \tag{31}$$

By inspecting this equation, we see that the time constant of the linearized model is 0.02 s.

In the last example, we can see from (30), as well as from Figure 9.10(b), that $\hat{i}_o = 24\hat{e}_o$. This equation has the form of Ohm's law for a linear resistor: $\hat{i}_o = (1/r)\hat{e}_o$, where $r = 1/24$ Ω. Figure 9.10(c) shows the linearized equivalent circuit that relates the time-varying incremental variables. It has the same form as Figure 9.10(a), except that the nonlinear resistor has been replaced by a linearized element. It is straightforward to show that (31) can be obtained directly from part (c) of the figure. Keep in mind that the value of the linearized element depends on the operating point.

Computer simulations are discussed in Chapter 15, which can be studied at any time. In the final two examples, we not only develop linearized models but also use such simulations to compare the nonlinear and linearized models. This is usually the only way to determine how large the time-varying component of the input can be and still have the linearized model give good results.

▶ *EXAMPLE 9.9*

Write the state-variable equations for the circuit shown in Figure 9.11(a), which contains a nonlinear resistor that obeys the element law $i_2 = \frac{1}{8}e_C^3$. Find the operating point when $e_i(t) = 2 + \hat{e}_i(t)$, and derive the linearized state-variable equations in terms of the incremental variables. Plot and compare i_L versus t for the nonlinear and linearized models when $\hat{e}_i(t) = [A \sin t]U(t)$ for (1)$A = 0.1$ V, (2)$A = 1.0$ V, and (3)$A = 10.0$ V.

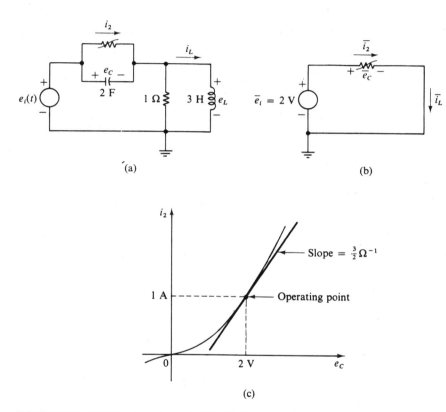

(a)   (b)

(c)

FIGURE 9.11 (a) Circuit for Example 9.9. (b) Circuit used for determining the operating point. (c) Characteristic curve for the nonlinear resistor.

Solution

We choose e_C and i_L as state variables and note that

$$e_L = e_i(t) - e_C \tag{32}$$

Applying Kirchhoff's current law to the upper right node gives

$$i_L + e_L - \frac{1}{8}e_C^3 - 2\dot{e}_C = 0$$

Inserting (32) into this equation and into the element law $di_L/dt = \frac{1}{3}e_L$ gives

$$\dot{e}_C = \frac{1}{2}\left[e_i(t) + i_L - \frac{1}{8}e_C^3 - e_C\right]$$

$$\frac{di_L}{dt} = \frac{1}{3}[e_i(t) - e_C] \tag{33}$$

which constitute the nonlinear state-variable equations.

At the operating point, the derivatives of the state variables are zero, and (33) reduces to the algebraic equations

$$\bar{e}_i + \bar{i}_L - \frac{1}{8}\bar{e}_C^3 - \bar{e}_C = 0$$

$$\bar{e}_i - \bar{e}_C = 0$$

With $\bar{e}_i = 2$ V, we find that $\bar{e}_C = 2$ V, $\bar{i}_L = 1$ A, and $\bar{i}_2 = 2^3/8 = 1$ A. An alternative way of determining the operating point is to recall from Section 6.2 that when all the voltages and currents are constant, we can replace the capacitors and inductors by open and short circuits, respectively. We do this in Figure 9.11(b), from which we again see that $\bar{e}_C = 2$ V and $\bar{i}_L = \bar{i}_2 = 1$ A.

Next we define the incremental variables $\hat{e}_C, \hat{i}_L$, and $\hat{e}_i(t)$ by the equations

$$e_C = 2 + \hat{e}_C$$

$$i_L = 1 + \hat{i}_L \tag{34}$$

$$e_i(t) = 2 + \hat{e}_i(t)$$

The Taylor-series expansion for the nonlinear resistor is

$$i_2 = \frac{1}{8}e_C^3 = \frac{1}{8}\bar{e}_C^3 + \frac{3}{8}\bar{e}_C^2(e_C - \bar{e}_C) + \cdots$$

Using the first two terms in the series, with $\bar{e}_C = 2$ V, we have

$$i_2 \simeq 1 + \frac{3}{2}\hat{e}_C \tag{35}$$

which is shown graphically by the straight line in Figure 9.11(c). Substituting (34) and (35) into (33) and canceling the constant terms, we obtain

$$\dot{\hat{e}}_C = \frac{1}{2}\left[\hat{e}_i(t) + \hat{i}_L - \frac{5}{2}\hat{e}_C\right] \tag{36a}$$

$$\frac{d\hat{i}_L}{dt} = \frac{1}{3}[\hat{e}_i(t) - \hat{e}_C] \tag{36b}$$

as the linearized state-variable equations.

The results of a computer solution for i_L of the nonlinear model given by (33) with $e_i(t) = 2 + [A \sin t]U(t)$ are shown in Figure 9.12 for three different values of the amplitude A. Plotted on the same axes are curves obtained by calculating $\hat{i}_L$ from the linearized model in (36) with $\hat{e}_i(t) = [A \sin t]U(t)$ and then forming the quantity $\bar{i}_L + \hat{i}_L$. Because $e_i(t) = \bar{e}_i$ for all $t < 0$, we used the initial conditions

$$e_C(0) = \bar{e}_C = 2 \text{ V}, \quad \hat{e}_C(0) = 0$$

$$i_L(0) = \bar{i}_L = 1 \text{ A}, \quad \hat{i}_L(0) = 0$$

Note that the responses of the nonlinear and linearized models are almost identical when $A = 0.1$ V, are in close agreement when $A = 1.0$ V, but differ significantly when $A = 10.0$ V. The steady-state response of the linearized model is always a sinusoidal oscillation about the operating point. For large values of A, however, the steady-state response of the nonlinear model is not symmetrical about the operating point.

We have plotted the three sets of curves with different vertical scales and different origins in order to get a good comparison of the responses of the nonlinear and linearized models for each of the three values of A. If we repeat the example when $\bar{e}_i = 0$ and $\hat{e}_i(t) = [A \sin t]U(t)$, then in the steady state we would expect the response of the nonlinear model to be symmetrical about the operating point. When we carry out a computer run for this case, we obtain not only the expected symmetry but also good agreement of the nonlinear and linearized responses for all three values of A.

▶ *EXAMPLE 9.10*

The voltage source $e_i(t)$ for the circuit shown in Figure 9.13(a) is

$$e_i(t) = \begin{cases} -2 & \text{for } t \leq 0 \\ 2 + A \cos 4t & \text{for } t > 0 \end{cases}$$

The element law for the nonlinear resistor is $e_2 = 2|i_L|i_L$.

1. Find a set of state-variable equations and an algebraic output equation for i_o. Give the initial conditions needed to solve the equations.

2. Find a linearized set of state-variable equations about the operating point corresponding to $\bar{e}_i = 2$ V. Write the necessary initial conditions and an algebraic output equation for $\hat{i}_o$. Also draw the linearized equivalent circuit.

3. Simulate the responses of the nonlinear and linearized models, and plot i_o versus time when $A = 1$ V, 5 V, and 20 V.

Solution

We make our usual choice of e_C and i_L as the state variables. The voltage at the top of the 1-Ω resistor is $e_C + 6$, so $i_1 = e_C + 6$. By Kirchhoff's

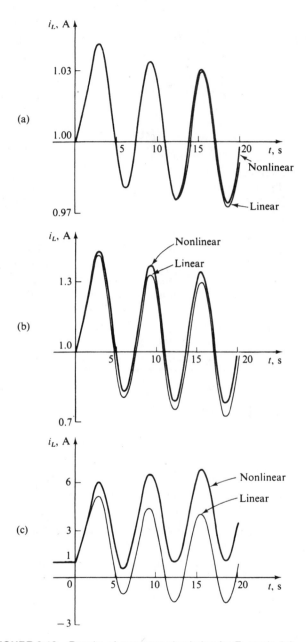

FIGURE 9.12 Results of computer simulation for Example 9.9 with $e_i(t) = 2 + [A \cos t]U(t)$. (a) $A = 0.1$ V. (b) $A = 1.0$ V. (c) $A = 10.0$ V.

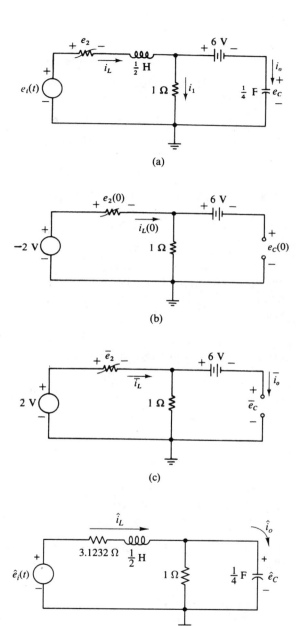

FIGURE 9.13 (a) Circuit for Example 9.10. (b) Circuit for determining the initial conditions. (c) Circuit for determining the operating point. (d) Linearized equivalent circuit.

current law,

$$i_o = i_L - i_1$$

$$= i_L - e_C - 6 \qquad (37)$$

which is the desired output equation. Because $i_o = \frac{1}{4}\dot{e}_C$, one state-variable equation is

$$\dot{e}_C = 4(i_L - e_C - 6) \qquad (38)$$

Summing voltages around the outside loop gives

$$e_C + 6 + \frac{1}{2}\frac{di_L}{dt} + 2|i_L|i_L - e_i(t) = 0$$

from which we have, for the second state-variable equation,

$$\frac{di_L}{dt} = 2[e_i(t) - 2|i_L|i_L - e_C - 6] \qquad (39)$$

To find the values of $e_C(0)$ and $i_L(0)$, we can use (38) and (39) with the derivatives replaced by zero and $e_i(t)$ replaced by -2 V. Equivalently, we can redraw the circuit as shown in Figure 9.13(b), replacing the capacitor and inductor by open and short circuits, respectively, and using the voltage source -2 V. Then

$$2|i_L(0)|i_L(0) + i_L(0) + 2 = 0$$

Only a negative value of $i_L(0)$ can satisfy this equation, so we rewrite it as

$$-2[i_L(0)]^2 + i_L(0) + 2 = 0 \qquad (40)$$

which has roots at -0.7808 and 1.2808. The latter root results from rewriting the equation in quadratic form and is extraneous, so

$$i_L(0) = -0.7808 \text{ A}$$
$$e_C(0) = -0.7808 - 6 = -6.7808 \text{ V} \qquad (41)$$

We can find the operating point corresponding to $\bar{e}_i = 2$ V from (38) and (39) or from the simplified circuit shown in Figure 9.13(c). We see that

$$2|\bar{i}_L|\bar{i}_L + \bar{i}_L - 2 = 0$$

This time only a positive value of $\bar{i}_L$ can satisfy the equation, so we rewrite it as

$$2\bar{i}_L^2 + \bar{i}_L - 2 = 0 \qquad (42)$$

Because (42) has the same form as (40) except that $i_L(0)$ is replaced by $-\bar{i}_L$, we know that the desired root is at 0.7808. Thus

$$\bar{i}_L = 0.7808 \text{ A}$$
$$\bar{e}_C = 0.7808 - 6 = -5.2192 \text{ V} \qquad (43)$$
$$\bar{i}_o = 0$$

We now introduce the incremental variables

$$\hat{e}_i(t) = e_i(t) - 2$$
$$\hat{i}_L = i_L - 0.7808$$
$$\hat{e}_C = e_C + 5.2192 \qquad (44)$$
$$\hat{i}_o = i_o$$

The Taylor-series expansion for e_2, the voltage across the nonlinear resistor, is

$$e_2 = 2|i_L|i_L = 2|\bar{i}_L|\bar{i}_L + \frac{de_2}{di_L}\bigg|_{\bar{i}_L} (i_L - \bar{i}_L) + \cdots$$

Because $\bar{i}_L$ is positive, $|\bar{i}_L| = \bar{i}_L$ and the approximate expression for e_2 becomes

$$e_2 \simeq 2\bar{i}_L^2 + (4\bar{i}_L)\hat{i}_L = 1.2193 + 3.1232\hat{i}_L \qquad (45)$$

Substituting (44) and (45) into (37), (38), and (39) and canceling the constant terms give the two state-variable equations

$$\dot{\hat{e}}_C = 4(\hat{i}_L - \hat{e}_C)$$
$$\frac{d\hat{i}_L}{dt} = 2[\hat{e}_i(t) - 3.1232\hat{i}_L - \hat{e}_C] \qquad (46)$$

and the output equation

$$\hat{i}_o = \hat{i}_L - \hat{e}_C \qquad (47)$$

The required initial conditions are

$$\hat{i}_L(0) = i_L(0) - 0.7808 = -1.5616 \text{ A}$$
$$\hat{e}_C(0) = e_C(0) + 5.2192 = -1.5616 \text{ V} \qquad (48)$$

To draw the linearized equivalent circuit, we first note from (45) that $\hat{e}_2 = 3.1232\hat{i}_L$. Thus, by a comparison with Ohm's law, the nonlinear resistor is replaced by a linear element whose resistance is $3.1232 \ \Omega$. We also replace all the voltages and currents in Figure 9.13(a) by their incremental components. Because the 6-V source has no incremental component, it becomes a short circuit. The complete linearized model is shown in Figure 9.13(d). If we so desire, we can obtain (46) and (47) directly from this figure.

The results of a computer solution of the nonlinear model when $e_i(t) = 2 + A\cos 4t$ for $t > 0$ and for the initial conditions in (41) are shown in Figure 9.14. A solution of the linearized model when $\hat{e}_i(t) = A\cos 4t$ and for comparable initial conditions is shown on the same set of axes. Because $\bar{i}_o = 0$, we can compare i_o from the nonlinear model to $\hat{i}_o$ from the linearized

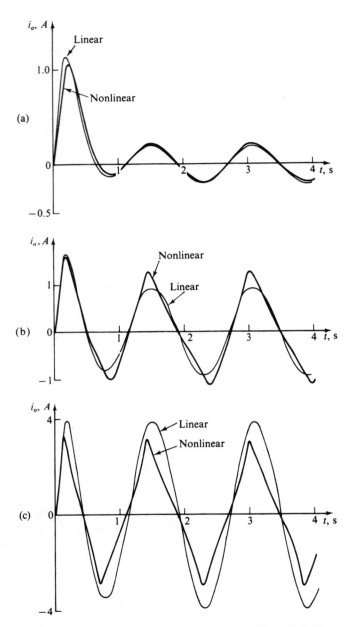

FIGURE 9.14 Results of computer simulation for Example 9.10 with $e_i(t) = 2 + A \cos 4t$ for $t > 0$. (a) $A = 1$ V. (b) $A = 5$ V. (c) $A = 20$ V.

model directly. The responses agree closely for $A = 1$ V. Note, however, that when $A = 5$ V and 20 V, the output waveshape for the nonlinear model begins to look triangular in the steady state. For the linearized model, the steady-state response to a sinusoidal input must remain sinusoidal regardless of the size of the input.

Reflecting on the results of this example and the preceding one, we see that even in the steady state, a nonlinearity can alter the average value of the output and also its waveshape. Its effect may be different for different operating points, and it is difficult to predict in advance the range of incremental inputs for which a linearized model will give a satisfactory approximation. Because it is difficult to establish general guidelines for approximating nonlinear systems, we must usually rely heavily on computer simulations.

SUMMARY

To linearize an element law about a particular operating point, we can use the first two terms in its Taylor-series expansion. This is equivalent to approximating its characteristic curve by a straight line tangent to the curve at the operating point.

For a system containing nonlinear elements, we first find the operating point corresponding to a specified constant value of the input. Then, in the nonlinear differential equations, we express the variables as the sum of constant and time-varying components, with nonlinear terms replaced by the first two terms in their Taylor-series expansions. After canceling the constant terms, we obtain linear equations that involve only the time-varying incremental variables.

In subsequent chapters, we shall use the same technique to obtain linearized approximations to some electromechanical, thermal, and hydraulic systems. The basic technique can also be extended to systems whose parameters vary with time and to nonlinearities that depend on two or more independent variables. Such extensions, along with nonlinear inductors and capacitors, are treated in some of the references in Appendix D.

PROBLEMS

In Problems 9.1 through 9.6, use a Taylor-series expansion to derive the linearized model for the element law and operating point(s) specified. In each case, show the linearized characteristic on a sketch of the nonlinear element law.

9.1 $f(x) = 0.5x^3$ where $\bar{x} = -2$, 0, and 2

* 9.2 $f(x) = \begin{cases} -A(1 - \epsilon^x) & \text{for } x < 0 \\ A(1 - \epsilon^{-x}) & \text{for } x \geq 0 \end{cases}$ where $\bar{x} = -1,\ 0,$ and 1

9.3 $f(\theta) = \begin{cases} -\sin^2\theta & \text{for } \theta < 0 \\ \sin^2\theta & \text{for } \theta \geq 0 \end{cases}$ where $\bar{\theta} = 0,\ \pi/4,\ \pi/2,$ and $3\pi/4$

9.4 $f(\theta) = \begin{cases} -\sin(\theta^2) & \text{for } \theta < 0 \\ \sin(\theta^2) & \text{for } \theta \geq 0 \end{cases}$ where $\bar{\theta} = 0,\ \sqrt{\pi}/2,$ and $\sqrt{\pi/2}$

* 9.5 $f(y) = 1/y$ where $y > 0$ and $\bar{y} = 0.5$

9.6 $f(z) = \begin{cases} -\sqrt{|z|} & \text{for } z < 0 \\ \sqrt{z} & \text{for } z \geq 0 \end{cases}$ where $\bar{z} = -2$ and 2

9.7 A nonlinear spring characteristic $f_K(x)$ is shown in Figure P9.7, where x denotes the total length. For each of the operating points specified, determine graphically the force exerted by the spring at the operating point, and evaluate graphically the linearized spring constant.

    a) $\bar{x} = 0.1$ m
    b) $\bar{x} = 0.2$ m
    c) $\bar{x} = 0.3$ m
    d) $\bar{x} = 0.4$ m

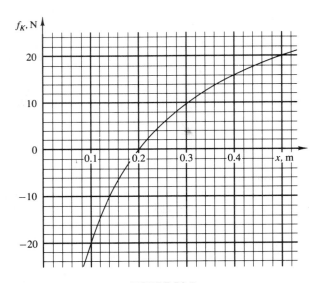

FIGURE P9.7

* 9.8 The nonlinear mechanical system shown in Figure P9.8 has $M = 1.5$ kg, $B = 0.5$ N·s/m, and the spring characteristic $f_K(x)$ plotted in Figure P9.7. The gravitational constant is 9.807 m/s². The variable x denotes the total length of the spring.

    a) Verify that the nonlinear input-output differential equation is $1.5\ddot{x} + 0.5\dot{x} + f_K(x) = 14.71$.

    b) Solve for the operating point $\bar{x}$.

c) Derive the linearized differential equation that is valid in the vicinity of the operating point.

d) Give the approximate range of x for which the linearized spring force is within 25% of the nonlinear spring force.

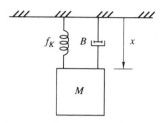

FIGURE P9.8

9.9 For the system shown in Figure P9.9, the mass is attached to the wall by a series combination of a linear spring and a nonlinear spring. The parameter values are $M = 4.0$ kg, $B = 0.3$ N·s/m, and $K = 25$ N/m. The applied force is $f_a(t) = 10 + 2\sin 3t$, and the nonlinear spring characteristic $f_K(x)$ is plotted in Figure P9.7. The position $z = 0$ corresponds to $f_a(t) = 0$ with both springs undeflected.

a) Find the nonlinear input-output differential equation relating z to $f_a(t)$.

b) Solve for the operating point $\bar{z}$.

c) Derive the linearized differential equation that is valid in the vicinity of the operating point.

d) Give the approximate range of z for which the linearized spring force is within 25% of the nonlinear spring force.

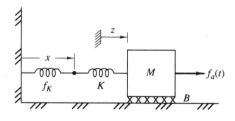

FIGURE P9.9

* 9.10 A mechanical system containing a nonlinear spring obeys the differential equation

$$\ddot{x} + 2\dot{x} + f(x) = A + B\sin 3t$$

where

$$f(x) = \begin{cases} -4\sqrt{|x|} & \text{for } x < 0 \\ 4\sqrt{x} & \text{for } x \geq 0 \end{cases}$$

a) Find the operating point $\bar{x}$ and derive the linearized model in numerical form for $A = 8$.

b) Find the operating point $\bar{x}$ and the linearized spring constant for $A = 4$ and -4.

c) Find $\hat{x}(0)$ and $\dot{\hat{x}}(0)$ when $A = 4$, $x(0) = 1.5$, and $\dot{x}(0) = 0.5$.

9.11 A nonlinear system obeys the equation

$$\ddot{x} + 2\dot{x} + \dot{x}^3 + \frac{4}{x} = A + B \cos t$$

a) Solve for the operating-point conditions on $\bar{x}$ and $\dot{\bar{x}}$. What restriction must be placed on the value of A?

b) Derive the linearized model, evaluating the coefficients in terms of A or numbers.

* 9.12 A system is described by the nonlinear equation

$$\ddot{y} + 2(\dot{y} + \dot{y}^3) + 2y + |y|y = A + B \cos t$$

a) For $A = -3$, find the operating point and derive the linearized model, expressing all coefficients in numerical form.

b) Repeat part (a) for $A = 15$.

9.13 The model of a nonlinear system is described by the equation

$$\ddot{x} + \dot{x} + 3x\sqrt{|x|} = A + B \sin \omega t$$

The equilibrium position is known to be $\bar{x} = 4$. Determine the linearized incremental model, and evaluate $\hat{x}(0)$ and $\dot{\hat{x}}(0)$ when $x(0) = 5$ and $\dot{x}(0) = 0$.

9.14 A nonlinear system obeys the equation

$$\dot{x} + 0.5x^2 = 2 + A \sin t$$

a) Sketch the nonlinear term $0.5x^2$ and indicate all possible operating points.

b) For each operating point you found in part (a), derive the linearized model for the system and indicate whether the linear model is stable or unstable.

9.15 A nonlinear system obeys the differential equation

$$\dot{y} + 4\sqrt{y} = 8 + B \cos 2t$$

for $y \geq 0$ and has the initial condition $y(0) = 5$.

a) Derive the linearized incremental model corresponding to the specified input.

b) Sketch the nonlinear element law for $y \geq 0$, and indicate the operating point and the linear approximation.

c) Evaluate the appropriate initial condition for the incremental variable.

9.16 A system obeys the differential equation

$$\ddot{x} + 3|\dot{x}|\dot{x} + 4x^3 = A + B \sin 2t$$

and has the initial conditions $x(0) = 2$ and $\dot{x}(0) = 1$.

a) Find the operating point and derive the linearized model for $A = 4$. Also, find the initial values of $\hat{x}$ and $\dot{\hat{x}}$.

b) Repeat part (a) for $A = 32$.

9.17 In developing the linearized model for a high-speed vehicle in Example 9.6, we assumed that $\bar{f}_a$, the nominal value of the driving force, was positive. Repeat the development for $\bar{f}_a < 0$, and find an expression for b, the effective damping coefficient of the linearized model, that is valid for both cases.

* **9.18** The disk shown in Figure P9.18 is supported by a nonlinear torsional spring and is subject to both linear and nonlinear frictional torques. The applied torque is $\tau_a(t) = 8 + \hat{\tau}_a(t)$.

    a) Find the operating point $\bar{\theta}$.

    b) Derive the linearized input-output equation in terms of $\hat{\theta}(t) = \theta - \bar{\theta}$.

    c) Find the initial values of the incremental variables $\hat{\theta}$ and $\dot{\hat{\theta}}$ if $\theta(0) = 0.5$ rad and $\dot{\theta}(0) = -0.5$ rad/s.

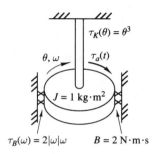

$$\tau_K(\theta) = \theta^3$$
$$\theta, \omega \qquad \tau_a(t)$$
$$J = 1\ \text{kg·m}^2$$
$$\tau_B(\omega) = 2|\omega|\omega \qquad B = 2\ \text{N·m·s}$$

FIGURE P9.18

9.19 The translational system shown in Figure P9.19 has a linear and a nonlinear spring and is subjected to the applied force $f_a(t)$.

    a) Show that the nonlinear model is $2\ddot{x} + 6\dot{x} + 3x + |x|x = f_a(t)$.

    b) Solve for the operating point $\bar{x}$ when $\bar{f}_a = 10$ N.

    c) Derive the linearized model when $f_a(t) = 10 + \hat{f}_a(t)$.

    d) Find the initial values $\hat{x}(0)$ and $\dot{\hat{x}}(0)$ if $x(0) = 3$ m and $\dot{x}(0) = 1$ m/s.

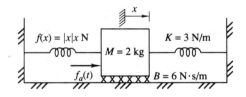

$$f(x) = |x|x\ \text{N} \qquad K = 3\ \text{N/m}$$
$$M = 2\ \text{kg}$$
$$f_a(t) \qquad B = 6\ \text{N·s/m}$$

FIGURE P9.19

9.20 The rotating cylinder shown in Figure P9.20 has damping vanes and a linear frictional torque such that the motion is described by the nonlinear equation

$$\dot{\omega} + 2|\omega|\omega + 2\omega = \tau_a(t)$$

where the applied torque is $\tau_a(t) = 12 + \hat{\tau}_a(t)$. Find the operating point and derive a linearized model in terms of the incremental angular velocity $\hat{\omega}$.

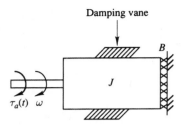

FIGURE P9.20

* **9.21 a)** Verify that the input-output differential equation for the mechanical system modeled in Problem 2.19 is

$$M\ddot{x} + B\dot{x} + x^3 = f_a(t) + Mg$$

b) Find the operating point and derive the linearized input-output equation for the system for the case when $\bar{f}_a = 0$.
c) Repeat part (b) for the case when $\bar{f}_a = Mg$.

9.22 A nonlinear system obeys the state-variable equations

$$\dot{x} = -x + y$$

$$\dot{y} = \frac{1}{y} + 4 + B \sin t$$

Find the operating point and derive the linearized equations in state-variable form. Also, evaluate the initial conditions on the incremental variables when $x(0) = 0$ and $y(0) = -0.5$.

* **9.23** A second-order nonlinear system having state variables x and y obeys the equations

$$\dot{x} = -2x + y^3$$

$$\dot{y} = x + 4 + \cos t$$

a) Find the operating-point values $\bar{x}$ and $\bar{y}$.
b) Find the linearized state-variable equations in numerical form.
c) Find the linearized model as an input-output equation relating $\hat{x}$ and its derivatives to the incremental input.

9.24 A nonlinear system with state variables x and y and input $u(t)$ obeys the equations

$$\dot{x} = -2|x|x - y + u(t) - 6$$

$$\dot{y} = x - y - 6$$

a) Verify that when $u(t) = 2 + B \cos 2t$, the operating point is $\bar{x} = 0.7808$, $\bar{y} = -5.2192$.
b) Evaluate the linearized model about this operating point.
c) Evaluate the initial conditions for the incremental variables when $x(0) = 1$ and $y(0) = -6$.

9.25 The nonlinear resistor in the circuit shown in Figure P9.25 obeys the element law $e_o = 2i^3$.

    a) Verify that the nonlinear input-output equation is

$$0.5\frac{di}{dt} + 3i + 2i^3 = 22 + \hat{e}_i(t)$$

    b) Find the operating-point values $\bar{i}$ and $\bar{e}_o$.

    c) Derive the linearized model that is valid in the vicinity of this operating point.

    d) Find the time constant of the linearized model.

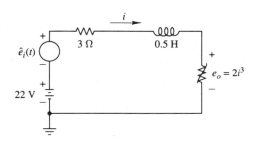

FIGURE P9.25

9.26 For the circuit shown in Figure 9.10(a), the nonlinear resistor is described by the equation $i_o = e_o/(1 + |e_o|)$.

    a) Verify that the nonlinear state-variable equation is

$$\dot{e}_o = 2\left[-e_o - \frac{e_o}{1 + |e_o|} + e_i(t)\right]$$

    b) If the operating point is defined by $\bar{e}_o = 2$ V, what must be $\bar{e}_i$, the nominal value of the input?

    c) Find the linearized state-variable equation for the operating point defined in part (b).

    d) Draw the linearized equivalent circuit.

* **9.27** The nonlinear resistor in the circuit shown in Figure P9.27 obeys the element law $e_o = 3|i_L|i_L$.

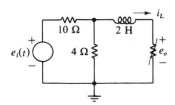

FIGURE P9.27

a) Verify that the nonlinear state-variable model is

$$\frac{di_L}{dt} = -\frac{10}{7}i_L - \frac{3}{2}|i_L|i_L + \frac{1}{7}e_i(t)$$

$$e_o = 3|i_L|i_L$$

b) Find the operating point and derive the linearized model when $e_i(t) = 5 + 0.4\cos t$ for $t > 0$.

c) Find the time constant of the linearized model.

* 9.28 For the circuit shown in Figure P9.28, $i_o = |e_o|e_o$ and $e_i(t) = 4 + \hat{e}_i(t)$.

a) Show that the nonlinear input-output differential equation is

$$2\ddot{e}_o + 6\dot{e}_o + 2e_o + \frac{d}{dt}(|e_o|e_o) = 4\dot{e}_i + 2e_i(t)$$

b) Find the operating-point values $\bar{e}_o$ and $\bar{i}_o$.

c) Find the linearized input-output equation relating $\hat{e}_o$ and $\hat{e}_i(t)$.

d) Draw the linearized equivalent circuit.

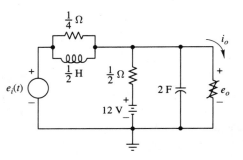

FIGURE P9.28

9.29 For the circuit shown in Figure P9.29, the element law for the nonlinear resistor is $i_2 = 2|e_C|e_C$.

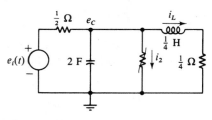

FIGURE P9.29

a) Verify that the circuit obeys the nonlinear state-variable equations

$$\dot{e}_C = -e_C - |e_C|e_C - \frac{1}{2}i_L + e_i(t)$$

$$\frac{di_L}{dt} = 4e_C - i_L$$

b) Determine the values of $\bar{e}_C$ and $\bar{i}_L$ when $e_i(t) = 10 + \hat{e}_i(t)$.

c) Derive the linearized state-variable equations that are valid in the vicinity of the operating point found in part (b).

d) Find $\hat{e}_C(0)$ and $\hat{i}_L(0)$ when $e_C(0) = 3$ V and $i_L(0) = 1$ A.

9.30 For the circuit shown in Figure P9.30, the element law for the nonlinear resistor is $e_2 = 0.5i_L^3$. The input voltage $e_i(t)$ is 4 V for $t \le 0$ and is $4 + \hat{e}_i(t)$ for $t > 0$.

a) Verify that the nonlinear state-variable model is

$$\dot{e}_C = -e_C + \frac{1}{2}i_L + \frac{1}{2}e_i(t)$$

$$\frac{di_L}{dt} = -2e_C - i_L^3 + 2e_i(t)$$

$$e_o = -e_C - \frac{1}{2}i_L^3 + e_i(t)$$

b) Find $e_C(0)$ and $i_L(0)$. Assume that steady-state conditions exist at $t = 0-$.

c) Find the values of the state variables at the operating point, and derive a set of linearized state-variable equations.

d) Find $\hat{e}_C(0)$ and $\hat{i}_L(0)$.

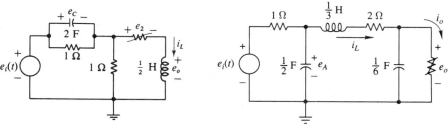

FIGURE P9.30   **FIGURE P9.31**

9.31 For the circuit shown in Figure P9.31, $i_o = \frac{1}{4}e_o^3$ and $e_i(t) = 8 + \hat{e}_i(t)$.

a) Verify that the state-variable equations are

$$\dot{e}_A = 2[-e_A - i_L + e_i(t)]$$

$$\dot{e}_o = 6\left[-\frac{1}{4}e_o^3 + i_L\right]$$

$$\frac{di_L}{dt} = 3[e_A - e_o - 2i_L]$$

b) Verify that the operating point is defined by $\bar{e}_o = 2$ V.

c) Find the linearized state-variable equations for the operating point in part (b) and draw the linearized equivalent circuit.

ELECTROMECHANICAL SYSTEMS

We can construct a wide variety of very useful devices by combining electrical and mechanical elements. Among the electromechanical devices that we shall consider are potentiometers, the galvanometer, the microphone, and motors and generators.

We first discuss coupling the electrical and mechanical parts of the system by mechanically varying a resistance. In the following section we consider the coupling associated with the movement of a current-carrying conductor through a magnetic field. Two new laws are needed to describe the additional forces and voltages caused by this action. A number of magnetically coupled devices are then considered in detail.

Some of the examples incorporate many of the analytical tools developed in the previous four chapters, such as damping ratio, steady-state response, transfer functions, and linearization. The chapter concludes with a comprehensive example that points out some of the important features that must be considered in the design of an electromechanical measuring device.

■ 10.1 RESISTIVE COUPLING

We can control a variable resistance by mechanical motion either continuously by moving an electrical contact or discretely by opening and closing a switch. Because resistors cannot store energy, this method of coupling electrical and mechanical parts of a system, in contrast to coupling by magnetic and electrical fields, does not involve mechanical forces that depend on electrical variables.

388

Figure 10.1(a) shows a strip of conducting material having resistivity ρ and cross-sectional area A. One terminal is fixed to the left end of the conductor. The other terminal, known as the **wiper**, is free to slide along the bar while maintaining a good electrical connection at all times—that is, zero resistance at the contact point. The resistance per unit length of the bar is ρ/A, so the resistance between the terminals is

$$R = \left[\frac{\rho}{A}\right] x(t) \tag{1}$$

where $x(t)$, the displacement of the wiper, can vary with time. The rotational equivalent of this device is shown in Figure 10.1(b). Here the resistance between the two terminals is a function of the angle $\theta(t)$, which defines the angular orientation of the wiper with respect to the fixed terminal.

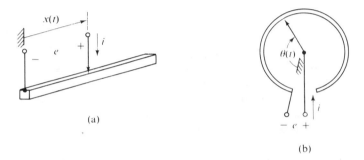

(a)

(b)

FIGURE 10.1   Variable resistors. (a) Translational. (b) Rotational.

A very useful device known as a **potentiometer** is obtained by adding a third terminal to the right ends of the variable resistors shown in Figure 10.1. For the translational potentiometer shown in Figure 10.2(a), the two end terminals are normally connected across a voltage source, and the voltage at the wiper is considered the output. The resistances R_1 and R_2 depend on the wiper position and are therefore labeled $R_1(x)$ and $R_2(x)$ in the figure. In our mathematical development, however, we shall omit the x in parentheses. We can regard either the position $x(t)$ or the voltage source $e_i(t)$, or both, as inputs.

The circuit diagram for the potentiometer is shown in Figure 10.2(b). Provided that no current flows through the wiper, we can apply the voltage-divider rule of (5.29) to obtain

$$e_o = \left[\frac{R_2}{R_1 + R_2}\right] e_i(t) \tag{2}$$

If the distance and the resistance between the fixed terminals are denoted by x_{max} and R_T, respectively, then $R_2 = [R_T/x_{max}]x(t)$ and $R_1 + R_2 = R_T$. Substituting these two expressions into (2), we can write the output voltage

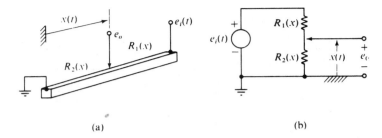

FIGURE 10.2   (a) Translational potentiometer. (b) Equivalent circuit.

as

$$e_o = \left[\frac{1}{x_{\max}}\right] x(t) e_i(t) \tag{3}$$

where the ratio $x(t)/x_{\max}$ must be between 0 and 1, inclusive.

We can interpret (3) as saying that the output voltage is proportional to the product of the input voltage $e_i(t)$ and the mechanical variable $x(t)$. For a constant input voltage, the output voltage is proportional only to the mechanical displacement $x(t)$. Sometimes, however, the electrical circuit includes an additional resistance across part of the potentiometer, which can complicate the desired relationship. This possible problem is illustrated in the following example.

▶ **EXAMPLE 10.1**

The rotary potentiometer shown in Figure 10.3 has a constant voltage E applied across its fixed terminais, and the wiper is connected to a constant resistance R_o, which might represent the resistance of a voltmeter or a recording device. Find the relationship between the output voltage e_o and the angular orientation of the mechanical rotor attached to the wiper. Assume that the resistance per unit length of the potentiometer is constant.

Solution

The wiper contact divides the total potentiometer resistance R_T into R_1 and R_2, such that in the circuit shown in Figure 10.4(a),

$$R_2 = \left[\frac{R_T}{\theta_{\max}}\right] \theta(t) \tag{4}$$

$$R_1 + R_2 = R_T$$

The values of R_1 and R_2 depend on $\theta(t)$, as we emphasize by labeling them $R_1(\theta)$ and $R_2(\theta)$ in the figure. Because R_o and R_2 are connected in parallel, they can be replaced by a single equivalent resistance $R_{eq} = R_o R_2/(R_o+R_2)$, which gives the circuit shown in Figure 10.4(b).

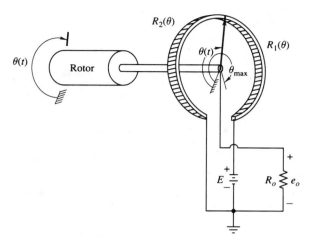

FIGURE 10.3 Potentiometer used to measure the angular orientation of a rotor.

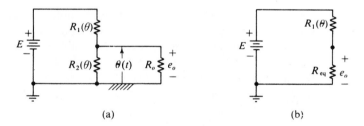

FIGURE 10.4 Equivalent circuits for Example 10.1.

By the voltage-divider rule, the output voltage is

$$
e_o = \left(\frac{R_{eq}}{R_{eq} + R_1} \right) E = \left(\frac{R_o R_2}{R_o R_2 + R_o R_1 + R_1 R_2} \right) E
$$

$$
= \left(\frac{R_o R_2}{R_o R_T + R_1 R_2} \right) E
$$

$$
= \left[\frac{1}{1 + \left(\dfrac{R_T}{R_o} \right) \left(\dfrac{R_1}{R_T} \right) \left(\dfrac{R_2}{R_T} \right)} \right] \left(\frac{R_2}{R_T} \right) E \tag{5}
$$

Substituting (4) into (5) gives

$$e_o = \left(\frac{E}{\theta_{max}}\right)\left[\frac{1}{1 + \left(\frac{R_T}{R_o}\right)\left[1 - \frac{\theta(t)}{\theta_{max}}\right]\left[\frac{\theta(t)}{\theta_{max}}\right]}\right]\theta(t) \qquad (6)$$

which is the desired result.

Unfortunately, (6) is a nonlinear relationship between the output voltage and the rotor angle because of the presence of $\theta(t)$ in the coefficient of $\theta(t)$. Although we could still use the potentiometer to measure $\theta(t)$, the voltmeter or recording device would require a nonlinear scale, which would be inconvenient.

However, if the output resistance R_o is large compared to the total potentiometer resistance R_T, then the coefficient in the brackets is approximately unity because $0 \le \theta(t)/\theta_{max} \le 1$. Then (6) reduces to the linear relationship

$$e_o = \left[\frac{E}{\theta_{max}}\right]\theta(t) \quad \text{for } R_o \gg R_T \qquad (7)$$

Equation (7) indicates that we can treat the potentiometer as a gain of E/θ_{max} volts per radian with $\theta(t)$ as its input and e_o as its output. This simplification can be used whenever the parallel combination of R_o and R_2 has a resistance equal to R_2. This is equivalent to saying that the current through R_o is negligible compared to that through R_2. When R_o is not sufficiently large for us to use (7), we say that the resistance R_o **loads** the potentiometer, and we use the nonlinear expression in (6).

■ 10.2 COUPLING BY A MAGNETIC FIELD

A great variety of electromechanical devices contain current-carrying wires that can move within a magnetic field. The physical laws governing this type of electromechanical coupling are given in introductory physics textbooks such as Halliday and Resnick (see Appendix D). These laws state that (1) a wire in a magnetic field that carries a current will have a force exerted on it, and (2) a voltage will be induced in a wire that moves relative to the magnetic field. The variables we need to model such devices are

f_e, the force on the conductor in newtons (N)

v, the velocity of the conductor with respect to the magnetic field in meters per second (m/s)

ℓ, the length of the conductor in the magnetic field in meters (m)

ϕ, the flux in webers (Wb)

$\mathscr{B}$, the flux density of the magnetic field in webers per square meter (Wb/m^2)

i, the current in the conductor in amperes (A)

e_m, the voltage induced in the conductor in volts (V)

In all of our examples the variables will be scalar quantities. However, we shall first introduce the basic laws in a very general way, where the force, velocity, length, and flux density can have any spatial orientation. For the general case we will represent these four quantities as vectors and use the boldface symbols $\mathbf{f_e}$, $\mathbf{v}$, $\boldsymbol{\ell}$, and $\mathscr{B}$.

The force on a conductor of differential length $d\ell$ carrying a current i in a magnetic field of flux density $\mathscr{B}$ is

$$d\mathbf{f_e} = i(d\boldsymbol{\ell} \times \mathscr{B}) \tag{8}$$

The cross in (8) represents the vector cross product. To obtain the total electrically induced force $\mathbf{f_e}$, we must integrate (8) along the length of the conductor.

In our applications, the wires will be either straight conductors that are perpendicular to a unidirectional magnetic field or circular conductors in a radial magnetic field. In either case, the differential length $d\ell$ will be perpendicular to a uniform flux density $\mathscr{B}$. Then (8) simplifies to the scalar relationship

$$f_e = \mathscr{B}\ell i \tag{9}$$

where the direction of the force is perpendicular to both the wire and the magnetic field and can be found by the following rule. If the bent fingers of the right hand are pointed from the positive direction of the current toward the positive direction of the magnetic field (through the right angle), the thumb will point in the positive direction of the force. Figure 10.5(a) shows that for a positive current into the page and a positive flux to the left, the force on a straight conductor is upward. The position of the right hand corresponding to this situation is shown in Figure 10.5(b).

The voltage induced in a conductor of differential length $d\ell$ moving with velocity $\mathbf{v}$ in a field of flux density $\mathscr{B}$ is

$$de_m = (\mathbf{v} \times \mathscr{B}) \cdot d\boldsymbol{\ell} \tag{10}$$

where the dot denotes the scalar product, or dot product, used with vector notation. We obtain the total induced voltage for a conductor by integrating (10) between the ends of the conductor.

In practice, the three vectors in (10) will be mutually perpendicular, so integrating (10) yields the scalar relationship

$$e_m = \mathscr{B}\ell v \tag{11}$$

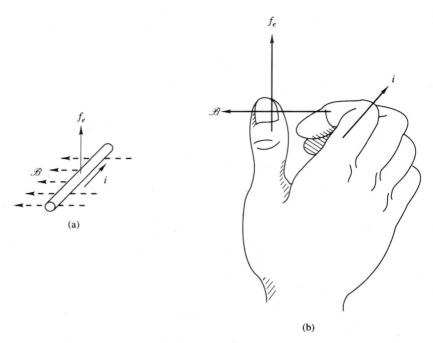

FIGURE 10.5 Right-hand rule for the force on a conductor.

If the bent fingers of the right hand are pointed from the positive direction of the velocity toward the positive direction of the magnetic field (through the right angle), the thumb will point in the direction in which the current caused by the induced voltage tends to flow. In Figure 10.6(a), a straight conductor is shown moving downward in a magnetic field directed to the left. As indicated by the polarity signs and by the sketch shown in Figure 10.6(b), the positive sense of the induced voltage is into the page. If the conductor were part of a complete circuit with no external sources, the current in the conductor would be into the page. According to Figure 10.5, this current would cause there to be exerted on the conductor an upward force that would oppose the downward motion.

Equations (9) and (11), which describe the force and induced voltage associated with a wire moving perpendicularly to a magnetic field, can be incorporated in a schematic representation of a translational electromechanical system as shown in Figure 10.7. The induced voltage is represented by a source in the electrical circuit, whereas the magnetically induced force is shown acting on the mass M to which the conductor is attached. We can determine the proper polarity marks for e_m and the reference direction for f_e by examining the specific device under consideration, but the figure indicates two combinations of reference directions that are consistent with the conservation of energy.

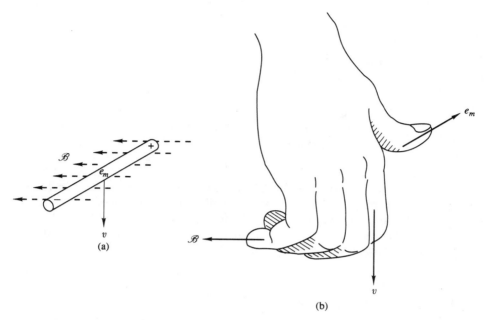

FIGURE 10.6 Right-hand rule for the voltage induced in a moving conductor.

In Figure 10.7(a), the polarity of the electrical source is such that power is absorbed from the remainder of the circuit when both e_m and i are positive. Likewise, when f_e and v are positive, there is a transfer of power into the mechanical part of the system. Conversely, for Figure 10.7(b), power flows from the mechanical side to the electrical side when all four variables are positive.

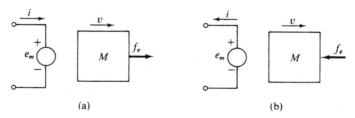

FIGURE 10.7 Representations of a translational electromechanical system. (a) Electrical-to-mechanical power flow. (b) Mechanical-to-electrical power flow.

It is instructive to evaluate the power involved in the coupling mechanism. The external power delivered to the electrical part of Figure 10.7(a) is

$$p_e = e_m i = (\mathscr{B}\ell v)i$$

whereas the power available to whatever mechanical elements are attached to the coil is

$$p_m = f_e v = (\mathscr{B}\ell i)v$$

Hence,

$$p_m = p_e$$

which says that any power delivered to the coupling mechanism in electrical form will be passed on undiminished to the mechanical portion. Of course, any practical system has losses resulting from the resistance of the conductor and the friction between the moving mechanical elements. However, any such dissipative elements can be modeled separately by a resistor in the electrical circuit or a viscous-friction element acting on the mass. In a similar way, you can demonstrate that for the coupling shown in Figure 10.7(b), the mechanical power supplied by the force f_e is transmitted to whatever electrical elements are connected across e_m.

■ 10.3   DEVICES COUPLED BY MAGNETIC FIELDS

Having introduced the basic laws that govern the behavior of a single conductor in a magnetic field, we shall describe several of the most common types of electromechanical systems and derive their mathematical models. In each case, we consider idealized versions of the device that omit certain aspects that may be important from a design standpoint but are not essential to understanding its operation as part of an overall system. We shall examine in turn the galvanometer, a microphone, and a motor.

The Galvanometer

The galvanometer is a device that produces an angular deflection dependent on the current passing through a coil attached to a pointer. It is widely used in electrical measurement devices. As shown in Figure 10.8(a), a permanent magnet supplies a radial magnetic field, and the flux passes through a stationary iron cylinder between the poles of the magnet. A coil of wire whose terminals can be connected to an external circuit is suspended by bearings so that it can rotate about a horizontal axis passing through the center of the cylinder. A torsional spring mounted on its axis restrains the coil.

The magnet provides a uniform flux density $\mathscr{B}$ within the air gaps between it and the iron cylinder directed from the north to the south pole. The moment of inertia of the coil is J, and the combination of bearing friction and damping due to the air is represented by the viscous-damping coefficient B. The torsional spring has the rotational spring constant K. It is assumed that the electrical connection between the external circuit and the

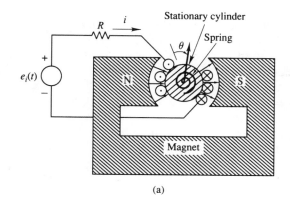

(a)

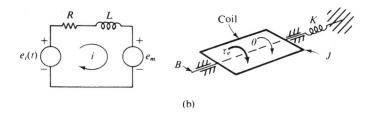

(b)

FIGURE 10.8 Galvanometer. (a) Physical device. (b) Diagrams used for analysis.

movable coils is made in such a way that the connection exerts no torque on the coil.

The coil consists of N rectangular turns, each of which has a radius of a and a length of ℓ along the direction of the axis of rotation, and it has a total inductance L. The dots in the wires on the left side of the coil and the crosses on the right side indicate that when i is positive, the current flows out of the page in the left conductors and into the page in the right conductors. The remainder of the circuit consists of a voltage source $e_i(t)$ and a resistance R that accounts for any resistance external to the galvanometer as well as for the resistance of the coils.

For purposes of analysis, we represent the idealized system by the circuit and mechanical diagrams shown in Figure 10.8(b). We have used the rotational equivalent of Figure 10.7(a) rather than Figure 10.7(b) to represent the electromechanical coupling, because the purpose of the device is to convert an electrical variable (current) into a mechanical variable (angular displacement). It remains to use (9) and (11), with the appropriate right-hand rules, to determine the expressions for e_m and τ_e, the electrically induced torque.

Assume that the rotation of the coil is sufficiently small that all the conductors remain in the region of constant flux density. Then we can obtain the torque τ_e acting about the axis of the coil by summing the torques on the $2N$ individual conductors of length ℓ. Because the magnetic field is confined to the iron cylinder as it passes between the air gaps, there is no contribution to the torque from the ends of the coil outside the gaps. If the current is positive, each conductor on the left side of the coil has a force of $f_e = \mathcal{B}\ell i$ acting upward, whereas the conductors on the right side have forces of the same magnitude acting downward. Because the arrow denoting the electrically induced torque τ_e was taken as clockwise in Figure 10.8(b), the expression for the torque is

$$\tau_e = (2N\mathcal{B}\ell a)i \tag{12}$$

Next we express the voltage induced in the coil in terms of the angular velocity $\dot{\theta}$. Because there are $2N$ conductors in series, which move with the velocity $a\dot{\theta}$ with respect to the magnetic field, a voltage of $2N\mathcal{B}\ell a\dot{\theta}$ is induced in the coil. We find the sign of the mechanically induced voltage e_m by applying the right-hand rule illustrated in Figure 10.6(b). The conductors on the right side of the coil in Figure 10.8(a) move downward when $\dot{\theta} > 0$ and the flux-density vector $\mathcal{B}$ points to the right, toward the south pole. Thus the positive sense of e_m is directed toward the viewer, and the corresponding current direction is out of the paper, opposite to the reference arrow for i in the figure. The circuit shown in Figure 10.8(b) was drawn with this assumed polarity for e_m, so we have

$$e_m = (2N\mathcal{B}\ell a)\dot{\theta} \tag{13}$$

Summing torques on the coil and using (12) give

$$J\ddot{\theta} + B\dot{\theta} + K\theta = (2N\mathcal{B}\ell a)i \tag{14}$$

Using (13) in a voltage-law equation for the single loop that makes up the electrical part of the system gives

$$L\frac{di}{dt} + Ri + (2N\mathcal{B}\ell a)\dot{\theta} = e_i(t) \tag{15}$$

Equations (14) and (15) constitute the complete model of the galvanometer, which is a third-order model. From these two equations we can determine the state-variable equations, the transfer function, and the input-output differential equation. In practical situations, the inductance of the coil is often sufficiently small to allow us to neglect the term $L\,di/dt$ in (15). This simplification is particularly helpful in solving for the response to an input voltage, because the model becomes second-order. When this term is dropped, we can solve (15) for the current, obtaining

$$i = \frac{1}{R}\left[e_i(t) - (2N\mathcal{B}\ell a)\dot{\theta}\right]$$

By substituting this expression into (14), we have, for the input-output equation,

$$\ddot{\theta} + \left(\frac{B}{J} + \frac{\alpha^2}{JR}\right)\dot{\theta} + \frac{K}{J}\theta = \frac{\alpha}{JR}e_i(t) \qquad (16)$$

where $\alpha = 2N\mathscr{B}\ell a$ is the electromechanical coupling coefficient. Comparing (16) with (6.49), we find that the undamped natural frequency ω_n and the damping ratio ζ of the galvanometer are

$$\omega_n = \sqrt{\frac{K}{J}}$$

$$\zeta = \frac{1}{2\sqrt{KJ}}\left(B + \frac{\alpha^2}{R}\right)$$

Hence the undamped natural frequency depends on the mechanical parameters K and J, and the damping ratio depends on both the mechanical and electrical parameters and the electromechanical coupling coefficient α.

We can find the sensitivity of the galvanometer in radians per volt by solving for the forced response to the constant excitation $e_i(t) = A$. The steady-state value of θ will be the particular solution of (16), namely

$$\theta_{ss} = \left(\frac{\alpha}{KR}\right)A \qquad (17)$$

which is a constant. The galvanometer sensitivity is $\theta_{ss}/A = \alpha/KR$. Thus a higher flux density will make the device more sensitive, and increasing either the spring stiffness or the electrical resistance will reduce its sensitivity.

We can arrive at the same result for the sensitivity by the following argument. Because in the steady state the rotor will be stationary, no voltage will be induced in the coils. Thus the steady-state current will be $i_{ss} = A/R$. The steady-state torque exerted on the rotor through the action of the magnetic field will be $(\tau_e)_{ss} = \alpha A/R$, which must be balanced entirely by the torsional spring that exerts the steady-state torque $K\theta_{ss}$. Equating these two torques gives (17).

If we wish to characterize the system by a set of state-variable equations, we can choose θ and ω as the state variables and use (16) to write

$$\dot{\theta} = \omega$$

$$\dot{\omega} = -\frac{K}{J}\theta - \left(\frac{B}{J} + \frac{\alpha^2}{JR}\right)\omega + \frac{\alpha}{JR}e_i(t)$$

Had we retained the inductance of the coil, the current i would have become the third state variable.

A Microphone

The microphone shown in cross section in Figure 10.9 consists of a diaphragm attached to a circular coil of wire that moves back and forth through a magnetic field when sound waves impinge on the diaphragm. The magnetic field is supplied by a cylindrical permanent magnet having concentric north and south poles, which result in radial lines of flux directed inward toward the axis of the magnet. The coil has N turns with a radius of a and is connected in series with an external resistor R, across which the output voltage is measured. The positive direction for the current i is assumed to be counterclockwise from the perspective of viewing the magnet from the diaphragm. In the figure, the resistance of the coil has been neglected, but the inductance of the coil is represented by the inductor L located externally to the coil. If the coil resistance were not negligible, another resistor could be added in series with the external resistor in order to account for it.

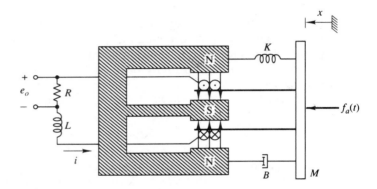

FIGURE 10.9   Representation of a microphone.

A single stiffness element K has been used to represent the stiffness of the entire diaphragm, and the viscous-friction element B has been used to account for the energy dissipation due to air resistance. The net force of the impinging sound waves is represented by $f_a(t)$, which is the input to the system. Although the forces acting on the diaphragm are certainly distributed in nature, it is a justifiable simplification to consider them as point forces associated with the lumped elements K, B, and M.

The first step in modeling the microphone is to construct idealized diagrams of the electrical and mechanical portions. In developing the equations for the galvanometer, we assumed at the outset positive senses for τ_e and e_m. Then we wrote expressions for these quantities, determining their signs by using the right-hand rules. This time, we shall first determine the positive directions of f_e, the electrically induced force on the diaphragm, and the mechanically induced voltage e_m when the other variables are positive. After that, we shall label the diagram with senses that agree with the positive directions of f_e and e_m. When we use this approach, we know in advance that the expressions for f_e and e_m will have plus signs.

Figure 10.10(a) shows the upper portion of a single turn of the coil as viewed from the diaphragm looking toward the magnet. Because the flux arrow points downward from the north to the south pole and the current arrow points to the left, the right-hand rule shown in Figure 10.5(b) indicates that the positive sense of f_e is toward the diaphragm. Because the velocity arrow points away from the diaphragm, the right-hand rule shown in Figure 10.6(b) indicates that the positive sense of the induced voltage is the same as that of the current. We can reach similar conclusions by examining any other part of the coil. Thus we can draw the complete diagram of the system, as shown in Figure 10.10(b).

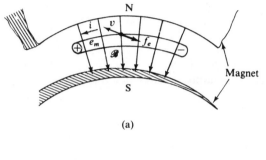

(a)

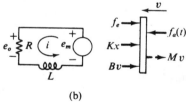

(b)

FIGURE 10.10   Microphone. (a) Relationships for a portion of a single coil. (b) Diagram used for analysis.

Because of the radial symmetry of the coil and the flux lines in the air gap, the entire coil of length $2\pi a N$ is perpendicular to the flux. Thus

$$f_e = \alpha i \tag{18a}$$

$$\tau_e = \alpha v \tag{18b}$$

where $\alpha = 2\pi a N \mathcal{B}$ is the electromechanical coupling coefficient for the system.

Summing forces on the free-body diagram for the diaphragm and using (18a), we obtain

$$M\dot{v} + Bv + Kx = -\alpha i + f_a(t) \tag{19}$$

We find the circuit equation by applying Kirchhoff's voltage law and using (18b), which yields

$$L\frac{di}{dt} + Ri = \alpha v \tag{20}$$

The system has three independent energy-storing elements (L, K, and M), so an appropriate set of state variables is i, x, and v. By rewriting (19) and (20), we obtain the state-variable equations

$$\frac{di}{dt} = \frac{1}{L}(-Ri + \alpha v)$$

$$\dot{x} = v$$

$$\dot{v} = \frac{1}{M}[-\alpha i - Kx - Bv + f_a(t)]$$

The output e_o is not a state variable, but we can find it from

$$e_o = Ri \tag{21}$$

In one of the end-of-chapter problems, you are asked to verify that the corresponding transfer function is

$$H(s) = \frac{E_o(s)}{F_a(s)} = \frac{\alpha R s}{MLs^3 + (MR + BL)s^2 + (KL + BR + \alpha^2)s + KR} \tag{22}$$

and that the input-output equation is

$$ML\ddot{e}_o + (MR + BL)\ddot{e}_o + (KL + BR + \alpha^2)\dot{e}_o + KRe_o = \alpha R\dot{f}_a \tag{23}$$

It is interesting to note that because the right side of (23) is proportional to $\dot{f}_a$ rather than to $f_a(t)$, the forced response for a constant-force input is zero. Thus a constant force applied to the diaphragm yields no output voltage in the steady state. This same conclusion can be reached by noting from (22) that $H(0) = 0$. In Figure 10.9, the constant applied force will be balanced by the steady-state spring force Kx_{ss}, the diaphragm will become stationary, and no voltage will be induced in the coil.

A Direct-Current Motor

A direct-current (dc) motor is somewhat similar to the galvanometer but differs from it in several significant respects. In all but the smallest motors, the magnetic field is established not by a permanent magnet but by a current in a separate field winding on the iron core that constitutes the stationary part of the motor, the **stator**. Figure 10.11 indicates the manner in which the field winding establishes the flux when the field current i_F flows. Because of the saturation effects of magnetic fields in iron, the flux ϕ is not necessarily proportional to i_F at high currents.

In a dc motor, the iron cylinder between the poles of the magnet is free to rotate and is called the **rotor**. The rotating coils are embedded in the surface

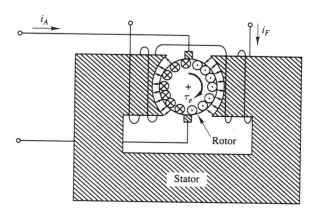

FIGURE 10.11 DC motor showing field and armature windings.

of the rotor and are known as the **armature winding**. There is no restraining torsional spring, and the rotor is free to rotate through an indefinite number of revolutions. However, this fact requires a significant deviation from the galvanometer in the construction of the rotor and the armature winding. First, if the rotor shown in Figure 10.11 rotates through 180° without a change in the direction of the currents in the individual armature conductors, then the torque exerted on it through the magnetic field will undergo a change in direction. Second, if there were a direct connection of the external armature circuit to the rotating armature, the wires would soon become tangled and halt the machine.

To solve both these problems, we use a **commutator**, which consists of a pair of low-resistance carbon brushes that are fixed with respect to the stator and make contact with the ends of the armature windings on the rotor (see the references in Appendix D for details). As indicated in Figure 10.11, when a conductor is located to the right of the commutator brushes, a positive value of i_A implies that the individual conductor current will be directed toward the reader. When the conductor is located to the left of the brushes, its current flows away from the reader when $i_A > 0$. As the ends of a particular conductor pass under the brushes, the direction of the current in that conductor changes sign. Under the arrangement just described, each conductor exerts a unidirectional torque on the rotor as it passes through a complete revolution. Hence the sliding contact at the brushes solves the mechanical problem of connecting the stationary and rotating parts of the armature circuit.

For modeling purposes, it is convenient to represent the important characteristics of the motor as shown in Figure 10.12. Representing the armature by a stationary circuit having resistance R_A, inductance L_A, and induced-voltage source e_m is justified by the presence of the commutator, which makes the armature behave as if it were stationary even though the individ-

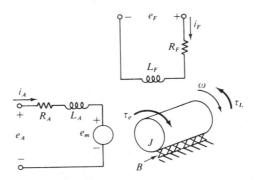

FIGURE 10.12   Diagram of the dc motor used for analysis.

ual conductors are indeed rotating. Likewise, the field circuit has resistance R_F and inductance L_F but no induced voltage. The rotor has moment of inertia J, rotational viscous-damping coefficient B, a driving torque τ_e caused by the forces acting on the individual conductors, and a load torque τ_L. The electrical inputs to the motor may be considered to be the currents i_A and i_F or the applied voltages e_A and e_F. The output is ω, the angular velocity of the rotor.

We begin the modeling process by expressing the voltage e_m and the torque τ_e in terms of the other system variables. We then write voltage-law equations for both the armature and field circuits, unless i_A or i_F is an input, and apply D'Alembert's law to the rotor.

When we are modeling dc motors and generators, it is convenient to express the flux density $\mathscr{B}$ as

$$\mathscr{B} = \frac{1}{A}\phi(i_F) \tag{24}$$

where $\phi(i_F)$ is the total flux established by the field current and A is the effective cross-sectional area of the flux path in the air gap between the rotor and stator. If ℓ denotes the total length of the armature conductors within the magnetic field and a denotes the radius of the armature, the electromechanical torque exerted on the rotor is

$$\tau_e = \left(\frac{\phi}{A}\right)\ell a i_A \tag{25}$$

Because the parameters ℓ, a, and A depend only on the geometry of the motor, we can define the motor parameter

$$\gamma = \frac{\ell a}{A} \tag{26}$$

and rewrite (25) in terms of the flux and armature current as

$$\tau_e = [\gamma\phi(i_F)]i_A \tag{27}$$

Similarly, the voltage induced in the armature is

$$e_m = [\gamma\phi(i_F)]\omega \tag{28}$$

Keep in mind that the flux $\phi(i_F)$ in (27) and (28) is a function of the field current i_F and, for that matter, is generally a nonlinear function.

Having established the model for the internal behavior of a dc motor represented by Figure 10.12 and (26), (27), and (28), we are prepared to develop models of complete electromechanical systems involving dc motors. We shall consider two such systems in the following examples.

▶ **EXAMPLE 10.2**

Derive the state-variable equations for a dc motor that has a constant field voltage E_F, an applied armature voltage $e_i(t)$, and a load torque $\tau_L(t)$. Also obtain the input-output equation with ω as the output, and determine the steady-state angular velocities corresponding to the following sets of inputs: (1) $e_i(t) = E$, $\tau_L(t) = 0$ and (2) $e_i(t) = 0$, $\tau_L(t) = T$.

Solution

The basic motor diagram in Figure 10.12 is repeated in Figure 10.13, with the specified field and armature input voltages added. The field voltage E_F is constant, so the field current will be the constant $i_F = E_F/R_F$. We can write the electromechanical driving torque τ_e and the induced voltage e_m as

$$\begin{aligned} \tau_e &= \alpha i_A \\ e_m &= \alpha\omega \end{aligned} \tag{29}$$

where α is a constant defined by

$$\alpha = \gamma\phi(i_F) \tag{30}$$

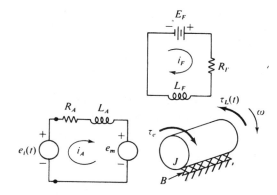

FIGURE 10.13 DC motor with a constant field current.

and γ is given by (26). We select i_A and ω as the state variables and write a voltage equation for the armature circuit and a torque equation for the rotor. Then, using (29) and solving for the derivatives of the state variables, we find the state-variable equations to be

$$\frac{di_A}{dt} = \frac{1}{L_A}[-R_A i_A - \alpha\omega + e_i(t)]$$

$$\dot{\omega} = \frac{1}{J}[\alpha i_A - B\omega - \tau_L(t)] \tag{31}$$

In order to find the system's transfer functions, we apply the Laplace transform to (31) and assume that there is no initial stored energy. With $i_A(0) = 0$ and $\omega(0) = 0$, we have

$$L_A s I_A(s) = -R_A I_A(s) - \alpha\Omega(s) + E_i(s)$$

$$Js\Omega(s) = \alpha I_A(s) - B\Omega(s) - \tau_L(s)$$

Eliminating $I_A(s)$ from this pair of algebraic equations and solving for the transformed output $\Omega(s)$, we find that

$$\Omega(s) = H_1(s)E_i(s) + H_2(s)\tau_L(s)$$

where

$$H_1(s) = \frac{\alpha/JL_A}{P(s)}$$

$$H_2(s) = \frac{-(1/J)s - (R_A/JL_A)}{P(s)}$$

$$P(s) = s^2 + \left(\frac{R_A}{L_A} + \frac{B}{J}\right)s + \left(\frac{R_A B + \alpha^2}{JL_A}\right)$$

The quantity $H_1(s)$ is the transfer function relating the output velocity and input voltage when $\tau_L(t) = 0$. $H_2(s)$ relates $\Omega(s)$ and $\tau_L(s)$ when $e_i(t) = 0$. The general input-output differential equation is

$$\ddot{\omega} + \left(\frac{R_A}{L_A} + \frac{B}{J}\right)\dot{\omega} + \left(\frac{R_A B + \alpha^2}{JL_A}\right)\omega = \frac{\alpha}{JL_A}e_i(t) - \frac{1}{J}\dot{\tau}_L - \frac{R_A}{JL_A}\tau_L(t) \tag{32}$$

As expected, both the electrical and the mechanical parameters contribute to the system's undamped natural frequency ω_n and to the damping ratio ζ.

To solve for the steady-state motor speed when the voltage source has the constant value $e_i(t) = E$ and when $\tau_L(t) = 0$, we omit all derivative terms in (32) and substitute these values for $e_i(t)$ and $\tau_L(t)$, obtaining

$$\omega_{ss} = \frac{\alpha E}{R_A B + \alpha^2} \tag{33}$$

In physical terms, the motor will run at a constant speed such that the driving torque $\tau_e = \alpha i_A$ exactly balances the viscous-frictional torque $B\omega_{ss}$. However, the steady-state armature current is $i_A = (E - e_m)/R_A$, where $e_m = \alpha\omega_{ss}$. Making the appropriate substitutions, we again obtain (33). We get the same expression by examining $H_1(0)$.

When $e_i(t) = 0$ and $\tau_L(t)$ has the constant value T, the steady-state solution to (32) is

$$\omega_{ss} = -\frac{R_A T}{R_A B + \alpha^2} \tag{34}$$

which indicates that the motor will be driven backward at a constant angular velocity. We can also obtain (34) by noting that $\omega_{ss} = T H_2(0)$. To understand the behavior of the motor under this condition, we observe that the electromechanical torque, $\tau_e = \alpha i_A$, must balance the sum of the load torque T and the viscous-frictional torque $B\omega_{ss}$. Thus an armature current must flow that will make $\alpha i_A = T + B\omega_{ss}$. Furthermore, because the applied armature voltage is zero and $e_m = \alpha\omega_{ss}$, it follows that $i_A R_A = -\alpha\omega_{ss}$. As anticipated, solving these two equations for ω_{ss} results in (34).

In this situation, the motor is acting as a **generator** connected to a load of zero resistance. Part of the mechanical power supplied by the load torque is being converted to electrical form and dissipated in the armature resistance R_A. Basically, we may think of a generator as a motor that is being driven mechanically and that delivers a portion of the power to an electrical load connected across the armature terminals.

You can verify that when the constant applied voltage is $e_i(t) = E$ and the constant load torque is $\tau_L(t) = \alpha E/R_A$, the steady-state motor speed is $\omega_{ss} = 0$. In this condition, the electromechanical driving torque τ_e exactly matches the load torque and the motor is stalled.

▶ *EXAMPLE 10.3*

A dc motor has a constant armature current $\bar{i}_A$ but a variable current source $i_F(t)$ supplying the field winding. The relationship between the flux ϕ and the field current $i_F(t)$ is nonlinear and is shown in Figure 10.14(a). A load having moment of inertia J_L and viscous-damping coefficient B_L is connected to the rotor by a rigid shaft. Find a linear model suitable for analyzing small perturbations about the operating point A indicated on the flux-versus-current curve.

Solution

In Figure 10.14(b), we have repeated the basic motor diagram in Figure 10.12 and have also added the specified current sources and the mechanical load. From (27), the electromechanical torque is

$$\tau_e = \gamma\phi\bar{i}_A \tag{35}$$

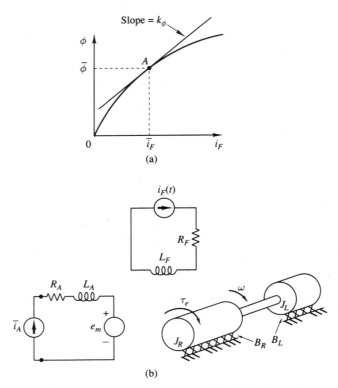

FIGURE 10.14 DC motor for Example 10.3. (a) Nonlinear field characteristic. (b) Diagram used for analysis.

where, in this case, γ and $\bar{i}_A$ are constants and $\phi = \phi(i_F)$. Because the armature current is constant and the field current is specified, there is no need to write an equation for either of the electrical circuits. Rather, we obtain the system model by summing torques on the rotor and load and using (35). This yields

$$(J_R + J_L)\dot{\omega} + (B_R + B_L)\omega = \gamma \bar{i}_A \phi(i_F) \tag{36}$$

To obtain the linearized model, we write the field current and angular velocity as $i_F(t) = \bar{i}_F + \hat{i}_F(t)$ and $\omega = \bar{\omega} + \hat{\omega}$, respectively. The operating-point values $\bar{i}_F$ and $\bar{\omega}$ must satisfy (36), which reduces to

$$\bar{\omega} = \frac{\gamma \bar{i}_A \phi(\bar{i}_F)}{B_R + B_L} \tag{37}$$

The flux is approximated by the first two terms in the Taylor-series expansion for $\phi(i_F)$ about the operating point, namely

$$\phi(\bar{i}_F) + k_\phi \hat{i}_F \tag{38}$$

where

$$k_\phi = \left.\frac{d\phi}{di_F}\right|_{\bar{i}_F} \tag{39}$$

Substituting (38) into (36), writing $\omega = \bar{\omega} + \hat{\omega}$, and using (37) to cancel the constant terms, we find the linearized model to be

$$(J_R + J_L)\dot{\hat{\omega}} + (B_R + B_L)\hat{\omega} = \gamma\bar{i}_A k_\phi \hat{i}_F(t) \tag{40}$$

where k_ϕ is the slope of the curve of ϕ versus i_F evaluated at the operating point.

In the last example note that (40) is a first-order equation, which implies that the system is only first-order. Although there are two inductors that can store energy, their currents are those of the current sources $\bar{i}_A$ and $i_F(t)$ and thus cannot be state variables.

Furthermore, it is apparent that the moments of inertia J_R and J_L and the friction coefficients B_R and B_L are merely added to obtain equivalent parameters for the system as a whole. If the motor had been connected to its load through a gear train (as would usually be the case), the equivalent parameters, when reflected to the motor, would be

$$J_{\text{eq}} = J_R + \frac{1}{N^2}J_L$$

$$B_{\text{eq}} = B_R + \frac{1}{N^2}B_L$$

The symbol N denotes the motor-to-load gear ratio; that is, the motor rotates at N times the angular velocity of the load.

10.4 A DEVICE FOR MEASURING ACCELERATION

In many areas of technology, it is important to be able to measure and record the acceleration of a moving body as a function of time. For example, deceleration measurements are required in the testing of automobiles for crash resistance. Accelerometers are important components in ship, aircraft, and rocket navigation and guidance systems.

Figure 10.15 shows an electromechanical device whose response depends on the acceleration of its case relative to an inertially fixed reference frame. The device is not intended to be representative of commonly used accelerometers, but modeling and analyzing its response will provide practice in using many of the techniques that we have discussed in this chapter and in Chapters 6 and 8.

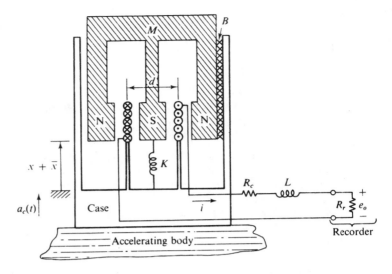

FIGURE 10.15 Acceleration-measuring device.

System Description

Basically, the device shown in Figure 10.15 consists of a case attached to the body or material whose motion is to be measured, a circular coil fixed to the case, and a permanent magnet supported on the case by a spring, with viscous damping between the magnet and the case. As the case moves vertically as a result of motion of the body supporting it, a voltage is induced in the coil because of the relative motion of the coil and the magnetic field. A recorder is attached to the terminals of the coil and draws a graph of the coil voltage e_o as a function of time.

The magnet has mass M and provides a flux density $\mathscr{B}$ in the annular space between its north and south poles. Although several springs would be used to support the mass, the single spring shown with spring constant K may be considered equivalent to whatever springs are present. The viscous-damping coefficient B accounts for all viscous effects between the magnet and the case.

The coil has N turns of diameter d, and the parameter $\ell = \pi d N$ denotes the length of the coil. The total coil resistance and inductance are modeled by lumped elements having values R_c and L, respectively. The dots and crosses associated with the coil in Figure 10.15 indicate that the assumed positive direction of current is clockwise as viewed from above. The recorder is attached directly to the terminals of the coil and is assumed to provide a resistance R_r in the coil circuit.

The acceleration of the case relative to a fixed inertial reference frame is denoted by $a_c(t)$ and is the input to the system. The vertical distance between the magnet and the case is $x + \bar{x}$, so the variable x denotes the incremental displacement of the magnet relative to the case, with the value $x = 0$ corresponding to the equilibrium condition. Likewise, the relative velocity of the magnet with respect to the case is $\dot{x}$.

System Model

We derive the differential equations describing the behavior of the system by drawing a free-body diagram for the magnet, drawing a circuit diagram for the coil and recorder, and expressing the electromechanically induced force and voltage in terms of the appropriate system variables. Three aspects of this task deserve specific mention.

First, the inertial force shown on the free-body diagram must use the acceleration of the mass relative to the inertial reference frame. Hence this force on the diagram shown in Figure 10.16(a) is $M[a_c(t) + \ddot{x}]$ in the

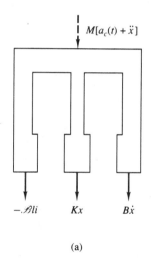

(a)

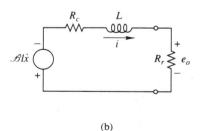

(b)

FIGURE 10.16 (a) Free-body diagram for the magnet. (b) Circuit diagram.

downward direction. Second, recall that the electrically induced force on the coil is given by $f_e = \mathscr{B}\ell i$. In this instance, however, we must show on the free-body diagram the force on the magnet, which, by the law of reaction forces, is $-\mathscr{B}\ell i$ in the downward direction. Finally, in order to determine the proper sign for the voltage induced in the coil, we note that when $\dot{x} > 0$, the coil is moving downward relative to the magnetic field. This is because the magnet is moving upward relative to the case, and the coil is attached to the case.

Taking these points into consideration, we can draw the free-body and circuit diagrams shown in Figure 10.16. Summing forces on the magnet and writing a voltage equation for the circuit, we obtain

$$L\frac{di}{dt} + (R_c + R_r)i = -\mathscr{B}\ell\dot{x} \tag{41a}$$

$$M\ddot{x} + B\dot{x} + Kx = \mathscr{B}\ell i - Ma_c(t) \tag{41b}$$

$$e_o = R_r i \tag{41c}$$

Transfer Function

To determine a single overall transfer function relating the input transform $A_c(s)$ to the output transform $E_o(s)$, we shall transform (41) with zero initial conditions. Doing this, we obtain the following set of three algebraic transform equations:

$$(Ls + R_c + R_r)I(s) = -\mathscr{B}\ell s X(s) \tag{42a}$$

$$(Ms^2 + Bs + K)X(s) = \mathscr{B}\ell I(s) - MA_c(s) \tag{42b}$$

$$E_o(s) = R_r I(s) \tag{42c}$$

We can combine these equations to eliminate the variables $X(s)$ and $I(s)$, obtaining a single equation relating the input transform $A_c(s)$ and the output transform $E_o(s)$.

First, if we combine (42a) and (42b) to eliminate $X(s)$, the result is

$$(Ms^2 + Bs + K)\left(\frac{Ls + R}{-\mathscr{B}\ell s}\right)I(s) - \mathscr{B}\ell I(s) = -MA_c(s)$$

where $R = R_c + R_r$. Combining the two terms involving $I(s)$ in this equation and then using (42c) to express $I(s)$ in terms of $E_o(s)$, we obtain the single transformed equation

$$\frac{1}{R_r}[(Ms^2 + Bs + K)(Ls + R) + \mathscr{B}^2\ell^2 s]E_o(s) = \mathscr{B}\ell Ms A_c(s)$$

Solving for the ratio $E_o(s)/A_c(s)$ yields the overall transfer function

$$\frac{E_o(s)}{A_c(s)} = \frac{R_r\mathscr{B}\ell Ms}{P(s)} \tag{43}$$

where $P(s)$ is the characteristic polynomial of the device and is

$$P(s) = MLs^3 + (BL + MR)s^2 + (BR + KL + \mathscr{B}^2\ell^2)s + KR \quad (44)$$

Because the acceleration, velocity, and displacement of the case are related by $a_c(t) = \dot{v}_c = \ddot{x}_c$, and because for zero initial conditions $A_c(s) = sV_c(s) = s^2X_c(s)$, we can also write the transfer functions corresponding to a velocity or displacement input:

$$\frac{E_o(s)}{V_c(s)} = \frac{R_r\mathscr{B}\ell Ms^2}{P(s)}$$

$$\frac{E_o(s)}{X_c(s)} = \frac{R_r\mathscr{B}\ell Ms^3}{P(s)}$$

The characteristic polynomial $P(s)$ is a cubic, so it is difficult to be very specific about the behavior of the system as a measuring device without substituting numerical values for the parameters and calculating the frequency response or simulating the response to specific inputs, such as the impulse and step function.

Rather than doing this, we shall make the approximation that the coil inductance can be neglected. In terms of the frequency response, this approximation should be well justified for low frequencies but not for high frequencies. Because our interest is principally in the response at low frequencies, we are justified in setting L equal to zero in (44). With this change $P(s)$ becomes quadratic. In essence, we have eliminated the current as a state variable, and (43) reduces to

$$\frac{E_o(s)}{A_c(s)} = \frac{R_r\mathscr{B}\ell Ms}{MRs^2 + (BR + \mathscr{B}^2\ell^2)s + KR}$$

$$= \frac{(\mathscr{B}\ell R_r/R)s}{s^2 + \left(\dfrac{B}{M} + \dfrac{\mathscr{B}^2\ell^2}{MR}\right)s + \dfrac{K}{M}} \quad (45)$$

Inspection of (45) indicates that the transfer function $E_o(s)/A_c(s)$ has a zero at $s = 0$ and a pair of poles that may be real or complex. To determine the undamped natural frequency ω_n and the damping ratio ζ associated with these poles, we compare (45) to

$$H(s) = \frac{Cs}{s^2 + 2\zeta\omega_n s + \omega_n^2} \quad (46)$$

which can be viewed as the standard form for a transfer function having a zero at $s = 0$ and two poles. Comparing the coefficients in (45) and (46), we obtain

$$C = \frac{\mathscr{B}\ell R_r}{R}$$

$$\omega_n = \sqrt{\frac{K}{M}} \qquad (47)$$

$$\zeta = \frac{1}{2}\sqrt{\frac{M}{K}}\left(\frac{B}{M} + \frac{\mathscr{B}^2\ell^2}{MR}\right)$$

If it were known what values of ζ and ω_n would result in a device that would perform well as a measuring instrument, a designer could attempt to select the physical parameters in order to achieve these values of ζ and ω_n. Frequency-response plots can be used to determine suitable values for ζ and ω_n.

Frequency Response

The steady-state response to a sinusoidal input is formed by examining $H(j\omega)$, as discussed in Section 8.5. A frequency-response analysis of (45) would be cumbersome unless specific numerical values were given for all but one or two of the physical parameters, so we shall work with (46). When s is replaced by $j\omega$, (46) becomes

$$H(j\omega) = \frac{jC\omega}{\omega_n^2 - \omega^2 + j2\zeta\omega_n\omega}$$

$$= \frac{j(C/\omega_n)(\omega/\omega_n)}{1 - (\omega/\omega_n)^2 + j2\zeta(\omega/\omega_n)} \qquad (48)$$

where the second form of the equation results from dividing both the numerator and the denominator by ω_n^2. The quantity ω/ω_n can be thought of as a normalized frequency. Because the factor C/ω_n in the numerator of (48) is a multiplying constant that does not affect the variation of $H(j\omega)$ with ω, we shall also normalize the magnitude of the transfer function by defining

$$H_N(j\omega) = \frac{\omega_n}{C}H(j\omega)$$

$$= \frac{j(\omega/\omega_n)}{1 - (\omega/\omega_n)^2 + j2\zeta(\omega/\omega_n)} \qquad (49)$$

We obtain the magnitude of $H_N(j\omega)$ by dividing the magnitude of its numerator by that of its denominator. This results in

$$|H_N(j\omega)| = \frac{\omega/\omega_n}{\sqrt{(\omega/\omega_n)^4 + (4\zeta^2 - 2)(\omega/\omega_n)^2 + 1}} \qquad (50)$$

Comparing $|H_N(j\omega)|$ for different values of ζ indicates the relative shapes of the frequency-response magnitudes corresponding to different values of the damping ratio. If the device is to be of value in measuring the acceleration of the case, there should be a range of frequencies for which $|H_N(j\omega)|$ is fairly flat—that is, independent of frequency.

From (50), we see that $|H_N(j\omega)| \simeq \omega/\omega_n$ for small values of ω/ω_n and that it approaches $1/(\omega/\omega_n)$ for large values of ω/ω_n. For $\omega/\omega_n = 1$, $|H_N(j\omega)| = 1/2\zeta$. Using this information and calculating a few additional points, we can draw the plots shown in Figure 10.17. Logarithmic scales are commonly used for frequency-response plots, and they enable us to include a wide range of values of $|H_N(j\omega)|$ and ω/ω_n.

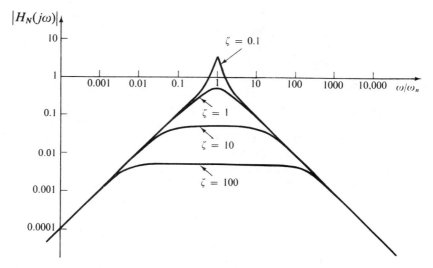

FIGURE 10.17 Frequency response of the acceleration-measuring device for several damping ratios.

It is apparent that the device must be heavily damped ($\zeta \gg 1$) if a range of frequencies is to be achieved for which $|H_N(j\omega)|$ is essentially constant. If $\zeta = 100$, $|H_N(j\omega)|$ will remain between 0.0045 and 0.0050 for $0.01 < \omega/\omega_n < 100$, which is a four-decade range of frequencies. In contrast, if $\zeta \leq 1$, there is no range of frequencies over which $|H_N(j\omega)|$ is essentially constant.

Because $|H_N(j\omega)| \simeq \omega/\omega_n$, as ω approaches zero, a constant acceleration will result in a zero steady-state output. We can also see this from (46) by noting that the steady-state response to a unit step-function input is $H(0) = 0$. When the acceleration $a_c(t)$ is constant, the velocity of the magnet will become equal to the velocity of the coil. There will then be no voltage induced in the coil, and the output of the recorder will be zero.

In order to read the relative displacement of the magnet with respect to the case, we could attach a pointer to the mass and put scale markings on the case. There would then be a steady-state output reading even for a constant acceleration of the case, and the device could sense acceleration of arbitrarily low frequencies. To obtain an electrical output for recording purposes, we can replace the pointer by the wiper of a potentiometer and use the voltage at the wiper arm as the output.

SUMMARY

In this chapter, we discussed two mechanisms for coupling the electrical and mechanical parts of a system. The potentiometer, which is an example of resistive coupling, can produce an output voltage that is proportional to a mechanical displacement, provided that the loading effect described in Example 10.1 is avoided.

The coupling for most of the electromechanical devices we considered was through a magnetic field. The applications used a current-carrying wire that moved perpendicularly to the current and to the mangetic field. When summing forces, we included the force on the wire, $f_e = \mathcal{B}\ell i$. When summing voltages, we included the induced voltage, $e_m = \mathcal{B}\ell v$. The characteristics of the overall systems depended on the electrical parameters, the mechanical parameters, and the strength of the magnetic coupling.

We presented several examples to illustrate the basic steps in modeling electromechanical devices. The references in Appendix D contain further information about nonlinear effects and construction details, including the commutator needed for a direct-current motor. They also discuss other possible types of electromechanical coupling, such as mechanically varying the characteristics of the flux path.

PROBLEMS

10.1 Use (6) to plot curves of e_o/E versus $\theta/\theta_{\max}$ for a rotary potentiometer with the load resistance R_o when (1) $R_o = 0.5R_T$, (2) $R_o = R_T$, and (3) $R_o = 10R_T$.

* **10.2** The potentiometer model shown in Figure 10.2(b) includes the resistances R_1 and R_2, both of which depend on $x(t)$. However, many potentiometers contain some inductance because they are constructed by winding many turns of wire about a core. The circuit shown in Figure P10.2 represents this inductance by the lumped elements whose values also depend on $x(t)$.

    a) Find the differential equation relating e_o to $x(t)$ and $e_i(t)$.

    b) Assume that R_2 and L_2 are proportional to the displacement $x(t)$. Let $L_2 = L_T[x(t)/x_{\max}]$ and $R_2 = R_T[x(t)/x_{\max}]$, where $L_1 + L_2 = L_T$ and $R_1 + R_2 = R_T$. Find the differential equation relating e_o to $x(t)$ and $e_i(t)$. Compare your answer to (3).

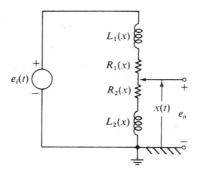

FIGURE P10.2

10.3 Two identical rotary potentiometers similar to the one shown in Figure 10.3 are connected across a constant voltage source E as indicated in Figure P10.3. The output wiper positions are denoted by $\theta_a(t)$ and $\theta_b(t)$. The various resistances satisfy the relationships

$$R_T = R_1 + R_2 = R_3 + R_4$$

$$R_2 = [\theta_a(t)/\theta_{\max}]R_T$$

$$R_4 = [\theta_b(t)/\theta_{\max}]R_T$$

a) Verify that when R_o is infinite (an open circuit),

$$e_o = \left(\frac{\theta_a - \theta_b}{\theta_{\max}}\right) E$$

b) Verify that when no restrictions are placed on R_o other than $R_o > 0$,

$$e_o = \left[\frac{\theta_a - \theta_b}{\theta_{\max} + \dfrac{R_T}{R_o}\left(1 - \dfrac{\theta_a}{\theta_{\max}}\right)\theta_a + \dfrac{R_T}{R_o}\left(1 - \dfrac{\theta_b}{\theta_{\max}}\right)\theta_b} \right] E$$

c) Show that when $R_T/R_o = 0$, the expression in part (b) for finite R_o reduces to the expression given in part (a).

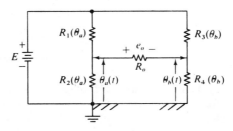

FIGURE P10.3

10.4 a) Find the state-variable equations, the transfer function, and the input-output differential equation for the galvanometer shown in Figure 10.8 when the inductance L of the coil is not neglected.

b) Find the steady-state response to a constant input by examining $H(0)$, and compare the result to (17).

10.5 Figure P10.5 shows a galvanometer whose flux is obtained from the same current i that passes through the movable coil, rather than from a permanent magnet as shown in Figure 10.8. The flux density in the air gaps is $\mathscr{B} = k_{\mathscr{B}} i$. The coil has moment of inertia J and viscous-damping coefficient B, and it is restrained by a torsional spring with spring constant K. The total length of the coil in the magnetic field is d, and its radius is a. Let $\alpha = adk_{\mathscr{B}}$.

a) Verify that a valid state-variable model is

$$\dot{\theta} = \omega$$

$$\dot{\omega} = \frac{1}{J}(-K\theta - B\omega + \alpha i^2)$$

$$\frac{di}{dt} = \frac{1}{L}[-\alpha i\omega - Ri + e_i(t)]$$

b) Find $\bar{\theta}$ corresponding to the operating point $\bar{e}_i$, where $e_i(t) = \bar{e}_i + \hat{e}_i(t)$.

c) Find a set of linearized state-variable equations valid in the vicinity of the operating point you found in part (b). To do this, first let $\theta = \bar{\theta} + \hat{\theta}$, $\omega = \bar{\omega} + \hat{\omega}$, and $i = \bar{i} + \hat{i}$. Then assume that the incremental variables are small, so that $(\hat{i})^2$ and the product $\hat{i}\hat{\omega}$ can be neglected.

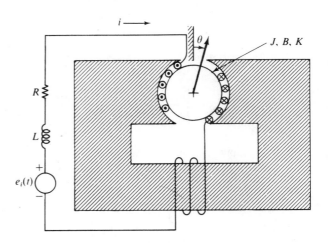

FIGURE P10.5

10.6 a) Verify (22) and (23) for the microphone shown in Figure 10.9 by transforming (19), (20), and (21) with zero initial conditions.

b) Write the input-output equation for the case $L = 0$. Find expressions for the damping ratio ζ and the undamped natural frequency ω_n in terms of the physical parameters M, K, B, R, and α.

* 10.7 A loudspeaker produces sound waves by the movement of a diaphragm in response to an electrical input. In the cross-sectional view shown in Figure P10.7, $e_i(t)$ is the input and the output is the displacement x. A coil of wire with N turns and radius a is attached to the diaphragm. Let $\alpha = 2\pi a N \mathscr{B}$, where $\mathscr{B}$ is the flux density in the air gap of the permanent magnet.

a) Verify that the equations

$$\dot{x} = v$$

$$\dot{v} = \frac{1}{M}(-Kx - Bv + \alpha i)$$

$$\frac{di}{dt} = \frac{1}{L}[-\alpha v - Ri + e_i(t)]$$

represent a valid state-variable model.

b) Find the transfer function and the input-output differential equation.

c) Rewrite the input-output equation for the case $L = 0$, and find expressions for the damping ratio ζ and the undamped natural frequency ω_n.

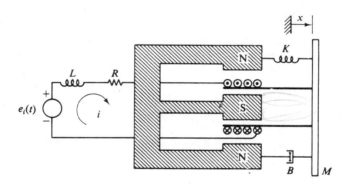

FIGURE P10.7

10.8 A transducer to measure translational motion is shown in Figure P10.8. The permanent magnet produces a uniform magnetic field in the air gap with flux density $\mathscr{B}$ and can move with a displacement x and velocity v. A wire that is fixed in space has a length d within the magnetic field. The inductance and resistance of the wire are included in the lumped elements L and R, and the output of the system is the voltage e_o across the resistor R_o.

a) Verify that the transfer function is

$$H(s) = \frac{E_o(s)}{X(s)} = \frac{d \mathscr{B} R_o s}{sL + (R + R_o)}$$

b) If $i(0) = 0$, find the response for all $t > 0$ when $x(t) = U(t)$. What is the steady-state response? What is the time constant?

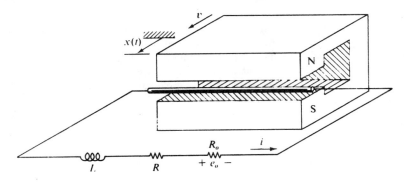

FIGURE P10.8

* 10.9 The magnet shown in Figure P10.8 and considered in Problem 10.8 has mass M and is separated from a fixed horizontal surface by an oil film with viscous friction coefficient B. Instead of a displacement input, a force $f_a(t)$ is applied to the magnet in the positive x direction. The wire of length d remains fixed in space. Find the transfer function $H(s) = E_o(s)/F_a(s)$.

10.10 A wire of length ℓ, rigidly attached to a mass M, is in a magnetic field with flux density $\mathcal{B}$. In the cross-sectional view shown in Figure P10.10, the wire is perpendicular to the page, with point a connected to the front of the wire and point b to the back. The input to the system is a 12-V battery. With no energy initially stored within the system, the switch closes at $t = 0$.

    a) Which way will the wire—and hence the mass—move when the switch is closed?

    b) What will be the steady-state displacement of the mass from its original position?

    c) Define a set of state variables and write the state-variable equations describing the behavior of the system for $t > 0$.

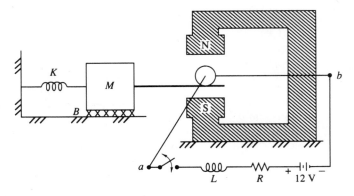

FIGURE P10.10

* 10.11 The conductor of mass M shown in Figure P10.11 can move vertically through a uniform magnetic field of flux density $\mathcal{B}$ whose positive sense is into

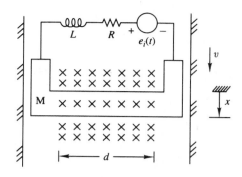

FIGURE P10.11

the page. There is no friction, the effective length of the conductor in the field is d, and $e_i(t)$ is a voltage source. The lumped elements $e_i(t)$, L, and R are outside the magnetic field.

    a) Write a set of state-variable equations.

    b) For what constant voltage $\bar{e}_i$ will the conductor remain stationary?

    c) What will be the steady-state velocity of the conductor if $e_i(t)$ is always zero?

10.12 A plunger is made to move horizontally through the center of a fixed cylindrical permanent magnet by the application of a voltage source $e_i(t)$. Attached to the plunger is a coil having N turns and radius a. Figure P10.12 shows the system, including a cross-sectional view of the magnet and plunger, and indicates typical paths for the magnetic flux by dashed lines. The magnetic field between the plunger and the south pole is assumed to have a constant flux density $\mathcal{B}$. The resistance and inductance of the coil are represented by the lumped elements R and L, respectively, and the plunger has mass M.

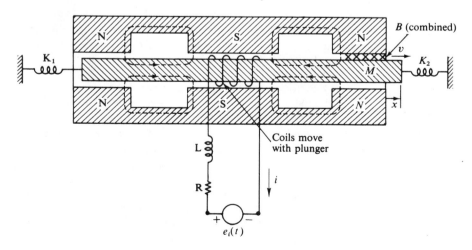

FIGURE P10.12

a) Verify that the following is a valid set of state-variable equations:

$$\dot{x} = v$$

$$\dot{v} = \frac{1}{M}[-(K_1 + K_2)x - Bv + \alpha i]$$

$$\frac{di}{dt} = \frac{1}{L}[-\alpha v - Ri + e_i(t)]$$

where $\alpha = 2\pi a N \mathscr{B}$.

b) Determine the direction in which the plunger will move if there is no initial stored energy and if $e_i(t) = U(t)$.

c) Find the steady-state displacement of the plunger for the input in part (b).

10.13 For the electric motor shown in Figure 10.14(b), let $i_F(t)$ have the constant value $\bar{i}_F$.

a) Write the differential equation describing the system and identify the time constant when $i_A(t)$ is the input and ω the output.

b) If $i_A(t) = i_{A_1}$ for all $t < 0$ and $i_A(t) = i_{A_2}$ for all $t > 0$, sketch ω versus t. Assume that steady-state conditions exist at $t = 0-$.

c) Repeat part (b) when i_{A_2} is replaced by $-i_{A_1}$. Find the value of t for which $\omega = 0$.

* 10.14 a) Write the differential equation describing the motor shown in Figure 10.14(b) when $i_A(t)$ and $i_F(t)$ are separate inputs and when $\phi = k_\phi i_F(t)$.

b) Find an expression for $\bar{\omega}$ at the operating point corresponding to $\bar{i}_A$ and $\bar{i}_F$.

c) If $i_A(t) = \bar{i}_A$ and $i_F(t) = \bar{i}_F + \hat{i}_F(t)$, find a linearized model that is valid in the vicinity of the operating point you found in part (b).

10.15 Let the shaft connecting J_R and J_L in Figure 10.14(b) have a stiffness constant K rather than being rigid. Also replace the current source $\bar{i}_A$ by a voltage source $e_i(t)$, with its positive sense upward. Assume that $\phi = k_\phi i_F$, and denote the angular displacements of the rotor and the load by θ_R and θ_L, respectively. Choose as state variables i_A, ω_R, ω_L, and $\theta = \theta_R - \theta_L$. Write the state-variable equations.

10.16 Assume that $L_A = 0$ for the motor shown in Figure 10.14(b). Replace the current source $\bar{i}_A$ by a voltage source that has a constant value of E_A volts.

a) Write the differential equation describing the system if the input is $i_F(t)$ and if $\phi = k_\phi i_F(t)$.

b) Find the operating point corresponding to $\bar{i}_F$.

c) Find a linearized model that is valid about the operating point you found in part (b). Identify its time constant. Let $\omega = \bar{\omega} + \hat{\omega}$ and $i_F = \bar{i}_F + \hat{i}_F$, and assume that terms involving $(\hat{i}_F)^2$ and the product $\hat{i}_F\hat{\omega}$ can be neglected.

* 10.17 For the motor depicted in Figure 10.13, replace $e_i(t)$ by a constant voltage source E_A, and replace the source in the field winding by a time-varying voltage $e_F(t)$. Assume that $\phi = k_\phi i_F$.

a) Using i_A, i_F, and ω as state variables, write the state-variable equations.

b) Find $\bar{\omega}$ for the operating point corresponding to $e_F(t) = \bar{e}_F$ and $\tau_L(t) = 0$.

c) Derive a linearized model valid about the operating point you found in part (b). Let $\omega = \bar{\omega} + \hat{\omega}$, $i_A = \bar{i}_A + \hat{i}_A$, and $i_F = \bar{i}_F + \hat{i}_F$. Assume that terms involving the products $\hat{i}_F\hat{\omega}$ and $\hat{i}_A\hat{\omega}$ can be neglected.

10.18 The field and armature windings of an electric motor are connected in parallel directly across a voltage source $e_i(t)$, as shown in Figure P10.18. The resistances of the field and armature windings are R_F and R_A, respectively, and the inductances of both windings are negligible.

    a) Verify that the differential equation relating ω to $e_i(t)$ and $\tau_L(t)$ is

$$J\dot{\omega} + B\omega = \frac{\gamma k_\phi}{R_F} \left(\frac{R_F - \gamma k_\phi \omega}{R_A R_F} \right) e_i^2(t) - \tau_L(t)$$

    b) Find an expression for $\bar{\omega}$ at the operating point corresponding to $e_i(t) = \bar{e}_i$ and $\tau_L(t) = 0$.

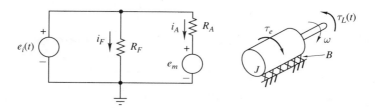

FIGURE P10.18

10.19 For the motor described in Problem 10.18, add an armature inductance L_A and a field inductance L_F in series with R_A and R_F, respectively.

    a) Verify that

$$\frac{di_A}{dt} = \frac{1}{L_A} \left[-R_A i_A - \gamma k_\phi i_F \omega + e_i(t) \right]$$

$$\frac{di_F}{dt} = \frac{1}{L_F} \left[-R_F i_F + e_i(t) \right]$$

$$\dot{\omega} = \frac{1}{J} \left[\gamma k_\phi i_F i_A - B\omega - \tau_L(t) \right]$$

constitute a suitable set of state-variable equations.

    b) Find an expression for $\bar{\omega}$ at the operating point corresponding to $e_i(t) = \bar{e}_i$ and $\tau_L(t) = 0$.

10.20 The rotor shown in Figure P10.20 is driven by a torque $\tau_a(t)$. The rotor has a moment of inertia J, but the friction is negligible. The field winding is excited by a constant voltage source, resulting in a constant magnetic flux. The armature resistance is denoted by R_A, and the armature inductance is negligible. Use (29) to obtain expressions for e_m and τ_e.

    a) With the rotor initially at rest and with the switch in the left-hand position connecting the armature to a short circuit, the applied torque is $\tau_a(t) = U(t)$. Find and sketch ω as a function of time.

    b) After the rotor has reached a steady-state speed under the conditions of part (a), the switch is thrown to the right, thereby connecting the armature to the battery. Find and sketch ω versus t if a constant unit torque continues to be applied to the rotor.

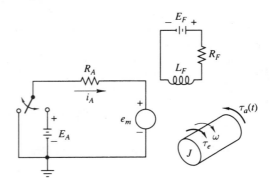

FIGURE P10.20

c) After a new steady-state speed has been reached under the conditions of part (b), the applied torque is removed, with the switch still in the right-hand position. Again find and sketch ω versus t.

* **10.21** The magnetic field of a small motor is supplied by a permanent magnet. The following two sets of measurements are made in the steady state with a 6-V battery connected across the armature. When there is no load and negligible friction, the motor rotates at 100 rad/s. When the motor is mechanically blocked to prevent its movement, the armature current is 2 A. The rotor is then attached to a propeller, which creates a viscous-friction load of 2.0×10^{-3} N·m·s, and the 6-V battery is again connected across the armature. Find the steady-state speed of the propeller.

10.22 Consider the electric motor shown in Figure 10.13 and discussed in Example 10.2. Taking i_A and ω as the state variables, write the state-variable equations in matrix form. Also write a matrix output equation for the output vector $\mathbf{y} = [\tau_e \; e_m]^T$. Identify the matrices $\mathbf{A}$, $\mathbf{B}$, $\mathbf{C}$, and $\mathbf{D}$.

THERMAL
SYSTEMS

Thermal systems are systems in which the storage and flow of heat are involved. Their mathematical models are based on the fundamental laws of thermodynamics. Examples of thermal systems include a thermometer, an automobile engine's cooling system, an oven, and a refrigerator. Generally thermal systems are distributed, and thus they obey partial rather than ordinary differential equations. We shall restrict our attention to lumped mathematical models by making approximations where necessary. Our purpose is to obtain linear ordinary differential equations that are capable of describing the dynamic response to a good approximation. We shall not examine the steady-state analysis of thermodynamic cycles that might be required in the design of a chemical process. Although systems that involve changes of phase (such as boiling or condensation) can be modeled, such treatment is beyond the scope of this book.

As in the previous chapters on modeling, we first introduce the variables and the element laws used to describe the dynamic behavior of thermal systems. Then we present a number of examples illustrating their application. A comprehensive example of the analysis of a thermal system appears in Section 11.4.

11.1 VARIABLES

The variables used to describe the behavior of a thermal system are

θ, temperature in kelvins (K) [1]

q, heat flow rate in joules per second (J/s) or in watts (W)

where 1 watt = 1 joule per second.

---

[1]Although the kelvin is the SI temperature unit, degrees Celsius (°C) may be more familiar. A temperature expressed in kelvins can be converted to degrees Celsius by subtracting 273.15 from its value.

The temperatures at various points in a distributed body usually differ from one another. For modeling and analysis, however, it is desirable to assume that all points in the body have the same temperature, presumably the average temperature of the body. If the temperature deviations from the average at various points do affect the validity of the single-temperature model, then the body may be partitioned into segments. Each of the segments can have a different average temperature associated with it, as illustrated in a later example. Unless otherwise noted, we shall use average temperatures for individual bodies. Furthermore, because the temperature is a measure of the energy stored in a body (provided there are no changes of phase), we normally select the temperatures as the state variables of a thermal system.

For most thermal systems, an equilibrium condition exists that defines the nominal operation. Generally, only deviations of the variables from their nominal values are of interest from a dynamic point of view. In these cases, **incremental temperatures** and **incremental heat flow rates** are defined by relationships of the form

$$\hat{\theta}(t) = \theta(t) - \bar{\theta}$$
$$\hat{q}(t) = q(t) - \bar{q}$$

where $\bar{\theta}$ and $\bar{q}$ are the nominal values. The ambient temperature of the environment surrounding the system is considered constant and is denoted by θ_a. In some problems, the nominal values of the temperature variables may be equal to θ_a, in which case we may refer to the incremental temperatures as **relative temperatures**.

■ 11.2 ELEMENT LAWS

A consequence of the laws of thermodynamics is that there are only two types of passive thermal elements: thermal capacitance and thermal resistance. Strictly speaking, thermal capacitance and thermal resistance are characteristics associated with bodies that are distributed in space and are not lumped elements. However, because we seek to describe the dynamic behavior of thermal systems by lumped models, we shall refer to them as elements. These elements are described next, and a brief discussion of thermal sources follows.

Thermal Capacitance

An algebraic relationship exists between the temperature of a physical body and the heat stored within it. Provided that there is no change of phase and that the range of temperatures is not excessive, this relationship can be considered linear.

If $q_{in}(t) - q_{out}(t)$ denotes the net heat flow rate into the body as a function of time, then the net heat supplied between time t_0 and time t is

$$\int_{t_0}^{t} [q_{in}(\lambda) - q_{out}(\lambda)]d\lambda$$

We assume that the heat supplied during this time interval equals a constant C times the change in temperature. If the temperature of the body at the reference time t_0 is denoted by $\theta(t_0)$, then

$$\theta(t) = \theta(t_0) + \frac{1}{C} \int_{t_0}^{t} [q_{in}(\lambda) - q_{out}(\lambda)]d\lambda \tag{1}$$

The constant C is known as the **thermal capacitance** and has units of joules per kelvin (J/K). For a body having a mass M and specific heat σ, with units of joules per kilogram-kelvin, the thermal capacitance is $C = M\sigma$.

Differentiating (1), we have

$$\dot{\theta} = \frac{1}{C}[q_{in}(t) - q_{out}(t)] \tag{2}$$

which relates the rate of temperature change to the instantaneous net heat flow rate into the body. Because we generally select the temperatures of the bodies that constitute a thermal system as the state variables, we shall use (2) extensively to write the state-variable equations. As indicated earlier, we can use (1) and (2) only when the temperature of the body is assumed to be uniform. If the thermal gradients within the body are so great that we cannot make this assumption, then the body should be divided into two or more parts with separate thermal capacitances.

Thermal Resistance

Heat can flow between points by three different mechanisms: conduction, convection, and radiation. We shall consider only conduction, whereby heat flows from one body to another through the medium connecting them at a rate proportional to the temperature difference between the points. Specifically, the flow of heat by conduction from a body at temperature θ_1 to a body at temperature θ_2 obeys the relationship

$$q(t) = \frac{1}{R}[\theta_1(t) - \theta_2(t)] \tag{3}$$

where R is the **thermal resistance** of the path between the bodies, with units of kelvin-seconds per joule (K·s/J) or kelvins per watt (K/W). For a path of cross-sectional area A and length d composed of material having a thermal conductivity α (with units of watts per meter-kelvin), the thermal resistance is

$$R = \frac{d}{A\alpha} \tag{4}$$

We can use (3) only when the material or body being treated as a thermal resistance does not store any heat. Should it become important to account for the heat stored in the resistance, then we must also include a thermal capacitance in the model.

In developing lumped models of thermal systems, we often find it convenient to combine two or more thermal resistances into a single equivalent resistance. The following two examples illustrate the techniques for doing this for combinations of two resistances.

▶ **EXAMPLE 11.1**

Figure 11.1(a) shows two bodies at temperatures θ_1 and θ_2 separated by two resistances R_1 and R_2. Heat flows through each of the resistances at the rate q but cannot flow through the perfect insulating material above and below the resistances. Find the value of the equivalent thermal resistance R_{eq} in Figure 11.1(b) and solve for the interface temperature θ_B.

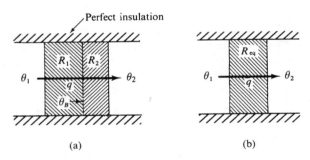

FIGURE 11.1   (a) Two thermal resistances in series. (b) Equivalent resistance.

Solution

We can use (3) for each of the thermal resistances to express the heat flow rate q in terms of the resistance and the temperature difference. Specifically,

$$q = \frac{1}{R_1}(\theta_1 - \theta_B) \tag{5a}$$

$$q = \frac{1}{R_2}(\theta_B - \theta_2) \tag{5b}$$

Combining the equations to eliminate θ_B and arranging the result in the form of (3), we find that

$$q = \frac{1}{R_1 + R_2}(\theta_1 - \theta_2)$$

Hence the equivalent thermal resistance is

$$R_{eq} = R_1 + R_2 \tag{6}$$

where R_1 and R_2 are said to be in **series** because the heat flow rate is the same through each.

To calculate the interface temperature θ_B, we combine (5a) and (5b) to eliminate q, getting

$$\theta_B = \frac{R_2\theta_1 + R_1\theta_2}{R_1 + R_2} \tag{7}$$

You should verify that equivalent forms of (7) are

$$\theta_B = \theta_1 - \frac{R_1}{R_{eq}}(\theta_1 - \theta_2)$$

$$\theta_B = \theta_2 + \frac{R_2}{R_{eq}}(\theta_1 - \theta_2)$$

▶ *EXAMPLE 11.2*

Figure 11.2 shows a hollow cylindrical vessel whose walls have thickness T and a material whose thermal conductivity is α. Calculate the thermal resistances of the side of the cylinder (R_c) and of each end (R_e). Then find the equivalent resistance of the entire vessel in terms of R_c and R_e.

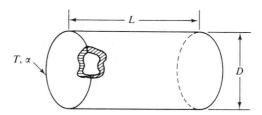

FIGURE 11.2 Cylindrical vessel for Example 11.2.

Solution

From (4), with d replaced by T and A replaced by $\pi D^2/4$, the resistance of each end of the vessel is

$$R_e = \frac{4T}{\pi D^2 \alpha} \tag{8}$$

Similarly, the resistance of the cylindrical portion is

$$R_c = \frac{T}{\pi D L \alpha} \tag{9}$$

The rate at which heat flows through each end is

$$q_e = \frac{\Delta\theta}{R_e}$$

where $\Delta\theta$ denotes the interior temperature minus the exterior temperature. Likewise, the heat flow rate through the cylindrical wall is

$$q_c = \frac{\Delta\theta}{R_c}$$

The total heat flow rate is

$$q_T = 2q_e + q_c$$

$$= \left(\frac{2}{R_e} + \frac{1}{R_c}\right)\Delta\theta \tag{10}$$

Because the equivalent thermal resistance R_{eq} must satisfy the relationship

$$q_T = \frac{\Delta\theta}{R_{eq}}$$

it follows from (10) that

$$\frac{1}{R_{eq}} = \frac{2}{R_e} + \frac{1}{R_c}$$

and

$$R_{eq} = \frac{R_c R_e}{2R_c + R_e} \tag{11}$$

Because the two ends and the cylindrical wall present independent paths for the heat to flow between the interior and exterior of the vessel, with the same temperature difference existing across each path, the three thermal resistances are said to be in **parallel**.

Thermal Sources

There are two types of ideal thermal sources. Figure 11.3 represents a source that adds or removes heat at a specified rate. Heat is added to the system when $q_i(t)$ is positive and removed when $q_i(t)$ is negative. On occasion, we shall consider the temperature of a body to be an input, in which case the temperature is a known function of time regardless of the rate at which heat flows between that body and the rest of the system.

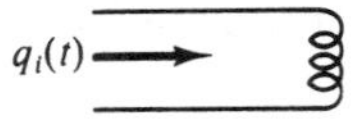

FIGURE 11.3   Representation of an ideal thermal source.

◼ 11.3 DYNAMIC MODELS OF THERMAL SYSTEMS

We shall demonstrate how to construct and analyze dynamic models of thermal systems by considering several examples. The general technique is to select the temperature of each thermal capacitance as a state variable and use (2) to obtain the corresponding state-variable equation. The net heat flow rate into a thermal capacitance depends on heat sources and heat flow rates through thermal resistances. By using (3), we can express the heat flow rates through the resistances in terms of the system's state variables, the temperatures of the thermal capacitances.

We first consider systems that have thermal capacitances from which heat can escape to the environment through thermal resistances. We then illustrate approximating a distributed system by a lumped model by analyzing two possible models for heating a bar. In the final example, a thermal capacitance is heated by both a heater and an incoming liquid stream.

▶ EXAMPLE 11.3

Figure 11.4 shows a thermal capacitance C enclosed by insulation that has an equivalent thermal resistance R. The temperature within the capacitance is θ and is assumed to be uniform. Heat is added to the interior of the system at the rate $q_i(t)$. The nominal values of $q_i(t)$ and θ are denoted by $\bar{q}_i$ and $\bar{\theta}$, respectively. The ambient temperature surrounding the exterior of the insulation is θ_a, a constant. Find the system model in terms of θ, $q_i(t)$, and θ_a and also in terms of incremental variables. Solve for the transfer function and the unit step response.

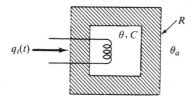

FIGURE 11.4 Thermal system with one capacitance.

Solution

The appropriate state variable is θ. We obtain an expression for its derivative by using (2) with

$$q_{in}(t) = q_i(t)$$

and, from (3),

$$q_{out}(t) = \frac{1}{R}(\theta - \theta_a)$$

Thus the state-variable model is

$$\dot{\theta} = \frac{1}{C}\left[q_i(t) - \frac{1}{R}(\theta - \theta_a)\right]$$

where we consider the ambient temperature θ_a an input to the system, along with $q_i(t)$. Rewriting the model, we have

$$\dot{\theta} + \frac{1}{RC}\theta = \frac{1}{C}q_i(t) + \frac{1}{RC}\theta_a \qquad (12)$$

which is readily recognized as the differential equation of a linear first-order system with the time constant $\tau = RC$ and the inputs $q_i(t)$ and θ_a. At the operating point, (12) reduces to

$$\frac{1}{RC}\bar{\theta} = \frac{1}{C}\bar{q}_i + \frac{1}{RC}\theta_a \qquad (13)$$

so

$$\bar{\theta} = \theta_a + R\bar{q}_i \qquad (14)$$

When the system is in equilibrium, the temperature of the thermal capacitance is constant, and the heat flow rate $\bar{q}_i$ supplied by the heater must equal the rate of heat flow through the thermal resistance. Then the temperature difference across the resistance is $R\bar{q}_i$, which agrees with (14).

To obtain a model in terms of incremental variables, we define

$$\hat{\theta}(t) = \theta(t) - \bar{\theta}$$

$$\hat{q}_i(t) = q_i(t) - \bar{q}_i$$

Substituting these expressions into (12) gives

$$\dot{\hat{\theta}} + \frac{1}{RC}(\hat{\theta} + \bar{\theta}) = \frac{1}{C}[\hat{q}_i(t) + \bar{q}_i] + \frac{1}{RC}\theta_a$$

By using (13), we can cancel the constant terms in the last equation, giving

$$\dot{\hat{\theta}} + \frac{1}{RC}\hat{\theta} = \frac{1}{C}\hat{q}_i(t) \qquad (15)$$

Examining (14) shows that if $\bar{q}_i > 0$, then $\bar{\theta} > \theta_a$ and the capacitance is being heated. If $\bar{q}_i < 0$, then $\bar{\theta} < \theta_a$ and the capacitance is being cooled. If $\bar{q}_i = 0$, then the nominal value of the temperature is $\bar{\theta} = \theta_a$ and $\hat{q}_i(t) = q_i(t)$. Because the system is linear, the incremental model given by (15) has the same coefficients regardless of the operating point.

Recall from Chapter 8 that the transfer function is $H(s) = Y(s)/U(s)$, where $U(s)$ is the transformed input and $Y(s)$ is the transform of the zero-state response. Thus we transform (15) with $\hat{\theta}(0) = 0$ to obtain

$$s\hat{\Theta}(s) + \frac{1}{RC}\hat{\Theta}(s) = \frac{1}{C}\hat{Q}_i(s)$$

We can rearrange this transformed equation to give the transfer function $H(s) = \hat{\Theta}(s)/\hat{Q}_i(s)$ as

$$H(s) = \frac{\dfrac{1}{C}}{s + \dfrac{1}{RC}}$$

which has a single pole at $s = -1/RC$. The response of $\hat{\theta}$ to a unit step function for $\hat{q}_i(t)$ will be

$$\hat{\theta} = R(1 - \epsilon^{-t/RC}) \quad \text{for } t > 0$$

which approaches a steady-state value of R with the time constant RC. Note that we can also find the steady-state value of $\hat{\theta}$ by evaluating $H(s)$ at $s = 0$. To find the response in terms of the actual temperature θ, we merely add $\bar{\theta}$ to $\hat{\theta}$, getting

$$\theta = \bar{\theta} + R(1 - \epsilon^{-t/RC}) \quad \text{for } t > 0$$

which is shown in Figure 11.5, along with the input $q_i(t)$.

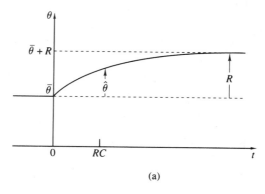

(a)

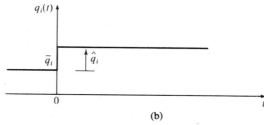

(b)

FIGURE 11.5 (a) Temperature response for Example 11.3. (b) Heat input rate.

▶ *EXAMPLE 11.4*

A system with two thermal capacitances is shown in Figure 11.6. Heat is supplied to the left capacitance at the rate $q_i(t)$ by a heater, and it is lost at the right end to the environment, which has the constant ambient temperature θ_a. Except for the thermal resistances R_1 and R_2, the enclosure is assumed to be perfectly insulated. Find the transfer function relating the transforms of the incremental variables $\hat{q}_i(t)$ and $\hat{\theta}_2$.

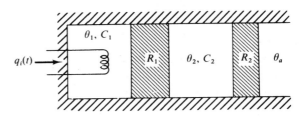

FIGURE 11.6   Thermal system with two capacitances.

Solution

Taking θ_1 and θ_2 as the two state variables and using (2) for each thermal capacitance, we can write the differential equations

$$\begin{aligned}
\dot{\theta}_1 &= \frac{1}{C_1}\left[q_i(t) - \frac{1}{R_1}(\theta_1 - \theta_2)\right] \\
\dot{\theta}_2 &= \frac{1}{C_2}\left[\frac{1}{R_1}(\theta_1 - \theta_2) - \frac{1}{R_2}(\theta_2 - \theta_a)\right]
\end{aligned} \tag{16}$$

At the operating point corresponding to the nominal input $\bar{q}_i$, (16) reduces to

$$\begin{aligned}
\bar{q}_i - \frac{1}{R_1}(\bar{\theta}_1 - \bar{\theta}_2) &= 0 \\
\frac{1}{R_1}(\bar{\theta}_1 - \bar{\theta}_2) - \frac{1}{R_2}(\bar{\theta}_2 - \theta_a) &= 0
\end{aligned} \tag{17}$$

from which

$$\bar{\theta}_2 = \theta_a + R_2\bar{q}_i \tag{18a}$$

$$\bar{\theta}_1 = \theta_a + (R_1 + R_2)\bar{q}_i \tag{18b}$$

At the operating point, where equilibrium conditions exist and the temperatures are constant, the heat flow rates through R_1 and R_2 must both equal $\bar{q}_i$. Because the rates of heat flow are the same, we can regard the two resistances as being in series. The equivalent resistance is $R_{eq} = R_1 + R_2$, as in (6), so $\bar{\theta}_1$ must be the temperature difference $(R_1 + R_2)\bar{q}_i$ plus the ambient temperature θ_a, which agrees with (18b).

We define the incremental temperatures $\hat{\theta}_1 = \theta_1 - \bar{\theta}_1$ and $\hat{\theta}_2 = \theta_2 - \bar{\theta}_2$ and substitute these expressions into (16). After canceling the constant terms by using (17), we obtain

$$\dot{\hat{\theta}}_1 + \frac{1}{R_1 C_1} \hat{\theta}_1 = \frac{1}{R_1 C_1} \hat{\theta}_2 + \frac{1}{C_1} \hat{q}_i(t)$$

$$\dot{\hat{\theta}}_2 + \left(\frac{1}{R_1 C_2} + \frac{1}{R_2 C_2} \right) \hat{\theta}_2 = \frac{1}{R_1 C_2} \hat{\theta}_1 \tag{19}$$

where the ambient temperature θ_a no longer appears. To find the transfer function $H(s) = \hat{\Theta}_2(s)/\hat{Q}_i(s)$, we transform (19) with $\hat{\theta}_1(0) = \hat{\theta}_2(0) = 0$, getting

$$\left(s + \frac{1}{R_1 C_1} \right) \hat{\Theta}_1(s) = \frac{1}{R_1 C_1} \hat{\Theta}_2(s) + \frac{1}{C_1} \hat{Q}_i(s)$$

$$\left[s + \left(\frac{1}{R_1 C_2} + \frac{1}{R_2 C_2} \right) \right] \hat{\Theta}_2(s) = \frac{1}{R_1 C_2} \hat{\Theta}_1(s)$$

Combining these equations to eliminate $\hat{\Theta}_1(s)$ and rearranging to form the ratio $\hat{\Theta}_2(s)/\hat{Q}_i(s)$, we get

$$H(s) = \frac{\dfrac{1}{R_1 C_1 C_2}}{s^2 + \left(\dfrac{1}{R_1 C_1} + \dfrac{1}{R_1 C_2} + \dfrac{1}{R_2 C_2} \right) s + \dfrac{1}{R_1 C_1 R_2 C_2}} \tag{20}$$

Note that the denominator of $H(s)$ is a quadratic function of s, which implies that it will have two poles. In fact, for any combination of numerical values for R_1, R_2, C_1, and C_2, these poles will be real, negative, and distinct. As a consequence, the transient response of the system consists of two decaying exponential functions.

▶ **EXAMPLE 11.5**

Consider a bar of length L and cross-sectional area A that is perfectly insulated on all its boundaries except at the left end, as shown in Figure 11.7. The temperature at the left end of the bar is $\theta_i(t)$, a known function of time that is the system's input. The interior of the bar is initially at the ambient temperature θ_a. The specific heat of the material is σ with units of joules per kilogram-kelvin, its density is ρ expressed in kilograms per cubic meter, and its thermal conductivity is α expressed in watts per meter-kelvin. Although the system is distributed and can be modeled exactly only by a partial differential equation, develop a lumped model consisting of a single thermal capacitance and resistance and then find the step response.

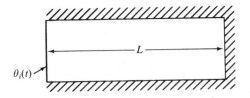

FIGURE 11.7   Insulated bar considered in Example 11.5.

Solution

Assume that all points within the bar have the same temperature θ except the left end, which has the prescribed temperature $\theta_i(t)$. Then the thermal capacitance is

$$C = \sigma\rho AL \tag{21}$$

with units of joules per kelvin. To complete the single-capacitance approximation, we assume that the thermal resistance of the entire bar, which from (4) is

$$R = \frac{L}{A\alpha} \tag{22}$$

with units of kelvins per watt, separates the left end from the remainder of the bar. The lumped approximation is shown in Figure 11.8, with C and R given by (21) and (22), respectively. From (2), with $q_{out} = 0$ because of the perfect insulation, and with

$$q_{in} = \frac{1}{R}[\theta_i(t) - \theta]$$

it follows that the single-capacitance model is

$$\dot{\theta} = \frac{1}{RC}[\theta_i(t) - \theta]$$

or

$$\dot{\theta} + \frac{1}{RC}\theta = \frac{1}{RC}\theta_i(t) \tag{23}$$

where $\theta(0) = \theta_a$.

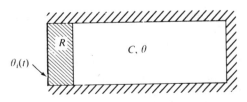

FIGURE 11.8   Single-capacitance approximation to the insulated bar shown in Figure 11.7.

If the input $\theta_i(t)$ is the sum of the constant ambient temperature θ_a and a step function of height B, we can write

$$\theta_i(t) = \theta_a + BU(t)$$

In this example, it is convenient to define the nominal values of the temperatures to be the ambient temperature θ_a and to let the incremental variables be the temperatures relative to θ_a. The relative input temperature is

$$\hat{\theta}_i(t) = \theta_i(t) - \theta_a$$
$$= BU(t)$$

and the relative bar temperature is

$$\hat{\theta} = \theta - \theta_a$$

With these definitions, (23) becomes

$$\dot{\hat{\theta}} + \frac{1}{RC}(\hat{\theta} + \theta_a) = \frac{1}{RC}[\theta_a + BU(t)]$$

which reduces to

$$\dot{\hat{\theta}} + \frac{1}{RC}\hat{\theta} = \frac{B}{RC}U(t) \qquad (24)$$

with the initial condition $\hat{\theta}(0) = 0$. The response of the relative temperature is

$$\hat{\theta} = B(1 - \epsilon^{-t/RC}) \qquad \text{for } t > 0$$

which indicates that the temperature of the bar will rise from the ambient temperature to that of its left end with the time constant

$$RC = \frac{\sigma\rho L^2}{\alpha}$$

▶ **EXAMPLE 11.6**

Analyze the step response of the insulated bar shown in Figure 11.7, using the two-capacitance approximation shown in Figure 11.9.

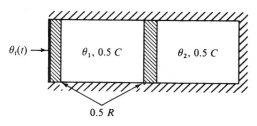

FIGURE 11.9 A two-capacitance approximation to the insulated bar shown in Figure 11.7.

Solution

As indicated in Figure 11.9, we take the value of each thermal capacitance as $0.5C$, where C is given by (21). Likewise, we take the value of each thermal resistance as $0.5R$, where R is given by (22). Applying (2) to the left capacitance with

$$q_{in} = \frac{1}{0.5R}[\theta_i(t) - \theta_1]$$

and

$$q_{out} = \frac{1}{0.5R}(\theta_1 - \theta_2)$$

gives the state-variable equation

$$\dot{\theta}_1 = \frac{1}{0.25RC}[\theta_i(t) - 2\theta_1 + \theta_2] \tag{25}$$

Applying (2) to the right capacitance with

$$q_{in} = \frac{1}{0.5R}(\theta_1 - \theta_2)$$

and $q_{out} = 0$ gives the second state-variable equation

$$\dot{\theta}_2 = \frac{1}{0.25RC}(\theta_1 - \theta_2) \tag{26}$$

To evaluate the responses of θ_1 and θ_2 to the input $\theta_i(t) = \theta_a + BU(t)$, we can define the relative temperatures $\hat{\theta}_1 = \theta_1 - \theta_a$, $\hat{\theta}_2 = \theta_2 - \theta_a$, and $\hat{\theta}_i(t) = \theta_i(t) - \theta_a$ and then derive the transfer functions $H_1(s) = \hat{\Theta}_1(s)/\hat{\Theta}_i(s)$ and $H_2(s) = \hat{\Theta}_2(s)/\hat{\Theta}_i(s)$. Knowing $H_1(s)$ and $H_2(s)$, we can write, for the step responses,

$$\hat{\theta}_1(t) = \mathcal{L}^{-1}\left[H_1(s)\frac{B}{s}\right]$$

$$\hat{\theta}_2(t) = \mathcal{L}^{-1}\left[H_2(s)\frac{B}{s}\right]$$

Rewriting (25) and (26) in terms of the relative temperatures, we have

$$\dot{\hat{\theta}}_1 + \frac{8}{RC}\hat{\theta}_1 = \frac{4}{RC}\hat{\theta}_2 + \frac{4}{RC}\hat{\theta}_i(t)$$

$$\dot{\hat{\theta}}_2 + \frac{4}{RC}\hat{\theta}_2 = \frac{4}{RC}\hat{\theta}_1 \tag{27}$$

Transforming (27) with $\hat{\theta}_1(0) = \hat{\theta}_2(0) = 0$ gives the pair of algebraic equations

$$\left(s + \frac{8}{RC}\right)\hat{\Theta}_1(s) = \frac{4}{RC}[\hat{\Theta}_2(s) + \hat{\Theta}_i(s)] \tag{28a}$$

$$\left(s + \frac{4}{RC}\right)\hat{\Theta}_2(s) = \frac{4}{RC}\hat{\Theta}_1(s) \tag{28b}$$

Solving (28b) for $\hat{\Theta}_2(s)$, substituting the result into (28a), and rearranging terms, we find that

$$\left[\left(s + \frac{8}{RC}\right)\left(s + \frac{4}{RC}\right) - \left(\frac{4}{RC}\right)^2\right]\hat{\Theta}_1(s) = \left[\frac{4}{RC}s + \left(\frac{4}{RC}\right)^2\right]\hat{\Theta}_i(s)$$

Simplifying the quadratic factor on the left side and solving for $H_1(s) = \hat{\Theta}_1(s)/\hat{\Theta}_i(s)$, we obtain

$$H_1(s) = \frac{4}{RC}\left[\frac{s + \dfrac{4}{RC}}{s^2 + \dfrac{12}{RC}s + \dfrac{16}{(RC)^2}}\right]$$

$$= \frac{4}{RC}\left[\frac{s + \dfrac{4}{RC}}{\left(s + \dfrac{1.528}{RC}\right)\left(s + \dfrac{10.472}{RC}\right)}\right] \tag{29}$$

The transfer function has poles at $s_1 = -1.528/RC$ and $s_2 = -10.472/RC$, and the free response has two terms that decay exponentially with the time constants

$$\tau_1 = \frac{RC}{1.528} = 0.6545RC$$

$$\tau_2 = \frac{RC}{10.472} = 0.0955RC$$

Because $H_1(0) = 1$ from (29), the steady-state value of $\hat{\theta}_1$ equals B when $\hat{\theta}_i(t) = BU(t)$. For this input,

$$\hat{\Theta}_1(s) = \frac{4}{RC}\left[\frac{s + \dfrac{4}{RC}}{\left(s + \dfrac{1.528}{RC}\right)\left(s + \dfrac{10.472}{RC}\right)}\right] \cdot \frac{B}{s}$$

$$= \frac{A_1}{s} + \frac{A_2}{s + \dfrac{1.528}{RC}} + \frac{A_3}{s + \dfrac{10.472}{RC}} \tag{30}$$

You can verify that the numerical values of the coefficients in the partial-fraction expansion are

$$A_1 = B$$
$$A_2 = -0.7235B$$
$$A_3 = -0.2764B$$

Substituting these values into (30) and taking the inverse transform, we find that for $t > 0$,

$$\hat{\theta}_1(t) = B(1 - 0.7235\epsilon^{-1.528t/RC} - 0.2764\epsilon^{-10.472t/RC})$$

From (28b),

$$\hat{\Theta}_2(s) = \frac{4}{RCs + 4}\hat{\Theta}_1(s)$$

$$= \frac{16}{(RC)^2}\left[\frac{B}{s\left(s + \dfrac{1.528}{RC}\right)\left(s + \dfrac{10.472}{RC}\right)}\right]$$

whose inverse transform can be shown to be

$$\hat{\theta}_2(t) = B(1 - 1.1708\epsilon^{-1.528t/RC} + 0.1708\epsilon^{-10.472t/RC})$$

The ratios $\hat{\theta}_1(t)/B$ and $\hat{\theta}_2(t)/B$ are shown in Figure 11.10 versus the normalized time variable t/RC. Other lumped-element approximations that lead to more accurate results for the insulated bar are investigated in some of the problems at the end of the chapter.

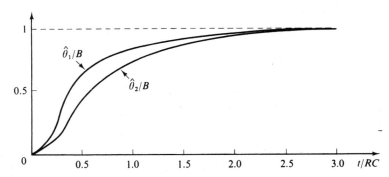

FIGURE 11.10   Response to a step function in $\hat{\theta}_i(t)$ for the two-capacitance approximation to the insulated bar shown in Figure 11.7.

▶ *EXAMPLE 11.7*

The insulated vessel shown in Figure 11.11 is filled with liquid at a temperature θ, which is kept uniform throughout the vessel by perfect mixing. Liquid enters at a constant volumetric flow rate of $\bar{w}$, expressed in units of cubic meters per second, and at a temperature $\theta_i(t)$. It leaves at the same rate and at the temperature θ_o. Because of the perfect mixing, the exit temperature θ_o is the same as the liquid temperature θ. The thermal resistance of the vessel and its insulation is R, and the ambient temperature is θ_a, a constant.

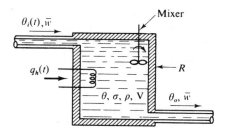

FIGURE 11.11   Insulated vessel with liquid flowing through it.

Heat is added to the liquid in the vessel by a heater at a rate $q_h(t)$. The volume of the vessel is V, and the liquid has a density of ρ (with units of kilograms per cubic meter) and a specific heat of σ (with units of joules per kilogram-kelvin). Derive the system model and find the appropriate transfer functions.

Solution

The thermal capacitance of the liquid is the product of the liquid's volume, density, and specific heat. The heat entering the vessel is the sum of that due to the heater and that contained in the incoming stream. The heat leaving the vessel is the sum of that taken out by the outgoing stream and that lost to the ambient through the vessel walls and insulation.

From (2),

$$\dot{\theta} = \frac{1}{C}(q_{\text{in}} - q_{\text{out}}) \qquad (31)$$

where

$$q_{\text{in}} = q_h(t) + \bar{w}\rho\sigma\theta_i(t)$$

$$q_{\text{out}} = \bar{w}\rho\sigma\theta + \frac{1}{R}(\theta - \theta_a)$$

$$C = \rho\sigma V$$

Substituting these expressions into (31) and rearranging, we obtain the first-order differential equation

$$\dot{\theta} + \left(\frac{\bar{w}}{V} + \frac{1}{RC}\right)\theta = \frac{\bar{w}}{V}\theta_i(t) + \frac{1}{C}q_h(t) + \frac{1}{RC}\theta_a \tag{32}$$

The time constant of the system is

$$\tau = \frac{1}{\dfrac{\bar{w}}{V} + \dfrac{1}{RC}} \tag{33}$$

which approaches RC as $\bar{w}$ approaches zero (no liquid flow). As R approaches infinity (perfect insulation), the time constant becomes $V/\bar{w}$, which is the time required to replace the total tank volume at the volumetric flow rate $\bar{w}$.

Because the initial values of the state variables must be zero when we calculate the transfer functions, we first rewrite the model in terms of incremental variables defined with respect to the operating point. Setting $\dot{\theta}$ equal to zero in (32) yields the relationship between the nominal values $\bar{q}_h$, $\bar{\theta}_i$, $\bar{\theta}$, and the ambient temperature θ_a. It is

$$\bar{q}_h + \frac{C\bar{w}}{V}(\bar{\theta}_i - \bar{\theta}) = \frac{1}{R}(\bar{\theta} - \theta_a) \tag{34}$$

Rewriting (32) in terms of the incremental variables $\hat{\theta} = \theta - \bar{\theta}$, $\hat{\theta}_i(t) = \theta_i(t) - \bar{\theta}_i$, and $\hat{q}_h(t) = q_h(t) - \bar{q}_h$ and using (34), we obtain for the incremental model

$$\dot{\hat{\theta}} + \frac{1}{\tau}\hat{\theta} = \frac{\bar{w}}{V}\hat{\theta}_i(t) + \frac{1}{C}\hat{q}_h(t) \tag{35}$$

The equilibrium condition, or operating point, corresponds to the initial condition $\hat{\theta}(0) = 0$ and to incremental inputs $\hat{q}_h(t) = \hat{\theta}_i(t) = 0$. To find the transfer function $H_1(s) = \hat{\Theta}(s)/\hat{Q}_h(s)$, we transform (35) with $\hat{\theta}(0) = 0$ and $\hat{\theta}_i(t) = 0$, obtaining

$$\left(s + \frac{1}{\tau}\right)\hat{\Theta}(s) = \frac{1}{C}\hat{Q}_h(s)$$

Solving for the ratio $\hat{\Theta}(s)/\hat{Q}_h(s)$ yields

$$H_1(s) = \frac{\dfrac{1}{C}}{s + \dfrac{1}{\tau}}$$

which has a single pole at $s = -1/\tau$. The steady-state value of $\hat{\theta}$ in response to a unit step change in the heater input is

$$H_1(0) = \frac{\tau}{C}$$

$$= \frac{1}{\bar{w}\rho\sigma + \dfrac{1}{R}}$$

Hence, either a high flow rate $\bar{w}$ or a low thermal resistance R tends to reduce the steady-state effect of a change in the heater input.

In similar fashion, you can verify that the transfer function $H_2(s) = \hat{\Theta}(s)/\hat{\Theta}_i(s)$ is

$$H_2(s) = \frac{\dfrac{\bar{w}}{V}}{s + \dfrac{1}{\tau}}$$

The steady-state response of $\hat{\theta}$ to a unit step change in the inlet temperature is

$$H_2(0) = \frac{\bar{w}\tau}{V} = \frac{\bar{w}\rho\sigma}{\bar{w}\rho\sigma + \dfrac{1}{R}}$$

$$= \frac{1}{1 + \dfrac{1}{\bar{w}\rho\sigma R}}$$

Thus a step change in the inlet temperature with constant heater input affects the steady-state value of the liquid temperature by only some fraction of the change. Either a high flow rate or a high thermal resistance will tend to make that fraction approach unity.

In an actual process for which θ must be maintained constant in spite of variations in $\theta_i(t)$, a feedback control system may be used to sense changes in θ and make corresponding adjustments in q_h. The type of mathematical modeling and transfer-function analysis that we have demonstrated here plays an important part in the design of such control systems.

11.4 A THERMAL SYSTEM

Producing chemicals almost always requires control of the temperature of liquids contained in vessels. In a continuous process, a vessel within which a reaction is taking place typically has liquid flowing into and out of it continuously, and a control system is needed to maintain the liquid at a constant temperature. Such a system was modeled in Example 11.7. In a batch process, a vessel would typically be filled with liquid, sealed, and then heated to a prescribed temperature. In the design and operation of batch processes, it is important to be able to calculate in advance the time required for the liquid to reach the desired temperature. Such a batch system is modeled and analyzed in this case study.

System Description

Figure 11.12 shows a closed, insulated vessel that is filled with liquid and contains an electrical heater immersed in the liquid. The heating element is contained within a metal jacket that has a thermal resistance of R_{HL}. The thermal resistance of the vessel and its insulation is R_{La}. The heater has a thermal capacitance of C_H, and the liquid has a thermal capacitance of C_L. The heater temperature is θ_H and that of the liquid is θ_L, which is assumed to be uniform because of the mixer in the vessel. The rate at which energy is supplied to the heating element is $q_i(t)$.

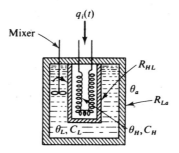

FIGURE 11.12   Vessel with heater.

The heater and the liquid are initially at the ambient temperature θ_a, with the heater turned off. At time $t = 0$, the heater is connected to an electrical source that supplies energy at a constant rate. We wish to determine the response of the liquid temperature θ_L and to calculate the time required for the liquid to reach a desired temperature, denoted by θ_d. The numerical values of the system parameters are

Heater capacitance: $C_H = 20.0 \times 10^3$ J/K

Liquid capacitance: $C_L = 1.0 \times 10^6$ J/K

Heater-liquid resistance: $R_{HL} = 1.0 \times 10^{-3}$ s·K/J

Liquid-ambient resistance: $R_{La} = 5.0 \times 10^{-3}$ s·K/J

Ambient temperature: $\theta_a = 300$ K

Desired temperature: $\theta_d = 365$ K

We will derive the system model for an arbitrary input $q_i(t)$ and for an arbitrary ambient temperature θ_a, using θ_L and θ_H as the state variables.

Then we will define a set of variables relative to the ambient conditions and find the transfer function relating the transforms of the relative liquid temperature and the input. Finally, we will calculate the time required for the liquid to reach the desired temperature.

System Model

Because θ_H and θ_L represent the energy stored in the system, we can write the state-variable model as

$$\dot{\theta}_H = \frac{1}{C_H}[q_i(t) - q_{HL}]$$
$$\dot{\theta}_L = \frac{1}{C_L}[q_{HL} - q_{La}]$$

(36)

where $q_{HL} = (\theta_H - \theta_L)/R_{HL}$ and $q_{La} = (\theta_L - \theta_a)/R_{La}$. Substituting these expressions for q_{HL} and q_{La} and the appropriate numerical parameter values into (36) leads to the pair of state-variable equations

$$\dot{\theta}_H = -0.050\theta_H + 0.050\theta_L + [0.50 \times 10^{-4}]q_i(t)$$
$$\dot{\theta}_L = -[1.20 \times 10^{-3}]\theta_L + 10^{-3}\theta_H + [0.20 \times 10^{-3}]\theta_a$$

(37)

where the initial conditions are $\theta_H(0) = \theta_L(0) = \theta_a$.

At this point, we could transform (37) for a specific ambient temperature and a specific input $q_i(t)$. Then we could solve for $\Theta_L(s)$ and take its inverse transform to find $\theta_L(t)$. Instead, we define the relative variables

$$\hat{\theta}_H = \theta_H - \theta_a \tag{38a}$$
$$\hat{\theta}_L = \theta_L - \theta_a \tag{38b}$$
$$\hat{q}_i(t) = q_i(t) \tag{38c}$$

where the last equation implies that $\bar{q}_i = 0$. Using (38) to rewrite (37), we find that the system model in terms of the relative variables is

$$\dot{\hat{\theta}}_H = -0.050\hat{\theta}_H + 0.050\hat{\theta}_L + [0.50 \times 10^{-4}]\hat{q}_i(t)$$
$$\dot{\hat{\theta}}_L = -[1.20 \times 10^{-3}]\hat{\theta}_L + 10^{-3}\hat{\theta}_H$$

(39)

where the initial conditions are $\hat{\theta}_H = \hat{\theta}_L(0) = 0$.

When transformed and rearranged, (39) becomes the pair of algebraic equations

$$(s + 0.050)\hat{\Theta}_H(s) = 0.050\hat{\Theta}_L(s) + (0.50 \times 10^{-4})\hat{Q}_i(s)$$
$$(s + 1.20 \times 10^{-3})\hat{\Theta}_L(s) = 10^{-3}\hat{\Theta}_H(s)$$

(40)

Combining the two equations in (40) to eliminate $\hat{\Theta}_H(s)$, we find that the transfer function $H(s) = \hat{\Theta}_L(s)/\hat{Q}_i(s)$ is

$$
\begin{aligned}
H(s) &= \frac{0.50 \times 10^{-4}}{1000s^2 + 51.20s + 0.010} \\
&= \frac{0.50 \times 10^{-7}}{s^2 + 0.05120s + 10^{-5}} \\
&= \frac{0.50 \times 10^{-7}}{(s + 0.0510)(s + 0.000196)}
\end{aligned}
\tag{41}
$$

System Response

Having found the transfer function $\hat{\Theta}_L(s)/\hat{Q}_i(s)$ given by (41), we can now solve for the response to various inputs. Specifically, we shall find $\theta_L(t)$ for the ambient temperature $\theta_a = 300$ K (approximately 27°C or 80°F) and for a step-function input $\hat{q}_i(t) = 1.50 \times 10^4$ W for $t > 0$.

To find $\hat{\Theta}_L(s)$, we multiply $\hat{Q}_i(s) = [1.50 \times 10^4](1/s)$ by $H(s)$ as given by (41), getting

$$
\hat{\Theta}_L(s) = \frac{0.750 \times 10^{-3}}{s(s + 0.0510)(s + 0.000196)}
\tag{42}
$$

Next we expand $\hat{\Theta}_L(s)$ in partial fractions to obtain

$$
\hat{\Theta}_L(s) = \frac{75.0}{s} + \frac{0.289}{s + 0.0510} - \frac{75.29}{s + 0.000196}
$$

Thus for $t > 0$, the relative liquid temperature is

$$
\hat{\theta}_L = 75.0 + 0.289\epsilon^{-0.0510t} - 75.29\epsilon^{-0.000196t}
\tag{43}
$$

We obtain the actual liquid temperature by adding the ambient temperature of 300 K to $\hat{\theta}_L$, getting

$$
\theta_L = 375.0 + 0.289\epsilon^{-0.0510t} - 75.29\epsilon^{-0.000196t}
\tag{44}
$$

which has a steady-state value of 375 K and is shown in Figure 11.13.

From inspection of either (43) or (44), we see that the transient response of the system has two exponentially decaying modes with time constants of

$$
\tau_1 = \frac{1}{0.0510} = 19.61 \text{ s}
$$

$$
\tau_2 = \frac{1}{0.000196} = 5102 \text{ s}
$$

Because τ_2 exceeds τ_1 by several orders of magnitude, the transient having the longer time constant dominates the response. The principal effect of the shorter time constant is to give θ_L a zero slope at $t = 0+$, which it would not have if the transient response were a single decaying exponential.

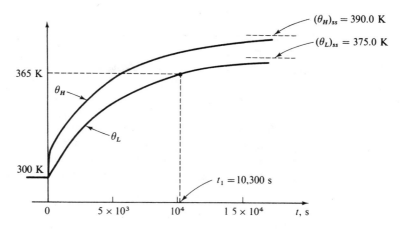

FIGURE 11.13 Responses of liquid and heater temperatures.

Finally, we must calculate the value of t_1, the time required for the liquid to reach the desired temperature $\theta_d = 365$ K. Because two exponential terms are present, an explicit solution of (44) is not possible. However by writing (44) in terms of the time constants τ_1 and τ_2 as

$$\theta_L = 375.0 + 0.289\epsilon^{-t/\tau_1} - 75.29\epsilon^{-t/\tau_2}$$

and noting that the solution for t_1 must be greater that τ_1, we can see that the term $0.289\epsilon^{-t/\tau_1}$ is negligible when $t = t_1$. Hence we can use the simpler approximate expression

$$\theta_L = 375.0 - 75.29\epsilon^{-t/5102} \qquad (45)$$

where the value of 5102 s has been substituted for τ_2. Because (45) contains only one exponential function, we can solve it explicitly for t_1. Replacing the left side of (45) by the value 365.0 and replacing t by t_1 on the right side, we have

$$365.0 = 375.0 - 75.29\epsilon^{-t_1/5102}$$

which leads to

$$t_1 = 5102 \ln\left(\frac{75.29}{375.0 - 365.0}\right)$$

$$= 10,300 \text{ s}$$

which is approximately 2.86 hours.

Though we have completed our original task, we can use the preceding modeling and analysis results to carry out a variety of additional tasks. For instance, we can find the response of the heater temperature θ_H for the specified $q_i(t)$ by eliminating $\Theta_L(s)$ from (40). The heater temperature θ_H is shown in Figure 11.13, and you are encouraged to evaluate the analytical expression for it. In practice, it might be important to evaluate the time t_1 for constant values of $\hat{q}_i(t)$ other than the value 1.50×10^4 W that we used. For example, if $\hat{q}_i(t)$ is doubled to 3.0×10^4 W, the desired liquid temperature $\theta_d = 365$ K will be reached in only 2916 s (48.6 minutes). On the other hand, if the constant energy-input rate is less than 1.30×10^4 W, the liquid will never reach 365 K. If we want to investigate the effects of replacing the constant power source by a variable source, we can multiply the transfer function $H(s)$ by $\hat{Q}_i(s)$ to give the transform of the relative temperature. After we find the inverse transform, we can add it to the ambient temperature to get θ_L.

SUMMARY

We first introduced the basic variables—temperature and heat flow rate—and then presented the element laws. In contrast to the three types of passive elements in mechanical and electrical systems, there are only two types of passive elements in thermal systems: thermal capacitance and thermal resistance. Also, a greater degree of approximation is often necessary in order to represent a thermal system by a lumped-element model.

The temperature of each body that can store heat is usually taken to be a state variable. Because there is only one type of energy-storing passive element, the poles of the transfer functions are real numbers, and the mode functions that characterize the free response are exponential rather than sinusoidal terms. Of course, adding mechanical or other elements to the thermal part of a system can change the nature of this response.

We investigated many examples, which culminated in the case study presented in Section 11.4. The procedures for finding a state-variable model, an input–output differential equation, or a transfer function are similar to those used for mechanical and electrical examples. In fact, the general methods of modeling and analysis introduced in earlier chapters are applicable to a wide variety of systems. In the next chapter, we shall apply them to hydraulic systems.

PROBLEMS

11.1 Find the equivalent thermal resistance for the three resistances shown in Figure P11.1. Also express the temperatures θ_A and θ_B at the interfaces in terms of θ_1 and θ_2.

* **11.2** The hollow enclosure shown in Figure P11.2 has four sides, each with resistance R_a, and two ends, each with resistance R_b. Find the equivalent thermal

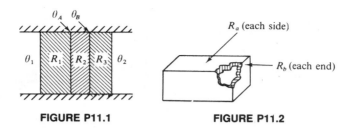

FIGURE P11.1	FIGURE P11.2

resistance between the interior and the exterior of the enclosure. Also calculate the total heat flow rate from the interior to the exterior when the interior of the enclosure is at a constant temperature θ_1 and the ambient temperature is θ_a.

11.3 A perfectly insulated enclosure containing a heater is filled with a liquid having thermal capacitance C. The temperature of the liquid is assumed to be uniform and is denoted by θ. The heat supplied by the heater is $q_i(t)$.

    a) Write the differential equation obeyed by the liquid temperature θ.

    b) Solve the equation you found in part (a) for θ in terms of the arbitrary initial temperature $\theta(0)$.

    c) Sketch θ versus t when $q_i(t) = 1$ for $10 < t \leq 20$ and zero otherwise.

11.4 Figure P11.4 shows a volume for which the temperature is θ_1 and the thermal capacitance is C. The volume is perfectly insulated from the environment except for the thermal resistances R_1 and R_2. Heat is supplied at the rate $q_i(t)$. The ambient temperature is θ_a.

    a) Write the system model.

    b) Find and sketch θ_1 versus t when $q_i(t) = AU(t)$ and $\theta_1(0) = \theta_a$. (*Hint:* First solve for the relative temperature $\hat{\theta}_1 = \theta_1 - \theta_a$.)

    c) Evaluate the transfer function $\hat{\Theta}_1(s)/Q_i(s)$ and sketch the magnitude of the frequency response versus ω.

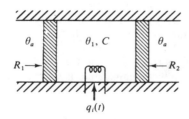

FIGURE P11.4

* 11.5 **a)** Repeat part (a) of Problem 11.4 when the temperature to the right of R_2 is $\theta_2(t)$ rather than the constant ambient temperature θ_a.

    b) Using the relative temperatures $\hat{\theta}_1 = \theta_1 - \theta_a$ and $\hat{\theta}_2(t) = \theta_2(t) - \theta_a$, rewrite the model and evaluate the transfer functions $H_1(s) = \hat{\Theta}_1(s)/\hat{\Theta}_2(s)$ and $H_2(s) = \hat{\Theta}_1(s)/Q_i(s)$.

11.6 The system shown in Figure P11.6 is composed of two thermal capacitances, three thermal resistances, and two heat sources.

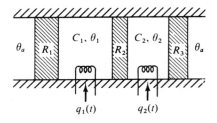

FIGURE P11.6

a) Verify that the model can be written in state-variable form as

$$\dot{\theta}_1 = \frac{1}{C_1}\left[-\left(\frac{1}{R_1}+\frac{1}{R_2}\right)\theta_1 + \frac{1}{R_2}\theta_2 + \frac{1}{R_1}\theta_a + q_1(t)\right]$$

$$\dot{\theta}_2 = \frac{1}{C_2}\left[\frac{1}{R_2}\theta_1 - \left(\frac{1}{R_2}+\frac{1}{R_3}\right)\theta_2 + \frac{1}{R_3}\theta_a + q_2(t)\right]$$

b) Derive the input–output differential equation relating θ_1, the inputs $q_1(t)$ and $q_2(t)$, and the ambient temperature θ_a.

c) Defining the relative temperature $\hat{\theta}_1$ as $\hat{\theta}_1 = \theta_1 - \theta_a$, write the transfer function $\hat{\Theta}_1(s)/\hat{Q}_1(s)$ and evaluate the steady-state response to a unit step-function input. Identify the three other transfer functions associated with the system, but do not solve for them.

* 11.7 a) Find the state-variable model for Figure P11.6 when the temperature to the right of R_3 is $\theta_3(t)$ rather than the constant ambient temperature θ_a.

b) Rewrite the model in terms of the relative temperatures $\hat{\theta}_1 = \theta_1 - \theta_a$, $\hat{\theta}_2 = \theta_2 - \theta_a$, and $\hat{\theta}_3(t) = \theta_3(t) - \theta_a$, and derive the transfer functions $H_1(s) = \hat{\Theta}_1(s)/\hat{\Theta}_3(s)$ and $H_2(s) = \hat{\Theta}_2(s)/\hat{\Theta}_3(s)$.

11.8 Figure P11.8 shows an electronic amplifier and a fan that can be turned on to cool the amplifier. The electronic equipment has a thermal capacitance C and generates heat at the constant rate $\bar{q}$ when it is operating. The amplifier's thermal conductivity to the ambient due to convection is K with the fan off and $2K$ with it on. The ambient temperature is θ_a, and the temperature of the amplifier is θ_1.

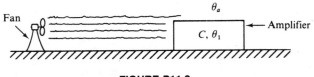

FIGURE P11.8

a) Verify that, with the fan off, the differential equation obeyed by θ_1 is

$$\dot{\theta}_1 + \frac{K}{C}\theta_1 = \frac{1}{C}(K\theta_a + \bar{q})$$

and that when the fan is on, the equation is

$$\dot{\theta}_1 + \frac{2K}{C}\theta_1 = \frac{1}{C}(2K\theta_a + \bar{q})$$

b) Solve for and sketch θ_1 when the system undergoes the following sequence of operations. In each case, indicate the steady-state temperature and the time constant.

(i) With $\theta_1(t_1) = \theta_a$ and the fan off, the amplifier is turned on at $t = t_1$.

(ii) After the system reaches steady-state conditions, the fan is turned on at $t = t_2$.

(iii) After the system reaches steady-state conditions, the amplifier is turned off at $t = t_3$ with the fan running.

c) Show how the response for $t > t_3$ in part (b) is affected when the fan also is turned off at $t = t_3$.

* 11.9 Figure P11.9 shows a piece of hot metal that has been immersed in a water bath to cool it. We can develop a simplified model by assuming that the temperatures of the metal and water, denoted by θ_m and θ_w, respectively, are uniform and that the rate of heat loss from the metal is proportional to the temperature difference $\theta_m - \theta_w$. The thermal capacitances are C_m and C_w, and the thermal resistance is R. We can neglect initially any heat lost to the environment at the surface.

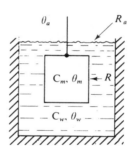

FIGURE P11.9

a) Verify that the mathematical model of the system subject to these assumptions can be written as

$$\dot{\theta}_m = \frac{1}{RC_m}(-\theta_m + \theta_w)$$

$$\dot{\theta}_w = \frac{1}{RC_w}(\theta_m - \theta_w)$$

b) Taking the initial metal temperature and water temperature as $\theta_m(0)$ and $\theta_w(0)$, respectively, solve for and sketch θ_m versus t and θ_w versus t.

c) Modify your answer to part (a) to allow for heat flow from the water to the environment. Denote the ambient temperature by θ_a and the thermal resistance between the water and the environment by R_a.

11.10 A heat exchanger in a chemical process uses steam to heat a liquid flowing in a pipe. We can apply an approximate linear model to relate changes in the temperature of the liquid leaving the heat exchanger to changes in the rate of steam flow. This model is given by the transfer function

$$\frac{\hat{\Theta}(s)}{\hat{W}(s)} = \frac{A\epsilon^{-sT_d}}{(\tau_1 s + 1)(\tau_2 s + 1)}$$

where $\hat{\Theta}(s)$ and $\hat{W}(s)$ are the Laplace transforms of the incremental outlet temperature and the incremental steam flow rate, respectively. We can determine the coefficient A, the time delay T_d, and the time constants τ_1 and τ_2 experimentally by recording the response to a step change in the steam flow rate with all other process conditions held constant. For parameter values $A = 0.5$ K·s/kg, $T_d = 20$ s, $\tau_1 = 15$ s, and $\tau_2 = 150$ s, evaluate and sketch the following:

  a) The response to a step in $\hat{w}(t)$ of 20 kg/s
  b) The unit impulse response $h(t)$
  c) The magnitude of the frequency response $H(j\omega)$ versus ω

* 11.11 Write the state-variable equations, using relative temperatures with respect to the ambient temperature, for a three-capacitance model of the insulated bar considered in Examples 11.5 and 11.6. Use three equal capacitances of value $C/3$ and three equal resistances of value $R/3$. Find the characteristic polynomial in terms of the parameter RC.

11.12 Repeat Problem 11.11, using nonuniform lengths for the three lumped segments of the bar. Specifically, take segments of length $0.2L$, $0.3L$, and $0.5L$, from left to right, where L is the length of the bar. Explain why such an approximation should yield greater accuracy than the equal-segment approximation of Problem 11.11.

11.13 a) Solve part (a) and part (b) of Problem 11.9 in numerical form for the following parameter values and initial conditions. The parameter values are

  Metal mass = 50 kg
  Metal specific heat = 460 J/(kg·K)
  Liquid volume = 0.15 m^3
  Liquid density = 1000 kg/m^3
  Liquid specific heat = 4186 J/(kg·K)
  Thermal resistance between the metal and the liquid = 10^{-3} s·K/J
  Thermal resistance between the liquid and the environment = 10^{-2} s·K/J
The initial conditions are
  Initial metal temperature = 750 K
  Initial liquid temperature = 320 K
  Ambient temperature = 300 K

  b) Do part (c) of Problem 11.9 and solve for θ_m. Sketch θ_m versus t and show qualitatively the shape of the curve for θ_w.

11.14 Using a digital computer, simulate the response of the insulated bar considered in Examples 11.5 and 11.6 by using N elements of equal length, as shown in Figure P11.14. Normalize the model by taking $RC = 1$ and finding the response to $\hat{\theta}_i(t) = U(t)$, where the initial relative temperature of each element is taken as zero.

  a) Use $N = 3$ and plot θ_a, θ_b, and θ_c versus time.

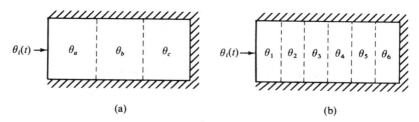

(a) (b)

FIGURE P11.14

b) Use $N = 6$ and plot the temperatures

$$\theta_a^* = 0.5(\theta_1 + \theta_2)$$

$$\theta_b^* = 0.5(\theta_3 + \theta_4)$$

$$\theta_c^* = 0.5(\theta_5 + \theta_6)$$

Compare the results for the two cases and comment on the difference.

11.15 The temperature of a uniform bar is analyzed in Example 11.5 and Example 11.6, and extensions of the analysis are proposed in Problems 11.11 and 11.12. For each of the following lumped models, using relative temperatures with respect to the ambient temperature, write the state-variable equations in matrix form and write an output equation for the average temperature of the bar.

    a) The two-capacitance model with uniform segment lengths analyzed in Example 11.6

    b) The three-capacitance model with uniform segment lengths described in Problem 11.11

    c) The three-capacitance model with nonuniform segment lengths described in Problem 11.12

HYDRAULIC SYSTEMS

A hydraulic system is one in which liquids, generally considered incompressible, flow. Hydraulic systems commonly appear in chemical processes, automatic control systems, and actuators and drive motors for manufacturing equipment. Such systems are usually interconnected to mechanical systems through pumps, valves, and movable pistons. A turbine driven by water and used for driving an electric generator is an example of a system with interacting hydraulic, mechanical, and electrical elements. We will not discuss here the more general topic of fluid systems, which would include compressible fluids such as gases and air.

An exact analysis of hydraulic systems is usually not feasible because of their distributed nature and the nonlinear character of the resistance to flow. For our dynamic analysis, however, we can obtain satisfactory results by using lumped elements and linearizing the resulting nonlinear mathematical models. On the other hand, the design of chemical processes requires a more exact analysis wherein static, rather than dynamic, models are used.

In most cases, hydraulic systems operate with the variables remaining close to a specific operating point. Thus we are generally interested in models involving incremental variables. This fact is particularly helpful because such models are usually linear, although the model in terms of the total variables may be quite nonlinear.

In the next two sections, we shall define the variables to be used and introduce and illustrate the element laws. Then we will present a variety of examples to demonstrate the modeling process and the application of the analytical techniques discussed in previous chapters, including Laplace transforms and transfer functions.

454

12.1 VARIABLES

Because hydraulic systems involve the flow and accumulation of liquid, the variables used to describe their dynamic behavior are

w, flow rate in cubic meters per second (m³/s)

v, volume in cubic meters (m³)

h, liquid height in meters (m)

p, pressure in newtons per square meter (N/m²)

Unless otherwise noted, a pressure will be the **absolute pressure**. In addition, we shall sometimes find it convenient to express pressures in terms of gauge pressures. A **gauge pressure**, denoted by p^*, is defined to be the difference between the absolute pressure and the atmospheric pressure p_a:

$$p^*(t) = p(t) - p_a \tag{1}$$

A pressure difference, denoted by Δp, is the difference between the pressures at two points.

12.2 ELEMENT LAWS

Hydraulic systems exhibit three types of characteristics that can be approximated by lumped elements: capacity, resistance to flow, and inertance. In this section we shall discuss the first two. The inertance, which accounts for the kinetic energy of a moving fluid stream, is usually negligible, and we will not consider it. A brief discussion of centrifugal pumps that act as hydraulic sources appears at the end of this section.

Capacitance

When liquid is stored in an open vessel, there is an algebraic relationship between the volume of the liquid and the pressure at the base of the vessel. If the cross-sectional area of the vessel is given by the function $A(h)$, where h is the height of the liquid level above the bottom of the vessel, then the liquid volume v is the integral of the area from the base of the vessel to the top of the liquid. Hence,

$$v = \int_0^h A(\lambda)d\lambda \tag{2}$$

where λ is a dummy variable of integration. For a liquid of density ρ expressed in kilograms per cubic meter, the absolute pressure p and the liquid height h are related by

$$p = \rho gh + p_a \tag{3}$$

where g is the gravitational constant (9.807 m/s^2) and where p_a is the atmospheric pressure, which is taken as 1.013×10^5 N/m^2.

Equations (2) and (3) imply that for any vessel geometry, liquid density, and atmospheric pressure, there is a unique algebraic relationship between the pressure p and the liquid volume v. A typical characteristic curve describing this relationship is shown in Figure 12.1(a).

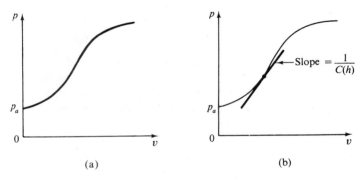

(a)   (b)

FIGURE 12.1 Pressure versus liquid volume for a vessel with variable cross-sectional area $A(h)$.

If the tangent to the pressure-versus-volume curve is drawn at some point, as shown in Figure 12.1(b), then the reciprocal of the slope is defined to be the **hydraulic capacitance**, denoted by $C(h)$. As indicated by the h in parentheses, the capacitance depends on the point on the curve being considered and hence on the liquid height h. Now

$$C(h) = \frac{1}{\dfrac{dp}{dv}} = \frac{dv}{dp}$$

and, from the chain rule of differentiation,

$$C(h) = \frac{dv}{dh}\frac{dh}{dp}$$

We see that $dv/dh = A(h)$ from (2) and that $dh/dp = 1/\rho g$ from (3). Thus for a vessel of arbitrary shape,

$$C(h) = \frac{A(h)}{\rho g} \tag{4}$$

which has units of m$^4 \cdot$s^2/kg or, equivalently, m^5/N.

For a vessel with constant cross-sectional area A, (2) reduces to $v = Ah$. We can substitute the height $h = v/A$ into (3) to obtain the pressure in terms of the volume:

$$p = \frac{\rho g}{A}v + p_a \tag{5}$$

Equation (5) yields a linear plot of pressure versus volume, as shown in Figure 12.2. The slope of the line is the reciprocal of the capacitance C, where

$$C = \frac{A}{\rho g} \tag{6}$$

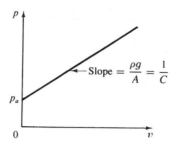

FIGURE 12.2 Pressure versus liquid volume for a vessel with constant A.

The volume of liquid in a vessel at any instant is the integral of the net flow rate into the vessel plus the initial volume. Hence we can write

$$v(t) = v(0) + \int_0^t [w_{\text{in}}(\lambda) - w_{\text{out}}(\lambda)]d\lambda$$

which can be differentiated to give the alternative form

$$\dot{v} = w_{\text{in}}(t) - w_{\text{out}}(t) \tag{7}$$

To obtain expressions for the time derivatives of the pressure p and the liquid height h that are valid for vessels with variable cross-sectional areas, we use the chain rule of differentiation to write

$$\frac{dv}{dt} = \frac{dv}{dh}\frac{dh}{dt}$$

where dv/dt is given by (7) and where $dv/dh = A(h)$. Thus the rate of change of the liquid height depends on the net flow rate according to

$$\dot{h} = \frac{1}{A(h)}[w_{\text{in}}(t) - w_{\text{out}}(t)] \tag{8}$$

Alternatively, we can write dv/dt as

$$\frac{dv}{dt} = \frac{dv}{dp}\frac{dp}{dt}$$

where $dv/dp = C(h)$. Hence the rate of change of the pressure at the base of the vessel is

$$\dot{p} = \frac{1}{C(h)}[w_{\text{in}}(t) - w_{\text{out}}(t)] \tag{9}$$

where $C(h)$ is given by (4).

Because any of the variables v, h, and p can be used as a measure of the amount of liquid in a vessel, we generally select one of them as a state variable. Then (7), (8), or (9) will yield the corresponding state-variable equation when w_{in} and w_{out} are expressed in terms of the state variables and inputs.

If the cross-sectional area of the vessel is variable, then the coefficient $A(h)$ in (8) will be a function of h, and the system model will be nonlinear. To develop a linearized model, we must find the operating point, define the incremental variables, and retain the first two terms in the Taylor-series expansion. Likewise, the term $C(h)$ in (9) will cause the differential equation to be nonlinear because the capacitance varies with h, which in turn is a function of the pressure.

▶ *EXAMPLE 12.1*

Consider a vessel formed by a circular cylinder of radius R and length L that contains a liquid of density ρ in units of kilograms per cubic meter. Find the hydraulic capacitance of the vessel when the cylinder is vertical, as shown in Figure 12.3(a). Then evaluate the capacitance when the cylinder is on its side, as shown in Figure 12.3(b).

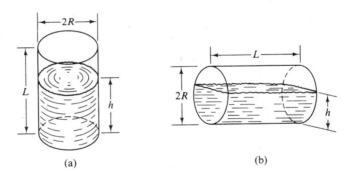

    (a)   (b)

FIGURE 12.3 Cylindrical vessel for Example 12.1. (a) Cylinder vertical. (b) Cylinder horizontal.

Solution

For the configuration shown in Figure 12.3(a), the cross-sectional area is πR^2 and so is independent of the liquid height. Thus we can use (6), and the vessel's hydraulic capacitance is $C_a = \pi R^2/\rho g$.

When the vessel is on its side, as shown in Figure 12.3(b), the cross-sectional area is a function of the liquid height h. You can verify that the width of the liquid surface is $2\sqrt{R^2 - (R - h)^2}$, which is zero when $h = 0$ and $h = 2R$ and which has a maximum value of $2R$ when $h = R$. Using

(4), we find that the capacitance is

$$C_b = \frac{2L}{\rho g}\sqrt{R^2 - (R - h)^2}$$

which is shown in Figure 12.4.

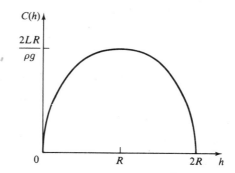

FIGURE 12.4 Capacitance of the vessel shown in Figure 12.3(b).

Resistance

As liquid flows through a pipe, there is a drop in the pressure of the liquid over the length of pipe. There is likewise a pressure drop if the liquid flows through a valve or through an orifice. The change in pressure associated with a flowing liquid results from the dissipation of energy and usually obeys a nonlinear algebraic relationship between the flow rate w and the pressure difference Δp. The symbol for a valve is shown in Figure 12.5; it can also be used for other energy-dissipating elements. A positive value of w indicates that liquid is flowing in the direction of the arrow; a positive value of Δp indicates that the pressure at the end marked $+$ is higher than the pressure at the other end. The expression

$$w = k\sqrt{\Delta p} \tag{10}$$

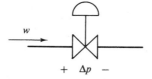

FIGURE 12.5 Symbol for a hydraulic valve.

describes an orifice and a valve and is a good approximation for turbulent flow through pipes. We can treat all situations of interest to us by using a nonlinear element law of the form of (10). In this equation, k is a constant that depends on the characteristics of the pipe, valve, or orifice. A typical curve of flow rate versus pressure difference is shown in Figure 12.6(a).

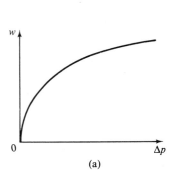 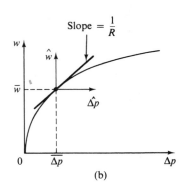

(a)   (b)

FIGURE 12.6   (a) Flow rate versus pressure difference given by (10). (b) Geometric interpretation of hydraulic resistance.

— steady state
↳ changing

Because (10) is a nonlinear relationship, we must linearize it about an operating point in order to develop a linear model of a hydraulic system. If we draw the tangent to the curve of w versus Δp at the operating point, the reciprocal of its slope is defined to be the **hydraulic resistance** R. Figure 12.6(b) illustrates the geometric interpretation of the resistance, which has units of newton-seconds per meter^5.

Expanding (10) in a Taylor series about the operating point gives

$$w = \overline{w} + \frac{dw}{d\,\Delta p}\bigg|_{\overline{\Delta p}} (\Delta p - \overline{\Delta p}) + \cdots$$

The incremental variables $\hat{w}$ and $\widehat{\Delta p}$ are defined by

$P = \hat{P} + \overline{P}$

$$\hat{w} = w - \overline{w} \tag{11a}$$

$$\widehat{\Delta p} = \Delta p - \overline{\Delta p} \tag{11b}$$

and the second- and higher-order terms in the expansion are dropped. Thus the incremental model becomes

$$\hat{w} = \frac{1}{R}\widehat{\Delta p} \tag{12}$$

where

$$\frac{1}{R} = \frac{dw}{d\,\Delta p}\bigg|_{\overline{\Delta p}}$$

We can express the resistance R in terms of either $\overline{\Delta p}$ or $\overline{w}$ by carrying out the required differentiation using (10). Specifically,

$$\frac{1}{R} = \frac{d}{d\,\Delta p}(k\,\Delta p^{1/2})\Big|_{\overline{\Delta p}}$$

$$= \frac{k}{2\sqrt{\overline{\Delta p}}}$$

so

$$R = \frac{2\sqrt{\overline{\Delta p}}}{k} \qquad (13)$$

To express the resistance in terms of $\overline{w}$, we note from (10) that

$$\overline{w} = k\sqrt{\overline{\Delta p}} \qquad (14)$$

Substituting (14) into (13) gives the alternative equation for the hydraulic resistance as

$$R = \frac{2\overline{w}}{k^2} \qquad (15)$$

Because liquids typically flow through networks composed of pipes, valves, and orifices, we must often combine several relationships of the form of (10) into a single equivalent expression. We use linearized models in much of our analysis of hydraulic systems, so it is important to develop rules for combining the resistances of linearized elements that occur in series and parallel combinations. In the following example, we consider the relationship of flow versus pressure difference and the equivalent resistance for two valves in series. The parallel-flow situation is treated in one of the end-of-chapter problems.

▶ **EXAMPLE 12.2**

Figure 12.7(a) shows a series combination of two valves through which liquid flows at a rate of w and across which the pressure difference is Δp. An equivalent valve is shown in Figure 12.7(b). The two valves obey

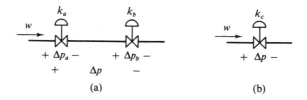

FIGURE 12.7   (a) Two valves in series. (b) Equivalent valve.

the relationships $w = k_a\sqrt{\Delta p_a}$ and $w = k_b\sqrt{\Delta p_b}$, respectively. Find the coefficient k_c of an equivalent valve that obeys the relationship $w = k_c\sqrt{\Delta p}$. Also evaluate the resistance R_c of the series combination in terms of the individual resistances R_a and R_b.

Solution

Because the two valves are connected in series, they have the same flow rate w, and the total pressure difference is $\Delta p = \Delta p_a + \Delta p_b$. To determine k_c, we write Δp in terms of w as

$$\Delta p = \Delta p_a + \Delta p_b = \left(\frac{1}{k_a^2} + \frac{1}{k_b^2} \right) w^2$$

and then solve for w in terms of Δp. After some manipulations, we find that

$$w = \left(\frac{k_a k_b}{\sqrt{k_a^2 + k_b^2}} \right) \sqrt{\Delta p} \tag{16}$$

Comparing (16) with (10) reveals that the equivalent valve constant is

$$k_c = \frac{k_a k_b}{\sqrt{k_a^2 + k_b^2}} \tag{17}$$

Using (15) for the resistance of the linearized model of the equivalent valve, we can write

$$R_c = \frac{2\overline{w}}{k_c^2} = 2\overline{w} \left(\frac{1}{k_a^2} + \frac{1}{k_b^2} \right) \tag{18}$$

However, by applying (15) to the individual valves, we see that their resistances are $R_a = 2\overline{w}/k_a^2$ and $R_b = 2\overline{w}/k_b^2$, respectively. Using these expressions for R_a and R_b, we can rewrite (18) as

$$R_c = R_a + R_b \tag{19}$$

which is identical to the result for a linear electrical circuit.

Sources

In most hydraulic systems, the source of energy is a pump that derives its power from an electric motor. Here we shall consider the centrifugal pump driven at a constant speed, which is widely used in chemical processes. The symbolic representation of a pump is shown in Figure 12.8. Typical input–output relationships for a centrifugal pump being driven at three different constant speeds are shown in Figure 12.9(a). Pump curves of Δp versus w

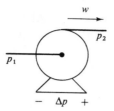

FIGURE 12.8 Symbolic representation of a pump.

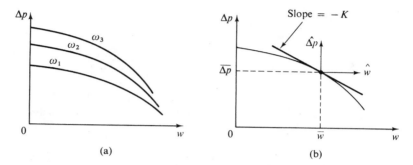

FIGURE 12.9 Typical centrifugal pump curves where $\Delta p = p_2 - p_1$. (a) For three different pump speeds ($\omega_1 < \omega_2 < \omega_3$). (b) Showing the linear approximation.

are determined experimentally under steady-state conditions and are quite nonlinear. To include a pump being driven at constant speed in a linear dynamic model, we first determine the operating point for the particular pump speed by calculating the values of $\overline{\Delta p}$ and $\overline{w}$. Then we find the slope of the tangent to the pump curve at the operating point and define it to be $-K$, which has units of newton-seconds per meter[5]. Having done this, we can express the incremental pressure difference $\widehat{\Delta p}$ in terms of the incremental flow rate $\hat{w}$ as

$$\widehat{\Delta p} = -K\hat{w} \tag{20}$$

where the constant K is always positive. Solving (20) for $\hat{w}$ yields

$$\hat{w} = -\frac{1}{K}\widehat{\Delta p} \tag{21}$$

Figure 12.9(b) illustrates the relationship of the linearized approximation to the nonlinear pump curve.

We can write the Taylor-series expansion for a pump driven at a constant speed as

$$w = \overline{w} + \frac{dw}{d\,\Delta p}\bigg|_{\overline{\Delta p}} (\Delta p - \overline{\Delta p}) + \cdots$$

where the coefficient $(dw/d\,\Delta p)|_{\overline{\Delta p}}$ is the slope of the tangent to the curve of w versus Δp, measured at the operating point, and has the value $-1/K$. By dropping the second- and higher-order terms in the expansion and using the incremental variables $\hat{w}$ versus $\widehat{\Delta p}$, we obtain the linear relationship (21).

The manner in which a constant-speed pump can be incorporated into the dynamic model of a hydraulic system is illustrated in Example 12.4 in the following section. References in Appendix D contain more comprehensive discussions of pumps and their models, including ones where variations in the pump speed are significant.

■ 12.3 DYNAMIC MODELS OF HYDRAULIC SYSTEMS

In this section, we apply the element laws presented in Section 12.2 and use many of the analytical techniques from previous chapters. We will develop and analyze dynamic models for a single vessel with a valve; a combination of a pump, vessel, and valve; and finally two vessels with two valves and a pump. In each case, we will derive the nonlinear model and then develop and analyze a linearized model.

▶ *EXAMPLE 12.3*

Figure 12.10 shows a vessel that receives liquid at a flow rate $w_i(t)$ and loses liquid through a valve that obeys the nonlinear flow-pressure relationship $w_o = k\sqrt{p_1 - p_a}$. The cross-sectional area is A and the liquid density is ρ. Derive the nonlinear model obeyed by the absolute pressure p_1 at the bottom of the vessel. Then develop the linearized version that is valid in the vicinity of the operating point, and find the transfer function relating the transforms of the incremental input $\hat{w}_i(t)$ and the incremental pressure $\hat{p}_1$.

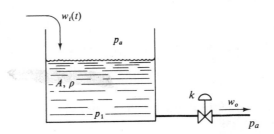

FIGURE 12.10 Hydraulic system for Example 12.3.

Having developed the system models in literal form, determine in numerical form the operating point, the transfer function, and the response to a

10% step-function increase in the input flow rate for the following parameter values:

$$A = 2 \text{ m}^2$$

$$\rho = 1000 \text{ kg/m}^3$$

$$k = 5.0 \times 10^{-5} \text{ m}^4/\text{s} \cdot N^{1/2}$$

$$\overline{w}_i = 6.0 \times 10^{-3} \text{ m}^3/\text{s}$$

$$p_a = 1.013 \times 10^5 \text{ N/m}^2$$

Solution

Taking the pressure p_1 as the single state variable, we use (9), with $C(h)$ replaced by the constant $C = A/\rho g$, to write

$$\dot{p} = \frac{1}{C}[w_{in}(t) - w_{out}(t)] \tag{22}$$

where

$$w_{in}(t) = w_i(t) \tag{23a}$$

$$w_{out}(t) = k\sqrt{p_1 - p_a} \tag{23b}$$

Substituting (23) into (22) gives the nonlinear system model as

$$\dot{p} = \frac{1}{C}[-k\sqrt{p_1 - p_a} + w_i(t)] \tag{24}$$

To develop a linearized model, we rewrite (24) in terms of the incremental variables $\hat{p}_1 = p_1 - \overline{p}_1$ and $\hat{w}_i(t) = w_i(t) - \overline{w}_i$. The nominal values $\overline{p}_1$ and $\overline{w}_i$ must satisfy the algebraic equation

$$k\sqrt{\overline{p}_1 - p_a} = \overline{w}_i$$

or

$$\overline{p}_1 = p_a + \frac{1}{k^2}\overline{w}_i^2 \tag{25}$$

which corresponds to an outflow rate equal to the inflow rate, resulting in a constant liquid level and pressure. The nominal height of the liquid is

$$\overline{h} = \frac{(\overline{p}_1 - p_a)}{\rho g} \tag{26}$$

Making the appropriate substitutions into (24) and using (12) with (15) for the linearized valve equation, we obtain

$$\dot{\hat{p}}_1 + \frac{1}{RC}\hat{p}_1 = \frac{1}{C}\hat{w}_i(t) \tag{27}$$

$R = \frac{2\overline{w_q}}{H}$ $C = \frac{A}{\rho g}$

$\frac{\hat{p}_1(s)}{w_i(s)} = \frac{1/C}{s + 1/RC}$

where $R = 2\overline{w}_i/k^2$. Transforming (27) with $\hat{p}_1(0) = 0$, which corresponds to $p_1(0) = \overline{p}_1$, we find that the system's transfer function $H(s) = \hat{P}_1(s)/\hat{W}_i(s)$ is

$$H(s) = \frac{\dfrac{1}{C}}{s + \dfrac{1}{RC}} \tag{28}$$

which has a single pole at $s = -1/RC$.

For the parameter values specified, the operating point given by (25) reduces to

$$\overline{p}_1 = 1.013 \times 10^5 + \left(\frac{6.0 \times 10^{-3}}{5.0 \times 10^{-5}}\right)^2 = 1.157 \times 10^5 \text{ N/m}^2$$

and from (26), the nominal liquid height is

$$\overline{h} = \frac{1.440 \times 10^4}{1000 \times 9.807} = 1.468 \text{ m}$$

The numerical values of the hydraulic resistance and capacitance are, respectively,

$$R = \frac{2 \times 6.0 \times 10^{-3}}{(5.0 \times 10^{-5})^2} = 4.80 \times 10^6 \text{ N} \cdot \text{s/m}^5$$

$$C = \frac{2.0}{1000 \times 9.807} = 2.039 \times 10^{-4} \text{ m}^5/\text{N}$$

Substituting these values of R and C into (28), we obtain the numerical form of the transfer function as

$$H(s) = \frac{4904.}{s + 1.0216 \times 10^{-3}} \tag{29}$$

If $w_i(t)$ is originally equal to its nominal value of $\overline{w}_i = 6.0 \times 10^{-3}$ m^3/s and undergoes a 10% step-function increase, then $\hat{w}_i(t) = [0.60 \times 10^{-3}]U(t)$ m^3/s and $\hat{W}_i(s) = 0.60 \times 10^{-3}$ (1/s). Thus

$$\hat{P}_1(s) = \frac{4904. \times 0.60 \times 10^{-3}}{s(s + 1.0216 \times 10^{-3})}$$

$$= \frac{2.942}{s(s + 1.0216 \times 10^{-3})}$$

From the final-value theorem, the steady-state value of $\hat{p}_1$ is $s\hat{P}_1(s)$ evaluated at $s = 0$, namely

$$\lim_{t \to \infty} \hat{p}_1(t) = \frac{2.942}{1.0216 \times 10^{-3}} = 2880. \text{ N/m}^2$$

The time constant of the linearized model is $\tau = RC$, which becomes

$$\tau = (4.80 \times 10^6)(2.039 \times 10^{-4})$$

$$= 978.7 \text{ s}$$

which is slightly over 16 minutes. Thus the response of the incremental pressure is

$$\hat{p}_1 = 2880.(1 - \epsilon^{-t/978.7})$$

The change in the incremental level is $\hat{p}_1/\rho g$, which becomes

$$\hat{h} = 0.2937(1 - \epsilon^{-t/978.7})$$

To obtain the responses of the actual pressure and liquid level, we merely add the nominal values $\overline{p}_1 = 1.157 \times 10^5$ N/m^2 and $\overline{h} = 1.468$ m to these incremental variables. It is interesting to note that because of the nonlinear valve, the 10% increase in the flow rate results in a 20% increase in both the gauge pressure $p_1 - p_a$ and the height h.

▶ **EXAMPLE 12.4**

Find the linearized model of the hydraulic system shown in Figure 12.11(a), which consists of a constant-speed centrifugal pump feeding a vessel from which liquid flows through a pipe and valve obeying the relationship $w_o = k\sqrt{p_1 - p_a}$. The pump characteristic for the specified pump speed $\overline{\omega}$ is shown in Figure 12.11(b).

Solution

The equilibrium condition for the system corresponds to

$$\overline{w}_i = \overline{w}_o \tag{30}$$

where $\overline{w}_i$ and $\overline{\Delta p} = \overline{p}_1 - p_a$ must be one of the points on the pump curve in Figure 12.11(b), and where $\overline{w}_o$ obeys the nonlinear flow relationship

$$\overline{w}_o = k\sqrt{\overline{\Delta p}} \tag{31}$$

To determine the operating point, we find the solution to (30) graphically by plotting the valve characteristic (31) on the pump curve. Doing this gives Figure 12.12(a), where the operating point is the intersection of the valve curve and the pump curve, designated as point A in the figure. Once we have located the operating point, we can draw the tangent to the pump curve as shown in Figure 12.12(b) and determine its slope $-K$ graphically.

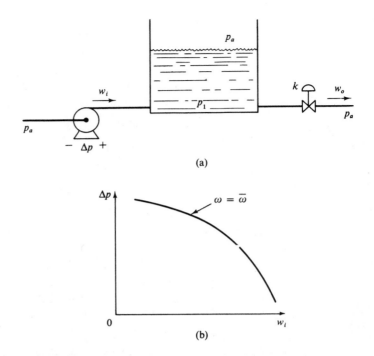

(a)

(b)

FIGURE 12.11 (a) System for Example 12.4. (b) Pump curve.

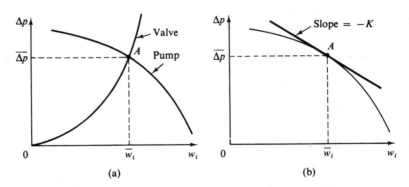

(a)   (b)

FIGURE 12.12 (a) Combined pump and valve curves for Example 12.4.
(b) Pump curve with linear approximation.

Following this preliminary step, we can use (9) to write the model of
the system as

$$\dot{p}_1 = \frac{1}{C}(w_i - w_o) \tag{32}$$

where, from (12), the approximate flow rate through the valve is

$$w_o = \overline{w}_o + \frac{1}{R}\widehat{\Delta p} \tag{33}$$

and where, from (21), the approximate flow rate through the pump is

$$w_i = \overline{w}_i - \frac{1}{K}\widehat{\Delta p} \tag{34}$$

Substituting (33) and (34) into (32), using $\dot{p}_1 = \dot{\hat{p}}_1$ and (30), and noting that $\widehat{\Delta p} = \hat{p}_1$ because p_a is constant, we find the incremental model to be

$$\dot{\hat{p}}_1 = \frac{1}{C}\left(-\frac{1}{K} - \frac{1}{R}\right)\hat{p}_1$$

which we can write as the homogeneous first-order differential equation

$$\dot{\hat{p}}_1 + \frac{1}{C}\left(\frac{1}{K} + \frac{1}{R}\right)\hat{p}_1 = 0 \tag{35}$$

Inspection of (35) indicates that the magnitude of the slope of the pump curve at the operating point enters the equation in exactly the same manner as the resistance associated with the valve. Hence, if we evaluate the equivalent resistance R_{eq} according to

$$R_{eq} = \frac{RK}{R + K}$$

(35) is the same as (27), which was derived for a vessel and a single valve, except for the absence of an input flow rate.

▶ *EXAMPLE 12.5*

The valves in the hydraulic system shown in Figure 12.13 obey the flow-pressure relationships $w_1 = k_1\sqrt{p_1 - p_2}$ and $w_2 = k_2\sqrt{p_2 - p_a}$. The atmospheric pressure is p_a, and the capacitances of the vessels are C_1 and C_2. Find the equations that determine the operating point, and show how the pump curve is used to solve them. Derive a linearized model that is valid about the operating point.

Solution

Because the pump and the two vessels are in series at equilibrium conditions, we define the operating point by equating the three flow rates $\overline{w}_p$, $\overline{w}_1$, and

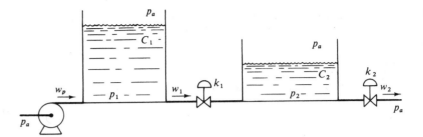

FIGURE 12.13   Hydraulic system with two vessels considered in Example 12.5.

$\overline{w}_2$. The flow rates through the two valves are given by

$$\overline{w}_1 = k_1\sqrt{\overline{p}_1 - \overline{p}_2} \tag{36a}$$

$$\overline{w}_2 = k_2\sqrt{\overline{p}_2 - p_a} \tag{36b}$$

The flow rate $\overline{w}_p$ through the pump and the pressure difference $\overline{\Delta p}_1 = \overline{p}_1 - p_a$ must correspond to a point on the pump curve. Equations (36a) and (36b) are those of two valves in series, and, as shown in Example 12.2, we can replace such a combination of valves by an equivalent valve specified by (16). Hence

$$\overline{w}_p = k_{eq}\sqrt{\overline{\Delta p}_1} \tag{37}$$

where, from (17),

$$k_{eq} = \frac{k_1 k_2}{\sqrt{k_1^2 + k_2^2}}$$

Plotting (37) on the pump curve as shown in Figure 12.12(a) yields the values of $\overline{\Delta p}_1$ and $\overline{w}_p$, from which we can find the other nominal values.

With this information, we can develop the incremental model. Using (9), (12), and (21), we can write the pair of linear differential equations

$$\dot{\hat{p}}_1 = \frac{1}{C_1}\left[-\frac{1}{K}\hat{p}_1 - \frac{1}{R_1}(\hat{p}_1 - \hat{p}_2)\right]$$

$$\dot{\hat{p}}_2 = \frac{1}{C_2}\left[\frac{1}{R_1}(\hat{p}_1 - \hat{p}_2) - \frac{1}{R_2}\hat{p}_2\right] \tag{38}$$

where the valve resistances are given by $R_1 = 2\overline{w}_1/k_1^2$ and $R_2 = 2\overline{w}_2/k_2^2$, and where $-K$ is the slope of the pump curve at the operating point. As indicated by (38), the incremental model has no inputs and hence can respond only to nonzero initial conditions—that is, $\hat{p}_1(0) \neq 0$ and/or $\hat{p}_2(0) \neq 0$.

In practice, there might be additional liquid streams entering either vessel, or the pump speed might be changed. It is also possible for either of the two valves to be opened or closed slightly. Such a change would modify the respective hydraulic resistance.

In the absence of an input, we can transform (38) to find the Laplace transform of the zero-input response. Doing this, we find that after rearranging,

$$\left[C_1 s + \left(\frac{1}{K} + \frac{1}{R_1} \right) \right] \hat{P}_1(s) = \frac{1}{R_1} \hat{P}_2(s) + C_1 \hat{p}_1(0) \qquad (39a)$$

$$\left[C_2 s + \left(\frac{1}{R_1} + \frac{1}{R_2} \right) \right] \hat{P}_2(s) = \frac{1}{R_1} \hat{P}_1(s) + C_2 \hat{p}_2(0) \qquad (39b)$$

We can find either $\hat{P}_1(s)$ or $\hat{P}_2(s)$ by combining these two equations into a single transform equation. The corresponding inverse transform will yield the zero-input response in terms of $\hat{p}_1(0)$ and $\hat{p}_2(0)$. The denominator of either $\hat{P}_1(s)$ or $\hat{P}_2(s)$ will be the characteristic polynomial of the system, which, as you may verify, is

$$s^2 + \left[\frac{1}{C_1} \left(\frac{1}{K} + \frac{1}{R_1} \right) + \frac{1}{C_2} \left(\frac{1}{R_1} + \frac{1}{R_2} \right) \right] s + \frac{1}{C_1 C_2} \left(\frac{1}{K R_1} + \frac{1}{K R_2} + \frac{1}{R_1 R_2} \right)$$

SUMMARY

The basic variables in a hydraulic system are flow rate and pressure. Other variables that are equivalent to the pressure at the bottom of a container are the volume of the liquid and the liquid height.

Because hydraulic systems are generally nonlinear, especially in the resistance to fluid flow, we developed linearized models valid in the vicinity of an operating point. We introduced the passive elements of hydraulic capacitance and hydraulic resistance in constructing such models. The former is associated with the potential energy of a fluid in a vessel, the latter with the energy dissipated when fluid flows through valves, orifices, and pipes. Another possible passive element is inertance, which is associated with the kinetic energy of fluids in motion. Because the inertance is normally negligible, we did not include it in our models.

A source may consist of a specified flow rate into a vessel. However, most practical hydraulic energy sources are mechanically driven pumps. We generally describe such pumps by a nonlinear relationship between pressure and flow rate, rather than specifying one of these two variables independently. This contrasts with the ideal force, velocity, voltage, and current sources used in earlier chapters. Because of the algebraic relationship between pressure and flow rate, a pump enters into the linearized system equations in a way somewhat similar to hydraulic resistance.

The pressure in each vessel (or else the volume or the liquid height) is normally chosen to be a state variable. The procedures for finding and solving hydraulic models, including state-variable equations and transfer functions, are generally the same as those used in the earlier chapters.

PROBLEMS

12.1 Figure P12.1 shows a conical vessel that has a circular cross section and contains a liquid. Evaluate and sketch the hydraulic capacitance as a function of the liquid height h. Also evaluate and sketch the gauge pressure $p^* = p - p_a$ at the base of the vessel as a function of the liquid volume v.

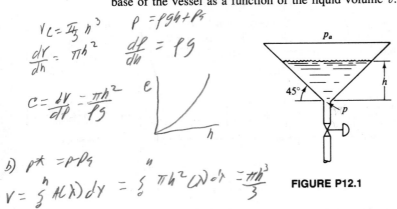

Handwritten annotations:

$$V_C = \frac{\pi}{3} h^3 \qquad p = \rho g h + p_a$$

$$\frac{dV}{dh} = \pi h^2 \qquad \frac{dp}{dh} = \rho g$$

$$C = \frac{dV}{dp} = \frac{\pi h^2}{\rho g} \qquad e$$

b) $p^* = p - p_a$

$$v = \int_0^h A(\lambda)\, d\lambda = \int_0^h \pi h^2 (\lambda)\, d\lambda = \frac{\pi h^3}{3}$$

$$h = \left(\frac{v \cdot 3}{\pi}\right)^{1/3}$$

$$p^* = \rho g \left(\frac{3v}{\pi}\right)^{1/3}$$

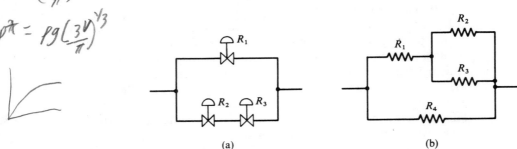

FIGURE P12.1

12.2 Find the equivalent hydraulic resistances for the linear models of hydraulic networks shown in Figure P12.2. Express your answers as single fractions.

(a)

(b)

FIGURE P12.2

12.3 Two valves that obey the relationships $w_a = k_a\sqrt{\Delta p}$ and $w_b = k_b\sqrt{\Delta p}$ are connected in parallel, as indicated in Figure P12.3.

  a) Determine the equivalent valve coefficient k_c in terms of k_a and k_b such that the total flow rate is given by $w = k_c\sqrt{\Delta p}$.

  b) Show that the hydraulic resistance of the equivalent linearized model is $R_c = 2\sqrt{\overline{\Delta p}}/k_c$, where $\overline{\Delta p}$ denotes the nominal pressure drop across the valves.

c) Show that $R_c = R_a R_b/(R_a + R_b)$, where R_a and R_b are the hydraulic resistances of the individual valves evaluated at the nominal pressure difference $\overline{\Delta p}$.

d) Assume curves for w_a versus Δp and w_b versus Δp, and sketch the corresponding curve for w_c. Indicate the linearized approximations at a typical value of $\overline{\Delta p}$.

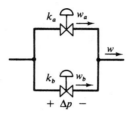

FIGURE P12.3

12.4 Consider the hydraulic system that was modeled in Example 12.3, consisting of a single vessel and a valve.

a) Obtain the linearized model in terms of the incremental pressure that is valid for the nominal flow rate $\overline{w}_i = 3.0 \times 10^{-3}$ m³/s, and evaluate the transfer function $\hat{P}_1(s)/\hat{W}_i(s)$. Also find $\overline{p}_1$.

b) Rewrite the model and transfer function you found in part (a) in terms of the incremental volume $\hat{v}$. Also find $\overline{v}$.

c) Solve for and sketch the incremental volume versus time when $\hat{w}_i(t) = 0.5 \times 10^{-3} U(t)$ m³/s and when the system starts at the nominal conditions found in part (a).

* 12.5 Write the state-variable equations for the system shown in Figure P12.5, using the incremental pressures $\hat{p}_1$ and $\hat{p}_2$ as state variables, where the pump obeys the relationship

$$w_p = \overline{w}_p - \frac{1}{K}(\hat{p}_2 - \hat{p}_1)$$

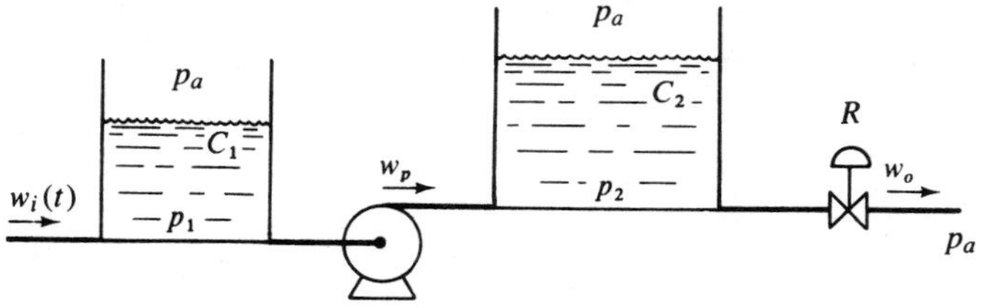

FIGURE P12.5

12.6 For the hydraulic system shown in Figure P12.6, the incremental input is $\hat{w}_i(t)$ and the incremental output is $\hat{w}_o$.

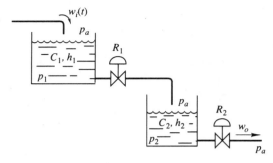

FIGURE P12.6

a) Verify that the following equations represent an appropriate state-variable model in terms of the incremental state variables $\hat{p}_1$ and $\hat{p}_2$.

$$\dot{\hat{p}}_1 = \frac{1}{C_1}\left[-\frac{1}{R_1}\hat{p}_1 + \hat{w}_i(t)\right]$$

$$\dot{\hat{p}}_2 = \frac{1}{C_2}\left[\frac{1}{R_1}\hat{p}_1 - \frac{1}{R_2}\hat{p}_2\right]$$

$$\hat{w}_o = \frac{1}{R_2}\hat{p}_2$$

b) Derive the system transfer function $\hat{W}_o(s)/\hat{W}_i(s)$.

c) Define the time constants $\tau_1 = R_1 C_1$ and $\tau_2 = R_2 C_2$, and evaluate the unit step response for the case $\tau_1 \neq \tau_2$. Sketch the response for the case where $\tau_1 = 2\tau_2$.

d) Evaluate the transfer function $\hat{H}_2(s)/\hat{W}_i(s)$ that relates the transform of $\hat{w}_i(t)$ to the transform of the incremental liquid height $\hat{h}t_2$.

* 12.7 The hydraulic system shown in Figure P12.7 has the incremental pressure $\hat{p}_i(t)$ as its input and the incremental flow rate $\hat{w}_o$ as its output.

a) Verify that the following equations represent an appropriate state-variable model in terms of the incremental state variables $\hat{p}_1$ and $\hat{p}_2$.

$$\dot{\hat{p}}_1 = -\frac{1}{R_3 C_1}\hat{p}_1 + \frac{1}{R_1 C_1}\hat{p}_i(t)$$

$$\dot{\hat{p}}_2 = \frac{1}{R_3 C_2}\hat{p}_1 - \frac{1}{R_4 C_2}\hat{p}_2 + \frac{1}{R_2 C_2}\hat{p}_i(t)$$

$$\hat{w}_o = \frac{1}{R_4}\hat{p}_2$$

b) Find the transfer function $\hat{W}_o(s)/\hat{P}_i(s)$.

c) Solve for the steady-state value of the unit step response.

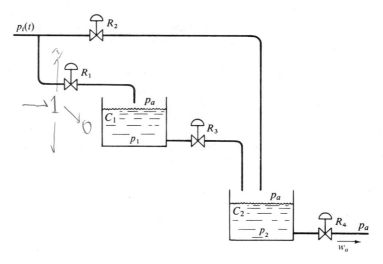

FIGURE P12.7

12.8 Figure P12.8 shows three identical tanks having capacitance C connected by identical lines having resistance R. An input stream flows into tank 1 at the incremental flow rate $\hat{w}_i(t)$, and an output stream flows from tank 3 at the incremental flow rate $\hat{w}_o(t)$.

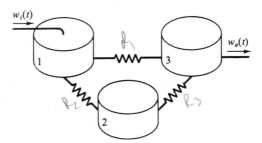

FIGURE P12.8

a) Verify that the following equations represent an appropriate state-variable model in terms of the incremental state variables $\hat{v}_1$, $\hat{v}_2$, and $\hat{v}_3$.

$$\dot{\hat{v}}_1 = -\frac{2}{RC}\hat{v}_1 + \frac{1}{RC}\hat{v}_2 + \frac{1}{RC}\hat{v}_3 + \hat{w}_i(t)$$

$$\dot{\hat{v}}_2 = \frac{1}{RC}\hat{v}_1 - \frac{2}{RC}\hat{v}_2 + \frac{1}{RC}\hat{v}_3$$

$$\dot{\hat{v}}_3 = \frac{1}{RC}\hat{v}_1 + \frac{1}{RC}\hat{v}_2 - \frac{2}{RC}\hat{v}_3 - \hat{w}_o(t)$$

b) Let $RC = 1$ and find $\hat{V}_2(s)$ in terms of $\hat{W}_1(s)$ and $\hat{W}_o(s)$ by transforming the three state-variable equations and eliminating $\hat{V}_1(s)$ and $\hat{V}_3(s)$.

c) Solve for $\hat{v}_2$ as a function of time when $\hat{w}_i(t) = U(t)$ and $\hat{w}_o(t) = 0$. Repeat the solution when $\hat{w}_i(t) = 0$ and $\hat{w}_o(t) = U(t)$. Sketch the responses.

12.9 The valve and pump characteristics for the hydraulic system shown in Figure P12.9(a) are plotted in Figure P12.9(b). Curves are given for the two pump speeds 100 rad/s and 150 rad/s. The cross-sectional area of the vessel is 2.0 m², and the liquid density is 1000 kg/m³.

a) Determine the steady-state flow rate, gauge pressure, and liquid height for each of the pump speeds for which curves are shown.

b) Derive the linearized models for each of the pump speeds in numerical form.

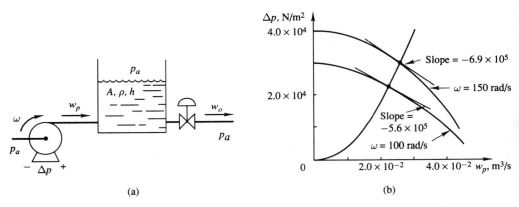

(a)   (b)

FIGURE P12.9

* 12.10 As shown in Figure P12.10(a), liquid can flow into a vessel through a pump and a valve. The assumed pump characteristic is shown in Figure P12.10(b), where α

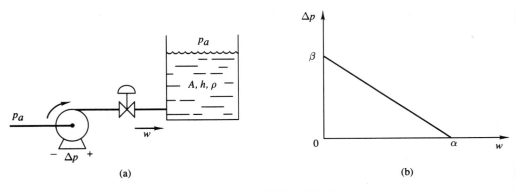

(a)   (b)

FIGURE P12.10

and β are the maximum flow rate and the maximum pressure difference, respectively. The valve is shut for all $t < 0$, is opened at $t = 0$, and presents no resistance to the flow of the liquid for $t > 0$.

a) Verify that the differential equation obeyed by the liquid height h after the valve is opened is

$$\dot{h} + \left(\frac{\alpha \rho g}{\beta A}\right) h = \frac{\alpha}{A}$$

b) Write expressions for the time constant and the steady-state height.

c) Solve for $h(t)$ and sketch it versus time.

12.11 Consider the hydraulic system described in Problem 12.10 with a pump having the nonlinear pressure-flow relationship shown in Figure P12.11.

a) Verify that the differential equation obeyed by the liquid height h after the valve is opened is

$$\dot{h} + \frac{\alpha}{A} \left(\frac{\rho g}{\beta}\right)^2 h^2 = \frac{\alpha}{A}$$

b) Using a digital computer and a nonlinear simulation language such as ACSL, plot $h(t)$ and $w(t)$ versus time. Use the parameter values $A = 1.50 \text{ m}^2$, $\rho = 1000 \text{ kg/m}^3$, $\alpha = 0.120 \text{ m}^3/\text{s}$, and $\beta = 3.0 \times 10^4 \text{ N/m}^2$.

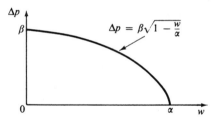

FIGURE P12.11

BLOCK
DIAGRAMS

A block diagram is an interconnection of symbols representing certain basic mathematical operations in such a way that the overall diagram obeys the system's mathematical model. In the diagram, the lines interconnecting the blocks represent the variables describing the system behavior, such as the input and state variables. Inspecting a block diagram of a system may provide new insight into the system's structure and behavior beyond that available from the differential equations themselves.

Throughout most of this chapter we shall restrict the discussion to fixed linear systems that contain no initial stored energy. After we transform the equations describing such a system, the variables that we shall use will be the Laplace transforms of the corresponding functions of time. The parts of the system can then be described by their transfer functions, as in Section 8.2. Recall that transfer functions give only the zero-state response. However, the steady-state response of a stable system does not depend on the initial conditions, so in that case there is no loss of generality in using only the zero-state response.

When we draw diagrams using functions of time as the variables, we generally call them simulation diagrams rather than block diagrams. Such diagrams can be useful in preparing a computer simulation. Unlike block diagrams, they can also be extended to include initial conditions and non-linear elements. We shall include an example of a simulation diagram for a nonlinear system, even though our emphasis will be on block diagrams and Laplace-transformed quantities.

After defining the components to be used in our diagrams, we first consider systems described by state-variable models. We then look at systems

478

described by input-output equations and by models in nonstandard form. Finally, we develop rules for simplifying block diagrams, emphasizing those that represent feedback systems.

■ 13.1 DIAGRAM BLOCKS

The operations that we generally use in block diagrams are summation, gain, and multiplication by a transfer function. Unless otherwise stated, all variables will be Laplace-transformed quantities.

Summer

The addition and subtraction of variables is represented by a **summer**, or **summing junction**. A summer is represented by a circle that has any number of arrows directed toward it (denoting inputs) and a single arrow directed away from it (denoting the output). Next to each entering arrowhead is a plus or minus symbol indicating the sign associated with the variable that the particular arrow represents. The output variable, appearing as the one arrow leaving the circle, is defined to be the sum of all the incoming variables, with the associated signs taken into account. A summer having three inputs $X_1(s)$, $X_2(s)$, and $X_3(s)$ appears in Figure 13.1.

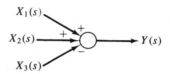

FIGURE 13.1 Summer representing $Y(s) = X_1(s) + X_2(s) - X_3(s)$.

Gain

The multiplication of a single variable by a constant is represented by a **gain** block. We place no restriction on the value of the gain, which may be positive or negative. It may be an algebraic function of other constants and/or system parameters. Several self-explanatory examples are shown in Figure 13.2.

Transfer Function

For a fixed linear system with no initial stored energy, the transformed output $Y(s)$ is given by

$$Y(s) = H(s)U(s)$$

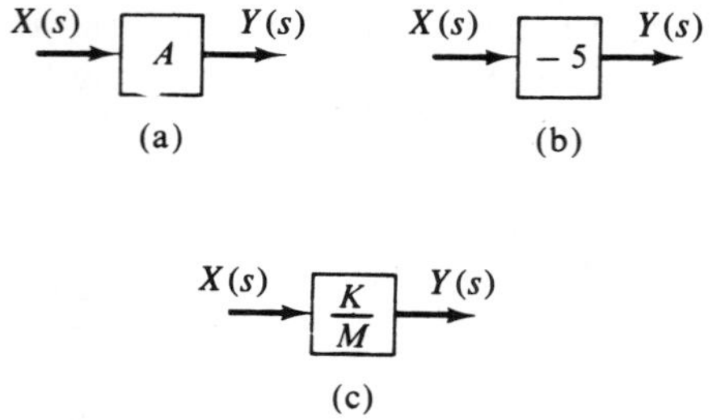

$$X(s) \rightarrow \boxed{A} \rightarrow Y(s)$$

(a)

$$X(s) \rightarrow \boxed{-5} \rightarrow Y(s)$$

(b)

$$X(s) \rightarrow \boxed{\dfrac{K}{M}} \rightarrow Y(s)$$

(c)

FIGURE 13.2 Gains. (a) $Y(s) = AX(s)$. (b) $Y(s) = -5X(s)$.
(c) $Y(s) = (K/M)X(s)$.

where $H(s)$ is the transfer function and $U(s)$ is the transformed input. When dealing with parts of a larger system, we often use $F(s)$ and $X(s)$ for the transfer function and transformed input of an individual part. Then

$$Y(s) = F(s)X(s) \tag{1}$$

Any system or combination of elements can be represented by a block containing its transfer function $F(s)$, as indicated in Figure 13.3(a). For example, the first-order system that obeys the input-output equation

$$\dot{y} + \frac{1}{\tau}y = Ax(t)$$

has as its transfer function

$$F(s) = \frac{A}{s + \dfrac{1}{\tau}}$$

Thus it could be represented by the block diagram shown in Figure 13.3(b). Note that the gain block in Figure 13.2(a) can be considered as a special case of a transfer function block, with $F(s) = A$.

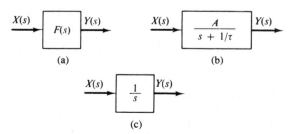

(a)

(b)

(c)

FIGURE 13.3 Basic block diagrams. (a) Arbitrary transfer function. (b) First-order system. (c) Integrator.

Integrator

Another important special case of a general transfer function block—one that will appear frequently in our diagrams—is the **integrator** block. An integrator that has an input $x(t)$ and an output $y(t)$ obeys the relationship

$$y(t) = y(0) + \int_0^t x(\lambda)d\lambda$$

where λ is the dummy variable of integration. Setting $y(0)$ equal to 0 and transforming the equation give

$$Y(s) = \frac{1}{s}X(s)$$

Hence the transfer function of the integrator is $Y(s)/X(s) = 1/s$, as shown in Figure 13.3(c).

The next three sections contain examples of constructing block diagrams using the above components. Because a block diagram is merely a pictorial representation of a set of algebraic Laplace-transformed equations, it is possible to combine blocks by calculating equivalent transfer functions and thereby to simplify the diagram. We shall now present procedures for handling series and parallel combinations of blocks. Methods for simplifying diagrams containing feedback paths will be discussed in Section 13.5.

Series Combination

Two blocks are said to be in **series** when the output of one goes only to the input of the other, as shown in Figure 13.4(a). The transfer functions of the individual blocks in the figure are $F_1(s) = V(s)/X(s)$ and $F_2(s) = Y(s)/V(s)$.

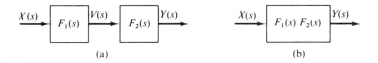

(a) (b)

FIGURE 13.4 (a) Two blocks in series. (b) Equivalent diagram.

When we evaluate the individual transfer functions, it is essential that we take any **loading effects** into account. This means that $F_1(s)$ is the ratio $V(s)/X(s)$ when the two subsystems are connected, so any effect the second subsystem has on the first is accounted for in the mathematical model. The same statement holds for calculating $F_2(s)$. For example, the input-output relationship for a linear potentiometer loaded by a resistor connected from its wiper to the ground node was shown in Example 10.1 to differ from that of the unloaded potentiometer.

In Figure 13.4(a), $Y(s) = F_2(s)V(s)$ and $V(s) = F_1(s)X(s)$. It follows that

$$Y(s) = F_2(s)[F_1(s)X(s)]$$
$$= [F_1(s)F_2(s)]X(s)$$

Thus the transfer function relating the input transform $X(s)$ to the output transform $Y(s)$ is $F_1(s)F_2(s)$, the product of the individual transfer functions. The equivalent block diagram is shown in Figure 13.4(b).

Parallel Combination

Two systems are said to be in **parallel** when they have a common input and their outputs are combined by a summing junction. If, as indicated in Figure 13.5(a), the individual blocks have the transfer functions $F_1(s)$ and $F_2(s)$ and the signs at the summing junction are both positive, the overall transfer function $Y(s)/X(s)$ will be the sum $F_1(s) + F_2(s)$, as shown in Figure 13.5(b). To prove this statement, we note that

$$Y(s) = V_1(s) + V_2(s)$$

where $V_1(s) = F_1(s)X(s)$ and $V_2(s) = F_2(s)X(s)$. Substituting for $V_1(s)$ and $V_2(s)$, we have

$$Y(s) = [F_1(s) + F_2(s)]X(s)$$

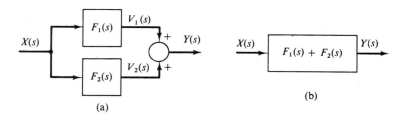

FIGURE 13.5   (a) Two blocks in parallel. (b) Equivalent diagram.

If either of the summing-junction signs associated with $V_1(s)$ or $V_2(s)$ is negative, we must change the sign of the corresponding transfer function in forming the overall transfer function. The following example illustrates the rules for combining blocks that are in parallel or in series.

▶ *EXAMPLE 13.1*

Evaluate the transfer functions $Y(s)/U(s)$ and $Z(s)/U(s)$ for the block diagram shown in Figure 13.6, giving the results as rational functions of s.

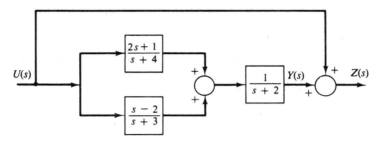

FIGURE 13.6 Block diagram for Example 13.1.

Solution

Because $Z(s)$ can be viewed as the sum of the outputs of two parallel blocks, one of which has $Y(s)$ as its output, we first evaluate the transfer function $Y(s)/U(s)$. To do this, we observe that $Y(s)$ can be considered the output of a series combination of two parts, one of which is a parallel combination of two blocks. Starting with this parallel combination, we write

$$\frac{2s+1}{s+4} + \frac{s-2}{s+3} = \frac{3s^2 + 9s - 5}{s^2 + 7s + 12}$$

and redraw the block diagram as shown in Figure 13.7(a). The series combination in this version has the transfer function

$$\frac{Y(s)}{U(s)} = \frac{3s^2 + 9s - 5}{s^2 + 7s + 12} \cdot \frac{1}{s+2}$$

$$= \frac{3s^2 + 9s - 5}{s^3 + 9s^2 + 26s + 24}$$

which leads to the diagram shown in Figure 13.7(b). We can reduce the final parallel combination to the single block shown in Figure 13.7(c) by writing

$$\frac{Z(s)}{U(s)} = 1 + \frac{Y(s)}{U(s)}$$

$$= 1 + \frac{3s^2 + 9s - 5}{s^3 + 9s^2 + 26s + 24}$$

$$= \frac{s^3 + 12s^2 + 35s + 19}{s^3 + 9s^2 + 26s + 24}$$

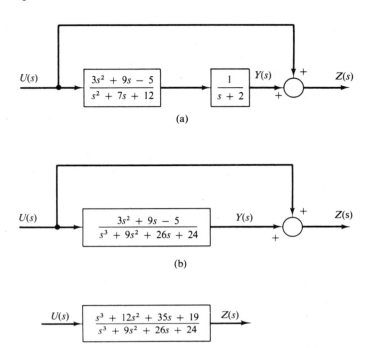

FIGURE 13.7   Equivalent block diagrams for the diagram shown in Figure 13.6.

In general, it is desirable to reduce the transfer functions of combinations of blocks to rational functions of s in order to simplify the subsequent analysis. This will be particularly important in Section 13.5 when we are reducing feedback loops to obtain an overall transfer function.

■ 13.2 DIAGRAMS FOR STATE-VARIABLE MODELS

Having defined the necessary building blocks, we next develop techniques for constructing the block diagram for a fixed linear system whose model is available in state-variable form. We shall transform the equations, with the initial condition terms set equal to zero, and then draw a diagram to fit the transformed equations. We start with a first-order system and then extend the procedure to systems of higher order.

First-Order Systems

Consider a fixed linear system that has a single state variable q, a single input u, and a single output y. The form of the state-variable model is

$$\dot{q} = aq + bu \qquad (2a)$$

$$y = cq + du \qquad (2b)$$

where a, b, c, and d are constants. Transforming these equations, with $q(0) = 0$, gives

$$sQ(s) = aQ(s) + bU(s) \qquad (3a)$$

$$Y(s) = cQ(s) + dU(s) \qquad (3b)$$

To construct the block diagram, we assume that the transformed input $U(s)$ is available for use in forming $sQ(s)$ and $Y(s)$ and that the coefficients a, b, c, and d are known. From (3a) we see that the quantity $sQ(s)$ can be formed by using gain and summing blocks, provided that $Q(s)$ is available. If we make $sQ(s)$ the input to an integrator, whose transfer function is $1/s$, then the output of the integrator will be $Q(s)$, which becomes available for use in implementing (3a). The process is circular in that $sQ(s)$ leads to $Q(s)$ via the integrator, whereas $Q(s)$, along with $U(s)$, is used to form $sQ(s)$ by (3a). We can then finish the diagram by using (3b) to form $Y(s)$ from the variables $Q(s)$ and $U(s)$. The steps in the process are as follows, and the diagram as it appears after each step is shown in Figure 13.8.

1. Draw an integrator block with input $sQ(s)$ and output $Q(s)$.

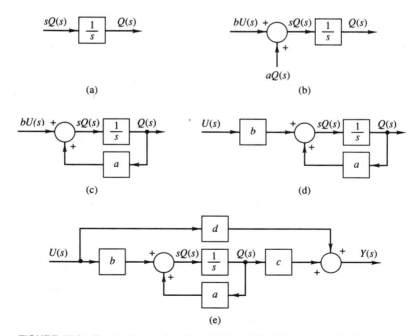

FIGURE 13.8 Block diagram for (3). (a), (b), (c) Partial diagrams for (3a). (d) Complete diagram for (3a). (e) Complete diagram for both equations.

2. Draw a summer to the left of the integrator having $sQ(s)$ as its output and $bU(s)$ and $aQ(s)$ as its inputs. Label both input arrows with plus signs.

3. Draw a block with gain a having $Q(s)$ as its input, and connect its output to the arrow labeled $aQ(s)$ entering the summer.

4. Draw a block with gain b having $U(s)$ as its input, and connect its output to the arrow labeled $bU(s)$ entering the summer. This step completes the simulation of (3a).

5. Append blocks with gains of c and d to the right side of the diagram, and make their inputs be $Q(s)$ and $U(s)$, respectively. Then draw a summer with inputs $cQ(s)$ and $dU(s)$ and output $Y(s)$. The diagram is now complete.

It is interesting to note that Figure 13.8 clearly illustrates the feedback nature of the system—that is, the fact that the rate of change of the output is dependent on the output itself, in addition to the input. The diagrams of most dynamic systems have such feedback paths from the outputs of one or more integrators back to the integrator input by way of gain blocks and summing junctions.

Second- and Higher-Order Systems

An nth-order fixed linear system having m inputs and p outputs is represented in state-variable form by a set of n first-order differential equations, each of which has the form

$$\dot{q}_i = a_{i1}q_1 + a_{i2}q_2 + \cdots + a_{in}q_n + b_{i1}u_1 + \cdots + b_{im}u_m \quad i = 1, 2, \ldots, n \quad (4)$$

The outputs are given by algebraic equations of the form

$$y_j = c_{j1}q_1 + c_{j2}q_2 + \cdots + c_{jn}q_n + d_{j1}u_1 + \cdots + d_{jm}u_m \quad j = 1, 2, \ldots, p \quad (5)$$

Transforming (4) and (5), with $q_i(0) = 0$ for all i, gives

$$sQ_i(s) = a_{i1}Q_1(s) + a_{i2}Q_2(s) + \cdots + a_{in}Q_n(s) + b_{i1}U_1(s)$$
$$+ \cdots + b_{im}U_m(s) \quad i = 1, 2, \ldots, n \quad (6a)$$

$$Y_j(s) = c_{j1}Q_1(s) + c_{j2}Q_2(s) + \cdots + c_{jn}Q_n(s) + d_{j1}U_1(s)$$
$$+ \cdots + d_{jm}U_m(s) \quad j = 1, 2, \ldots, p \quad (6b)$$

Generalizing the method we outlined for a first-order system, we draw n integrator blocks. We label the input and output of each integrator $sQ_i(s)$ and $Q_i(s)$, respectively, where $i = 1, 2, \ldots, n$. Then, for each value of i, we construct $sQ_i(s)$ according to (6a) from the n transformed state variables that appear as the integrator outputs and from the m inputs, using gain and summer blocks. Finally, we form the p outputs according to (6b) with additional gain and summer blocks.

In the following example, we illustrate this procedure for the general second-order fixed linear system having a single input and a single output.

▶ **EXAMPLE 13.2**

Draw a block diagram for the system described by the state-variable equations

$$\dot{q}_1 = a_{11}q_1 + a_{12}q_2 + b_1 u \tag{7a}$$

$$\dot{q}_2 = a_{21}q_1 + a_{22}q_2 + b_2 u \tag{7b}$$

and the output equation

$$y = c_1 q_1 + c_2 q_2 + du \tag{8}$$

Solution

The transformed equations, with $q_1(0) = q_2(0) = 0$, are

$$s Q_1(s) = a_{11} Q_1(s) + a_{12} Q_2(s) + b_1 U(s) \tag{9a}$$

$$s Q_2(s) = a_{21} Q_1(s) + a_{22} Q_2(s) + b_2 U(s) \tag{9b}$$

and

$$Y(s) = c_1 Q_1(s) + c_2 Q_2(s) + dU(s) \tag{10}$$

The system has two state variables, so we need two integrator blocks that have outputs of $Q_1(s)$ and $Q_2(s)$ and inputs of $s Q_1(s)$ and $s Q_2(s)$, respectively. Each of the integrator inputs is the output of a summer which itself has three inputs as defined by (9a) and (9b). The output $Y(s)$ is also formed by using a summer with three inputs according to (10). The resulting diagram is shown in Figure 13.9.

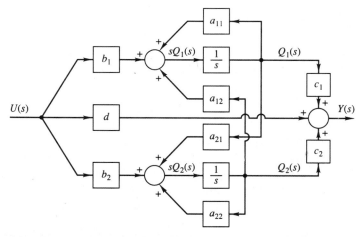

FIGURE 13.9 Block diagram for a general fixed linear second-order system with a single input and a single output in state-variable form.

Simulation Diagrams

For a fixed linear system, the form of the **simulation diagram** is essentially the same as that of the corresponding block diagram, except that all variables are functions of time rather than transformed quantities. The summer and gain blocks are exactly the same except for the labeling of the variables. The integrator, instead of being represented by the transfer function $1/s$ as in Figure 13.10(a), is shown by a block containing an integral sign as in part (b) of the figure. The input-output relationship is

$$y(t) = y(0) + \int_0^t x(\lambda)d\lambda \tag{11}$$

where the initial condition $y(0)$ is generally not explicitly shown. However, $y(0)$, which for transfer function analysis would be assumed to be zero, can be included if desired, as in Figure 13.10(c). Note that (11) can also be written in its differential form as

$$\dot{y}(t) = x(t) \tag{12}$$

leading to the representation in part (d) of the figure.

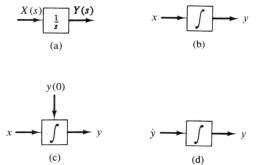

FIGURE 13.10 Integrators. (a) Transfer-function representation. (b) Without initial condition shown. (c) With initial condition shown. (d) Showing differential relationship.

The simulation diagram for Example 13.2 would be the same as that shown in Figure 13.9 except for the following changes. The transformed functions $U(s)$, $Q_1(s)$, $Q_2(s)$, and $Y(s)$ would be changed to the corresponding functions of time, and $sQ_1(s)$ and $sQ_2(s)$ would be replaced by $\dot{q}_1$ and $\dot{q}_2$, respectively. Finally, the integrators would be represented by blocks like the one in Figure 13.10(d) rather than by the transfer function $1/s$.

When considering nonlinear or time-varying systems, we may need additional blocks. A **multiplier** is represented by a block that is labeled MULT and has two inputs and one output. The output variable is the product of the two input variables; thus it is a nonlinear block, unlike the summer, gain, and integrator. Using multipliers in simulation diagrams, we may implement a variety of nonlinear characteristics and time-varying coefficients. Several examples are shown in Figure 13.11. In Figure 13.11(c), the time-varying coefficient $a(t)$ is assumed to be available as an input to the simulation diagram, as are the inputs to the system.

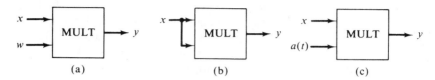

FIGURE 13.11 Multipliers. (a) $y = wx$. (b) $y = x^2$. (c) $y = a(t)x$.

Other nonlinear operations can be represented by a rectangular box that shows the appropriate symbol (if there is one) or a sketch of the function. Three examples are shown in Figure 13.12.

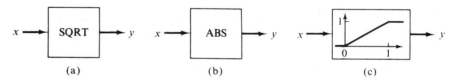

FIGURE 13.12 Nonlinearities. (a) $y = \sqrt{x}$. (b) $y = |x|$. (c) $y = 0$ for $x < 0$, $y = x$ for $0 \le x \le 1$, and $y = 1$ for $x > 1$.

To construct a simulation diagram directly from a state-variable model, we use an integrator for each state variable. The input of the integrator is $\dot{q}_i$ and its output is q_i. Then we combine gains, summers, and any necessary nonlinear blocks to form $\dot{q}_i$ as given by the corresponding state-variable equation. The general procedure is similar to that used for the block diagrams discussed earlier. It is illustrated for a nonlinear system in the following example.

▶ *EXAMPLE 13.3*

Draw a simulation diagram for the high-speed vehicle discussed in Example 9.6 and described by the equation

$$M\dot{v} + Bv + D|v|v = f_a(t)$$

where $f_a(t)$ is the driving force and v is the velocity of the vehicle.

Solution

The model for this vehicle is a first-order nonlinear differential equation with the velocity v as both the state variable and the output. The input is the applied force $f_a(t)$. In state-variable form, the model is

$$\dot{v} = \frac{1}{M}[-Bv - D|v|v + f_a(t)] \qquad (13)$$

We initiate the simulation diagram by drawing an integrator with input $\dot{v}$ and output v. The coefficient $1/M$ appears as a gain whose output is $\dot{v}$ and whose input corresponds to the three terms inside the brackets in (13). The bracketed term is the output of a summer with the three inputs Bv, $D|v|v$, and $f_a(t)$, each having the appropriate sign at the corresponding arrowhead. The term $|v|v$ is formed by using a nonlinear block for the absolute value and a multiplier. The completed diagram is shown in Figure 13.13.

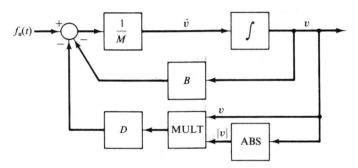

FIGURE 13.13   Simulation diagram for high-speed vehicle.

■ 13.3 DIAGRAMS FOR INPUT-OUTPUT MODELS

The input-output form of the model of an nth-order fixed linear system with input $u(t)$ and output y is the single differential equation

$$a_n y^{(n)} + a_{n-1} y^{n-1} + \cdots + a_0 y = b_m u^{(m)} + \cdots + b_0 u(t) \qquad (14)$$

where $y^{(k)}$ denotes $d^k y/dt^k$, and where in practice $m \le n$. Transforming this equation with the initial-condition terms set equal to zero gives

$$(a_n s^n + a_{n-1} s^{n-1} + \cdots + a_0) Y(s) = (b_m s^m + \cdots + b_0) U(s)$$

corresponding to the transfer function

$$H(s) = \frac{Y(s)}{U(s)} = \frac{b_m s^m + \cdots + b_0}{a_n s^n + a_{n-1} s^{n-1} + \cdots + a_0} \qquad (15)$$

In this section we shall present a general method of representing these equations by a block diagram consisting only of summers, gains, and integrators. We also want to be able to write a state-variable model corresponding to a given input-output equation. Because the choice of state variables is not unique, our method will result in only one of several possible state-variable models.

We shall develop the method in two stages. First we consider systems for which (14) contains no derivatives of the input, and then we extend the method to include input derivatives. For a first-order system, the state-variable and input-output models involve a single first-order differential equation and are essentially identical. Thus we start with second-order systems and generalize the results to apply to higher-order systems.

Second-Order Systems

We shall consider the input-output differential equation

$$a_2\ddot{y} + a_1\dot{y} + a_0 y = F(t)$$

for three choices of the forcing function: (1) $F(t) = u(t)$, (2) $F(t) = b_1\dot{u} + b_0 u(t)$, and (3) $F(t) = b_2\ddot{u} + b_1\dot{u} + b_0 u(t)$. We shall construct the corresponding block diagrams in the following three examples, the last one of which will constitute the most general case of a second-order fixed linear system.

▶ **EXAMPLE 13.4**

Construct the block diagram for the system described by the differential equation

$$a_2\ddot{y} + a_1\dot{y} + a_0 y = u(t) \tag{16}$$

Then use the block diagram to find a state-variable model for the system.

Solution

With $y(0) = \dot{y}(0) = 0$, the transformed equation is

$$a_2 s^2 Y(s) + a_1 s Y(s) + a_0 Y(s) = U(s)$$

so

$$s^2 Y(s) = \frac{1}{a_2}[-a_1 s Y(s) - a_0 Y(s) + U(s)] \tag{17}$$

We begin by drawing a series combination of two integrators in Figure 13.14(a), which shows the variables $Y(s)$, $sY(s)$, and $s^2 Y(s)$. Using gain blocks and a summer, we then form $s^2 Y(s)$ according to (17). The complete diagram is shown in Figure 13.14(b).

In order to write the state-variable equations, it can be helpful to draw or visualize the simulation diagram, where the variables are shown as functions of time. The simulation diagram corresponding to part (b) of Figure 13.14 is given in part (c). We usually take the output of each integrator as a state

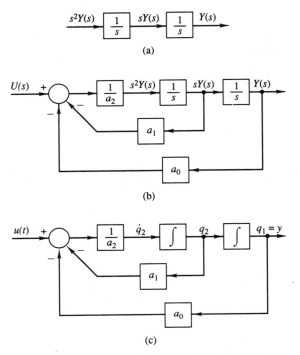

FIGURE 13.14 Diagrams for Example 13.4. (a) Partial diagram.
(b) Complete block diagram. (c) Simulation diagram.

variable, and we have labeled the diagram in this way. If the output of an integrator is q_i, then its input is $\dot{q}_i$ and we can get an equation for $\dot{q}_i$ by inspection of the diagram. In our example,

$$\dot{q}_1 = q_2 \tag{18a}$$

$$\dot{q}_2 = \frac{1}{a_2}[-a_0 q_1 - a_1 q_2 + u(t)] \tag{18b}$$

$$y = q_1 \tag{18c}$$

In the last example, note that (18a) and (18b) do have the correct form for the state-variable equations describing a second-order fixed linear system. It is easy to check (18) by showing that these equations satisfy the input-output equation in (16). To do this, we need only substitute (18a) into (18b) and then replace q_1 by y. We also note that the transfer function corresponding to (16) is

$$H(s) = \frac{Y(s)}{U(s)} = \frac{1}{a_2 s^2 + a_1 s + a_0} \tag{19}$$

By the methods to be presented in Section 13.5, we can show as a further check that the block diagram in Figure 13.14(b) does indeed have this transfer function.

▶ *EXAMPLE 13.5*

Draw the block diagram and write the state-variable model when

$$a_2 \ddot{y} + a_1 \dot{y} + a_0 y = b_1 \dot{u} + b_0 u(t) \tag{20}$$

Solution

With zero initial conditions, the transformed output can be written as

$$Y(s) = \frac{b_1 s + b_0}{a_2 s^2 + a_1 s + a_0} U(s) \tag{21}$$

If we define $Q(s)$ to be

$$Q(s) = \left[\frac{1}{a_2 s^2 + a_1 s + a_0} \right] U(s) \tag{22}$$

we can rewrite (21) as

$$\begin{aligned} Y(s) &= (b_1 s + b_0) Q(s) \\ &= b_1 s Q(s) + b_0 Q(s) \end{aligned} \tag{23}$$

The quantity inside the brackets in (22) is the transfer function corresponding to (16) in Example 13.4. Thus (22) is described by the block diagram in Figure 13.14(b) if we replace the symbol $Y(s)$ by $Q(s)$. This is done in Figure 13.15(a). Once $Q(s)$ and $sQ(s)$ are available in the block diagram, we use two additional gain blocks and a summer to satisfy (23), which results in the complete diagram in Figure 13.15(b).

The corresponding simulation diagram is drawn in part (c) of the figure, where we have again used the outputs of the integrators as the state variables. We can write the state-variable model as

$$\begin{aligned} \dot{q}_1 &= q_2 \\ \dot{q}_2 &= \frac{1}{a_2} [-a_0 q_1 - a_1 q_2 + u(t)] \\ y &= b_0 q_1 + b_1 q_2 \end{aligned} \tag{24}$$

Comparing these equations with the results of Example 13.4, we see that the only effect of the more complicated forcing function has been to change the algebraic output equation to include both state variables.

In order to avoid having to draw a simulation diagram before writing the state-variable equations, we have shown in Figure 13.15(b) the transformed

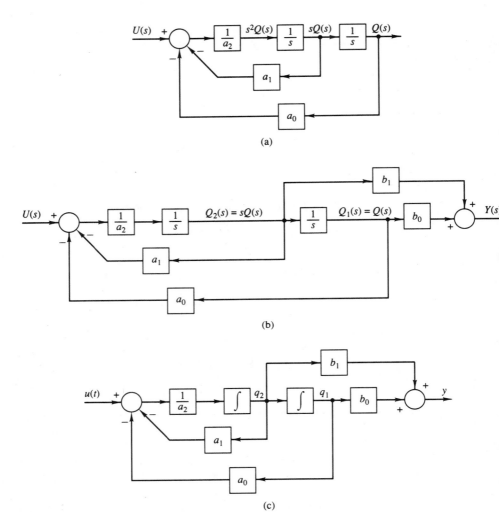

FIGURE 13.15 Diagram for Example 13.5. (a) Diagram for $Q(s)$. (b) Complete block diagram. (c) Simulation diagram.

variables $Q_1(s) = Q(s)$ and $Q_2(s) = sQ(s)$. Then, directly from the figure, we have

$$sQ_1(s) = Q_2(s)$$
$$sQ_2(s) = \frac{1}{a_2}[-a_0Q_1(s) - a_1Q_2(s) + U(s)] \tag{25}$$
$$Y(s) = b_0Q_1(s) + b_1Q_2(s)$$

Remember that when constructing block diagrams, we always assume the initial conditions to be zero. Because $\mathcal{L}[\dot{q}_1] = sQ_1(s)$ and $\mathcal{L}[\dot{q}_2] = sQ_2(s)$

for zero initial conditions, (24) follows immediately from (25). With a little practice, it is possible to write the state-variable model directly from the block diagram, and we shall do this in subsequent examples.

▶ **EXAMPLE 13.6**

Repeat the previous example when

$$a_2 \ddot{y} + a_1 \dot{y} + a_0 y = b_2 \ddot{u} + b_1 \dot{u} + b_0 u(t) \tag{26}$$

Solution

We can write the zero-state transformed output as

$$Y(s) = \left[\frac{b_2 s^2 + b_1 s + b_0}{a_2 s^2 + a_1 s + a_0} \right] U(s) \tag{27}$$

or, with $Q(s)$ defined by (22),

$$Y(s) = (b_2 s^2 + b_1 s + b_0) Q(s)$$

$$= b_2 s^2 Q(s) + b_1 s Q(s) + b_0 Q(s) \tag{28}$$

The definition of $Q(s)$ is the same as for Example 13.5, so the relationship between $Q(s)$ and $U(s)$ is still described by Figure 13.15(a). To satisfy (28), we can add three gain blocks and a summer to obtain the complete block diagram in Figure 13.16(a). In order to facilitate writing the state-variable equations, we have replaced $Q(s)$ and $sQ(s)$ by $Q_1(s)$ and $Q_2(s)$ when labeling the outputs of the integrators. From this diagram we see that

$$\dot{q}_1 = q_2 \tag{29a}$$

$$\dot{q}_2 = \frac{1}{a_2}[-a_0 q_1 - a_1 q_2 + u(t)] \tag{29b}$$

$$y = b_0 q_1 + b_2 \dot{q}_2 + b_1 q_2 \tag{29c}$$

Note, however, that (29c) does not have the standard form of the output equation in a state-variable model, because y is given as a function of the *derivative* of one of the state variables, in addition to the state variables themselves. In spite of this feature, (29c) is a useful form of the output equation for many purposes, particularly because each of the six gains appearing in the block diagram is a coefficient of the input-output differential equation. Thus we can draw the diagram without performing any calculations to evaluate the gains.

The basic reason for the form of (29c) is that one of the signals entering the output summer in Figure 13.16(a) does not come from the output of an integrator. This in turn is caused by the fact that the numerator of the transfer function in (27) is not of lower order than the denominator. When this situation occurs, we can carry out a preliminary step of long division, as

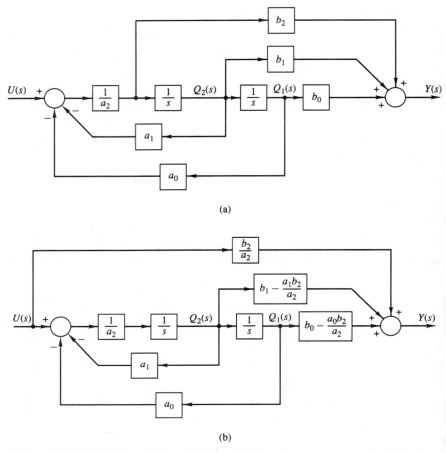

(a)

(b)

FIGURE 13.16 Diagrams for Example 13.6. (a) Block diagram corresponding to (28). (b) Block diagram corresponding to (30).

was done in Section 7.3 whenever a function of s was not a strictly proper rational function. Then (27) becomes

$$
Y(s) = \left[\frac{b_2}{a_2} + \frac{(b_1 - a_1 b_2 / a_2)s + (b_0 - a_0 b_2 / a_2)}{a_2 s^2 + a_1 s + a_0} \right] U(s)
$$

$$
= \frac{b_2}{a_2} U(s) + [(b_1 - a_1 b_2 / a_2)s + (b_0 - a_0 b_2 / a_2)]Q(s) \qquad (30)
$$

The quantity $Q(s)$ is still given by (22), and the relationship between $Q(s)$ and $U(s)$ is still shown in Figure 13.15(a). Starting with that figure, adding the extra blocks needed to implement (30), and replacing $Q(s)$ and $sQ(s)$ by $Q_1(s)$ and $Q_2(s)$, we obtain the diagram in Figure 13.16(b). The state-variable equations corresponding to the diagram are again given by (29a) and (29b), but the output equation becomes

$$y = \left(b_0 - \frac{a_0 b_2}{a_2}\right) q_1 + \left(b_1 - \frac{a_1 b_2}{a_2}\right) q_2 + \frac{b_2}{a_2} u(t) \tag{31}$$

which includes the input $u(t)$ in addition to the state variables q_1 and q_2.

Higher-Order Systems

Generalizing the three previous examples to systems of higher order than two is straightforward. The general input-output differential equation and the corresponding transfer function are given by (14) and (15), respectively. We first consider the related differential equation

$$a_n q^{(n)} + a_{n-1} q^{(n-1)} + \cdots + a_0 q = u(t) \tag{32}$$

where the forcing function is assumed to be just the input $u(t)$. Transforming (32) with zero initial conditions, we have

$$a_n s^n Q(s) + a_{n-1} s^{n-1} Q(s) + \cdots + a_0 Q(s) = U(s) \tag{33}$$

and

$$Q(s) = \left[\frac{1}{a_n s^n + a_{n-1} s^{n-1} + \cdots + a_0}\right] U(s) \tag{34}$$

We rearrange (33) as

$$s^n Q(s) = \frac{1}{a_n} \left[-a_{n-1} s^{n-1} Q(s) - \cdots - a_0 Q(s) + U(s)\right] \tag{35}$$

which is described by the block diagram shown in Figure 13.17.

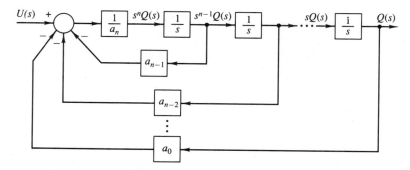

FIGURE 13.17 Block diagram for (32) through (35).

Returning to the more general model given by (14), we rewrite (15) as

$$Y(s) = \left[\frac{b_m s^m + \cdots + b_0}{a_n s^n + a_{n-1} s^{n-1} + \cdots + a_0} \right] U(s)$$

$$= (b_m s^m + \cdots + b_0) Q(s)$$

$$= b_m s^m Q(s) + \cdots + b_0 Q(s) \tag{36}$$

where $Q(s)$ is defined by (34) and where the relationship between $Q(s)$ and $U(s)$ is represented by the diagram in Figure 13.17. To form the block diagram corresponding to (14) and (15), we merely add to Figure 13.17 additional gain and summer blocks according to (36).

As long as $m < n$, this procedure will give an entirely satisfactory diagram. For the case of $m = n$, we may choose to carry out a preliminary step of long division on the transfer function $H(s)$ in (15). The following two examples illustrate the method for third-order systems.

▶ **EXAMPLE 13.7**

Draw the block diagram for the system described by

$$\dddot{y} + 5\ddot{y} + 2\dot{y} + y = 3\ddot{u} + 4u(t)$$

Also find a state-variable model.

Solution

The block diagram corresponding to

$$\dddot{q} + 5\ddot{q} + 2\dot{q} + q = u(t)$$

is shown in Figure 13.18(a). Noting that

$$Y(s) = (3s^2 + 4)Q(s) = 3s^2 Q(s) + 4Q(s)$$

we add to that figure two gain blocks and a summer in order to obtain the block diagram in Figure 13.18(b).

The outputs of the integrators are labeled $Q_1(s)$, $Q_2(s)$, and $Q_3(s)$ from right to left. Then we can write the state-variable model as

$$\begin{aligned}
\dot{q}_1 &= q_2 \\
\dot{q}_2 &= q_3 \\
\dot{q}_3 &= -q_1 - 2q_2 - 5q_3 + u(t) \\
y &= 4q_1 + 3q_3
\end{aligned} \tag{37}$$

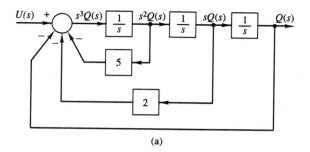

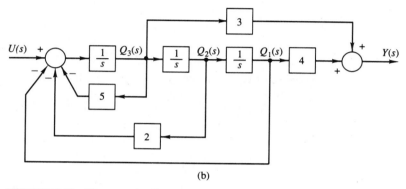

FIGURE 13.18 Diagrams for Example 13.7. (a) Partial block diagram. (b) Complete block diagram.

▶ *EXAMPLE 13.8*

Repeat the previous example for the input-output equation

$$0.5\ddot{y} + 2\ddot{y} + \dot{y} + y = 2\ddot{u} - 3\dot{u} + u(t)$$

Solution

We can write

$$Y(s) = \left[\frac{2s^3 - 3s + 1}{0.5s^3 + 2s^2 + s + 1}\right] U(s) \tag{38}$$

where the quantity inside the bracket is the system's transfer function $H(s)$. Then

$$Y(s) = (2s^3 - 3s + 1)Q(s)$$
$$= 2s^3 Q(s) - 3s Q(s) + Q(s) \tag{39}$$

where

$$Q(s) = \left[\frac{1}{0.5s^3 + 2s^2 + s + 1} \right] U(s) \tag{40}$$

The block diagram for (40) is shown in Figure 13.19(a). Adding the gain and summer blocks called for by (39) gives the complete diagram in Figure 13.19(b). Then we have

$$\dot{q}_1 = q_2 \tag{41a}$$

$$\dot{q}_2 = q_3 \tag{41b}$$

$$\dot{q}_3 = 2[-q_1 - q_2 - 2q_3 + u(t)] \tag{41c}$$

$$y = q_1 - 3q_2 + 2\dot{q}_3 \tag{41d}$$

Because of the presence of the term $2\dot{q}_3$, the last equation does not have the standard form for the output equation in a state-variable model. For an alternative block diagram, we perform a step of long division on the transfer function within the brackets in (38). Then

$$Y(s) = \left[4 + \frac{-8s^2 - 7s - 3}{0.5s^3 + 2s^2 + s + 1} \right] U(s)$$

$$= 4U(s) - 8s^2 Q(s) - 7s Q(s) - 3Q(s)$$

Again starting with Figure 13.19(a), we add four gain blocks and a summer to obtain the diagram in part (c) of the figure. The corresponding state-variable model consists of (41a), (41b), and (41c), together with the new output equation

$$y = -3q_1 - 7q_2 - 8q_3 + 4u(t) \tag{42}$$

which does not contain any derivatives. This output equation can also be obtained by substituting (41c) into (41d) to eliminate the derivative on the right side of (41d).

■ 13.4 MODELS IN NONSTANDARD FORM

The free-body diagram for a single mass or moment of inertia in a mechanical system will generally result in a second-order differential equation that contains one or more variables not directly associated with the motion of that element. If the system consists of several such elements, each having its own free-body diagram, then the overall model will probably appear first as a set of coupled second-order equations.

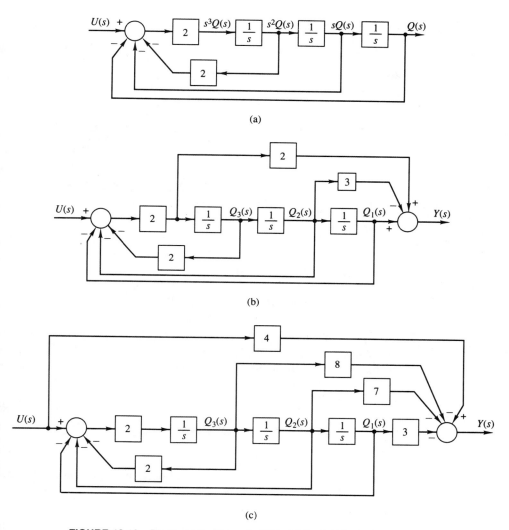

FIGURE 13.19 Diagrams for Example 13.8. (a) Partial block diagram. (b) Complete block diagram. (c) Alternative block diagram.

In such situations, we may wish to draw a block diagram directly from the nonstandard form of the model, which is in neither state-variable nor input-output form. Because the variables associated with a single mass are the position, velocity, and acceleration, the corresponding portion of the diagram generally consists of a chain of two integrators with the variables being fed back to a summer at the input of the first integrator. Hence the complete diagram is an interconnection of subdiagrams that contain two-integrator chains. These ideas are illustrated in the following example.

▶ **EXAMPLE 13.9**

Draw a block diagram for the mechanical system shown in Figure 13.20 and modeled in Example 4.11.

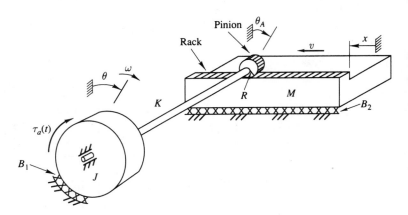

FIGURE 13.20   System for Example 4.11 with rack and pinion gear.

Solution

In the solution of Example 4.11, we drew free-body diagrams for the rotor, the pinion gear, and the mass. These diagrams lead to the three equations

$$J\ddot{\theta} + B_1\dot{\theta} + K(\theta - \theta_A) = \tau_a(t) \tag{43a}$$

$$M\ddot{x} + B_2\dot{x} = f_c \tag{43b}$$

$$Rf_c = K(\theta - \theta_A) \tag{43c}$$

which are identical to (4.61) except for a minor rearrangement of the terms and the use of the identities $\dot{\theta} = \omega$ and $\dot{x} = v$. In addition to (43), we have the geometric relationship

$$R\theta_A = x \tag{44}$$

Transforming (43) and (44) with zero initial conditions, we obtain

$$s^2\Theta(s) = \frac{1}{J}\{-B_1 s\Theta(s) - K[\Theta(s) - \Theta_A(s)] + \tau_a(s)\} \tag{45a}$$

$$s^2 X(s) = \frac{1}{M}[-B_2 s X(s) + F_c(s)] \tag{45b}$$

$$F_c(s) = \frac{1}{R}K[\Theta(s) - \Theta_A(s)] \tag{45c}$$

$$\Theta_A(s) = \frac{1}{R}X(s) \tag{45d}$$

We start the block diagram with a pair of two-integrator chains, whose outputs are $\Theta(s)$ and $X(s)$ and whose inputs are $s^2\Theta(s)$ and $s^2X(s)$. From (45c) and (45d) we construct $F_c(s)$ and $\Theta_A(s)$ in terms of $X(s)$ and $\Theta(s)$. Finally, we use (45a) and (45b) to determine the inputs to the summers that precede the integrator chains. The completed diagram is shown in Figure 13.21(a).

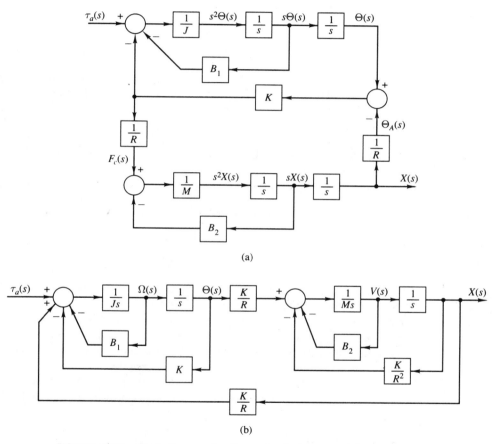

(a)

(b)

FIGURE 13.21 Block diagrams for the mechanical system of Example 13.9. (a) Nonstandard form. (b) State-variable form.

When discussing block diagrams for specific physical systems, engineers often refer to transformed variables by their original time-domain names. For example, the quantity $K[\Theta(s) - \Theta_A(s)]$ is the *transform* of the torque transmitted by the shaft connecting the pinion gear to the rotational inertia. However, it would commonly be referred to as simply the torque transmitted by the shaft. Note that the two parallel two-integrator chains in Figure 13.21(a) are coupled by this torque.

We can also draw a block diagram to correspond to the state-variable form of the model given by (4.63), which is repeated here:

$$\dot{\theta} = \omega$$

$$\dot{\omega} = \frac{1}{J}\left[-K\theta - B_1\omega + \frac{K}{R}x + \tau_a(t)\right]$$

$$\dot{x} = v$$

$$\dot{v} = \frac{1}{M}\left(\frac{K}{R}\theta - \frac{K}{R^2}x - B_2v\right)$$

The reader should verify that these equations lead to the diagram shown in Figure 13.21(b). As drawn, the diagram has the two-integrator chains arranged in series rather than in parallel. Although the contact force $F_c(s)$ is not explicitly shown in this version, it can be generated from $\Theta(s)$ and $X(s)$ by using gains and a summer. In comparing the two diagrams, remember that in order to draw the state-variable version, we had to use the two algebraic equations (43c) and (44) to eliminate $F_c(s)$ and $\Theta_A(s)$. In contrast, the diagram in Figure 13.21(a) can be drawn directly from the free-body diagrams and (44).

■ 13.5 BLOCK DIAGRAMS OF FEEDBACK SYSTEMS

The block diagrams in the previous three sections contained only integrators, gain blocks, and summers. Feedback paths were formed around the integrators by multiplying the transformed state variables by constants and then feeding these signals back to an input summer. In this section and also in the next chapter, we shall consider the more general situation where the individual blocks can have arbitrary transfer functions.

Figure 13.22(a) shows the block diagram of a general feedback system that has a forward path from the summing junction to the output and a feed-

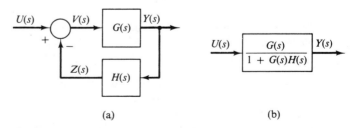

(a)   (b)

FIGURE 13.22   (a) Block diagram of a feedback system.
(b) Equivalent diagram.

back path from the output back to the summing junction. The transforms of the system's input and output are $U(s)$ and $Y(s)$, respectively. The transfer function $G(s) = Y(s)/V(s)$ is known as the **forward transfer function**, and $H(s) = Z(s)/Y(s)$ is called the **feedback transfer function**. We must evaluate both of these transfer functions with the system elements connected in order properly to account for the loading effects of the interconnections. The product $G(s)H(s)$ is referred to as the **open-loop transfer function**. The sign associated with the feedback signal from the block $H(s)$ at the summing junction is shown as minus because a minus sign naturally occurs in the majority of feedback systems, particularly in control systems.

Given the model of a feedback system in terms of its forward and feedback transfer functions $G(s)$ and $H(s)$, it is often necessary to determine the **closed-loop transfer function** $T(s) = Y(s)/U(s)$. We do this by writing the algebraic transform equations corresponding to the block diagram shown in Figure 13.22(a) and solving them for the ratio $Y(s)/U(s)$. We can write the following transform equations directly from the block diagram.

$$V(s) = U(s) - Z(s)$$

$$Y(s) = G(s)V(s)$$

$$Z(s) = H(s)Y(s)$$

If we combine these equations in such a way as to eliminate $V(s)$ and $Z(s)$, we find that

$$Y(s) = G(s)[U(s) - H(s)Y(s)]$$

which can be rearranged to give

$$[1 + G(s)H(s)]Y(s) = G(s)U(s)$$

Hence the closed-loop transfer function $T(s) = Y(s)/U(s)$ is

$$T(s) = \frac{G(s)}{1 + G(s)H(s)} \tag{46}$$

where it is implicit that the sign of the feedback signal at the summing junction is negative. It is readily shown that when a plus sign is used at the summing junction for the feedback signal, the closed-loop transfer function becomes

$$T(s) = \frac{G(s)}{1 - G(s)H(s)} \tag{47}$$

A commonly used simplification occurs when the feedback transfer function is unity—this is, when $H(s) = 1$. Such a system is referred to as a

unity-feedback system, and (46) reduces to

$$T(s) = \frac{G(s)}{1 + G(s)} \tag{48}$$

We now consider three examples that use (46) and (47). The first two illustrate determining the closed-loop transfer function by reducing the block diagram. They also show the effects of feedback gains on the closed-loop poles, time constant, damping ratio, and undamped natural frequency. In the third example, a block diagram is drawn directly from the system's state-variable equations and then reduced to give the system's transfer functions.

▶ *EXAMPLE 13.10*

Find the closed-loop transfer function for the feedback system shown in Figure 13.23(a), and compare the locations of the poles of the open-loop and closed-loop transfer functions in the s-plane.

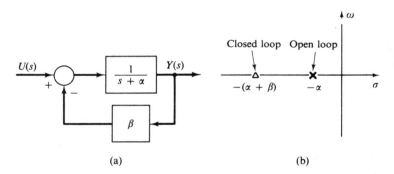

(a)   (b)

FIGURE 13.23   Single-loop feedback system for Example 13.10.

Solution

By comparing the block diagram shown in Figure 13.23(a) with that shown in Figure 13.22(a), we see that $G(s) = 1/(s+\alpha)$ and $H(s) = \beta$. Substituting these expressions into (46) gives

$$T(s) = \frac{\dfrac{1}{s+\alpha}}{1 + \left(\dfrac{1}{s+\alpha}\right)\beta}$$

which we can write as a rational function of s by multiplying the numerator and denominator by $s + \alpha$. Doing this, we obtain the closed-loop transfer function

$$T(s) = \frac{1}{s + \alpha + \beta}$$

This result illustrates an interesting and useful property of feedback systems: the fact that the poles of the closed-loop transfer function differ from the poles of the open-loop transfer function $G(s)H(s)$. In this case, the single open-loop pole is at $s = -\alpha$, whereas the single closed-loop pole is at $s = -(\alpha + \beta)$. These pole locations are indicated in Figure 13.23(b) for positive α and β. Hence, in the absence of feedback, the pole of the transfer function $Y(s)/U(s)$ is at $s = -\alpha$, and the free response will be of the form $\epsilon^{-\alpha t}$. With feedback, however, the free response will be $\epsilon^{-(\alpha+\beta)t}$. Thus the time constant of the open-loop system is $1/\alpha$, whereas that of the closed-loop system is $1/(\alpha + \beta)$.

▶ **EXAMPLE 13.11**

Find the closed-loop transfer function of the two-loop feedback system shown in Figure 13.24. Also express the damping ratio and the undamped natural frequency of the closed-loop system in terms of the gains a_0 and a_1.

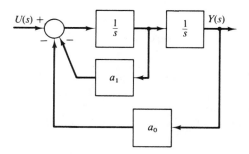

FIGURE 13.24 System with two feedback loops for Example 13.11.

Solution

Because the system's block diagram contains one feedback path inside another, we cannot use (46) directly to evaluate $Y(s)/U(s)$. However, we can redraw the block diagram such that the summing junction is split into two summing junctions, as shown in Figure 13.25(a). Then it is possible to use (46) to eliminate the inner loop by calculating the transfer function $W(s)/V(s)$. Taking $G(s) = 1/s$ and $H(s) = a_1$ in (46), we obtain

$$\frac{W(s)}{V(s)} = \frac{\dfrac{1}{s}}{1 + \dfrac{a_1}{s}} = \frac{1}{s + a_1}$$

Redrawing Figure 13.25(a) with the inner loop replaced by a block having $1/(s + a_1)$ as its transfer function gives Figure 13.25(b). The two

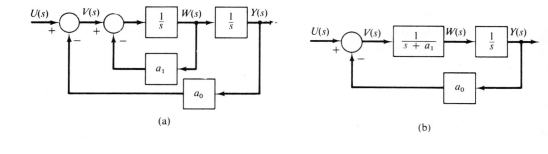

(a) (b)

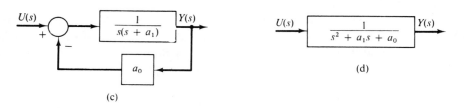

(c) (d)

FIGURE 13.25 Equivalent block diagrams for the system shown in Figure 13.24.

blocks in the forward path of this version are in series and can be combined by multiplying their transfer functions, which gives the block diagram shown in Figure 13.25(c). Then we can apply (46) again to find the overall closed-loop transfer function $T(s) = Y(s)/U(s)$ as

$$T(s) = \frac{\dfrac{1}{s(s+a_1)}}{1 + \dfrac{1}{s(s+a_1)} \cdot a_0} = \frac{1}{s^2 + a_1 s + a_0} \tag{49}$$

The block-diagram representation of the feedback system corresponding to (49) is shown in Figure 13.25(d).

The poles of the closed-loop transfer function are the roots of the equation

$$s^2 + a_1 s + a_0 = 0 \tag{50}$$

which we obtain by setting the denominator of $T(s)$ equal to zero and which is the characteristic equation of the closed-loop system. Equation (50) has two roots, which may be real or complex, depending on the sign of the quantity $a_1^2 - 4a_0$. However, the roots of (50) will have negative real parts and the closed-loop system will be stable provided that a_0 and a_1 are both positive.

If the poles are complex, it is convenient to rewrite the denominator of $T(s)$ in terms of the damping ratio ζ and the undamped natural frequency

ω_n, which were introduced in Section 6.4. When the parameter r is replaced by s, the characteristic equation in (6.50) can be compared to (50). Doing this, we see that

$$a_0 = \omega_n^2 \tag{51a}$$

$$a_1 = 2\zeta\omega_n \tag{51b}$$

Solving (51a) for ω_n and substituting it into (51b) give the damping ratio and the undamped natural frequency of the closed-loop system as

$$\zeta = \frac{a_1}{2\sqrt{a_0}}$$

$$\omega_n = \sqrt{a_0}$$

We see from these expressions that a_0, the gain of the outer feedback path in Figure 13.24, determines the undamped natural frequency ω_n and that a_1, the gain of the inner feedback path, affects only the damping ratio. If we can specify both a_0 and a_1 at will, then we can attain any desired values of ζ and ω_n for the closed-loop transfer function.

▶ *EXAMPLE 13.12*

Draw a block diagram for the translational mechanical system studied in Example 3.7, whose state-variable equations are given by (3.14). Reduce the block diagram to determine the transfer functions $X_1(s)/F_a(s)$ and $X_2(s)/F_a(s)$ as rational functions of s.

Solution

Transforming (3.14) with zero initial conditions, we have

$$sX_1(s) = V_1(s) \tag{52a}$$

$$MsV_1(s) = -K_1X_1(s) - B_1V_1(s) + K_1X_2(s) + F_a(s) \tag{52b}$$

$$B_2sX_2(s) = K_1X_1(s) - (K_1 + K_2)X_2(s) \tag{52c}$$

We use (52b) to draw a summing junction that has $MsV_1(s)$ as its output. After the summing junction, we insert the transfer function $1/Ms$ to get $V_1(s)$, which, from (52a), equals $sX_1(s)$. Thus an integrator whose input is $V_1(s)$ has $X_1(s)$ as its output. Using (52c), we form a second summing junction that has $B_2sX_2(s)$ as its output. Following this summing junction by the transfer function $1/B_2s$, we get $X_2(s)$ and can complete the four feedback paths required by the summing junctions. The result of these steps is the block diagram shown in Figure 13.26(a).

To simplify the block diagram, we use (46) to reduce each of the three inner feedback loops, obtaining the version shown in Figure 13.26(b). To evaluate the transfer function $X_1(s)/F_a(s)$, we can apply (47) to this single-

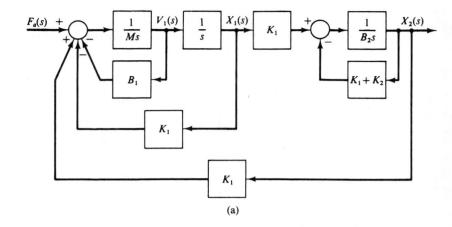

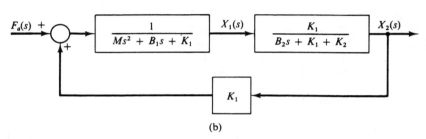

FIGURE 13.26 Block diagrams for the system in Example 13.12. (a) As drawn from (52). (b) With the three inner feedback loops eliminated.

loop diagram because the sign associated with the feedback signal at the summing junction is positive rather than negative. Doing this with

$$G(s) = \frac{1}{Ms^2 + B_1s + K_1}$$

and

$$H(s) = \frac{K_1^2}{B_2s + K_1 + K_2}$$

we find

$$
\begin{aligned}
\frac{X_1(s)}{F_a(s)} &= \frac{\dfrac{1}{Ms^2 + B_1s + K_1}}{1 - \dfrac{1}{Ms^2 + B_1s + K_1} \cdot \dfrac{K_1^2}{B_2s + K_1 + K_2}} \\[2mm]
&= \frac{B_2s + K_1 + K_2}{(Ms^2 + B_1s + K_1)(B_2s + K_1 + K_2) - K_1^2} \\[2mm]
&= \frac{B_2s + K_1 + K_2}{P(s)} \tag{53}
\end{aligned}
$$

where

$$P(s) = MB_2s^3 + [(K_1 + K_2)M + B_1B_2]s^2$$
$$+ [B_1(K_1 + K_2) + B_2K_1]s + K_1K_2$$

To obtain $X_2(s)/F_a(s)$, we can write

$$\frac{X_2(s)}{F_a(s)} = \frac{X_1(s)}{F_a(s)} \cdot \frac{X_2(s)}{X_1(s)}$$

where $X_1(s)/F_a(s)$ is given by (53) and, from Figure 13.26(b),

$$\frac{X_2(s)}{X_1(s)} = \frac{K_1}{B_2s + K_1 + K_2} \qquad (54)$$

The result of multiplying (53) and (54) is a transfer function with the same denominator as (53) but with a numerator of K_1. Note that the two transfer functions are consistent with the corresponding input-output differential equations found in (3.27) and (3.28) for this system.

In the previous examples, we used the rules for combining blocks that are in series or in parallel, as shown in Figures 13.4 and 13.5. We also repeatedly used the rule for simplifying the basic feedback configuration given in Figure 13.22(a). A number of other operations can be derived to help simplify block diagrams. To conclude this chapter, we present and illustrate two of these additional operations.

Keep in mind that a block diagram is just a means of representing the algebraic Laplace-transformed equations that describe a system. Simplifying or reducing the diagram is equivalent to manipulating the equations. In order to prove that a particular operation on the block diagram is valid, we need only show that the relationships among the transformed variables of interest are left unchanged.

Moving a Pick-Off Point

A **pick-off point** is a point where an incoming variable in the diagram is directed into more than one block. In the partial diagram of Figure 13.27(a),

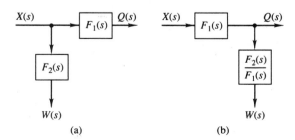

(a)   (b)

FIGURE 13.27 Moving a pick-off point.

the incoming signal $X(s)$ is used not only to provide the output $Q(s)$ but also to form the signal $W(s)$, which in practice might be fed back to a summer that appears earlier in the complete diagram. The pick-off point can be moved to the right of $F_1(s)$ if the transfer function of the block leading to $W(s)$ is modified as shown in Figure 13.27(b). Both parts of the figure give the same equations:

$$Q(s) = F_1(s)X(s)$$
$$W(s) = F_2(s)X(s)$$

▶ **EXAMPLE 13.13**

Use Figure 13.27 to find the closed-loop transfer function for the system shown in Figure 13.24.

Solution

The pick-off point leading to the gain block a_1 can be moved to the output $Y(s)$ by replacing a_1 by a_1s, as shown in Figure 13.28(a). Then the two integrator blocks, which are now in series, can be combined to give the transfer function $G(s) = 1/s^2$. The two feedback blocks are now in parallel and can be combined into the single transfer function $a_1s + a_0$, as shown in Figure 13.28(b). Finally, by (46),

$$T(s) = \frac{Y(s)}{U(s)} = \frac{1/s^2}{1 + (a_1s + a_0)/s^2} = \frac{1}{s^2 + a_1s + a_0}$$

which agrees with (49), as found in Example 13.11.

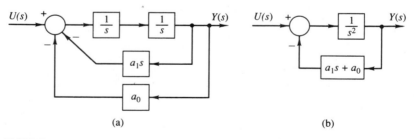

(a)   (b)

FIGURE 13.28 Equivalent block diagrams for the system shown in Figure 13.24.

Moving a Summing Junction

Suppose that, in the partial diagram of Figure 13.29(a), we wish to move the summing junction to the left of the block that has the transfer function

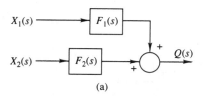

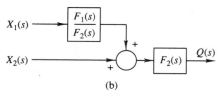

FIGURE 13.29   Moving a summing junction.

$F_2(s)$. We can do this by modifying the transfer function of the block whose input is $X_1(s)$, as shown in part (b) of the figure. For each part of the figure,

$$Q(s) = F_1(s)X_1(s) + F_2(s)X_2(s)$$

▶ **EXAMPLE 13.14**

Find the closed-loop transfer function $T(s) = Y(s)/U(s)$ for the feedback system shown in Figure 13.30(a).

Solution

We cannot immediately apply (46) to the inner feedback loop consisting of the first integrator and the gain block a_1, because the output of block b_1 enters a summer within that loop. We therefore use Figure 13.29 to move this summer to the left of the first integrator block, where it can be combined with the first summer. The resulting diagram is given in Figure 13.30(b).

Now (46) can be applied to the inner feedback loop to give the transfer function

$$G_1(s) = \frac{1/s}{1 + a_1/s} = \frac{1}{s + a_1}$$

The equivalent block with the transfer function $G_1(s)$ is then in series with the remaining integrator, which results in a combined transfer function of $1/[s(s + a_1)]$. Also, the two blocks with gains of sb_1 and 1 are in parallel and can be combined into a single block. These simplifications are shown in Figure 13.30(c).

We can now repeat the procedure and move the right summer to the left of the block labeled $1/[s(s + a_1)]$, where it can again be combined with

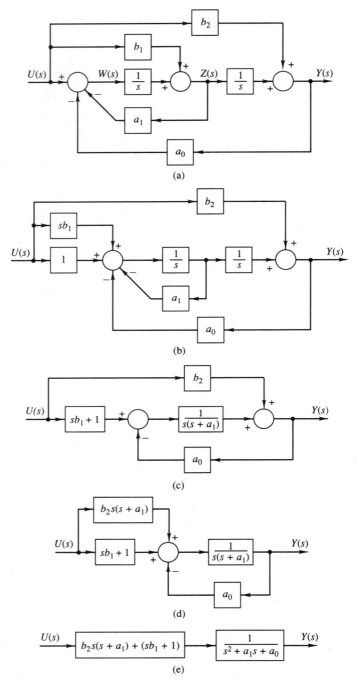

FIGURE 13.30 (a) Block diagram for Example 13.14. (b), (c), (d), (e) Equivalent block diagrams.

the first summer. This is done in part (d) of the figure. The two blocks in parallel at the left can now be combined by adding their transfer functions, and (46) can be applied to the right part of the diagram to give

$$\frac{\dfrac{1}{s(s+a_1)}}{1+\dfrac{a_0}{s(s+a_1)}}=\frac{1}{s^2+a_1s+a_0}$$

These steps yield Figure 13.30(e), from which we see that

$$T(s)=\frac{b_2s^2+(a_1b_2+b_1)s+1}{s^2+a_1s+a_0} \tag{55}$$

Because performing operations on a given block diagram is equivalent to manipulating the algebraic equations that describe the system, it may sometimes be easier to work with the equations themselves. As an alternative solution to the last example, suppose that we start by writing the equations for each of the three summers in Figure 13.30(a):

$$W(s)=U(s)-a_0Y(s)-a_1Z(s) \tag{56a}$$

$$Z(s)=\frac{1}{s}W(s)+b_1U(s) \tag{56b}$$

$$Y(s)=\frac{1}{s}Z(s)+b_2U(s) \tag{56c}$$

Substituting (56a) into (56b), we see that

$$Z(s)=\frac{1}{s}[U(s)-a_0Y(s)-a_1Z(s)]+b_1U(s)$$

from which

$$Z(s)=\frac{1}{s+a_1}[-a_0Y(s)+(b_1s+1)U(s)] \tag{57}$$

Substituting (57) into (56c) gives

$$Y(s)=\frac{1}{s(s+a_1)}[-a_0Y(s)+(b_1s+1)U(s)]+b_2U(s)$$

Rearranging this equation, we find that

$$\frac{Y(s)}{U(s)}=\frac{b_2s^2+(a_1b_2+b_1)s+1}{s^2+a_1s+a_0}$$

which agrees with (55), as found in Example 13.14.

SUMMARY

Block diagrams are an important way of representing the structure and properties of fixed linear systems. We start the construction of a block diagram by transforming the system equations, assuming zero initial conditions. When the system is described by a state-variable model, by an input-output model, or by coupled equations in nonstandard form, we can construct a diagram using integrators, gain blocks, and summers. For a system of order n we need n integrators, each with a transfer function of $1/s$. We feed the signals represented by the integrator outputs through individual gain blocks and then back to an input summer, in accordance with the transformed equations. For general state-variable models or input-output equations containing derivatives of the input, we also feed signals forward to an output summer.

If a block diagram is drawn for a given input-output differential equation or for a given transfer function, we can use the diagram to obtain a state-variable model. The integrator outputs are usually taken to be the Laplace-transformed state variables.

In simulation diagrams, the variables are functions of time rather than transformed quantities. For fixed linear systems, they have a form that is essentially the same as that of the block diagrams. The use of simulation diagrams, however, can be extended to systems where the initial stored energy is important or where there are time-varying or nonlinear elements.

The blocks used in diagrams for feedback systems may contain transfer functions of any degree of complexity. We developed a number of rules, including those for series and parallel combinations and for the basic feedback configuration in Figure 13.22(a), for simplifying block diagrams. Reducing block diagrams and adding components to improve the performance of feedback systems will be important in the next chapter.

PROBLEMS

13.1 Find the transfer functions of the blocks shown in parts (b) and (c) of Figure P13.1 such that the transfer functions $Y(s)/X_1(s)$ and $Y(s)/X_2(s)$ are identical to those for part (a) of the figure.

13.2 Find the transfer functions of the blocks shown in parts (b) and (c) of Figure P13.2 such that the transfer functions $Y_1(s)/X(s)$ and $Y_2(s)/X(s)$ are identical to those for part (a) of the figure.

* **13.3** Evaluate the transfer functions $T_1(s) = Y(s)/U(s)$ and $T_2(s) = Z(s)/U(s)$ as rational functions for the block diagram shown in Figure P13.3.

13.4 Draw block diagrams for each of the following sets of state-variable equations.
    a) $\dot{x} = -4x + 6y + 2u(t)$
        $\dot{y} = -2x - 3y$

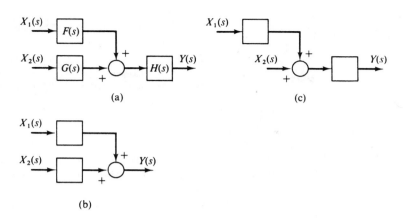

FIGURE P13.1

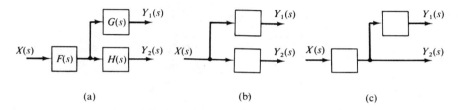

FIGURE P13.2

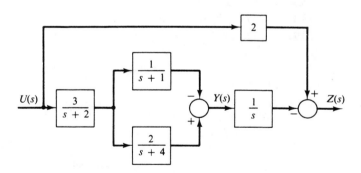

FIGURE P13.3

b) $\dot{x}_1 = -3x_1 + 5x_2 + 3u(t)$
$\dot{x}_2 = 4x_1 - 6x_2 - u(t)$

c) $\dot{\theta} = \omega$
$\dot{\omega} = -8\theta - 4\omega + 2x$
$\dot{x} = v$
$\dot{v} = 6\theta - 3x + u(t)$

13.5 Draw simulation diagrams for each of the following nonlinear models.

    a) $\dot{v}_1 = -3v_1 + 2|v_2|v_2 + 3\cos 2t$

        $\dot{v}_2 = v_1 - v_2$

    b) $\ddot{y} + 2|\dot{y}|\dot{y} + y^3 = 5u(t)$

13.6 Draw block diagrams for each of the following input-output models.

    a) $\dot{y} + 3y = 2u(t)$

    b) $\dot{y} + 3y = 2\dot{u} + u(t)$

    c) $\ddot{z} + 4\dot{z} + 2z = u(t)$

    d) $\ddot{z} + 4\dot{z} + 2z = 3\dot{u} + 2u(t)$

* 13.7 Draw block diagrams for each of the following input-output models. Also write a set of state-variable equations for each of the models.

    a) $\ddot{y} + 5\dot{y} + 6y = 12u(t)$

    b) $\ddot{y} + 5\dot{y} + 6y = 2\ddot{u} + \dot{u} + 2u(t)$

    c) $\dddot{y} + 2\ddot{y} + 3\dot{y} + 4y = 2\ddot{u} - \dot{u} + 4u(t)$

13.8 Repeat Problem 13.7 for each of the following models.

    a) $2\ddot{y} + 3\dot{y} + 6y = 4u(t)$

    b) $2\ddot{y} + 3\dot{y} + 6y = -2\dot{u} + 3u(t)$

    c) $\ddot{z} + 4\dot{z} + 3z = \ddot{u} + 2u(t)$

13.9 Draw a block diagram for the rotational mechanical system described by the following two equations, where $\theta_a(t)$ is the input. Let $\dot{z} = 2\dot{\theta}_1 - \dot{\theta}_a$.

$$2\ddot{\theta}_1 + \dot{\theta}_1 + 3(\dot{\theta}_1 - \dot{\theta}_2) + \theta_1 = \dot{\theta}_a + \theta_a(t)$$

$$2\ddot{\theta}_2 + \dot{\theta}_2 = 3(\dot{\theta}_1 - \dot{\theta}_2) + \theta_2$$

In Problems 13.10 through 13.19, draw block diagrams for the systems that were modeled in the examples indicated, using the equations cited.

13.10 (2.19) in Example 2.4.

13.11 (2.25) in Example 2.6.

13.12 (3.3) and (3.4) in Example 3.2.

13.13 (3.8) and (3.9) in Example 3.5.

13.14 (3.21) and (3.22) in Example 3.8.

13.15 (3.23) and (3.24) in Example 3.9.

13.16 a) (4.27) in Example 4.2.

    b) (4.29) in Example 4.2.

13.17 (4.64) and (4.66) in Example 4.12.

13.18 a) (5.21) in Example 5.3.

    b) (5.41), (5.42), and (5.43) in Example 5.8.

13.19 (5.47) in Example 5.9.

In Problems 13.20 through 13.23, draw a simulation diagram for the nonlinear system that was modeled in the example indicated, using the equation(s) cited. Also draw a simulation diagram for the linearized model.

13.20 (9.23) in Example 9.7.

13.21 (9.27) in Example 9.8.

13.22 (9.33) in Example 9.9.

13.23 (9.37), (9.38), and (9.39) in Example 9.10.

In Problems 13.24 through 13.26, determine the closed-loop transfer function $Y(s)/U(s)$ as a rational function of s for the block diagram shown in the figure cited.

* 13.24 Figure P13.24.

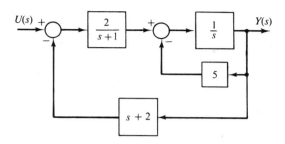

FIGURE P13.24

13.25 Figure P13.25.

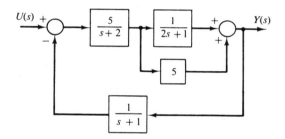

FIGURE P13.25

* 13.26 Figure 13.21(b), where $U(s) = \tau_a(s)$ and $Y(s) = X(s)$.

13.27 **a)** Draw a block diagram for the rotational mechanical system modeled in Example 4.5 by transforming (4.42) and drawing the corresponding diagram.
b) Set $\tau_L(s)$ equal to zero and reduce the block diagram to find the transfer function $T_1(s) = \Omega_2(s)/\tau_a(s)$.
c) Set $\tau_a(s)$ equal to zero and reduce the block diagram you found in part (a) to obtain the transfer function $T_2(s) = \Omega_2(s)/\tau_L(s)$.
d) Transform (4.43) and use the result to verify your answers to parts (b) and (c).

13.28 **a)** Draw a block diagram for the electromechanical system modeled in Example 10.2 by (10.31).
b) Obtain the transfer functions $T_1(s) = \Omega(s)/E_i(s)$ and $T_2(s) = \Omega(s)/\tau_L(s)$ by reducing the block diagram, first with $\tau_L(s) = 0$ and then with $E_i(s) = 0$. Compare your answers with the transfer functions $H_1(s)$ and $H_2(s)$ derived in Example 10.2.

13.29 **a)** Draw a block diagram for the thermal system modeled in Example 11.4 by (11.19).

b) Obtain the transfer function $T(s) = \hat{Q}_2(s)/\hat{Q}_i(s)$ by reducing the block diagram. Compare your answer with (11.20).

* 13.30 a) For the block diagram shown in Figure P13.30, find the closed-loop transfer function $T(s) = Y(s)/U(s)$ as a ratio of polynomials.

b) Determine the steady-state response to a unit step-function input in terms of K.

c) Write the damping ratio ζ and the undamped natural frequency ω_n in terms of K. Solve for the value of K for which $\zeta = 1/\sqrt{2}$, and find the corresponding value of ω_n.

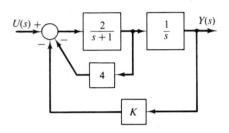

FIGURE P13.30

13.31 a) Find the closed-loop transfer function $T(s) = Y(s)/U(s)$ as a ratio of polynomials for the block diagram shown in Figure P13.31.

b) Determine the undamped natural frequency ω_n and the damping ratio ζ of the closed-loop system. Solve for the value of K for which $\omega_n = 5$ rad/s, and find the corresponding value of ζ.

c) Find the steady-state value of the response when the input is a step function of height 5 and when K has the value determined in part (b).

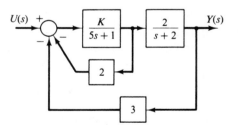

FIGURE P13.31

* 13.32 Consider the feedback system shown in Figure P13.32, which has inputs $U(s)$ and $V(s)$ and output $Y(s)$.

a) Find the transfer function $T_1(s) = Y(s)/U(s)$ as a ratio of polynomials. *Note:* $V(s)$ should be set equal to zero for this calculation.

b) Find the transfer function $T_2(s) = Y(s)/V(s)$ as a ratio of polynomials, taking $U(s) = 0$. *Hint:* Define the output of the right summing junction as

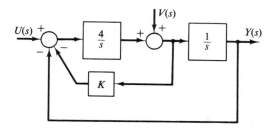

FIGURE P13.32

$Z(s)$, and write the algebraic transform equations relating $V(s)$, $Z(s)$, and $Y(s)$.

c) Determine the damping ratio ζ and the undamped natural frequency ω_n of the closed-loop system. Determine the value of K for which $\zeta = 1$.

d) Find the steady-state response when $u(t)$ is the unit step function and $v(t) = 0$. Repeat the solution when $u(t) = 0$ and $v(t)$ is the unit step function, and comment on the difference in the results.

13.33 a) Find the closed-loop transfer function $T(s) = Y(s)/U(s)$ as a ratio of polynomials for the block diagram shown in Figure P13.33.

b) Express the damping ratio ζ and the undamped natural frequency ω_n in terms of K. Show that both poles of $T(s)$ are on the negative real axis for $0 \leq K \leq 1/4$.

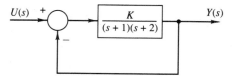

FIGURE P13.33

* 13.34 a) Find the closed-loop transfer function $T(s) = Y(s)/U(s)$ as a ratio of polynomials for the block diagram shown in Figure P13.34.

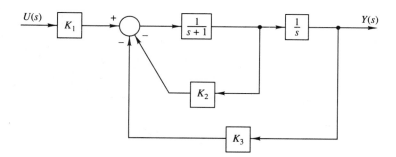

FIGURE P13.34

b) Express the damping ratio ζ and the undamped natural frequency ω_n in terms of the gains K_2 and K_3. Assume that K_3 is positive but that K_2 can be either positive or negative. Explain why ζ and ω_n are not affected by K_1.

c) For what values of K_2 is the system stable?

d) For what values of K_2 will the zero-input response contain decaying oscillations?

e) Determine the values of K_2 and K_3 such that $\omega_n = 2$ rad/s and $\zeta = 1/2$.

13.35 a) Write a set of state-variable equations for the system represented by the block diagram in Figure P13.35.

b) Determine the closed-loop transfer function $T(s) = \Theta(s)/F_a(s)$ as a ratio of polynomials.

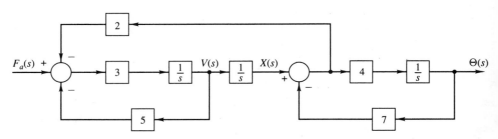

FIGURE P13.35

* 13.36 Find the closed-loop transfer functions $T_1(s) = Y(s)/U(s)$ and $T_2(s) = Z(s)/U(s)$ in terms of the individual transfer functions $A(s), \ldots, E(s)$ for the block diagram shown in Figure P13.36. Give your answer as a ratio of terms that involve only sums, differences, and products of the individual transfer functions.

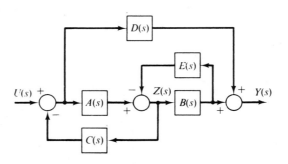

FIGURE P13.36

13.37 Repeat Problem 13.36 for the block diagram shown in Figure P13.37.

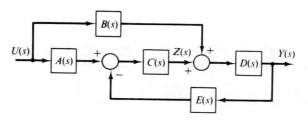

FIGURE P13.37

FEEDBACK SYSTEM MODELING AND DESIGN TOOLS

This chapter uses techniques developed previously, especially those in Section 13.5, to consider some of the problems encountered in modeling and designing feedback control systems. In order to introduce the reader to some of the typical concerns, we first examine in detail a particular electromechanical system. We construct a block-diagram model, find the transfer function, and then improve the performance by adjusting those parameters that are under the designer's control.

Two important graphical design aids are described in Sections 14.2 and 14.3. The first of these shows how the poles of the transfer function move when one of the system parameters is varied. The second represents the sinusoidal steady-state response by diagrams that are convenient for system design.

In the final two sections we explain and illustrate some of the practical design criteria and ways of meeting those criteria. We include stability considerations, the transient response, the steady-state errors corresponding to particular inputs, the need for satisfactory performance even if the system parameters change somewhat, minimizing the response to unwanted disturbance inputs, and rejecting unwanted noise.

■ 14.1 APPLICATION TO A CONTROL SYSTEM

Most control systems use feedback to force the output variable to follow a reference input while remaining relatively insensitive to the effects of one or more disturbance inputs. A common type of control system is the **servomechanism**. Here a mechanical input variable, such as the position or angular rotation of an element, is required to follow a reference input, such as the orientation of a knob or dial that is varied by a human operator. For example, a mechanical manipulator used for working with radioactive materials would require several servomechanisms to translate the operator's hand motion into equivalent physical motion at a remote location behind the shielding material.

In this section, we model and analyze a simple servomechanism whose purpose is to make the angular orientation of an output shaft follow that of a manually adjusted dial. First, we will develop a mathematical model of the feedback system by writing the algebraic and differential equations that describe the individual elements, transforming these equations and drawing a block diagram, and then reducing the block diagram to give a single transfer function. Finally, we shall analyze the system's performance and consider means of improving it.

System Description

The positional servomechanism we will consider is shown in Figure 14.1. The manually set input potentiometer at the left has its two ends connected to constant voltage sources, and its wiper voltage e_1 obeys the algebraic relationship

$$e_1 = K_\theta \theta_i(t) \tag{1}$$

where K_θ is a constant, provided that the potentiometer is linear and that no current is drawn by the amplifier—that is, there is no loading. The output potentiometer at the right of the figure is identical to the input potentiometer, except that its wiper is mechanically connected to the output shaft. Hence the voltage of the wiper of the output potentiometer obeys the equation

$$e_2 = K_\theta \theta_o \tag{2}$$

If both potentiometers are constrained to one full revolution and if the constant voltage sources are $\pm A$ volts, then $K_\theta = A/\pi$ volts per radian.

The amplifier's output voltage is

$$e_a = K_A(e_1 - e_2) \tag{3}$$

where K_A is the amplifier gain in volts per volt. It is assumed that (3) holds regardless of the current i flowing in the armature circuit of the motor and that the amplifier draws no current from the wipers of the input and output potentiometers. Note that the amplifier is described by an algebraic rather than a differential equation, which implies that (3) holds regardless of how rapidly e_1 or e_2 may vary.

The motor is assumed to have a constant field current and negligible inductance in the armature winding. The electromechanical driving torque τ_e and the induced voltage e_m are given, as in (10.29), by

$$\tau_e = \alpha i$$

$$e_{m} = \alpha \dot{\phi}$$

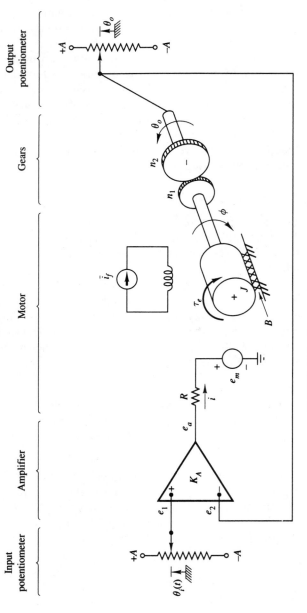

FIGURE 14.1   Servomechanism components.

where the coupling coefficient α has units of volt-seconds or, equivalently, newton-meters per ampere and is dependent on the field current $\bar{i}_f$. The symbol ϕ denotes the angular displacement of the motor shaft. If the armature resistance is denoted by R, the viscous-friction coefficent by B, and the moment of inertia by J, the motor can be modeled by the pair of equations

$$i = \frac{1}{R}(e_a - \alpha\dot{\phi}) \qquad (4a)$$

$$J\ddot{\phi} + B\dot{\phi} = \alpha i \qquad (4b)$$

The motor shaft is connected to the output shaft through a pair of gears having the gear ratio $N = n_2/n_1$. Hence the motor angle ϕ and the output wiper angle θ_o are related by

$$\theta_o = \frac{1}{N}\phi \qquad (5)$$

Although Figure 14.1 does not indicate a moment of inertia attached to the right gear or moments of inertia for the gears themselves, such moments of inertia could be referred to the motor shaft and incorporated in the value of J if they were not negligible. Likewise, any viscous friction associated with the output shaft could be referred to the motor and combined with B.

System Model

In order to obtain a block diagram for the system, we transform (1) through (5) with zero initial conditions. For the combination of the input and output potentiometers and the amplifier, substituting (1) and (2) into (3) and taking the Laplace transform yield

$$E_a(s) = K_A K_\theta [\Theta_i(s) - \Theta_o(s)] \qquad (6)$$

which is represented by the two gains of K_θ, the summing junction, and the gain of K_A within the dashed rectangle shown in Figure 14.2.

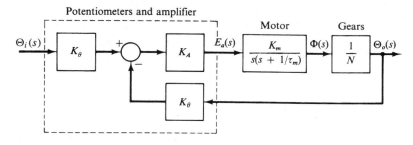

FIGURE 14.2 Servomechanism block diagram.

When (4) is transformed and $I(s)$ is eliminated, we obtain the single transformed equation

$$\left[Js^2 + \left(B + \frac{\alpha^2}{R} \right) s \right] \Phi(s) = \frac{\alpha}{R} E_a(s)$$

for the motor, which yields the transfer function

$$\frac{\Phi(s)}{E_a(s)} = \frac{\dfrac{\alpha}{RJ}}{s \left[s + \left(\dfrac{B}{J} + \dfrac{\alpha^2}{JR} \right) \right]}$$

If we define the parameters

$$K_m = \frac{\alpha}{RJ}$$

$$\tau_m = \frac{1}{\dfrac{B}{J} + \dfrac{\alpha^2}{JR}}$$

the transfer function of the motor becomes

$$\frac{\Phi(s)}{E_a(s)} = \frac{K_m}{s \left(s + \dfrac{1}{\tau_m} \right)} \tag{7}$$

which results in a single block located in the forward path of the diagram shown in Figure 14.2. Finally, we describe the gears by the gain $1/N$ according to

$$\Theta_o(s) = \frac{1}{N} \Phi(s) \tag{8}$$

and draw the feedback path from the output to the output-potentiometer block.

Closed-Loop Transfer Function

To calculate $T(s) = \Theta_o(s)/\Theta_i(s)$, the transfer function of the closed-loop system, we note that the first block with gain K_θ is in series with the feedback-loop portion of the system. We can obtain the transfer function of the feedback loop by applying (13.46) with

$$G(s) = \frac{K_A K_m / N}{s(s + 1/\tau_m)}$$

$$H(s) = K_\theta$$

Then

$$T(s) = K_\theta \left[\frac{G(s)}{1 + G(s)H(s)} \right] = \frac{K_A K_m K_\theta / N}{s^2 + (1/\tau_m)s + K_A K_m K_\theta / N} \tag{9}$$

By inspection of (9), we can observe several important aspects of the behavior of the closed-loop system. First, the system model is second-order, and its closed-loop transfer function $T(s)$ has two poles and no zeros in the finite s-plane. Assuming that the values of all the parameters appearing in $T(s)$ are positive, the poles of $T(s)$ will be in the left half of the complex plane, and the closed-loop system will be stable regardless of the specific numerical values of the parameters.

We obtain the steady-state value of the unit step response of the closed-loop system by setting s equal to zero in (9).

$$T(0) = \frac{K_A K_m K_\theta / N}{K_A K_m K_\theta / N} = 1$$

Hence a step input for $\theta_i(t)$ will result in an output angle θ_o that is identical to the input angle in the steady state. This steady-state condition of zero error will occur regardless of the specific numerical values for the system parameters. This property is a result of the feedback structure of the servomechanism, whereby a signal that is proportional to the error signal $\theta_i(t) - \theta_o$ is used to drive the motor. Because the motor acts like an integrator (its transfer function $\Phi(s)/E_a(s)$ has a pole at $s = 0$), the armature voltage e_a must become zero if the system is to reach steady state with a constant input; otherwise, $\dot{\phi}$ would not be zero. Because of (3), the difference of the wiper voltages e_1 and e_2 must be zero in the steady state, and this condition requires that $(\theta_o)_{ss} = \theta_i$.

Design for Specified Damping Ratio

In practice, all the parameter values except one are often fixed and we must select the remaining one to yield some specific response characteristic such as the damping ratio, undamped natural frequency, or steady-state response. Suppose that all the parameters except the amplifier gain K_A are fixed at the values listed in Table 14.1 and that we must select K_A to yield a value of 0.50 for the damping ratio.

TABLE 14.1   Numerical Values of Servomechanism Parameters

Parameter	Value
A (magnitude of potentiometer voltages)	15.0 V
K_m (for the motor)	150. $V \cdot rad/s^2$
τ_m (for the motor)	0.40 s
N (gear ratio)	10.

Because the potentiometer gains are $K_\theta = A/\pi$, it follows that $K_\theta = 15.0/\pi = 4.775$ V/rad. Substituting the known parameter values into (9) results in the closed-loop transfer function

$$
\begin{aligned}
T(s) &= \frac{(150 \times 4.775/10)K_A}{s^2 + (1/0.40)s + (150 \times 4.775/10)K_A} \\
&= \frac{71.62K_A}{s^2 + 2.50s + 71.62K_A}
\end{aligned}
\tag{10}
$$

Comparing the denominator of (10) to the polynomial $s^2 + 2\zeta\omega_n s + \omega_n^2$, which is used to define the damping ratio ζ and the undamped natural frequency ω_n, we see that

$$
2\zeta\omega_n = 2.50
\tag{11a}
$$

$$
\omega_n^2 = 71.62K_A
\tag{11b}
$$

Setting ζ equal to its specified value of 0.50 in (11a), we get $\omega_n = 2.50$ rad/s. Substituting for ω_n^2 in (11b) gives the required amplifier gain as

$$
K_A = 0.08727 \text{ V/V}
$$

Substituting this value of K_A into (10) yields the closed-loop transfer function in numerical form as

$$
T(s) = \frac{6.25}{s^2 + 2.50s + 6.25}
\tag{12}
$$

You can verify that the denominator of $T(s)$ results in a pair of complex poles having $\zeta = 0.50$ as specified.

Proportional-Plus-Derivative Feedback

The system designed in the foregoing paragraphs is constrained in several ways that turn out to be undesirable in practice. For example, although we obtained the specified damping ratio of 0.50, the value of ω_n was dictated by the requirement on ζ and could not have been specified independently. In practice, one might want to specify both ζ and ω_n for the closed-loop system. We shall demonstrate that this can be done, provided that a signal proportional to the angular velocity of the motor shaft (or output shaft) is fed back and added to the amplifier input.

Assume that a tachometer is attached directly to the motor and a potentiometer is placed across the output terminals of the tachometer, such that the voltage on the potentiometer wiper is

$$
e_3 = K_T \dot{\phi}
$$

where K_T has units of volt-seconds and is adjustable between zero and some positive maximum value. The signal e_3 is added to e_2, such that the armature voltage is now

$$e_a = K_A(e_1 - e_2 - e_3)$$
$$= K_A[K_\theta \theta_i(t) - K_\theta \theta_o - K_T \dot\phi]$$

Then the transform of the armature voltage becomes

$$E_a(s) = K_A[K_\theta \Theta_i(s) - K_\theta \Theta_o(s) - K_T s \Phi(s)] \tag{13}$$

The modified system can be represented by the block diagram shown in Figure 14.3, which we obtain by separating the motor transfer function $K_m/[s(s+1/\tau_m)]$ into the pair of blocks in series shown in the figure and then adding the inner feedback path corresponding to the term $K_T s \Phi(s)$. Because we assume zero initial conditions when evaluating transfer functions, the input to the gain block K_T is $s\Phi(s) = \mathcal{L}[\dot\phi(t)]$. Thus a signal proportional to the angular velocity of the motor shaft is being fed through the inner feedback path to the summing junction.

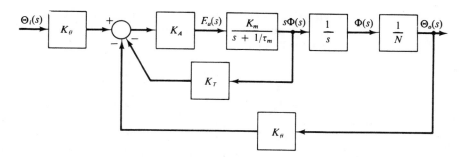

FIGURE 14.3 Block diagram of servomechanism with tachometer feedback added.

To determine the effect of the tachometer feedback on the closed-loop transfer function, we can reduce the inner loop shown in Figure 14.3 by using (13.46) with $G(s) = K_A K_m/(s + 1/\tau_m)$ and $H(s) = K_T$ to give

$$T'(s) = \frac{K_A K_m}{s + (1/\tau_m) + K_A K_m K_T}$$

Applying (13.46) again with $G(s) = T'(s)/sN$ and $H(s) = K_\theta$ and then multiplying the result by K_θ, we obtain the overall transfer function

$$T(s) = \frac{K_A K_m K_\theta/N}{s^2 + [(1/\tau_m) + K_A K_m K_T]s + K_A K_m K_\theta/N} \tag{14}$$

Comparing (14) to (9) indicates that the only effect of the tachometer feedback is to modify the coefficient of s in the denominator of the transfer function. Hence the damping ratio and undamped natural frequency now satisfy the relationships

$$2\zeta\omega_n = (1/\tau_m) + K_A K_m K_T$$
$$\omega_n^2 = K_A K_m K_\theta / N \tag{15}$$

If the values of both K_A and K_T can be selected with τ_m, K_m, K_θ, and N fixed as before, we can specify values for both ζ and ω_n. For example, using the parameter values given in Table 14.1 with $\zeta = 0.50$, we find that (15) reduces to

$$\omega_n = 2.50 + 150 K_A K_T \tag{16a}$$
$$\omega_n^2 = 71.62 K_A \tag{16b}$$

If, for example, we want ω_n to be 5.0 rad/s, it follows that

$$K_A = 0.3491 \text{ V/V}$$
$$K_T = 0.04775 \text{ V·s/rad}$$

When we substitute these parameter values and those listed in Table 14.1 into (14), the numerical form of the closed-loop transfer function with tachometer feedback is

$$T(s) = \frac{25.0}{s^2 + 5.0s + 25.0}$$

It is easy to verify that the two poles of $T(s)$ are complex and have $\zeta = 0.50$ and $\omega_n = 5.0$ rad/s, as required.

In concluding this example, we note that the control law given by (13) uses a combination of the output-shaft angle θ_o and the motor angular velocity $\dot{\phi}$ as the feedback signals. It is also possible to think in terms of having the output-shaft angular velocity $\dot{\theta}_o$ fed back by noting that the two angular velocities in question are proportional to one another: $\dot{\theta}_o = \dot{\phi}/N$. Hence we can rewrite (13) in the time domain and in terms of the output-shaft angle as

$$e_a = K_A[K_\theta \theta_i(t) - K_\theta \theta_o - K_{\dot{\theta}} \dot{\theta}_o] \tag{17}$$

where $K_{\dot{\theta}} = N K_T$, which is the gain of the angular-velocity term. The block diagram corresponding to this version of the control law can take either of the equivalent forms shown in Figure 14.4. If we combine the two parallel feedback paths shown in Figure 14.4(b) to yield the single feedback transfer function $K_\theta + K_{\dot{\theta}}s$, using (13.46) gives the same expression for $T(s) = \Theta_o(s)/\Theta_i(s)$ as found in (14).

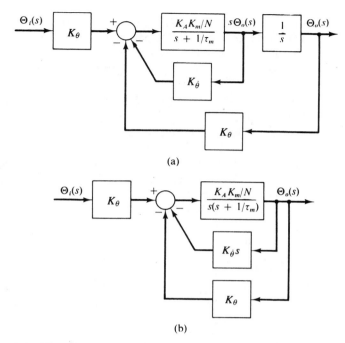

FIGURE 14.4   Equivalent block diagrams for servomechanism with tachometer feedback.

14.2 ROOT-LOCUS DIAGRAMS

The poles of a system's overall transfer function determine whether the system is stable and, for a stable system, determine the nature of the transient response. Because the positions of the poles in the complex s-plane constitute one of the key design considerations, it is important to know how these positions change when one of the parameters of the system is varied.

The effect of the pole positions on stability and on the transient response was discussed in detail in Chapters 6 and 8. Keep in mind that the poles of the transfer function are roots of the characteristic polynomial used in Chapter 6. If all the poles are inside the left half of the s-plane, then the free response decays to zero and the system is stable. If the transfer function has a pole inside the right half-plane or repeated poles on the imaginary axis, the free response increases without limit and the system is unstable. Finally, if all the poles are inside the left half-plane except for first-order poles on the imaginary axis (possibly including the origin), a nonzero but finite component of the free response remains for large values of t, and the system is said to be marginally stable.

The nature of the free response corresponding to various pole positions was illustrated in Figures 6.17 through 6.20. For a single pole on the negative real axis of the s-plane, the distance from the vertical axis is the reciprocal of the time constant. For a pair of first-order poles at $s = -\alpha \pm j\beta$ in the left half-plane, the free response has the form

$$y_H(t) = K\epsilon^{-\alpha t} \cos(\beta t + \phi)$$

where α, the distance from the vertical axis, is again the reciprocal of the time constant for the exponential factor.

The movement of the pole positions when a particular parameter is varied can be shown by drawing the path traced out in the s-plane as the parameter is increased from very small to very large values. Because poles of the transfer function are roots of the characteristic equation, such a path is called a **root locus**. It can help us select appropriate values for some of the elements. Although we shall not use it in this way, it can also help us determine how sensitive the pole positions are to unwanted variations in the system components.

Most root-locus diagrams are drawn for the closed-loop transfer function of a standard feedback configuration, and this will be our primary interest. However, we shall first illustrate the concept of a locus of possible pole positions by examining two mechanical systems that do not have external feedback paths.

▶ **EXAMPLE 14.1**

For the first-order system shown in Figure 14.5(a), find the locus traced out by the pole of $T(s) = V(s)/F_a(s)$ when the friction coefficient B is varied from zero to infinity.

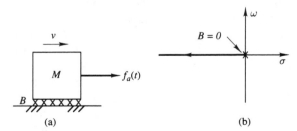

FIGURE 14.5 (a) Mechanical system for Example 14.1.
(b) Locus of pole positions when B is varied.

Solution

The differential equation describing the system is $M\dot{v} + Bv = f_a(t)$, so the transfer function is

$$T(s) = \frac{1}{Ms + B}$$

which has a single pole at $s = -B/M$. When $B = 0$, the pole is at the origin of the s-plane and is shown by the cross in Figure 14.5(b). The free response will not decay to zero for this case, because there is no retarding frictional force.

As B increases, the pole moves to the left, as indicated by the arrow in the figure. As expected, we see that the free response decays more and more quickly as B is increased.

Finding the locus for each part of the next example is more complicated, but the general procedure is the same. At the end of this section, we shall show how to put the transfer function into a form that enables us to use some special techniques to obtain the locus more easily.

▶ **EXAMPLE 14.2**

Consider the transfer function $T(s) = X(s)/F_a(s)$ for the second-order mechanical system shown in Figure 14.6(a). First assume that M and B have fixed values. Find the locus traced out by the poles of $T(s)$ as the spring constant K is increased from zero toward infinity. Repeat the problem when M and K are fixed, while the friction coefficient B is varied from zero toward infinity.

Solution

The input-output differential equation is easily shown to be $M\ddot{x} + B\dot{x} + Kx = f_a(t)$, so the transfer function is

$$T(s) = \frac{1}{Ms^2 + Bs + K} = \frac{\dfrac{1}{M}}{s^2 + \dfrac{B}{M}s + \dfrac{K}{M}}$$

Because the denominator of $T(s)$ is a quadratic, there are two poles. When $K = 0$, these poles are at $s = 0$ and $s = -B/M$, as indicated by the crosses in Figure 14.6(b). When $K = B^2/4M$, the denominator becomes

$$s^2 + \frac{B}{M}s + \frac{B^2}{4M^2} = \left(s + \frac{B}{2M}\right)^2$$

For this value of K, there is a double pole at $s = -B/2M$. For values of K larger than $B^2/4M$, it is convenient to rewrite the denominator of the transfer function by completing the square (Section 7.3):

$$T(s) = \frac{\dfrac{1}{M}}{\left(s + \dfrac{B}{2M}\right)^2 + \left(\dfrac{K}{M} - \dfrac{B^2}{4M^2}\right)}$$

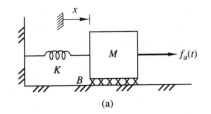

(a)

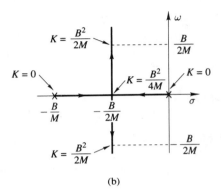

(b)

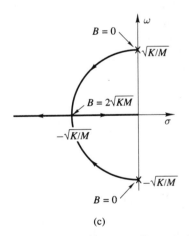

(c)

FIGURE 14.6 (a) Mechanical system for Example 14.2. (b) Locus of pole positions when K is varied. (c) Locus of pole positions when B is varied.

which has poles at

$$
s = -\frac{B}{2M} \pm j\sqrt{\frac{K}{M} - \frac{B^2}{4M^2}} = \frac{1}{2M}\left[-B \pm j\sqrt{4KM - B^2}\right] \tag{18}
$$

For constant values of M and B, the real part of this expression is constant, whereas the size of the imaginary part increases as K increases. The heavy lines in Figure 14.6(b) constitute the complete locus of all possible pole positions for nonnegative values of K. The arrows on the locus indicate the directions in which the poles move as K is increased. The values of K corresponding to some of the specific points are also shown.

For the case where M and K are fixed, we first let $B = 0$. The poles of $T(s)$ are then at $s = \pm j\sqrt{K/M}$, as indicated by the crosses in Figure 14.6(c). For $0 < B < 2\sqrt{KM}$, we have a pair of complex conjugate poles in the left half-plane, as given by (18). The distance of these poles from the origin of the s-plane is

$$\frac{1}{2M}[B^2 + (4KM - B^2)]^{1/2} = \sqrt{K/M}$$

Thus for constant values of K and M, this part of the locus is the arc of a circle of radius $\sqrt{K/M}$. When $B = 2\sqrt{KM}$, the denominator of $T(s)$ becomes

$$M(s^2 + 2\sqrt{K/M}s + K/M) = M\left(s + \sqrt{K/M}\right)^2$$

corresponding to a double pole on the negative real axis at $s = -\sqrt{K/M}$. For values of B larger than $2\sqrt{KM}$, there are two distinct poles on the negative real axis. The complete locus traced out by the pole positions is shown by the heavy lines. The arrows indicate increasing values of B.

Although a locus of possible pole positions can be drawn for any system in which only one of the parameters is varied, it is particularly important for us to be able to do this for the feedback configuration shown in Figure 13.22(a), which is repeated in Figure 14.7. From (13.46), the closed-loop transfer function is

$$T(s) = \frac{G(s)}{1 + G(s)H(s)} \tag{19}$$

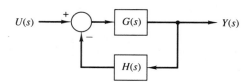

FIGURE 14.7 Block diagram of a feedback system.

We shall assume that the open-loop transfer function $G(s)H(s)$ can be expressed in factored form as

$$G(s)H(s) = K\frac{(s - z_1) \cdots (s - z_m)}{(s - p_1) \cdots (s - p_n)} \tag{20a}$$

$$= KF(s) \tag{20b}$$

Note from this definition that $F(s)$ contains all the factors of $G(s)H(s)$ except the multiplying constant K. Parts of $G(s)H(s)$ are normally under the control of the designer, who typically takes a particular $F(s)$ and then sketches a locus of the poles of $T(s)$ as K is varied. The designer can do this *without* having first to write $T(s)$ as an explicit rational function and without having to factor high-order polynomials.

The quantities z_1 through z_m in (20) are the zeros of $F(s)$ in the finite s-plane, which are referred to as the **open-loop zeros**. The quantities p_1 through p_n are the poles, referred to as the **open-loop poles**. For all practical physical systems $m \leq n$. If $m < n$, then $F(s)$ is said to have a zero of order $n - m$ at infinity. We seek a locus of the poles of $T(s)$ as the positive constant K is varied. The poles of the closed-loop transfer function $T(s)$ will lie on the root locus and will be called roots. In the ensuing discussion, the terms *poles* and *zeros* refer to p_i and z_j, respectively, in the open-loop transfer function $KF(s)$.

Chapter 15 will describe a computer program that can be used to construct the root locus when $F(s)$ is given. However, it is helpful to be able to predict the general shape of the locus, even if one plans to rely on a computer program for an exact final plot. Books on feedback control systems, including several of the references in Appendix D, develop a number of rules for sketching the locus by hand. We shall present here, without proof, the most useful of these rules.

Angle and Magnitude Criteria

We see from (19) that the poles of $T(s)$, which are the points on the root locus, will be those values of s for which

$$1 + G(s)H(s) = 0$$

With $G(s)H(s)$ replaced by $KF(s)$, this requires that $1 + KF(s) = 0$, so

$$KF(s) = -1 \tag{21}$$

The quantity on the right-hand side of (21) has a magnitude of 1 and an angle of π radians (or any odd multiple of π radians). Thus if the constant K is restricted to positive values, the angle criterion is

$$\arg F(s) = \pm n\pi \text{ for } n = 1, 3, 5, \cdots \tag{22}$$

and the magnitude criterion is

$$K = \frac{1}{|F(s)|} \tag{23}$$

We use (22), which does not involve K, to find the locus of *all possible* root positions for $K \geq 0$. Then we can use (23) to calibrate the locus—that is, to find the values of K that correspond to particular points on the locus.

Rules for Constructing a Root Locus

Some of the rules may seem intuitively obvious. For example, because any complex poles must occur in conjugate pairs, the root locus must be symmetrical about the real axis. Root locations must satisfy (23), so K must be small for points on the locus close to the poles of $F(s)$. Similarly, K must be large for points close to the zeros of $F(s)$. Other rules are much less obvious, but they are summarized below for the case where $K \geq 0$ and where the poles and zeros are distinct. We let n denote the number of poles of $F(s)$, and m the number of finite-plane zeros. After presenting the rules, we shall illustrate them with several examples.

1. The locus is symmetrical with respect to the real axis of the s-plane.

2. The locus has n branches.

3. A point on the real axis is part of the locus if and only if the total number of real poles and zeros to the right of that point is odd.

4. If a single pair of branches in the locus leaves or enters the real axis, those branches do so at angles of ± 90 degrees.

5. As K increases from zero, one branch of the locus departs from each of the poles of $F(s)$.

6. As K approaches infinity, the branches of the locus approach the zeros of $F(s)$. There will be m branches approaching the finite-plane zeros. If $m \neq n$, the remaining $n - m$ branches will approach infinity.

7. The branches approaching infinity will be asymptotic to equally spaced straight lines emanating from the center of mass for the poles and zeros. This center can be found by regarding each pole as a positive unit mass and each zero as a negative unit mass, and it is a point on the real axis given by

$$\sigma_0 = \frac{1}{n - m} \left[\sum_{k=1}^{n} p_k - \sum_{i=1}^{m} z_i \right] \tag{24}$$

The angles of the equally spaced asymptotes can be determined by remembering that the branches of the locus must be symmetrical about the real axis of the s-plane. Figure 14.8 shows these angles when $n - m$, the number of branches approaching infinity, is 4, 3, or 2. In all cases, the poles of $F(s)$ are at $s = -1, -2, -4$, and -7. The points on the real axis at which the asymptotes meet can be found from (24) and are at $\sigma = -3.5, -3$, and -4, respectively. Whenever $n - m$ is an odd integer, one of the asymptotes is the negative real axis.

Other rules can also be developed. One of these gives the angles at which the branches depart from a pair of complex poles of $F(s)$ and the

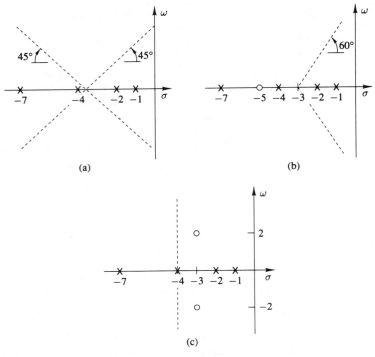

FIGURE 14.8 Asymptotes for branches going to infinity. (a) $n - m = 4$.
(b) $n - m = 3$. (c) $n - m = 2$.

angles at which they approach any complex zeros. However, rather than investigating any other rules, we shall consider a number of examples, which should give some appreciation for the forms of typical loci. The examples will also illustrate the rules already discussed.

When sketching the locus by hand, we first mark the open-loop poles and zeros by crosses and circles, determine which parts of the real axis belong to the locus, and draw the asymptotes for any branches going to infinity. One branch must start from each pole of the open-loop transfer function $KF(s)$ and eventually go either to a finite-plane zero or to infinity. When two branches move toward each other along the real axis and meet, they then leave the axis at angles of ± 90 degrees. We shall not describe the sketching process in great detail, because the locus is normally generated by an appropriate computer package. We used MATLAB[1] for most of the examples in this chapter. The figures are not exact copies of the computer output, but have been modified in order to emphasize the salient features of each plot.

---

[1]MATLAB is described and illustrated in Sections 15.1 and 15.2.

▶ *EXAMPLE 14.3*

Find the locus for the poles of the closed-loop transfer function when

$$KF(s) = \frac{K}{s^3 + 7s^2 + 14s + 8} = \frac{K}{(s+1)(s+2)(s+4)}$$

Solution

The parts of the real axis that belong to the locus are indicated by heavy lines. Between $s = -1$ and $s = -2$ there is one pole to the right; for points to the left of $s = -4$ there are three poles to the right (in both cases, an odd integer). Because $F(s)$ has no finite-plane zeros, all three branches of the locus eventually go to infinity. According to (24), the center from which the asymptotes emanate is $\sigma_0 = (-1 - 2 - 4)/3 = -7/3$. The complete plot is shown in Figure 14.9. Arrows indicate the directions in which the closed-loop poles move as K is increased.

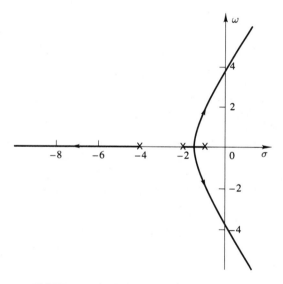

FIGURE 14.9 Root locus for Example 14.3.

Although a root locus shows how the closed-loop poles move as K is increased, it is usually necessary to calibrate the locus by showing the values of K that correspond to specific points. A computer program such as MATLAB can easily list the points on the locus corresponding to specified values of K. If the locus has been sketched by hand, then (23) can be used to evaluate K corresponding to a given point. In the last example, two branches of the locus pass into the right half-plane when K gets sufficiently large, after which the system becomes unstable. Of particular interest is the value of K for which these two branches are right on the imaginary axis of the s-plane.

▶ EXAMPLE 14.4

For the function $KF(s)$ in Example 14.3, find the values of the positive constant K for which the closed-loop system is stable.

Solution

We must first determine the height of the two right-hand branches in Figure 14.9 when they are on the imaginary axis. If the locus has been plotted to scale, this can be done by inspection of the figure. For this example, we shall show that the branches cross the axis at $s = \pm j\sqrt{14}$. According to (23), the corresponding value of K is

$$K = \left| \frac{1}{F(s)} \right|_{s=j\sqrt{14}} = |(s+1)(s+2)(s+4)|_{s=j\sqrt{14}}$$

$$= |j\sqrt{14} + 1||j\sqrt{14} + 2||j\sqrt{14} + 4|$$

$$= \sqrt{15}\sqrt{18}\sqrt{30} = \sqrt{8100} = 90$$

For all the branches of the locus to be inside the left half-plane, as is required for a stable system, the positive constant K is restricted to $K < 90$.

The references in Appendix D present special schemes for evaluating the factors in $|F(s)|$ for a particular point in the s-plane. Routh's criterion is useful for finding the value of K that corresponds to a point on the imaginary axis. However, when $F(s)$ has four or fewer poles, the following alternative approach, based on (21), is feasible. In the equation $KF(s) = -1$, we replace s by $j\omega$, corresponding to a point on the imaginary axis a distance ω from the origin. In this example,

$$\frac{K}{-j\omega^3 - 7\omega^2 + j14\omega + 8} = -1$$

Cross-multiplying gives

$$K = (7\omega^2 - 8) + j(\omega^3 - 14\omega)$$

from which we have the pair of equations

$$K = 7\omega^2 - 8 \tag{25a}$$

$$0 = \omega(\omega^2 - 14) \tag{25b}$$

Equation (25b) could be satisfied by $\omega = 0$, but this would correspond to a negative value of K in (25a). Thus we use $\omega = \pm\sqrt{14}$. Substituting this into (25a) gives $K = 98 - 8 = 90$, which agrees with the answer we found before.

▶ *EXAMPLE 14.5*

Find the root locus when

$$KF(s) = \frac{K}{(s+1)(s+6-j2)(s+6+j2)}$$

Solution

It is straightforward to find the part of the real axis that belongs to the locus and to draw the asymptotes for the three branches going to infinity. The asymptotes meet at $\sigma_0 = (-1 - 6 + j2 - 6 - j2)/3 = -13/3$. The two branches starting from the complex poles meet at the real axis and then split. One of these branches then meets the branch starting at $s = -1$, after which they eventually move into the right half-plane. The complete locus is shown in Figure 14.10. By the method used in the last example, it can be shown that the overall system is stable when the positive constant K is less than 636.

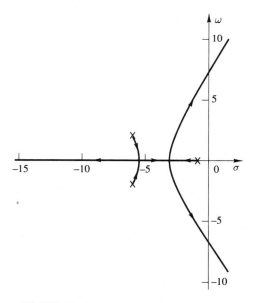

FIGURE 14.10 Root locus for Example 14.5.

▶ *EXAMPLE 14.6*

Find the root locus for

$$KF(s) = \frac{K(s+\alpha)}{(s+1)(s+2)(s+10)}$$

when $\alpha = 6$ and when $\alpha = 2.5$.

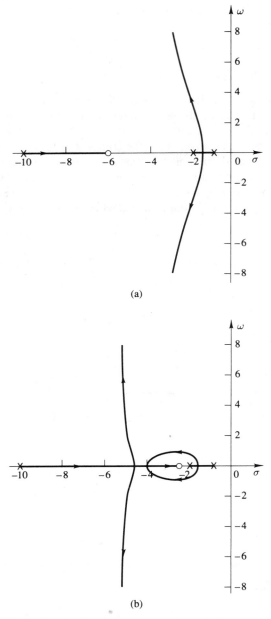

(a)

(b)

FIGURE 14.11 Root locus for Example 14.6. (a) Zero of $F(s)$ at -6. (b) Zero of $F(s)$ at -2.5.

Solution

In both cases, there is one zero of $F(s)$ between the poles at $s = -2$ and $s = -10$. However, the two root-locus plots, as generated by the MATLAB program and as shown in Figure 14.11, are significantly different. When the zero of $F(s)$ is at $s = -6$, the branches starting at $s = -1$ and $s = -2$ are affected in only a relatively minor way by the presence of the other pole-zero combination. When the zero is moved closer to the rightmost branches, it attracts these branches strongly enough to force them to return to the real axis. This is an example of how the shape of the locus can be affected not just by the general nature of the pole-zero pattern for $F(s)$ but also by the specific numerical values used for the poles and zeros.

▶ **EXAMPLE 14.7**

Construct the root locus and find the values of the positive constant K for which the overall system is stable when

$$KF(s) = \frac{K(s+2)}{s^4 + 11s^3 + 34s^2 + 24s} = \frac{K(s+2)}{s(s+1)(s+4)(s+6)}$$

Solution

The parts of the real axis that belong to the locus are found in the usual way. The asymptotes for the three branches that go to infinity meet at the point $\sigma_0 = (-1 + 2 - 4 - 6)/3 = -3$. The complete locus is shown in Figure 14.12. For the points where two of the branches cross the imaginary axis, we may set $KF(j\omega) = -1$, getting

$$K(j\omega + 2) = -(\omega^4 - j11\omega^3 - 34\omega^2 + j24\omega)$$

from which

$$2K = -\omega^4 + 34\omega^2 \tag{26a}$$

$$\omega K = \omega(11\omega^2 - 24) \tag{26b}$$

The solutions of (26b) are $\omega = 0$ (corresponding to $K = 0$) and $K = 11\omega^2 - 24$. Substituting this latter expression into (26a) gives

$$22\omega^2 - 48 = -\omega^4 + 34\omega^2$$

or

$$\omega^4 - 12\omega^2 - 48 = 0$$

The only positive value of ω^2 that satisfies this equation is $\omega^2 = 15.17$, for which $K = 142.8$. The system is marginally stable for $K = 0$ and for $K = 142.8$, and it is stable for $0 < K < 142.8$.

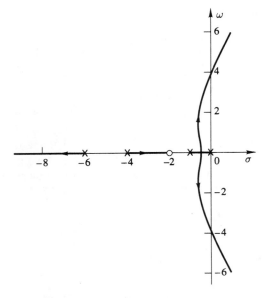

FIGURE 14.12   Root locus for Example 14.7.

▶ **EXAMPLE 14.8**

The value of K can be chosen to give a specified damping ratio ζ for a pair of poles in the closed-loop transfer function. Construct the root locus for

$$KF(s) = \frac{K(s^2 + 6s + 10)}{s^2 + 2s + 10} = \frac{K(s + 3 - j1)(s + 3 + j1)}{(s + 1 - j3)(s + 1 + j3)}$$

and determine the range of possible values of ζ when K can be any positive constant.

Solution

The root locus as K is increased from zero to infinity is shown in Figure 14.13. From (6.52), we know that $\zeta = \cos\theta$ for any pair of points on this locus. When $K = 0$, $\zeta = 1/\sqrt{10} = 0.3162$. When K approaches infinity, $\zeta = 3/\sqrt{10} = 0.9487$. By the appropriate choice of K, we can make the damping ratio take on any value between these two limits.

Because this particular example is fairly simple, we can easily find a general expression for ζ in terms of K. Setting $KF(s) = -1$ and cross-multiplying, we have

$$K(s^2 + 6s + 10) = -(s^2 + 2s + 10)$$

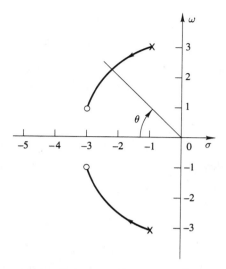

FIGURE 14.13   Root locus for Example 14.8.

Collecting terms and dividing by $K + 1$ give

$$s^2 + \left(\frac{6K + 2}{K + 1}\right) s + 10 = 0$$

This is the closed-loop characteristic equation, whose roots are the poles of the closed-loop transfer function. We can compare this with the standard form of the second-order characteristic equation, $s^2 + 2\zeta\omega_n s + \omega_n^2 = 0$, which was first given in (6.50). Then we see that $\omega_n = \sqrt{10}$ and $2\zeta\omega_n = (6K + 2)/(K + 1)$, so

$$\zeta = \frac{3K + 1}{(K + 1)\sqrt{10}}$$

Replacing K by zero and infinity yields $\zeta = 1/\sqrt{10}$ and $\zeta = 3/\sqrt{10}$, respectively, which agrees with the previous result. If, for example, we want $\zeta = 1/2$, then $(K+1)\sqrt{10} = 2(3K+1)$, from which $\sqrt{10}-2 = (6-\sqrt{10})K$ and $K = 0.4094$.

In each of the next two examples, the open-loop transfer function $K F(s)$ is unstable. In the first case there is a pole in the right half-plane, and in the second, a double pole at the origin. Such poles might be an unavoidable characteristic of one part of the system that cannot be changed. However, the other factors in $K F(s)$ allow the locus to move inside the left half-plane as K is increased.

▶ *EXAMPLE 14.9*

Show the root locus and find the values of K for which the overall system is stable when

$$KF(s) = \frac{K(s+2)}{s(s-1)}$$

Solution

The complete locus is shown in Figure 14.14. To find the point where the branches cross the imaginary axis, we can write $KF(j\omega) = -1$. Then $K(j\omega + 2) = -j\omega(j\omega - 1)$, so

$$2K = \omega^2 \tag{27a}$$

$$\omega K = \omega \tag{27b}$$

As expected, one solution is $\omega = 0$ and $K = 0$. For the other solution, $K = 1$ from (27b) and $\omega = \sqrt{2}$ from (27a). The system is stable for all $K > 1$.

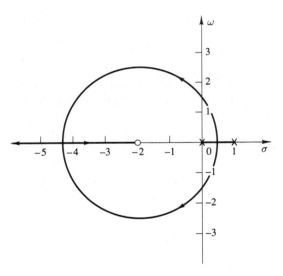

FIGURE 14.14   Root locus for Example 14.9.

▶ *EXAMPLE 14.10*

Find the root locus when

$$KF(s) = \frac{K(s+1)}{s^2(s+10)}$$

The double pole at the origin might come from an essential part of the open-loop system. The zero at $s = -1$ might have been added in order to move the locus to the left, but in practice the component that provided this zero might also have added an extra pole. In such a case, the pole can be placed far enough from the origin that it will not adversely affect the desired result.

Solution

The asymptotes corresponding to large values of K cross the axis at $\sigma_0 = (-10 + 1)/2 = -9/2$. The complete locus appears in Figure 14.15. It can be shown that two branches enter the real axis at $s = -5/2$ and that two branches leave the real axis at $s = -4$. If the pole of $KF(s)$ at $s = -10$ were moved considerably closer to the zero, than the branches leaving the double pole at the origin would not be drawn all the way to the real axis but would instead approach directly the asymptotes for large K.

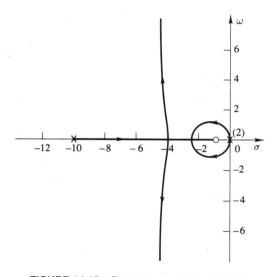

FIGURE 14.15 Root locus for Example 14.10.

The concepts that we have developed for the construction of a root locus can be extended to other situations. If the sign of the signal fed back to the summer in Figure 14.7 is changed from minus to plus, then the closed-loop transfer function is

$$T(s) = \frac{G(s)}{1 - G(s)H(s)}$$

By comparing this equation with (19) and (20), we see that the only change has been to replace K by $-K$. For this reason, we sometimes wish to start with the pole-zero pattern of $KF(s)$ and then draw the root locus for negative values of K.

Root Locus For Negative Values of K

The locus is still symmetrical with respect to the real axis of the s-plane, and it still has one branch starting from each of the poles of $F(s)$. As the magnitude of K increases, the branches again either approach the finite-plane zeros of $F(s)$ or approach infinity. The asymptotes for those branches that approach infinity will still have equally spaced angles and will still meet at a point on the real axis given by (24). However, if there is an odd number of such asymptotes, one of them will be the positive (rather than the negative) real axis. A point on the real axis will belong to the locus if and only if the number of real poles and zeros to the right of that point is even (rather than odd).

Equation (21) is valid for both positive and negative values of K. Sometimes, however, people prefer to rewrite it specifically for negative values of K as

$$|K|F(s) = 1 \qquad (28)$$

Equations (22) and (23) were written only for the case where K is restricted to positive values. The corresponding equations for negative values of K are

$$\arg F(s) = \pm n\pi \quad \text{for } n = 0, 2, 4, \cdots$$

$$K = -\frac{1}{|F(s)|}$$

The applications for negative values of K are illustrated by a single example.

▶ *EXAMPLE 14.11*

Repeat Examples 14.3 and 14.4 for negative values of K. Recall that the open-loop transfer function is

$$KF(s) = \frac{K}{s^3 + 7s^2 + 14s + 8} = \frac{K}{(s+1)(s+2)(s+4)}$$

Solution

The parts of the real axis that belong to the locus are indicated by heavy lines in Figure 14.16. All three branches of the locus eventually go to infinity. The asymptotes still meet at $\sigma_0 = (-1 - 2 - 4)/3 = -7/3$, but one of them is now the positive real axis. The arrows on the locus indicate increasing magnitudes for the negative constant K.

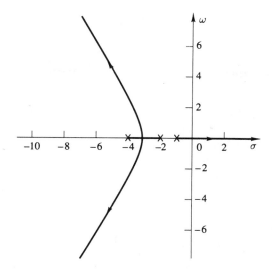

FIGURE 14.16 Root locus for Example 14.11.

In Example 14.4 we used (21) to write $KF(j\omega) = -1$, from which we obtained

$$K = 7\omega^2 - 8$$
$$0 = \omega(\omega^2 - 14)$$

which are valid for both positive and negative values of K. The only solution for negative K is $\omega = 0$ and $K = -8$, which describes the point at which the right branch passes into the right half-plane. Thus the system is stable for $|K| < 8$. If we were to use (28) with s replaced by $j\omega$, we would get

$$|K| = -7\omega^2 + 8$$
$$0 = \omega(\omega^2 - 14)$$

which yield the same result. Combining this solution with that for Example 14.4, we see that if K is allowed to have both positive and negative values, the condition for stability is $-8 < K < 90$.

Root Locus for Systems not in Standard Feedback Form

Our root-locus rules may be useful even when the system is not presented in the standard feedback configuration shown in Figure 14.7. We require only that the denominator of the overall transfer function be written in the form $1 + KF(s)$. Recall the mechanical system that is shown in Figure 14.6(a) and considered in Example 14.2 and that has the transfer function

$$T(s) = \frac{\dfrac{1}{M}}{s^2 + \dfrac{B}{M}s + \dfrac{K}{M}}$$

We want the locus of the poles of $T(s)$ when first K/M and then B/M are varied. To put the expression into a suitable form, we divide both halves of the fraction by those denominator terms that do not contain the parameter to be varied. Thus we write

$$T(s) = \frac{\dfrac{1/M}{s(s + B/M)}}{1 + \dfrac{K/M}{s(s + B/M)}} \qquad (29a)$$

$$T(s) = \frac{\dfrac{1/M}{s^2 + K/M}}{1 + \dfrac{(B/M)s}{s^2 + K/M}} \qquad (29b)$$

In each case, the denominator is in the right form. In (29a), we regard the open-loop transfer function as having poles at $s = 0$ and at $s = -B/M$, and we then draw the root locus as K/M is increased from zero to infinity. This gives the diagram that was shown in Figure 14.6(b).

Using (29b), we can define an open-loop transfer function that has poles at $s = \pm j\sqrt{K/M}$ and a zero at the origin. Drawing the locus as B/M increases from zero to infinity gives Figure 14.6(c).

■ 14.3 BODE DIAGRAMS

A designer often characterizes parts of a feedback control system by their sinusoidal-steady-state responses. The basic ideas were presented in Section 8.5 and can be summarized by (8.44), (8.49), and (8.51). We shall start this section with these same equations. However, we shall use $T(s)$ rather than $H(s)$ for a general transfer function in order to avoid confusion with the use of $H(s)$ for the feedback transfer function in feedback systems. To obtain an expression for the frequency-response function $T(j\omega)$, we replace s by $j\omega$ in $T(s)$ and then write the resulting complex quantity in polar form as

$$T(j\omega) = M(\omega)\epsilon^{j\theta(\omega)} \qquad (30)$$

where $M(\omega)$ is the magnitude of $T(j\omega)$ and $\theta(\omega)$ is its angle. If the input of a stable system is the sinusoidal function

$$u(t) = \sin \omega t \qquad (31)$$

then the steady-state response is

$$y_{ss}(t) = M \sin(\omega t + \theta) \tag{32}$$

More generally, the steady-state response to the sinusoidal input $u(t) = B \sin(\omega t + \phi_1)$ is

$$y_{ss}(t) = BM \sin(\omega t + \phi_1 + \theta)$$

If we draw curves of $M(\omega)$ and $\theta(\omega)$ versus ω, we can see how the magnitude and angle of the steady-state response change as the frequency of the input is changed, as was illustrated in Section 8.5. However, it is often more useful to express the magnitude of $T(j\omega)$ in decibels, to use semilog paper, and to present the two curves in the form of a Bode diagram.

Bode diagrams have several advantages. A wide range of values of $M(\omega)$ and of ω can be included (although the point corresponding to $\omega = 0$ can never be shown because of the logarithmic frequency scale). A number of rules can be developed to enable a designer quickly to sketch reasonable approximations to the Bode diagrams, although we shall emphasize computer-generated plots. Conversely, the transfer function $T(s)$ can be approximated from Bode diagrams that have been constructed from experimental measurements. For subsystems in series, the corresponding Bode diagrams can be added to obtain the diagram for the combination. For feedback systems, the diagrams for the open-loop transfer function provide important information about the stability of the overall systems.

To express a real, positive, dimensionless quantity in decibels (usually abbreviated dB), we take its logarithm (to the base 10) and then multiply by 20. Thus

$$M(\omega)|_{dB} = 20 \log_{10} M(\omega) \tag{33}$$

Note that the decibel gain $M(\omega)|_{dB}$ is positive when $M(\omega) > 1$ and negative when $M(\omega) < 1$. When the magnitude of the transfer function is 1, 10, 100, and 1000, respectively, the corresponding decibel gain is 0, 20, 40, and 60.

Construction of Bode Diagrams

We begin the discussion by presenting several simple cases. The diagrams can easily be drawn by hand and turn out to be important to understanding the asymptotic behavior in more complicated cases. Keep in mind that the ω scale is logarithmic and that the curves are drawn on semilog paper. Unless otherwise stated, any gain constant K is assumed to be a positive number.

▶ **EXAMPLE 14.12**

Construct the magnitude curve for each of the following frequency-response functions: $T_1(j\omega) = K$, $T_2(j\omega) = j\omega K$, $T_3(j\omega) = K/j\omega$, and $T_4(j\omega) = K/(j\omega)^2$. Because all of the angle functions turn out to be constants in this example, we shall not plot the angle curves.

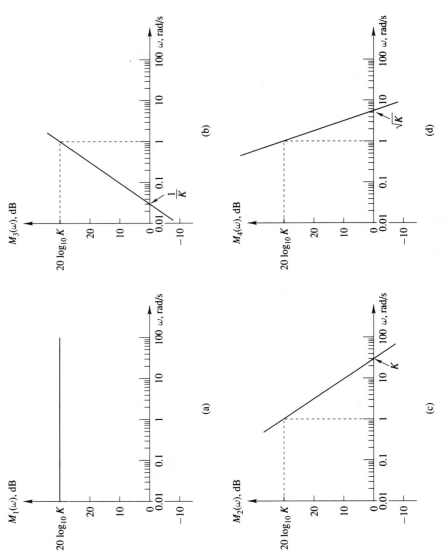

FIGURE 14.17   Magnitude curves for Example 14.12. (a) $T_1(j\omega) = K$. (b) $T_2(j\omega) = j\omega K$. (c) $T_3(j\omega) = K/j\omega$.

Solution

For $T_1(j\omega) = K$, $M_1(\omega)|_{\text{dB}} = 20\log_{10}K$, which gives the horizontal line shown in Figure 14.17(a). The angle $\theta_1(\omega)$ is zero for all values of ω.

For $T_2(j\omega) = j\omega K$, we can write $M_2(\omega)|_{\text{dB}} = 20\log_{10}\omega K = 20\log_{10}K + 20\log_{10}\omega$, which describes the straight line shown in Fig. 14.17(b). The slope of the line is usually expressed in units of decibels per decade or decibels per octave. A decade corresponds to increasing the frequency by a multiplying factor of 10, an octave to doubling the frequency. For this part of the example, when the frequency is increased from ω_a to $10\omega_a$ the resulting magnitude change is

$$20\log_{10}(10\omega_a K) - 20\log_{10}(\omega_a K) = 20\log_{10}10 = 20 \text{ dB}$$

If we double the frequency, the magnitude change is

$$20\log_{10}(2\omega_a K) - 20\log_{10}(\omega_a K) = 20\log_{10}2 \simeq 6 \text{ dB}$$

Thus the slope of the line in Figure 14.17(b) is 20 dB per decade and 6 dB per octave. The angle $\theta_2(\omega)$ is $90°$ for all values of ω.

For $T_3(j\omega) = K/(j\omega)$, we have $M_3(\omega)|_{\text{dB}} = 20\log_{10}(K/\omega) = 20\log_{10}K - 20\log_{10}\omega$, which describes a straight line with a slope of -20 dB per decade, as shown in part (c) of the figure. The angle $\theta_3(\omega)$ is $-90°$ for all values of ω.

For the general case where $T(j\omega) = K/(j\omega)^n$, we see that

$$M(\omega)|_{\text{dB}} = 20\log_{10}(K/\omega^n) = 20\log_{10}K - 20n\log_{10}\omega$$

Then the magnitude curve is a straight line with a slope of $-20n$ dB per decade, and the angle is a constant $-90n°$. Similarly, if $T(j\omega) = K(j\omega)^n$, the magnitude curve has a slope of $+20n$ dB per decade, and the angle curve is $+90n°$.

The results of the last example will be important when we draw the low- and high-frequency asymptotes for more complicated functions. For very small or very large values of ω, frequency-response functions usually reduce to the cases examined in Example 14.12. Remember that the slope of the magnitude curve is $-20n$ dB per decade for $T(j\omega) = K/(j\omega)^n$ and is $+20n$ dB per decade for $T(j\omega) = (j\omega)^n K$. In addition to the slope, we shall need to locate one point on these magnitude curves. One way to do so (illustrated in Figure 14.17) is to note that when $\omega = 1$, $M(\omega)|_{\text{dB}} = 20\log_{10}K$. Another easy way is to note that the line (extended if necessary) crosses the zero-dB axis when $|T(j\omega)| = 1$. For $T(j\omega) = K/(j\omega)^n$, this occurs when $\omega = \sqrt[n]{K}$; for $T(j\omega) = (j\omega)^n K$, it occurs when $\omega = \sqrt[n]{1/K}$.

The next three examples provide additional background for understanding the construction of Bode diagrams for cases of arbitrary complexity. Following these examples, we shall discuss briefly a general method for drawing approximate curves for any transfer function, even though our emphasis will be on the use of computer-generated plots.

▶ *EXAMPLE 14.13*

Construct the Bode diagram for $T(s) = 1/(1 + \tau s)$ by examining the frequency-response function

$$T(j\omega) = \frac{1}{1 + j\omega\tau} \qquad (34)$$

Solution

The computer-generated curves are shown in Figure 14.18. For very small values of ω, $T(j\omega)$ approaches 1, so the magnitude curve approaches a constant value of 0 dB, and the angle curve approaches 0°. At very high frequencies, where $\omega\tau \gg 1$, $T(j\omega)$ approaches $1/(j\omega\tau)$. From the previous example, the high-frequency asymptote for the magnitude curve has a slope of −20 dB per decade and crosses the zero-dB axis at $\omega = 1/\tau$. The curve of $\theta(\omega)$ must approach −90° for large values of ω.

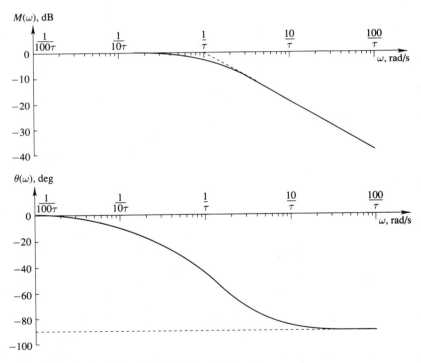

FIGURE 14.18   Bode diagram for $T(s) = 1/(1 + \tau s)$.

In part (a) of the figure, note that the low- and high-frequency asymptotes meet at $\omega = 1/\tau$, which is sometimes called the **corner frequency** or **break frequency**. Together, these asymptotes could serve as a rough approximation to the exact curve, especially if correction factors were used near the break frequency. Although we shall rely on computer-generated plots, the references in Appendix D contain further guidelines that enable a designer to draw approximate curves quickly.

▶ *EXAMPLE 14.14*

Suppose that two frequency-response functions are related by the equation

$$T_2(j\omega) = \frac{1}{T_1(j\omega)}$$

and that the Bode diagram for $T_1(j\omega)$ is available. Develop a procedure for constructing the diagram for $T_2(j\omega)$.

Solution

If $T_1(j\omega) = M_1(\omega)\epsilon^{j\theta_1(\omega)}$, then

$$T_2(j\omega) = \frac{1}{M_1(\omega)}\epsilon^{-j\theta_1(\omega)}$$

and we see that $M_2(\omega) = 1/M_1(\omega)$ and $\theta_2(\omega) = -\theta_1(\omega)$. Thus the new angle curve is just the negative of the original one. Furthermore,

$$M_2(\omega)|_{dB} = 20\log_{10}[1/M_1(\omega)]$$
$$= -20\log_{10}M_1(\omega) = -M_1(\omega)|_{dB}$$

so the new magnitude curve is also the negative of the original one. As a specific example, we can use the results of Example 14.13 to draw immediately the curves shown in Figure 14.19 for $T(j\omega) = 1 + j\omega\tau$.

▶ *EXAMPLE 14.15*

Construct the Bode diagram for $T(s) = \omega_n^2/(s^2 + 2\zeta\omega_n s + \omega_n^2)$, for which

$$T(j\omega) = \frac{\omega_n^2}{-\omega^2 + j(2\zeta\omega_n)\omega + \omega_n^2} = \frac{1}{1 + j2\zeta(\omega/\omega_n) - (\omega/\omega_n)^2} \quad (35)$$

Solution

The complete magnitude and angle curves when the damping ratio $\zeta = 1$, 0.5, and 0.1 are shown in Figure 14.20. Note that in order to make the curves more generally applicable, we have made the abscissa the normalized frequency ω/ω_n.

From (35), we see that for very small values of ω, $T(j\omega)$ approaches 1. Thus the low-frequency asymptotes are 0 dB and 0°. For large values of ω, $T(j\omega)$ approaches $1/(j\omega/\omega_n)^2$. Then the high-frequency magnitude asymptote must have a slope of −40 dB per decade and must cross the

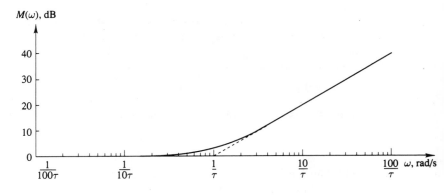

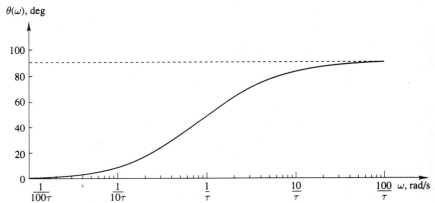

FIGURE 14.19   Bode diagram for $T(s) = 1 + \tau s$.

zero-dB axis at $\omega = \omega_n$. The high-frequency asymptote for the angle is $-180°$.

We could try to approximate the magnitude curve in part (a) of the figure by using only the low- and high-frequency asymptotes. If we do this, however, very large errors could occur near the break frequency, especially if ζ is very small. Special correction curves would usually be required.

Frequently it is desirable to express a transfer function as the product of several factors. For example, let

$$T(s) = T_1(s)T_2(s)T_3(s) \tag{36}$$

in which case

$$T(j\omega) = T_1(j\omega)T_2(j\omega)T_3(j\omega) \tag{37}$$

Using the appropriate subscripts, we let $M(\omega)$ and $\theta(\omega)$ denote the magnitude and angle of the individual frequency-response functions in the

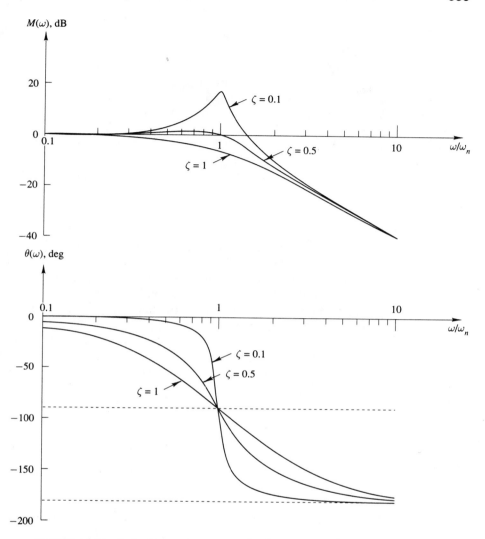

FIGURE 14.20   Bode diagram for $T(s) = \omega_n^2/(s^2 + 2\zeta\omega_n s + \omega_n^2)$.

usual way. By the rules for complex numbers, we can write, for the overall function $T(j\omega)$,

$$M(\omega) = M_1(\omega)M_2(\omega)M_3(\omega) \tag{38a}$$

$$\theta(\omega) = \theta_1(\omega) + \theta_2(\omega) + \theta_3(\omega) \tag{38b}$$

Furthermore, $M(\omega)|_{dB} = 20\log_{10}[M_1(\omega)M_2(\omega)M_3(\omega)]$, so

$$M(\omega)|_{dB} = M_1(\omega)|_{d3} + M_2(\omega)|_{dB} + M_3(\omega)|_{dB} \tag{39}$$

Thus the individual magnitude curves can be added, as can the individual angle curves.

One application of (38b) and (39) occurs when a block diagram contains several blocks in series. The overall transfer function for the partial diagram in Figure 14.21 is given by (36). To construct the Bode diagram for the overall frequency-response function, we merely add the magnitude and angle curves for the individual blocks.

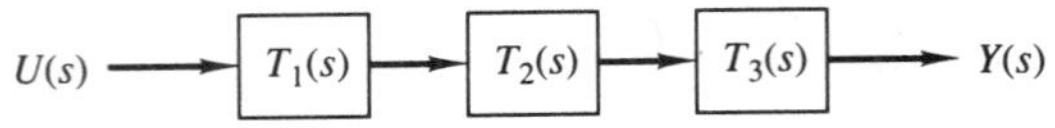

FIGURE 14.21   Blocks in series corresponding to (36).

As will be discussed in Section 14.4, it is sometimes necessary to insert additional components in series with the original open-loop system in order to meet the design specifications. Using (38b) and (39) enables us to determine, for these additional components, the magnitude and angle characteristics needed in order to allow the complete Bode diagram to be appropriately modified.

Suppose that we have a transfer function in factored form. For any real poles or zeros, we would have factors of the form $s + \alpha$ in the denominator or numerator. A quadratic factor corresponding to a pair of complex poles or zeros inside the left half-plane would have the form $s^2 + 2\zeta \omega_n s + \omega_n^2$, where $0 < \zeta < 1$. Thus a typical transfer function might be

$$T(s) = \frac{K(s + \alpha)}{s(s + \beta)(s^2 + 2\zeta \omega_n s + \omega_n^2)}$$

which we can rewrite as

$$T(s) = \left(\frac{\alpha K}{\beta \omega_n^2}\right)\left(\frac{1}{s}\right)\left(1 + \frac{s}{\alpha}\right)\left(\frac{1}{1 + s/\beta}\right)\left(\frac{\omega_n^2}{s^2 + 2\zeta \omega_n s + \omega_n^2}\right)$$

When s is replaced by $j\omega$ to give the frequency-response function $T(j\omega)$, we can see that each of the factors was among those treated in the previous examples. The magnitude curve for the constant $\alpha K / \beta \omega_n^2$ is a horizontal line, and the angle is zero. Corresponding to the factor $1/s$, we have a magnitude curve with a slope of -20 dB per decade and an angle of $-90°$. The curves for the final three factors are similar to those in Figures 14.19, 14.18, and 14.20, respectively. The magnitude and angle curves for $T(j\omega)$ can be found by adding the individual curves.

This approach is especially useful when we draw approximate curves by hand. However, we shall generally use computer-generated curves, in which case there is no need to break the transfer function up into individual factors.

Stability Criteria

Consider again the standard feedback configuration that is shown in Figures 13.22(a) and 14.7 and is repeated in Figure 14.22. We discussed in Section 14.2 the importance of being able to predict the nature of the free response of the overall system from a knowledge of the open-loop transfer function $G(s)H(s)$. If the behavior of the overall system needs to be modified, we can consider changing the gain constant associated with $G(s)H(s)$ or can even arrange to give it additional poles and zeros.

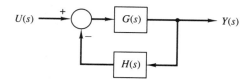

FIGURE 14.22 Block diagram of a feedback system.

The most fundamental way of relating the frequency-response function $G(j\omega)H(j\omega)$ to the stability of the overall system is to construct a polar plot. We would regard $G(j\omega)H(j\omega)$ as a vector drawn from the origin of a new complex plane (different from the s-plane) and would look at the path traced out by the tip of that vector as ω increases. A test known as the **Nyquist stability criterion** can be applied to determine whether the system is stable. Furthermore, that test can give considerable insight into whether the system will remain stable even if some of the characteristics of the open-loop transfer function undergo moderate changes.

Knowledge of the Nyquist criterion is necessary for a complete understanding of how the Bode diagram for $G(s)H(s)$ can be related to the stability of the overall system. Unfortunately, developing the Nyquist criterion is fairly involved, so we must refer those interested in it to the references in Appendix D. In the following discussion, we shall assume that all the poles of the open-loop transfer function are inside the left half-plane, except for a possible first-order pole at the origin. Then we can state, without proof, the following definitions and properties.

The Bode diagram in Figure 14.23 represents the open-loop transfer function $G(s)H(s)$. The frequency at which the magnitude curve crosses the zero-dB line is denoted by ω_{pm} and is sometimes called the **magnitude crossover frequency**. The **phase margin** ϕ_m is the amount by which the angle curve would have to be moved down in order to make the angle $\theta(\omega_{pm})$ be $-180°$.

The frequency at which the angle curve crosses $-180°$, sometimes called the **phase crossover frequency**, is denoted by ω_{gm}. The **gain margin** k_m is the number of decibels by which the magnitude curve would have to be moved up in order to make $M(\omega_{gm})|_{dB} = 0$. The gain and phase margins are

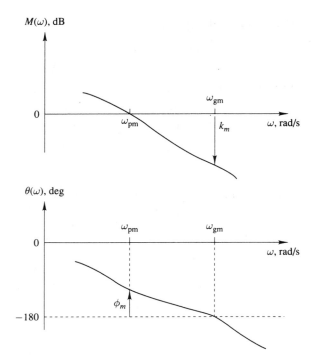

FIGURE 14.23 Bode diagram showing the phase margin ϕ_m and the gain margin k_m.

labeled in Figure 14.23. For the overall system to be stable, both the gain margin and the phase margin must be positive, as is assumed in the figure.

There are no standard symbols for the gain and phase margins or for the frequencies at which these quantities are measured. The subscripts we have used in the symbols ω_{pm} and ω_{gm} indicate the frequencies at which the phase margin and gain margin, respectively, are measured. Although the nature of the plots in Figure 14.23 is fairly typical, cases exist for which our definitions of k_m and ϕ_m do not apply. For example, it is possible for the curve of $\theta(\omega)$ never to cross the $-180°$ axis or to cross it more than once. Similarly, the curve of $M(\omega)|_{dB}$ could cross the zero-dB axis more than once.

In order for the closed-loop system not to be too lightly damped and in order to be sure that it will remain stable even if there are some variations in the parameters, a designer would insist on certain minimum values for the gain and phase margins. The ranges of desired gain and phase margins depend on the particular system being considered and on the intended applications. However, a gain margin of about 10 dB and a phase margin of $45°$ are typical for many systems.

Increasing the phase margin generally increases the damping ratio ζ associated with a pair of complex poles. For specific second-order systems, explicit relationships between ϕ_m and ζ can be derived. Some of the references in Appendix D contain curves of ζ versus ϕ_m, but it is important to note the specific open-loop transfer function for which they apply.

In order to give some plausibility to the foregoing statements about the gain and phase margin, let us look at the steady-state behavior of the feedback system in Figure 14.22 when the input is sinusoidal. At the frequency ω_{gm}, the angle of the open-loop transfer function is $-180°$. Because of the signs shown on the summer, the signal fed back from the $G(s)H(s)$ path is then in phase with the input and adds directly to it.

Suppose the input is now removed. If the magnitude of the open-loop gain is less than unity at the frequency ω_{gm}, then the signal fed back to the summer continually diminishes, and the output goes to zero. If $|M(\omega_{gm})| = 1$, corresponding to 0 dB, the signal fed back to the summer is just large enough to sustain the sinusoidal oscillations at a constant amplitude. Such a condition describes a marginally stable system. If $|M(\omega_{gm})| > 1$, then the oscillations continually grow in magnitude, and the system is unstable.

A positive gain margin means that $M(\omega_{gm})|_{dB} < 0$, corresponding to a stable system. A gain margin of zero occurs when $M(\omega_{gm})|_{dB} = 0$. A negative gain margin means that $M(\omega_{gm})|_{dB} > 0$, corresponding to an unstable system.

The MATLAB computer program can not only yield the Bode diagram for a given open-loop transfer function but can also list the gain and phase margins and the frequencies at which they are measured. The gain margin can be expressed both in decibels and as the additional multiplying factor needed to make $M(\omega_{gm}) = 1$. As in any computer program that produces a smooth curve from discrete numerical calculations, values corresponding to special points on the curve are only approximations to the exact numbers. Although a designer would require only reasonably close answers, more accurate values can always be achieved by increasing the number of points at which calculations are made. We now make use of MATLAB to draw and interpret the Bode diagram for the system that was considered in Examples 14.3 and 14.4.

▶ *EXAMPLE 14.16*

Draw the Bode diagram for the open-loop transfer function

$$G(s)H(s) = \frac{K}{(s+1)(s+2)(s+4)} = \frac{K/8}{(1+s)(1+s/2)(1+s/4)}$$

when $K = 20$. Find the gain and phase margins. Determine the values of the positive constant K for which the closed-loop transfer function is stable.

Solution

Although we could add the magnitude and angle curves for $K/8$, $1/(1 + j\omega)$, $1/(1 + j\omega/2)$, and $1/(1 + j\omega/4)$ in order to construct the diagram for

$G(j\omega)H(j\omega)$, we use MATLAB to obtain the plots shown in Figure 14.24. The gain and phase margins are shown in the figure. Their numerical values are $k_m = 13.13$ dB (corresponding to a multiplying factor of 4.535, where $13.13 = 20 \log_{10} 4.535$) and $\phi_m = 64.1°$. Other values of interest are $\omega_{gm} = 3.75$ rad/s and $\omega_{pm} = 1.54$ rad/s.

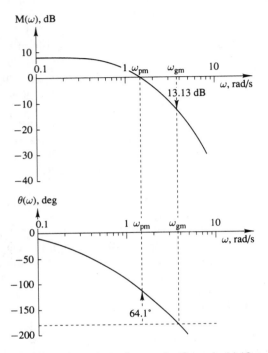

FIGURE 14.24   Bode diagram for Example 14.16.

Multiplying the transfer function by a positive constant A raises the magnitude curve by the constant $20 \log_{10} A$ without changing the angle curve. For a marginally stable system, $k_m = 0$ dB. In our case this would correspond to $A = 4.535$ and to a value of $K = 4.535 \times 20 = 90.70$. This is in reasonable agreement with the result of Example 14.4, where we found from the root-locus magnitude criterion that the overall system is stable for gains in the interval $0 < K < 90$.

■ 14.4 DESIGN GUIDELINES

The block diagram for a basic feedback configuration is shown in Figure 14.25(a). Particular systems may have more complicated diagrams with a number of additional feedback and feedforward paths. However, many

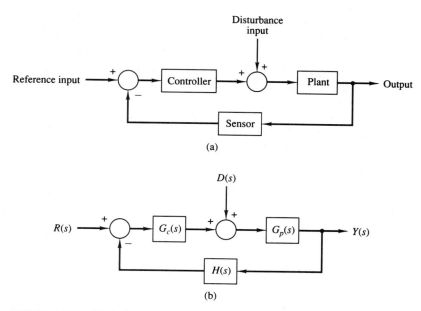

FIGURE 14.25 Block diagrams for a basic feedback system.

diagrams can be reduced to the one in the figure, and analyzing it will provide an introduction to some of the design techniques most often used.

The **plant** is the system to be controlled. It may contain almost any collection of linearized components or processes, and its parameters are generally already fixed and beyond the designer's control. The purpose of the **sensor** is to measure the output and feed a signal back to the input summing device. The engineer may also choose to add other components within the sensor block to improve the system performance. The **controller** not only provides the excitation for the plant but also can be designed to meet the specifications for the overall system behavior. Its characteristics and implementation are chosen by the engineer.

The notation that we shall use is shown in Figure 14.25(b). The transfer functions for the controller, plant, and sensor are denoted by $G_c(s)$, $G_p(s)$, and $H(s)$, respectively. Because the diagram has two inputs, we distinguish their Laplace transforms by using $R(s)$ for the reference input and $D(s)$ for the disturbance input. We assume that we want the output $y(t)$ to follow closely any changes in the reference input $r(t)$. For the system examined in Section 14.1, the input and output variables were the angular displacements of mechanical components. However, they might equally well be any other type of variable.

A system may be subjected to unpredictable disturbances that tend to affect the output adversely. Examples include wind gusts on a moving vehicle and a load torque exerted on a rotating shaft to which a cutting tool is attached. Such unwanted inputs are usually exerted directly on the plant and are represented in the figure by the transformed variable $D(s)$. We want the output to be relatively insensitive to a disturbance input. An additional concern, which we shall discuss only in a qualitative way, is the need for the system's behavior to remain acceptable even if some of its parameters undergo moderate changes or if random noise signals arise within the system.

We define the following two transfer functions for the system shown in Figure 14.25(b): $T_R(s) = Y(s)/R(s)$ when the disturbance input $D(s)$ is zero, and $T_D(s) = Y(s)/D(s)$ when the reference input $R(s)$ is zero. By (13.46),

$$T_R(s) = \frac{Y(s)}{R(s)} = \frac{G_c(s)G_p(s)}{1 + G_c(s)G_p(s)H(s)} \tag{40a}$$

$$T_D(s) = \frac{Y(s)}{D(s)} = \frac{G_p(s)}{1 + G_c(s)G_p(s)H(s)} \tag{40b}$$

We would of course like $T_R(s)$ to approach unity and $T_D(s)$ to approach zero. Because both transfer functions have the same denominator, they will have the same poles. Thus consideration of stability and consideration of the form of the transient response will yield the same results, no matter which of the two functions is used. Information about these items can be obtained from root-locus or Bode plots corresponding to the open-loop transfer function $G_c(s)G_p(s)H(s)$.

One design criterion is the steady-state response to common reference inputs, such as the unit step function. Because we want the output to follow the reference input, we define the error function

$$e(t) = r(t) - y(t) \tag{41}$$

which, when transformed, gives

$$E(s) = R(s) - Y(s)$$

For the special case where $H(s) = 1$, $E(s)$ is the transformed output of the first summer and the input to the controller. For the general case, however, $E(s)$ does not appear in the block diagram.

When examining steady-state responses, we can apply the final-value theorem, which was presented in (7.83) and is repeated here:

$$f(\infty) = \lim_{s \to 0} s F(s) \tag{42}$$

provided that $s F(s)$ has no poles on the imaginary axis or in the right half of the complex plane. We can also write a partial-fraction expansion, omitting those terms that do not contribute to the steady-state response.

In order to investigate the effects of different types of controllers, we shall use for purposes of illustration the following second-order transfer function for the plant:

$$G_p(s) = \frac{K_p}{(s + a)(s + b)} \tag{43}$$

where a and b are nonnegative real constants. For the servomechanism treated in Section 14.1, the transfer function of the motor had this form with $a = 0, b = 1/\tau_m$, and $K_p = K_m$. If we include an input for the hydraulic system shown in Figure 12.13, it will have a transfer function similar to (43) with real positive values for a and b.

In the ensuing discussion, we shall also let $H(s) = 1$. Then the system diagram in Figure 14.25(b) reduces to the one in Figure 14.26, for which

$$T_R(s) = \frac{G_c(s)\dfrac{K_p}{(s+a)(s+b)}}{1 + G_c(s)\dfrac{K_p}{(s+a)(s+b)}} \tag{44a}$$

$$T_D(s) = \frac{\dfrac{K_p}{(s+a)(s+b)}}{1 + G_c(s)\dfrac{K_p}{(s+a)(s+b)}} \tag{44b}$$

where the open-loop transfer function is

$$\frac{K_p G_c(s)}{(s+a)(s+b)}$$

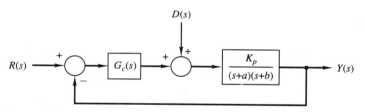

FIGURE 14.26 Block diagram for second-order plant and unity feedback.

Proportional Control

We first let $G_c(s)$ be the positive constant K_c. Then (44) reduces to

$$T_R(s) = \frac{\dfrac{K_c K_p}{(s+a)(s+b)}}{1 + \dfrac{K_c K_p}{(s+a)(s+b)}} = \frac{K_c K_p}{s^2 + (a+b)s + (ab + K_c K_p)} \tag{45a}$$

$$T_D(s) = \frac{\dfrac{K_p}{(s+a)(s+b)}}{1 + \dfrac{K_c K_p}{(s+a)(s+b)}} = \frac{K_p}{s^2 + (a+b)s + (ab + K_c K_p)} \tag{45b}$$

When the disturbance input is zero and the reference input is the unit step function, $R(s) = 1/s$ and

$$Y(s) = \frac{K_c K_p}{s[s^2 + (a + b)s + (ab + K_c K_p)]}$$

By the final-value theorem, the steady-state response is

$$y_{ss} = \frac{K_c K_p}{ab + K_c K_p} \tag{46}$$

The steady-state error is

$$e_{ss} = 1 - \frac{K_c K_p}{ab + K_c K_p} = \frac{ab}{ab + K_c K_p} \tag{47}$$

Although this is not zero, it can be made small by choosing K_c such that $K_c K_p \gg ab$.

The step input $r(t)$ and a possible curve for the output $y(t)$ are shown in Figure 14.27(a). The nature of the transient response depends on the poles of the closed-loop transfer function $T_R(s)$, which for the plot shown have been assumed to be on the negative real axis.

We next let the reference input be the unit ramp function

$$r(t) = \begin{cases} 0 \text{ for } t \leq 0 \\ t \text{ for } t > 0 \end{cases} \tag{48}$$

If $r(t)$ and $y(t)$ are angular displacements of rotating mechanical components, then the input in (48) corresponds to a constant angular velocity of 1 for all $t > 0$. Then $R(s) = 1/s^2$ and

$$Y(s) = \frac{K_c K_p}{s^2[s^2 + (a + b)s + (ab + K_c K_p)]}$$

for which the beginning of the partial-fraction expansion is

$$Y(s) = \frac{K_c K_p/(ab + K_c K_p)}{s^2} + \cdots$$

so that

$$y(t) = \frac{K_c K_p}{ab + K_c K_p} t + \cdots \tag{49}$$

The dots represent terms that are either constant or decaying with time. Thus for large values of time, $y(t)$ approaches a straight line with a slope of $K_c K_p/(ab + K_c K_p)$. For any finite value of $K_c K_p$, this slope will be less than 1, and the error will continually increase, as shown in Figure 14.27(b). For a rotating mechanical system, this means that the steady-state output angular velocity is less than that for the input, so the output angular displacement lags further and further behind the input. This lag can be reduced by making K_c very large.

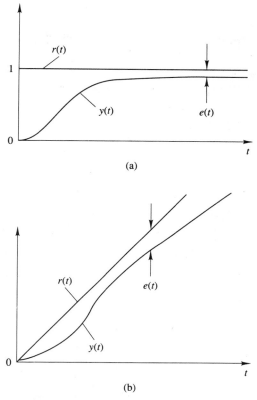

FIGURE 14.27 Response to the reference input when
$G_c(s) = K_c$. (a) Unit step response. (b) Unit ramp response.

We consider next the response to an unwanted disturbance input. If
$r(t) = 0$ and $d(t)$ is the unit step function, then $D(s) = 1/s$,

$$Y(s) = \frac{K_p}{s[s^2 + (a + b)s + (ab + K_c K_p)]}$$

and

$$y_{ss} = \frac{K_p}{ab + K_c K_p} \tag{50}$$

For the disturbance response to be small, we require $K_c \gg K_p$. Once again,
we see that a large controller gain will improve the steady-state response.
The reader may wish to show that if $d(t)$ is the unit ramp function, then

$$Y(s) = \frac{K_p}{s^2[s^2 + (a + b)s + (ab + K_c K_p)]}$$

and

$$y(t) = \frac{K_p}{ab + K_c K_p} t + \cdots \tag{51}$$

which again indicates the need for a large value of K_c.

We now look at the nature of the transient response, which is governed by the poles of the closed-loop transfer function. These are points on the root locus that corresponds to the open-loop transfer function

$$\frac{K_c K_p}{(s + a)(s + b)}$$

and is shown in Figure 14.28. As long as a, b, and $K_c K_p$ are positive numbers, the system is always stable because the locus remains in the left half-plane. For large values of $K_c K_p$, however, the roots will be complex and far from the real axis, corresponding to a small damping ratio ζ. The transient response will then contain stronger oscillations than would normally be desired.

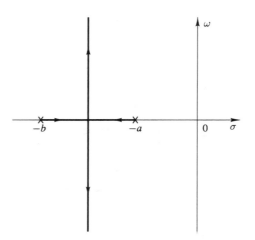

FIGURE 14.28   Root locus when $G_c(s) = K_c$.

Note that there are conflicting priorities concerning the choice of the controller gain K_c. For the best steady-state behavior, the gain should be very large. However, this can result in an undesirable transient response.

A typical Bode diagram is sketched in Figure 14.29. The magnitude curve has an initial slope of zero and a final slope of -40 dB per decade. As expected, the phase margin ϕ_m is always positive. Increasing $K_c K_p$ raises the magnitude curve without affecting the phase angle. This improves the steady-state behavior of the system but decreases ϕ_m. The gain margin k_m is not defined, because the angle curve never crosses $-180°$.

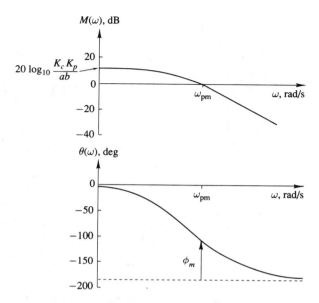

FIGURE 14.29 Bode diagram when $G_c(s) = K_c$.

Proportional-Plus-Derivative Control

We now take the controller's transfer function to be

$$G_c(s) = K_c(1 + K_D s) \tag{52}$$

Because the transfer function for a component described by $y(t) = K_D \dot{x}$ is $K_D s$, the controller includes both proportional and derivative action. Equations (44) become

$$
T_R(s) = \frac{\dfrac{K_c K_p (1 + K_D s)}{(s + a)(s + b)}}{1 + \dfrac{K_c K_p (1 + K_D s)}{(s + a)(s + b)}}
$$

$$
= \frac{K_c K_p (1 + K_D s)}{s^2 + (a + b + K_c K_p K_D)s + (ab + K_c K_p)} \tag{53}
$$

and

$$
T_D(s) = \frac{\dfrac{K_p}{(s + a)(s + b)}}{1 + \dfrac{K_c K_p (1 + K_D s)}{(s + a)(s + b)}}
$$

$$
= \frac{K_p}{s^2 + (a + b + K_c K_p K_D)s + (ab + K_c K_p)} \tag{54}
$$

We can examine the steady-state responses to the reference and disturbance inputs by the procedure used for the proportional controller. Because K_D does not affect the limit of $T_R(s)$ or $T_D(s)$ as $s \to 0$, the key expressions turn out to be the same as before. For large values of time, $y(t)$ is again given by (46) and (49) when $r(t)$ is the unit step and unit ramp, respectively. It is also given by (50) and (51) when $d(t)$ is the unit step and unit ramp, respectively.

Although K_D does not influence the steady-state response, it can change the transient behavior significantly. The open-loop transfer function

$$K_c K_p \frac{1 + K_D s}{(s + a)(s + b)}$$

has a zero at $s = -1/K_D$. Root-locus plots for three different zero positions are shown in Figure 14.30. In all three cases, the locus is confined to the left half-plane and the system is always stable. Recall, however, that the distances of the roots from the imaginary axis are the reciprocals of the time constants in the corresponding transient terms. The time constants should be reasonably small so that the transient response dies out quickly. Thus we usually want to move the roots away from the vertical axis. In order to accomplish this, we choose K_D such that the zero at $s = -1/K_D$ is to the left of both open-loop poles, as in part (a) of the figure.

Figure 14.31 shows a typical Bode diagram for the open-loop pole-zero pattern in Figure 14.30(a). The phase margin ϕ_m is always positive, but the gain margin k_m is again undefined because the angle curve does not cross the $-180°$ line.

Proportional-Plus-Integral Control

For a third basic type of controller action, we let

$$G_c(s) = K_c \left(1 + \frac{K_I}{s} \right) = \frac{K_c(s + K_I)}{s} \tag{55}$$

where K_I/s is the transfer function for a component described by $y(t) = K_I \int_0^t x(\lambda)d\lambda$. Inserting (55) into (44) gives

$$T_R(s) = \frac{\dfrac{K_c K_p(s + K_I)}{s(s + a)(s + b)}}{1 + \dfrac{K_c K_p(s + K_I)}{s(s + a)(s + b)}}$$

$$= \frac{K_c K_p(s + K_I)}{s^3 + (a + b)s^2 + (ab + K_c K_p)s + K_c K_p K_I} \tag{56}$$

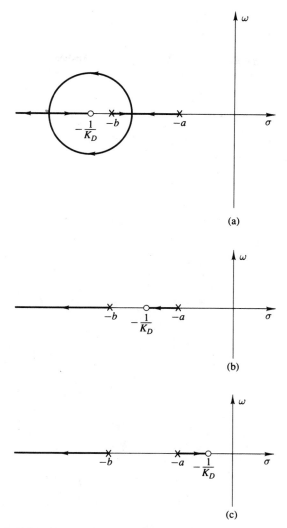

FIGURE 14.30 Possible root-locus plots when $G_c(s) = K_c(1 + K_D s)$.

and

$$T_D(s) = \frac{\dfrac{K_p}{(s+a)(s+b)}}{1 + \dfrac{K_c K_p (s + K_I)}{s(s+a)(s+b)}}$$

$$= \frac{K_p s}{s^3 + (a+b)s^2 + (ab + K_c K_p)s + K_c K_p K_I} \qquad (57)$$

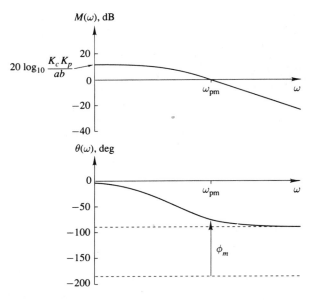

FIGURE 14.31   Bode diagram when $G_c(s) = K_c(1 + K_D s)$.

We first look at the steady-state response when the disturbance input is zero. When $r(t) = U(t)$, $Y(s) = T_R(s)/s$ and

$$y_{ss} = T_R(0) = \frac{K_c K_p K_I}{K_c K_p K_I} = 1$$

In contrast to the results for the previous types of controllers, the steady-state error is zero for all nonzero values of $K_c K_p K_I$. When $r(t)$ is the unit ramp function,

$$Y(s) = \frac{K_c K_p (s + K_I)}{s^2 [s^3 + (a + b)s^2 + (ab + K_c K_p)s + K_c K_p K_I]}$$

$$= \frac{1}{s^2} - \frac{ab/(K_c K_p K_I)}{s} + \cdots$$

and

$$y(t) = t - \frac{ab}{K_c K_p K_I} + \cdots$$

The dots represent those terms that decay to zero as t becomes large. Thus the steady-state error to the unit ramp is

$$e_{ss} = \frac{ab}{K_c K_p K_I}$$

Again in contrast to the controllers previously considered, the error for large values of t does not continually increase. In fact, it can be made arbitrarily small by making $K_c K_p K_I$ sufficiently large.

The response to a unit step disturbance input, when $r(t) = 0$, is $Y(s) = T_D(s)/s$. From (57) and the final-value theorem, we see that

$$y_{ss} = 0$$

When $d(t)$ is the unit ramp function, $Y(s) = T_D(s)/s^2$ and

$$y_{ss} = \frac{K_p}{K_c K_p K_I} = \frac{1}{K_c K_I}$$

which becomes small for large values of $K_c K_I$.

For the transient response, we look at the root-locus and Bode diagrams corresponding to the open-loop transfer function

$$\frac{K_c K_p (s + K_I)}{s(s + a)(s + b)}$$

The location of the open-loop zero at $s = -K_I$ is usually chosen close to the pole at the origin, as shown in Figure 14.32. Then the main part of the root-locus diagram will not differ greatly from that for proportional control. There will be another branch of the locus near the origin, and this will result in an additional term in the transient response. Although this term will decay relatively slowly, its magnitude will be small because of the short distance between the pole and the zero of $G_c(s)$.

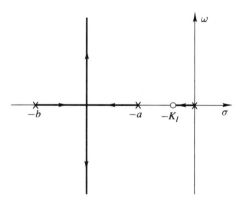

FIGURE 14.32 Root-locus diagram for $G_c(s) = K_c(1 + K_I/s)$.

The Bode diagram will be similar to the one for proportional control, except at low frequencies. For very small values of ω, the magnitude plot will have a slope of -20 dB per decade, and the angle curve will approach $-90°$.

Other Types of Control

We have seen that proportional-plus-integral control gives very good steady-state behavior for both reference and disturbance inputs. The dynamic response, however, will be slower than with proportional-plus-derivative control. In order to get both good steady-state and good dynamic characteristics, we can use a controller that combines derivative and integral action. A general proportional-plus-integral-plus-derivative (PID) controller has the transfer function

$$G_c(s) = K_c \left(1 + K_D s + \frac{K_I}{s} \right) \tag{58}$$

Three other basic types of controller characteristics are represented by lead, lag, and lag-lead transfer functions, whose pole-zero patterns are displayed in Figure 14.33. Because some of the poles or zeros may be quite close to the origin and others far away, it can be difficult to indicate their true positions in a single diagram. In the figure, therefore, the diagrams are not to scale but show only the relative pole and zero locations. For comparison, the pole-zero patterns for the PD, PI, and PID controllers are repeated

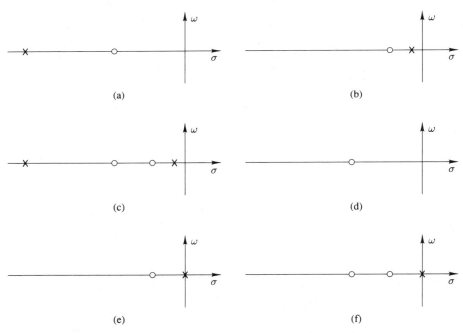

FIGURE 14.33 Relative locations of poles and zeros. (a) Lead compensator. (b) Lag compensator. (c) Lag-lead compensator. (d) PD controller. (e) PI controller. (f) PID controller.

in parts (d), (e), and (f) of the figure. We can see how in some respects they might approximate the lead, lag, and lag-lead transfer functions.

In Figure 14.34, we show Bode plots for typical lead and lag compensators. The Bode diagram for the lag-lead case will be included in the next section. The names for these transfer functions refer to their phase-angle characteristics. Positive and negative values of $\theta(\omega)$ are called leading and lagging angles, respectively. For a lag network, the majority of the changes in the curves normally take place at lower frequencies than for a lead network. Keep in mind that Figures 14.33 and 14.34 show the characteristics only of the controller and not of the entire open-loop transfer function.

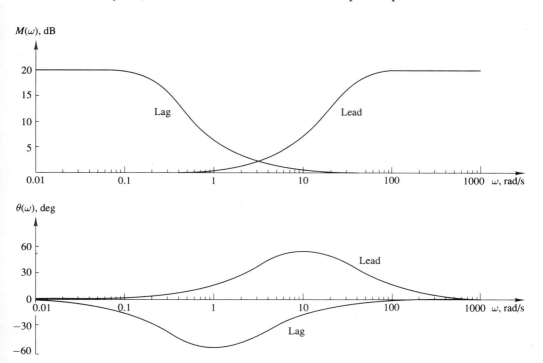

FIGURE 14.34 Bode diagrams for lead and lag compensators.

Many useful transfer functions can be implemented with electrical, mechanical, hydraulic, or pneumatic components. Except for digital controllers, networks employing operational amplifiers are most frequently used. Two of the problems at the end of Chapter 8 presented op-amp networks that can be used for lag, lead, and PID control. Some of the problems at the end of this chapter examine op-amp networks for achieving other types of transfer functions. Because such devices can be incorporated into the controller to compensate for deficiencies that would otherwise exist in the system's behavior, they are often called **compensators**. In some cases, appropriate compensators are put in the sensor block of Figure 14.25(a) or in an inner feedback loop, rather than in the controller block.

Additional Concerns

A mathematical model provides only an approximate description of the physical system. In the construction of the components, some deviations from the nominal parameter values are to be expected. Wear and environmental factors might further modify their characteristics over time. In any event, not all the secondary features can be incorporated into the model. In fact, there may be some uncertainty in the complete description of the plant to be controlled.

It is important to be sure that the system's behavior will remain acceptable when the parameters undergo moderate changes. It is possible to calculate the effects of individual parameter changes on the responses of the model. Fortunately, the very structure of feedback systems tends to reduce these effects. Even then, however, a safety margin is needed because of uncertainty about how closely the model describes the actual system. Often, factors that may be relatively unimportant under most conditions play a more significant role as the open-loop gain becomes large. Even though the original model might have indicated that the system is always stable, additional poles and zeros may need to be included and may even drive the root locus into the right half-plane for large values of the gain constant K. Nonlinear effects also become increasingly important. More sophisticated models, extensive computer simulation, and testing may be necessary.

The operation of practical sensors and other system components often produces unwanted high-frequency signals in addition to the desired responses. It is important that such internally generated signals, referred to as noise, be attenuated rapidly as they travel around the feedback loop. Thus the decibel curve should fall off sufficiently fast at high frequencies. Associated with the Bode plot there may be specified a cut-off frequency, above which the open-loop gain must be sufficiently small. If the designer is willing to use more costly high-performance components, then this cut-off requirement can be relaxed somewhat.

■ 14.5 APPLICATIONS

We shall illustrate the concepts discussed in Section 14.4 by considering two relatively simple systems. In each case, we shall assume that the system can be represented by Figure 14.25(b) so that $T_R(s)$ and $T_D(s)$ are given by (40). The transfer function of the plant will be specified, will have distinct poles only on the negative real axis, and will have no zeros in the finite s-plane. We assume that we may choose the transfer function $G_c(s)$ for the controller, with no restriction on the values of its coefficients.

In the solutions, we shall assume that there are no constraints other than those given in the problem statements. We shall, however, comment on some of the practical difficulties that one should consider when choosing $G_c(s)$. The design choices that we make will not represent an approach that should always be used, nor will our results be unique. The purpose of this section is simply to introduce some of the important design techniques.

▶ **EXAMPLE 14.17**

Let the transfer function of the plant in Figure 14.25(b) be

$$G_p(s) = \frac{10}{(s+1)(s+10)} \tag{59}$$

Assume a unity-feedback system, so that $H(s) = 1$. The steady-state error for a reference step input should not exceed 2% of the input. Similarly, the steady-state response to a disturbance step input should not exceed 2%.

The poles of the closed-loop transfer function $T_R(s)$ should meet the following conditions. The time constants of the corresponding exponential factors in the transient response should be less than 0.1 s. And for any pair of complex conjugate poles, the damping ratio ζ should be at least 0.8.

Determine whether it is possible to satisfy these design constraints by using proportional control. If it is not, use proportional-plus-derivative control to do so.

Solution

The transfer function for the plant is given by (43) with $K_p = 10$, $a = 1$, and $b = 10$. For proportional control, where $G_c(s) = K_c$, we can substitute these numerical values into (45) through (51). From (45), the closed-loop transfer functions for a reference or disturbance input are

$$T_R(s) = \frac{10K_c}{s^2 + 11s + 10(1 + K_c)}$$

$$T_D(s) = \frac{10}{s^2 + 11s + 10(1 + K_c)} \tag{60}$$

When $r(t)$ is the unit step function, the steady-state error is, from (47),

$$e_{ss} = \frac{10}{10 + 10K_c} = \frac{1}{1 + K_c} \tag{61}$$

which should not exceed 0.02. Because we find it generally unwise to choose the controller gain K_c larger than necessary, we let $K_c = 49$.

When $d(t)$ is the unit step function, we see from (50) that the steady-state response is $y_{ss} = 1/(1 + K_c)$. Thus selecting $K_c = 49$ also limits the steady-state response to a constant disturbance input to 2%.

Once K_c has been chosen to meet the steady-state requirements, we have no further means of affecting the dynamic behavior. The denominator in (60) is the closed-loop characteristic polynomial. Thus with $K_c = 49$, the characteristic equation is

$$s^2 + 11s + 500 = 0 \qquad (62)$$

from which the closed-loop poles are at $s = -5.50 \pm j21.67$. The time constant of the exponential factor associated with these poles is $1/5.50 = 0.182$ s. To find the damping ratio, we can compare (62) with $s^2 + 2\zeta\omega_n s + \omega_n^2 = 0$ or we can use (6.52) to write $\zeta = \cos[\tan^{-1}(21.67/5.50)] = 0.246$. The dynamic behavior does not come close to meeting the specifications.

In order to improve the transient response without adversely affecting the steady-state characteristics, we can use a PD controller that has the transfer function

$$G_c(s) = K_c(1 + K_D s)$$

Then the open-loop transfer function becomes

$$G_c(s)G_p(s) = \frac{10K_c(1 + K_D s)}{(s + 1)(s + 10)} \qquad (63)$$

The expressions for $T_R(s)$ and $T_D(s)$ are those in (53) and (54) with $K_p = 10$, $a = 1$, and $b = 10$. As explained in Section 14.4, the parameter K_D has no effect on $T_R(0)$ and $T_D(0)$. Thus we again take $K_c = 49$ in order to satisfy the steady-state specifications.

The extra zero at $s = -1/K_D$ in the open-loop transfer function in (63) should be placed to the left of both the poles, as shown in Figure 14.30(a). Suppose we choose this zero at $s = -15$, plot the root-locus diagram, and then find the point on the locus corresponding to $K_c = 49$. We use MATLAB to do this, with the results shown in Figure 14.35. The pair of closed-loop poles turn out to be at $s = -21.83 \pm j4.83$, corresponding to a time constant $\tau = 0.0458$ s and a damping ratio $\zeta = 0.976$. This is more than satisfactory, so we let $K_D = 1/15 = 0.06667$.

If the dynamic response was not satisfactory, we could reposition the zero at $s = -1/K_D$ and plot a new root-locus diagram. Actually, because the overall transfer function in this example is only second-order, we could achieve the necessary results without plotting an accurate root locus. However, drawing such diagrams is generally a key step in the design of a controller.

▶ **EXAMPLE 14.18**

For the plant specified in Example 14.17, we want zero steady-state error when $r(t) = U(t)$ and also zero steady-state response when $d(t) = U(t)$. The conditions on the closed-loop poles are the same as before. The new steady-state requirements could be met with a PI controller, as in (55) through (57). However, the transient response would be no better than that achieved with proportional control. In order to get the improved dynamic

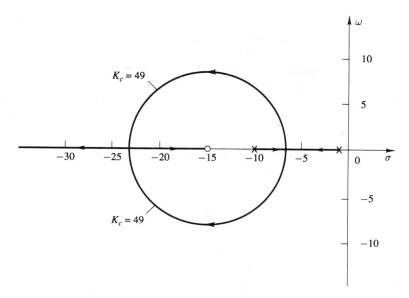

FIGURE 14.35 Root locus for Example 14.17 with PD control.

characteristics associated with derivative action and the excellent steady-state behavior associated with integral action, we use a PID controller that has the transfer function given in (58), which is repeated here.

$$G_c(s) = K_c \left(1 + K_D s + \frac{K_I}{s} \right) = \frac{K_c(K_D s^2 + s + K_I)}{s} \qquad (64)$$

Solution

The open-loop transfer function is

$$G_c(s)G_p(s) = \frac{10K_c(K_D s^2 + s + K_I)}{s(s+1)(s+10)} \qquad (65)$$

Inserting this expression into (40), with $H(s) = 1$, gives

$$T_R(s) = \frac{10K_c(K_D s^2 + s + K_I)}{s^3 + (11 + 10K_c K_D)s^2 + 10(1 + K_c)s + 10K_c K_I}$$

$$T_D(s) = \frac{10s}{s^3 + (11 + 10K_c K_D)s^2 + 10(1 + K_c)s + 10K_c K_I} \qquad (66)$$

Because $T_R(0) = 1$, the steady-state error when $r(t) = U(t)$ is zero for all nonzero values of $K_c K_I$. And because $T_D(0) = 0$, the steady-state response to a constant disturbance input is also zero.

The controller has contributed to the open-loop transfer function in (65) a pole at the origin and two zeros. We shall let one of these zeros be at

$s = -15$, as for the PD controller. The other zero is normally placed close to the pole at the origin, so that the dynamic behavior of the overall system will not be too different from that exhibited when the PD controller is used. We find it convenient to select this zero position at $s = -1$, which is the location of one of the open-loop poles.

Specifying the two zeros of $G_c(s)$ indirectly determines the values of K_D and K_I. For our choice, we find that $K_D = 1/16$ and $K_I = 15/16$. Then (65) can be rewritten as

$$G_c(s)G_p(s) = \frac{(10/16)K_c(s^2 + 16s + 15)}{s(s+1)(s+10)} = \frac{(5/8)K_c(s+1)(s+15)}{s(s+1)(s+10)} \tag{67}$$

We again use MATLAB for this open-loop transfer function to plot the root locus, which is shown in Figure 14.36. Because the steady-state specification is satisfied for all values of K_c, we are now free to select this parameter to place the closed-loop poles anywhere on the locus. The computer program can easily calculate the points on the locus for a given value of K_c and can also determine the value of K_c that corresponds to a specified point. If, for example, $K_c = 20$, the closed-loop poles are at $s = -11.25 \pm j7.81$. The time constant and damping ratio for this pair of poles are $\tau = 1/11.25 = 0.889$ s and $\zeta = \cos[\tan^{-1}(7.81/11.25)] = 0.822$.

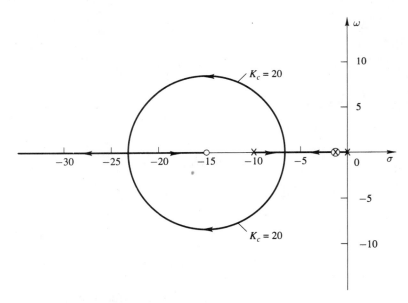

FIGURE 14.36 Root locus for Example 14.18 with PID control.

Although the foregoing choice of K_c satisfies the problem specifications, we should point out two possible problems. First, because of normal tolerances in the physical system, the pole and zero at $s = -1$ in $G_c(s)G_p(s)$ cannot be expected to cancel exactly. In addition to modifying the existing branches of the locus somewhat, this creates a third branch, which in turn yields another term in the transient response, with a time constant of about 1 s. However, this transient term is small because of the short distance between the pole and zero.

The second possible problem becomes apparent when we carefully examine the expression for the closed-loop disturbance transfer function. It turns out that, unlike $T_R(s)$, $T_D(s)$ contains a pole at $s = -1$ even if there is an exact cancellation of the pole and zero of $G_c(s)G_p(s)$ at that point. We shall not take the time to investigate the effects of this, but the reader should be aware of it.

Two practical difficulties arise with a PID controller, which was used in the last example. First, it is very difficult with an electronic controller to put a pole of $G_c(s)$ right at the origin of the s-plane. It is more realistic to move this pole slightly to the left of $s = 0$. Second, unwanted noise may be generated within the controller or may appear in the signals leading to it. Because noise contains high-frequency components that should not be amplified, we do not want the magnitude of the controller's frequency-response function $G_c(j\omega)$ to increase at high frequencies.

Consider the Bode diagram shown in Figure 14.37 for the PID controller described by (64), with K_c chosen to be unity and with the values of K_D and K_I that we used in the last example. For very low and very high frequencies, $|G_c(j\omega)|$ becomes K_I/ω and $K_D\omega$, respectively. Thus the low- and high-frequency asymptotes for the magnitude curve have slopes of -20 dB per decade and $+20$ dB per decade, respectively. The low- and high-frequency asymptotes for the angle curve are $-90°$ and $+90°$. The fact that the magnitude approaches infinity as $\omega \to 0$ and as $\omega \to \infty$ results in the difficulties described in the previous paragraph. To avoid this, we can use a lag-lead transfer function with the pole-zero pattern shown in part (c) of Figure 14.33.

In order to compare the characteristics of the two controllers, we assume that their multiplying constants have been adjusted so that for both cases, $M(\omega)$ approaches unity in the mid-frequency range. For any controller, increasing the value of K_c just raises the entire magnitude curve by a constant amount without affecting the angle curve. A Bode diagram for the lag-lead controller used in the next example is also shown in Figure 14.37, again for $K_c = 1$. Note that except at low and high frequencies, the two diagrams are quite similar.

▶ *EXAMPLE 14.19*

Determine a suitable lag-lead compensator for the plant considered in the last two examples. The steady-state and transient requirements are the same as those given in Example 14.17.

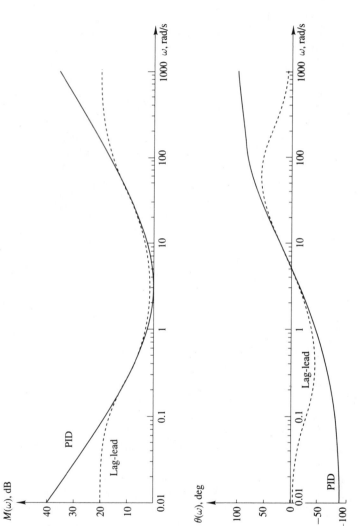

FIGURE 14.37 Bode diagrams for PID and lag-lead controllers.

Solution

The transfer function for the PID controller used in Example 14.18 was

$$\frac{K_c(s+1)(s+15)}{16s}$$

For the lag-lead controller, we keep the same zero positions but move the pole at the origin to $s = -0.1$. We place the new pole at $s = -150$. Then

$$G_c(s) = \frac{10K_c(s+1)(s+15)}{(s+0.1)(s+150)} \tag{68}$$

The multiplying factor of 10 has been added to the numerator so that in the mid-frequency range (say, $3 < \omega < 5$), $M(\omega)$ is approximately the same for the two controllers when the values of K_c are the same. This makes possible a more meaningful comparison of the values of K_c needed for the two cases.

Using (68), we have for the open-loop transfer function

$$G_c(s)G_p(s) = \frac{100K_c(s+1)(s+15)}{(s+0.1)(s+1)(s+10)(s+150)} \tag{69}$$

Substituting this expression into (40), with $H(s) = 1$, gives

$$T_R(s) = \frac{100K_c(s+15)}{s^3 + 160.1s^2 + (1516 + 100K_c)s + (150 + 1500K_c)}$$

$$T_D(s) = \frac{10(s+0.1)(s+150)}{(s+1)[s^3 + 160.1s^2 + (1516 + 100K_c)s + (150 + 1500K_c)]}$$

We see that $T_R(0) = 10K_c/(1+10K_c)$. When $r(t) = U(t)$, the steady-state error is

$$e_{ss} = 1 - \frac{10K_c}{1 + 10K_c} = \frac{1}{1 + 10K_c} \tag{70}$$

Because $T_D(0) = 1/(1+10K_c)$, the steady-state response when $d(t) = U(t)$ is

$$y_{ss} = \frac{1}{1 + 10K_c} \tag{71}$$

The expressions in (70) and (71) cannot exceed 0.02, so we require $K_c \geq 4.9$.

The root-locus plot for the open-loop transfer function in (69) is shown in Figure 14.38. The values of K_c corresponding to several points of interest are labeled on the diagram. Keep in mind that we may select any value of K_c greater than 4.9. We are not able to show all the branches of the locus,

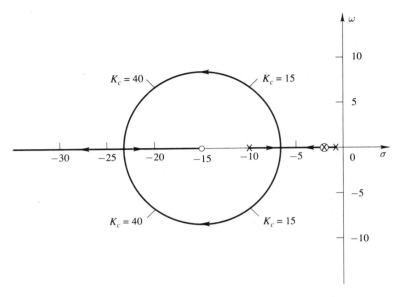

FIGURE 14.38   Root locus for Example 14.19 with lag-lead control.

because the open-loop pole at $s = -150$ is too far to the left. However, the time constant associated with the branch starting at that pole will always be very small.

If a pair of complex closed-loop poles has a real part of -10, the exponential factor in the corresponding terms in the transient response has a time constant of 0.1 s. This just satisfies one of the conditions on the dynamic behavior. For our locus, it occurs when $K_c = 14.41$. The pair of complex poles are then at $s = -10 \pm j7.443$, which corresponds to a damping ratio $\zeta = \cos[\tan^{-1}(7.443/10)] = 0.802$. Because this value is greater than the minimum value allowed by the problem statement, we may choose $K_c = 14.41$. By substituting this value into (70) and (71), we find that in the steady state, the error to a reference step input and the response to a constant disturbance input have both been reduced to 0.69%.

We can improve both the steady-state and the dynamic behavior by making K_c even larger. When $K_c = 40$, for example, the closed-loop poles are at $s = -21.29 \pm j7.65$ and $s = -117.5$. For the pair of complex poles, $\zeta = 0.941$ and the time constant is $\tau = 1/21.29 = 0.047$ s. The steady-state error for a constant input, found from (70), is $1/401 = 0.25\%$.

For the plant characteristics given by (59), we can use MATLAB to plot the unit step response for a reference input for different choices of $G_c(s)$. In Figure 14.39, the curves for proportional control and PD control are for

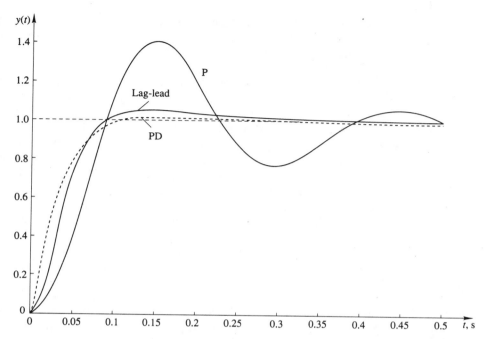

FIGURE 14.39 Unit step responses for a reference input for Examples 14.17 and 14.19.

Example 14.17, both with $K_c = 49$. The curve for lag-lead compensation is for Example 14.19 with $K_c = 40$.

For proportional control, we could have anticipated the large oscillations and the relatively long time to approach the steady state. Recall that the closed-loop poles had a damping ratio $\zeta = 0.246$ and a time constant $\tau = 0.182$ s. The curve for proportional-plus-derivative control exhibits excellent dynamic characteristics (corresponding to closed-loop poles with $\zeta = 0.976$ and $\tau = 0.046$ s). However, a PD controller would be more sensitive to unwanted noise and in practice would be implemented with a lead compensator.

For the lag-lead design, the pair of dominant complex poles were quite close to those for the PD controller. Because the damping ratio was slightly smaller and the time constant slightly larger, the overshoot and the time to approach the steady state have increased slightly. However, the lag-lead design has a far better steady-state behavior, with an error of only 0.25% instead of 2.0%. Finally, the value of K_c is less than for the other cases.

For any of the designs, a large value of K_c may cause practical difficulties. At some point, the linear model will no longer represent the physical system with reasonable accuracy. As the open-loop gain is increased, unmodeled modes and nonlinearities generally become important. Before selecting a final value of K_c, the designer might run additional computer simulations using a more complex but more accurate model. In Example 14.19, it may be better to choose $K_c = 15$, which will meet all the specifications given in Example 14.17, than to seek a faster response by using $K_c = 40$.

In the final example, the transfer function $G_p(s)$ for the plant will have three poles and no finite-plane zeros. Increasing the number of poles of $G_p(s)$ without increasing the number of zeros tends to make the system's transient response more difficult to control. Consider the case of a unity-feedback system with proportional control. Then the poles and zeros of the open-loop transfer function $K_c G_p(s)$ are the same as those of $G_p(s)$. From Section 14.2, the number of branches in the root locus that approach infinity is $n - m$, where n and m are the numbers of open-loop poles and zeros, respectively, in the finite s-plane. If $n - m \geq 3$, some of these branches pass into the right half-plane as the gain increases, making the overall system unstable.

Even if a more complicated function were to be used for $G_c(s)$, it would be difficult in practice to add more zeros than poles to the open-loop transfer function. This is because we want to attenuate any high-frequency noise. Nevertheless, we can still choose the poles and zeros of $G_c(s)$ in such a way as to try to pull the root locus to the left in the s-plane.

When the transfer function of the plant has a pole at the origin, the steady-state error for a reference step input is zero. However, there can still be a nonzero steady-state response to a constant disturbance input. In order to illustrate this, let

$$G_p(s) = \frac{K_p}{s(s+a)(s+b)}$$

and $G_c(s) = K_c$. With $H(s) = 1$, we obtain from (40)

$$T_R(s) = \frac{K_c K_p}{s^3 + (a+b)s^2 + abs + K_c K_p}$$

$$T_D(s) = \frac{K_p}{s^3 + (a+b)s^2 + abs + K_c K_p} \tag{72}$$

We see that $T_R(0) = 1$, so there is no steady-state error when $r(t)$ is constant. Because $T_D(0) = 1/K_c$, the steady-state response to $d(t) = U(t)$ is $1/K_c$.

▶ **EXAMPLE 14.20**

A particular feedback system can be represented by Figure 14.25(b), with $H(s) = 1$ and with

$$G_p(s) = \frac{500}{s(s+10)(s+50)} \tag{73}$$

The unit step response to $r(t)$ should have a steady-state value of unity, should have an overshoot of less than 15%, and should be within 4% of the steady-state value for all $t > 0.5$ s. The steady-state response to a constant disturbance input should be limited to 1% of the input. Determine a transfer function for the controller that meets these specifications. Because of the practical considerations discussed earlier in this section, the number of finite-plane zeros of $G_c(s)$ should not exceed the number of poles, and none of its poles should be at the origin.

Solution

If $G_c(s) = K_c$, the only poles of the open-loop transfer function will be at $s = 0$, -10, and -50, which leads to the root-locus plot shown in Figure 14.40. The expressions for $T_R(s)$ and $T_D(s)$ are given by (72) with $K_p = 500$, $a = 10$, and $b = 50$. In order to limit to 1% the steady-state response to a constant disturbance input, we must choose K_c to be at least 100. With $K_c = 100$, the closed-loop poles are at $s = 2.16 \pm j27.80$ and -64.31, and the system is unstable.

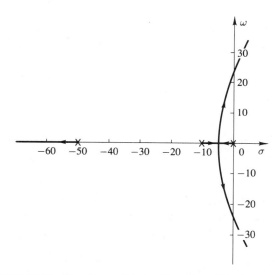

FIGURE 14.40 Root-locus plots for Example 14.20 with $G_c(s) = K_c$.

In order to meet the requirements on both the steady-state and transient behavior, we shall use a lag-lead compensator. We put one zero of $G_c(s)$ at $s = -12$, which is a little to the left of the pole of $G_p(s)$ at -10, in order to pull to the left the two right-hand branches of the locus. We also put a pole of $G_c(s)$ close to the origin (specifically, at $s = -0.1$) to reduce the steady-state error to a disturbance input.

Associated with the pole at $s = -0.1$ we include a zero at $s = -1$, so that the shape of the root-locus branches moving toward the right half-plane will not be greatly altered. Associated with the zero at $s = -12$ we add a pole at $s = -120$, so that $G_c(s)$ will not have more zeros than poles in the finite s-plane. Once we have selected the zero at $s = -12$ and the pole at $s = -0.1$, it is not uncommon to use a multiplying factor of 10 to locate the additional zero at $-(10)(0.1) = -1$ and the additional pole at $-(10)(12) = -120$. Thus we let

$$G_c(s) = \frac{10K_c(s + 1)(s + 12)}{(s + 0.1)(s + 120)}$$

Then the open-loop transfer function becomes

$$G_c(s)G_p(s) = \frac{5000K_c(s + 1)(s + 12)}{s(s + 0.1)(s + 10)(s + 50)(s + 120)} \tag{74}$$

We find that

$$T_R(s) = 5000K_c(s + 1)(s + 12)/P(s)$$
$$T_D(s) = 500(s + 0.1)(s + 120)/P(s)$$

where

$$P(s) = s^5 + 180.1s^4 + 7718s^3 + (60,770 + 5000K_c)s^2$$
$$+ (6000 + 52,000K_c)s + 60,000K_c$$

We see that $T_R(0) = 1$ and $T_D(0) = 0.1/K_c$. In order to satisfy the steady-state conditions, we require $K_c \geq 10$.

The root locus for (74) is plotted in Figure 14.41(a). It is difficult to show the entire locus clearly in a single diagram, so the portion near the origin is enlarged in part (b) of the figure. If we choose $K_c = 16$, the closed-loop poles are at $s = -1.96, -19.16, -16.01 \pm j10.63$, and -127.85. Note that the time constant corresponding to the pole at $s = -1.96$ is $\tau = 1/1.96 = 0.51$ s. However, the magnitude of this term in the transient response will be relatively small because of the presence of the closed-loop zero at $s = -1$.

The response to $r(t) = U(t)$ is shown in Figure 14.42. There is some overshoot because of the complex poles. Because of the pole at $s = -1.96$, the response takes some time to approach its final steady-state value. However, it does satisfy all the conditions in the problem statement.

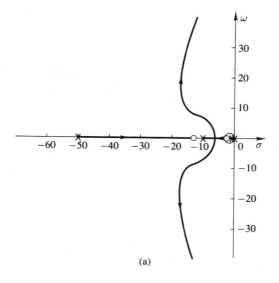

(a)

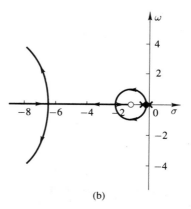

(b)

FIGURE 14.41 (a) Root locus for Example 14.20 with lag-lead control. (b) Enlargement of locus near the origin.

We have chosen the examples in this section to illustrate some of the techniques for handling feedback systems and some of the concerns encountered in practice. The availability of computer programs such as MATLAB for quickly plotting root-locus diagrams, Bode diagrams, and time responses is an important asset. An actual design would normally include many more diagrams than we have plotted, showing the effect of varying the controller's characteristics and allowing for the tolerances in physical devices.

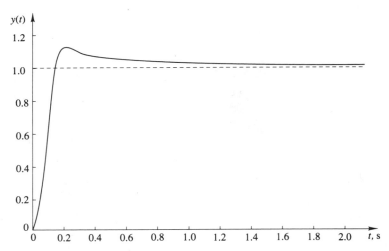

FIGURE 14.42   Unit step response for Example 14.20 with lag-lead control and with $K_c = 16$.

In all our examples, we assumed a simple unity-feedback system, with the compensator placed only in the controller block in the forward path. Had space permitted, we could also have discussed the merits of inserting compensators in the sensor block or in separate inner feedback loops. Note, for example, that the servomechanism examined in Section 14.1 does not exactly fit the configuration assumed in this section.

SUMMARY

Root-locus and Bode diagrams are important tools for analysis and design. Although there are a number of rules to aid a person sketching the diagrams by hand, accurate plots can be obtained easily via standard computer programs. This is especially helpful in an iterative design process, wherein changes in parts of the system are introduced in order to try to improve system performance.

When applied to a feedback system, a root locus shows how the poles of the closed-loop transfer function move in the s-plane as the open-loop gain is increased. Once the locus is drawn, a program such as MATLAB can locate the points corresponding to a particular gain. It can also determine the gain needed to place a closed-loop pole at a particular point on the locus. If the general shape of the locus is not satisfactory, changes can be made in those parameters that are under the designer's control, and a new locus can be plotted.

For any transfer function $T(s)$, we can obtain the frequency-response function by replacing s by $j\omega$ and writing the resulting complex quantity as $T(j\omega) = M(\omega)\epsilon^{j\theta(\omega)}$. To express the magnitude in decibels, we write $M(\omega)|_{dB} = 20 \log_{10} M(\omega)$. In a Bode diagram, we plot $M(\omega)|_{dB}$ versus ω and $\theta(\omega)$ versus ω, using a logarithmic scale for the frequency ω. For a standard feedback configuration, a Bode diagram for the open-loop transfer function can give important information about the behavior of the closed-loop system. An indirect indication of the form of the free response is given by the gain margin and phase margin, which were defined in Figure 14.23. Increasing the open-loop gain raises the magnitude curve by a constant amount without affecting the angle curve.

Among the typical constraints given to the designer of a feedback system are conditions on the steady-state responses to reference and disturbance inputs, as well as conditions on the nature of the transient response. In simple systems, increasing the open-loop gain tends to improve the steady-state response but adversely affects the dynamic behavior. In order to satisfy all the constraints, a more complicated controller may be needed. Root-locus and Bode diagrams help the designer investigate the effects of possible changes in the poles and zeros of the open-loop transfer function.

PROBLEMS

14.1 This problem involves the servomechanism considered in Section 14.1, and the numerical values of the parameters given in Table 14.1 should be used where they are needed.

   a) Calculate the value of K_A for a proportional-only controller that will result in a damping ratio of $\zeta = 0.7071$ for the closed-loop system. Give its transfer function $T(s)$ as a ratio of polynomials.

   b) Assuming that a tachometer signal $e_3 = K_T \dot{\phi}$ is available for proportional-plus-derivative control, calculate the values of K_A and K_T that will yield a closed-loop system with $\zeta = 0.7071$ and $\omega_n = 8$ rad/s. Determine the closed-loop transfer function and verify that its poles have the specified values for ζ and ω_n.

* 14.2 Repeat Problem 14.1 when the desired damping ratio is $\zeta = 1.0$ and, for part (b), the desired undamped natural frequency is $\omega_n = 10$ rad/s.

14.3 Repeat the analysis of Example 14.2 for the series RLC circuit with a voltage source that was studied in Example 5.1.

   a) Write the transfer function $T(s) = E_R(s)/E_i(s)$, and find its poles in terms of R, L, and C.

   b) Assuming that L and C are fixed, find the locus of the poles of $T(s)$ as the resistance R is increased from zero toward infinity. Sketch the locus in the s-plane.

   c) Give the value R for which $T(s)$ has a repeated pole ($\zeta = 1$), and give the location of this pole in the s-plane.

14.4 Repeat the analysis of Example 14.2 for the parallel RLC circuit with a current source that was studied in Example 5.2.

   a) Write the transfer function $T(s) = E_o(s)/I_i(s)$, and find its poles in terms of R, L, and C.

b) Assuming that L and C are fixed, find the locus of the poles of $T(s)$ as the resistance R is decreased from infinity toward zero. Sketch the locus in the s-plane.

c) Give the value R for which $T(s)$ has a repeated pole ($\zeta = 1$), and give the location of this pole in the s-plane.

* 14.5 a) Find the closed-loop transfer function $Y(s)/U(s)$ in terms of the parameter K for the feedback system shown in Figure P14.5.

b) Write an expression for the closed-loop poles in terms of K, and sketch the locus of these poles in the complex plane for $K \geq 0$. Indicate the pole locations for $K = 0, 1, 2,$ and 3 on the locus.

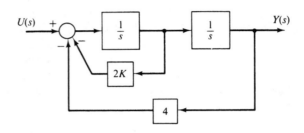

FIGURE P14.5

In Problems 14.6 through 14.14, use the root-locus construction rules presented in Section 14.2 to sketch the root locus for the open-loop transfer function for positive values of the gain K. Also use MATLAB, or another computer package, to obtain a plot of the root locus. Where branches cross the imaginary axis, use the magnitude criterion to find the corresponding value of K, denoted by K^*. Identify the open-loop zeros and poles with the symbols $\circ$ and $\times$, respectively, and use arrows to show the directions in which the roots move for increasing gain. Give the value for σ_0, the center of the large-gain asymptotes, where it exists.

14.6 $G(s)H(s) = \dfrac{K}{s(s+4)(s+6)}$

14.7 $G(s)H(s) = \dfrac{K}{(s+2)(s+5-j3)(s+5+j3)}$

14.8 $G(s)H(s) = \dfrac{K(s+2)}{(s+1)(s+3)(s+6)}$

* 14.9 $G(s)H(s) = \dfrac{K(s+9)}{(s+1)(s+2)(s+4)(s+8)}$

14.10 $G(s)H(s) = \dfrac{K(s^2+12s+37)}{s^2+4s+29}$

14.11 $G(s)H(s) = \dfrac{K(s+4)}{(s+1)(s-1)}$

14.12 $G(s)H(s) = \dfrac{K(s+2)}{(s+1)^2(s+8)}$

14.13 $G(s)H(s) = \dfrac{K(s+6)}{(s+1)(s+4)^2}$

* 14.14 $G(s)H(s) = \dfrac{K}{(s+1)(s+3)(s+6)(s+12)}$

14.15 Repeat Example 14.5 when $K < 0$.

* 14.16 Repeat Problem 14.9 when $K < 0$.

In Problems 14.17 through 14.21, sketch Bode plots for the frequency-response functions specified. In each case, include a magnitude curve in decibels and a phase-angle curve in degrees. Use a logarithmic frequency axis for both curves. Also use MATLAB, or another analysis package, to obtain a computer-generated Bode plot.

14.17 $T(j\omega) = \dfrac{1 + j\omega/2}{1 + j\omega/50}$

14.18 $T(j\omega) = \dfrac{1 + j\omega/5}{(1 + j\omega/40)^2}$

14.19 $T(j\omega) = \dfrac{1 + j\omega/20}{(1 + j\omega/2)(1 + j\omega/50)}$

14.20 $T(j\omega) = \dfrac{1}{j\omega(1 + j\omega/50)}$

14.21 $T(j\omega) = \dfrac{j\omega}{1 + j\omega/40}$

14.22 Construct the Bode diagram for the transfer function

$$T(s) = \frac{\omega_n(s + \omega_n)}{s^2 + 2\zeta\omega_n s + \omega_n^2}$$

when the damping ratio is $\zeta = 1$, 0.5, and 0.1. Use the normalized frequency ω/ω_n for the abcissa. Compare the curves with those for Example 14.15, giving special attention to the low- and high-frequency asymptotes and to the point at $\omega/\omega_n = 1$.

14.23 a) Obtain a computer-generated Bode diagram for the open-loop transfer function in Example 14.5, with $K = 100$. Determine the gain margin and the phase margin.

b) Find the value of K that will give a gain margin of 10 dB.

c) Find K^*, the maximum value of K for which the closed-loop transfer function will be stable.

* 14.24 Repeat Problem 14.23 for the open-loop transfer function in Example 14.7, with $K = 40$.

14.25 a) Use the result of Example 8.16 to verify that the transfer function for the circuit shown in Figure P14.25 is

$$\frac{E_o(s)}{E_i(s)} = -\frac{R_3(R_4 C_4 s + 1)[(R_1 + R_2)C_2 s + 1]}{R_1(R_2 C_2 s + 1)[(R_3 + R_4)C_4 s + 1]}$$

b) Express the poles and zeros in terms of the resistances and capacitances. Plot the pole-zero pattern, assuming that $R_4 C_4 > (R_1 + R_2)C_2$.

c) By referring to Figure 14.33, identify the type of controller or compensator that the circuit implements.

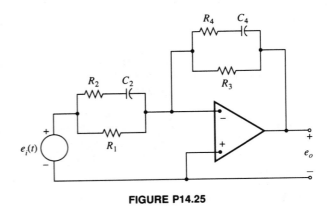

FIGURE P14.25

* **14.26** **a)** Use the result of Example 8.16 to determine the transfer function $E_o(s)/E_i(s)$ for the circuit shown in Figure P14.26.
b) Express the poles and zeros in terms of R_1, R_2, and C. Plot the pole-zero pattern.
c) By referring to Figure 14.33, identify the type of controller or compensator that the circuit implements.

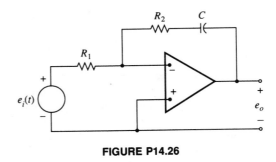

FIGURE P14.26

14.27 Repeat Problem 14.26 for the circuit shown in Figure P14.27.

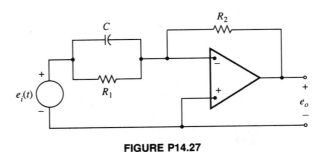

FIGURE P14.27

* **14.28** The servomechanism discussed in Section 14.1 has a disturbance torque $\tau_d(t)$ applied to the shaft to which the output potentiometer is attached. In Figure 14.1, the positive sense of this torque is clockwise.

    a) Show that the block diagram of Figure 14.2 must be modified to appear as in Figure P14.28(a).

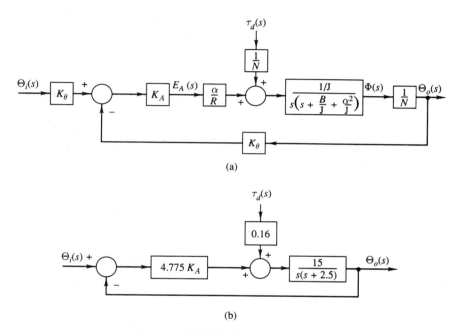

(a)

(b)

FIGURE P14.28

    b) When $R = 8\ \Omega$, $\alpha = 5.0\ \text{V}\cdot\text{s/rad}$, and the two potentiometer gain blocks K_θ are moved to the output of the summing junction and combined with the amplifier gain block K_A, verify that the model can be represented as shown in Figure P14.28(b). Use the numerical values in Table 14.1.

    c) Assume that proportional control is used with $K_A = 0.08727$ V/V. Determine the steady-state errors to

        (i) A unit ramp input in the reference angle $\theta_i(t)$.

        (ii) A unit step in the disturbance torque $\tau_d(t)$.

    d) Draw a root-locus plot and determine the value of K_A that will result in a closed-loop system having $\zeta = 0.8$. Find the corresponding value of ω_n.

    e) Draw a Bode plot for the open-loop system when $K_A = 0.4$ and determine the phase margin. Explain why the gain margin is not defined.

14.29 The servomechanism discussed in Section 14.1 is to be controlled by inserting a proportional-plus-derivative (PD) compensator immediately after the amplifier.

    a) Verify that the system can be represented by the block diagram shown in Figure P14.29, where K_D is the derivative gain, in seconds.

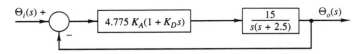

FIGURE P14.29

b) Show analytically that when the derivative gain is $K_D = 0.1$ s, it is possible to have closed-loop poles with $\zeta = 0.5$ and $\omega_n = 5.0$ rad/s. Determine the required value of the amplifier gain K_A.

c) Draw a root-locus plot and verify the locations of the closed-loop poles for the value of K_A found in part (b).

d) Using MATLAB or another computer program, compute and plot the response of the closed-loop system to a unit step in the reference input $\theta_i(t)$.

14.30 The servomechanism discussed in Section 14.1 is to be controlled by inserting a lead compensator immediately after the amplifier.

a) Verify that when the magnitude of the lead pole is 10 times that of the lead zero, the system can be represented by the block diagram shown in Figure P14.30.

FIGURE P14.30

b) Draw the root-locus plot with the lead zero placed at $s = -10$, and show that the upper branch of the locus passes close to the point in the s-plane that corresponds to $\zeta = 0.5$ and $\omega_n = 5.0$ rad/s. Select a value for the amplifier gain K_A that will result in closed-loop poles close to this point, and determine the locations of all the closed-loop poles for this value of K_A.

c) Using MATLAB or another computer program, compute and plot the response of the closed-loop system to a unit step in the reference input $\theta_i(t)$.

14.31 The servomechanism discussed in Section 14.1 has a disturbance torque $\tau_d(t)$ as described in Problem 14.28 and is to be controlled with a lag-lead compensator.

a) Adapt the block diagram in Figure P14.28(b) to have the controller transfer function

$$G_c(s) = \frac{10K_A(s+1)(s+10)}{(s+0.1)(s+100)}$$

in place of the gain K_A.

b) Evaluate the closed-loop transfer functions from each of the inputs to the output.

c) Solve for the steady-state error in θ_o that is due to a unit step in the disturbance torque $\tau_d(t)$.

d) Draw the root-locus plot and determine the value of K_A that will result in closed-loop poles with $\zeta = 0.7$. Determine the locations of all the closed-loop poles for this value of K_A.

e) Using MATLAB or another computer program, compute and plot the response of the closed-loop system to a unit step in the reference input $\theta_i(t)$.

* 14.32 Figure P14.32 shows a thermal process with a feedback temperature controller. The controller receives the desired temperature $\theta_d(t)$ and the measured temperature θ_m as inputs and determines the heat q_h supplied by the heater. The uncontrolled process was modeled in Example 11.7, where we derived transfer functions for $\hat{\Theta}(s)/\hat{Q}_h(s)$ and $\hat{\Theta}(s)/\hat{\Theta}_i(s)$. Assume that the thermal resistance R is infinite and that the liquid flow rate is $\bar{w}$, a constant. In terms of incremental variables, the controller is modeled by the relationship

$$\hat{Q}_h(s) = G_c(s)[\hat{\Theta}_d(s) - \hat{\Theta}_m(s)]$$

where $G_c(s)$ is the controller transfer function and the quantity $\hat{\Theta}_d(s) - \hat{\Theta}_m(s)$ is the transform of the measured temperature error. It is assumed that the sensor measures the actual temperature exactly—that is, $\hat{\theta}_m = \hat{\theta}$.

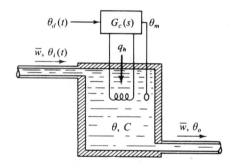

FIGURE P14.32

a) Draw a block diagram representing the closed-loop system that has the incremental inputs $\hat{\Theta}_d(s)$ and $\hat{\Theta}_i(s)$ and the incremental output $\hat{\Theta}(s)$.

b) Evaluate the closed-loop transfer functions $\hat{\Theta}(s)/\hat{\Theta}_d(s)$ and $\hat{\Theta}(s)/\hat{\Theta}_i(s)$ in terms of the unspecified controller transfer function $G_c(s)$.

c) Using proportional control with $G_c(s) = K_c$, evaluate the two closed-loop transfer functions $\hat{\Theta}(s)/\hat{\Theta}_d(s)$ and $\hat{\Theta}(s)/\hat{\Theta}_i(s)$. Show that for step inputs in $\hat{\theta}_d(t)$ and $\hat{\theta}_i(t)$, taken separately, the steady-state temperature error is not zero for finite values of K_c.

d) Using proportional-plus-integral control with $G_c(s) = K_c(1 + K_I/s)$, reevaluate the closed-loop transfer functions. Show that for step inputs in $\hat{\theta}_d(t)$ and $\hat{\theta}_i(t)$, taken separately, the steady-state temperature error is zero for all positive values of K_c and K_I.

14.33 Repeat the analysis of the temperature-control system described in Problem 14.32 when a dynamic model for the temperature sensor is included. Ignore possible fluctuations in the inlet temperature so that $\hat{\theta}_i(t)$ can be taken to be zero. In terms of the incremental variables, the sensor is assumed to have the transfer function

$$\frac{\hat{\Theta}_m(s)}{\hat{\Theta}(s)} = \frac{1}{as+1}$$

where a is the sensor time constant.

a) Find the closed-loop transfer function $\hat{\Theta}(s)/\hat{\Theta}_d(s)$ for proportional control, where $G_c(s) = K_c$. Determine the steady-state error to a step input in $\hat{\theta}_d(t)$.

b) Repeat part (a) for PI control, where $G_c(s) = K_c(1 + K_I/s)$.

14.34 Figure P14.34 shows a liquid-level control system such as might be found in a typical chemical process. The sensed level signal h_s is obtained by measuring the gauge pressure $p_1{}^*$ at the bottom of the tank. The controller also receives a signal $h_d(t)$ indicating the desired level. The controller output x is used to position a linear control valve in a bypass line connected around a centrifugal pump. The bypass flow rate w_b is given by

$$w_b = k\sqrt{\overline{\Delta p}}\left(\frac{x}{x_m}\right)$$

where x_m is the maximum valve opening, x is the actual valve opening, Δp is the pressure difference developed by the pump, and k is the valve coefficient. The pump is driven at a constant speed, and at the operating point, the slope of the curve of Δp versus w is $-K$.

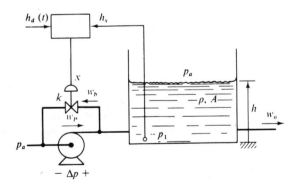

FIGURE P14.34

a) Derive the linearized model of the control valve by finding the coefficients α and β in the expression $\hat{w}_b = \alpha\widehat{\Delta p} + \beta\hat{x}$.

b) Write the linearized system equations in terms of the incremental variables $\hat{h}$, $\hat{w}_o$, $\hat{w}_b$, $\hat{w}_p$, $\widehat{\Delta p}$, and $\hat{p}_1$. Then draw the block diagram of the open-loop system with $\hat{X}(s)$ and $\hat{W}_o(s)$ as the inputs and $\hat{H}(s)$ as the output. Evaluate the transfer functions $\hat{H}(s)/\hat{X}(s)$ and $\hat{H}(s)/\hat{W}_o(s)$.

c) Taking $\hat{W}_o(s) = 0$, draw a block diagram of the closed-loop system when the controller is described by $\hat{X}(s) = K_c[\hat{H}_d(s) - \hat{H}_s(s)]$ and the sensor is described by $\hat{H}_s(s) = \hat{H}(s)$. Find the closed-loop transfer function $\hat{H}(s)/\hat{H}_d(s)$. Explain why the controller gain K_c should be negative.

d) Repeat part (c), using a dynamic model of the sensor such that $\hat{H}_s(s)/\hat{H}(s) = 1/(\tau s + 1)$.

COMPUTER ANALYSIS

We have presented methods for analyzing linear models of dynamic systems by using classical differential equations, Laplace transforms, and transfer functions. For nonlinear systems, we have shown how one can develop a linear approximation that is valid when the variables remain within some region.

For most linear models of third and higher order, and for nearly all nonlinear models, computers are used to obtain solutions for the time responses. They can also carry out other types of analyses for linear models. In this chapter we will describe two commercially available software packages: Pro-MATLAB[1] for linear models and ACSL[2] for nonlinear models. Other packages exist for this type of analysis and simulation, but these two will serve to illustrate the capabilities that are available. Both of these packages can be run on a large variety of machines, including personal computers (PCs), and both are widely used in educational and industrial settings.

We will illustrate the use of MATLAB for building and combining linear models in several different forms. Then we will show how these models can be analyzed. Finally, we will use ACSL to simulate the response of nonlinear models to arbitrary inputs.

---

[1]Pro-MATLAB is a product of The MathWorks, Inc. (Natick, Massachusetts) that runs on engineering workstations and a variety of other high-performance platforms. PC-MATLAB is the personal computer version.

[2]ACSL stands for Advanced Continuous Simulation Language and is a product of MGA, Inc. of Concord, Massachusetts. It runs on a wide range of machines, including engineering workstations and personal computers.

15.1 BUILDING LINEAR MODELS

MATLAB allows four different types of models for linear, continuous-time systems and the same four types for linear, discrete-time systems. We will deal only with continuous-time systems and will restrict our attention to three of the four model types: transfer-function, zero-pole, and state-space. The fourth form, which corresponds to the partial-fraction expansion of the system's transfer function, will not be covered. For each of the three types we will illustrate how the model can be created. Then we will show how to convert a model from one form to either of the remaining two and how to combine the models for subsystems in series, parallel, and feedback configurations. Methods for analyzing these models, such as computing and plotting step and impulse responses, are considered in Section 15.2.

Most of the commands we will discuss belong to the Control System Toolbox[3] that has been developed for use with Pro-MATLAB and PC-MATLAB. This toolbox consists of a set of files, all having extension .M, that contain MATLAB commands for implementing the model-building and analytical operations that one commonly encounters when working with control systems. Other toolboxes have been developed for areas such as signal processing and system identification. The interested reader is referred to the *MATLAB User's Guide* for details on MATLAB itself and to the *Control System Toolbox User's Guide* for more information on most of the commands we shall use here. MATLAB and its toolboxes have an online help facility that can be used to obtain detailed information about commands while the program is running.

We will introduce some of the notation and capabilities of MATLAB but will not attempt to be comprehensive. All the examples will be for single-input, single-output (SISO) systems. However, the procedures can readily be extended to include systems with multiple inputs and/or multiple outputs.

Transfer-Function Form

The usual form for the transfer function of a single-input, single-output linear model is a ratio of polynomials—that is, a rational function of the variable s. To create the model in MATLAB, we represent the numerator and denominator polynomials by row vectors whose elements are the coefficients of the corresponding powers of s in the polynomials. For example, if the numerator of $G(s)$ is the polynomial $N(s) = 3s^2 + 4s + 5$, it can be expressed by entering the command numG = [3 4 5], where the symbol numG is the name we have assigned to the numerator polynomial.

If the denominator of $G(s)$ is the polynomial $D(s) = s^3 + 2s^2 + 4s + 8$, we can give it the name denG and express it by entering denG = [1 2

---

[3]A product of The MathWorks, Inc., Natick, Massachusetts.

4 8]. If we enter these two commands exactly as shown here, we will have created the transfer function

$$G(s) = \frac{3s^2 + 4s + 5}{s^3 + 2s^2 + 4s + 8}$$

without any further keystrokes.

If we want to perform some operation on $G(s)$, such as computing the step response, the quantities numG and denG are used as arguments, *in this order*, to the command. Most any other names with fewer than 20 characters can be used for the numerator and denominator vectors, in place of numG and denG, as long as they are listed in the proper order in any subsequent commands. One should keep in mind that MATLAB is case-sensitive, so numG and numg are two distinct entities. MATLAB will display the names and values of the arguments on the screen, which facilitates verifying that they have been entered correctly. This echoing by MATLAB can, however, be suppressed by appending a semicolon to the line.

Zero-Pole Form

We know from Chapter 8 that a transfer function $G(s) = N(s)/D(s)$ can be expressed in terms of a gain constant, its zeros [the solutions of $N(s) = 0$], and its poles [the roots of $D(s) = 0$]. To create a model for a single-input, single-output linear system in this form, we enter the gain as a scalar and the zeros and poles as column vectors.

For example, to build a MATLAB model for a SISO system whose transfer function has a gain of 5.5, zeros at $s = -3$ and -5, and poles at $s = -1$, $-2 + j3$, and $-2 - j3$, we could enter the lines

```
k = 5.5
zro = [-3; -5]
pol = [-1; -2+3*i; -2-3*i]
```

Again, different names could have been selected in place of k, zro, and pol. The symbol i is predefined by MATLAB to represent $\sqrt{-1}$, which we have denoted by j throughout this book. The semicolons within the brackets indicate to MATLAB that the element that follows is on a new row. Thus the quantities zro and pol are column vectors. An alternative method of specifying them is to omit the semicolons and transpose the resulting row vector by appending the symbol ', as in

```
zro = [-3   -5]'
pol = [-1   -2+3*i   -2-3*i]'
```

In either case, the transfer function defined by the foregoing commands is

$$G(s) = \frac{5.5(s + 3)(s + 5)}{(s + 1)(s + 2 - j3)(s + 2 + j3)}$$

The numerical values for the gain, zeros, and poles can be entered in any order. However, when using any MATLAB command to operate on $G(s)$, we must list the *arguments* in the command in the following order: zeros, poles, and gain.

State-Space Form

For a fixed linear system, the matrix form of the state-variable model was given in (3.33) as

$$\dot{\mathbf{q}} = \mathbf{Aq} + \mathbf{Bu}$$
$$\mathbf{y} = \mathbf{Cq} + \mathbf{Du}$$
(1)

We enter this model form in MATLAB by defining the four matrices **A**, **B**, **C**, and **D**. To analyze a model that exists in state-variable form within MATLAB, we need only specify the names that have been assigned to the four coefficient matrices for that particular model as arguments of the appropriate command.

For example, the four matrices corresponding to the third-order system described by

$$\dot{q}_1 = q_2$$
$$\dot{q}_2 = q_3$$
$$\dot{q}_3 = -q_1 - 4q_2 - 2q_3 + 2u$$
$$y = q_1 - 3q_2 + 2q_3 + 0.5u$$

are

$$\mathbf{A} = \begin{bmatrix} 0 & 1 & 0 \\ 0 & 0 & 1 \\ -1 & -4 & -2 \end{bmatrix} \qquad \mathbf{B} = \begin{bmatrix} 0 \\ 0 \\ 2 \end{bmatrix} \qquad \mathbf{C} = \begin{bmatrix} 1 & -3 & 2 \end{bmatrix} \qquad \mathbf{D} = 0.5$$

We define this model in MATLAB by entering the lines

```
A = [0 1 0; 0 0 1; -1 -4 -2]
B = [0; 0; 2]
C = [1 -3 2]
D = 0.5
```

Changing Forms

The commands that will transform a model among the three commonly used forms of the Control System Toolbox are shown in Table 15.1. In each case, the names of the quantities to be determined are entered in square brackets

TABLE 15.1 MATLAB Commands for Changing the Form of a Model

ss2tf	State-space form to transfer-function form
ss2zp	State-space form to zero-pole form
tf2ss	Transfer-function form to state-space form
tf2zp	Transfer-function form to zero-pole form
zp2ss	Zero-pole form to state-space form
zp2tf	Zero-pole form to transfer-function form

on the left side of the equals sign, and the names of the known quantities appear as arguments of the command. For the two commands that start with the state-variable form (ss2tf and ss2zp), it is necessary to include an additional integer argument that designates the particular input involved. For single-input, single-output systems, this integer is always 1.

The syntax for using these six commands follows. We have used the names num and den to represent the numerator and denominator coefficient vectors of the transfer-function form; k, zro, and pol to represent the gain and the column vectors of the zero-pole form; and A, B, C, and D to represent the matrices of the state-space form. These symbols would be replaced with the user-assigned names in an actual application. The commands are

```
[num,den] = ss2tf(A,B,C,D,1)
[zro,pol,k] = ss2zp(A,B,C,D,1)
[A,B,C,D] = tf2ss(num,den)
[zro,pol,k] = tf2zp(num,den)
[A,B,C,D] = zp2ss(zro,pol,k)
[num,den] = zp2tf(zro,pol,k)
```

We will illustrate the use of these commands in the following example by entering a system model in zero-pole form, transforming it to the two other forms, and finally returning it to the original form.

▶ **EXAMPLE 15.1**

Enter the model of a system whose transfer function is

$$G(s) = \frac{4(s+1)(s+4)(s+12)}{s(s+5)(s+3-j6)(s+3+j6)}$$

and use the appropriate MATLAB commands to obtain the model that has $G(s)$ as a rational function and also the state-space model.

Solution

We begin by entering the values for the gain, zeros, and poles.

```
k = 4
z = [-1; -4; -12]
p = [0; -5; -3+6*i; -3-6*i]
```

Because there are no semicolons at the ends of the lines, MATLAB echoes the values and yields the following output.

```
k =     4
z =    -1
       -4
      -12
p =     0
       -5.0000
       -3.0000 + 6.0000i
       -3.0000 - 6.0000i
```

To obtain the coefficients of the numerator and denominator polynomials of $G(s)$, we enter the command

```
[num,den] = zp2tf(z,p,k)
```

which results in the output

```
num =     0     4     68    256    192
den =     1    11     75    225      0
```

From these two row vectors of polynomial coefficients, we can write the transfer function as

$$G(s) = \frac{4s^3 + 68s^2 + 256s + 192}{s^4 + 11s^3 + 75s^2 + 225s}$$

To obtain the state-space form of the model from the numerator and denominator polynomials, we enter the line

```
[A,B,C,D] = tf2ss(num,den)
```

which yields the following list of the four matrices.

```
A =   -11    -75   -225      0
        1      0      0      0
        0      1      0      0
        0      0      1      0
B =     1
        0
        0
        0
C =     4     68    256    192
D =     0
```

We see that A has four rows and four columns, corresponding to four state variables. This also implies that B will have four rows and that C will have four columns. Because there is one input, B and D have one column, and because there is one output, C and D have one row.

As a final step in this example, we compute the zeros, poles, and gain of the model from the state-space matrices. To distinguish their values from the original set, we refer to them as zz, pp, and kk. We enter the command

```
[zz,pp,kk] = ss2zp(A,B,C,D,1)
```

which results in the output

```
zz =    -1.0000
        -4.0000
       -12.0000
pp =     0
        -3.0000 + 6.0000i
        -3.0000 - 6.0000i
        -5.0000
kk =     4.0000
```

These values agree with the original values of z, p, and k. The fact that there are only three zeros in the list indicates that the degree of the numerator polynomial is one less than that of the denominator. Hence $G(s)$ approaches zero as s approaches infinity.

Series Connection

Figure 15.1(a) shows two single-input, single-output subsystems that have been defined in transfer-function form and are to be connected in series, resulting in the equivalent system shown in part (b) of the figure. We know from Chapter 8 that the transfer function of the resulting system will be the product of the individual transfer functions, namely

$$G_{12}(s) = G_1(s)G_2(s)$$

Assume that the polynomials numG1 and denG1 represent the first subsystem, and numG2 and denG2 the second subsystem. MATLAB can create the polynomials numG12 and denG12 via the command

```
[numG12,denG12] = series(numG1,denG1,numG2,denG2)
```

A series connection of two subsystems can also be done if both systems are expressed in state-space form in terms of their four matrices, **A**, **B**, **C**, and **D**. We assume that the outputs of the first subsystem are the same as the inputs of the second. In this case the appropriate form of the MATLAB command is

```
[A12,B12,C12,D12] = series(A1,B1,C1,D1,A2,B2,C2,D2)
```

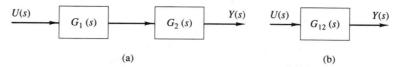

(a)

(b)

FIGURE 15.1 (a) Series connection of two subsystems in transfer-function form. (b) Equivalent system.

▶ **EXAMPLE 15.2**

Using MATLAB, enter the subsystems that have the transfer functions

$$G_1(s) = \frac{2(s+1)}{s(s+4)}$$

and

$$G_2(s) = \frac{3}{s^2 + 2s + 5}$$

and connect them in series to form a new system that has the transfer function

$$G_{12}(s) = G_1(s)G_2(s)$$

Then obtain the zero-pole and state-space forms of $G_{12}(s)$.

Solution

Because we know the zeros, poles, and gain of $G_1(s)$, we enter it with the commands `kG1 = 2`, `zerG1 = -1`, and `polG1 = [0; -4]` and transform the model to transfer-function form with the command

    [numG1,denG1] = zp2tf(zerG1,polG1,kG1)

The resulting matrices for the transfer-function model of subsystem 1 are

    numG1 =   0   2   2
    denG1 =   1   4   0

Because $G_2(s)$ is given in polynomial form, we enter the numerator and denominator polynomials as

    numG2 = 3
    denG2 = [1 2 5]

If we want to know the poles of $G_2(s)$, we can convert the transfer function to zero-pole form by entering

    [zerG2,polG2,kG2] = tf2zp(numG2,denG2)

Doing so yields

```
zerG2 =    [ ]
polG2 =    -1.0000 + 2.0000i
           -1.0000 - 2.0000i
kG2 =      3
```

We see that $G_2(s)$ has a pair of complex poles at $s = -1 + j2$ and $s = -1 - j2$ and a gain of 3. The symbol [ ] that is shown for zerG2 denotes an empty matrix. This means that the symbol has been defined but at present has no value. Because the numerator of $G_2(s)$ is just the constant 3, the transfer function has no zeros in the finite s-plane. In other words, the set of finite zeros of $G_2(s)$ is empty, which is what MATLAB is expressing with this notation.

Now that both subsystems have been defined in transfer-function form, we can make the series connection by giving the command

```
[num_ser,den_ser] = series(numG1,denG1,numG2,denG2)
```

which results in

```
num_ser =     0     0     0     6     6
den_ser =     1     6    13    20     0
```

This is MATLAB's representation of the rational function

$$G_{12}(s) = \frac{6s + 6}{s^4 + 6s^3 + 13s^2 + 20s}$$

To verify that the poles and zeros of the series combination are the union of those of the two subsystems, we enter the command

```
[zer_ser,pol_ser,k_ser] = tf2zp(num_ser,den_ser)
```

and obtain the result

```
zer_ser =    -1
pol_ser =     0
             -4.0000
             -1.0000 + 2.0000i
             -1.0000 - 2.0000i
k_ser =       6
```

which agrees with the form

$$G_{12}(s) = \frac{6(s + 1)}{s(s + 4)(s^2 + 2s + 5)}$$

where the complex poles correspond to the quadratic term in the denominator.

To obtain a state-space representation of the series connection, we enter

`[A_ser,B_ser,C_ser,D_ser] = tf2ss(num_ser,den_ser)`

and obtain

```
A_ser =     -6    -13    -20     0
             1      0      0     0
             0      1      0     0
             0      0      1     0

B_ser =      1
             0
             0
             0

C_ser =      0      0      6      6

D_ser =      0
```

From the dimensions of these matrices, we can see that the resulting system has four state variables, one input, and one output.

Feedback Connection

Figure 15.2(a) shows two subsystems that are connected in the feedback configuration introduced in Section 13.5 and shown in Figure 13.22(a). When each subsystem has a single input and a single output, and when the feedback signal has a negative sign where it enters the summing junction, the MATLAB command

`[num_fbk,den_fbk]=feedback(num_G,den_G,num_H,den_H)`

will create the numerator and denominator polynomials for the feedback interconnection.

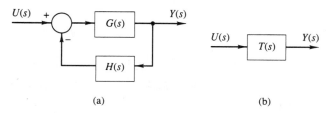

(a)   (b)

FIGURE 15.2 (a) Feedback connection of two subsystems. (b) Equivalent system.

Alternatively, we can handle the feedback interconnection of two multi-input, multi-output subsystems via the state-space representations, provided that we take care to ensure that the numbers of inputs and outputs are consistent at each connection point. The default condition is for a negative sign on the feedback signal where it enters the summing junction, although it is possible to obtain a positive sign by using an additional argument in the `feedback` command.

▶ **EXAMPLE 15.3**

The two subsystems used in the last example appear in the feedback configuration shown in Figure 15.3. Find the closed-loop transfer function and also its gain, zeros, and poles.

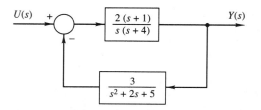

FIGURE 15.3   Feedback connection for Example 15.3.

Solution

The two blocks that were created in the previous example can be connected in a feedback configuration (with a negative sign where the feedback signal enters the summing junction) by issuing the command

    [num_fbk,den_fbk]=feedback(numG1,denG1,numG2,denG2)

which will create the following coefficients for the numerator and denominator polynomials in the closed-loop transfer function.

    num_fbk =   0   2   6   14   10
    den_fbk =   1   6   13   26   6

Thus

$$T(s) = \frac{2s^3 + 6s^2 + 14s + 10}{s^4 + 6s^3 + 13s^2 + 26s + 6} \qquad (2)$$

To determine the closed-loop poles and zeros, we use the `tf2zp` command

    [zer_fbk,pol_fbk,k_fbk] = tf2zp(num_fbk,den_fbk)

and obtain

```
zer_fbk =    -1.0000 + 2.0000i
             -1.0000 - 2.0000i
             -1.0000

pol_fbk =    -4.3083
             -0.7154 + 2.1969i
             -0.7154 - 2.1969i
             -0.2609

k_fbk =       2
```

Note that all four of the closed-loop poles differ from those of $G_1(s)$ and $G_2(s)$. This is usually the case when two blocks are joined in a feedback configuration, whereas the poles and zeros for a series connection are the same as those of the individual blocks. We can see that the closed-loop zeros are $s = -1$, which is the zero of $G_1(s)$, and $s = -1 + j2$ and $s = -1 - j2$, which are the poles of $G_2(s)$. It is a general property of feedback systems that the closed-loop zeros are the *zeros* of the *forward*-path transfer function and the *poles* of the *feedback*-path transfer function.

15.2 ANALYSIS WITH MATLAB

Having illustrated how the model of a fixed, linear system can be expressed in a variety of forms, we now turn our attention to using MATLAB to analyze such models. Complete coverage of MATLAB's varied capabilities is well beyond our scope here, but a number of the most basic and most commonly used commands will be presented. We will show how to compute and plot the responses to step functions and impulses, and then the responses to arbitrary inputs. Next we will illustrate generation of the frequency response in the form of a Bode diagram. The section concludes with a demonstration of how root-locus plots such as those shown in Chapter 14 are created.

The commands we will discuss can be used either with or without arguments on the left side of an equals sign. When one or more arguments are present, as in the command [y,x,t] = step(num,den), MAT-LAB supplies the numerical values of the variables listed inside the square brackets to the left of the equals sign. If a plot is to be drawn, such as y versus t, it is up to the user to enter the appropriate plotting command(s). Alternatively, when a command is given without the equals sign and any arguments to the left of it, as in step(num,den), MATLAB generates the plot automatically but does not supply any numerical values.

Each of the commands we will illustrate can be done with the model expressed in either transfer-function or state-space form. For the most part, we will use the transfer-function form where the model is given in terms of its numerator and denominator coefficients. For systems of relatively low order, say 10 or less, the choice is not critical. For systems of higher order, the state-space form, which uses the four coefficient matrices, is generally less susceptible than the transfer-function form to numerical errors.

Step and Impulse Responses

MATLAB computes time responses for specified inputs and initial conditions by using the system's state-transition matrix (see Section 6.6). The user generally selects the length of time for which the plot is desired and also the time interval between adjacent points. There are commands for computing the step and impulse responses, and they will yield the values of both the outputs and the state variables, if desired. A more general command called lsim exists for obtaining the responses to rather arbitrary inputs; it will be demonstrated shortly. In the following example, we illustrate the use of the step and impulse commands.

▶ *EXAMPLE 15.4*

Compute and plot the unit step response for the feedback system constructed in Example 15.3, for the interval $0 \le t \le 20$.

Solution

Because, from the solution of Example 15.3, the model exists as the arrays num_fbk and den_fbk, we need only define the time vector before computing the time responses. MATLAB requires uniformly spaced time points, defined by either a row vector or a column vector. To use an interval of 0.10 seconds and to define the time variable as a row vector, we enter

```
time = [0:0.1:20];
```

where the semicolon suppresses the printing of the 201 values. The step-response values of the output variable are generated and plotted in response to the command

```
step(num_fbk,den_fbk,time)
```

Grid lines and a title can be added to the plot via the line

```
grid;title('step response of fdbk configuration')
```

The resulting plot appears as Figure 15.4. In order to see the response to a unit impulse, we can issue the same commands, with step replaced by impulse.

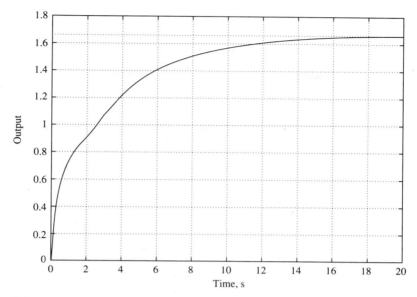

FIGURE 15.4   Unit step response of the closed-loop system for Examples 15.3 and 15.4.

Responses to Arbitrary Inputs

In addition to finding the step and impulse responses of a linear model, MATLAB can also compute the responses to arbitrary inputs, both with and without initial conditions on the state variables. The command that accomplishes this is called lsim, which stands for *linear simulation.*

The model can be in either state-space or transfer-function form, and the user must define both the time vector and the input. For single-input models, the input variable must be a column vector that has one element per time point. For multi-input models, it must be a matrix that has one column for each of the model's inputs. The time vector is defined as for the step and impulse responses—that is, as a row or column vector of uniformly spaced time points. If the initial state is not zero, the state-space form of the model must be used.

▶ *EXAMPLE 15.5*

The feedback system shown in Figure 15.5 is the same as that in Figure 15.3, except that an adjustable gain K has been included in the forward path. Obtain the zero-state response over the interval $0 \leq t \leq 50$ seconds with $K = 2.5$. The input is the signal shown in Figure 15.6, where $A = 1$, $t_1 = 1$ s, $t_2 = 16$ s, and $t_3 = 31$ s.

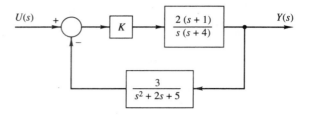

FIGURE 15.5 Feedback system from Example 15.4 with adjustable gain K added to the forward path.

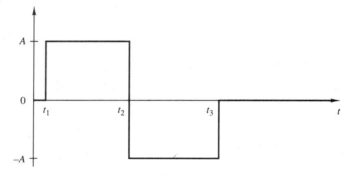

FIGURE 15.6 Input signal for Example 15.5.

Solution

To build the MATLAB model of the closed-loop system with the gain K set to 2.5, we start with the transfer functions $G_1(s)$ and $G_2(s)$ that were created in Example 15.2, create the transfer function of the forward path by multiplying $G_1(s)$ by the constant 2.5, and use the feedback command.

```
K = 2.5;
[num_K,den_K] = feedback(K*numG1,denG1,numG2,denG2)
```

Because there is no semicolon at the end of the feedback statement, the results are displayed.

```
num_K =      0    5   15   35   25
den_K =      1    6   13   35   15
```

We now have the model of the closed-loop system in transfer-function form and are ready to define the time and input vectors. To create a column vector for the time, with the points separated by 0.1 s, we enter

```
time = [0:0.1:50]';
```

which will give us 501 time points. The apostrophe after the closing bracket denotes the transpose of the matrix.

The length of the input vector must always be the same as the length of the time vector. We shall first initialize the input vector in to be a column of 501 zeros. Then we shall change the input values to 1 for $1 < t \leq 16$ and to -1 for $16 < t \leq 31$, as required by Figure 15.6.

```
in = 0*time;
for i=11:160, in(i) = 1.0;end;
for i=161:310, in(i) = -1.0;end;
```

Because the initial states are to be zero, we are ready to compute the response of the output y and plot it, along with the input, via the commands

```
y = lsim(num_K,den_K,in,time);
plot(time,y,time,in);grid
title('Response of feedback system with K=2.5')
```

The resulting plot is shown in Figure 15.7, which indicates that the closed-loop system is stable but lightly damped. The labels for the input and output curves have been added by hand. To find the values of the system's closed-loop poles, we need only enter the commands

```
[zcl,pcl,kcl] = tf2zp(num_K,den_K);
pcl
```

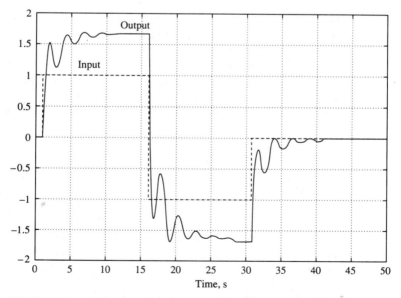

FIGURE 15.7 Response to pulse input of feedback system for Example 15.5 with $K = 2.5$.

which result in

```
pcl =    -4.6739
         -0.4119 + 2.4937i
         -0.4119 - 2.4937i
         -0.5024
```

As a check on the nature of the output plot, we note that the pair of complex poles has a damping ratio $\zeta = \cos[\tan^{-1}(2.4937/0.4119)] = 0.163$ and a time constant $\tau = 1/0.4119 = 2.43$ s. The steady-state value of the unit step response must be $T(0) = 25/15 = 1.60$, which is again consistent with the figure.

Bode Diagrams

As described in Section 14.3, Bode plots of a system's open-loop frequency response are often used in the analysis and design of feedback systems. MATLAB has a `bode` command that can produce magnitude and phase angle curves for models in either state-space or transfer-function form. The models may be either open-loop (no feedback active) or closed-loop. Also, the user has the option of either specifying the frequency values for which the calculations are to be done or letting MATLAB make the selection on the basis of the poles and zeros of the system's transfer function.

If the frequency values are to be specified, the user must first create a row vector of frequency values, expressed in radians per unit of time (typically, seconds). Because we use the logarithm of the frequency as the independent variable, it is customary to have the elements of the frequency list spaced logarithmically so that adjacent values in the list have the same ratio rather than the same difference. This is easily done in MATLAB by means of the `logspace` command, for which the first two arguments are the beginning and ending frequencies, expressed as powers of 10. The optional third argument is the number of points in the list, 50 being the default value.

For each of the frequencies in the list, the `bode` command calculates the magnitude and phase angle of the frequency response, expressed as a magnitude ratio and in degrees, respectively. To obtain a plot with the magnitude expressed in decibels, we must convert the magnitude ratios to decibels by taking $20 \log_{10}$ of each element. This is done by operating on the entire vector of magnitude ratios, as illustrated below. For plotting with a logarithmic horizontal scale and a linear vertical scale, MATLAB has the command `semilogx`, which is used in just the same way as the `plot` command.

There is also a `margin` command that can be used with *open-loop* models for finding the gain and phase margins, provided that they are defined for the specific model being analyzed. Recall that $|G(j\omega)H(j\omega)|$ must cross the zero-dB axis for the phase margin to exist, and $\arg[G(j\omega)H(j\omega)]$ must cross $-180°$ for the gain margin to exist.

▶ **EXAMPLE 15.6**

Draw plots of the frequency response magnitude (in decibels) and phase angle (in degrees) for the closed-loop system created in Example 15.3. Use the state-space form of the model.

Solution

The steps to be taken are (1) create the list of frequencies, (2) compute the magnitude ratio and the phase angle at each frequency value, (3) convert the magnitude ratios to decibels, and (4) construct the magnitude and phase plots versus frequency. The commands that will accomplish these steps, along with some comments, follow.

```
%-- 100 freq values from 0.01 to 100 rad/s
freq = logspace(-2,2,100);
%-- magnitude in dB and phase in degrees
[mag_ratio,phase,w] ...
       = bode(A_fbk,B_fbk,C_fbk,D_fbk,1,freq);
mag_db = 20*log10(mag_ratio);
%-- plot magnitude in dB vs logarithmic frequency
subplot(211)
semilogx(freq,mag_db);
grid;xlabel('freq - rad/s');ylabel('mag - dB')
title('Closed-loop frequency-response')
%-- plot phase angle versus logarithmic frequency
subplot(212)
semilogx(freq,phase);grid
xlabel('freq - rad/s');ylabel('phase - deg')
subplot      %-- return to normal plotting format
```

The desired Bode diagram is shown in Figure 15.8.

From the upper part of Figure 15.8 we see that for low frequencies, $|T(j\omega)|$ is asymptotic to a value of just less than 5 dB. The actual value is 4.437 dB $= 20\log_{10}(10/6)$, which can be obtained by taking the limit as $\omega \to 0$ of $T(s)$ as given by (2). The lower part of the figure shows that for low frequencies, the phase is asymptotic to zero. As ω increases, the magnitude of the frequency response of the closed-loop system remains flat until about $\omega = 0.1$ rad/s and then begins to fall off, with a slight peak near $\omega = 2$ rad/s. It continues to decrease at a slope of -20 dB/decade as the frequency increases. The phase plot exhibits a similar behavior as the frequency increases but becomes asymptotic to $-90°$ as $\omega \to \infty$.

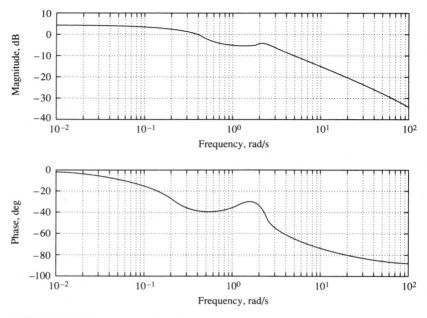

FIGURE 15.8   Bode diagram for Example 15.6.

Root-Locus Plots

In Section 14.2, we showed how a root-locus plot can be used to determine how the closed-loop poles of a feedback system will vary as the open-loop gain is varied. As with the other MATLAB commands that we are discussing, the user has several options available for the `rlocus` command. The model can be given in either transfer-function or state-space form. A list of gain values can be specified, or MATLAB will select a set that it considers appropriate. The user can have MATLAB either draw the plot without returning the numerical values of the roots or return the values without automatically drawing the plot. The region within the s-plane covered by the plot can also be specified or left to MATLAB. There is an additional command called `rlocfind` that allows the user to select any point on the locus once it has been drawn and to obtain both the value of the gain parameter corresponding to that point and the values of all n of the closed-loop characteristic roots for that value of gain.

The following example illustrates how root-locus plots can be created with MATLAB and how the gain can be determined for specific points on the locus.

▶ *EXAMPLE 15.7*

Generate a root-locus plot for the feedback system shown in Figure 15.5. Use the plot to determine the value of the gain K for which the closed-loop system will become marginally stable.

Solution

Recognizing that the forward and feedback transfer functions, excluding the gain K, are the functions $G_1(s)$ and $G_2(s)$ that were built and connected in series in Example 15.2, we can specify the open-loop model in transfer-function form in terms of the existing polynomial coefficient vectors num_ser and den_ser. The gain K in the forward path is included automatically. Thus, to generate the root-locus plot with the region and gains determined by MATLAB, we enter the commands

```
rlocus(num_ser,den_ser)
grid;title('root-locus plot for Example 15.7')
```

The plot shown in Figure 15.9 will appear on the screen. Note that the symbol x has been placed at each of the four open-loop poles and the symbol o at the single open-loop zero.

To determine the value of K for which the complex branches cross into the right half of the s-plane, we enter

```
[k,clpoles] = rlocfind(num_ser,den_ser)
```

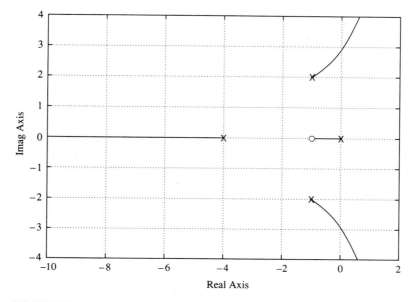

FIGURE 15.9 Root-locus plot for Example 15.7.

MATLAB will prompt the user to select the point for which the gain is to be found by clicking with the mouse directly on the root-locus plot that has just been drawn in the graphics window. We get $K^* = 5.85$.

■ 15.3 BUILDING ACSL MODELS

In the previous two sections we showed how a digital computer can be used to obtain numerical solutions for fixed, linear models. Now we direct our attention to the equally important task of numerically solving for the responses of nonlinear models. It is not usually possible to find a closed-form solution for nonlinear dynamic systems. What we can do is numerically integrate the nonlinear differential equations that describe the system, for a specific set of inputs and initial conditions. By repeating this process for a number of inputs and initial conditions, we can develop a good understanding of the dynamic behavior of the nonlinear model. In this section we will describe the **nonlinear simulation** program ACSL, which is representative of a number of such programs.

The starting point for developing a simulation is to write the model in state-variable form. If the model has n state variables and m inputs, we write the n first-order differential equations

$$\dot{q}_1 = f_1(q_1, \cdots, q_n, u_1, \cdots, u_m, t)$$
$$\dot{q}_2 = f_2(q_1, \cdots, q_n, u_1, \cdots, u_m, t)$$
$$\vdots \qquad\qquad\qquad\qquad\qquad (3)$$
$$\dot{q}_n = f_n(q_1, \cdots, q_n, u_1, \cdots, u_m, t)$$

where the f_i can be nonlinear functions of the state variables, the inputs, and possibly the time t. If the model has p outputs, there will be p algebraic output equations expressing the outputs in terms of the state variables, inputs, and perhaps t. The key feature of (3) is that the derivatives of all of the state variables can be calculated for any instant at which the state variables and inputs are known. These derivatives can be used to determine, by numerical integration, the approximate values of the state variables at the next instant. This iterative process can be started at the initial time t_0 from a known set of initial conditions $q_i(t_0)$. At the end of the computer run we will have the solution—actually, an approximation to the true solution—at a set of discrete time points.

A variety of methods exist for doing numerical integration, and they involve different amounts of calculation and have different error characteristics. Perhaps the most commonly used is the fourth-order Runga-Kutta algorithm, which does four sets of evaluations of the state-variable derivatives for each step forward in time.

The flow chart in Figure 15.10 shows the steps that must be taken for a numerical simulation. There is a section that is done initially but does not have to be repeated. Then there is a section that is done repetitively, as time advances, until the stopping condition is satisfied. Output in numerical form can be displayed as the run progresses. At the conclusion of the calculations, plots are generated from values that have been stored during the run. As we shall see, ACSL is set up to implement exactly this scenario. The user is also able to make modifications to parameter values (such as constants and initial conditions) between runs, without having to change the computer code for the model.

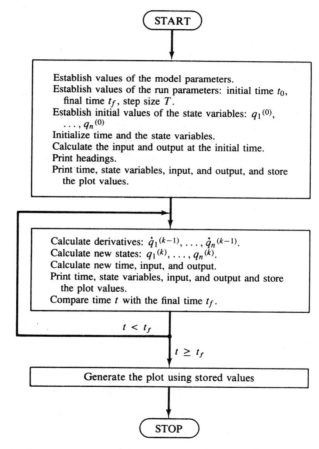

FIGURE 15.10 Operations required for the numerical solution of system models.

Two types of computer files are used for an ACSL simulation. These are the **model file**, which contains the equations that describe the system's mathematical model, and the **command file**, which describes how the simulation is to be conducted. For example, the command file contains the names of the variables whose values are to be displayed at certain intervals as the solution progresses.

Once the model file has been prepared, it is automatically translated into Fortran code, which is then compiled and linked with the appropriate libraries to yield an executable module. When execution begins, the command file is read and its instructions are carried out. At the completion of the command file, the keyboard becomes active so that the user can enter new commands, change the values of constants, and make additional runs.

Structure of an ACSL Program

Figure 15.11 shows the structure of a simplified ACSL program that will simulate any continuous-time system we are likely to encounter. There may be other elements in a more complicated situation, but they need not concern us. Note that each keyword that begins the program or a section must be matched by an end statement. Any text on a line following an exclamation point is a comment and is ignored by ACSL. In the initial section, any calculations that need be done only once should be performed, such as calculating coefficients that are used in expressions for derivatives and calculating constants that depend on the initial conditions. Although it is not essential, it is good practice to declare all constants and assign them values here.

```
program
initial

    - declare constants and assign values
    - do initial calculations (parameters, initial values)

end ! of initial section
derivative

    - evaluate inputs
    - evaluate derivatives of state variables
    - integration statements
    - evaluate outputs
    - check termination condition

end ! of derivative section
end ! of program
```

FIGURE 15.11 Simplified structure of an ACSL program for continuous-time models.

The `derivative` section contains all the computations that must be performed at each time step. This includes testing for the stopping condition. This test usually involves comparing the actual simulation time to an ending time. However, other types of stopping conditions can be used, such as the displacement of a mass reaching a specified value.

Integration

The heart of a simulation program is integration of the first-order differential equations of the state-variable model. To accomplish this integration, we must know the initial conditions and must evaluate the derivative of each state variable. Then we use the `integ` command with the derivative and initial condition as its arguments to obtain the values of the variable at subsequent time points.

For example, to solve the first-order nonlinear differential equation $\dot{x} + 2x^3 = 0$ with the initial condition $x(0) = 2$, we first write $\dot{x} = -2x^3$. If we then denote $\dot{x}$ by `xdot` and $x(0)$ by `xic`, we enter the statements

```
constant   xic = 2
xdot = -2*x*x*x
x = integ(xdot,xic)
```

At any point in time, the derivative `xdot` is evaluated and is used by the integration algorithm to determine the value of `x` at the next time point. The user need not be concerned with the details of these calculations for most simulation tasks, provided that the step size is kept sufficiently small. If we are using a fixed-step-size method, we can generally verify that the step size is satisfactory by running the simulation for several step sizes and comparing the results. Some of the nine built-in integration algorithms that ACSL has automatically vary the step size in order to maintain the integration error within bounds. The default is the fourth-order Runga-Kutta algorithm, which can be changed by specifying a different value for the ACSL parameter `ialg`. The variable `t` is automatically computed by ACSL as the independent time variable.

Functions

ACSL has the usual mathematical functions, including sine, cosine, tangent, square root, exponential, and logarithm. There are also functions for obtaining the absolute value, maximum, and minimum of a variable. Such common time functions as the step, ramp, and pulse are available. And a variety of nonlinear functions such as saturation, dead zone, and a switch exist.

Timing Parameters

The key timing parameter is the communication interval (`cint`), which determines how often the values of the variables are to be displayed and stored for printing. The calculation interval—that is, the integration step size—can never exceed the communication interval. For fixed-step-size methods such as the Runga-Kutta algorithm, there are `nstp` integration steps per communication interval, and the default value of `nstp` is 10. Thus we can easily investigate the effects of integration step size by doing several runs with different values for `nstp`.

Usually a simulation run is terminated by the time variable's reaching a specified maximum value. We ensure this by using the `termt` statement in the `derivative` section as in

```
termt (t .ge. tstop,'reached final time')
```

where the value of `tstop` is set with a `constant` statement or entered by the user from the keyboard. When the time variable `t` reaches `tstop`, the run terminates and the message `reached final time` appears in the output display. More complicated stopping conditions, such as a variable's reaching a predetermined value, are also possible.

Run-Time Statements

Once the ACSL model has been entered and converted to executable code, run-time commands must be given to tell ACSL what is to be done. Typical commands are to define a title for the particular case being run, to specify some parameter values and/or initial conditions, to identify certain variables to be printed on the display as the run progresses, to identify variables whose values should be saved for plotting, and to indicate that a run should be started. Rather than discussing these statements individually, we will illustrate their use in the examples that follow.

There are several ways in which the run-time commands can be entered. First, they can be typed at the keyboard. Second, they can be read in from a file that has the same name as the model file but also includes the extension `.cmd`, which designates the command file. The third method involves the definition of blocks of run-time statements, called procedures, in the command file. When this is done, the entire block of commands can be executed merely by entering the name of the specific procedure. In fact, the procedures can have arguments that are specified by the user when invoked.

■ 15.4 RUNNING ACSL MODELS

This section gives two examples of ACSL models and uses them to simulate the response of a dynamic system. We start with a simple linear system and then simulate a nonlinear mechanical system that has both translational and rotational motion with a nonlinear stiffness characteristic.

▶ *EXAMPLE 15.8*

Create an ACSL model for the second-order linear system described by the state-variable equations

$$\dot{q}_1 = q_2$$

$$\dot{q}_2 = -aq_1 - bq_2 + x(t)$$

$$y = q_1 + q_2$$

where q_1 and q_2 are the state variables, y is the output, and $x(t)$ is the input. Simulate the zero-state response to a pulse of height 2.0 starting at $t = 0.5$ s and ending at $t = 4.5$ s. The simulation should be done for the parameter values $a = 1.5$ and $b = 2.0$ and should cover the time interval $0 \le t \le 10$ seconds.

Solution

An ACSL model file that implements this linear model is shown in Figure 15.12. Note that constants are defined in the `initial` section for the coefficients of the differential equation, the initial conditions, the time at which the input begins and ends, and the time at which the simulation terminates. Because these parameters are defined by `constant` statements, any of them can be changed at run time from the keyboard, from the command file, or with a procedure call.

The remainder of the model is contained in the `derivative` section: the expressions for the two state-variable derivatives, the input, the two

```
program example15-8
initial !-- initialize parameters and constants
constant    a = 1.5,   b = 2.0
constant    q1ic = 0.0,   q2ic = 0.0
constant    tstep1 = 0.5,   tstep2 = 4.5
constant    xamp = 2.0,   tstop = 10.0
end ! of initial section
derivative !-- create dynamic model
x = xamp*(step(tstep1)-step(tstep2))
q1dot = q2      ! derivatives of states
q2dot = x - (a*q1 + b*q2)
q1 = integ(q1dot,q1ic)      ! state variables
q2 = integ(q2dot,q2ic)
y = q1 + q2      ! output
termt(t .ge. tstop,'reached final time')
end   ! of derivative section
end   ! of program
```

FIGURE 15.12 ACSL model file for Example 15.8.

`integ` statements that provide the integration of the derivatives, the output expression, and the stopping condition. Note that there is nothing in the model file that says what is to be done with the model—the model file just defines the model itself. The reader must understand this important distinction in order to prepare simulations of more complicated systems properly.

To run the simulation, we will use the command file shown in Figure 15.13. The command `set title` makes the message between the apostrophes start at the beginning of the first line at the top of the output plot; `set title(41)` shifts the corresponding message by 41 spaces (which in this case is at the start of the second line). The fourth line in Figure 15.13 sets the plotting device to be the standard one for the particular computer system in use. Some of the other options for the variable `devplt` are 3 for Tektronix format, 5 for Postscript format, and 6 for an X-windows driver. Setting the ACSL variable `nciout` to 10 causes the printed output to appear for only every tenth communication interval, thereby reducing the volume of the output. The `output` command tells ACSL which of the variables and parameters are to be printed at time intervals of `nciout*cint`. The `prepar` command indicates which variables are to have their values saved every `cint` units of time so that they can be plotted if desired. Note that the variable `t` appears in both the `output` and `prepar` lists. The simulation time `t` is the *only* variable that does not have to be defined separately.

Unless instructed otherwise, ACSL draws solid grid lines, which can be confused with the response curves. By setting the value of the ACSL plotting parameter `gltplt` to 200, we obtain dashed grid lines.

```
! Command file for running example 15-8
set title = 'Ex 15.8: linear example with 2 states'
set title(41) = 'a=1.5, b=2.0'
set devplt = 1 ! use default plot output device
set nciout = 10 ! print every 10th comm interval
output  t,x,y,q1,q2,a,b,xamp ! print these
prepare t,x,y,q1,q2 ! store for later plotting
set gltplt=200      ! dashed grid lines
start
!--- plot output and input
plot/xaxis=t/xtag=', sec' y,x/hi=2.5/lo=-0.5
pause
!--- plot the states
plot   q1,q2
!--- keyboard becomes active here
```

FIGURE 15.13 Command file for Example 15.8.

The `start` command tells ACSL to begin a simulation that will terminate when the logical expression that is the first argument of the `termt` statement in the `derivative` section of the model file is satisfied. At the conclusion of the run, the command file tells ACSL to draw two plots, with a pause between them. The first plot will show the output y and the input x versus time; it appears in Figure 15.14(a). The axes are scaled automatically unless the user specifies the scale. The command for the first plot makes the scale for x extend from −0.5 to 2.5.

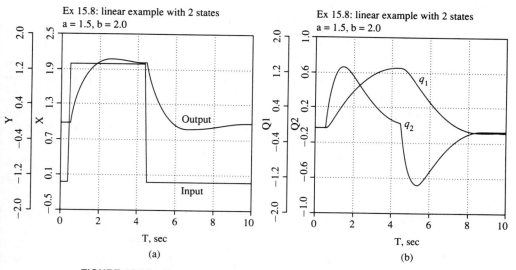

FIGURE 15.14 Responses to pulse input computed by the ACSL simulation of Example 15.8. (a) Output and input. (b) State variables.

After the user has viewed the first plot, a carriage return initiates the second plot, which shows the two state variables (Figure 15.14b). To differentiate between two or more curves in the same plot, ACSL has commands to add symbols or to use different types of lines. The labels on the individual curves in Figure 15.14 were added by hand.

When the last command in the file has been completed, the keyboard will be active, and the user can enter further commands manually. For example, the coefficients a and b might be changed and the simulation repeated. To do this and to view just the plot of the output and input, the user would enter

```
set a=3.0, b=1.0
start
plot y,x
```

It is not necessary to enter the other run-time commands that were in the file, because their settings are retained until modified by the user.

Having illustrated the main features of ACSL in the context of a simple linear system, we now show how it can be used to obtain responses of a nonlinear system that cannot be handled analytically.

▶ **EXAMPLE 15.9**

Develop an ACSL simulation of the mechanical system shown in Figure 15.15(a) and use it to compute the zero-input response and the zero-state response to $\tau_a(t)$. Include the force due to gravity on the mass M in all parts of the problem. The front end of the shaft attached to J_2 is fixed in the wall, and the shaft obeys the nonlinear torque-displacement relationship $\tau_K = \alpha|\theta_2|\theta_2$. The gear ratio is defined to be $N = R_2/R_1$. The outputs are x, the displacement of the mass, and f_K, the tensile force exerted by the translational spring. Because of the presence of the flexible cable, the force f_K is zero whenever the spring is not in tension. The parameter values are

$J_1 = 0.25$ kg·m^2	$J_2 = 12$ kg·m^2	$M = 50$ kg
$R_1 = 0.075$ m	$R_2 = 0.30$ m	$K = 1500$ N/m
$B = 25$ N·m·s/rad	$\alpha = 215$ N·m/rad^2	$A = 50$ N·m

The gravitational constant is 9.807 m/s^2. Angles are measured in radians, and translational displacements are in meters. When $\theta_2 = x = 0$, both the torsional shaft and the translational spring are undeflected. The numerical values of the input torque and the state variables should be printed. The translational displacement x and the applied torque $\tau_a(t)$ should be plotted. The following specific tasks are to be accomplished:

1. Write the model as a set of first-order differential equations (not necessarily in state-variable form) and use them to solve analytically for the equilibrium values $\bar{\theta}_2$ and $\bar{x}$ when the applied torque $\bar{\tau}_a$ is zero.

2. Develop an ACSL program to simulate the response to an applied torque that is a step function of height A commencing at 0.5 s, where the initial conditions for θ_2 and x are specified relative to their equilibrium values and where the initial velocities are always zero.

3. Simulate the zero-input response when the mass is released from the position where $\theta_2 = x = 0$. Plot the displacement x versus time.

4. Simulate the response when the amplitude of the applied torque is $A = 50$ N·m and the initial conditions are $\theta_2(0) = \bar{\theta}_2$ and $x(0) = \bar{x}$. Plot the input torque $\tau_a(t)$ and the displacement x versus time.

5. Repeat the previous step when the damping coefficient B is increased to 200 N·m·s/rad.

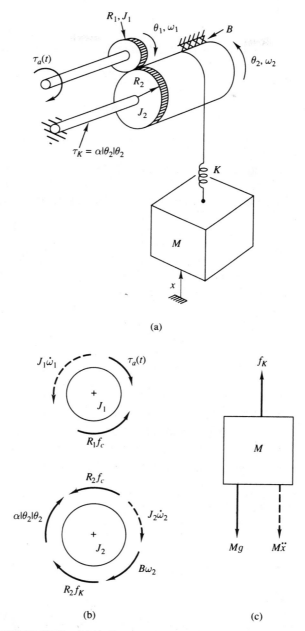

(a)

(b)   (c)

FIGURE 15.15 (a) Nonlinear mechanical system for Example
15.9. (b), (c) Free-body diagrams.

Solution

To develop the modeling equations, we first draw the free-body diagrams shown in parts (b) and (c) of Figure 15.15. Summing moments on the two rotational bodies and summing forces on the mass yield the following equations:

$$J_1 \dot{\omega}_1 + R_1 f_c - \tau_a(t) = 0 \tag{4a}$$

$$J_2 \dot{\omega}_2 + B \omega_2 + \alpha |\theta_2| \theta_2 - R_2 f_c + R_2 f_K = 0 \tag{4b}$$

$$M \dot{v} - f_K + M g = 0 \tag{4c}$$

where f_c denotes the contact force on the gears and $\omega_1 = N \omega_2$, where the gear ratio has been defined as $N = R_2/R_1$. Because the translational spring K is attached to a flexible cable, it is unable to exert a compressive force. Hence the force f_K obeys the nonlinear relationship

$$f_K = \begin{cases} K(R_2 \theta_2 - x) & \text{for } R_2 \theta_2 \geq x \\ 0 & \text{for } R_2 \theta_2 < x \end{cases} \tag{5}$$

To obtain the model in a form suitable for ACSL, we select a set of state variables and write an equation for each of their derivatives. However, because of the complexity of the expression for the force f_K, we do not attempt to express these derivatives as explicit functions of only the state variables and the input. Rather, we use (5) to compute f_K and then use it where needed in the expressions for the derivatives. The steps to be taken are as follows:

1. Select x, v, θ_2, and ω_2 as state variables.
2. Use the relationship $\omega_1 = N \omega_2$ to eliminate ω_1 in (4a).
3. Combine (4a) and (4b) to eliminate the contact force f_c and define the equivalent moment of inertia $J_{eq} = J_2 + N^2 J_1$.
4. Rearrange the terms to obtain expressions for the derivative of each of the four state variables.

We obtain the following set of first-order differential equations for the derivatives of the state-variables.

$$\begin{aligned}
\dot{x} &= v \\
\dot{v} &= (f_K - M g)/M \\
\dot{\theta}_2 &= \omega_2 \\
\dot{\omega}_2 &= -[\alpha |\theta_2| \theta_2 + B \omega_2 + R_2 f_K - N \tau_a(t)]/J_{eq}
\end{aligned} \tag{6}$$

where f_K is given by (5).

At any equilibrium position, the translational spring will be in tension and all derivatives will be zero. Then (5) and (6) become

$$\bar{f}_K = K(R_2\bar{\theta}_2 - \bar{x})$$

$$\bar{f}_K - Mg = 0$$

$$\alpha|\dot{\theta}_2|\dot{\theta}_2 + R_2\bar{f}_K - N\bar{\tau}_a = 0$$

from which

$$|\dot{\theta}_2|\dot{\theta}_2 = (N\bar{\tau}_a - R_2Mg)/\alpha$$

$$\bar{x} = R_2\bar{\theta}_2 - Mg/K \tag{7}$$

An ACSL model file that can be used with a command file or with user-entered run-time commands to obtain the required responses is given in Figure 15.16. In the `initial` section, the values of the physical parameters are specified, and a number of quantities are computed for use in the `derivative` section. Note that the equilibrium values $\bar{\theta}_2$ and $\bar{x}$ for $\bar{\tau}_a = 0$ are computed from (7). The initial conditions for θ_2 and x are then defined relative to this equilbrium condition. Various constants that appear in the differential equations, including the gear ratio N and the equivalent moment of inertia J_{eq}, are evaluated once in this section. Finally, the communication interval is set to 0.05 s so that the plots will be smooth. This also forces the default integration step size to be 0.005 s, which is a satisfactory value for this problem.

In the `derivative` section, all of the time-varying quantities are evaluated and the terminal condition is tested. Equation (5), which switches between two different expressions for f_K when $R_2\theta_2 - x$ changes sign, is implemented by a real switch designated by `rsw` in the file. Note that each of the derivatives is evaluated explicitly, although it is permissible to use the expression for a derivative as the first argument in the `integ` statement. However, the approach taken here is preferable because the values of the derivatives can be printed or plotted. Although we generally do not need to see a derivative of a state variable explicitly, this information can be very helpful in debugging a simulation that is not correct. Likewise, the initial conditions of the states are defined explicitly, and their symbols, rather than the values themselves, are used as the arguments of the `integ` statements.

A command file to run the model is shown in Figure 15.17. The first portion of the file contains commands that set the title, the frequency at which the output is printed, the variables and constants whose values are to be printed each `cint*nciout` seconds, and the variables whose values will be available for plotting at the end of the run. The last portion of the file establishes a `procedure` called `task3` that will simulate and plot the zero-input response (the third task in the example statement) when the user enters the command `task3`. By examining the command file, we see that the plot title is modified to reflect the specific conditions in effect, the proper initial conditions are set, the amplitude of the input torque is set to zero, the solution is started, the minimum and maximum values of the spring force

```
program ex15-9 ! trans + rot mechanical system
initial
constant J1=0.25, J2=12.0      ! kg-m^2
constant M=50.      ! kg
constant R1=0.075, R2=0.30      ! m
constant K=1500.      ! N/m
constant B=25.      ! N-m-s/rad
constant alpha=215.      ! N-m/rad^2
constant G=9.807      ! m/s^2
constant delx=0, delth2=0      ! ICs rel to equil
constant vic=0, w2ic=0
constant Ataua=0, tauabar=0, tstop=10.0, tstep=0.5
!--- compute nominal values, ICs, constants
delta = N*tauabar - R2*M*G
th2bar = sign(sqrt(abs(delta/alpha)),delta)
xbar = R2*th2bar-M*G/K
xic = xbar + delx
th2ic = th2bar + delth2
N = R2/R1
Jeq = J2+(N**2)*J1    ! equiv moment of inertia
cinterval cint=0.05 !-- communication interval
end    ! of initial section
derivative
taua = Ataua*step(tstep)
xdot = v
vdot = (fK-M*G)/M
th2dot = w2
w2dot = (-alpha*th2*abs(th2) - R2*fK &
                - B*w2 + N*taua)/Jeq
x = integ(xdot,xic)
v = integ(vdot,vic)
th2 = integ(th2dot,th2ic)
w2 = integ(w2dot,w2ic)
fK = rsw(R2*th2.ge.x, K*(R2*th2 - x), 0)
termt (t.ge.tstop,'reached final time')
end    ! of derivative section
end    ! of program
```

FIGURE 15.16 ACSL model file for Example 15.9.

f_K are displayed by the range command, and the displacement x is plotted versus time. The command file could be expanded to define procedures for carrying out the simulations defined in the fourth and fifth tasks of the list, but no such instructions are included in the figure.

```
set title = 'Example 15.9'
set ialg=4 ! second-order Runga-Kutta algorithm
set symcpl=.t.,npccpl=100    ! symbols on plots
set nciout=20 ! output every 20th comm interval
output t,x,v,th2,w2,taua,fK,alpha,K,B,Ataua
prepar t,x,th2,taua,fK ! store for plotting
plot/xaxis=t
procedure task3    ! zero-input response
  set title(13) = ', Task 3'
  set title(41) = 'alpha=220, K=1500, B=25'
  set title(81) = &
            'delx=-xbar, delth2=-th2bar, Ataua=0'
  set delx=0.5751,delth2=0.8272 ! x(0)=th2(0)=0
  set Ataua=0
  start
  range fK ! make sure fK stays nonnegative
  plot x/hi=0.2/lo=-0.8
end    ! of task3
```

FIGURE 15.17   ACSL command file for Example 15.9.

Figure 15.18 shows the zero-input response to an initial displacement of the mass that starts at $x = 0$ and settles to its equilibrium (for $\bar{\tau}_a = 0$) value of -0.5751 m. Note that the oscillations take over 10 s to damp out.

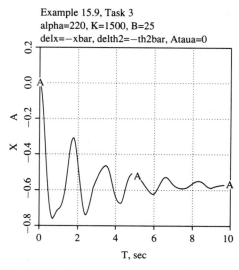

FIGURE 15.18   Zero-input response of the mechanical system in Example 15.9.

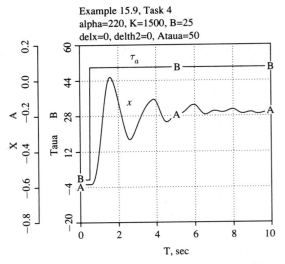

FIGURE 15.19 Zero-state response to a step input for the mechanical system in Example 15.9 with $B = 25$.

Figure 15.19 shows the zero-state response (where zero-state refers to the equilibrium condition with gravity but with no applied torque acting) when $\tau_a(t)$ undergoes a step change of 50 N·m at $t = 0.5$ s and when the rotational damping coefficient is $B = 25$ N·m·s/rad. The displacement of

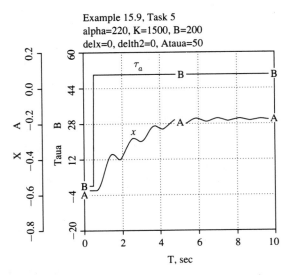

FIGURE 15.20 Zero-state response to a step input for the mechanical system in Example 15.9 with $B = 200$.

the mass starts at its unforced equilibrium value of -0.5751 m and settles out to a value of -0.1777 m, following a series of decaying oscillations. This behavior is consistent with the arrows in Figure 15.15(a) that show the positive senses of these variables.

Figure 15.20 shows the response under the same conditions as before, except that the rotational viscous damping coefficient B has been increased from 25 to 200 N·m·s/rad. Comparing Figure 15.20 with 15.19, we see that the starting and ending values of the displacement remain the same. The rise of the mass is substantially slower, and the amplitude of the oscillations has been reduced. However, the oscillations take about the same amount of time to damp out, because the increased damping directly affects only the drum J_2. The mass M has no damping force acting directly on it.

SUMMARY

Computer methods are required at some stage in the design of all but the simplest systems. In this chapter, we have illustrated key features of MAT-LAB and ACSL, two widely available software packages. ACSL can be introduced and applied as early as Chapter 3. Because important aspects of MATLAB are based on transfer functions, its use would normally be deferred until Chapter 8. Both programs are important tools for the analysis and design of dynamic systems.

For linear systems, MATLAB models can be created from the transfer functions or from the matrix state-variable equations. We can combine the models for subsystems that are connected in various configurations. We can then ask for the time responses to step functions, impulses, and other inputs. We can also obtain Bode diagrams for the frequency-response function of any part of the system. In the design of feedback systems, two important graphical aids based on the open-loop transfer function are Bode diagrams and root-locus plots. In Chapter 14 we used MATLAB to produce many such plots.

ACSL is used to simulate nonlinear systems. We first build a model file, usually from the state-variable equations describing the system. We also need a command file (or some alternative way to enter run-time commands) to tell ACSL how the simulation is to be done and how the results are to be presented. Even for a nonlinear system, it is easy to plot the responses to a variety of inputs and initial conditions, thereby gaining a good understanding of the system's dynamic behavior under a wide range of conditions.

PROBLEMS

In Problems 15.1 through 15.16, use MATLAB or another suitable software package. You should produce a diary file that shows the input, the numerical results, and (where appropriate) computer-generated plots.

15.1 The transfer function of a linear system has zeros at $s = -1, -4+j2, -4-j2$, poles at $s = -0.6, -1+j8, -1-j8, -15$, and a gain of 2.

    a) Obtain the transfer function as a ratio of polynomials.

    b) Find the four matrices that describe the state-space model.

    c) Compute the zeros, poles, and gain of the transfer function from the state-space matrices.

15.2 The transfer function of a linear system is

$$T(s) = \frac{2s^2 + 4s + 1}{3s^4 + 8s^3 + 9s^2 + 10s}$$

    a) Determine the zeros, poles, and gain of the transfer function.

    b) Find the four matrices that describe the state-space model.

    c) Compute the numerator and denominator polynomials of the transfer function from the state-space matrices.

* 15.3 The state-space matrices for a linear system are

$$A = \begin{bmatrix} 0 & 1 & 2 & 0 \\ -3 & -2 & 0 & 1 \\ -2 & 0 & 0 & 1 \\ 0 & 0 & -1 & -5 \end{bmatrix} \quad B = \begin{bmatrix} 0 \\ 1 \\ 0 \\ 2 \end{bmatrix} \quad C = \begin{bmatrix} 1 & 0 & -2 & 3 \end{bmatrix} \quad D = 0$$

    a) Obtain the transfer function as a ratio of polynomials.

    b) Determine the zeros, poles, and gain of the transfer function.

15.4 a) Use (13.37) to develop a state-space model of the system that was studied in Example 13.7, whose block diagram is shown in Figure 13.18(b).

    b) Convert this model to transfer-function form and compare the result with the differential equation given in the example statement.

* 15.5 a) Use (13.41a), (13.41b), (13.41c), and (13.42) to develop a state-space model of the system that was studied in Example 13.8, whose block diagram is shown in Figure 13.19(c).

    b) Convert this model to transfer-function form and compare the result with the differential equation given in the example statement.

15.6 Obtain state-space models for the individual subsystems defined in Example 15.2. Then, for the series combination, obtain both the zero-pole and transfer-function forms of the overall transfer function $G_{12}(s)$. Verify that the results agree with those found in the example.

* 15.7 For the series connection shown in Figure P15.7, obtain the zero-pole model and the transfer-function model.

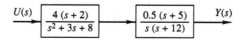

$$U(s) \rightarrow \boxed{\frac{4(s+2)}{s^2 + 3s + 8}} \rightarrow \boxed{\frac{0.5(s+5)}{s(s+12)}} \rightarrow Y(s)$$

FIGURE P15.7

15.8 a) Use the series and parallel commands of MATLAB to build the model represented in Figure 13.6 in transfer-function form.

    b) Determine the zeros, poles, and gain of $T(s) = Z(s)/U(s)$.

15.9 Repeat Problem 15.8 for the block diagram shown in Figure P15.9.

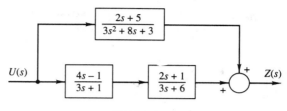

FIGURE P15.9

15.10 For the feedback connection shown in Figure P15.10, obtain the model for the closed-loop system in zero-pole form, transfer-function form, and state-space form.

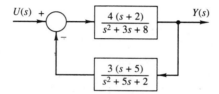

FIGURE P15.10

15.11 Repeat Problem 15.10 when the negative sign at the summing junction is changed to a plus sign—that is, when the feedback is positive rather than negative.

* 15.12 Repeat Problem 15.10 for the feedback system shown in Figure P15.12.

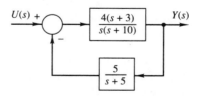

FIGURE P15.12

15.13 Obtain plots of the unit step and unit impulse responses for the linear system given in Problem 15.2.

15.14 Obtain plots of the unit step and unit impulse responses for the linear system given in Problem 15.3.

* 15.15 Obtain the zero-state response of the system described in Problem 15.2 to the input shown in Figure P15.15 over the interval $0 \le t \le 50$ s. Plot the input and the output on the same axes.

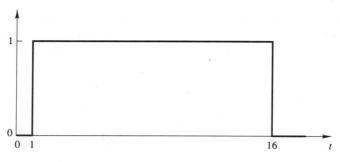

FIGURE P15.15

15.16 Obtain the zero-state response of the system described in Problem 15.3 to the input shown in Figure P15.16 over the interval $0 \leq t \leq 20$ s. Plot the input and the output on the same axes.

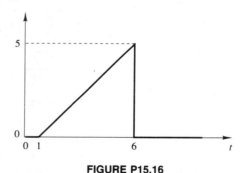

FIGURE P15.16

15.17 Obtain the Bode plots shown in Figure 14.20.

15.18 **a)** Obtain the Bode plot for the system that was considered in Examples 14.3, 14.4, and 14.16 when $K = 10$.
b) Determine the gain and phase margins and the frequencies at which they are defined.
c) Use the gain margin to determine the maximum value of K for which the closed-loop system is stable.

*15.19 Repeat Problem 15.18 for the system that was studied in Example 14.5 when $K = 150$.

15.20 Repeat Problem 15.18 for the system that was studied in Example 14.7 when $K = 40$.

15.21 **a)** Obtain a root-locus plot similar to the one shown in Figure 14.9 for the feedback system studied in Example 14.3.
b) Determine the value of K that will result in a complex closed-loop pole having an imaginary part of $+2$. Find the other closed-loop poles that cor. e-spond to this value of gain.

15.22 **a)** Obtain a root-locus plot similar to the one shown in Figure 14.10 for the feedback system studied in Example 14.5.

b) Determine the value of K that will result in a complex closed-loop pole having a real part of -2. Find the other closed-loop poles that correspond to this value of gain.

15.23 Repeat Example 14.6 when $\alpha = 20$. Determine the maximum value of K for which the closed-loop system is stable.

* 15.24 **a)** Obtain a root-locus plot similar to the one shown in Figure 14.12 for the feedback system studied in Example 14.7.

b) Determine the value of K that will result in a complex closed-loop pole having an imaginary part of $+2$. Find the other closed-loop poles that correspond to this value of gain.

In Problems 15.25 through 15.32, use the nonlinear simulation language ACSL or any equivalent software package.

* 15.25 Consider the linear system that was discussed in Example 13.7, whose block diagram is shown in Figure 13.18(b). Simulate the zero-state response of the system to the inputs described below. In each case, generate two plots. The first plot should show the input and the output, and the second should show each of the state variables.

a) A unit step function starting at $t = 1$ s.

b) The function shown in Figure P15.16.

15.26 Repeat Problem 15.25 for the linear system that was discussed in Example 13.8, whose block diagram is shown in Figure 13.19(c). Use the following inputs.

a) A unit ramp function starting at $t = 1$ s.

b) The function shown in Figure P15.26.

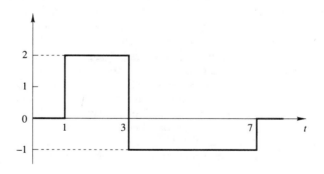

FIGURE P15.26

15.27 Repeat Problem 15.25 for the linear system whose transfer function is

$$T(s) = \frac{3s^2 + 4s + 6}{2s^3 + 2s^2 + 5s + 4}$$

* 15.28 Simulate the response of the second-order nonlinear system considered in Example 9.7 and described by (9.23) over the interval $0 \le t \le 10$ s. Verify by simulation that the system is in equilibrium when $x = -1$, $y = 0$, and the input is -3. Then simulate the response to the following conditions. In each case, plot the input and the output y.

    a) $x(0) = -0.5$, $y(0) = 0$, and the input is -3.

    b) $x(0) = -1$, $y(0) = 0$, and the input is $-3 + 0.2 \cos t$.

15.29 Simulate the response of the nonlinear circuit shown in Figure 9.11(a) that was studied in Example 9.9. Use the initial conditions $e_C(0) = 2$ V and $i_L(0) = 1$ A, which correspond to the operating point. Let the amplitude of the incremental input have the values $A = 0.1$ V, 1.0 V, and 10.0 V and plot the inductor current i_L. The responses should agree with the curves that are marked "nonlinear" in Figure 9.12.

15.30 Simulate the response of the nonlinear circuit shown in Figure 9.13 that was analyzed in Example 9.10. Use the initial conditions $e_C(0) = -6.7808$ V and $i_L(0) = -0.7808$ A, which correspond to the steady-state condition when the input voltage is $e_i(t) = -2$ V. For $t > 0$, $e_i(t) = 2 + A \cos 4t$. Let the amplitude of the incremental input have the values $A = 1.0$ V, 5.0 V, and 20.0 V and plot the output current i_o. The responses should agree with the curves that are marked "nonlinear" in Figure 9.14.

15.31 Simulate the zero-input and zero-state responses of the rack and pinion system that was modeled in Example 4.11, for which a block diagram was drawn in Example 13.9. The physical system is shown in Figures 4.27 and 13.20. The following parameter values should be used: $M = 500$ kg, $J = 40$ kg·m^2, $R = 0.50$ m, $K = 2000$ N/m, $B_1 = 25$ N·m·s/rad, and $B_2 = 25$ N·s/m. The simulation should cover the interval $0 \le t \le 40$ s. Specifically,

    a) Simulate the zero-input response when $x(0) = 0.5$ m and $\theta(0) = \omega(0) = v(0) = 0$.

    b) Simulate the zero-state response when the applied torque is 50 times the function shown in Figure P15.26.

In each case plot the horizontal displacement of the mass, the contact force on the mass (positive sense to the left), and the applied torque.

15.32 Prepare a simulation of the nonlinear pendulum shown in Figure 4.23(a) that was modeled in Example 4.7. The parameter values to be used are $M = 20$ kg, $L = 2.0$ m, and $B = 50$ N·m·s/rad. The gravitational constant is 9.807 m/s^2. Select the lengths of the runs so that all transients have died out.

    a) Simulate the zero-input response when the initial angle is $\theta(0) = 0.1$, 1.5, 3.0, 3.3, and 6.0 rad and the initial angular velocity is zero. Plot the angle of rotation θ. Comment on the character of the responses and compare them with the behavior of a linearized model.

    b) Simulate the zero-state response to a step-applied torque of 275 N·m. Plot the angle of rotation and the applied torque.

Units

We use the **International System of Units**, abbreviated as SI for **Système International d'Unités**. In Section A.1, we list the seven basic SI units, of which we use only the first five in this book. A supplementary unit for plane angles is the radian (rad).

In Section A.2, we give those derived SI units that we use. In addition to the physical quantity, the unit, and its symbol, there is a fourth column that expresses the unit in terms of units previously given. For example, $1 \text{ N} = 1 \text{ kg} \cdot \text{m/s}^2$.

■ A.1 BASIC UNITS

TABLE A.1   Names and Symbols of the Basic Units

Physical Quantity	Name	Symbol
Length	meter	m
Mass	kilogram	kg
Time	second	s
Electrical current	ampere	A
Thermodynamic temperature	kelvin	K
Luminous intensity	candela	cd
Amount of substance	mole	mol

■ A.2 DERIVED UNITS

TABLE A.2   Names, Symbols, and Equivalents of the Derived Units

Physical Quantity	Name	Symbol	In Terms of Other Units
Force	newton	N	$kg \cdot m/s^2$
Energy	joule	J	$kg \cdot m^2/s^2$
Power	watt	W	J/s
Electrical charge	coulomb	C	$A \cdot s$
Voltage	volt	V	W/A
Electrical resistance	ohm	Ω	V/A
Electrical capacitance	farad	F	$A \cdot s/V$
Inductance	henry	H	$V \cdot s/A$
Magnetic flux	weber	Wb	$V \cdot s$

■ A.3 PREFIXES

The standard prefixes for decimal multiples and submultiples of a unit are given in elementary physics books. The only ones used in this book are kilo (k), milli (m), and micro (μ). The terms in which they appear are as follows: $1 \text{ k}\Omega = 10^3 \ \Omega$, $1 \text{ mV} = 10^{-3} \text{ V}$, $1 \ \mu\text{F} = 10^{-6} \text{ F}$.

■ A.4 CONSTANTS

The following three constants are used in the numerical solution of many examples and problems.

Atmospheric pressure at sea level: $p_a = 1.013 \times 10^5 \text{ N/m}^2$

Base of natural logarithms: $\epsilon = 2.718$

Gravitational constant at the surface of the earth: $g = 9.807 \text{ m/s}^2$

Laplace Transforms

In Table B.1, we list the Laplace transforms for common functions of time. When using the table to take inverse transforms, the reader should keep in mind that the time functions are valid only for positive values of t.

Table B.2 contains the most important properties that are needed in the application of the transform method to dynamic models. The restrictions on the use of these properties are not included in the table but may be found in Chapter 7. In that chapter, we discuss the proper interpretation of the initial-condition terms and the conditions on the initial-value and final-value theorems. The functions of time are again valid only for $t > 0$.

TABLE B.1 Transforms of Functions

Time Functions	Transformed Functions
$\delta(t)$	1
$U(t)$	$\dfrac{1}{s}$
A	$\dfrac{A}{s}$
t	$\dfrac{1}{s^2}$
t^2	$\dfrac{2!}{s^3}$
t^n for $n = 1, 2, 3, \ldots$	$\dfrac{n!}{s^{n+1}}$
ϵ^{-at}	$\dfrac{1}{s+a}$
$t\epsilon^{-at}$	$\dfrac{1}{(s+a)^2}$
$t^2\epsilon^{-at}$	$\dfrac{2!}{(s+a)^3}$
$\sin \omega t$	$\dfrac{\omega}{s^2 + \omega^2}$
$\cos \omega t$	$\dfrac{s}{s^2 + \omega^2}$
$\epsilon^{-at} \sin \omega t$	$\dfrac{\omega}{(s+a)^2 + \omega^2}$
$\epsilon^{-at} \cos \omega t$	$\dfrac{s+a}{(s+a)^2 + \omega^2}$
$\epsilon^{-at}\left[B \cos \omega t + \left(\dfrac{C - aB}{\omega} \right) \sin \omega t \right]$	$\dfrac{Bs + C}{(s+a)^2 + \omega^2}$
$2K\epsilon^{-at} \cos(\omega t + \phi)$	$\dfrac{K\epsilon^{j\phi}}{s + a - j\omega} + \dfrac{K\epsilon^{-j\phi}}{s + a + j\omega}$

TABLE B.2 Transform Properties

Time Functions	Transformed Functions
$f(t)$	$F(s)$
$af(t)$	$aF(s)$
$f(t) + g(t)$	$F(s) + G(s)$
$\epsilon^{-at} f(t)$	$F(s + a)$
$tf(t)$	$-\dfrac{d}{ds} F(s)$
$f(t/a)$	$aF(as)$
$[f(t - a)]U(t - a)$	$\epsilon^{-sa} F(s)$
$\dot{f}(t)$	$sF(s) - f(0)$
$\ddot{f}(t)$	$s^2 F(s) - sf(0) - \dot{f}(0)$
$\dddot{f}(t)$	$s^3 F(s) - s^2 f(0) - s\dot{f}(0) - \ddot{f}(0)$
$\dfrac{d^n f}{dt^n}$ for $n = 1, 2, 3, \ldots$	$s^n F(s) - s^{n-1} f(0) - \cdots - sf^{(n-2)}(0) - f^{(n-1)}(0)$
$\displaystyle\int_0^t f(\lambda)d\lambda$	$\dfrac{1}{s} F(s)$
$f(0+)$	$\displaystyle\lim_{s\to\infty} sF(s)$
$f(\infty)$	$\displaystyle\lim_{s\to 0} sF(s)$

▶ A P P E N D I X C

Matrices

This appendix is intended as a refresher for the reader who has had an introductory course in linear algebra and is studying those sections of the book that use matrix methods. It is not a suitable introduction for someone who has not had formal exposure to matrices. Only those aspects of the subject that are used in Sections 3.3, 6.6, and 8.7 are emphasized. References to more complete treatments appear in Appendix D.

◼ C.1 DEFINITIONS

A **matrix** is a rectangular array of elements that are either constants or functions of time. We refer to a matrix having m rows and n columns as being of **order** $m \times n$. The element in the ith row and the jth column of the matrix **A** is denoted by a_{ij}, such that

$$\mathbf{A} = \begin{bmatrix} a_{11} & a_{12} & \cdots & a_{1n} \\ a_{21} & a_{22} & \cdots & a_{2n} \\ \vdots & \vdots & & \vdots \\ a_{m1} & a_{m2} & \cdots & a_{mn} \end{bmatrix}$$

A matrix having the same number of rows as columns, in which case $m = n$, is a **square matrix** of order n. A matrix with a single column is a **column vector**. Examples of column vectors are

$$\mathbf{b} = \begin{bmatrix} b_1 \\ b_2 \\ \vdots \\ b_m \end{bmatrix} \qquad \mathbf{c} = \begin{bmatrix} 4 \\ -1 \\ 3 \end{bmatrix} \qquad \mathbf{x}(t) = \begin{bmatrix} x_1(t) \\ x_2(t) \\ \vdots \\ x_n(t) \end{bmatrix}$$

A matrix with a single row is called a **row vector**.

A matrix that consists of a single element—that is, one that has only one row and one column—is referred to as a **scalar**. A square matrix of n rows and n columns that has unity for each of the elements on its main

649

diagonal and zero for the remaining elements is the **identity matrix** of order n, denoted by **I**. For example,

$$\begin{bmatrix} 1 & 0 \\ 0 & 1 \end{bmatrix} \quad \text{and} \quad \begin{bmatrix} 1 & 0 & 0 \\ 0 & 1 & 0 \\ 0 & 0 & 1 \end{bmatrix}$$

are the identity matrices of order 2 and 3, respectively. A matrix all of whose elements are zero is the **null matrix**, denoted by **0**.

We obtain the **transpose** of a matrix by interchanging its rows and columns such that the ith row of the original matrix becomes the ith column of the transpose, for all rows. Hence if **A** is of order $m \times n$ with elements a_{ij}, then its transpose, $\mathbf{A}^T$, is of order $n \times m$ and has elements $(\mathbf{A}^T)_{ij} = a_{ji}$.

■ C.2 OPERATIONS

We can add or subtract two matrices that have the same order by adding or subtracting their respective elements. For example, if **A** and **B** are both $m \times n$, the ijth element of $\mathbf{A} + \mathbf{B}$ is $a_{ij} + b_{ij}$. We can form the product $\mathbf{C} = \mathbf{AB}$ only if the number of rows of **B**, the right matrix, is equal to the number of columns of **A**, the left matrix. If this condition is met, we find the $i\ell$th element of **C** by summing the products of the elements in the ith row of **A** with the corresponding elements in the ℓth column of **B**. If **A** is $m \times n$ and **B** is $n \times p$, then **C** is $m \times p$ and

$$c_{i\ell} = \sum_{j=1}^{n} a_{ij} b_{j\ell} \quad \text{for } i = 1, 2, \ldots, m \quad \text{and} \quad \ell = 1, 2, \ldots, p \quad (1)$$

For example, if

$$\mathbf{A} = \begin{bmatrix} 2 & -1 & 3 \\ 1 & 0 & 4 \end{bmatrix} \quad \text{and} \quad \mathbf{B} = \begin{bmatrix} 1 & -1 \\ 2 & 3 \\ -2 & 1 \end{bmatrix}$$

then

$$c_{11} = (2)(1) + (-1)(2) + (3)(-2) = -6$$
$$c_{12} = (2)(-1) + (-1)(3) + (3)(1) = -2$$
$$c_{21} = (1)(1) + (0)(2) + (4)(-2) = -7$$
$$c_{22} = (1)(-1) + (0)(3) + (4)(1) = 3$$

giving

$$\mathbf{C} = \begin{bmatrix} -6 & -2 \\ -7 & 3 \end{bmatrix}$$

We obtain the product of a matrix and a scalar by multiplying each element of the matrix by the scalar. For example, if k is a scalar, the ijth element of $k\mathbf{A}$ is ka_{ij}.

Some properties of matrices are summarized in Table C.1, where $\mathbf{A}$, $\mathbf{B}$, and $\mathbf{C}$ denote general matrices and where $\mathbf{I}$ and $\mathbf{0}$ are the identity matrix and the null matrix, respectively. Some of the properties that hold for scalars are not always valid for matrices. For example, except in special cases, $\mathbf{AB} \neq \mathbf{BA}$. Also, the equation $\mathbf{AB} = \mathbf{AC}$ does not necessarily imply that $\mathbf{B} = \mathbf{C}$. Furthermore, the equation $\mathbf{AB} = \mathbf{0}$ does not necessarily imply that either $\mathbf{A}$ or $\mathbf{B}$ is zero.

TABLE C.1 Matrix Properties

$\mathbf{A} + \mathbf{B} = \mathbf{B} + \mathbf{A}$
$\mathbf{A} + (\mathbf{B} + \mathbf{C}) = (\mathbf{A} + \mathbf{B}) + \mathbf{C}$
$\mathbf{A}(\mathbf{B} + \mathbf{C}) = \mathbf{AB} + \mathbf{AC}$
$\mathbf{AI} = \mathbf{IA} = \mathbf{A}$
$\mathbf{0A} = \mathbf{0}$
$\mathbf{A0} = \mathbf{0}$
$\mathbf{A} + \mathbf{0} = \mathbf{A}$

■ C.3 THE DETERMINANT AND THE INVERSE MATRIX

Associated with any square matrix $\mathbf{A}$ is a scalar quantity called the **determinant** and denoted by $|\mathbf{A}|$. For the 2×2 matrix

$$\mathbf{A} = \begin{bmatrix} a_{11} & a_{12} \\ a_{21} & a_{22} \end{bmatrix}$$

the determinant is defined as

$$|\mathbf{A}| = a_{11}a_{22} - a_{12}a_{21} \tag{2}$$

One way of evaluating the determinant for larger matrices is in terms of the determinants of some of its submatrices, as indicated in the following discussion.

The **minor** of the ijth element of an $n \times n$ matrix $\mathbf{A}$ is the determinant of the $(n-1) \times (n-1)$ submatrix we obtain by deleting the ith row and the jth column of $\mathbf{A}$. It is denoted by M_{ij}. The **cofactor** of the ijth element is denoted by C_{ij} and is

$$C_{ij} = (-1)^{i+j} M_{ij} \tag{3}$$

Thus the ijth cofactor is identical to the ijth minor if $i+j$ is an even integer and is the negative of the ijth minor if $i+j$ is odd. The **cofactor matrix** of an $n \times n$ matrix $\mathbf{A}$ is another $n \times n$ matrix whose elements are the cofactors of $\mathbf{A}$. For the 3×3 matrix

$$\mathbf{A} = \begin{bmatrix} 2 & 1 & 0 \\ 3 & -2 & 1 \\ -1 & 2 & 1 \end{bmatrix} \tag{4}$$

the minors of the 1, 1 and 2, 1 elements are

$$M_{11} = \begin{vmatrix} -2 & 1 \\ 2 & 1 \end{vmatrix} = (-2)(1) - (1)(2) = -4$$

and

$$M_{21} = \begin{vmatrix} 1 & 0 \\ 2 & 1 \end{vmatrix} = (1)(1) - (0)(2) = 1$$

The corresponding cofactors are $C_{11} = -4$ and $C_{21} = -1$. Evaluating the cofactors of the remaining elements of $\mathbf{A}$, we find the cofactor matrix to be

$$\mathbf{C} = \begin{bmatrix} -4 & -4 & 4 \\ -1 & 2 & -5 \\ 1 & -2 & -7 \end{bmatrix} \tag{5}$$

We can evaluate the determinant of $\mathbf{A}$ by selecting any one row or column of $\mathbf{A}$ and summing the products of the elements a_{ij} and their respective cofactors. Expanding along the ith row gives

$$|\mathbf{A}| = \sum_{j=1}^{n} a_{ij} C_{ij} \qquad \text{for } i = 1, 2, \ldots, n \tag{6}$$

while expanding down the jth column gives

$$|\mathbf{A}| = \sum_{i=1}^{n} a_{ij} C_{ij} \qquad \text{for } j = 1, 2, \ldots, n \tag{7}$$

For example, consider the matrix $\mathbf{A}$ defined by (4) and its cofactor matrix given by (5). Expanding $|\mathbf{A}|$ along the first row, we have

$$|\mathbf{A}| = a_{11} C_{11} + a_{12} C_{12} + a_{13} C_{13}$$
$$= (2)(-4) + (1)(-4) + (0)(4) = -12$$

Expanding the determinant along any other row or down any column will give the same result.

For a 4×4 matrix, each cofactor is a determinant of order 3×3, which can in turn be evaluated in terms of three 2×2 determinants. We can always continue this process for any square matrix until only 2×2 arrays are left, and we can then use (2) to evaluate each of these 2×2 determinants.

The **adjoint** of the square matrix **A** is denoted by adj[**A**] and is the transpose of the cofactor matrix; that is,

$$(\text{adj}[\mathbf{A}])_{ij} = C_{ji}$$

For the matrix **A** in (4),

$$\text{adj}[\mathbf{A}] = \begin{bmatrix} -4 & -1 & 1 \\ -4 & 2 & -2 \\ 4 & -5 & -7 \end{bmatrix}$$

If a matrix **B** can be found such that $\mathbf{AB} = \mathbf{BA} = \mathbf{I}$, then **B** is called the **inverse** of **A**, written $\mathbf{A}^{-1}$. Thus

$$\mathbf{AA}^{-1} = \mathbf{A}^{-1}\mathbf{A} = \mathbf{I} \tag{8}$$

If the inverse exists, it is unique. A necessary but not a sufficient condition for **A** to have an inverse is that **A** must be square. A square matrix **A** of order $n \times n$ has an inverse $\mathbf{A}^{-1}$ if and only if $|\mathbf{A}| \neq 0$. If $|\mathbf{A}|$ is nonzero, it can be shown that

$$\mathbf{A}^{-1} = \frac{\text{adj}[\mathbf{A}]}{|\mathbf{A}|} \tag{9}$$

For the matrix **A** in (4), $|\mathbf{A}| = -12$ and

$$\mathbf{A}^{-1} = -\frac{1}{12} \begin{bmatrix} -4 & -1 & 1 \\ -4 & 2 & -2 \\ 4 & -5 & -7 \end{bmatrix} = \begin{bmatrix} 1/3 & 1/12 & -1/12 \\ 1/3 & -1/6 & 1/6 \\ -1/3 & 5/12 & 7/12 \end{bmatrix} \tag{10}$$

You can readily verify that (4) and (10) satisfy both of the relationships in (8). Although the methods described here for evaluating determinants and inverses are satisfactory for hand calculations with small matrices, other methods exist that are better suited for computer use with large matrices.

C.4 CHARACTERISTIC VALUES

Any square matrix of order n has associated with it a **characteristic equation** which, when written in terms of the variable s, is

$$|s\mathbf{I} - \mathbf{A}| = 0 \tag{11}$$

where **I** is the $n \times n$ identity matrix, and where

$$
s\mathbf{I} - \mathbf{A} =
\begin{bmatrix}
s - a_{11} & -a_{12} & \cdots & -a_{1n} \\
-a_{21} & s - a_{22} & \cdots & -a_{2n} \\
\vdots & \vdots & & \vdots \\
-a_{n1} & -a_{n2} & \cdots & s - a_{nn}
\end{bmatrix}
\tag{12}
$$

To evaluate $|s\mathbf{I} - \mathbf{A}|$, we can apply either (6) along any row or (7) down any column of the right side of (12). Regardless of the choice made, $|s\mathbf{I} - \mathbf{A}|$ is a unique polynomial of degree n in the variable s, and it is called the **characteristic polynomial**. Thus

$$
|s\mathbf{I} - \mathbf{A}| = s^n + \alpha_{n-1}s^{n-1} + \cdots + \alpha_1 s + \alpha_0
\tag{13}
$$

where the coefficients $\alpha_0, \alpha_1, \ldots, \alpha_{n-1}$ depend on the elements of **A**.

Because the characteristic polynomial is of degree n, the characteristic equation given by (11) will have at most n distinct solutions, known as the **characteristic values (eigenvalues)** of the matrix **A**. Should (11) have fewer than n distinct solutions, one or more of its solutions must be a multiple solution such that the total number of solutions, each one counted according to its multiplicity, is exactly n. The characteristic values may be real or complex, but because the coefficients in (13) are real, any complex characteristic values must occur in complex conjugate pairs.

To find the characteristic values of the matrix **A** in (4), we form

$$
s\mathbf{I} - \mathbf{A} =
\begin{bmatrix}
s - 2 & -1 & 0 \\
-3 & s + 2 & -1 \\
1 & -2 & s - 1
\end{bmatrix}
$$

and then evaluate its determinant. Expanding along the first row, we find that

$$
\begin{aligned}
|s\mathbf{I} - \mathbf{A}| &= (s - 2)
\begin{vmatrix}
s + 2 & -1 \\
-2 & s - 1
\end{vmatrix}
- (-1)
\begin{vmatrix}
-3 & -1 \\
1 & s - 1
\end{vmatrix} \\
&= (s - 2)[(s + 2)(s - 1) - 2] + [(-3)(s - 1) + 1] \\
&= s^3 - s^2 - 9s + 12
\end{aligned}
$$

Since $|s\mathbf{I} - \mathbf{A}|$ is a cubic function of s, we use a digital computer or a calculator to find that the three characteristic values are $s_1 = 1.432$, $s_2 = 2.687$, and $s_3 = -3.119$.

Selected Reading

This appendix suggests a number of books that are suitable for undergraduates. Some provide background for specific topics or can be used as collateral reading. Others extend the topics we treat to a more advanced level or offer an introduction to additional areas. The works cited here are included in the list of references that follows. This appendix and the references provide typical starting points for further reading, but these lists are not intended to be comprehensive.

Background Sources

Introductory college physics textbooks describe the basic mechanical, electrical, and electromechanical elements and some other components as well. They also illustrate simple applications of physical laws to such systems. One good reference is *Halliday and Resnick*. Comprehensive lists of units and conversion factors are given in *Wildi*.

A good example of a book on differential equations is *Boyce and DiPrima*. For a background in linear algebra and matrices, such as would be useful for Sections 3.3, 6.6, and 8.7, see *Anton*.

Books at a Comparable Level

The following three introductory systems books discuss a variety of physical components, as well as analysis techniques: *Rosenberg and Karnopp*, *Ogata* (1992), and *Palm*. Included are electrical, mechanical, hydraulic, pneumatic, and thermal systems. The references include several books, easily recognized by their titles, that illustrate the application of the MATLAB and ACSL computer programs.

Most books dealing with modeling and analysis are restricted to a particular discipline. *Kimbrell, Meriam and Kraige*, and *Thomson* deal with mechanical components. *Thorpe* and *de Silva* also include hydraulic and mechanical devices. Textbooks on chemical processes include *Seborg, Edgar, and Mellichamp* and *Luyben*.

655

Two of the standard books on electrical circuits are *Johnson, Johnson, and Hilburn* and *Nilsson*. *Sedra and Smith* covers electronic circuits in detail. Books such as *Smith and Dorf, Carlson and Gisser*, and *Del Toro* treat devices and applications in both electrical and electromechanical systems. *Krause and Wasynczuk, Guru and Hiziroglu*, and *McPherson* are confined to electromechanical machinery.

Books that Extend the Analytical Techniques

It is natural to follow up your study of this book with more advanced books on feedback control systems, such as *D'Souza, Raven, Ogata* (1990), and some others in the list of references. Some of these include discrete-time systems in addition to continuous systems. Two books that emphasize discrete-time control systems are *Phillips and Nagle*, and *Franklin, Powell, and Workman*.

A number of books broaden the study of transform methods to include both the Fourier and *z* transforms, as well as the Laplace transform. Good examples are *Chen, Kamen*, and *Sinha*.

▶ APPENDIX E

Answers to Selected Problems

CHAPTER 2

2.1 $M_1\ddot{x}_1 + B_1\dot{x}_1 + (K_1 + K_2)x_1 - K_2x_2 = f_a(t),$
$-K_2x_1 + M_2\ddot{x}_2 + B_2\dot{x}_2 + K_2x_2 = 0$

2.4 $M_1\ddot{x}_1 + (B_1 + B_3)\dot{x}_1 + (K_1 + K_3)x_1 - B_3\dot{x}_2 - K_3x_2 = f_a(t),$
$-B_3\dot{x}_1 - K_3x_1 + M_2\ddot{x}_2 + (B_2 + B_3)\dot{x}_2 + (K_2 + K_3)x_2 = 0$

2.7   (a) $M_1\ddot{x}_1 + B_1\dot{x}_1 + (K_1 + K_2)x_1 = K_2x_2(t)$
(b) $f_2 = -K_2x_1 + M_2\ddot{x}_2 + B_2\dot{x}_2 + K_2x_2(t)$

2.10 $M_1\ddot{x}_1 + K_1x_1 - K_2x_2 = 0, \quad M_2\ddot{x}_1 + B\dot{x}_1 + M_2\ddot{x}_2 + B\dot{x}_2 + K_2x_2 = f_a(t)$

2.12 $M_1\ddot{x}_1 + K_1x_1 + B\dot{x}_2 = K_1x_3(t),$
$-M_2\ddot{x}_1 - K_2x_1 + M_2\ddot{x}_2 + B\dot{x}_2 + K_2x_2 = 0$

2.15   (a) $M_1\ddot{x}_1 + B\dot{x}_1 + K_1x_1 - B\dot{x}_2 - K_1x_2 = M_1g,$
$-B\dot{x}_1 - K_1x_1 + M_2\ddot{x}_2 + B\dot{x}_2 + (K_1 + K_2)x_2 = M_2g + f_a(t)$
(b) $x_{1_0} = [(M_1 + M_2)/K_2 + (M_1/K_1)]g, \quad x_{2_0} = [(M_1 + M_2)/K_2]g$
(c) $M_1\ddot{z}_1 + B\dot{z}_1 + K_1z_1 - B\dot{z}_2 - K_1z_2 = 0,$
$-B\dot{z}_1 - K_1z_1 + M_2\ddot{z}_2 + B\dot{z}_2 + (K_1 + K_2)z_2 = f_a(t)$

2.18   (a) $M_1\ddot{x}_1 + B\dot{x}_1 + 2Kx_1 - B\dot{x}_2 - Kx_2 = M_1g,$
$-B\dot{x}_1 - Kx_1 + M_2\ddot{x}_2 + B\dot{x}_2 + 3Kx_2 - Kx_3 = M_2g,$
$-Kx_2 + M_3\ddot{x}_3 + Kx_3 = M_3g - f_a(t)$
(b) $x_{1_0} = (2M_1 + M_2 + M_3)g/(3K),$
$x_{2_0} = (M_1 + 2M_2 + 2M_3)g/(3K),$
$x_{2_0} - x_{1_0} = (-M_1 + M_2 + M_3)g/(3K), \quad x_{3_0} - x_{2_0} = M_3g/K$

2.22 $M_1\ddot{x}_1 + (K_1 + K_2)x_1 - K_2x_2 = M_1g,$
$-K_1x_1 + M_2\ddot{x}_2 + B\dot{x}_2 + (K_2 + K_3)x_2 = -M_2g$

2.25 $\dot{x}_1 = [B_2/(B_1 + B_2)]\dot{x}_2, \quad B_{eq} = B_1B_2/(B_1 + B_2)$

2.27 $M\ddot{x}_1 + (B_1 + B_2)\dot{x}_1 + (K_1 + K_2)x_1 - B_2\dot{x}_2 - K_2x_2 = 0,$
$-B_2\dot{x}_1 - K_2x_1 + B_2\dot{x}_2 + (K_2 + K_3)x_2 = K_3x_3(t)$

CHAPTER 3

3.3 $\dot{y} = v,\quad \dot{v} = -2y - 4v + x,\quad \dot{x} = -y - x + f_a(t)$

3.5 $\dot{x}_1 = v_1,\quad \dot{v}_1 = [-K_1 x_1 - (B_1 + B_2 + B_3)v_1 + B_2 v_2]/M_1,\quad \dot{x}_2 = v_2,$
$\dot{v}_2 = [B_2 v_1 - K_2 x_2 - B_2 v_2 + f_a(t)]/M_2,\quad y_1 = B_2(v_2 - v_1),$
$y_2 = K_2 x_2$

3.9 $\dot{x}_1 = v_1,\quad \dot{v}_1 = [-K_1 x_1 - Bv_1 + K_1 x_2 + Bv_2 + M_1 g]/M_1,\quad \dot{x}_2 = v_2,$
$\dot{v}_2 = [K_1 x_1 + Bv_1 - (K_1 + K_2)x_2 - Bv_2 + M_2 g + f_a(t)]/M_2,$
$y_1 = x_1 - x_2,\quad a_1 = [-K_1 x_1 - Bv_1 + K_1 x_2 + Bv_2 + M_1 g]/M_1$

3.11 $\dot{x}_1 = v_1,\quad \dot{v}_1 = [-3Kx_1 - Bv_1 + Kx_2 + M_1 g]/M_1,\quad \dot{x}_2 = v_2,$
$\dot{v}_2 = [Kx_1 - Kx_2 + M_2 g + f_a(t)]/M_2,\quad y = x_2 - x_1$

3.13 $\dot{x}_1 = v_1,\quad \dot{v}_1 = [-K_1 x_1 - B_1 v_1 - K_3 x_2 + K_3 x_3(t)]/M,$
$\dot{x}_2 = [K_2 x_1 + B_2 v_1 - (K_2 + K_3)x_2 + K_3 x_3(t)]/B_2,$
$y = K_2 x_1 - (K_2 + K_3)x_2 + K_3 x_3(t)$

3.15 $\dot{q}_1 = -3q_1 + 2q_2 + 3u_1(t) - 6u_2(t),\quad \dot{q}_2 = 2q_1 + q_2 + u_1(t) + 4u_2(t),$
$y = q_1 - q_2 - u_1(t) + 3u_2(t)$ where $q_1 = x_1 - 2u_2(t)$ and
$q_2 = x_2 - u_1(t)$

3.18 $\dot{x}_1 = q_1 + (B_1/M_1)x_3(t),$
$\dot{q}_1 = [-(K_1 + K_2)x_1 - B_1 q_1 + K_2 x_2 + (K_1 - B_1^2/M_1)x_3(t) + f_a(t)]/M_1,$
$\dot{x}_2 = q_2 + (B_2/M_2)x_3(t),$
$\dot{q}_2 = [K_2 x_1 - K_2 x_2 - B_2 q_2 - (B_2^2/M_2)x_3(t)]/M_2,$
$v_1 = q_1 + (B_1/M_1)x_3(t),\quad v_2 = q_2 + (B_2/M_2)x_3(t)$

3.21 $\dot{x}_1 = v_1,\quad \dot{v}_1 = [-Kx_1 - Bv_1 + Bv_2 - f_a(t)]/M_1,\quad \dot{x}_2 = v_2,$
$\dot{v}_2 = [Bv_1 - Bv_2 + M_2 g]/M_2,\quad m_1 = M_1 v_1,\quad m_2 = M_2 v_2,$
$f_c = B(v_2 - v_1)$

3.24 $M_1 \ddot{x}_1 + B\dot{x}_1 + (K_1 + K_2)x_1 = B\dot{x}_2 + K_2 x_2(t)$

3.26 $x_1^{(iv)} + 2x_1^{(iii)} + 5\ddot{x}_1 + \dot{x}_1 + 2x_1 = 4g + \ddot{f}_a + \dot{f}_a + 2f_a(t)$

3.29 $\dot{\mathbf{q}} = \begin{bmatrix} 0 & -1 & 1 \\ K_2/M_1 & -B/M_1 & B/M_1 \\ -K_2/M_2 & B/M_2 & -B/M_2 \end{bmatrix} \mathbf{q} + \begin{bmatrix} 0 \\ 0 \\ 1/M_2 \end{bmatrix} f_a(t),$

$\mathbf{y} = \begin{bmatrix} K_2 & 0 & 0 \\ 0 & M_1 & M_2 \end{bmatrix} \mathbf{q} + \begin{bmatrix} 0 \\ 0 \end{bmatrix} f_a(t)$

CHAPTER 4

4.2 $J_1 J_2 \dddot{\omega}_2 + B J_2 \ddot{\omega}_2 + K(J_1 + J_2)\dot{\omega}_2 + KB\omega_2 = BK\omega_a(t)$

4.6 (a) With $\theta_1,\ \omega_1,\ \theta_2,\ \omega_2$ as state variables: $\dot{\theta}_1 = \omega_1,$
$\quad \dot{\omega}_1 = [-K_1 \theta_1 - B\omega_1 + B\omega_2 + \tau_a(t)]/J_1,\quad \dot{\theta}_2 = \omega_2,$
$\quad \dot{\omega}_2 = (B\omega_1 - K_2 \theta_2 - B\omega_2)/J_2,\quad \tau_B = B(\omega_2 - \omega_1)$
(b) $\theta_2^{(iv)} + 2\theta_2^{(iii)} + 2\ddot{\theta}_2 + 2\dot{\theta}_2 + \theta_2 = \dot{\tau}_a$

4.7 $J\ddot{\theta} + K_{eq}\theta = \tau_a(t)$ where $K_{eq} = K_1 + [K_2K_3/(K_2 + K_3)]$

4.10 (a) $\dot{x}_1 = v_1$, $\dot{v}_1 = [-(K_1 + K_2)x_1 - B_1v_1 + (K_2L/4)\theta]/M$,
$\dot{\theta} = (16/9B_2L)[(K_2/4)x_1 - (K_2L/16)\theta - (3/4)f_a(t)]$
(b) $f_r = (4K_2/3)x_1 - (K_2L/3)\theta$

4.13 With x_1, v_1, θ, ω as state variables: $\dot{x}_1 = v_1$,
$\dot{v}_1 = [-(K_1 + K_2)x_1 - B_1v_1 + (1/4)K_2L\theta]/M$, $\dot{\theta} = \omega$,
$\dot{\omega} = (3/7ML)[4K_2x_1 - LK_2\theta - 9LB_2\omega - 12f_a(t)]$
$f_{K_2} = -K_2x_1 + (1/4)LK_2\theta$

4.18 (a) $J_1\ddot{\theta}_1 + B\dot{\theta}_1 - R_1f_c = \tau_a(t)$, $J_2\ddot{\theta}_2 + K\theta_2 + R_2f_c = 0$
(b) With θ_1, ω_1 as state variables: $\dot{\theta}_1 = \omega_1$,
$\dot{\omega}_1 = [-(K/N^2)\theta_1 - B\omega_1 + \tau_a(t)]/[J_1 + (J_2/N^2)]$
$m_T = [J_1 + (J_2/N)]\omega_1$, $\tau_B = -B\omega_1$
(c) $[J_1 + (J_2/N^2)]\ddot{\theta}_1 + B\dot{\theta}_1 + (K/N^2)\theta_1 = \tau_a(t)$

4.19 $\dot{\theta}_1 = \omega_1$, $\dot{\omega}_1 = [-K_1\theta_1 - B\omega_1 + K_1\theta_2 + \tau_a(t)]/J_1$, $\dot{\theta}_2 = \omega_2$,
$\dot{\omega}_2 = [K_1\theta_1 - (K_1 + N^2K_2)\theta_2]/(J_2 + N^2J_3)$, $\theta_3 = -N\theta_2$

4.26 With θ, ω as state variables: $\dot{\theta} = \omega$,
$\dot{\omega} = [-KR\theta - (B/R)\omega + Mg + f_a(t)]/[(J/R) + MR]$
$z = R\theta - Mg/K$

4.29 With θ, ω, x_2, v_2 as state variables: $\dot{\theta} = \omega$,
$\dot{\omega} = [-(R_1K_1 + K_2)\theta + (K_2/R_2)x_2 + R_1K_1x_1(t)]/J_1$, $\dot{x}_2 = v_2$,
$\dot{v}_2 = [(K_2/R_2)\theta - (K_2/R_2^2 + 2K_3)x_2 - Bv_2 + M_2g]/M_2$,
$y = K_2\theta - K_2R_2x_2$

4.32
$$\frac{d}{dt}\begin{bmatrix} \theta \\ \omega \\ x \\ v \end{bmatrix} = \begin{bmatrix} 0 & 1 & 0 & 0 \\ -(K_1 + K_2R^2)/J & -B/J & K_2R/J & 0 \\ 0 & 0 & 0 & 1 \\ K_2R/M & 0 & -K_2/M & 0 \end{bmatrix}\begin{bmatrix} \theta \\ \omega \\ x \\ v \end{bmatrix}$$

$$+ \begin{bmatrix} 0 & 0 \\ 0 & 0 \\ 0 & 0 \\ 1/M & 1/M \end{bmatrix}\begin{bmatrix} Mg \\ f_a(t) \end{bmatrix}$$

CHAPTER 5

5.3 $\dot{e}_o + e_o = (7/24)\dot{e}_i + (2/3)e_i(t)$

5.7 $2\ddot{e}_o + 2\dot{e}_o + 4e_o = 3e_i(t)$

5.9 $\ddot{e}_o + \dot{e}_o + (1/2)e_o = 2di_i/dt$

5.12 $\ddot{e}_o + 2\dot{e}_o + 2e_o = \ddot{e}_i + (1/2)\dot{e}_i$

5.17 $e_o = 12$ V

5.18 (a) With i_L (positive to right), e_C (positive at upper node) as
state variables: $\dot{e}_C = [-e_C - R_1i_L + R_1i_i(t) - 6]/(R_1C)$,
$di_L/dt = (e_C - R_2i_L)/L$

(b) $i_o = i_i(t) - (e_C + 6)/R_1$

5.21 With i_L (positive downward), e_o as state
variables: $\dot{e}_o = -(1/2)e_o - 2i_L + 2i_i(t)$,
$di_L/dt = (1/8)e_o - (1/2)i_L + (1/2)i_i(t)$

5.24 With i_L (positive to right), e_C (positive at upper node)
as state variables: $\dot{e}_C = [-e_C + 2i_L + e_i(t)]/3$,
$di_L/dt = [-e_C - 4i_L + e_i(t)]/6$, $\quad e_o = (2/3)[-e_C + 2i_L + e_i(t)]$

5.27 $\dot{e}_{C_1} = -i_L + i_i(t)$, $\quad \dot{e}_{C_2} = [-e_{C_2} - 2i_L + 6i_i(t)]/12$,
$di_L/dt = (3e_{C_1} + e_{C_2} - 4i_L)/9$, $\quad i_o = (1/6)e_{C_2} + (1/3)i_L$

5.31 $6\dot{e}_o + (10 - \alpha)e_o = [1 + (\alpha/2)]i_i(t)$

5.34 $e_o = -(R_3/R_1)e_1(t) - (R_3/R_2)e_2(t)$, $\quad$ summer with gains
determined by R_1, R_2, and R_3.

5.37 $C_2\dot{e}_o + (1/R_2)e_o = -C_1\dot{e}_i - (1/R_1)e_i(t)$

5.41 $\dfrac{d}{dt}\begin{bmatrix} e_C \\ i_L \end{bmatrix} = \begin{bmatrix} -0.6 & 0.3 \\ -1.2 & -0.8 \end{bmatrix}\begin{bmatrix} e_C \\ i_L \end{bmatrix} + \begin{bmatrix} 0.2 \\ 0.4 \end{bmatrix}e_i(t)$,

$e_o = \begin{bmatrix} -0.6 & -0.2 \end{bmatrix}\begin{bmatrix} e_C \\ i_L \end{bmatrix} + \begin{bmatrix} 0.2 \end{bmatrix}e_i(t)$

CHAPTER 6

Note: Expressions for time functions are valid for $t \geq 0$ unless noted otherwise.

6.2 **(a)** $y(t) = 0.4\epsilon^{-t/2} + 1.2\sin t - 0.4\cos t$
(b) $y(t) = \epsilon^{-t/2} + t\epsilon^{-t/2}$

6.5 $y(t) = 2\epsilon^{-t} - \epsilon^{-2t} + t - 1$

6.8 $y(t) = (A/2)(1 - \epsilon^{-2t/3})$, $\quad \tau = 3/2$ s,
$y_{ss} = A/2$, $y_{transient} = -(A/2)\epsilon^{-2t/3}$

6.12 **(a)** $\tau = 3/2$ s
(b) $e_o(t) = 2 + K\epsilon^{-2t/3}$
(c) $e_o(0+) = 2/3$ V, $K = -4/3$
(d) $e_o(t) = 2 - (4/3)\epsilon^{-2t/3}$
(e) $(e_o)_{ss} = 2$ V

6.16 **(a)** $y_U(t) = 2(1 - \epsilon^{-t/2})$
(b) $y(t) = 4 - 5\epsilon^{-t/2}$
(c) $y(t) = 2(1 - \epsilon^{-t/2})$ for $0 \leq t \leq 2$ and $y(t) = 2(\epsilon - 1)\epsilon^{-t/2}$ for
$t \geq 2$
(d) $h(t) = \epsilon^{-t/2}$

6.20 **(b)** $\zeta = [(B_1 + B_2)/2]/\sqrt{K_2(M_1 + M_2)}$ and $\omega_n = \sqrt{K_2/(M_1 + M_2)}$
(c) $x_{ss} = (1 - M_2 g)/K_2$

6.25 **(a)** $\zeta = 1/\sqrt{2}$, $\omega_n = \sqrt{2}$
(b) $y_U(t) = -0.5\epsilon^{-t}(\cos t + \sin t) + 0.5$, $\quad h(t) = \epsilon^{-t}\sin t$

6.27 **(a)** $\zeta = 1/\sqrt{5} = 0.4472$, $\omega_n = \sqrt{5} = 2.236$
     (b) $h(t) = 3.414\delta(t) - 4.467\epsilon^{-t}[\sin(2t + 1.249)]U(t)$

6.28 $y(t) = 2 - \epsilon^{-2t} - \cos t + 3\sin t$

6.34 **(a)** $\phi(t) = \begin{bmatrix} 2\epsilon^{-t} - \epsilon^{-2t} & \epsilon^{-t} - \epsilon^{-2t} \\ -2\epsilon^{-t} + 2\epsilon^{-2t} & -\epsilon^{-t} + 2\epsilon^{-2t} \end{bmatrix}$
     (b) $y_{zi}(t) = (2\epsilon^{-t} - 3\epsilon^{-2t})q_1(0) + (\epsilon^{-t} - 3\epsilon^{-2t})q_2(0)$

6.35 $y(t) = \begin{bmatrix} 12.5\epsilon^{-t} - 20\epsilon^{-2t} + 7.5\epsilon^{-3t} \\ -5.5\epsilon^{-t} + 10\epsilon^{-2t} - 4.5\epsilon^{-3t} \end{bmatrix}$

CHAPTER 7

Note: Expressions for time functions are valid for $t > 0$.

7.3 **(a)** $F_1(s) = (s^2 + 4s - 5)/[(s^2 + 4s + 13)^2]$
     (b) $F_2(s) = (6\omega s^2 - 2\omega^3)/[(s^2 + \omega^2)^3]$
     (c) $F_3(s) = 2s/[(s + 1)^3]$
     (d) $F_4(s) = 2/[s(s + 1)^3]$

7.7 **(a)** $f(t) = 2 - (5 + t)\epsilon^{-t} + 4\epsilon^{-2t}$
     (b) $f(t) = 2 + 2\sqrt{2}\,\epsilon^{-t}\cos(2t - \pi/4)$
     (c) $f(t) = 3\delta(t) + (1/3) - [(37/3) - 20t]\epsilon^{-3t}$
     (d) $f(t) = \delta(t) + 3\epsilon^{-t} - 8\epsilon^{-2t}$

7.8 **(a)** $f(t) = 2\epsilon^{-2t} + 2.692\epsilon^{-t}\cos(2t + 1.190)$
     (b) $f(t) = 2\epsilon^{-2t} + \epsilon^{-t}\cos 2t - 2.5\epsilon^{-t}\sin 2t$

7.10 $f(t) = 1.25 - 2\epsilon^{-t} + 0.75\epsilon^{-4t}$

7.14 $y(t) = 2.5t - 3.75 + 6\epsilon^{-t} - 1.25\epsilon^{-2t}$

7.17 $e_o(t) = 2 - (4/3)\epsilon^{-2t/3}$

7.21 **(a)** $x_0 = -M_2g/K_2$
     (b) $X(s) = 1/s[(M_1 + M_2)s^2 + (B_1 + B_2)s + K_2] - (M_2g/sK_2)$
     (c) $x(t) = 1 - \epsilon^{-0.5t}(\cos 0.5t + \sin 0.5t) - g$

7.23 $\theta(t) = \theta(0)\cos\sqrt{g/L}\,t + \dot\theta(0)\sqrt{L/g}\,\sin\sqrt{g/L}\,t,\quad \phi(t) =$
     $0.5\left[\phi(0) - \sqrt{L/g}\,\dot\phi(0)\right]\epsilon^{-\sqrt{g/L}\,t} + 0.5\left[\phi(0) + \sqrt{L/g}\,\dot\phi(0)\right]\epsilon^{+\sqrt{g/L}\,t}$

7.25 $e_o(t) = 1 + (1/3)\epsilon^{-t} + (2/3)\epsilon^{-4t}$

7.28 **(b)** $E_o(s) = 2se_A(0)/(16s^3 + 19s^2 + 10s + 8)$

7.32 **(a)** $F_1(s) = A(1 - 2\epsilon^{-s} + \epsilon^{-2s})/s$
     (b) $F_2(s) = A(1 - \epsilon^{-s} - \epsilon^{-2s} + \epsilon^{-3s})/s^2$

7.35 **(a)** $f(0+) = 1$, $f(\infty) = 2$
     (b) $f(0+) = 4$, $f(\infty) = 2$
     (c) The initial-value theorem is not applicable, $f(\infty) = 1/3$
     (d) The initial-value theorem is not applicable, $f(\infty) = 0$

CHAPTER 8

Note: Expressions for time functions are valid for $t > 0$.

8.2 $\theta_1(t) = 0.6552 \sin 0.6622t + 0.0319 \sin 2.136t$

8.5 $e_o(t) =$
$\epsilon^{-2t}\left\{-e_C(0)\cos\sqrt{12}\,t + (2/\sqrt{12})\,[e_C(0) - i_L(0)]\sin\sqrt{12}\,t\right\}$,
$\epsilon^{-2t}\cos\sqrt{12}\,t$ is absent if $e_C(0) = 0$, $\epsilon^{-2t}\sin\sqrt{12}\,t$ is absent if
$i_L(0) = e_C(0)$

8.7 $X_R(s)/F_a(s) = M_1/[M_1 M_2 s^2 + (M_1 + M_2)Bs + (M_1 + M_2)K_2]$

8.10 $X(s)/\tau_a(s) = (K/R)/P(s)$ where $P(s) = s[JMs^3 + (B_1 M + JB_2)s^2 + (KM + B_1 B_2 + JK/R^2)s + KB_2 + (KB_1/R^2)]$

8.12 (a) $E_o(s) = [-(30s + 12)e_C(0) - (10s + 15)i_L(0)]/P(s)$ where
$P(s) = 50s^2 + 70s + 42$
(b) $E_o(s)/E_i(s) = (10s^2 + 4s)/P(s)$

8.14 (a) Double pole at $s = -2$, zeros at $s = -1 \pm j1$
(b) $y_{zi}(t) = (K_1 + K_2 t)\epsilon^{-2t}$, $\ddot{y} + 4\dot{y} + 4y = \ddot{u} + 2\dot{u} + 2u(t)$
(c) $y_U(0+) = 1$, $y_U(\infty) = 0.5$
(d) $y_U(t) = 0.5 + (0.5 - t)\epsilon^{-2t}$, $h(t) = \delta(t) - 2(1 - t)\epsilon^{-2t}$

8.17 (a) Poles at $s = -0.5, \pm j2$, double zero at $s = 0$
(b) $y_{zi}(t) = K_1\epsilon^{-0.5t} + K_2\cos(2t + \phi)$ or
$y_{zi}(t) = K_1\epsilon^{-0.5t} + K_3\cos 2t + K_4\sin 2t$, $2\ddot{y} + \ddot{y} + 8\dot{y} + 4y = \ddot{u}$
(c) $y_U(0+) = 0$, $y_U(\infty) = 0$
(d) $y_U(t) = -0.05882\epsilon^{-0.5t} + 0.2426\cos(2t - 1.326)$,
$h(t) = 0.02941\epsilon^{-0.5t} + 0.4850\cos(2t + 0.2450)$

8.20 $h(t) = 10.91\epsilon^{-2t}\sin 4.583t$,
$y_U(t) = 2 - 2.182\epsilon^{-2t}\cos(4.583t - 0.4115)$ or
$y_U(t) = 2 - \epsilon^{-2t}[2\cos\sqrt{21}\,t + (4/\sqrt{21})\sin\sqrt{21}\,t]$

8.23 $h(t) = \delta(t) + t\epsilon^{-2t} - 2\epsilon^{-2t}$, $y_U(t) = 0.25 - 0.5t\epsilon^{-2t} + 0.75\epsilon^{-2t}$

8.27 (a) Pole at $s = -1$, zero at $s = +1$, $M(\omega) = 1$ for all ω,
$\theta(\omega) = \pi - 2\tan^{-1}\omega$
(b) Poles at $s = 0, -5$, double zero at
$s = -1$, $M(\omega) = (1 + \omega^2)/(\omega\sqrt{25 + \omega^2})$,
$\theta(\omega) = 2\tan^{-1}\omega - \pi/2 - \tan^{-1}(\omega/5)$
(c) Double poles at $s = -0.1 \pm j10$, zero at
$s = 0$, $M(\omega) = \omega/[(100 - \omega^2)^2 + 0.04\omega^2]$,
$\theta(\omega) = \pi/2 - 2\tan^{-1}[0.2\omega/(100 - \omega^2)]$

8.29 $A = 0.0667$, $B = 5.0$, $C = 0.120$, $A/B = 0.01333$, $C/B = 0.0240$

8.31 (a) $H(s) = Cs/(LCs^2 + RCs + 1)$
(b) $\omega = 1/\sqrt{LC}$

8.35 (b) $E_o(s)/E_i(s) = (s^2 + 2s + 1)/(s^2 + 4s + 4)$

8.38 (b) $E_o(s)/E_i(s) = (s^2 + 0.5s)/(s^2 + 2s + 2)$

(c) $\ddot{e}_o + 2\dot{e}_o + 2e_o = \ddot{e}_i + 0.5\dot{e}_i$

8.42 (a) $\Phi(s) = \begin{bmatrix} \dfrac{s+3}{(s+1)(s+2)} & \dfrac{1}{(s+1)(s+2)} \\ \dfrac{-2}{(s+1)(s+2)} & \dfrac{s}{(s+1)(s+2)} \end{bmatrix}$

(b) $\phi(t) = \begin{bmatrix} 2\epsilon^{-t} - \epsilon^{-2t} & \epsilon^{-t} - \epsilon^{-2t} \\ -2\epsilon^{-t} + 2\epsilon^{-2t} & -\epsilon^{-t} + 2\epsilon^{-2t} \end{bmatrix}$

(c) $q_1(t) = (2\epsilon^{-t} - \epsilon^{-2t})q_1(0) + (\epsilon^{-t} - \epsilon^{-2t})q_2(0)$,
$q_2(t) = (-2\epsilon^{-t} + 2\epsilon^{-2t})q_1(0) + (-\epsilon^{-t} + 2\epsilon^{-2t})q_2(0)$

8.46 (a) 2 state variables, 2 inputs, 1 output

(b) $\mathbf{H}(s) = \begin{bmatrix} \dfrac{s+3}{(s+1)(s+2)} & \dfrac{1}{(s+1)(s+2)} \end{bmatrix}$

(c) $\mathbf{h}(t) = \begin{bmatrix} 2\epsilon^{-t} - \epsilon^{-2t} & \epsilon^{-t} - \epsilon^{-2t} \end{bmatrix}$

CHAPTER 9

9.2 For $\bar{x} = -1$, $f(x) \simeq A(0.6321 + 0.3679\hat{x})$; for
$\bar{x} = 0$, $f(x) \simeq A\hat{x}$; for $\bar{x} = +1$, $f(x) \simeq A(-0.6321 + 0.3679\hat{x})$

9.5 $f(y) \simeq 2 - 4\hat{y}$

9.8 (b) $\bar{x} = 0.39$ m
(c) $1.5\ddot{\hat{x}} + 0.5\dot{\hat{x}} + 55\hat{x} = 0$
(d) Satisfactory for at least $0.27 < x < 0.60$

9.10 (a) $\bar{x} = 4$, $\ddot{\hat{x}} + 2\dot{\hat{x}} + \hat{x} = B\sin 3t$
(b) For $A = 4$, $\bar{x} = 1$, $k = 2$; for $A = -4$, $\bar{x} = -1$, $k = 2$
(c) $\hat{x}(0) = 0.5$, $\dot{\hat{x}}(0) = 0.5$

9.12 (a) $\bar{y} = -1$, $\ddot{\hat{y}} + 2\dot{\hat{y}} + 4\hat{y} = B\cos t$
(b) $\bar{y} = 3$, $\ddot{\hat{y}} + 2\dot{\hat{y}} + 8\hat{y} = B\cos t$

9.18 (a) $\bar{\theta} = 2$
(b) $\ddot{\hat{\theta}} + 2\dot{\hat{\theta}} + 12\hat{\theta} = \hat{\tau}_a(t)$
(c) $\hat{\theta}(0) = -1.5$ rad, $\dot{\hat{\theta}}(0) = -0.5$ rad/s

9.21 (b) $\bar{x} = \sqrt[3]{Mg}$, $M\ddot{\hat{x}} + B\dot{\hat{x}} + 3(Mg)^{(2/3)}\hat{x} = \hat{f}_a(t)$
(c) $\bar{x} = 1.260\sqrt[3]{Mg}$, $M\ddot{\hat{x}} + B\dot{\hat{x}} + 4.762(Mg)^{(2/3)}\hat{x} = \hat{f}_a(t)$

9.23 (a) $\bar{x} = -4$, $\bar{y} = -2$
(b) $\dot{\hat{x}} = -2\hat{x} + 12\hat{y}$, $\dot{\hat{y}} = \hat{x} + \cos t$
(c) $\ddot{\hat{x}} + 2\dot{\hat{x}} - 12\hat{x} = 12\cos t$

9.27 (b) $\bar{i}_L = 0.3622$ A, $\bar{e}_o = 0.3936$ V,
$d\hat{i}_L/dt = -2.515\hat{i}_L + 0.05714\cos t$, $\hat{e}_o = 2.173\hat{i}_L$
(c) $\tau = 0.3976$ s

9.28 (b) $\bar{e}_o = 4$ V, $\bar{i}_o = 16$ A
(c) $\ddot{\hat{e}}_o + 7\dot{\hat{e}}_o + \hat{e}_o = 2\dot{\hat{e}}_i + \hat{e}_i(t)$

CHAPTER 10

10.2 (a) $L_T \dot{e}_o + R_T e_o = L_2(x)\dot{e}_i + R_2(x)e_i(t)$

(b) $L_T \dot{e}_o + R_T e_o = [x(t)/x_{\max}][L_T \dot{e}_i + R_T e_i(t)]$

10.7 (b) $X(s)/E_i(s) = \alpha/P(s)$ where
$P(s) = MLs^3 + (BL + MR)s^2 + (KL + BR + \alpha^2)s + KR,$
$ML\ddot{x} + (BL + MR)\ddot{x} + (KL + BR + \alpha^2)\dot{x} + KRx = \alpha e_i(t)$

(c) $MR\ddot{x} + (BR + \alpha^2)\dot{x} + KRx = \alpha e_i(t),$
$\zeta = (\alpha^2 + BR)/(2R\sqrt{MK}), \quad \omega_n = \sqrt{K/M}$

10.9 $E_o(s)/F_a(s) = d.\mathscr{B}R_o/P(s)$ where
$P(s) = MLs^2 + (BL + MR + MR_o)s + B(R + R_o) + (d.\mathscr{B})^2$

10.11 (a) $di/dt = [-Ri + \mathscr{B}dv + e_i(t)]/L, \quad \dot{v} = (-\mathscr{B}di + Mg)/M$

(b) $\bar{e}_i = RMg/\mathscr{B}d$

(c) $\bar{v} = RMg/(\mathscr{B}d)^2$

10.14 (a) $(J_R + J_L)\dot{\omega} + (B_R + B_L)\omega = \gamma k_\phi i_F(t)i_A(t)$

(b) $\bar{\omega} = [\gamma k_\phi/(B_R + B_L)]\bar{i}_F \bar{i}_A$

(c) $(J_R + J_L)\dot{\hat{\omega}} + (B_R + B_L)\hat{\omega} = \gamma k_\phi[\bar{i}_F \hat{i}_A(t) + \bar{i}_A \hat{i}_F(t)]$

10.17 (a) $di_A/dt = (-R_A i_A - \gamma k_\phi i_F \omega + E_A)/L_A, \quad di_F/dt = [-R_F i_F + e_F(t)]/L_F, \quad \dot{\omega} = [\gamma k_\phi i_F i_A - B\omega - \tau_L(t)]/J$

(b) $\bar{\omega} = \gamma k_\phi \bar{i}_F \bar{i}_A/B$ where $\bar{i}_F = \bar{e}_F/R_F$ and
$\bar{i}_A = BR_F^2 E_A/[BR_A R_F^2 + (\gamma k_\phi \bar{e}_F)^2]$

(c) $d\hat{i}_A/dt = (-R_A \hat{i}_A - \gamma k_\phi \bar{\omega}\hat{i}_F - \gamma k_\phi \bar{i}_F \hat{\omega})/L_A, \quad d\hat{i}_F/dt = [-R_F \hat{i}_F + \hat{e}_F(t)]/L_F, \quad \dot{\hat{\omega}} = [\gamma k_\phi \bar{i}_F \hat{i}_A + \gamma k_\phi \bar{i}_A \hat{i}_F - B\hat{\omega} - \hat{\tau}_L(t)]/J$

10.21 $\omega_{ss} = 37.5$ rad/s

CHAPTER 11

11.2 $R_{eq} = R_a R_b/(2R_a + 4R_b), \quad q = [(4/R_a) + (2/R_b)](\theta_1 - \theta_a)$

11.5 (a) $\dot{\theta}_1 = [-(1/R_{eq})\theta_1 + (1/R_1)\theta_a + (1/R_2)\theta_2(t) + q_i(t)]/C$ where
$1/R_{eq} = (1/R_1) + (1/R_2)$

(b) $H_1(s) = (1/R_2)/[Cs + (1/R_{eq})], \quad H_2(s) = 1/[Cs + (1/R_{eq})]$

11.7 (a) $\dot{\theta}_1 = [-(1/R_1 + 1/R_2)\theta_1 + (1/R_2)\theta_2 + (1/R_1)\theta_a + q_1(t)]/C_1,$
$\dot{\theta}_2 = [(1/R_2)\theta_1 - (1/R_2 + 1/R_3)\theta_2 + (1/R_3)\theta_3(t) + q_2(t)]/C_2$

(b) $\dot{\hat{\theta}}_1 = [-(1/R_1 + 1/R_2)\hat{\theta}_1 + (1/R_2)\hat{\theta}_2 + q_1(t)]/C_1, \quad \dot{\hat{\theta}}_2 = [(1/R_2)\hat{\theta}_1 - (1/R_2 + 1/R_3)\hat{\theta}_2 + (1/R_3)\hat{\theta}_3(t) + q_2(t)]/C_2, \quad H_1(s) = R_1/P(s)$ and $H_2(s) = (R_1 R_2 C_1 s + R_1 + R_2)/P(s)$ where $P(s) = R_1 R_2 R_3 C_1 C_2 s^2 + [R_1 C_1(R_2 + R_3) + R_3 C_2(R_1 + R_2)]s + R_1 + R_2 + R_3$

11.9 (b) $\theta_m = \{C_w\theta_w(0) + C_m\theta_m(0) + C_w[\theta_m(0) - \theta_w(0)]\epsilon^{-t/\tau}\}/(C_m + C_w), \quad \theta_w = \{C_w\theta_w(0) + C_m\theta_m(0) - C_m[\theta_m(0) - \theta_w(0)]\epsilon^{-t/\tau}\}/(C_m + C_w)$
for $t \geq 0$ where $\tau = RC_m C_w/(C_m + C_w)$

(c) $\dot{\theta}_m$ is unchanged,
$$\dot{\theta}_w = [(1/R)\theta_m - (1/R + 1/R_a)\theta_w + (1/R_a)\theta_a]/C_w$$

11.11 $\dot{\theta}_1 = (9/RC)[-2\hat{\theta}_1 + \hat{\theta}_2 + \hat{\theta}_i(t)], \quad \dot{\theta}_2 =$
$(9/RC)(\hat{\theta}_1 - 2\hat{\theta}_2 + \hat{\theta}_3), \quad \dot{\theta}_3 = (9/RC)(\hat{\theta}_2 - \hat{\theta}_3), \quad P(s) =$
$s^3 + (45/RC)s^2 + [486/(RC)^2]s + [729/(RC)^3]$

CHAPTER 12

12.1 $C = \pi h^2/\rho g, \quad p^* = \rho g\sqrt[3]{3v/\pi}$

12.5 $\dot{p}_1 = [-(1/K)\hat{p}_1 + (1/K)\hat{p}_2 + \hat{w}_i(t)]/C_1,$
$\dot{p}_2 = [(1/K)\hat{p}_1 - (1/K + 1/R)\hat{p}_2]/C_2$

12.7 **(b)** $\hat{W}_o(s)/\hat{P}_i(s) =$
$[(R_3C_1s + 1)/R_2 + (1/R_1)]/[(R_4C_2s + 1)(R_3C_1s + 1)]$
(c) $(\hat{w}_o)_{ss} = (1/R_1) + (1/R_2)$

12.10 **(b)** $\tau = \beta A/\alpha\rho g, \quad h_{ss} = \beta/\rho g$
(c) $h(t) = (\beta/\rho g)(1 - \epsilon^{-t/\tau})$ for $t \geq 0$

CHAPTER 13

13.3 $T_1(s) = (3s - 6)/(s^3 + 7s^2 + 14s + 8), \quad T_2(s) =$
$(2s^4 + 14s^3 + 28s^2 + 13s + 6)/(s^4 + 7s^3 + 14s^2 + 8s)$

13.7 **(a)** $\dot{q}_1 = q_2, \quad \dot{q}_2 = -6q_1 - 5q_2 + 12u(t), \quad y = q_1$

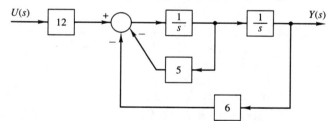

(b) $\dot{q}_1 = q_2, \quad \dot{q}_2 = -6q_1 - 5q_2 + u(t), \quad y = 10q_1 + 9q_2 + 2u(t)$

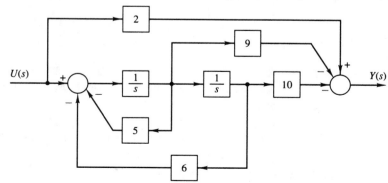

(c) $\dot{q}_1 = q_2$, $\dot{q}_2 = q_3$, $\dot{q}_3 = -4q_1 - 3q_2 - 2q_3 + u(t)$
 $y = 4q_1 - q_2 + 2q_3$

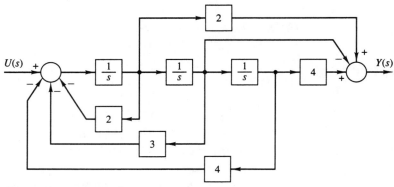

13.24 $Y(s)/U(s) = 2/(s^2 + 8s + 9)$

13.26 $X(s)/\tau_a(s) = (K/R)/P(s)$ where $P(s) = JMs^4 + (MB_1 + JB_2)s^3 + [MK + B_1B_2 + (JK/R^2)]s^2 + [B_2K + (B_1K/R^2)]s$

13.30 (a) $T(s) = 2/(s^2 + 9s + 2K)$
 (b) $y_{ss} = 1/K$
 (c) $\zeta = 9/(2\sqrt{2K})$, $\omega_n = \sqrt{2K}$, $K = 20.25$, $\omega_n = 6.364$ rad/s

13.32 (a) $T_1(s) = 4/(s^2 + 4Ks + 4)$
 (b) $T_2(s) = s/(s^2 + 4Ks + 4)$
 (c) $\omega_n = 2$ rad/s, $\zeta = K$, so use $K = 1$.
 (d) For $u(t) = U(t)$, $y_{ss} = 1$; for $v(t) = U(t)$, $y_{ss} = 0$.

13.34 (a) $T(s) = K_1/[s^2 + (K_2 + 1)s + K_3]$
 (b) $\zeta = (K_2 + 1)/(2\sqrt{K_3})$, $\omega_n = \sqrt{K_3}$
 (c) $K_2 > -1$
 (d) $-1 < K_2 < 2\sqrt{K_3} - 1$
 (e) $K_2 = 1$, $K_3 = 4$

13.36 $T_1(s) = (AB + BDE + D)/(1 + BE + AC)$,
 $T_2(s) = A/(1 + BE + AC)$

CHAPTER 14

14.2 (a) $K_A = 0.0218$, $T(s) = 1.563/(s^2 + 2.50s + 1.563)$
 (b) $K_A = 1.396$, $K_T = 0.0836$ V·s/rad, $T(s) = 100/(s^2 + 20s + 100)$

14.5 (a) $T(s) = 1/(s^2 + 2Ks + 4)$
 (b) Poles at $s = -K \pm \sqrt{K^2 - 4}$;   for $K = 0$, $s = \pm j2$;
 for $K = 1$, $s = -1 \pm j\sqrt{3}$; for $K = 2$, $s = -2, -2$; for
 $K = 3, s = -0.764, -5.236$

14.9 $\sigma_0 = -2$, $K^* = 75.4$

14.14 $\sigma_0 = -5.5$, $K^* = 1825$

14.16 $\sigma_0 = -2$, $K^* = -64/9 = -7.11$

14.24 (a) $k_m = 11.1$ dB, $\phi_m = 28.9°$
   (b) $K = 45.1$
   (c) $K^* = 143$

14.26 (a) $H(s) = -(R_2Cs + 1)/(R_1Cs)$
   (b) Pole at $s = 0$, zero at $s = -1/(R_2C)$
   (c) PI compensator

14.28 (c) (i) $\theta_{ss} = 0.400$ rad, (ii) $\theta_{ss} = -0.384$ rad
   (d) $K_A = 0.0341$ V/V, $\omega_n = 1.563$ rad/s
   (e) $\phi_m = 26°$, phase is always $\geq -180°$.

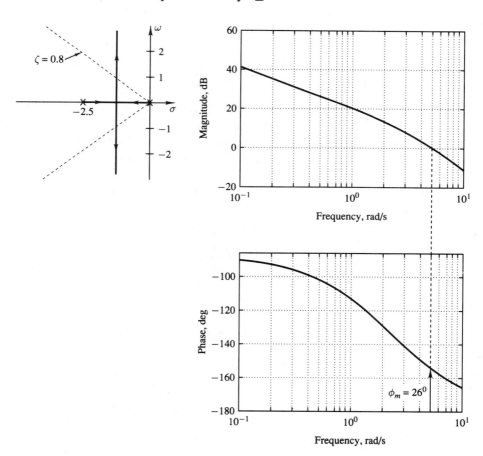

14.32 (a) The block diagram is based on the equation
   $\hat{\Theta}(s) = \tau\hat{Q}_h(s)/[C(\tau s + 1)] + \hat{Q}_i(s)/(\tau s + 1)$.

(b) $\hat{\Theta}(s)/\hat{\Theta}_d(s) = \tau G_c(s)/P(s)$, $\hat{\Theta}(s)/\hat{\Theta}_i(s) = C/P(s)$ where
$P(s) = \tau Cs + C + \tau G_c(s)$

(c) For unit step in $\hat{\theta}_d(t)$, $\hat{\theta}_{ss} = \tau K_c/(C + \tau K_c)$;   for unit step in
$\hat{\theta}_i(t)$, $\hat{\theta}_{ss} = C/(C + \tau K_c)$

(d) $\hat{\Theta}(s)/\hat{\Theta}_d(s) = \tau K_c(s + K_I)/P(s)$ and $\hat{\Theta}(s)/\hat{\Theta}_i(s) = Cs/P(s)$
where $P(s) = \tau Cs^2 + (C + \tau K_c)s + \tau K_c K_I$

CHAPTER 15

15.3 (a) $T(s) = (6s^3 + 9s^2 + 49s + 79)/(s^4 + 7s^3 + 18s^2 + 45s + 41)$

(b) Zeros are $s = 0.0429 \pm j2.881, -1.586$;   poles are
$s = -0.4218 \pm j2.502, -1.316, -4.840$;   gain = 6

15.5 (a) $A = \begin{bmatrix} 0 & 1 & 0 \\ 0 & 0 & 1 \\ -2 & -2 & -4 \end{bmatrix}$, $B = \begin{bmatrix} 0 \\ 0 \\ 2 \end{bmatrix}$

$C = \begin{bmatrix} -3 & -7 & -8 \end{bmatrix}$, $D = 4$

(b) $T(s) = (4s^3 - 6s + 2)/(s^3 + 4s^2 + 2s + 2)$

15.7 Zeros are $s = -2, -5$;   poles are $s = 0, -1.500 \pm j2.398, -12.00$;
gain = 2; $T(s) = (2s^2 + 14s + 20)/(s^4 + 15s^3 + 44s^2 + 96s)$

15.12 Zeros are $s = -3, -5$; poles are $s = -1.0956, -6.952 \pm j2.536$,
$T(s) = (4s^2 + 32s + 60)/(s^3 + 15s^2 + 70s + 60)$,

$A = \begin{bmatrix} -15 & -70 & -60 \\ 1 & 0 & 0 \\ 0 & 1 & 0 \end{bmatrix}$, $B = \begin{bmatrix} 1 \\ 0 \\ 0 \end{bmatrix}$, $C = \begin{bmatrix} 4 & 32 & 60 \end{bmatrix}$, $D = 0$

15.15

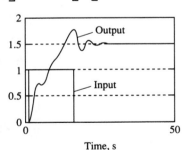

Time, s

15.19 (a)

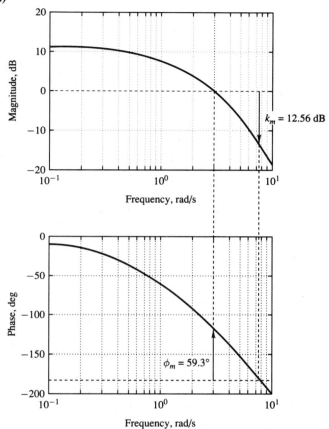

(b) $k_m = 12.56$ dB, $\omega_{gm} = 7.21$ rad/s, $\phi_m = 59.3°$, $\omega_{pm} = 3.00$ rad/s
(c) $K = 636$

15.24 (b) $K = 39.7$, $s = -0.574 \pm j2.00$, -2.50, -7.36

15.25 (a) Unit step function starting at $t = 1$ s.

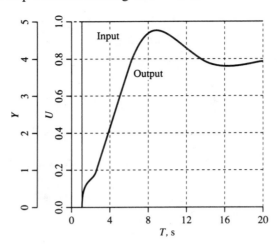

(b) Triangular signal in Figure P15.16.

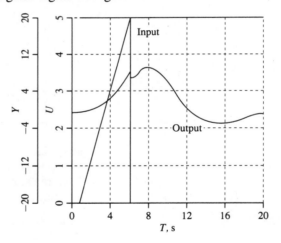

15.28 **(a)**

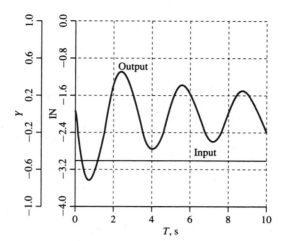

(b)

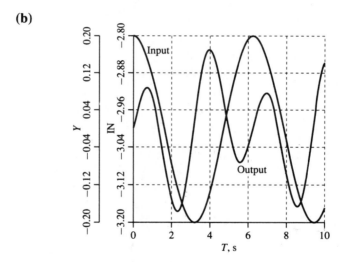

▶ REFERENCES

Anton, A. *Elementary Linear Algebra*, 6th ed. Wiley, New York, 1991.

Boyce, W.E. and R.C. DiPrima. *Elementary Differential Equations*, 5th ed. Wiley, New York, 1992.

Carlson, A.B. and D.G. Gisser. *Electrical Engineering, Concepts and Applications*, 2d ed. Addison-Wesley, Reading, Mass., 1990.

Chen, C.T. *System and Signal Analysis*. Saunders College Publishing, Philadelphia, 1989.

Del Toro, V. *Electrical Engineering Fundamentals*, 2d ed. Prentice-Hall, Englewood Cliffs, N.J., 1986.

de Silva, C.W. *Control Sensors and Actuators*. Prentice-Hall, Englewood Cliffs, N.J., 1989.

Doebelin, E.O. *Measurement Systems*, 4th ed. McGraw-Hill, New York, 1990.

Dorf, R.C. *Modern Control Systems*, 6th ed. Addison-Wesley, Reading, Mass., 1992.

D'Souza, A.F. *Design of Control Systems*, Prentice-Hall, Englewood Cliffs, N.J., 1988.

Franklin, G.F., J.E. Powell, and M.L. Workman. *Digital Control of Dynamic Systems*, 2d ed. Addison-Wesley, Reading, Mass., 1990.

Franklin, G.F., J.D. Powell, and A. Emami-Naeini. *Feedback Control of Dynamic Systems*, 2d ed. Addison-Wesley, Reading, Mass., 1991.

Grace, A., A.J. Laub, J.N. Little, and C. Thompson. *CONTROL SYSTEM TOOLBOX User's Guide*. The MathWorks, Inc., Natick, Mass., 1990.

Guru, B.S. and H.R. Hiziroglu. *Electrical Machinery and Transformers*, Saunders College Publishing, Philadelphia, 1988.

Halliday, D., and R. Resnick. *Fundamentals of Physics*, 3d ed. Wiley, New York, 1988.

Hayt, W.H., Jr. and J.E. Kemmerly. *Engineering Circuit Analysis*, 4th ed. McGraw-Hill, New York, 1986.

Johnson, D.E., J.R. Johnson, and J.L. Hilburn. *Electric Circuit Analysis*, 2d ed. Prentice-Hall, Englewood Cliffs, N.J., 1992.

Kamen, E.W. *Introduction to Signals and Systems*, 2d ed. Macmillan, New York, 1990.

Kimbrell, J.T. *Kinematics Analysis and Synthesis*, McGraw-Hill, New York, 1991.

Krause, P.C. and O. Wasynczuk. *Electromechanical Motion Devices*. McGraw-Hill, New York, 1989.

Kuo, B.C. *Automatic Control Systems*, 6th ed. Prentice-Hall, Englewood Cliffs, N.J., 1991.

Luyben, W.L. *Process Modeling, Simulation and Control for Chemical Engineers*, 2d ed. McGraw-Hill, New York, 1990.

The MathWorks, *PRO-MATLAB User's Guide*, The MathWorks, Inc., Natick, Mass., 1990.

The MathWorks, *The Student Edition of MATLAB*. Prentice-Hall, Englewood Cliffs, N.J., 1992.

McPherson, G. *An Introduction to Electrical Machines and Transformers*, 2d ed. Wiley, New York, 1990.

Meriam, J.L. and L.G. Kraige. *Engineering Mechanics, Volume 2*, 3d ed. Wiley, New York, 1992.

Mitchell and Gauthier Associates. *ACSL Reference Manual*, Edition 10.0. MGA, Inc., Concord, Mass., 1991.

Nilsson, J.W. *Electric Circuits*, 3d ed. Addison-Wesley, Reading, Mass., 1990.

Ogata, K. *Modern Control Engineering*. Prentice-Hall, Englewood Cliffs, N.J., 1990.

Ogata, K. *System Dynamics*, 2d ed. Prentice-Hall, Englewood Cliffs, N.J., 1992.

Palm, W.J. *Modeling, Analysis, and Control of Dynamic Systems*. Wiley, New York, 1983.

Phillips, C.L. and H.T. Nagle. *Digital Control System Analysis and Design*, 2d ed. Prentice-Hall, Englewood Cliffs, N.J., 1990.

Raven, F.H. *Automatic Control Engineering*, 4th ed. McGraw-Hill, New York, 1987.

Rosenberg, R.C. and D.C. Karnopp. *Introduction to Physical Systems Dynamics*. McGraw-Hill, New York, 1983.

Seborg, D.E., T.E. Edgar, and D.A. Mellichamp. *Process Dynamics and Control.* Wiley, New York, 1989.

Sedra, O.S. and K.C. Smith. *Microelectronic Circuits*, 3d ed. Saunders College Publishing, Philadelphia, 1991.

Sinha, N.K. *Linear Systems.* Wiley, New York, 1991.

Smith, R. J. and R.C. Dorf. *Circuits, Systems, and Devices*, 5th ed. Wiley, New York, 1992.

Thomson, W.T. *Theory of Vibrations with Applications*, 3d ed. Prentice-Hall, Englewood Cliffs, N.J., 1988.

Thorpe, J.F. *Mechanical System Components.* Allyn and Bacon, Boston, 1989.

Wildi, T. *Units and Conversion Charts.* IEEE Press, Piscataway, N.J., 1991.

$$H(s) = \frac{Y(s)}{U(s)} = \frac{output}{input} \quad \frac{X(s)}{F_s(s)}$$

$$\begin{bmatrix} s^2 + 2s + 2 & -s-1 \\ -s-1 & s^2 + 2s + 2 \end{bmatrix} \begin{Bmatrix} X_1(s) \\ X_2(s) \end{Bmatrix} = \begin{Bmatrix} f_1(s) \\ 0 \end{Bmatrix}$$

$$\Delta(s) = (s^2+2s+2)(s^2+2s+2) - (-s-1)(-s-1)$$

$$X_1(s) = \frac{\begin{vmatrix} f_1(s) & -s-1 \\ 0 & s^2+2s+2 \end{vmatrix}}{p(s)} = \frac{f_1(s)(s^2+2s+2) - (0)(-s-1)}{p(s)}$$

$$H_1(s) = \frac{X_1(s)}{F_1(s)} = \frac{(s^2+2s+2) - (0)(-s-1)}{p(s)}$$

$$X_2(s) = \frac{\begin{vmatrix} s^2+2s+2 & f_1(s) \\ -s-1 & 0 \end{vmatrix}}{p(s)} = \frac{0 - (-s-1)(f_1(s))}{p(s)}$$

$$H_2(s) = \frac{X_2(s)}{F_1(s)} = \frac{s+1}{p(s)}$$

▶ Index